METHODS OF SOIL ANALYSIS

Part 1

AGRONOMY

A Series of Monographs Published by the

AMERICAN SOCIETY OF AGRONOMY

General Editor, Monographs 1 to 6, A. G. NORMAN

1 C. EDMUND MARSHALL: The Colloid Chemistry of the Silicate Minerals, 1949

2 BYRON T. SHAW, *Editor:* Soil Physical Conditions and Plant Growth, 1952

3 K. D. JACOB, *Editor:* Fertilizer Technology and Resources in the United States, 1953

4 W. H. PIERRE and A. G. NORMAN, *Editors:* Soil and Fertilizer Phosphate in Crop Nutrition, 1953

5 GEORGE F. SPRAGUE, *Editor:* Corn and Corn Improvement, 1955

6 J. LEVITT: The Hardiness of Plants, 1956

7 JAMES N. LUTHIN, *Editor:* Drainage of Agricultural Lands, 1957
                                             General Editor, D. E. GREGG

8 FRANKLIN A. COFFMAN, *Editor:* Oats and Oat Improvement, 1961
                                             Managing Editor, H. L. HAMILTON

9 C. A. BLACK, *Editor-in-Chief,* and D. D. EVANS, J. L. WHITE, L. E. ENSMINGER, and F. E. CLARK, *Associate Editors:* Methods of Soil Analysis, 1965

> Part 1—Physical and Mineralogical Properties, Including Statistics of Measurement and Sampling
> Part 2—Chemical and Microbiological Properties
> *Managing Editor, R. C. DINAUER*

Monographs 1 through 6, published by Academic Press, Inc., should be ordered from:

Academic Press, Inc.
111 Fifth Avenue
New York, New York 10003

Monographs 7, 8, and 9, published by the American Society of Agronomy, should be ordered from:

American Society of Agronomy
677 South Segoe Road
Madison, Wisconsin, USA 53711

METHODS OF SOIL ANALYSIS

Part 1

Physical and Mineralogical Properties, Including Statistics of Measurement and Sampling

C. A. BLACK, *Editor-in-Chief*

and

D. D. EVANS
J. L. WHITE

L. E. ENSMINGER
F. E. CLARK

Associate Editors

R. C. DINAUER, *Managing Editor*

Sponsored jointly by the
AMERICAN SOCIETY OF AGRONOMY
and
AMERICAN SOCIETY FOR TESTING AND MATERIALS

Number 9 in the series
AGRONOMY

American Society of Agronomy, Inc., *Publisher*
Madison, Wisconsin, USA
1965

THE AMERICAN SOCIETY OF AGRONOMY, INC.
677 SOUTH SEGOE ROAD, MADISON, WISCONSIN, USA 53711

LIBRARY OF CONGRESS CATALOG CARD NUMBER: 65-15800

PRINTED IN THE UNITED STATES OF AMERICA

GENERAL FOREWORD

AGRONOMY—An ASA Monograph Series

The need for comprehensive treatments of specific subject matter areas was realized by members of the American Society of Agronomy several years ago. As a result, the first monograph of a series entitled "Agronomy" was published in 1949. Dr. A. G. Norman, an eminent member of the Society, was appointed general editor and served in this capacity for the first six publications. Since the Society, a nonprofit organization, was not initially able to finance the project, arrangements were made with Academic Press, Inc., of New York to publish the monographs. This procedure was used for the first six monographs. This fact explains why these six publications are not available at the Society Headquarters Office but instead from Academic Press, Inc.

By 1957, the Society had developed considerably and had in operation a Headquarters Office with a competent editorial staff which made it possible to editorially manage its publications. Also, the financial stability of the Society now enabled it to pursue independently the monograph project, including complete financing and publishing of the series.

The ASA now presents its ninth contribution, with several more in preparation. In contrast to the first eight "volumes," the ninth and succeeding issues will be referred to as "numbers." As reported in the Preface, the project which was to become this monograph on Methods of Soil Analysis was conceived and initiated in 1957 by the Soil Science Society of America. During the course of development of the project it became apparent that the publication would be a particularly large and expensive one. The American Society of Agronomy had in its organization a Monographs Committee to which was assigned the responsibility to decide on the appropriateness of subject-matter for ASA monographs while at the same time taking note of the financial obligations related to this project. With the agreement of the SSSA, the Monographs Committee recommended the sponsorship and complete financing of this monograph to the ASA. Approval to proceed was given by the American Society of Agronomy.

It may interest readers to know that members of the SSSA are members of the ASA and that members of the Crop Science Society of America are also members of the ASA. The three societies, while administratively separate, autonomous, and individually incorporated organizations in Wisconsin, are closely associated, work harmoniously together, and share a Headquarters Office and staff in Madison, Wisconsin. The readiness of the ASA to sponsor a project initiated and successfully carried through by an SSSA committee, the members of which are also ASA members, is a further indication of the desirability and practicality of the existing favorable inter-relationship among these associated societies.

December 1964

MATTHIAS STELLY
Executive Secretary-Treasurer
American Society of Agronomy
Crop Science Society of America
Soil Science Society of America

v

FOREWORD

Cooperation on a project like this monograph on soil analysis is appropriate for the American Society of Agronomy and the American Society for Testing and Materials. The American Society of Agronomy has primary concern for efficient agricultural production while ASTM interest covers standards and test methods used in engineering and industrial applications. Numerous soil characteristics are significant and important to both, and both societies subscribe to full use of applicable science in making soil of maximum benefit to man.

Historically the processes of testing and analyzing soil have relied heavily on standardized apparatus and standardized procedures. With a complex, heterogeneous and reactive material like soil, we have been fortunate when the purpose of a measurement has been sufficiently understood that a realistic and useful testing procedure could be devised.

As knowledge increases of the components, principles and mechanisms represented in soil, soil scientists can deal increasingly with properties that can be defined, ideally, in such a way that measured values are independent of apparatus or method and can be expressed in standard units. There are some who would restrict the technical meaning of the term "property" to such "qualities" of matter. For soil it is not always possible to define such properties that will serve our needs. The reader will be interested to see how far we have progressed in this direction.

For ASTM, standardization of specifications and methods of testing is an important consideration. Even though there are properties for which different methods may yield similar results, the ultimate objective would be to establish a single standard method.

Skill is required in the definition of useful soil properties, in devising suitable measuring methods and in making the determinations. It is the purpose of this intersociety monograph to assemble and disseminate these skills for the analysis of soil. We are much indebted to the Editor, to his staff, and to the many contributing authors.

December 1964

LORENZO A. RICHARDS, *President*
American Society of Agronomy

CHARLES L. KENT, *President*
American Society for Testing and Materials

PREFACE

The need for authoritative information on soil analysis is shared by most soil scientists, whether or not they are actively engaged personally in making analyses. Comprehensive and authoritative coverage of a range of subject matter as great as that of soil analysis, however, is hardly possible for a single individual and may be accomplished more readily by cooperation of specialists in the different areas of work. This monograph is a result of the cooperative endeavor of many specialists.

In January 1957, L. B. Nelson, then president of the Soil Science Society of America, appointed a committee to study and recommend whether or not the SSSA should prepare a book on methods of soil analysis and to consider the fields to be covered and the method of organization, selection of methods, and editing. This committee included W. H. Gardner, E. R. Graham, J. J. Hanway, M. L. Jackson, R. F. Reitemeier, R. L. Starkey, and L. V. Wilcox, with C. I. Rich as chairman. The committee recommended that the SSSA prepare such a book. The committee recommended further that the standing committees on methods of soil analysis already existing in the Society, with the addition of a committee on microbiological properties, be given the responsibility of selecting and editing the methods; and that the chairmen of these committees, together with an individual elected by them to be the editor-in-chief, should comprise the editorial board. The recommendations were approved by the executive subcommittee of the SSSA in August 1957 and by the entire executive committee at the annual meeting held in November 1957 in Atlanta, Georgia.

At the same time a parallel and independent development was taking place in the American Society for Testing and Materials. ASTM Committee D-18 on Soils and Rocks for Engineering Purposes, Subcommittee R-6, with the late D. T. Davidson as chairman, was developing plans for a monograph on methods of soil analysis to supplement the methods of tests already published by ASTM. Because the monograph project of the Soil Science Society of America was further advanced than that of the American Society for Testing and Materials when the duplication of efforts was discovered, the ASTM committee offered their full support and cooperation to the SSSA in completing the project.

Contact was then made with the Monographs Committee of the American Society of Agronomy to determine whether the proposed publication would be suitable as a number in the series of monographs sponsored by the ASA; and contact was made with the American Society for Testing and Materials to determine whether the ASTM wished to join with the ASA in sponsorship. Approval was obtained, and work on the monograph was completed under the supervision of the SSSA committees and editorial board, with the ASA and ASTM serving as joint sponsors of the publication.

The members of the SSSA and ASTM committees who participated in development of this monograph are as follows:

Soil Science Society of America
Committees on Soil Analysis and Measurement

PHYSICAL MEASUREMENT

D. D. EVANS, *Chairman,* University of Arizona, Tucson, Ariz.

D. M. ANDERSON, Cold Regions Research Laboratory, U. S. Army, Hanover, N. H.

G. R. BLAKE, University of Minnesota, St. Paul, Minn.

R. R. BRUCE, ARS, USDA, and Mississippi State University, State College, Miss.

W. H. GARDNER, Washington State University, Pullman, Wash.

W. R. GARDNER, ARS, USDA, U. S. Salinity Laboratory, Riverside, Calif.

V. C. JAMISON, ARS, USDA, Columbia, Mo.

D. B. PETERS, ARS, USDA, and University of Illinois, Urbana, Ill.

J. S. ROBINS, ARS, USDA, Boise, Idaho

SOIL MINERAL ANALYSIS

J. L. WHITE, *Chairman,* Purdue University, Lafayette, Ind.

I. BARSHAD, University of California, Berkeley, Calif.

A. H. BEAVERS, University of Illinois, Urbana, Ill.

G. W. KUNZE, Texas A & M University, College Station, Tex.

M. M. MORTLAND, Michigan State University, East Lansing, Mich.

R. C. VANDEN HEUVEL, SCS, USDA, Soil Survey Laboratory, Beltsville, Md.

L. D. WHITTIG, University of California, Davis, Calif.

CHEMICAL ANALYSIS

L. E. ENSMINGER, *Chairman,* Auburn University, Auburn, Ala.

H. D. CHAPMAN, University of California, Riverside, Calif.

B. N. DRISKELL, Denham Laboratory, University of Alabama, Tuscaloosa, Ala.

M. E. HARWARD, Oregon State University, Corvallis, Oregon

V. J. KILMER, Tennessee Valley Authority, Wilson Dam, Ala.
KIRK LAWTON, Michigan State University, East Lansing, Mich.
C. D. MOODIE, Washington State University, Pullman, Wash.
A. B. PRINCE, University of New Hampshire, Durham, N. H.

SOIL MICROBIOLOGICAL METHODS

F. E. CLARK, *Chairman,* ARS, USDA, Fort Collins, Colo.
M. ALEXANDER, Cornell University, Ithaca, N. Y.
F. E. BROADBENT, University of California, Davis, Calif.
L. R. FREDERICK, Iowa State University, Ames, Iowa

American Society for Testing and Materials Committee D-18 Subcommittee R-6 on Physico-Chemical Properties of Soils

D. T. DAVIDSON, *Chairman,* Iowa Engineering Experiment Station, Ames, Iowa
R. L. HANDY, Iowa State University, Ames, Iowa
R. G. EDHOLM, General Electric Co., Milwaukee, Wis.
H. A. FACCI, Washington, D. C.
W. A. GOODWIN, University of Tennessee, Knoxville, Tenn.
R. E. GRIM, University of Illinois, Urbana, Ill.
J. H. HAVENS, Highway Research Laboratory, Lexington, Ky.
C. D. JEFFRIES, Pennsylvania State University, University Park, Pa.
A. L. JOHNSON, New Castle, Pa.
E. J. KILCAWLEY, Rensselaer Polytechnic Institute, Troy, N. Y.
T. W. LAMBE, Massachusetts Institute of Technology, Cambridge, Mass.
C. E. MARSHALL, University of Missouri, Columbia, Mo.
R. T. MARTIN, Massachusetts Institute of Technology, Cambridge, Mass.
J. K. MITCHELL, University of California, Berkeley, Calif.
R. F. REITEMEIER, U. S. Atomic Energy Commission, Washington, D. C.
C. S. ROSS, U. S. Geological Survey, Washington, D. C.
C. B. TANNER, University of Wisconsin, Madison, Wis.
T. I. TAYLOR, Columbia University, New York, N. Y.
H. F. WINTERKORN, Princeton University, Princeton, N. J.
C. J. WOODS, Electronics, Inc., Mt. Vernon, N. Y.

Immediately following approval of the project by the SSSA, the committee on physical analysis, then under the chairmanship of W. H. Gardner, prepared an outline of subject matter for the portion of the monograph to deal with physical properties. The other committees on soil analysis soon prepared outlines for their respective areas, and the individual outlines were organized into an over-all outline by the editorial board.

Authors for individual sections were selected by the standing committees, and contacts were made by chairmen of these committees. Authors were selected on the basis of their special knowledge of the subject on which they were asked to write, and the choice of methods to be described was left to them. In some instances authors include several methods for making a particular measurement and, when so, usually provide supplementary information to aid the reader in deciding which method best suits his purpose. Thus, with the exception of some ASTM methods, the methods described have not been included because of any specific official action of the Soil Science Society of America, the American Society of Agronomy, or the American Society for Testing and Materials; hence, they should not be considered to be standard or official methods of any of these Societies.

Most of the sections deal with methods of soil analysis, as the title implies. The few that do not have been included because the methods and related information they contain are of importance to people working with soils and frequently are needed by them.

Although a monograph entitled methods of analysis might be strictly a set of directions for performing the operations required to make the measurements, the editorial board was in unanimous agreement from the beginning that this style of presentation would not fulfill the total need of readers for information about the methods. Authors, therefore, were asked to include not only the specific directions for the measurements but also the principles of the method, comments on such matters as limitations, pitfalls, and precision, and reference to sources in the literature to which the reader might go for further study.

The standard pattern of treatment is followed with most subjects, but it is inapplicable for a few; and, in such instances, departures from the standard format are made. In the subject of analysis of nitrogenous gases, for example, the authors do not consider that proven methods are available; accordingly, they give no methods in detail but instead provide an analysis of the literature to serve as a basis for research to develop suitable methods.

An attempt has been made to produce a treatise that is self-sufficient, so that a reader with good background knowledge of science can obtain what he needs to know of the theory and practice without having to consult other sources, which might not be readily available. This objective has been accomplished to different degrees in the different sections. In some, the breadth of material is so great that a considerable compromise has been necessary. For example, in the subject of petrographic methods, standard techniques may be found in books on optical mineralogy. Because the material is so extensive, the author does not attempt to repeat it in the form of specific directions. Rather, he confines his remarks principally to the special aspects of petrographic methods that have to do with soils, and he makes reference to sources in the literature where the specific directions may be obtained.

Considerable thought was given to the subject of indexes of availability of plant nutrients. From the standpoint of numbers of analyses performed, such measurements undoubtedly are of first importance. Nevertheless, measurements on soils to obtain indexes of availability of plant nutrients have an empirical aspect that is not so generally present in measurements of other properties. Moreover, the number of methods in use is large, and there is relatively little standardization among different laboratories. Because it was obvious that all methods found to be useful and perhaps satisfactory in one location or another could not be included, a compromise was made, and only a few methods have been given, again at the discretion of the authors.

Manuscripts submitted by authors were reviewed by the committee chairman or by one or more other persons (usually members of the SSSA committees on soil analysis) and sometimes by both, as well as the editor-in-chief; and the comments prepared were transmitted to the authors, as is customary with journal papers. Because a period of several years was required to complete the monograph, authors were given an opportunity, immediately prior to typesetting, to make revisions in their manuscripts. A number of authors made revisions and added new material at that time.

Throughout the monograph, frequent reference is made to specific commercial products and manufacturers. Such information is included for the convenience of the reader and should not be taken as an endorsement of the products or manufacturers to the exclusion of others by the Soil Science Society of America, the American Society of Agronomy, the American Society for Testing and Materials, or the author's employer.

Special recognition is due Oscar Kempthorne for the counsel and assistance he so generously provided in connection with the parts of the monograph dealing with statistics of measurement and sampling. Similar recognition is due Donald T. Davidson, late chairman of ASTM Subcommittee R-6 on physico-chemical properties of soils, and his successor, R. L. Handy, for their contributions to the sections of the monograph dealing with soil mechanics. Thanks are due L. Boersma for his work in an editorial capacity in the area of physical properties during the temporary absence of the chairman of the committee. Thanks are due P. F. Low for his advice on technical matters. And finally, appreciation must be expressed to the many anonymous reviewers who provided their time and talents to aid in maintaining high standards in the technical subject matter of the monograph and to R. C. Dinauer, of the Headquarters Staff of the American Society of Agronomy, for his painstaking job of editing the final copy for publication.

Editorial Board

Ames, Iowa
September 1964

CONTRIBUTORS

Fred Adams

Associate Professor of Soil Chemistry, Department of Agronomy and Soils, Auburn University, Auburn, Alabama

M. Alexander

Associate Professor of Soil Microbiology, Department of Agronomy, Cornell University, Ithaca, New York

L. E. Allison

Soil Scientist, U. S. Salinity Laboratory, Soil and Water Conservation Research Division, Agricultural Research Service, U. S. Department of Agriculture, Riverside, California

R. R. Allmaras

Soil Scientist, North Central Soil Conservation Research Center, Soil and Water Conservation Research Division, Agricultural Research Service, U. S. Department of Agriculture, Morris, Minnesota

Jack Altman

Assistant Professor of Botany and Plant Pathology, Department of Botany and Plant Pathology, Colorado State University, Fort Collins, Colorado

D. M. Anderson

Geologist, Materials Research Branch, U. S. Army Cold Regions Research and Engineering Laboratory, Hanover, New Hampshire

Edward S. Barber

Consulting Engineer, Soil Mechanics and Foundations, Arlington, Virginia

C. E. Bardsley

Associate Professor of Agronomy, South Carolina Agricultural Experiment Station, Clemson College, Clemson, South Carolina

Isaac Barshad

Soil Chemist, Department of Soils and Plant Nutrition, University of California, Berkeley, California

W. E. Beard

Chemist, Nitrogen Laboratory, Soil and Water Conservation Research Division, Agricultural Research Service, U. S. Department of Agriculture, Fort Collins, Colorado

Kenneth C. Beeson

Formerly Director, U. S. Plant, Soil and Nutrition Laboratory, Soil and Water Conservation Research Division, Agricultural Research Service, U. S. Department of Agriculture, Ithaca, New York (now with USAID to Sudan)

Anson R. Bertrand	Chief, Southern Branch, Soil and Water Conservation Research Division, Agricultural Research Service, U. S. Department of Agriculture, University of Georgia, Athens, Georgia
C. A. Black	Professor of Soils, Department of Agronomy, Iowa State University, Ames, Iowa
G. R. Blake	Professor of Soils, Department of Soils, University of Minnesota, St. Paul, Minnesota
Louis C. Boawn	Soil Scientist, Soil and Water Conservation Research Division, Agricultural Research Service, U. S. Department of Agriculture, Prosser, Washington
L. Boersma	Assistant Professor of Soils, Department of Soils, Oregon State University, Corvallis, Oregon
W. B. Bollen	Professor of Soil Microbiology, Department of Microbiology, Oregon State University, Corvallis, Oregon
C. A. Bower	Director, U. S. Salinity Laboratory, Soil and Water Conservation Research Division, Agricultural Research Service, U. S. Department of Agriculture, Riverside, California
J. M. Bremner	Professor of Soils, Department of Agronomy, Iowa State University, Ames, Iowa
Robert F. Brewer	Associate Chemist, Department of Soils and Plant Nutrition, University of California, Riverside, California
F. E. Broadbent	Professor of Soil Microbiology, Department of Soils and Plant Nutrition, University of California, Davis, California
C. H. M. van Bavel	Physicist, U. S. Water Conservation Laboratory, Soil and Water Conservation Research Division, Agricultural Research Service, U. S. Department of Agriculture, Tempe, Arizona
F. B. Cady	Assistant Professor of Statistics, Department of Statistics, Iowa State University, Ames, Iowa
John G. Cady	Soil Scientist, Soil Survey Laboratory, Soil Conservation Service, U. S. Department of Agriculture, Beltsville, Maryland

L. D. Calvin

Professor of Statistics and Chairman, Department of Statistics, Oregon State University, Corvallis, Oregon

H. D. Chapman

Professor of Soils and Plant Nutrition, Department of Soils and Plant Nutrition, University of California, Riverside, California

H. H. Cheng

Research Associate, Department of Agronomy, Iowa State University, Ames, Iowa

W. S. Chepil
(deceased)

Research Investigations Leader, Soil Erosion, Soil and Water Conservation Research Division, Agricultural Research Service, U. S. Department of Agriculture, Kansas State University, Manhattan, Kansas

Francis E. Clark

Microbiologist, Nitrogen Laboratory, Soil and Water Conservation Research Division, Agricultural Research Service, U. S. Department of Agriculture, Fort Collins, Colorado

H. T. David

Professor of Statistics, Department of Statistics, Iowa State University, Ames, Iowa

Donald T. Davidson
(deceased)

Professor of Civil Engineering, Department of Civil Engineering, Iowa State University, Ames, Iowa

Paul R. Day

Professor of Soil Physics, Department of Soils and Plant Nutrition, University of California, Berkeley, California

L. A. Dean

Director, U. S. Soils Laboratory, Soil and Water Conservation Research Division, Agricultural Research Service, U. S. Department of Agriculture, Beltsville, Maryland

W. J. Dixon

Professor of Preventive Medicine, Health Sciences Computing Facilities, Department of Preventive Medicine, School of Medicine, University of California, Los Angeles, California

L. W. Durrell

Professor of Botany and Plant Pathology and Dean Emeritus, Department of Botany and Plant Pathology, Colorado State University, Fort Collins, Colorado

D. D. Evans

Professor, Department of Agricultural Chemistry and Soils, University of Arizona, Tucson, Arizona

Earl J. Felt
(deceased)
Manager of Transportation Development, Transportation Development Section, Research and Development Division, Portland Cement Association, Skokie, Illinois

L. O. Fine
Professor and Head, Department of Agronomy, South Dakota State University, Brookings, South Dakota

John G. A. Fiskell
Biochemist, Department of Soils, Agricultural Experiment Stations, University of Florida, Gainesville, Florida

Lloyd R. Frederick
Professor of Agronomy, Department of Agronomy, Iowa State University, Ames, Iowa

Walter H. Gardner
Professor of Soils, Department of Agronomy, Washington State University, Pullman, Washington

W. A. Goodwin
Research Professor, University of Tennessee, Knoxville Tennessee (now with Highway Research Board, National Cooperative Research Program, Washington, D. C.)

Walter R. Heald
Soil Scientist, U. S. Soils Laboratory, Soil and Water Conservation Research Division, Agricultural Research Service, U. S. Department of Agriculture, Beltsville, Maryland

W. G. Holtz
Assistant Chief Research Scientist, Soils Engineering Branch, Bureau of Reclamation, U. S. Department of Interior, Denver Federal Center, Denver, Colorado

M. L. Jackson
Professor of Soil Science, Department of Soil Science, University of Wisconsin, Madison, Wisconsin

Ray D. Jackson
Physicist, U. S. Water Conservation Laboratory, Soil and Water Conservation Research Division, Agricultural Research Service, U. S. Department of Agriculture, Tempe, Arizona

C. M. Johnson
Chemist, Department of Soils and Plant Nutrition, University of California, Berkeley, California

Yoshinori Kanehiro
Assistant Professor of Soils, Agronomy and Soil Science Department, University of Hawaii, College of Tropical Agriculture, Honolulu, Hawaii

W. D. Kemper	Soil Scientist and Associate Professor of Soils, Soil and Water Conservation Research Division, Agricultural Research Service, U. S. Department of Agriculture, and the Department of Agronomy, Colorado State University, Fort Collins, Colorado
Oscar Kempthorne	Professor of Statistics, Department of Statistics, Iowa State University, Ames, Iowa
Victor J. Kilmer	Soil Scientist, Office of Agricultural and Chemical Development, Tennessee Valley Authority, Wilson Dam, Alabama
J. A. Kittrick	Associate Professor of Soils, Department of Agronomy, Washington State University, Pullman, Washington
Arnold Klute	Professor of Soil Physics, Department of Agronomy, University of Illinois, Urbana, Illinois
Joe Kubota	Soil Scientist, Soil Conservation Service, U. S. Department of Agriculture, U. S. Plant, Soil and Nutrition Laboratory, Ithaca, New York
George W. Kunze	Professor of Soil Mineralogy, Department of Soil and Crop Sciences, Texas A & M University, College Station, Texas
J. D. Lancaster	Professor of Soil Chemistry and Nitrogen, Mississippi State University, State College, Mississippi
V. A. Lazar	Soil Scientist, U. S. Plant, Soil and Nutrition Laboratory, Soil and Water Conservation Research Division, Agricultural Research Service, U. S. Department of Agriculture, Ithaca, New York
Torrence H. MacDonald	Meteorologist, Solar Radiation Research Project, Office of Meteorological Research, U. S. Weather Bureau, Washington, D. C.
E. O. McLean	Professor of Agronomy, Department of Agronomy, Ohio State University and the Ohio Agricultural Experiment Station, Columbus, Ohio
Ronald G. Menzel	Soil Scientist, U. S. Soils Laboratory, Soil and Water Conservation Research Division, Agricultural Research Service, U. S. Department of Agriculture, Beltsville, Maryland

J. D. Menzies	Microbiologist, U. S. Soils Laboratory, Soil and Water Conservation Research Division, Agricultural Research Service, U. S. Department of Agriculture, Beltsville, Maryland
C. D. Moodie	Professor of Soils, Department of Agronomy, Washington State University, Pullman, Washington
J. L. Mortensen (deceased)	Professor of Agronomy, Department of Agronomy, Ohio State University and the Ohio Agricultural Experiment Station, Columbus, Ohio
M. M. Mortland	Professor of Soil Science, Department of Soil Science, Michigan State University, East Lansing, Michigan
Alfred T. Myers	Geochemist, Geological Survey, U. S. Department of the Interior, Denver, Colorado
Uteana Oda	Chemist, Geological Survey, U. S. Department of the Interior, Denver, Colorado
S. R. Olsen	Soil Scientist, Soil Phosphorus Laboratory, Soil and Water Conservation Research Division, Agricultural Research Service, U. S. Department of Agriculture, Colorado State University, Fort Collins, Colorado
R. V. Olson	Professor and Head, Department of Agronomy, Kansas State University, Manhattan, Kansas
Michael Peech	Professor of Soil Science, Department of Agronomy, Cornell University, Ithaca, New York
D. B. Peters	Soil Scientist and Associate Professor, Soil and Water Conservation Research Division, Agricultural Research Service, U. S. Department of Agriculture, Department of Agronomy, University of Illinois, Urbana, Illinois
R. G. Petersen	Associate Professor of Design and Analytical Experiments, Department of Experimental Statistics, North Carolina State of the University of North Carolina at Raleigh, North Carolina
Lynn K. Porter	Soil Scientist, Nitrogen Laboratory, Soil and Water Conservation Research Division, Agricultural Research Service, U. S. Department of Agriculture, Fort Collins, Colorado
P. F. Pratt	Professor and Chemist, Department of Soils and Plant Nutrition, University of California, Riverside, California

Allan B. Prince   Professor of Soil and Water Science, Department of Soil and Water Science, University of New Hampshire, Durham, New Hampshire

R. C. Reeve   Research Investigations Leader, Soil and Water Conservation Research Division, Agricultural Research Service, U. S. Department of Agriculture, Ohio State University, Columbus, Ohio

H. M. Reisenauer   Associate Research Soil Scientist, M. Theodore Kearney Foundation of Soil Science, University of California, Davis, California

C. I. Rich   Professor of Agronomy, Department of Agronomy, Virginia Polytechnic Institute, Blacksburg, Virginia

L. A. Richards   Physicist, U. S. Salinity Laboratory, Soil and Water Conservation Research Division, Agricultural Research Service, U. S. Department of Agriculture, Riverside, California

S. J. Richards   Professor of Soil Physics, Department of Soils and Plant Nutrition, University of California, Riverside, California

J. S. Robins   Chief, Northwest Branch, Soil and Water Conservation Research Division, Agricultural Research Service, U. S. Department of Agriculture, Boise, Idaho

John R. Sallberg   Highway Research Engineer, Soil Research Branch, Materials Research Division, Bureau of Public Roads, U. S. Department of Commerce, Washington, D. C.

G. Donald Sherman   Associate Director of the Agricultural Experiment Station and Senior Professor of Soils, University of Hawaii, College of Tropical Agriculture, Honolulu, Hawaii

George F. Sowers   Professor of Civil Engineering and Consulting Engineer, School of Civil Engineering, Georgia Institute of Technology, Atlanta, Georgia (also Law Engineering Testing Co., Atlanta, Georgia)

Alston W. Specht   Chemist, U. S. Soils Laboratory, Soil and Water Conservation Research Division, Agricultural Research Service, U. S. Department of Agriculture, Beltsville, Maryland

F. J. Stevenson   Professor of Soil Chemistry, Department of Agronomy, University of Illinois, Urbana, Illinois

G. Stotzky

Chairman, Research Department, Kitchawan Research Laboratory, Brooklyn Botanic Garden, Ossining, New York

P. R. Stout

Professor and Head, Department of Soils and Plant Nutrition, University of California, Davis, California

Sterling A. Taylor

Professor of Soil Physics, Department of Agronomy, Utah State University, Logan, Utah

R. C. Vanden Heuvel

Soil Scientist, Soil Survey Laboratory, Soil Conservation Service, U. S. Department of Agriculture, Beltsville, Maryland

Frank G. Viets, Jr.

Research Investigations Leader, Soil and Water Conservation Research Division, Agricultural Research Service, U. S. Department of Agriculture, Fort Collins, Colorado

James A. Vomocil

Associate Professor of Soil Physics, Department of Soils and Plant Nutrition, University of California, Davis, California

John I. Wear

Soil Chemist, Department of Agronomy and Soils, Auburn University, Auburn, Alabama

L. V. Wilcox

Formerly Assistant to Director, U. S. Salinity Laboratory, Soil and Water Conservation Research Division, Agricultural Research Service, U. S. Department of Agriculture, Riverside, California (now retired)

J. L. White

Professor of Agronomy, Department of Agronomy, Purdue University, Lafayette, Indiana

L. D. Whittig

Associate Soil Chemist, Department of Soils and Plant Nutrition, University of California, Davis, California

Tyler A. Woolley

Professor, Department of Zoology, Colorado State University, Fort Collins, Colorado

CONTENTS

Part 1

CONTENTS

Part 2

80   Selenium

L. O. FINE

81   Chlorine and Bromine

P. R. STOUT AND C. M. JOHNSON

82   Fluorine

ROBERT F. BREWER

83   Total Nitrogen

J. M. BREMNER

84   Inorganic Forms of Nitrogen

J. M. BREMNER

1 | Errors of Observation

OSCAR KEMPTHORNE
Iowa State University
Ames, Iowa

R. R. ALLMARAS
Agricultural Research Service, USDA
Morris, Minnesota

1–1 INTRODUCTION

The experimenter is confronted nearly every day with the examination of results from his own experiments as well as those of others. He needs to know the methods by which the data were obtained and what confidence he may place in the numerical results. Significant aspects of these matters involve the principles and methods of statistics, and the objective of this chapter is to describe the basic ideas of statistics that are relevant to errors of observations.

A measurement is a quantization of an attribute of the material under investigation, directed to the answering of some question that the experimenter has. The quantization implies a sequence of operations or steps that yields the resultant measurement. Thus, the concept of measurement may be said to include not only the steps used to obtain measurement but also the use of the measurement by the experimenter to draw conclusions.

The result of a particular process of measurement serves as part of the basis upon which an experimenter makes a judgment about the attribute under investigation. Some judgments may require a more reliable basis than others. The reliability desired in the measurements will depend on the purpose for which the measurements are to be used, but the degree of reliability may be limited by the resources available to the experimenter. He may exercise control of the reliability by choosing a measurement process making use of a number of relevant scientific principles, by controlling attributes of the environment in which measurement is made, and by repeating the measurements. Different combinations of these control alternatives may be suitable for a given measurement process; and the suitability

[1] Contribution from the Department of Statistics, Iowa State University, Ames, and the Soil and Water Conservation Research Division, ARS, USDA, Morris, Minn. Journal Paper No. J-4633 of the Iowa Agr. & Home Econ. Exp. Sta., Ames. Project No. 890.

of a particular combination of control alternatives varies among measurement processes, and depends on the reliability desired.

The number, which the experimenter uses to judge about the substance under investigation, may not be a single measurement but may be a derived number, that is, some function of several measurements utilizing the same or different measurement processes. The best function will be dictated by the scientific nature of the investigation as well as by the theory of combination of observations and related statistical concepts.

1–2 CLASSIFICATION OF ERRORS OF MEASUREMENT

From the standpoint of errors of measurement, the simplest situation is that of obtaining an attribute of an object which is not affected by the measuring process, so that the measuring process can be applied again and again to the unchanged object, as, for example, determining the length of a bar of steel. Repeated application of the measuring process to this unchanged object, following the directions laid down in the specifications, will yield a sequence of nonidentical numbers. The variation in the numbers results because no sequence of operations or "state of nature" is perfectly reproducible. In other words, no human or machine can do exactly the same sequence of operations again and again, and the identical circumstances and object of measurement cannot be achieved perfectly. If the measurement is coarse, the lack of reproducibility of the measuring process may have no effect, as for instance would be the case with most adults measuring the length of a 5¾-inch rod to the nearest inch with a ruler graduated in inches. In general, however, the lack of reproducibility of operations will produce variability. For instance the instruction to bring the pH of a solution to 6 by adding 1.0 N HCl can be performed only to a certain degree of correctness, depending on the indicator and the operator. Supposedly simple operations like weighing a precipitate will not lead to the same answer on repetition with a sufficiently sensitive balance. Of course, much of the training in elementary analytical chemistry is directed to the performance of operations in a manner sufficiently exact to achieve negligible variability in results and conclusions, but this ideal can rarely be achieved. The variability among results of a measuring process applied to a constant object may be called measurement error or, for emphasis, pure measurement error.

In contrast to the above situation, we may imagine that the object of measurement, which may be a batch of material, is heterogeneous and can be measured only in parts which are unlike, but that the measurement process is perfectly reproducible for each part. If we could apply the measuring process to all parts of the whole under these ideal circumstances, there would be no error in the final result, but the circumstances under which one can process the whole are very rare. To give an obvious example, suppose we wish to characterize the potassium status of plots of land in connection with study of uptake of applied potassium fertilizer. We cannot process all the soil of the plot for obvious reasons, of which perhaps the most compelling is that if we did so we would not then have the plot of land to experiment on. We, therefore, have to determine the status of the land by drawing samples and applying a measurement process to these samples. The samples will not be equal with regard to the attributes under examination, and the variation among the sample results will lead to uncertainty in the final result. Variation of this type, in which it is supposed that the measuring process itself is exactly reproducible, is called pure sampling error.

We can, of course, take the view that what we called pure measurement error arises from sampling a population of repetitions of the measurement process.

In practice few measurement situations lie at either of the two extremes we have mentioned. In the majority of cases the measurement process destroys the object being measured, so that repetition of the measuring process on the object of measurement cannot be performed. A common way out of this difficulty in soil analysis is to homogenize the sample by passing it through a fine sieve and mixing it thoroughly. The homogenized sample is then subdivided, and one performs repeated measurements on subsamples, which one has good reason to regard as identical. Where analyses are made in this way, the total error of an observation on a subsample will include both measurement error and sampling error, the latter because the total sample from which the subsamples are derived is only a small part of the whole for which information is desired. In soil analytical practice, of course, there is always a lower limit to the subsample size that can be taken "without sampling error" from even a sample that has been finely ground and mixed. This problem is of considerable importance in some kinds of soil analysis.

The measurement process consists of a sequence of operations, and at each step in the sequence there will be a certain lack of perfect repeatability of the operation. The measurement error may, therefore, have a structure, in the sense that part arises from step 1 of the sequence of operations, part from step 2, and so on. Similarly the total operation of sampling may in each particular situation be broken down into distinct steps, perhaps according to the sampling design, and each step will introduce a part of the sampling error.

The total "error" is that arising from measurement and sampling. In practice we must attempt to control this total error, so that conclusions based on results will not differ in any important respect from conclusions that would be made in the absence of error, or so that the effect of the error on subsequent conclusions can be assessed.

In general, "error" in the sense discussed above is *not* the result of incorrect procedure; also, it is to be distinguished from mistakes in following the directions, which will lead to large deviations of single measurements from other measurements made with the same measurement process. The detection of gross mistakes is discussed in section 3.

1–3 SCIENTIFIC VALIDITY OF MEASUREMENTS

In general, the measurement process is aimed at the characterization of an object of measurement in terms of scientific concepts. We might, for instance, wish to measure the total content of combined nitrogen in a soil that contains appreciable amounts of NO_3^-. We can imagine a highly reproducible Kjeldahl analysis wherein no additives were used to assure conversion of the NO_3^- to NH_4^+ in the digestion. The measurement would not give the desired answer, because the total content of combined nitrogen is the answer sought, while the measurement process does not measure all the nitrogen present as NO_3^-. The occurrence of such a defect in the measurement process can be found only on the basis of scientific principles or by special tests of validity.

Underlying any measurement process applied to an object of measurement is what one may term the "scientific true value," which can be visualized as being approached more and more closely by refinement of measurement operations and by appropriate changes in the process in accordance with scientific principles. For example, in the instance just considered, the scientific true value would be approached more closely if the process were changed to include NO_3^-.

The scientific relevance of the measurement process is not a matter of the theory of "error," which involves the "wandering" of the results. Clearly, however, the theory of "error" enters into what we may call the validation of a measurement process, because such validation will require the comparison of results obtained in different ways, each way having its own peculiar error characteristics. It is because the scientific validation of a measurement process involves such comparisons that the experimenter must have some awareness of the concept of "error" and of procedures for drawing conclusions in the presence of "error."

It is, one supposes, obvious that examination of the results given by a single measurement process cannot *per se* lead to scientific validation of the measurement process, but it is equally obvious that validation involves consideration of the variability exhibited by the results of applying the measurement process. We, therefore, take up the problem of characterizing the numbers one will obtain by repeating the measurement process.

1–4 CHARACTERIZATION OF VARIABILITY

We suppose that we have at hand a large sample of soil which can be subdivided into a very large number of smaller samples, to each of which we can apply the measurement process. We suppose that a large number of the smaller samples have been analyzed. Under these circumstances the variability among analytical values may arise from pure measurement error or sampling (of the large sample) error, or both. We can then construct a frequency distribution or histogram of the resulting numbers, which could have the appearance of Fig. 1–1, in which the area of the block between *a* and *b* is the relative frequency of numbers between *a* and *b,* and the units of area are chosen so that the total area of all the blocks is unity. This distribution is an empirical or observed distribution.

We have supposed that we could have obtained an indefinitely large number of results, and we can imagine making successive histograms in which the intervals become progressively narrower until we have essentially a continuous curve rather than a curve which proceeds by steps. The distribution which we would so obtain may be called the true distribution underlying the whole measurement operation, and it may take a particular mathematical form, of which examples will be given later.

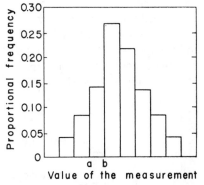

Fig. 1–1. Frequency distribution of arbitrary measurements.

The mean of this essentially infinite population, which will be hypothetical in all cases, that is, the arithmetic average of an indefinitely large number of results, may be called the "statistical true value" or "limiting mean" associated with the measurement process and the object of measurement. It may also be called the "operational true value," in the sense that it is a mean value associated with the operations of the measurement process.

This "statistical true value" may be different from the "scientific true value" which is being sought, for one or more of the following reasons:

(*1*) The specifications of the measurement process may be inadequate. The deficiency may be one of selectivity, in which the process does not permit inclusion of all that is desired; or it may include more than is intended. Alternatively, the specifications may not provide for the problem encountered with some measurements that the quantitative expression of the property being measured is not entirely independent of the nature of the material on which the analysis is performed. Inadequate specification of a measurement process may be characterized as a scientific deficiency of the process, and the resulting deviation of the statistical true value from the scientific true value may be termed "scientific bias."

(*2*) The auxiliary apparatus or materials used in making the measurement may be faulty, so that the results tend to be too high or too low. Differences between the scientific and statistical true values arising in this way may be called "measurement bias."

(*3*) The process for obtaining the samples to be measured may result in selection of samples that are not representative of the whole. A difference between the scientific and statistical true values arising in this way may be called "sampling bias."

These are very generalized statements of what may go wrong with a measurement process. Another source of discrepancy arises from the human element. We can imagine two different operators analyzing comparable samples of the same soil by the same method but obtaining different distributions because of differences in performance such as filling pipettes to consistently different levels. The purpose of training is, of course, to attempt to eliminate this type of "personal" effect as much as possible, but one cannot assume that the training has been effective or has not been forgotten. Operator variability is discussed briefly in section 4.

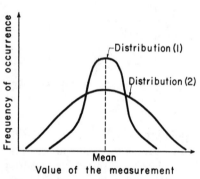

Fig. 1–2. Frequency distributions expected in two different arbitrary situations of (*a*) reproducibility of the measurement process or (*b*) sample homogeneity.

The spread or dispersion of the distribution of Fig. 1–1 must now be considered. One can imagine two measurement processes with distributions (*1*) and (*2*) in Fig. 1–2 in which the means of the two distributions are the same, but distribution (*2*) is clearly more spread out than distribution (*1*). If the sampling procedure in the two processes is the same, so that for instance the two distributions were estimated by first drawing 2,000 samples and then partitioning these into two sets of 1,000 samples, one set for each measurement process, then process (*1*) may be said to give more *precise* measurements than process (*2*).

Precision is inversely related to the variability among results obtained by applying a measurement process again and again to an object of measurement or to samples from a population which is the object of measurement. This variability can be represented by the construction of a histogram or frequency distribution of the results, and we can imagine a mathematically defined form for the distribution which would result with indefinitely many repetitions. Usually one is satisfied with a mathematically defined distribution which is developed from a model of the measurement process.

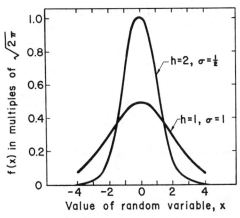

Fig. 1-3. Frequency distribution of random variable x for two values of h and σ.

The commonest distribution in measurement work is the "normal" distribution, and most of our ideas on precision and modes of handling imprecision are based on the normal distribution. Let us suppose that the total error of an observation, say e, is made up additively of components, say, e_1 arising from taking a prescribed aliquot imperfectly, e_2 arising from not adding the prescribed amount of one reagent, and so on. Then

$$e = e_1 + e_2 + \ldots + e_n.$$

Then it is a mathematical fact that if these component errors are not associated, e.g., an extreme value of e_1 does not induce an extreme value for e_2, and if the number of constituent errors is large, the total error will follow a distribution close to the normal distribution. If $f(x)\,dx$ denotes the relative frequency that e has in the interval x to $x + dx$, then

$$f(x) = [1/\sigma(2\pi)^{1/2}] \exp(-x^2/2\sigma^2). \qquad [1]$$

Classical writers liked to write this in another form, obtained by writing h in place of $1/\sigma$, so that

$$f(x) = [h/(2\pi)^{1/2}] \exp(-h^2x^2/2). \qquad [2]$$

This gives the familiar bell-shaped curve of error which is characterized by one parameter σ, which is called the standard deviation, or by h. We give in Fig. 1-3 the two curves for:

        (a) $\sigma = 1$, or $h = 1$, and
        (b) $\sigma = 1/2$, or $h = 2$.

A numerical quantity for which the relative frequency of possible values is specified is called a random variable (actually a real-valued random variable). It is purely a mathematical exercise to determine the frequency with which errors lie in particular ranges, and the most useful symmetrical ones are given in Table 1-1. To facilitate presentation, the situation is considered where $\sigma = 1$ and equation [1] is integrated between specified

Table 1–1. Frequencies of errors in particular segments for a normal
distribution with zero mean and unit standard deviation.

Segment of the random variable	Confined proportion of the total frequency	Usual name of segment denoted
-0.674 to 0.674	0.50	Probable error
-1.0 to 1.0	0.67	Standard deviation
-1.96 to 1.96	0.95	"95% confidence region"
-2.58 to 2.58	0.99	"99% confidence region"

limits corresponding to particular segments of the random variable. An empirical distribution which is virtually "normal" in appearance is presented in Fig. 1–4. In practice one may not get a normal distribution because sets of observations have common errors, and for other reasons.

The fact that the normal distribution of error is determined by one parameter, σ or h, makes the definition of a measure of precision for such errors easy to specify, and the idea that less variability should be associated with higher precision led classical writers to use the quantity h as a measure of precision. If then we have normally distributed errors, the matter of quantifying precision is simple. It is more usual nowadays to use σ, which is called the standard deviation, so that the lower the value of σ the higher the precision.

The concept of "probable error" was frequently used in the past, and its meaning is given in Table 1–1. Instead of considering one standard deviation, only 0.674 σ is considered. The frequency of occurrence of errors within the range $\pm 0.674\ \sigma$ is equal to the frequency of occurrence of errors outside this range, so that the confined proportional frequency is 0.50.

Occasionally the experimenter may observe that a plot of the frequency versus the magnitude of the random variable reveals a positive skewness

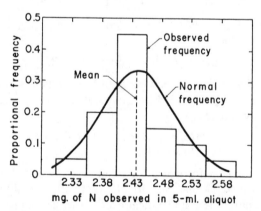

Fig. 1–4. Histogram and distribution of Kjeldahl determinations of N in 20 aliquots taken from a homogeneous $(NH_4)_2SO_4$ solution (Personal communication, D. R. Timmons, Morris, Minnesota).

(i.e., an excess of frequencies for random variables less than the mean). Sometimes such a skewed distribution will approach in shape more closely the normal type of distribution if the frequency is plotted against the logarithm of the magnitude of the random variable. These distributions are called log-normal distributions. In studies of soil properties the log-normal distribution is observed from some size (logarithm of the diameter) distributions of aggregates and primary particles (Gardner, 1956). Austin (1939) demonstrated experimentally that dispersed clays follow this distribution. Menzel and Heald (1959) observed that both exchangeable calcium and strontium were log-normally distributed.

Analogous to the situation in the normal case where the magnitude of the random variables is the additive effect of a large number of small independent causes, the arithmetic magnitude of the log-normally distributed random variable is the multiplicative effect of a large number of independent causes. This analogy is discussed by Aitchison and Brown (1957) and Gaddum (1945). As an example, we may consider the diameter of an aggregate of soil particles in relation to two causes that may bring about a change in diameter. The proportionate-effect hypothesis predicts that the diameter change, resulting from the action of a cause, is some proportion of the initial diameter. Let the initial diameter be d_1, the diameter after the first cause acts be d_2, and the final diameter after the second cause acts be d_3. The effect resulting from the first cause is $(d_2 - d_1)/d_1 = e_1$ and that after the second cause acts is $(d_3 - d_2)/d_2 = e_2$. Hence

$$d_3 = d_1(1 + e_1)(1 + e_2)$$
or
$$\ln d_3 = \ln d_1 + \ln(1 + e_1) + \ln(1 + e_2)$$
or
$$\ln d_3 = \ln d_1 + f_1 + f_2$$

where f_1 is $\ln(1 + e_1)$, and f_2 is $\ln(1 + e_2)$. With a large number of independent causes, $\ln d$ will have an error which is the sum of a large number of independent errors and will tend to have a normal distribution.

The Poisson distribution has a position of some importance, especially in count or enumeration data. This distribution arises where discrete events occur at random over a long time or a large area, and where the random variable is the frequency of occurrence of these events in any small time interval or small area chosen at random. The total number of possible events should be large (infinite, theoretically), but the probability of occurrence of any individual event in the time interval or area considered should be small. The underlying random variable can then have the integral values, $0, 1, 2, \ldots$, and the probability that x will be observed is

$$f(x) = e^{-m}(m^x/x!); \qquad 0 \le x < \infty \qquad [3]$$

where m is the limiting mean or statistical true value.

The Poisson distribution arises, for example, in counts of disintegrations of radioactive elements. Experimentally, the Poisson distribution of radio-

Table 1–2. Number of α-particle emissions per unit of time from polonium observed by scintillation counting, and the χ^2 goodness of fit to the Poisson distribution (data from Rutherford and Geiger, 1910).

Number of α-particles observed per unit time x	Number of times observed in 2,608 trials f_0	$f_0 x$	Expected number of times based on Poisson distribution* f_ϵ	$\dfrac{(f_0 - f_\epsilon)^2}{f_\epsilon}$
0	57	0	54	0.17
1	203	203	210	0.23
2	383	766	407	1.42
3	525	1,575	525	0.00
4	532	2,128	508	1.13
5	408	2,040	394	0.50
6	273	1,638	254	1.42
7	139	973	141	0.03
8	45	360	68	7.78
9	27	243	29	0.14
10	10	100	11	0.09
11	4	44	4	0.00
12	0)	0	2)	0.00
	)		)	
13	1)	13	)	
	)		)	
14	1)	14	)	
Sum	2,608	10,097	χ^2 (11 d.f.) = 12.91	

* Estimates from assumed Poisson distribution:

$$\hat{m} = \frac{10097}{2608} = 3.87$$

$$f(0) = 2,608 \left\{ \frac{(3.87)^0}{0!} e^{-3.87} \right\} = 54$$

$$f(1) = 2,608 \left\{ \frac{(3.87)^1}{1!} e^{-3.87} \right\} = 210$$

$$\vdots$$

$$f(14) = 2,608 \left\{ \frac{(3.87)^{14}}{14!} e^{-3.87} \right\} = 0.11$$

active counts per unit time may be verified by repeatedly counting for short periods of time a nuclide having a long half-life. An example is the number of alpha particles emitted per unit time from a polonium source, shown in Table 1–2. The observed frequencies and the fitted Poisson distribution are shown in Fig. 1–5.

In passing, it should be noted that there are instances where frequencies of radioactive counts do not assume the Poisson form. Counts of nuclides having short half-lives tend to show distribution forms more closely approximating the normal in general shape. A tendency for the distribution to shift toward the normal form is caused also by the internal and external conditions playing upon the measurement process. For example, the scalers commonly used in measuring radioactivity consist of many electronic components, each of which conceivably could add some directional effect to the count. The observed count thus contains not only the factors deter-

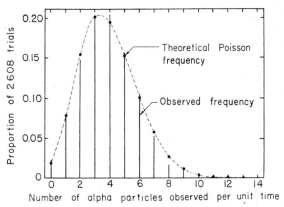

Fig. 1–5. Observed frequency distribution of alpha-particle emission per unit time from polonium, and the theoretical Poisson distribution (Data from Rutherford and Geiger, 1910).

mined by sampling from the Poisson population, but also a number of other factors. As the latter become determinant relative to the former, the distribution should show increasing normality of form. Other situations to which the Poisson distribution applies include the numbers of microbial colonies within a given area on agar plates in the agar-plate method for numbers of soil microorganisms, and the numbers of particles of a mineral species within given fields on microscope slides in the statistical-count method for determining the content of a mineral species in a particular particle-size fraction of soil.

Of other mathematical distributions which will occur occasionally in measurement work, we mention only the binomial distribution and the multinomial distribution. The binomial distribution has reference to outcomes which are dichotomous, such as success or failure, or presence or absence. With n trials the probability of r "successes" is

$$n!/[r!(n - r)!]p^r(1 - p)^{n-r}$$

where p is the probability of "success" on any one trial. This distribution is interesting *per se*, and also in that the more important distributions in measurement work, the normal and the Poisson, arise as limiting forms of the binomial distribution. If the number of trials n increases with p remaining constant, the quantity $(r - np)/[np(1 - p)]^{1/2}$ tends to have a normal distribution with zero mean and unit standard deviation. If the number of trials n increases and p decreases, so that np remains constant, the number of "successes" tends to have a Poisson distribution with mean np. The multinomial distribution arises when the outcome is multichotomous such as would arise when judgments are made about the semiquantitative or qualitative occurrence of some attribute. A reaction might be categorized as "absent," "weak" or "strong," to give a multinomial with 3 classes.

In general, measures of precision and procedures for handling imprecision of data are based on an assumed mathematical distribution. There are, however, basic measures and concepts which can be applied to any distribution.

The variance of any distribution that can occur in a measurement situation is defined as the average of squared deviations of results from the mean of an essentially infinite number of measurements by a given process on a given object (known as the statistical true value). The variance is generally denoted by μ_2, or by σ^2. The square root of the variance is the standard deviation. If the distribution is normal it is specified completely by the statistical true value and the standard deviation, as we have seen; but, of course, the distribution may not always be normal. The standard deviation σ is useful for any distribution because of a fundamental concept known as Tchebychef's Theorem, which states that the relative frequency with which an error exceeds $t\sigma$ in absolute magnitude is less than or equal to $1/t^2$ for any distribution (t is an arbitrary constant). In symbols, using probability in place of relative frequency, as is usually done,

$$\text{Probability } (|\epsilon| > t\sigma) \leq 1/t^2 \,,$$

where $|\epsilon|$ is the absolute magnitude of the error. For example, the probability that an error greater than 2σ will arise is less than $1/4$ for any distribution of error. Note that if the distribution of error were "normal," this statement could be replaced by the much stronger one

$$\text{Probability } (|\epsilon| > 2\sigma) = 1/20 \text{ (approximately)} \,.$$

Thus we pay for ignorance of the nature of the distribution by being able only to make a weaker probability statement.

There are several other measures of variability. The interquartile range is the interval such that 25% of the observations are above the interval and 25% are below the interval. Other percentile ranges can be envisaged. In a normal distribution these ranges are simply related to the standard deviation, as shown in Table 1–1. The variance measures the second moment of inertia around the mean, and other moments may also be considered, such as the third moment which is the average value of the cube of deviations of observations from the mean. Usually the second moment will be adequate to characterize the variability.

1–5   THE ESTIMATION OF PRECISION

In practice we do not have an infinite number of samples, so that we have to estimate the unknown true properties of the distributions we meet. We can give only introductory ideas with regard to the general problem, which forms a substantial part of the body of statistical theory.

We shall assume that the distributions encountered are such that they may reasonably be characterized by mean and variance, and that they are approximately normal in form, so that mathematically developed procedures for normal distributions can be used.

To estimate the variance, a standard procedure with n results x_1, $x_2, \ldots, x_n$ is to calculate

$$\Sigma (x_i - \bar{x})^2/(n - 1),$$

where $\bar{x}$ is the arithmetic average. The result is taken as an estimate of μ_2 or σ^2, and is commonly denoted by s^2. It is an unbiased estimate, so that if one made a large number of estimates from independent samples, the arithmetic average of the s^2 values obtained would approach the true variance. One can take s^2 to be the estimated variance of a single observation. The positive square root of s^2, which is usually denoted by s, is called the estimated standard deviation of a single observation, or the "standard error" of a single observation. It is a measure of the precision of a single observation. The convenient aspects of the use of this measure of precision are that it is easily calculated, and that one can readily obtain a measure of precision for the observed arithmetic mean (which is the common "estimate" of the statistical true value) by forming $s/(n)^{1/2}$. This quantity is the estimated standard deviation of the observed mean or the standard error of the observed mean. One can say forthrightly that any proposed method of analysis should be accompanied by an estimated standard deviation or standard error of a single result, with a statement of the number of observations on which this estimate is based. More commonly, rather than giving the sample size, it is appropriate to give the "degrees of freedom" on which the standard error is based, which for a simple random sample of size n is equal to $n - 1$.

A particularly simple estimation of variance arises when only two observations are obtained because the formula given above reduces to half of the squared difference of the two observations. This measure of variability has only one degree of freedom and is the absolute minimum which can be regarded as scientific in nature.

Rather than use the formula above for variance, one can estimate the standard deviation directly from the range, i.e., the difference between the smallest and largest observation. To convert the range to an estimate of standard deviation, one has to divide the range by a number which depends on the sample size. This number is given in many statistical texts, e.g., Snedecor (1956, Table 5.5). For sample sizes of 2, 3, 4, 5, and 6, the divisors are 1.13, 1.69, 2.06, 2.33, and 2.53, respectively. This estimate of standard deviation is not as good as the earlier estimate given if the distribution is normal, but is probably good enough for most routine assessments of precision.

A rather commonly used measure of precision is the coefficient of variation (CV). For a population this is defined as σ/μ, where σ is the true standard deviation, and μ is the statistical true value. This is estimated with a sample by $s/\bar{x}$, where s is the estimate of standard deviation. It measures, in a rough way, the relative variability of the observations. If one adopted as rough limits of uncertainty for a particular observation say

$$x - 2s \text{ to } x + 2s,$$

then the relative spread is approximately

$$1 - (2s/x) \text{ to } 1 + (2s/x)$$

which is approximated by the interval

$$1 - 2CV \text{ to } 1 + 2CV.$$

An approximate interval of uncertainty of a sample mean based on n observations can then be taken as

$$\bar{x} - [2s/(n)^{1/2}] \text{ to } \bar{x} + [2s/(n)^{1/2}]$$

so that the relative spread of uncertainty is

$$1 - 2CV/(n)^{1/2} \text{ to } 1 + 2CV/(n)^{1/2}.$$

The coefficient of variation (CV) may therefore be used to judge what sample size is desirable to have reasonable relative uncertainty on the sample mean.

We have used the term "approximate interval of uncertainty" without specifying at all what is meant. This term and the computational formula are based on the idea of "confidence intervals," as related to normal distributions. If the observations are from a normal distribution with statistical true value μ, then the quantity

$$(\bar{x} - \mu)/[s/(n)^{1/2}]$$

is a random variable with a distribution that depends only on sample size, or rather on the degrees of freedom on which s is based, which in the case of a simple random sample is one less than the sample size. This quantity follows Student's "t" distribution. From this distributional fact, one can assert that if one determines from a table of the "t" distribution (which is given in essentially every book on statistical methods), the quantity $t_{\alpha,k}$ such that

$$\text{Probability } (|t| \leq t_{\alpha,k}) = 1 - \alpha$$

where the subscript k indicates the degrees of freedom, then one can assert that the interval

$$\bar{x} - t_{\alpha,n-1}[s/(n)^{1/2}] \text{ to } \bar{x} + t_{\alpha,n-1}[s/(n)^{1/2}]$$

contains the unknown statistical true value with the probability $1 - \alpha$ that the statement is true. Conventionally $1 - \alpha$ is taken to be 0.95 or 0.99, and the resulting interval is called the 95% confidence interval or the 99% confidence interval, on the unknown statistical true value.

In writing an approximate interval of uncertainty as

$$\bar{x} - 2s/(k)^{1/2} \text{ to } \bar{x} + 2s/(k)^{1/2}$$

we are using a "t" value of 2 which corresponds to a probability of about 0.95 if the sample size is 40 or more. If the sample size is as low as 5 the associated probability is about 0.90; and if the sample size is only 2, so that s is based on only one degree of freedom, the associated probability is 0.50.

1–6 PRECISION OF DERIVED OBSERVATIONS

A derived number or observation is considered to be some function of a single attribute of the substance investigated by the measurement process, or a function of single attributes, each observed from a different measurement process. The objective of this section is to consider the precision of these derived numbers.

This topic is treated by Topping (1957) and Beers (1957) by essentially the same method. The advantage of the method of estimation of precision of derived numbers is that it is not necessary to assume that the attribute belongs to any particular parent distribution, i.e., normally distributed or otherwise. Its disadvantage is that, in the absence of an assumed parent distribution, and by virtue of the assumptions, the method is an approximation. Exposition of this method of estimating variance of derived numbers will help to extend the experimenter's objective evaluation of data throughout the continuum from measurement to reporting of results. Two cases of the general problem are treated.

1–6.1 Case 1: A Single-Valued Function of an Observation

Suppose we have an observation x, with mean μ and variance σ^2, and we wish to assess the precision of a single-valued function of x, say, $f(x)$. Examples are $f(x) = \ln x$, $f(x) = x^2$, $f(x) = \sin x$. The approximate procedure is to note that

$$f(x) = f(\mu + x - \mu)$$
$$= f(\mu + \delta), \text{ where } \delta = x - \mu ,$$

and to suppose that this function can be expanded by a Taylor series:

$$f(\mu + \delta) = f(\mu) + \delta f'(\mu) + [\delta^2/(2!)][f''(\mu)] + \text{remainder} .$$

Now suppose that the remainder can be ignored, and consider the average value in repetitions, or the "expectation," denoted by E, of $f(x)$. We have

$$E[f(x)] = f(\mu) + [f''(\mu)/2]\sigma^2$$

since

$$E(\delta) = 0, \text{ and } E(\delta^2) = \sigma^2.$$

Hence we note that, approximately,

$$f(x) - [f''(x)/2]\sigma^2$$

is an unbiased estimate of $f(\mu)$. Here, of course, σ^2 would have to be replaced by an estimate. A first approximation to $f(\mu)$ would be to take $f(x)$.

Turning now to precision, we note that if $f''(\mu)$ is small,

$$\text{Variance } [f(x)] = \text{Variance } [f(\mu) + \delta f'(\mu)]$$
$$= [f'(\mu)]^2 \sigma^2$$

because variance $= E\{f(x) - E[f(x)]\}^2$ and variance $(cx) = c^2\sigma^2$. In practice one would use the approximation

$$\text{Variance } [f(x)] = [f'(x)]^2 s^2$$

where s^2 is an estimate of σ^2. When $f(\bar{x})$ is desired and $\bar{x}$ is the mean of n observations, the quantities s^2 and σ^2 are replaced by s^2/n and σ^2/n, respectively. Simple examples are as follows:

$f(x)$	Estimated variance of $f(x)$
$\ln x$	s^2/x^2
$1/x$	s^2/x^4
$\sin x$	$(\cos^2 x)s^2$
x^p	$p^2 x^{2(p-1)} s^2$

In the case when a function of $\bar{x}$, the mean of n observations, is desired, the quantity s^2 in the above formulas is replaced by s^2/n.

The importance of adjustment of the variance of the mean of the measurements when a derived number is calculated may be appreciated by considering several examples. The first example concerns the precision of the estimate of the area A of a circle (a derived number) when the diameter d is measured. In this example $f(\bar{d}) = \pi(\bar{d})^2/4$. The area, $\bar{A} = f(\bar{d})$, is approximated as $\pi(\Sigma_{i=1}^n d_i/n)^2/4$, where the d_i are the individual measurements of diameter, and there are n of these measurements. The variance $\sigma_{\bar{A}}^2$ of the estimate of area of the circle is approximated by

$$\sigma_{\bar{A}}^2 = [\pi(\Sigma_1^n d_i)/2n]^2 \sigma_{\bar{d}}^2 ,$$

because $f'(\bar{d}) = (\pi\bar{d}/2)$. The disperson of the mean area is, therefore, inflated with respect to the dispersion of the diameter. Furthermore, with a lower specified limit of precision on the area, the required lower limit of precision of the mean diameter can be calculated. In practice this application is important because the variance of the mean diameter can be controlled not only by the measurement process itself but also by the number of diameter measurements.

A second example concerns the situation where x is measured, and it is desired to estimate $f(\bar{x}) = \ln (\bar{x})$ and the precision of $f(\bar{x})$. The quantity $f(\bar{x})$ would be estimated approximately by $\ln (\Sigma_1^n x_i/n)$, and its variance is observed to be $(n/\Sigma_{i=1}^{n} x_i)^2 \sigma_{\bar{x}}^2$. This example is mentioned because of the possibility of a misleading implication about the precision involved in measuring the arithmetic value when the variance of $\ln x$ or $\ln (\bar{x})$ is reported.

A very simple example is when the derived number is expressed in different units of measurement than the unit of measurement for the measurements themselves. Thus $f(\bar{x}) = k\bar{x}$, where k is a constant related to the change in units of measurement. The estimate of $f(\bar{x})$ is then $k(\Sigma_1^n x_i/n)$ and the variance of $f(\bar{x}) = k^2 \sigma_{\bar{x}}^2$, which is an exact result because there is no error in the Taylor expansion. Incidentally, this result agrees with the result obtained by first changing the measurements to the unit of measurement for the derived number and then considering the variance of the derived number. The derived number would be kx_i. Its mean would be $k \Sigma_{i=1}^{n} x_i/n$ and its variance,

$$\text{Variance } (k \Sigma_1^n x_i/n) \quad \text{is } k^2 n \sigma_x^2/n^2 = k^2 \sigma_{\bar{x}}^2 \, .$$

1–6.2   Case 2: A Number Derived from Measurements of More Than One Attribute on the Same Sample

This case is more complex than Case 1, but utilizes some of its properties. We illustrate the situation with the case of a number based on two attributes, x and y. Consider the function $f(x,y)$, and suppose it is a "smooth" function. Then it can be expanded around μ_x, μ_y, the limiting means, in a Taylor series expansion

$$f(x,y) = f(\mu_x,\mu_y) + (x - \mu_x)(\partial f/\partial \mu_x) + (y - \mu_y)(\partial f/\partial \mu_y) + \text{remainder} \, .$$

If the remainder is small, the expectation of $f(x,y)$ is nearly equal to $f(\mu_x,\mu_y)$, so that $f(x,y)$ is nearly unbiased. We could obtain a more nearly unbiased estimate by taking account of second derivatives as in the case of a single attribute. The variance of $f(x,y)$ is approximately the expectation of

$$[(x - \mu_x)(\partial f/\partial \mu_x) + (y - \mu_y)(\partial f/\partial \mu_y)]^2$$

which is equal to

$$(\partial f/\partial \mu_x)^2 \sigma_x^2 + (\partial f/\partial \mu_y)^2 \sigma_y^2 + 2(\partial f/\partial \mu_x)(\partial f/\partial \mu_y)\sigma_{xy}$$

where σ_{xy} is the expectation of $(x - \mu_x)(y - \mu_y)$, that is, the covariance of x and y. In using this relationship, the variances, σ_x^2 and σ_y^2, and the covariance σ_{xy} are estimated by

$$s_x^2 = \Sigma (x - \bar{x})^2/(n - 1)$$
$$s_y^2 = \Sigma (y - \bar{y})^2/(n - 1)$$
$$s_{xy} = \Sigma (x - \bar{x})(y - \bar{y})/(n - 1) \, .$$

Also, to use the formula one has to insert $\bar{x}$ and $\bar{y}$ for μ_x and μ_y. The whole procedure is approximate, but if the standard deviations of x and y are small relative to x and y, it will give a reasonable guide to the precision of the estimate $f(x,y)$. To base the result on means instead of individual observations, the estimated variances, s_x^2 and s_y^2, and estimated covariance s_{xy} would be divided by n, the sample size.

We give in Table 1–3 some elementary functions which arise with some frequency. The formulas shown in the table were derived in the manner described above.

The argument given above is applicable also to the case where x and y are obtained from independent samples, with the modification that s_{xy} would be zero. The type of argument above can be extended easily to the case of a function of several means.

Two particular cases with many attributes have moderate frequency of occurrence. Let $Z_1, Z_2, \ldots, Z_n$ be random variables, and $a_1, a_2, \ldots, a_n$ be constants. Then the variance of a linear function

$$a_1 Z_1 + a_2 Z_2 + \ldots + a_n Z_n$$

is equal to

$$a_1^2 \sigma_{Z_1}^2 + a_2^2 \sigma_{Z_2}^2 + \ldots + a_n^2 \sigma_{Z_n}^2 + 2a_1 a_2 \sigma_{Z_1 Z_2} + 2a_1 a_3 \sigma_{Z_1 Z_3} + \text{etc} .$$

In the particular case when the Z's are uncorrelated, so that $\sigma_{Z_i Z_j}$ is zero, the variance function reduces to the simple form

$$a_1^2 \sigma_{Z_1}^2 + a_2^2 \sigma_{Z_2}^2 + \ldots + a_n^2 \sigma_{Z_n}^2 ,$$

of which simpler forms with equal values for a_i can be recognized. Consider also a product function, say

$$P = Z_1^{a_1} Z_2^{a_2}, \ldots, Z_n^{a_n}$$

in which $a_1, a_2, \ldots, a_n$ are constants. Then

$$\log P = a_1 \log Z_1 + a_2 \log Z_2 + \ldots + a_n \log Z_n$$

and

$$(1/P)\Delta P = (a_1/Z_1)\Delta Z_1 + (a_2/Z_2)\Delta Z_2 + \ldots + (a_n/Z_n)\Delta Z_n$$

where $\Delta P, \Delta Z_1, \ldots, \Delta Z_n$ are small errors in the respective variables. If now

Table 1–3. Approximate precision of $f(x,y)$ measured by variance
in terms of variability of x and y.

Estimate of $f(x, y)$	Variance of $f(x, y)$
$x \pm y$	$s_x^2 + s_y^2 \pm 2s_{xy}$
xy	$y^2 s_x^2 + x^2 s_y^2 + 2xy\, s_{xy}$
x/y	$\{ s_x^2 + (x/y)^2\, s_y^2 - 2(x/y)s_{xy} \}/y^2$
$\ln (x/y)$	$(1/x^2)\, s_x^2 + (1/y^2)\, s_y^2 - (2/xy)\, s_{xy}$
$\ln (xy)$	$(1/x^2)\, s_x^2 + (1/y^2)\, s_y^2 + (2/xy)\, s_{xy}$

the errors in $Z_1, Z_2, \ldots, Z_n$ are uncorrelated, we obtain by squaring, replacing $Z_1, Z_2, \ldots, Z_n$ by their expected values, and taking expectations,

$$\text{CV}^2(P) = a_1^2 \text{CV}^2(Z_1) + a_2^2 \text{CV}^2(Z_2) + \ldots + a_n^2 \text{CV}^2(Z_n)$$

where CV (P), CV (Z_1), etc. are coefficients of variation of P, Z_1, etc. In the simple case of a pure product, all a_i being equal to unity, or if the a_i are all plus or minus unity, this function would reduce to

CV^2 (Product of uncorrelated variables) = Sum of CV^2 (each variable) .

This expression serves for products the same role as variance does for sums of uncorrelated variables in that

Variance (sum of uncorrelated variables)
                        = Sum of variances of each variable .

1-7 THE ROLES OF BIAS AND PRECISION

We have defined bias as the deviation of the statistical true value (limiting mean of repetitions) from the scientific true value. Also precision has been defined as a measure of variability of an observation around statistical true value. Bias and precision have intrinsically different roles. One can note, for instance, that precision can be increased merely by making more repetitions, since the precision of the mean of n independent measurements (i.e., independent samples and independent application of the unchanged measurement process) is equal to the precision of a single observation multiplied by n, with almost any reasonable definition. Hence with sufficient expenditure of resources in sampling and measuring, the precision can be made arbitrarily high (unless the material to be measured is used up). Thus in a general way a choice between processes of different precisions must be made not only on the basis of the precision of a single observation with each process but also on the relative costs of observations with the different processes. If for example a measurement with process A gives an unbiased answer with a standard deviation of 1 unit at a cost of \$9, while with process B one gets an unbiased number with a standard deviation of 2 units at a cost of \$1, process B is the better one for the research worker with a shortage of money but plenty of time. Four repetitions with process B would lead to a standard deviation of 1 unit at a cost of \$4 which is clearly cheaper than what process A can achieve.

To examine the bias of a measurement process, we have to consider the precision of observations so that we can form judgments as to whether underlying statistical true values are really different and by how much. Consequently the logical process of examining experimental results *per se* must start first with estimation of precision and lead up to the comparison of means and the like.

Repetition achieves nothing with respect to bias because every repeated measurement (and hence the average of repeated measurements) contains a constant bias. One's attitude to bias is, however, based on its magnitude relative to the precision as measured by the standard deviation. For example, suppose we have two processes, A and B, with distributions as in Fig. 1–6. Here it is supposed that A gives unbiased results while B does not. It is clear, however, that process B will give answers which deviate from the scientific true value by less than one standard deviation with much higher frequency than A. In the comparison of methods a composite measure of goodness combining effects of both bias and precision is the root-mean-square error defined as

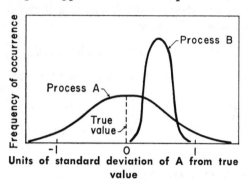

Fig. 1–6. Frequency distributions of two processes differing both in precision and in statistical true value.

$$(\text{Bias}^2 + \text{Standard Deviation}^2)^{1/2}.$$

If one used n independent measurements with the same bias, the root-mean-square error of the average would be

$$(\text{Bias}^2 + \text{Standard Deviation}^2/n)^{1/2}.$$

This measure shows how the comparison of processes depends on the two aspects, bias and precision.

The attitude of the experimental scientists to bias should also be based on the type of investigation he is pursuing. In a general sense of purpose for which measurements are taken, two types of experimentation may be defined. With absolute experimentation, measurements are made to assess the absolute magnitude of the attribute of the object of measurement under consideration; but, in comparative experimentation, comparative magnitudes of the attribute are measured when specific environmental changes have been imposed to bring about a quantitative change in the attribute. The distinction between absolute and comparative experimentation may be illustrated by considering, respectively, the conductivity of the saturation extract of soil for specification of a critical level, and the comparative conductivity of the saturation extract of soil from control and irrigated plots in the same field. In the first case, specification of a critical level implies that other laboratories may use this conductivity, in which case absolute values are important since measurement processes may not be the same among laboratories. In the second case, absolute values are not so important if the comparative conductivities are determined under comparable conditions by the same analyst because consistent bias may not seriously interfere with certain types of inferences about the effect of irrigation on the conductivity. Precision of course must be considered in both absolute and comparative experimentation.

1–8 A NOTE ON TERMINOLOGY

It appears that everyone who writes on the topic "errors of observation" uses slightly different terminology, and this will be a source of confusion to the reader. The following terms frequently arise in the various descriptions: random error, systematic error, precision, bias, accuracy. We shall give our understanding of these terms.

The taking of a measurement is the application of a process, with more or less human intervention, which leads to a number. One can imagine applying this process to a constant object of measurement or to independent samples of an object of measurement. In certain cases this is easily done, as for instance when we make up, say, 10 liters of solution, and draw out successively 1-ml. samples to which we apply the measurement process. We can do this again and again, being careful to assure no carry-over of information or of variations in process conditions from one sample to the next. We can then consider the sequence of results and can examine this sequence for structure or system; in other words we can check for randomness. If we can find no system in the sequence of results, we say that the fluctuations of the results are random, and that each result contains a "random error." We could estimate the random error of any particular result exactly if we knew the statistical true value, which would be the mean of infinitely many results—the limiting mean.

In so far as a sequence of results obtained in the above manner does exhibit some system, we should properly describe that system of deviation of the results from the limiting mean as systematic error of the process. More commonly a "systematic error" is thought of as the difference between the limiting mean obtained by the process in question and the limiting mean obtained by some other process which is deemed to give the correct result, perhaps by edict, or perhaps by calculation when samples are made up chemically to check the measurement process. We have mentioned that one individual may consistently underevaluate a titration or a reading, this presumably being relative to some highly trained individual whose results can be accepted as being the correct ones, subject only to lack of precision because of finiteness of number of results. Such a difference would be classified as a systematic error. If, however, we had in mind a population of possible individuals of which we were going to use one at random, this systematic error would then become a random error, in relation to the results of other individuals.

We have already discussed in nontechnical terms what we mean by "precision" which we can summarize as the inverse of the degree of variability among results which arise in a random sequence.

We have also discussed the matter of "bias," a concept which can be analyzed extensively. Initially it seemed appropriate to us to mention "scientific bias" of a method, which relates to deviation of a limiting mean (the statistical true value) from a scientifically defined true value, which may not be easily obtained. This "scientific bias" may be referred to as a systematic error of the measurement method. Also we have mentioned "measurement bias," an example of which would be a tendency to obtain high values as a result of use of an impure substance as a primary standard. We have also mentioned what may be termed "sampling bias," which is attributable to nonrandom sampling of material to be measured.

The term "accuracy" has been used very loosely. It appears that a method is described as "accurate" if it has no biases of any sort and has high precision. It appears, therefore, to be a summary type of categorization, including many identifiable or partially identifiable facets of the method. Under some circumstances a reasonable measure of "accuracy" would be the root-mean-square error, defined as average (observation-scientific true value).[2]

1–9 STATISTICAL PROBLEMS AND TECHNIQUES IN GENERAL

The presentation of detailed statistical techniques for the vast variety of situations that can occur is neither appropriate nor possible in this book. We can refer the worker to several "standard" texts on statistical methods, such as Fisher (1958), Snedecor (1956), Goulden (1952), Steel and Torrie (1960), and Brownlee (1960). Introductory texts include those by Youden (1951), Fryer (1954), and Finney (1962).

It does, however, seem appropriate to discuss briefly the simpler problems the experimenter will meet.

We have discussed briefly the precision of a single mean. Frequently the experimenter will have to compare two or more means, for instance, to check one method of analysis against another. Statistical texts contain procedures for comparing means. The comparison of methods of analysis may also involve comparisons of precision, and this would ordinarily be done by comparing estimated variances. In some cases the experimenter will wish to check whether his data are satisfactorily represented by a particular mathematical distribution, and will have to use some goodness-of-fit test. Problems of relationships between methods of analysis will involve the fitting and testing of mathematical models, using what is commonly called regression analysis. [See, e.g., Kempthorne (1952).] An excellent treatment of problems of straight-line data is given by Acton (1959).

It will be more common than not that the observations the experimenter obtains have a structure, as with, for example, methods, samples for each method, and aliquots for each sample. The treatment of such data is usually best handled by the analysis of variance, which serves as a procedure for estimating variance arising from different origins. Extensive treatment of analysis-of-variance procedures is given in the chapter on sampling methods for studying soil variation.

Also, mention should be made of the existence of what are called nonparametric tests of significance, as for instance the comparison of two means. The word "nonparametric" means that the test procedure does not depend on an assumed mathematical form for the underlying distribution and requires only that the observations be a random sample from some arbitrary distribution.

1-10 LITERATURE CITED

Acton, Forman S. 1959. Analysis of Straight-Line Data. John Wiley & Sons, Inc., New York.

Aitchison, J., and Brown, J. A. C. 1957. The Lognormal Distribution. Cambridge University Press, New York.

Austin, J. B. 1939. Methods of representing distribution of particle size. Ind. Eng. Chem., Anal. Ed. 11:334–339.

Beers, Yardley. 1957. Introduction to the Theory of Error. Revised Edition. Addison-Wesley Publishing Company, Inc., Reading, Mass.

Brownlee, K. A. 1960. Statistical Theory and Methodology in Science and Engineering. John Wiley & Sons, Inc., New York.

Finney, D. J. 1962. An Introduction to Statistical Science in Agriculture. Munksgaard, Copenhagen.

Fisher, R. A. 1958. Statistical Methods for Research Workers, Ed. 13. Oliver and Boyd, Ltd., London.

Fryer, H. C. 1954. Elements of Statistics. John Wiley & Sons, Inc., New York.

Gaddum, J. H. 1945. Lognormal distributions. Nature (London) 156:463–466.

Gardner, W. R. 1956. Representation of soil aggregate—size distribution by logarithmic—normal distribution. Soil Sci. Soc. Am. Proc. 20:151–153.

Goulden, C. H. 1952. Methods of Statistical Analysis. Ed. 2. John Wiley & Sons, Inc., New York.

Kempthorne, Oscar. 1952. The Design and Analysis of Experiments. John Wiley & Sons, Inc., New York.

Menzel, R. G., and Heald, W. R. 1959. Strontium and calcium contents of crop plants in relation to exchangeable strontium and calcium of the soil. Soil Sci. Soc. Am. Proc. 23:110–112.

Rutherford, E., and Geiger, H. 1910. The probability variations in the distribution of α particles. Phil. Mag. J. Sci. Ser. 6, 20:698–704.

Snedecor, George W. 1956. Statistical Methods. Ed. 5. Iowa State College Press, Ames.

Steel, Robert G. D., and Torrie, James H. 1960. Principles and Procedures of Statistics. McGraw-Hill Book Co., Inc., New York.

Topping, J. 1957. Errors of Observation and Their Treatment. Revised Edition. The Institute of Physics, 47 Belgrave Square, London.

Youden, W. J. 1951. Statistical Methods for Chemists. John Wiley & Sons, Inc., New York.

2

Bias[1]

R. R. ALLMARAS

Agricultural Research Service, USDA
Morris, Minnesota

2–1 GENERAL INTRODUCTION

The term bias, as applied to measurements in scientific work, means a component of error that causes the limiting mean of repeated measurements to be higher or lower than the scientific true value (to use the nomenclature developed in section 1).

The significance of bias and its relationship to other concepts of measurement may be clarified by an example. If 5.0-g. samples of finely ground and thoroughly mixed soil are analyzed for total combined nitrogen, there is no question that each separate sample will have a certain number of atoms of combined nitrogen. This number, expressed in any appropriate units, is the scientific true value for each sample. If all aspects of the measurement process can be performed without bias, the individual measurements in general will not give the scientific true values but will sometimes give higher values and sometimes lower values because of random errors. (The concept of precision, discussed in section 1, has to do with these random errors. Small random errors lead to high precision, and large random errors to low precision.) In the absence of bias, however, the mean of a large number of measurements containing only random errors will approach the scientific true value as a limit, irrespective of the degree of precision with which individual measurements are made. If, on the other hand, the 5.0-g. weight used to weigh all samples should have a mass of 4.9 g., all other aspects of the measurement process being carried out as before, the measurements would be biased. A consistent component of error would be introduced by attributing to the 4.9-g. samples a weight of 5.0 g. Although some of the individual measurements might yield results in excess of the scientific true value for 5.0-g. samples, depending on the degree of precision, the tendency would be for a preponderance of measurements below the scientific true value for 5.0-g. samples. The value ap-

[1] Contribution from the Soil and Water Conservation Research Division, ARS, USDA, Morris, Minn.

proached by the mean of a large number of observations would be the statistical true value for the 5.0-g. samples (following the terminology of section 1) or the scientific true value for the 4.9-g. samples. From this example, it may be inferred that high precision is necessary if the scientific true value is to be approached closely by the mean of a small number of repetitions of the measurement process; precision, however, does not ensure that bias is absent. That is to say, the degree of precision does not determine whether or not the statistical true value is the same as the scientific true value.

Precision is easily evaluated by standard mathematical operations outlined in books on statistics. Although the importance of bias is at least as great as that of precision, bias usually cannot be evaluated readily. In fact, bias usually cannot be evaluated in the sense employed here. By use of proper techniques, one may discover the existence of bias; and one may discover, measure, and reduce or eliminate certain biases; but one cannot prove that undiscovered biases do not exist; hence, one cannot be certain that any discovered bias is the total bias.

Good experimental practice dictates that attention be given to bias in learning to make measurements. In such preliminary studies, increasing the number of repetitions of the measurement process is helpful only indirectly by enhancing the precision of estimation and thereby permitting a more precise evaluation of bias. Special experiments must be performed to evaluate sources of bias and to correct for them by empirical mathematical processes, by alteration of the original process of measurement, or by selection of a different process of measurement. Discovery and evaluation of bias depend heavily on the experimenter's knowledge of the scientific principles involved in the measurement as well as the skillful manipulation of certain apparatus.

2–2 MATHEMATICAL FORMS OF BIAS AND THEIR CONSEQUENCES

Bias may occur in different mathematical forms, some of which are complex. Two simple and distinctly different mathematical forms are algebraic addition of a constant and multiplication of the true value by a constant. Additive bias may be represented by $X_i = k + Z_i$ and multiplicative bias by $X_i = bZ_i$, where X_i is the i'th biased value, Z_i is the i'th scientific true value, and k and b are parameters. For simplicity, the term for experimental error or imprecision is omitted from these models.

Additive and multiplicative bias may be illustrated by two errors in the gravimetric estimation of calcium by precipitating it as $CaC_2O_4 \cdot H_2O$. If the source of NH_4OH employed to cause precipitation should contain an impurity that precipitates as the oxalate, the addition of a constant quantity of NH_4OH would result in addition of a constant weight to the precipitate.

If, before weighing, the precipitate is not heated to eliminate the water of crystallization, the quantity of water remaining in the precipitate may be expected to be approximately proportional to the weight of precipitate; and bias of the multiplicative type will then be present if the quantity of calcium is calculated on the assumption that the precipitate is CaC_2O_4.

The consequences of bias in measurements will depend on the form of the bias as well as the way in which derived numbers are obtained. If one is interested in the difference between two similarly biased measurements, the bias will disappear if it is of the type in which a constant value is added algebraically but will remain if it is of the type in which the true value is multiplied by a constant figure. If one is interested in the ratio or product of two measurements, bias will always persist in the derived result if the bias is of the additive type and will persist except under special circumstances if it is of the multiplicative type. Table 2–1 indicates the consequences of additive and multiplicative bias in several kinds of statistical computations. The information in Table 2–1 illustrates the fact that generalization about the effect of bias in statistical computations can be hazardous. Each computation must be examined individually. Because it is not difficult to estimate the effects of additive and multiplicative bias by algebraic manipulations using $k + Z_i$ for the former and bZ_i for the latter, the experimenter may find it worthwhile to calculate the effects of certain forms of bias that he suspects are present, to see whether the inferences he wishes to make are reasonable in the presence of such bias.

2–3   EXPERIMENTAL INVESTIGATION OF BIAS

2–3.1   Introduction

The investigation of bias should begin with tests made by each investigator to verify the validity of the method of measurement in question as he makes the measurements. The various techniques employed are not equally applicable to all kinds of measurements. Selections and adaptations must be made to fit the purpose at hand. The following sections will describe some of the techniques in general terms, with examples of their use.

2–3.2   Method of Standard Additions

The method of standard additions involves carrying out the measurement process in the absence and presence of one or preferably more known quantities of the substance for which the analysis is made. The measurements y obtained then may be represented as a function of the known quantities x that were added. The first test of validity is provided by the

Table 2–1. Bias introduced in statistical computations in the presence of additive and multiplicative forms of bias in measurements.

Form of bias in observations X_i	Bias introduced in indicated statistical computation			
	Mean, $\overline{X}$, estimated by $\frac{1}{n}\Sigma X_i$	Variance estimated by, $\frac{\Sigma (X_i-\overline{X})^2}{n-1}$	Test of hypothesis that $\mu = \mu_0$ *	Confidence interval containing μ*
Additive: Constant k added to true value Z_i	k added to $\overline{X}$	Unchanged	Number of rejections & acceptances depends on value of k relative to $\overline{X}$ and μ	Position of interval affected by k but length of interval unaffected
Multiplicative: true value Z_i multiplied by constant b	$\overline{X}$ multiplied by b	Magnitude increased by square of b	Unaffected by bias only when $\mu_0=0$	Length of interval increased and position shifted by b

* μ_0 may be any constant including zero, and μ is the statistical true value of the population of which $\overline{X}$ is the sample mean.

nature of the function. Bias is indicated if the function cannot be represented by the linear relationship

$$y = a + b_1 x \qquad [1]$$

where a and b_1 are parameters, $a \geq 0$, and precision errors are small. If the units of x and y are the same, the value of b_1 should be unity; and significant deviations from unity will indicate bias of the proportional type.

Several modifications of the method of standard additions are in common use. In the first modification, the analyses for the standard additions are carried out in the absence of soil. In the second modification, soil is present in constant quantity. The applicability of these two modifications depends on the possibility of mutual influence of the standard addition and the soil. With a technique such as the air-pycnometer method for measuring the volumes of solids and gases in dry soil (section 21–4.3), addition of known volumes of nonreactive solid will clearly produce no interaction with soil solids, and so the test should be equally valuable for detecting bias in the absence and presence of soil solids. On the other hand, if the analytical value obtained for some soil constituent may be affected by the presence of an interfering substance, which is a possibility with various chemical measurements, analysis for the standard addition should be made in the presence of soil. In this way, the analysis for both the substance in the soil and the standard addition may be influenced adversely by any interfering substances.

With the second modification, as with the first, a test of validity is provided by the value of b_1. Because the quantity present in the soil (plus control) in the absence of a standard addition is estimated by a/b_1, a value of b_1 equal to unity evidently will indicate that the quantity found in the absence of the standard addition is exactly equal to the quantity present. If $b_1 < 1$, the indications will be that the quantity found by analysis of the soil plus control is too low; and, if $b_1 > 1$, the indications will be that the quantity found by analysis of the soil plus control is too high.

With both modifications, due precautions must be observed to ensure that the standard addition has suitable properties relative to those of the constituent sought by the test method and relative to the method itself. For example, although KCl can be obtained readily in highly purified form, KCl would not be a suitable standard substance for testing the validity of measurements of total soil Cl by the method of water extraction. Use of KCl as a standard substance under these circumstances could yield results indicating a valid measurement, but the validity would apply to water-soluble Cl in the soil. The value for total Cl would be biased, and the bias could remain undetected. The problem exemplified by the illustration of KCl additions leads to the use of what might be called a third modification, which is to employ a substance for the standard addition similar to the one under investigation. Because there are so few standard substances suitable for use in soil analysis, this modification can be employed only in selected instances. The National Bureau of Standards supplies samples of clays and rocks that are useful as standard substances in checking analyses for certain elemental constituents in soils. A circular listing the available standard samples is published at intervals.

A fourth modification of the method of standard additions involves use of an isotope to label the standard. This modification has advantages in certain applications because of its sensitivity and because of the unique technique of detection, where radioactive isotopes are concerned. For example, Anderson[2] used the method of standard additions of P^{32}-tagged inorganic orthophosphate to investigate the validity of a method of analysis he developed for separating soil organic phosphorus from the inorganic orthophosphate extracted along with it. The method involves adsorbing the organic phosphorus from the extract by a column of carbon, washing the inorganic phosphorus from the carbon by leaching the column with dilute HCl, and then estimating the organic phosphorus by ashing the carbon and analyzing the ash for inorganic phosphorus. The method of standard additions was employed to test the validity of the inference that, after correction for the inorganic phosphorus in the carbon of a control column, the balance of the inorganic phosphorus in the ash of the carbon is derived completely from the organic phosphorus added in the extract and not from the inorganic phosphorus. Because the quantities of inorganic phosphorus in

[2] Anderson, Carl Andrew. 1962. Quantitative chromatographic separation of total organic phosphorus from soil extracts. Ph.D. Thesis, Iowa State University.

question could not be measured precisely from the difference between inorganic phosphorus added and inorganic phosphorus eluted, the isotope measurements were made directly on the ash. The apparent divergence of the example just described from the general pattern of the method of standard additions illustrates the fact that the general method is flexible and may be applied in different ways for different purposes.

In making the standard additions it is important to choose the proper quantities for the purpose. Where the standard additions are to be analyzed in the absence of soil, the relevance of the findings as indicators of bias will usually be greatest if the quantities of x are chosen to be in the same range as the quantities found in the soils. Although the precision of analyses frequently is improved by selecting quantities of x that are relatively large compared with the analytical values for the soils, the findings obtained with both relatively large and relatively small values may be of questionable relevance. For example, precipitation of a test substance from solution may be difficult to initiate where the concentration is low, thus leading to indication of a negative bias in standard additions where, in fact, no such bias exists in measurements on soils yielding more concentrated solutions. Conversely, if the concentration of solution obtained with soils is in the range where precipitation does not take place readily, and if the standard additions are above this range, the standard additions may indicate no bias even though bias exists in analyses of the soils. To ensure the relevance of the findings where soil is present in constant quantity, the quantities of x employed should usually be the smallest that will permit precise estimation of the increases produced by addition of the standard quantities. This procedure will keep the analytical values within the same general range as those for the soils in the absence of the standard additions. In some instances, however, a more sensitive test may be obtained by use of quantities of x that are relatively large compared with the analytical values for soils; this is true in the example described above from Anderson's[3] work with standard additions tagged with a radioisotope.

In carrying out the method of standard additions, one must recognize that additions made at different stages may test the validity of different parts of the procedure. For example, if one wished to measure the content of a particular amino acid in soil, he could make the standard addition before hydrolysis to release the soil amino acids from combination with other constituents. This stage of the procedure would be the proper point to make the addition to check the validity of the entire procedure. Alternatively, the standard addition could be made after the hydrolysis and before the chromatographic separation. Addition at this stage would provide a check of the validity of the chromatographic separation and final analysis, but it would not check the validity of the hydrolysis process, where

---

[3] Ibid.

some loss of the amino acid might occur. The standard addition could be made also at the stage following the chromatographic separation, where an addition would provide a check of the final analysis but not the hydrolysis or the chromatographic separation.

2–3.3 Method of Internal Consistency

The method of internal consistency is an application of the fact that, where analyses are made on different amounts of a uniform mixture of soil, the quantity of any component or the magnitude of any quantitative property found by analysis using a method that is without bias should be proportional to the total amount of the mixture employed for analysis.

In mathematical terms, if increasing quantities or volumes z of soil are analyzed for a quantity, the measurements y will be a function of z. Bias is indicated if the functional relationship between y and z cannot be represented in the linear form,

$$y = a + b_2 z \qquad [2]$$

where a and b_2 are parameters, and where $a \gtrless 0$. In this method, the critical point is the linearity of the relation between y and z; nonlinearity indicates the existence of bias. In contrast to the method of standard additions, the actual value of b_2 is dependent upon the proportion of the component for which the analysis is made, even where the same units are employed for y and z.

The parameter a also has some diagnostic significance. It should not have a value less than zero. In many analyses, it should have a positive value, the magnitude of which cannot be specified. For example, in analyses for combined nitrogen, the value of a should be positive because of the presence of nitrogen in the reagents. Because different quantities of nitrogen may be present in the reagents, the parameter a has diagnostic value only where it is negative. A negative value for a coupled with a constant value for b_2 would indicate the existence of a constant negative bias. In a few instances, the value of a clearly should be zero. An example is in measurement of soil mass and volume for bulk-density analysis. The mass of dry soil found should obviously be zero where the volume is zero. A positive or negative value for a coupled with a satisfactory linear relation would indicate constant positive or negative bias. In neither of the two situations described here does a provide information on existence of the proportional type of bias.

2–3.4 Combined Methods of Standard Addition and Internal Consistency

The method of internal consistency provides no information on existence of the proportional type of bias. To obtain such information, it may be convenient to employ a combination of the method of standard additions and the method of internal consistency. Bias is indicated if the functional relationship of measurements to additions cannot be expressed in the general form,

$$y = a + b_1x + b_2z \qquad [3]$$

where the meaning of the symbols and the interpretation of the findings is the same as before. Equation [3] simplifies to equation [1] where $z = 0$ and to equation [2] where $x = 0$. Use of the combined methods of internal consistency and standard addition in simplest form requires four treatments, including a control, two quantities of z alone, and one quantity of z in the presence of a single quantity of x.

2–3.5 Analytical Methods Differing in Principle

One of the best ways to detect bias is to make the analysis in question using analytical methods that differ in principle. Detection of bias by this technique is based on the fact that biases usually differ among methods, even though some bias may be common to the various methods for reasons such as use of the same weighing and volumetric apparatus.

If a significant difference in results between two methods is found with a single soil, there is little doubt that a bias exists in one or both methods in this particular instance. Finding bias in one instance immediately leads to the suspicion that bias exists in other instances that have not been tested, and so the experimenter is encouraged by his finding to analyze other soils by the two methods. On the other hand, if a significant difference in results between the two methods is not found in a single instance, there is some evidence that significant bias does not exist in either method, where the particular soil is concerned. Because the testing of methods is unproductive of results, the experimenter is encouraged to infer from the absence of a difference with a particular soil that similar results will be obtained where the method is applied to other soils. Where one has gone so far as to prepare himself to make analyses by two different methods, however, the extra effort required to make analyses of several different soils is usually a relatively small additional task that is well worthwhile because of the security provided against the possibility that the failure to find a difference between methods in analyses of a single soil was a mere chance occurrence.

As a possible aid in clarifying the concept, the example of measurement of combined nitrogen in soils by the Dumas and Kjeldahl methods may be mentioned (see section 83–1). The Dumas method involves measurement of the volume of nitrogen gas evolved upon heating the soil and reducing the gaseous oxides of nitrogen to the elemental form. The Kjeldahl method involves measurement of the ammonium nitrogen after digestion of the soil with concentrated H_2SO_4 and other additives to change the nitrogen to ammonium. Analyses of various mineral soils by the two methods have shown that closely agreeing results can be obtained, thus providing evidence for the absence of any considerable bias in either method. Analyses of peat soils, however, have shown that higher values are obtained by the Dumas method than by the Kjeldahl method, thus indicating the presence of a bias in one or both methods. Further investigation has shown that where precautions are taken to remove adsorbed gaseous nitrogen from peat soils before analysis, the results obtained by the Dumas method on peat soils are lowered (although not necessarily to the values obtained by the Kjeldahl method). Presumably, therefore, the results on peat soils obtained by the Dumas method are biased because this method measures nitrogen in the elemental form, and thus includes elemental nitrogen adsorbed by the soil. The Kjeldahl method does not measure elemental nitrogen but only combined nitrogen. Because adsorbed nitrogen is present in mineral soils as well as in peat soils, the Dumas method may be said to contain a bias that operates in all soils but is of significance only in those soils where relatively large quantities of nitrogen are adsorbed. Alternatively, it may be said that the Kjeldahl method is biased because it does not provide a measurement of the elemental nitrogen present in adsorbed form. In deciding between these two alternatives, it is necessary to keep in mind the purpose for which the analysis is made. Ordinarily the purpose of the analysis is to find the content of combined nitrogen in soils and not the content of total nitrogen. The expression "total nitrogen" is therefore a misnomer where it is applied to the Kjeldahl method, and it would be more correct to use the term "combined nitrogen" or "total combined nitrogen."

Under certain circumstances, elementary probability theory can be a useful aid in interpreting results obtained using different methods of analysis. One may conceive of the hypothetical situation in which the mean of many individual measurements is obtained using each of a large number of methods for making the same analysis. If the methods are truly independent, the biases will be relatively large with some methods and small with others, positive with some methods and negative with others. With enough data, one might expect to find a normal distribution of means for the different methods with the scientific true value at the center of the distribution. If the distribution is indeed normal, the probability that the scientific true value lies within the range covered by means of methods chosen at random is nearly 0.5 for any two methods, 0.75 for any three methods, and so on (Youden, 1961).

The difficulty in applying the probability theory lies in obtaining truly independent methods and in developing the competence needed to obtain the means suitable for comparison. This limitation applies also to general use of analytical methods differing in principle.

2–3.6 Method of Independent Analyses

The method of independent analyses employs repeated analysis of one or more soils by each of two or more experimenters. It provides a test of difference in bias among experimenters but not a test of bias of the analytical method employed. A broader discussion of the subject of operator variation is found in section 4.

The method of independent analyses is closely related to the method of section 2–3.5. The basic concept is that a difference in bias is indicated if two experimenters obtain mean values that differ significantly. In general, the most rigorous test is provided where the experimenters are in different laboratories, because these circumstances provide opportunity for expression of greater differences among analyses than would be expected within a single laboratory.

The method of independent analyses is employed in several modifications. In the first and simplest of these, two experimenters make repeated analyses of the same soil, using the same analytical method. If the mean values differ significantly, it is evident that bias exists in at least one of the mean values, and it is possible that both are biased. On the other hand, if no significant difference is found, bias may be present, but the data supply no evidence for its existence.

Because it is possible that bias may not be expressed in individual instances because of peculiarities of the soil in relation to the nature of the bias, the absence of a significant difference in analytical values with a single soil provides no substantial evidence that a difference will not exist with other soils. Hence, in the absence of evidence of bias with a single soil, it is advisable to analyze several soils. This is the second modification of the method of independent analyses. The analyses obtained by one experimenter are then plotted against those obtained by the other. If no difference in bias exists, the results can be expressed by a linear relationship in which the intercept does not differ significantly from zero, the slope does not differ significantly from unity, and the points representing individual samples do not deviate significantly from the straight-line relationship. If desired, statistical tests can be made to find whether the data meet each of these requirements. Figure 2–1 is an example taken from a paper by Attoe (1959), showing analyses of 12 soils for exchangeable magnesium. It is clear from the figure that the two individuals obtained almost the same value with a few soils but that in most instances individual 2 obtained higher

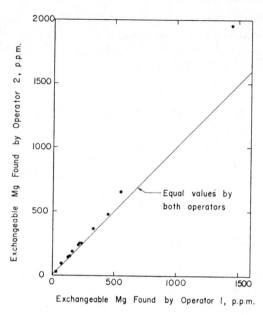

Fig. 2–1. Exchangeable Mg found in each of 12 soils by two different operators (Attoe, 1959).

values than individual 1. Youden (1959) discussed statistical analysis of data of this type by the method of paired comparisons.

In the third modification of the method of independent analyses, each of a pair of soils is analyzed repeatedly by each of two or more individuals. The samples should be chosen carefully to be similar qualitatively but to differ quantitatively in the character to be measured. The purpose of this qualification in respect of sample composition is to increase the probability that, if bias exists, it will find expression in the same way with both samples. (Because several causes of bias may be operating concurrently, it is conceivable that experimenter 1 could obtain higher values than experimenter 2 with one sample and lower values than experimenter 2 with another sample that differs qualitatively from the first.)

The mean values obtained in analyses of soil Y are then plotted against those obtained in analyses of soil X in a two-way diagram such as Fig. 2–2, where the vertical axis is the mean of all values obtained for soil X, and the horizontal axis is the mean of all values obtained for soil Y. Each pair of analyses made by one individual thus is plotted as a single point. If desired a vertical straight line may then be drawn through each point to indicate the confidence interval (see section 1–4) of the analyses of the particular individual on soil Y, and a horizontal line to indicate the confidence interval of analyses on soil X.

The results then are interpreted in the following manner. If there is no

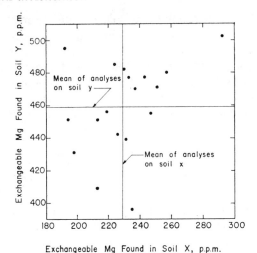

Fig. 2–2. Exchangeable Mg found in each of two soils by each of 18 different operators (Attoe, 1959).

difference in bias among experimenters, the distance of the points from the mean will not exceed the appropriate confidence interval except by statistical chance. Moreover, it is equally probable that, because of random error (including sample heterogeneity), the values obtained for the two soils will be higher with one experimenter than the other, or that one value will be higher and the other lower. Hence, it is equally probable that the two points representing results of two experimenters will lie in the first and third quadrants or in the second and fourth quadrants. On the other hand, if the confidence intervals in the X direction, the Y direction, or both should not overlap, the existence of bias in analyses made by one or both experimenters is likely, and the probability is greater that the two points will lie in quadrants 1 and 3 than in 2 and 4. The reason for this location of points is that, if a bias exists, it may be expected to occur in both soils, so that one experimenter will tend to have results that are higher than the other. If desired, a chi-square test may be made on the distribution of data points among quadrants.

The value of the third modification for indicating bias may be enhanced by increasing the number of independent analyses. The reason is that, as the number of independent analyses is increased, the probability is decreased that a concentration of points in the first and third quadrants will result from random error. Application of this modification may be illustrated by Attoe's (1959) work on exchangeable magnesium. Figure 2–2 gives a plot of values for exchangeable magnesium found in soil Y against those found in soil X by each of 18 operators. Most of the points lie in the first and third quadrants, and some of these points lie far from the means. This distribution of points verifies the existence of differences in bias among operators in their use of the flame photometric method. The wide scatter of points about an imaginary diagonal line passing through the intersection of the "mean lines" indicates existence of considerable random error. Existence of such error is verified by the frequent substantial differences in analyses reported for unlabeled duplicate samples submitted to the operators for analysis.

2–3.7 Method of Systematic Variation of Factors

The method of systematic variation of factors is used primarily in efforts to identify possible causes of bias, the magnitude of their effects, and the interaction among causes. Usually the method of systematic variation of factors is not employed at the outset but is used only after other tests have indicated the existence of bias. The factors investigated may exist in discrete form, such as different kinds of condensers in a Kjeldahl apparatus for nitrogen; or, they may exist as continuous variables, such as the rate of distillation or the concentration of magnesium in extracts to be analyzed for calcium.

The method consists essentially of making repeated analyses for a fixed quantity of the test constituent as other factors are varied one at a time or in some other fashion, such as a factorial design. The factorial design is advantageous because of the efficiency of effort and the knowledge of interactions that it provides. Cochran and Cox (1957) and Kempthorne (1952) discussed the concepts of factorial designs, confounding, and fractional replication that are useful in carrying out the method of systematic variation of factors. Youden (1961) and Kempthorne (1948) discussed the advantages and disadvantages of fractional replication in relation to the possible interaction among factors.

Although the method may be applied in the presence of fixed quantities of soil, it is usually applied to standard additions of the test constituent in the absence of soil. The advantage of the latter approach is that, where chemical work is concerned, reagent-grade chemicals of high purity can be employed to obtain mixtures of known composition without the necessity for making analyses of soils. By observing the change in analytical values obtained as the composition or other factors are varied, the effect of individual factors and of factor interaction on bias can be observed. The information obtained then may be used in efforts to reduce bias, as mentioned in section 2–4. In any event, an important step is that of correlating the findings with the conditions encountered in soils.

As an example of the use of the method of systematic variation of factors, the work of Shaw and Veal (1956) on flame photometric estimation of calcium and magnesium in soil extracts may be mentioned. These investigators examined the effect of different adjustments of the flame photometer, the nature of the fuel gas, and the concentrations of aluminum, iron, manganese, phosphate, calcium, and magnesium.

Bremner and Shaw (1955) used the method of systematic variations to provide a test of specificity of their method for ammonium extracted from soil. They added known quantities of different organic nitrogenous compounds that might decompose to some extent and release ammonium, which would be measured. Also, they added nitrite, which might cause loss of ammonium by reaction with it to form ammonium nitrate, with subsequent decomposition to give nitrogen gas.

2–3.8 Method of Qualitative Examination

The method of qualitative examination is an application of the principle that the quantity of a constituent found by analysis should consist entirely of that constituent and of nothing else. A number of applications of this principle may be made in soil analysis. For example, in the agar-plate method for microorganisms (section 99), one may count as colonies some specks in the plates that are not actually colonies. Qualitative study of the supposed colonies by microscopic examination or by making smears on fresh agar could confirm their nature. In chemical analysis, for example, one may test a precipitate of magnesium ammonium phosphate for manganese, a common contaminant. As another example, the molybdenum-blue colorimetric method for phosphate responds also to arsenate. Hence, in soils where arsenical sprays have been used, it may be important to test soil extracts for arsenate to see whether the desired analyses for phosphate are actually measurements of phosphate. In practice, of course, what begins as a qualitative test may end as a quantitative measurement designed to provide the correction needed.

2–3.9 Method of Summation

The method of summation is an application of the principle that the whole is equal to the sum of the parts. Occasionally this method can be applied in soil analysis. In the pipette method of particle-size analysis (section 43–4), for example, the sand and "residual silt" are collected together on a fine sieve and weighed. The material is then separated into fractions by passing it through a nest of sieves with the coarsest sieve at the top and successively finer sieves toward the bottom, ending with the fine sieve on which the material was collected originally. The sand fractions and the residual silt that passes through all sieves into the pan beneath are weighed.

Bias is indicated by the occurrence of summation weights that are consistently higher or lower than the total weight. The same principle was earlier employed extensively in total chemical analysis of rocks and soils. Where the sample is ignited and weighed prior to analysis, the summation of all sample constituents expressed as oxides (with due correction for halogens) should be equal to the total weight of ignited material in the absence of bias.

The sensitivity of the method of summation as a test for the existence of bias in measurements of individual components is decreased by the compensating effect of positive and negative biases. Sometimes there is even a definite association of a negative bias of one measurement with a positive bias in another. For example, in total chemical analysis of soil, some of the silica may escape precipitation in the intended step and may be carried down with the hydrous oxides in a later step. In this instance the sum of weights of material obtained in the two steps might be accurate even though the weight is too low in one step and too high in the other.

2–3.10   Method of Charge-Balance

This method is based on the principle that numbers of positive and negative charges must be equal. This method complements the method of summation, as applied to total chemical analysis.

In practical soil analysis work, the method of charge-balance is of principal value in checking analyses of soluble salts (section 62). Here the number of ionic constituents present in quantity is usually relatively small, and analyses sometimes are made for all of them.

2–3.11   Method of Comparative Values

Under circumstances where there is reason to think that biases leading to high values are absent, the method that yields the highest value may be inferred to provide the answer that is closest to the scientific true value. The work of Bremner (1960) on different modifications of the Kjeldahl method for determining nitrogen in soil may be cited as an example. In all the modifications tested, the final steps in the analysis were those of distilling the nitrogen as ammonia from a digest of the sample and using a standard method to titrate the ammonium thus obtained. The distillation and titration are highly selective, precise, and generally satisfactory. The principal problems arise in the prior digestion, where the incomplete digestion of organic nitrogen or the use of a procedure that does not include all the inorganic nitrogen are likely to lead to low results, and where high results are unlikely. Figure 2–3 gives the results obtained where two

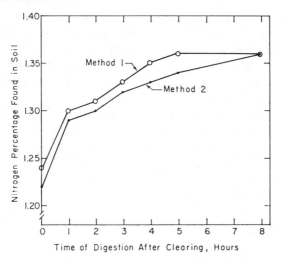

Fig. 2–3. Nitrogen percentages found in analyses of samples of a soil with two Kjeldahl methods, each employed with different times of digestion following clearing (Bremner, 1960).

methods were used on samples of a given soil. Values obtained using method 1 are higher than those obtained with method 2 at all periods of digestion less than 8 hours, from which one may infer that the bias is smaller with method 1 than with method 2 if employed with such digestion periods. With a digestion of 8 hours following clearing, the results are the same with both methods, thus providing no evidence of a difference in bias.

2–4 PRACTICAL SIGNIFICANCE OF BIAS

As the number of methods employed to test for bias is increased, and as the techniques of testing are refined, the likelihood increases that bias will be discovered. However, no single method of testing and no combination of such methods is sufficient to prove that bias is absent. One can only prove beyond reasonable doubt that bias is present.

Once bias has been demonstrated, the significance to be attached to the findings, and the action to be taken, depend upon the objectives and judgment of the individual concerned. If the objective is that of perfecting a method, the decision will probably lie between work to reduce or eliminate bias and work to reduce random error. Ordinarily little benefit is derived from attempts to reduce bias to a level much lower than that of random error. Work to reduce or eliminate bias is facilitated by knowledge of the cause or causes of the bias, and discovery of such causes may be an important aspect of research on the method. If the objective is not the improvement of the method but rather the elucidation of some question with the aid of analyses obtained by the method, a more tolerant attitude may be taken. Here the most important consideration is that the bias is not great enough to alter the interpretation or conclusions although admittedly a certain amount of personal pride may be involved in a decision to use or not to use a method in which bias is known to exist.

In some instances a mathematical correction is applied to the results to provide an adjustment for bias. Most, if not all, such corrections are inaccurate. Although the true values may be approached more closely by the adjusted values than by the unadjusted values, it is well to retain some reservation regarding the validity of the correction for soils in general.

2–5 OPERATIONAL CONTROL OF BIAS IN COMPARATIVE ANALYSES

The methods for experimental investigation of bias discussed in section 2–3 are concerned with detection of bias and not with the problems of carrying out a given method in a manner that will prevent injection of undue bias into analyses for part of the soils relative to the others. Frequently several sources of differential bias may affect the comparative values obtained in analyses on individual samples. These sources are generally associated with either space or time. As an example of the space factor, the variation of temperature between shelves in an incubator may be mentioned. If all samples of soil A are placed on the upper shelf and all samples of soil B are placed on the lower shelf, a difference in temperature between locations obviously could produce a differential effect on analyses of A and B samples. As examples of time effects, changes in analytical results with deterioration of a reagent or with a decrease in voltage of a storage battery may be mentioned. Repeated measurements on samples of soil A and soil B in the same order obviously could result in differential bias of the analyses.

Two basic techniques are employed to control the differential bias among samples. The first may be called randomization and the second, systematization.

The technique of randomization involves assigning individual samples of the group of soils to locations and times in random or chance order. Ideally, the differential bias among soils will be negligible in means of a large number of replicate analyses made in this way. The technique of systematization involves distributing the samples and operations in space and time in such a way that ideally the differential bias will occur entirely among replicate analyses on the group of soils, with none of it appearing among soils. Although these ideals cannot be attained in practice, they may be approached with the aid of appropriate experimental designs, which involve a combination of randomization and systematization.

The techniques of randomization and systematization, and the effects of their use, may be illustrated by reference to an example in which the temperature in an incubator differs between the upper and lower shelves and also varies somewhat among locations within the space on each shelf. If an experiment requiring analyses of incubated samples of soil is to be carried out using the incubator, one set of samples of all soils could be placed on the upper shelf for replicate 1, and another set of samples of all soils could be placed on the lower shelf for replicate 2. This placement is an example of systematization. With an arrangement such as this, the mean value for each soil would be derived from analysis of one sample on the upper shelf and one sample on the lower shelf. Thus, although the effect of the mean difference in temperature between shelves would still be present, it would not be a source of differential bias among soils. The effect of the smaller difference in temperature among locations within the space on individual shelves may now be considered. In a single replicate, and in any larger number of replicates in which the samples of the various soils are placed in the same relative position, the difference in temperature within a shelf will introduce a differential bias. Unless auxiliary temperature measurements are made, there is no way to separate the effect of temperature from the effect of soils in such an arrangement. Randomization of a single replicate would be of no value in controlling differential bias in analyses of a group of samples of different soils, where one sample of each soil occurs in the replicate (although it could be useful where samples of a single soil form a series to which increasing quantities of some substance may be added). Rerandomization of each successive replicate, however, would have the effect of causing the differential bias to appear in part as experimental error or lack of precision instead of apparent soil differences. With a small number of replicates the differential bias among soils would still be present, but the higher experimental error would tend to discourage attachment of undue significance to mean differences. With a large number of replicates, on the other hand, the mean of analyses for each soil would approach the mean for that soil for the shelf as a whole, thus effectively eliminating the differential bias.

The foregoing example might be extended to a more complex situation in which both time of analysis and location may introduce differential effects. If the time effect occurs among days, one design to keep the differential bias from appearing among soils would be to stagger the dates of loading the shelves in the incubator, so that all samples in replicate 1 on the upper shelf could be analyzed on one day, and all samples in replicate 2 on the lower shelf could be analyzed on the next day. This procedure would cause both the space bias and the time bias to be associated with replicates and not with soils. For the situation in which the effect of time is continuous, Mulligan and Haught (1958) adopted the technique of randomizing the samples in pairs, each sample with every other, and of analyzing both members of each pair together. Youden (1954) used a more complex method.

Where small numbers of soils are involved, it is usually not difficult to find some simple arrangement that will have the effect of placing among replicates much of the variation that otherwise would appear as differential bias among soils. With larger numbers the problem becomes more complex. Several different statistical designs are available for handling such problems (Cochran and Cox, 1957; Kempthorne, 1952). Maximum advantage can be derived from statistical designs only where the design is selected to fit the circumstances. Where little or no information on differential bias is available, use of a statistical design as an aid in controlling the occurrence of differential bias among soils is almost certain to be of some value and in any event will do no harm.

2–6 LITERATURE CITED

Attoe, O. J. 1959. Report on flame photometric determination of exchangeable magnesium in soils. Soil Sci. Soc. Am. Proc. 23:460–462.

Bremner, J. M. 1960. Determination of nitrogen in soil by the Kjeldahl method. J. Agr. Sci. 55:11–33.

Bremner, J. M., and Shaw, K. 1955. Determination of ammonia and nitrate in soil. J. Agr. Sci. 46:320–328.

Cochran, W. G., and Cox, G. M. 1957. Experimental Designs. Ed. 2. John Wiley and Sons, Inc., New York.

Kempthorne, O. 1948. The factorial approach to the weighing problem. Ann. Math. Stat. 19:238–245.

Kempthorne, O. 1952. Design and Analysis of Experiments. John Wiley and Sons, Inc., New York.

Mulligan, B. W., and Haught, A. F. 1958. Instrument drift applied to flame photometry. J. Res. Natl. Bur. Stand. 61:499–501.

Shaw, W. M., and Veal, N. Claire. 1956. Flame photometric determination of exchangeable calcium and magnesium in soils. Soil Sci. Soc. Am. Proc. 20:328–333.

Youden, W. J. 1954. Instrument drift. Sci. 120:627–631.

Youden, W. J. 1959. Accuracy and precision: evaluation and interpretation of analytical data. In I. M. Kolthoff and Philip J. Elving, ed. Treatise on Analytical Chemistry. Vol. 1, pp. 47–66. The Interscience Encyclopedia Inc., New York.

Youden, W. J. 1961. Systematic errors in physical constants. Phys. Today 14, No. 9:32–34, 36, 38, 40–43.

3 Extraneous Values

W. J. DIXON

University of California
Los-Angeles, California

3-1 INTRODUCTION

Every experimenter has at some time or other faced the problem of whether certain of his observations properly belong in his presentation of measurements obtained. He must decide whether these observations are valid. If they are not valid the experimenter will wish to discard them, or at least treat his data in a manner which will minimize their effect on his conclusions. Frequently, interest in this topic arises only in the final stages of data processing. It is the author's view that a consideration of this sort is more properly made at the recording stage or perhaps at the stage of preliminary processing.

This problem will be discussed in terms of the following general models: We assume that observations are independently drawn from a particular distribution; alternatively, we assume that an observation is occasionally obtained from some other population, and that there is nothing in the experimental situation to indicate that this has happened except what may be inferred from the observational reading itself.

We assume that if no extraneous observations occur, the observations (or some transformation of them, such as logs) follow a normal distribution. The rules to be recommended are based on the assumption that the occasional extraneous observations are either from a population with a shifted mean, or from a population with the same mean and a larger variance. These assumptions may not be completely realistic, but procedures developed for these alternatives should be helpful.

If one is taking observations where either of these models applies, there remain two distinct problems.

First, one may attempt to designate the particular observation or observations which are from the different populations. One may be interested in this selection either to decide that something has gone wrong with the experimental procedure resulting in this observation (in which case he will not wish to include the result), or that this observation gives an indication of some unusual occurrence which the investigator may wish to explore further.

The second problem is not concerned with designating the particular observation which is from a different population, but with obtaining a procedure of analysis not appreciably affected by the presence of such observations. This second problem is of importance whenever one wishes to *estimate* the mean or variance of the basic distribution in a situation where unavoidable contamination occasionally occurs.

The first problem—designating the particular observation—is of importance in looking for "gross errors" or outliers, or the best or largest of several different products. Frequently the analysis of variance test for difference in means is used in the latter case. This is not a particularly good procedure, since many types of inequality of means have the same chance of being discovered. It should be noted that the power of the analysis of variance test decreases as more products are considered when testing a situation of one product different from others which are all alike.

The problem of testing particular apparently divergent observations (outliers) was discussed in a paper by Dixon (1953). The power of numerous criteria was investigated, and recommendations were made for various circumstances.

3–2 THE PROBLEM OF ESTIMATION (USE OF THE MEDIAN AND RANGE)

The median M of a small number of observations can usually be determined by inspection. Although it is less efficient than the average $\bar{x}$ if the population is normally distributed, M may be more efficient than the average $\bar{x}$ if gross errors are present. A chemist is frequently faced with the problem of deciding whether or not to reject an observation that deviates greatly from the rest of the data. If the observation is actually a gross error, it will have an undesirable effect on estimates using that value. The median is obviously less influenced by a gross error than is the average. It may be desirable to use the median to avoid deciding whether a gross error is present. It has been shown by Lieblein (1952) that, for three observations from a normal population, the median is better than the "best two out of three," i.e., the average of the two closest observations. It has also been shown (Dixon, 1953) that the median is better than the mean if as many as 3 to 5% of the observations are displaced by as much as 3 or 4 standard deviations from the mean.

No attempt is made to give a complete treatment of the problem of gross errors here, but an approach based on a fairly complete summary of this problem (Dixon, 1950; Dixon, 1953; Dixon and Massey, 1957) is given in section 3–5.

The following series of observations represents calculated percentages of

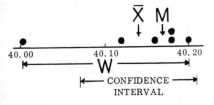

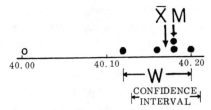

Fig. 3-1. Graphical presentation of data chosen in example.

Fig. 3-2. Graphical presentation of changes produced by rejection of a questionable observation (compare with Fig. 3-1).

sodium oxide in soda ash. The data have been arranged in order of magnitude, and are presented graphically in Fig. 3–1 and 3–2.

$$
\begin{array}{ll}
40.02 & x_1 \\
40.12 & x_2 \\
40.16 & x_3 \\
40.18 & x_4 \\
40.18 & x_5 \\
40.20 & x_6 \\
\bar{x} = 40.14 \quad & M = 40.17
\end{array}
$$

The first value may be considered doubtful. The average is 40.14, and the median is 40.17. We may wish to place more confidence in the median 40.17 than in the average 40.14. (If the series were obtained in the order given, we might justifiably rule out the first observation as the result of unfamiliarity with the techniques involved.)

The range of the observations w is the difference between the greatest and least value; $w = x_n - x_1$. The range w is a convenient measure of the dispersion. It is highly efficient for ten or fewer observations, as is evident from column 3 of Table 3–1. This high relative efficiency arises in part from

Table 3–1. Numerical values for various statistical parameters for numbers of observations from 2 to 10.

1	2	3	4	5	6	7	8	9	10	11
n	K_w	E_w	$t_{.95}$	$t_{.99}$	$t_{w.95}$	$t_{w.99}$	$Q_{.90}$	$Q_{.80}$	$(w/\sigma)_{.95}$	$(w/\sigma)_{.99}$
2	.886	1.00	12.7	63.7	6.35	31.8	–	–	2.77	3.64
3	.591	0.99	4.30	9.92	1.30	3.01	.941	.886	3.31	4.12
4	.486	0.98	3.18	5.84	0.717	1.32	.765	.679	3.63	4.40
5	.430	0.96	2.78	4.60	0.507	0.843	.642	.557	3.86	4.60
6	.395	0.93	2.57	4.03	0.399	0.628	.560	.482	4.03	4.76
7	.370	0.91	2.45	3.71	0.333	0.507	.507	.434	4.17	4.88
8	.351	0.89	2.36	3.50	0.288	0.429	.554*	.479*	4.29	4.99
9	.337	0.87	2.31	3.36	0.255	0.374	.512*	.441*	4.39	5.08
10	.325	0.85	2.26	3.25	0.230	0.333	.477*	.409*	4.47	5.16

* These critical values are for a modified Q ratio: $Q^1 = (x_2 - x_1)/(x_{n-1} - x_1)$ or $(x_n - x_{n-1})/(x_n - x_2)$.

the fact that the standard deviation is a poor estimate of the dispersion for a small number of observations, even though it is the best known estimate for a given set of data. The range is also more efficient than the average deviation for fewer than eight observations. To convert the range to a measure of dispersion independent of the number of observations, we must multiply by the factor K_w, which is tabulated in column 2 of Table 3–1. This factor adjusts the range w so that on the average we estimate the standard deviation of the population. The product $wK_w = s_w$ is therefore an estimate of the standard deviation which can be obtained from the range. In the series presented above, the range is 0.18. From the table we find that K_w for six observations is 0.40, and so $s_w = 0.072$. The standard deviation s, calculated according to the following equation, equals 0.066.

$$s = \sqrt{\frac{\Sigma (x - \bar{x})^2}{n - 1}}$$

As the number of observations n increases, the efficiency of the range decreases. If the data are randomly presented, such as in order of production rather than in order of size, the average of the ranges of successive subgroups of 6 or 8 is more efficient than a single range. The same table of multipliers is used, the appropriate K_w being determined by the subgroup size.

3–3 CONFIDENCE LIMITS AS ESTIMATES

Although s and s_w are useful measures of the dispersion of the original data, we are usually more interested in the confidence interval or confidence limits. By the confidence interval, we mean the distance on either side of $\bar{x}$ in which we would expect to find, with a given probability, the "true" central value. For example, we would expect the true average to be covered by the 95% confidence limits 95% of the time. By taking wider confidence limits, say 99% limits, we can increase our chances of covering the "true" average, but the interval will necessarily be longer. The shortest interval for a given probability corresponds to the "t test" of Student (Fisher and Yates, 1957; Merrington, 1942). $\bar{x} \pm ts/(n)^{1/2}$ is the confidence interval, where the quantity t varies with the number of observations and the degree of confidence desired. For convenience, t is tabulated for 95 and 99% confidence values (Table 3–1 columns 4 and 5).

Confidence limits might be calculated in a similar manner, using s_w obtained from the range and a corresponding but different table for t. However, it is more convenient to calculate the limits directly from the range as $\bar{x} \pm wt_w$. The factor for converting w to s_w has been included in the quantity t_w, which is tabulated in column 6 of Table 3–1 for 95% confidence and in column 7 for 99% confidence (Dixon and Massey, 1957, p. 408; Lord, 1947).

For a set of six observations, t_w is 0.40, and the range of the set previously listed is 0.18; therefore, wt_w equals 0.072. Hence, we can report as a 95% confidence interval, 40.14 ± 0.072. If we calculate a confidence interval using the tables of t and the calculated value of s, we find $t = 2.6$ at the 95% level and $ts/(6)^{1/2} = 0.070$. We would report 40.14 ± 0.070, a result substantially the same as that obtained from the range of this particular sample.

If the standard deviation of a given population is known or assumed from previous data, we can use the normal curve to calculate the confidence limits. This situation may arise when a given analysis has been used for 50 or so sets of analyses of similar samples. The standard deviation of the population may be estimated by averaging the variance s^2 of the sets of observations, or from K_w times the average range of the sets of observations. The interval $\bar{x} \pm 1.96s/(m)^{1/2}$, where x is computed from a new set of m observations, can be expected to include the population average 95% of the time.

3-4 THE PROBLEM OF DESIGNATING EXTRANEOUS VALUES

Simplified statistics have been presented which enable one to obtain estimates of a central value and to set confidence limits on the result. Let us consider now the problem of extraneous values. The use of the median eliminates a large part of the effect of extraneous values on the estimate of the central value. The range, on the other hand, obviously gives unnecessary weight to an extraneous value in an estimate of the dispersion; for this reason, we may wish to eliminate values which fail to pass a screening test.

One very simple test, the Q test, is as follows:

Calculate the distance of a doubtful observation from its nearest neighbor; then divide this distance by the range. The ratio is Q where

$$Q = (x_2 - x_1)/w$$

or

$$Q = (x_n - x_{n-1})/w .$$

If Q exceeds the tabulated values (see Table 3–1), the questionable observations may be rejected with 90% confidence (Dixon, 1950; Dixon, 1953; Dixon and Massey, 1957). In the example cited, 40.02 is the questionable value and

$$Q = (40.12 - 40.02)/(40.20 - 40.02) = 0.56$$

This value of Q just equals the tabulated value of 0.56 for 90% confidence.

If we had decided to reject an extreme low value if Q was as large or larger than would occur 90% of the time in sets of observations from a normal population, we would now reject the observation 40.02. In other words, a deviation, this great or greater, would occur by chance only 10% of the time at one or the other end of a set of observations from a normally distributed population.

By rejecting the first value, we increase the median from 40.17 to 40.18, and the average from 40.14 to 40.17 (see Fig. 3–2). The standard deviation s falls from 0.066 to 0.030 (it might be greater than 0.030 if we have erred in rejecting the value 40.02), and s_w falls from 0.072 to 0.034. The 95% confidence interval corresponding to the t test is now 40.17 ± 0.038 and, from the median and range, is 40.18 ± 0.040, a reduction of about one-half in the length of the interval. (The 95% is only approximate, as we have performed an intermediate statistical test.)

3–5 RECOMMENDED RULES FOR DESIGNATING EXTRANEOUS VALUES

The problem of a test of significance for designating an extraneous value is straightforward. We choose a level of significance, using the standard considerations, and make a test on the set of observations we are processing. If a significant ratio is obtained, we declare the extreme value to be from a population differing from that of the remaining observations. Depending on the practical situation, we then declare the apparently extraneous value to represent a gross error or an exceptional individual. The best[1] statistic for this test, if the standard deviation σ is known from extensive data, is the range over σ for divergent values in either direction (see Table 3–1 for critical values) or the ratio $(x_n - \bar{x})/\sigma$ for a one-sided test. x_n represents the largest observation. For a one-sided test in the other direction, we substitute $\bar{x} - x_1$ for $x_n - \bar{x}$. Here x_1 represents the smallest observation. The power of these tests is discussed by Dixon (1950). Critical values for range over σ are given by Dixon (1950), and for $(x_n - \bar{x})/\sigma$ by Pearson and Hartley (1958).

If an independent estimate of σ is available, the best tests for extraneous values are the same as above, with s replacing σ. Critical values for these tests are given by Pearson and Hartley (1958). If no external estimate of σ is available, the best statistic is the Q-ratio given here. Critical values for these ratios are given in Table 3–1.

3–6 RECOMMENDED RULES FOR ESTIMATION IN THE PRESENCE OF EXTRANEOUS VALUES

Now let us suppose that in place of designating an individual value as an extraneous observation from some different distribution, we wish to estimate

---

[1] Best is used here in the sense of power greater than or equal to all other tests investigated by Dixon (1950).

the parameters of the basic distribution free from this contaminating effect. How might we process the data to come closer to the mean and variance of this basic distribution?

If little is known about the contamination to be expected, about the best one can do is to label particular observations as extraneous values, as described in section 3–5, and remove them from estimates of the mean and standard deviation.

If even a moderate amount of information about the type of contamination to be expected is available, a process can be prescribed which will minimize the effects of contamination on the estimates of mean and dispersion in small samples. Dixon (1953) gives detailed rules. However, if more than 10% of the observations deviate from the mean by 3σ or more, one should test for and remove the extraneous values and then use the median and range. If somewhat fewer observations are expected to deviate to that extent, one should test for and remove the extraneous values and use the mean and range. In either case, it seems advantageous to use a fairly large α; i.e., in general one would use $Q_{0.80}$ in place of $Q_{0.90}$.

3-7 LITERATURE CITED

American Society for Testing and Materials. 1945. Manual on presentation of data. Am. Soc. Testing Mater. Philadelphia.

Dean, R. B., and Dixon, W. J. 1951. Simplified statistics for small numbers of observations. Anal. Chem. 23:636–638.

Dixon, W. J. 1950. Ratios involving extreme values. Ann. Math. Statist. 21:488–506.

Dixon, W. J. 1953. Processing data for outliers. Biometrics 9:74–89.

Dixon, W. J., and Massey, F. J. 1957. Introduction to Statistical Analysis. Ed. 2, pp. 408, 412. McGraw-Hill Book Co., New York.

Fisher, R. A., and Yates, Frank. 1957. Statistical Tables for Biological, Agricultural and Medical Research. Ed. 5. Oliver and Boyd, Edinburgh.

Grant, E. L. 1946. Statistical Quality Control, p. 536. McGraw-Hill Book Co., New York.

Lieblein, Julius. 1952. Properties of certain statistics involving the closest pair in a sample of three observations. Natl. Bur. Std. J. Res. 48:255–268.

Lord, E. 1947. The use of range in place of standard deviation in the t-test. Biometrika 34:41–67.

Lord, E. 1950. Power of the modified t-test (u-test) based on range. Biometrika 37:64–77.

Merrington, Maxine. 1942. Table of percentage points of the t-distribution. Biometrika 32:300.

Pearson, E. S. 1950. Some notes on the use of range. Biometrika 37:88–92.

Pearson, E. S., and Hartley, H. O. 1958. Biometrika Tables for Statisticians. Vol 1. Cambridge Univ. Press, Cambridge.

4 | Operator Variation [1]

C. A. BLACK

Iowa State University
Ames, Iowa

4–1 INTRODUCTION

Operator variation may be defined as divergence among operators in results of measurements made on the same materials by a given method and by a given instrument. There are two general kinds of divergence, and these may occur singly or together. The first is variation in reproducibility or precision, and the second is variation in estimated population means.

The first kind of operator variation, that of reproducibility or precision, results in differences in sensitivity of experimental work. The reason is that the difference among means required for significance decreases as the precision of the measurements increases. The second kind of operator variation, that of differences among operators in estimated population means, may cause no problem where only one operator is concerned and where only relative values are needed; however, where there are two or more operators, where absolute values are needed, or both, consistent differences among operators can be a cause of error, disagreement, and inconsistent interpretation.

For information and coverage of the literature beyond the brief account given here, the review by Griffiths and Rosenfeld (1954) should be consulted.

4–2 EXAMPLE

The two kinds of operator variation are exemplified by the data of Hardin (1952) in Table 4–1. The data are from a collaborative investigation of a method for determining fluorine in soil. Each collaborator received a sample of the same soil, together with detailed directions for

[1] Journal Paper No. J-4406 of the Iowa Agr. & Home Econ. Exp. Sta. Ames. Project No. 1183. Contribution from the Department of Agronomy.

Table 4–1. Fluorine content of soil as found by three operators (Hardin, 1952).

Operator	Fluorine in soil, ppm.		Standard deviation	95% confidence interval on mean
	Individual analyses	Mean		
A	36, 38, 40	38	2	33–43
B	60, 61, 62	61	1	58–63
C	38, 55, 66	53	14	18–88

performing the analysis. Each collaborator was asked to make one or more trial runs and then to make triplicate determinations and to report the results of the latter.

The first kind of operator variation, that of precision, is shown by the standard deviations in Table 4–1. Evidently the precision of analyses by operators A and B is much greater than that of analyses by operator C. The second kind of variation, that of estimated population means, is shown by the means and the associated confidence intervals. The 95% confidence intervals of analyses by operators A and B do not overlap. Thus, the evidence indicates that the estimated population means obtained by these two operators are really different. (Despite the relatively good precision of the measurements, of course, it is clear that both answers cannot be correct.) With operator C, on the other hand, the 95% confidence interval is so broad that the estimated population mean cannot be said to differ from that obtained by either A or B.

4–3 CAUSES

Causes of operator variation may be classified into two groups. The first is differences in technique, and the second is differences in judgment.

With regard to technique, some operators may not follow the written directions exactly. For example, an operator may add two reagents consecutively instead of swirling the test solution, as directed, to mix the first reagent with the test solution before adding the second. Because of a high local concentration of the two reagents, an undesired reaction may occur that will affect the results.

Of perhaps greater importance is the fact that the technique is never specified completely in written procedures. Many points are taken for granted. The conditions are not specified exhaustively. Differences among workers in performance of the unwritten parts of the procedure may have important consequences. For example, if the procedure calls for use of 100-mesh soil, one operator may do enough grinding to obtain the quantity of 100-mesh soil he needs, discarding the oversize material, and another may grind the total sample to 100-mesh size. The result is almost certain to be a difference in the nature of the material the two operators are analyzing.

Differences in judgment in such matters as estimating fractions of a scale division on a recording instrument may cause operator variation. Judgment may be an important source of operator variation in such quantitative measurements made close to the limits of sensitivity of a method; but, in measurements made in the sensitive range, technique probably is of greater importance.

Differences in judgment are especially important as a source of operator variation in quantitative measurements involving a qualitative aspect, such as evaluating the mineralogical composition of a particular particle-size fraction of soil from counts of the number of particles of each kind of mineral in a number of microscopic fields. In measurements of this kind, the operator must make a choice among two or more alternatives on the basis of the attributes of the materials with which he is dealing. Differences in judgment may be expected to be most pronounced where the number of attributes required for differentiation is large, where the difference in individual attributes among qualitative classes is one of degree, and where the attributes are not measured quantitatively.

4–4 REMEDIES

With the causes of operator variation in mind, the remedies follow directly. Operator variation can be decreased by increasing the precision with which the procedures and bases for qualitative decisions are specified and by increased effort of the operators to understand and follow the directions. Training a group of operators together is a useful adjunct because it provides each operator with direct evidence of the nature of his performance in comparison with that of his fellows. Of inestimable importance is the practice of making the trial runs and special tests (see section 2) needed to ensure the desired reliability before measurements are reported. Analysts know that preliminary practice and checking are important; but, because of carelessness, haste, or pressure to produce results, they may make analyses without them. They are well aware that another analyst may obtain different results; however, until it is proved otherwise, they may rationalize the situation by assuming that the other operator is wrong. Because there is usually no easy way to demonstrate unreliability with natural materials such as soils that differ greatly from place to place, individual operators may persist indefinitely, without detection, in reporting unreliable results.

Most of the methods described in this monograph are used almost exclusively for research purposes, and they will be used by individual workers who must decide for themselves how far they will go in verifying the reliability of their results. There are relatively few instances where several workers in the same laboratory make the same kind of measurements on a large-scale, routine basis. In such instances, however, a simple technique can be employed with great effectiveness to ensure that operator variation is held to an acceptable level. The technique is for the supervisor to insert one or more check samples at random in each group of samples analyzed by the individual operators. When the results are reported, the supervisor knows immediately whether the values obtained with the check samples correspond to the values that have been obtained in many analyses in the past. If the values are out of line, the entire group can be submitted for re-analysis. If the values are out of line persistently, the cause of the divergence can be investigated. A modification of this technique can be used by an individual operator to check his own results.

4–5 LITERATURE CITED

Griffiths, J. C., and Rosenfeld, M. A. 1954. Operator variation in experimental research. J. Geol. 62:74–91.

Hardin, L. J. 1952. Report on the determination of fluorine content of soils. J. Assoc. Offic. Agr. Chem. 35:621–633.

5 | Sampling

R. G. PETERSEN

*N. C. State of the University of North Carolina
Raleigh, North Carolina*

L. D. CALVIN

*Oregon State University
Corvallis, Oregon*

5–1 INTRODUCTION

The purpose of any soil sample is to obtain information about a particular soil. The sample itself is seldom, if ever, the entire soil mass in which we are interested. This larger aggregate of material, in which we are ultimately interested, is called the "population" or "universe." Information from the sample is of interest only insofar as it yields information about the population, and the information may or may not be representative, depending on how the sample is selected.

The population itself may be large or small, or even a part of what would ordinarily be considered a larger population. For example, a population might be all the soil in a field to a depth of 36 inches, the clay portion in the top 6 inches of a field plot, or the organic matter in the B horizon over several fields of a common soil type. It is that portion of the soil for which we want additional information.

For any population, there are certain characteristics which describe it. For soils, these may include the thickness of each horizon in a soil, the percent organic matter, the amount of soluble salts, or the pH. The true value of each such characteristic in the population is called a parameter. The purpose of sampling is to estimate these parameters with an accuracy which will meet our needs at the lowest possible cost. All practical studies are limited in funds, and sampling therefore becomes a necessity in nearly all scientific investigations. If the population is relatively homogeneous, a very small sample may tell us all we desire to know about the population. With soils, however, variation and heterogeneity seem the rule rather than the exception.

5–2 VARIATION OF SOILS

Soils are characterized by several types of variation, and if we are to do an adequate job of representing a particular soil population by means of a sample, it is necessary that we consider the nature of these types of variation. The soil is not a homogeneous mass but a rather heterogeneous body of material. And because of this heterogeneity, systems have been set up which attempt to delineate soil classification units which approach homogeneity within themselves, but which, at the same time, are distinctly different from all other units. Thus, one type of soil variation is the variation among the several units which have been classified as homogeneous. Differences among these units may be large or small depending, among other things, on the differential effect of the factors which formed the soils. Poorly drained soils formed from recent alluvium, for example, are usually different in most of their properties from well-drained soils formed from residual parent material. The variation in properties among soils formed from the same parent material under similar conditions, on the other hand, may be rather small even though the soils be classified as different soils.

Because of the nature of the soil-forming processes, distinct boundaries between soil classification units are rare. Although the modal profiles of two adjacent soils series may be distinctly different, there is usually a gradual transition, in the field, between one series and another. Superimposed on this pattern of slowly changing characteristics, however, we may find rather marked local variations.

These local variations may result from natural causes, such as sharp vegetative or topographic variations, or from man-made variation. Available phosphorus, for example, may vary widely within a series because of differential fertilization or liming practices in the past. A similar pattern of variation is found in the subsoil.

Soil properties vary not only from one location to another but also among the horizons of a given profile. The horizon boundaries may be more distinct than are the surface boundaries of a soil classification unit. Here, also, however, zones of transition are found between adjacent horizons. Furthermore, considerable local variation may occur within a particular horizon.

These characteristics should be kept in mind when sampling soils. The soil population to be sampled should be subdivided, both horizontally and vertically, into sampling units which are as homogeneous as possible, and the several sources of variation within the population should be sampled if valid inferences are to be made about the population from the sample.

The intensity with which a soil must be sampled to estimate with given accuracy some characteristic will depend on the magnitude of the variation within the soil population under consideration. The more heterogeneous the population, the more intense must be the sampling rate to attain a given accuracy. Few data are available, however, from which the magnitudes of the several sources of variation in soils may be estimated. In general, although differences have been found to exist among soil classification units, considerable variation may be expected within the units for such characteristics as pH, available P, exchangeable K, exchangeable Na, conductivity, volume weight, permeability, and porosity (Allmaras and Gardner, 1956; Mason et al., 1957; Olson et al., 1958; Sayegh et al., 1958). In some instances, the variation within contiguous classification units is so great that it is not feasible to estimate differences among the units with any degree of accuracy. For most characteristics, the variation, both within and among units, decreases with increasing depth in the profile. Hence, fortunately, it is usually necessary to sample the subsoil at a lower rate than the topsoil to attain comparable accuracy.

5–3   SAMPLING PLANS

When a sample is actually drawn from the population, it is necessary to think of the population as composed of a number of separate units. These may be the number of cores, 3 inches square and 7 inches long, that can be taken from a field, or the number of spade loads which would comprise the area under study. They may be natural units of the population such as an individual plant, or they may be artificial ones such as fields within a soil series. The essential feature is that they be separate and distinct units and that their total number comprise the entire population.

The sampling plan designates which units of the population are to be included in the sample. There are always a number of different plans or designs which can be used. Some are more precise than others (provide a smaller error), and some may be carried out at a much lower cost. In general, the best design is one that provides the maximum precision at a given cost or that provides a specified precision (error) at the lower cost.

The principles of soil sampling were outlined by Cline (1944) and have not changed materially. There has been a greater appreciation of the systematic sample since then, and new methods have been suggested for estimating sampling error; however, very few studies have been made upon which to base sound sampling procedures. Perhaps the cost of making intensive studies has discouraged such work, but if progress is to be forthcoming, further investigation of the reliability and efficiency of different sampling plans is needed.

5–3.1   Judgment Sample

The research worker ordinarily knows something about his population and would like to use this information in obtaining a representative sample. His effort has often been directed toward the use of his judgment in selecting the most "typical" sites from which to draw the sample. These "typical" sites are obtained by selecting the sites, which in the sampler's judgment, present a representative picture of the population. Because the sampling units are selected with different but unknown probabilities, samples selected in this manner are biased. As an example, some workers are very careful to include the extremes of the population (and may therefore oversample the extremes), while others attempt to exclude all extremes as being unrepresentative of the bulk of the population.

Unfortunately, unless additional data are available or the true characteristics are known for the population, there is no way of assessing the accuracy of the results from such a sample. The sample may represent the population very well or it may not; any confidence in the results must rest entirely on faith in the sampler's judgment.

If a small sample is to be taken, a judgment sample may have a lower error than a random sample. As sample size increases, however, the error with a random sample becomes progressively smaller, whereas with a judgment sample, the error drops much more slowly and eventually becomes larger than with a random sample. Unless the research worker is particularly skillful in selecting "typical" sites, the error with a random sample becomes smaller than that with a judgment sample at a relatively small sample size. As sample size increases, the selection of "typical" sites also becomes more difficult and time-consuming. However, if low accuracy is satisfactory and no estimate of precision needed, a judgment sample may be satisfactory for the purpose.

5–3.2 Simple Random Sample

If n units are to be selected from the population, a simple random sample is defined as a sample obtained in such a manner that each possible combination of n units has an equal chance of being selected. In practice, it is usually drawn by selecting each unit separately, randomly, and independently of any units previously drawn. This, of course, requires that each unit can be listed or potentially listed. With a field, for example, it is not necessary to list all possible core samples which can be taken, although it could be done if necessary.

In soil investigations, the unit to be included in the sample is usually a volume of soil, although it may be an area of ground, a plant, or a volume of water. If the units are listed, a random sample can easily be taken by the use of a table of random numbers (Fisher and Yates, 1948). Often, however, it is more convenient to spot the field location by selecting random distances on a coordinate system and using the intersection of the two random distances as the point at which the unit is to be taken. This system works well for fields of both regular and irregular shape, since the points outside the area of interest are merely discarded, and only the points inside the area are used in the sample.

The location of the point at which each sampling unit is to be taken is often reached in two steps. The two steps provide a fairly simple method to use and also ensure an objectivity to prevent a selection bias which can occur when only a single step is used. The first step is to reach an approximate point in the field. This can be accomplished by (*1*) mapping the area, and establishing two base lines at right angles to each other which intersect at an arbitrarily selected origin, say the southwest corner; (*2*) establishing a scale interval to be used in locating the selected point, e.g., a pace, yard, chain, or 0.1 mile; (*3*) drawing two random numbers representing the number of basic scaling units to be measured along the two directions; and (*4*) locating the intersection of two distances in the field as an approximate point for sampling. Using this point as the origin of a new coordinate system, a second random coordinate is measured off to provide an exact point for the sampling unit. The sampling unit to be taken is then defined as the soil unit for which the selected point is some prescribed point, say the center or the southwest corner of the sampling tool. The scale interval for the second random coordinate should be of the same dimensions as the sampling tool with the maximum value of the second coordinate equal to the scale interval of the first coordinate system. For example (see Fig. 5–1), if the first scale interval is a pace and a 4 by 4-inch sampling unit is to be used, then the second set of random distances should be selected from numbers 0 to 9 (9 four-inch units per pace). This procedure provides an unbiased method of selecting the sample, since every unit has an equal chance of being included in the sample. With large fields or areas, it is sometimes advisable to use a three-step procedure as an easier method of locating the sampling unit. In this case the first scale interval may be in miles. For very

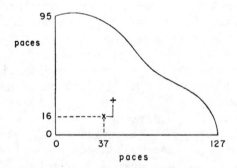

Fig. 5–1. Selection of randomly selected points in a field by a two-step procedure. Random lengths were 37 and 16 paces along the east and north axes, respectively, to establish the approximate point for sampling (x). Random 4-inch units drawn were 2 and 8 to the east and north, respectively, to establish an exact point (+) for locating the southwest corner of the 4 by 4-inch sampling tool. Subsequent sampling units are selected in a like manner. *Note:* The 4-inch units are not drawn to scale, but are exaggerated to illustrate the procedure.

small areas, a one-step procedure may be used. When a circular sampling tool is used, this procedure could conceivably introduce some bias into the estimates; however, this is not thought to be important in practice.

Sometimes a sample is taken from a one-dimensional population, such as a list of cards, a row of pots, or distances along a line. A simple random sample of this type can be taken in the same manner as the sample of distances in one direction only in the coordinate or two-dimensional system. Ordinarily only a single-step procedure is used, drawing one random number for each unit to be sampled. Sampling is usually without replacement, i.e., no unit is used more than once in the sample.

If more than one sampling unit is included in the sample, the random sample provides an estimate of the sampling error. Estimates of the mean $\bar{y}$ and variance $V(\bar{y})$ of the mean are given by

$$\bar{y} = (\Sigma_{i=1}^{n} y_i)/n \qquad [1]$$

$$V(\bar{y}) = \Sigma_{i=1}^{n} (y_i - \bar{y})^2/n(n - 1) = s^2/n \qquad [2]$$

where y_i is the value observed for the ith sampling unit and n is the number of sampling units in the sample. If more than 10% of the population is included in the sample, an adjustment should be made in the estimate of the variance of the mean. Discussions of this correction for sampling from finite populations and other details of analysis are ably presented by several authors (Cochran, 1953; Deming, 1950; Hansen et al., 1953; Hendricks, 1956).

Once the variance of the mean has been estimated, the usual confidence limits may be placed around the mean by the relationship

$$L = \bar{y} \pm t_\alpha(s^2/n)^{1/2} \qquad [3]$$

in which L is the confidence limit, t_α is the Student's t with $(n - 1)$ degrees of freedom (which is tabulated in most textbooks on statistics) at the α probability level, and s^2/n is as previously defined.

If an estimate of the variance is available from previous samples of the population or can be arrived at from knowledge of the population, then an estimate of the number of samples necessary in future sampling to obtain a given precision with a specified probability may be obtained in the following manner from equations [2] and [3]:

$$n = t_\alpha^2 s^2 / D^2 \qquad [4]$$

where D is the specified limit.

As an example of the application of these equations, suppose we have taken 10 cores at random from the 0- to 6-inch layer of soil in a particular field and have obtained the following estimates of exchangeable potassium (K) in ppm.:

$$59, 47, 58, 80, 57, 58, 62, 52, 50, 47 .$$

The mean exchangeable K level, estimated using equation [1], would be

$$\bar{y} = (59 + 47 + \ldots + 47)/10 = 570/10 = 57.0 \text{ ppm} .$$

The variance of the mean would be, from equation [2],

$$V(\bar{y}) = (834.00)/(10)(9) = 92.67/10 = 9.267 .$$

The 95% confidence limits are then obtained using equation [3]:

$$L = 57.0 \pm 2.26(9.267)^{1/2} = 57.0 \pm (2.26)(3.04)$$
$$L = 57.0 \pm 6.87 .$$

Thus, we can say that unless a 1 in 20 chance has occurred in sampling, the true population mean lies within the range 50.13 to 63.87 ppm. K; that is, the probability is 0.95 that the true mean lies within the range 50.13 to 63.87 ppm. K.

Suppose we are interested in determining the number of observations required in future sampling of the population to estimate the mean within ± 5.00 ppm. at the 95% probability level. The necessary number of samples would be estimated using equation [4]:

$$n = (2.26)^2 (92.67)/(5.00)^2 = (5.11)(92.67)/25.00$$
$$n = 18.94.$$

Hence, to obtain the desired precision it is estimated that the sampling rate should be increased from 10 to 19 in future sampling.

5–3.3   Stratified Random Sample

With stratified random sampling the population is broken into a number of subpopulations, and a simple random sample is taken from each subpopulation; e.g., a field may be mapped by series (subpopulations) and a random sample taken from each series. The reasons for sampling soils in this manner include the desire (*1*) to make statements about each of the subpopulations separately, and (*2*) to increase the precision of estimates over the entire population. For the first reason, the sampling can be considered a series of separate sampling studies on a number of different populations. The second reason, however, raises some special considerations, both from the standpoint of design and analysis.

If the stratified random sample is to have greater precision than the simple random sample, stratification must eliminate some of the variation from the sampling error. Since every subpopulation, or stratum, is sampled, the differences among the stratum means are eliminated from the error, and only the within-stratum variation contributes to the sampling error. If strata are constructed in such a manner as to make the units within each stratum very homogeneous compared to the variation among the stratum means, the stratified random sample will have much greater precision than the simple random sample. The basis for making effective stratification may be another variable related to or correlated with the characteristic of interest, previous knowledge about the distribution of the characteristic, or merely geographic proximity. Any prior information which will aid in making homogeneous groups of units of the population can be used.

In general, the more stratification the greater the increase in precision. There are several precautions that should be considered, though, to prevent excessive stratification. Precision increases at a decreasing rate as strata are divided more and more until a point is reached where no further gain in precision is obtained. The additional strata also complicate the analysis so that the gain in precision must be considered in relation to the effort required to obtain it. Since at least two units must be sampled in each stratum to have an estimate of the sampling error from that stratum, it is usually advisable to keep the number of strata small enough to allow satisfactory estimates of error.

The total number of sampling units is usually allocated to the strata proportionately; e.g., if a stratum contains 20% of the population then 20% of the sampling units will be taken from that stratum. This allocation is not optimum in the sense that the variance of the mean will be a minimum; however, unless the variation within the strata differs markedly from stratum to stratum it will be nearly as good an allocation as possible. Optimum allocation, both with equal and unequal costs per unit in different strata, is discussed at length by Cochran (1953), and Hansen et al. (1953).

The estimate of the mean over all strata, $\bar{\bar{y}}$, and the variance of this mean, $V(\bar{\bar{y}})$, are given by

$$\bar{\bar{y}} = (\Sigma_{h=1}^{L} N_h \bar{y}_h)/N \qquad [5]$$

$$V(\bar{\bar{y}}) = (1/N^2) \Sigma_{h=1}^{L} N_h^2 (s_h^2/n_h) \qquad [6]$$

where N_h is the total number of units in the hth stratum, L is the total number of strata, N is the total number of units in all strata, and

$$s_h^2/n_h = V(\bar{y}_h)$$

as given in section 5–3.2. It may be noted that N_h/N is the proportion of all sampling units in the hth stratum; hence the proportion of the population in the hth stratum may be used in the equation rather than the total number.

When the allocation is proportional and all strata have a common variance, which is a common occurrence in soil sampling, then the estimation of the mean and variance are simplified:

$$\bar{\bar{y}} = (\Sigma_{i=1}^{n} y_i)/n \qquad [7]$$

$$V(\bar{\bar{y}}) = s_p^2/n \qquad [8]$$

where n is the total number of units in the sample and $s_p{}^2$ is the pooled variance within strata ($s_p{}^2$ measures the variation among samples within strata).

If more than 10% of the units in any stratum are included in the sample, use should be made of the finite population correction referred to previously in section 5–3.2.

To illustrate the computations involved in stratified random sampling, suppose we are interested in estimating the cation-exchange capacity of the surface soil in a field which contains three soil types: A, B and C. Suppose further, that type A represents 1/6 of the total area of the field, type B 1/3, and C 1/2 of the total area. We might stratify the field with respect to soil type and draw a simple random sample of cores from each stratum, the number of cores from each stratum being proportioned to the fraction of the total area occupied by each soil type. That is, we might take 2 samples from type A, 4 from type B, and 6 from type C. The results of such a sampling plan are shown in Table 5–1.

The mean exchange capacity would be estimated using equation [7] as

$$\bar{y} = (11.6 + 13.4 + \ldots + 17.1 + 19.5)/12 = 16.62 \text{ me. per } 100 \text{ g}.$$

Assuming a common within-stratum variance, the variance of the mean could be estimated using an analysis of variance of the sample data, shown in Table 5–2.

Table 5–1. Cation-exchange capacity of soil samples from a field stratified according to soil type.

	Cation-exchange capacity (me. /100 g.) of samples from indicated type		
	A	B	C
	11.6	19.0	14.2
	13.4	21.4	16.5
		18.1	15.7
		17.8	15.2
			17.1
			19.5
Total	25.0	76.3	98.2
Mean	12.50	19.08	16.37

Table 5–2. Analysis of variance of cation-exchange capacity (me./100 g.) of soil samples in Table 5–1.

Source of variation	Degrees of freedom	Mean square
Among strata	2	29.22
Among samples within strata	9	2.94

The variance of the mean, $V(\bar{y})$, would then be estimated using the "within-strata" mean square and equation [8]:

$$V(\bar{y}) = 2.94/12 = 0.24.$$

And, by analogy to simple random sampling, we might place the 95% confidence limits about the mean using equation [3]:

$$L = 16.62 \pm 2.26(0.24)^{1/2} = 16.62 \pm (2.26)(.49) = 16.62 \pm 1.11.$$

Thus we can say that the true population mean lies within the range of 15.51 to 17.73 me. per 100 g. with probability 0.95.

5–3.4 Systematic Sample

As the stratified random sample is an attempt to ensure that better coverage of the population is obtained than with a simple random sample, so also is the use of a systematic sample a further step in this same direction. It is a natural extension and one that is receiving increasing attention. The fact that it is easy to use in practice has undoubtedly been a factor in its wide usage.

The definition of a systematic sample which is used here covers samples in which the selected units are at regular distances away from each other, either in one or two dimensions. If the population is of one dimension, e.g., units along a line, in a list, or in any linear order, the first unit is assumed to be selected at random from the first k units and subsequent units at each kth interval (Cochran, 1953). If the population is of two dimensions, e.g., plots in a field or sections of an area, the surface can be considered to be composed of a number of strata of common size and shape. In one stratum a unit is selected at random, and all units in comparable positions in all strata are included in the sample. Alternatively, the

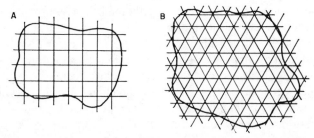

Fig. 5–2. Systematic samples in two dimensions. Design A is composed of all units at the intersections of equidistant parallel lines at right angles to each other. Design B is composed of all units at the intersections of equidistant parallel lines, each set at 60° from vertical. Triangles are formed by drawing horizontal lines through the intersections.

stratum pattern can be imposed at random on the surface and the center unit from each stratum included in the sample (see Fig. 5–2). In practice, it is not necessary that the stratum outlines actually be designated, although the procedure must permit them. This definition includes the type of systematic sample most common in practice, although many others could be designed. This type of systematic sample can also be considered as a single complex sampling unit selected at random from such k units in the population.

For the one-dimensional case, systematic samples have been compared with random and stratified random samples, both theoretically (Cochran, 1946; Madow and Madow, 1944; Madow 1949, 1953; Yates, 1948), and empirically (Finney, 1948; Hasel, 1938; Osborne, 1942; Williams, 1956; Yates, 1948). The results have favored systematic samples in nearly all cases. An exception pointed out by several workers (Cochran, 1953; Finney, 1948; Madow and Madow, 1944; Yates, 1948) may occur when the population has a periodic trend, such as might be experienced by a line across hills and valleys in a forested area, or across a field with row effects caused from previous fertilizer treatment. When this occurs, the systematic sample is much less precise than random sampling if the interval between the sampling units in the systematic sample is equal to an integral multiple of the period, e.g., sampling units taken on each row and none between rows. If the interval is equal to an odd multiple of the half period, systematic sampling will be more precise. Milne (1959) states that such periodicities seldom occur in nature; however, Matérn (1960) gives several examples, but indicates that a considerable loss of precision occurs only when the interval coincides closely with the periodicity.

The two-dimensional case, applicable for most field sampling, has been studied theoretically (Das, 1950; Matérn, 1960; Quenouille, 1949; Zubrzycki, 1958) for several types of populations. Empirical studies have been very limited and confined to crops and forested areas. The theoretical studies have all assumed that a correlation exists between units close to each other and that this correlation decreases exponentially with the distance between the units. This seems to be a realistic assumption, and it has been supported by empirical studies (Finney, 1948; Milne, 1959; Rigney and Reed, 1946). The results are similar to the one-dimensional case in that the systematic sample has greater precision than random or stratified random samples, if the correlation between plots decreases exponentially with distance between the plots in both directions. Dalenius et al.[1] have also shown that the optimum pattern for several classes of populations is the triangular grid shown in Fig. 5–2B, although the square grid is almost as precise.

[1] Dalenius, Tore, Jaroslav, Hajek, and Zubrzycki, Stefan. 1960. On plane sampling and some related problems. Unpubl. mimeo. paper.

The effect of additional trends in the population has not yet been fully studied, although such trends may be a more important factor than the correlation in the precision of systematic sampling. It has been pointed out (Madow and Madow, 1944; Yates, 1948) that the systematic grid pattern is inefficient when there is a fertility gradient along rows or columns of a field. Since this may be the case in fields which have a slope or drainage problem (or other not such obvious conditions imposing a gradient effect), it is apparent that systematic designs cannot be used without consideration of the form of the population distribution.

The empirical comparisons have shown somewhat conflicting results. In sampling for crop yield on 14 fields, Haynes[2] found that the systematic square grid pattern (see Fig. 5–2A) had about the same precision as the simple random sample and less precision than the stratified random sample. Matérn (1960) found that square and triangular grids gave greater precision than the stratified random and considerably greater precision than the random sample when sampling for percent forested area and percent lake area in a region. Haynes hypothesized that a linear trend might be the cause of his results and showed on the basis of theory that the systematic sample is indeed less precise in the presence of such a trend. It can be shown that the precision also depends on relative gradients in the two directions. In general, when linear trends are present, more sampling units should be selected in the direction of the strongest gradient.

One of the main problems with the systematic sample has been in the estimate of sampling error from the sample itself. A number of methods have been suggested (Hansen et al., 1953; Madow, 1953; Milne, 1959; Osborne, 1942; Smith, 1938; Williams, 1956), but those most commonly used in practice are the following: (1) assume that the population was in random order before the systematic sample was drawn and estimate the sampling error as with a simple random sample; (2) block or stratify the sample, assuming that the variation among units within a block or stratum is only sampling variation, and estimate the sampling error as with a stratified random sample; and (3) take a number of separate systematic samples, each drawn at random from all possible systematic samples of the same type, i.e., each systematic sample is drawn with a separate randomly selected starting point. The sample mean is calculated from each sample, and these means are treated as the data from a simple random sample of size equal to the number of separate systematic samples. Method (3) is the only unbiased method of assessing the sampling error without making some assumptions about the form of the population; however, if the assumptions made under methods (1) and (2) are reasonably valid, these methods give greater precision.

---

[2] Haynes, J. D. 1948. An empirical investigation of sampling methods for an area. Unpubl. M.S. thesis, North Carolina State College, Raleigh, N. C.

5–4 SOURCES OF ERRORS

Errors arising from soil sampling (Das, 1950) fall into three general categories, viz., sampling error, selection error, and measurement error. Each contributes to the total error, and consideration of each of them is necessary to ensure a satisfactory sampling procedure.

Sampling error is the error arising from the fact that the sample includes only the selected sampling units rather than the entire population. It is caused by the inherent variation among the units of the population and can be avoided completely only by including all of the population in the sample.

Selection error arises from any tendency to select some units of the population with a greater or lesser probability than was intended, e.g., a tendency to avoid rocky sites in a field or to oversample the borders of a field. There is some tendency for selection errors to cancel each other; and yet, as sample size increases, bias resulting from the selection procedure may become an increasing portion of the total error. The two-step procedure outlined in section 5–3.2 is a method designed to minimize selection error, and analogous procedures can usually be devised.

Measurement error is that error caused by the failure of the observed measurement to be the true value for the unit. It includes both the random errors of measurement which tend to cancel out with increased sample size and biases which are independent of sample size. Examples of random errors are those caused by assuming constant weights for cores of soil which have variable weights and those caused by chance variations of technique in the analytical procedure. Biases, independent of sample size, would result if tare weights were ignored or if a calibration curve were offset to one side of the appropriate curve.

If a biased technique is used, such as subsampling from the top of a container of improperly mixed soil (selection error), or using an analytical test which gives a reading too high (measurement error), then this error, or bias, would not be included in the computed sampling error. Only constant attention to technique can hold these biases to a minimum, and even then no estimate of their magnitude is usually available.

Although considerable study is needed on the sources of error in practical surveys, some evidence would point to sampling error generally being larger than random measurement error (Cline, 1944; Hammond et al., 1958; Rigney and Reed, 1946).

5–5 SUBSAMPLING

In many types of soil investigation, the use of subsampling, or multistage sampling, is advantageous. With this technique, the sampling unit, selected by one of the previously described methods, is divided into a number of smaller elements. The characteristic under consideration is then measured on a sample of these elements drawn at random from the unit. For example, a sample of cores may be taken from a field plot, and a number of small samples taken from each core for chemical analysis.

The primary advantage of subsampling is that it permits the estimation of some characteristic of the larger sampling unit without the necessity of measuring the entire unit. Hence, by using subsampling, the cost of the investigation might be considerably reduced. At the same time, however, subsampling will usually decrease the precision with which the characteristic is estimated. At each stage of sampling, an additional component of variation, the variation among smaller elements within the larger units, is added to the sampling error. Thus, the efficient use of subsampling depends on striking a balance between cost and precision.

To illustrate the statistical considerations involved in subsampling, suppose we draw n sampling units at random from a population, and from each unit we select, at random, m elements. The mean, on a per element basis, may be estimated from

$$\bar{\bar{y}} = (\Sigma_{i=1}^{n} \Sigma_{j=1}^{m} y_{ij})/nm \qquad [9]$$

in which $\bar{\bar{y}}$ is the sample mean, y_{ij} is the observation on the jth element in the ith unit, n is the number of units in the sample, and m is the number of elements sampled per unit.

The variance of the mean, $V(\bar{\bar{y}})$, on a per element basis, is given by

$$V(\bar{\bar{y}}) = \sigma_b^2/n + \sigma_w^2/mn \qquad [10]$$

where σ_b^2 is the variation among units, σ_w^2 is the variation among elements within units, and n and m are as previously defined.

The components of variance, σ_b^2 and σ_w^2, may be estimated from an analysis of variance of the sample data, shown in Table 5–3.

The variation among elements, σ_w^2, is estimated by the mean square

Table 5–3. Analysis of variance of the sample (on a per element basis).

Source of variation	Degrees of freedom	Mean square*	Mean square is an estimate of
Among units	$(n-1)$	s_b^2	$\sigma_w^2 + m\sigma_b^2$
Among elements within units	$n(m-1)$	s_w^2	σ_w^2

$$* \quad s_b^2 = m\Sigma_i(\bar{y}_i - \bar{\bar{y}})^2 /(n-1)$$

$$s_w^2 = \Sigma_i \Sigma_j (y_{ij} - \bar{y}_i)^2 /n(m-1)$$

where $\bar{y}_i$ = the mean of the ith unit = $(\Sigma_{j=1}^{m} y_{ij})/m$.

among elements within units, $s_w{}^2$. The variation among units, $\sigma_b{}^2$, is estimated from

$$\sigma_b^2 = (s_b^2 - s_w^2)/m . \qquad [11]$$

If the sample includes more than 10% of the units in the population, an adjustment should be made in the estimate of the variance of the mean. The proper adjustment is adequately discussed by several authors (Cochran, 1953; Deming, 1950; Hansen et al., 1953).

If estimates of $\sigma_w{}^2$ and $\sigma_b{}^2$ are available from previous samples, or can be arrived at from a knowledge of the population, we can use equation [10] to predict the variance of the mean in future sampling from the same type of population. The proposed sampling and subsampling rates, n and m, and the estimates of the variance components, $\sigma_w{}^2$ and $\sigma_b{}^2$, are substituted into the appropriate equation.

It is apparent from [10] that the variance of the mean may always be reduced at a more rapid rate by increasing the number of units sampled than by increasing the sampling rate within units. This may not be the most efficient procedure, however, if the cost of taking the sample is considered. The optimum sampling and subsampling rate will depend on the relative cost of sampling the unit and that of sampling the element within the unit. A cost relationship which has been useful in many types of soil investigation is given by

$$C = nc_b + nmc_w \qquad [12]$$

in which C is the total cost of obtaining an estimate of the mean, c_b is the cost per unit, directly assignable to the unit and independent of the number of elements per units, c_w is the cost per element, and n and m are the number of units and the number of elements per unit, respectively, in the sample.

When the variance of the mean is of the form given by [10] and the cost relationship is that given by [12], it can be shown (Cochran, 1953) that the optimum subsampling rate, m', may be obtained from

$$m' = [(c_b\sigma_w^2)/(c_w\sigma_b^2)]^{1/2} . \qquad [13]$$

That is, m' can be shown to give the smallest variance for a given cost, or alternatively, the least cost for a given variance. The sample rate, n, is found by solving either [10] or [12], depending on whether the variance or the cost has been specified.

In practice, m' will usually not be an integer, and the nearest integer should be selected. In addition, the variance usually changes rather slowly for values of m in the region of the optimum. Thus some latitude in the selection of m' can be tolerated.

As an example of the computations involved in subsampling, suppose we were interested in estimating the effect of continuous grazing on the bulk

Table 5–4. Bulk density of three subsamples of soil in each of five sampling units.

Subsample	Bulk density of soil in indicated sampling unit				
	1	2	3	4	5
1	1.53	1.63	1.47	1.59	1.64
2	1.48	1.58	1.41	1.36	1.58
3	1.64	1.67	1.50	1.41	1.50

Table 5–5. Analysis of variance of bulk density data in Table 5–4.

Source of variation	Degrees of freedom	Mean square
Among units	4	0.0168
Among cores within units	10	0.0061

density of a pasture soil. And suppose that we drew a random sample of five 10- by 10-foot sampling units, and within each unit we selected, at random, three subsamples in the form of 3–inch cores upon which the bulk density measurements were made. The resultant observations might appear as in Table 5–4.

The mean bulk density may be estimated from [9] as

$$\bar{\bar{y}} = \frac{(1.53 + 1.48 + \ldots + 1.58 + 1.50)}{5 \times 3} = \frac{22.99}{15} = 1.53 .$$

The analysis of variance of the data is shown in Table 5–5.

The variance components may then be estimated as

$$\sigma_w^2 = 0.0061$$
$$\sigma_b^2 = (0.0168 - 0.0061)/3 = 0.0036 .$$

Thus from [10] the variance of the mean, on a core basis, is found to be

$$V(\bar{\bar{y}}) = 0.0036/5 + 0.0061/5 \times 3 = 0.0007 + 0.0004 = 0.0011 .$$

Now suppose we are interested in determining the effect on the variance of reducing the number of sampling units to 3, and increasing the number of cores per unit to 5. Again we would use equation [10] to obtain

$$V(\bar{\bar{y}}) = 0.0036/3 + 0.0061/3 \times 5 = 0.0012 + 0.0004 = 0.0016 .$$

Now suppose we wish to estimate what the optimum sampling rate would be in future sampling from the same type of population, and suppose that it costs five times as much to sample an additional unit as it does to take an additional core in each unit. From [13] we would find the optimum sampling rate to be

$$m' = [(5 \times 0.0061)/(1 \times 0.0036)]^{1/2} = (0.0305/0.0036)^{1/2} = (8.47)^{1/2}$$
$$m' = 2.91 .$$

Thus, in sampling from a similar population, we would expect the maximum precision for a given cost by taking 3 cores per unit.

It should be pointed out that subsampling need not be restricted to a two-stage procedure. In some instances, the sample may be taken in three or more stages. A core of soil, for example, might be subsampled to provide small quantities of soil for chemical analysis which, in turn, might be subsampled to provide aliquots for the final measurement. The principles involved in multistage sampling are essentially extensions of the principles discussed here. The statistical considerations are adequately presented by several authors (Cochran, 1953; Deming, 1950; Hansen et al., 1953).

5–6　COMPOSITE SAMPLES

In many soil investigations, a substantial saving in total cost can result if laboratory analyses are performed on a composite of the field samples rather than on the individual samples. The procedure consists of taking a number of field samples adequate to represent the population in question, thoroughly mixing these samples to form one composite or bulk sample, and performing the laboratory analyses on the composite sample or on a subsample of the composite. The assumption, of course, is that a valid estimate of the mean of some characteristic of the population may be obtained from this single analysis of the composite sample. This assumption is true only under certain conditions. All samples which form the composite must be drawn from the population under consideration, and each sample must contribute the same amount to the composite.

For example, suppose a study is initiated to determine the changes in available soil phosphorus which have taken place in a field experiment which involved the annual application of varying increments of phosphorus to certain of the plots in the experiment. A composite sample for each plot could be obtained by pooling a number of borings taken at random from the plot. Similarly, if no estimate of precision is needed, the mean available phosphorus for a given treatment would be obtained from a composite of equal numbers of samples from all plots with a common treatment. Forming a composite by pooling samples taken from several treatments, however, is seldom if ever justified.

It should be pointed out that the composite samples provide only an estimate of the mean of the population from which the samples forming the composite are drawn. No estimate of the variance of the mean, and hence, the precision with which the mean is estimated can be obtained from a composite sample. It is not sufficient to analyze two or more subsamples from the same composite to obtain an estimate of the variation within the population. Such a procedure would permit the estimation of variation among subsamples within the composite, but not the variation among samples in the field. Similarly, if composites are formed from samples within different parts of a population, the variability among the parts, but not the variability within the parts, can be estimated. If an estimate of the variability among sampling units within the population is required, two or more samples taken at random within the population must be analyzed separately.

The accuracy with which a population mean is estimated from a composite is dependent on the variability among sampling units within the population and the number of such units included in the composite. Because of the difference in variability among the several characteristics of a soil and among the several types of sampling units, no generalizations can be made regarding the number of sampling units required for a composite sample. If an estimate of the variability among units is available, it can be used to determine the number of units to include in the composite to attain a given precision. The procedure is the same as that given in section 5–3.2 for estimating the size of a simple random sample. If no estimate of variability is available, compositing should be avoided if possible.

Subject to the foregoing restrictions, compositing may prove valuable in soil investigation. It permits the precision with which the mean is estimated to be increased by increasing the number of units included in the sample without, at the same time, increasing the cost of analysis.

5–7 LITERATURE CITED

Allmaras, R. R., and Gardner, C. O. 1956. Soil sampling for moisture determination in irrigation experiments. Agron. J. 48:15–17.

Cline, Marlin D. 1944. Principles of soil sampling. Soil Sci. 58:275–288.

Cochran, W. G. 1946. Relative accuracy of systematic and stratified samples for a certain class of populations. Ann. Math. Statist. 17:164–177.

Cochran, W. G. 1953. Sampling Techniques. John Wiley and Sons, Inc., New York.

Das, A. C. 1950. Two-dimensional systematic sampling and associated stratified and random sampling. Sankhya 10:95–108.

Deming, W. E. 1950. Some Theory of Sampling. John Wiley and Sons, Inc., New York.

Finney, D. J. 1948. Random and systematic sampling in timber surveys. J. Forestry 22:64–99.

Fisher, R. A., and Mackenzie, W. A. 1922. The correlation of weekly rainfall. Quart. J. Roy. Meteorol. Soc. 48:234–245.

Hammond, L. C., Pritchett, W. L., and Chew, V. 1958. Soil sampling in relation to soil heterogeneity. Soil Sci. Soc. Am. Proc. 22:548–552.

Hansen, M. H., Hurwitz, W. N., and Madow, W. G. 1953. Sample Survey Methods and Theory, Vols. I and II. John Wiley and Sons, New York.

Hasel, A. A. 1938. Sampling errors in timber surveys. J. Agr. Res. 57:713–736.

Hendricks, W. A. 1956. The Mathematical Theory of Sampling. Scarecrow Press, New Brunswick, N. J.

Madow, W. G. 1949. On the theory of systematic sampling: II. Ann. Math. Statist. 20:333–354.

Madow, W. G. 1953. On the theory of systematic sampling: III. Ann. Math. Statist. 24:101–106.

Madow, W. G., and Madow, L. H. 1944. On the theory of systematic sampling: I. Ann. Math. Statist. 15:1–24.

Mason, D. D., Lutz, J. F., and Petersen, R. G. 1957. Hydraulic conductivity as related to certain soil properties in a number of great soil groups—sampling errors involved. Soil Sci. Soc. Am. Proc. 21:554–560.

Matérn, Bertel. 1960. Spatial variation. Stochastic models and their application to some problems in forest surveys and other sampling investigations. Meddelanden Fran Statens Skogsforskningsinstitut. Band. 49, NR. 5.

Milne, A. 1959. The centric system area-sample treated as a random sample. Biometrics 15:270–297.

Olson, R. A., Drier, A. F., and Sorensen, R. C. 1958. The significance of subsoil and soil series in Nebraska soil testing. Agron. J. 50:185–188.

Osborne, J. G. 1942. Sampling errors of systematic and random surveys of cover-type areas. J. Am. Statist. Assoc. 37:256–264.

Quenouille, M. H. 1949. Problems in plane sampling. Ann. Math. Statist. 20:355–375.

Rigney, J. A., and Reed, J. F. 1946. Some factors affecting the accuracy of soil sampling. Soil Sci. Soc. Am. Proc. 10:257–259. (1945)

Sayegh, A. H., Alban, L. A., and Petersen, R. G. 1958. A sampling study in a saline and alkali area. Soil Sci. Soc. Am. Proc. 22:252–254.

Smith, H. F. 1938. An empirical law governing soil heterogeneity. J. Agr. Sci. 28:1–23.

Williams, R. M. 1956. The variance of the mean of systematic samples. Biometrika 43:137–148.

Yates, F. 1948. Systematic sampling. Phil. Trans. Roy. Soc. London, Ser. A. 241:345–377.

Yates, F. 1953. Sampling Methods for Censuses and Surveys, Ed. 2. Charles Griffen and Co. Ltd., London.

Zubrzycki, S. 1958. Remarks on random, stratified and systematic sampling in a plane. Colloquium Mathematicum 6:251–264.

6 | Calibration

H. T. DAVID AND F. B. CADY

Iowa State University
Ames, Iowa

6–1 THE NATURE OF CALIBRATION

In calibration, a functional relationship is assumed to exist between some magnitude X, commonly the amount of a substance, and an observed instrumental measurement Y of that magnitude. This relationship is expressible as $Y = f(X)$. A common example of this functional relationship is the calibration curve of a flame photometer for potassium. Here the observed photometer reading is a function of the known potassium concentration. This functional relationship may be pictured by plotting a series of points, the X-coordinate of a point being a known potassium concentration, and the Y-coordinate, the corresponding observed instrumental measurement.

However, the resulting points do not provide an entirely satisfactory picture of the functional relationship in question. This is because the X-coordinates can usually be assumed to be measured without experimental error, while such an assumption can not be made for the Y-coordinates. As a result of this experimental error, the Y-coordinates of the plotted points are imprecise, and the picture provided by these points does not correspond exactly to the functional relationship.

The problem then arises how to deduce the functional relationship from the plotted points. A reasonable way to do this is to assume that any irregularity displayed by the plotted points is attributable to experimental error, i.e., to assume that the functional relationship is estimated from the plotted points by "smoothing" the latter. This may be done by the standard methods of regression analysis (Snedecor, 1956; Williams, 1959).

Smoothing an observed curve by regression to obtain an estimated theoretical curve is, of course, not peculiar to the calibration problem. Rather, it underlies any experimental situation where a functional relationship is estimated from experimental data. Thus, the least-squares regression procedures applicable, for example, to yield prediction from fertilizer-response data apply equally to estimating the calibration curve for the flame photometer.

Once the regression calculations have yielded an estimate of the calibration curve, the latter is used to estimate the value of the hypothetical standard corresponding to a further observed measurement. The calibration problem becomes conceptually simplest whenever it can be assumed that this "value of the hypothetical standard" can be interpreted as "true concentration of the unknown."

Specifically, the calibration problem as illustrated by the flame photometer problem is as follows:

(1) n photometer readings Y are observed for n potassium standards X, and the resulting n points (X,Y) are plotted.

(2) The form of the calibration curve is assumed, e.g., a straight line, $Y = \beta X$, through the origin.

(3) The estimated functional relationship, $Y = \hat{\beta} X$, where $\hat{\beta}$ is the estimate of β, is fitted by standard regression methods. Note that the proper regression is that of Y on X rather than X on Y because it is the Y's that are subject to error.[1]

(4) A photometer reading Y_0 is taken for a potassium sample of unknown concentration. The estimated calibration curve, $Y = \hat{\beta} X$, is entered at ordinate Y_0, and the corresponding abscissa X_0 is recorded. This amounts of course to solving for X the equation $Y_0 = \hat{\beta} X$. As indicated in 3, X_0 is obtained from the inverse regression equation $X_0 = Y_0/\hat{\beta}$ via the regression of Y on X rather than that of X on Y (see footnote 1).

6–2 STATISTICAL ASPECTS OF CALIBRATION

It is desirable not only to estimate "true concentration," but also to assess the goodness (precision) of this estimate. Such an assessment usually involves constructing a confidence interval that contains the true concentration with a predetermined high probability. The two statistical problems are, then, to give an estimate of the unknown X_0 and to construct a confidence interval for it. This estimate and confidence interval will be based on the corresponding observed Y_0 and the estimated calibration curve. As is typical of most applications of statistics to experimentation, the allowances for error in the unknown Y and in the estimated calibration curve do not take into account possible biases, i.e., inaccuracy in these variables. In other words, while allowance is made for random error (imprecision), allowance is not made for the possibility of systematic errors such as the lack

---

[1] Eisenhart (1939, see pp. 167 with a change in notation) draws attention to this point: "Thus when the research worker selects the X values in advance, and holds X to these values without error, and then observes the corresponding Y values, the errors are in the Y values, so that even if he is interested in using observed values of Y to estimate X he should nevertheless fit $Y = \beta X$ and then use the inverse of this relation to estimate X, i.e., $X = Y/\hat{\beta}$."

of correspondence in the chemical reactions of standards and unknowns, parallax, instrumental drift, or the deterioration of the standards. These possible biases should be seriously considered, as they are not taken into account by the methods described below. These methods are predicated on, and the experimenter is responsible for, the absence of any such biases.

It will be convenient to examine the estimation and construction of the confidence interval for the unknown X_0 in terms of three examples typifying situations frequently met in practice.

These examples are concerned with the case where an initial standardizing adjustment ensures a zero standard, i.e., ensures that the calibration curve passes through the origin. These examples are not concerned with cases where a standardizing adjustment also is made at the other end of the scale.

The first two examples refer to cases where the form of the calibrating curve is linear, but the first and second differ in the assumed structure of the experimental error. The third illustrates an application of an approximate method intended to deal with cases where the assumption of linearity is not valid.

Some symbols useful in the further discussion are as follows:

X_i: Values of the standards ($i = 1, 2, \ldots, n$)
Y_i: Corresponding observed measurements ($i = 1, 2, \ldots, n$)
X_0: Hypothetical value of the unknown
Y_0: Corresponding observed measurement
$\hat{X}_0$: Estimate of X_0 based on Y_0 and the estimated curve
$\sigma(X), \sigma(Y)$: Standard deviation (dispersion or imprecision)
$t_{.05}(n - 1df)$: Useful constants tabulated for example in Table 2.7.1, page 46, of Snedecor (1956) in the column headed 0.050, with degrees of freedom listed in the first column of the table.

It will be assumed in all the examples given below that the n X-measurements $X_1, X_2, \ldots, X_n$ on the n standards underlying the estimated calibration curve are known without error. This assumption greatly simplifies the requisite theoretical problems and is warranted in most applications, at least in the sense that Y measurements typically are considerably less precise than X measurements.[2] This assumption is expressed symbolically as $\sigma(X_1) = \sigma(X_2) = \ldots = \sigma(X_n) = 0$.

---

[2] If the assumption that X is measured essentially without error cannot be made, e.g., in the calibration of one method of chemical determination with respect to an alternative method, the required methods of analysis are not routine. An excellent presentation of possible avenues of approach under these circumstances is given by Lindley (1947, see pp. 231–234).

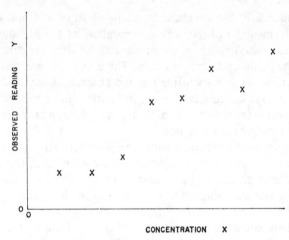

Fig. 6–1. Typical data plot when standard deviation of Y is constant.

6–3   EXAMPLES

6–3.1   Example 1

The critical features of the set of points $(X_1, Y_1), (X_2, Y_2), \ldots, (X_n, Y_n)$ in Fig. 6–1 are:

(*1*) It seems plausible that the true calibration curve is a straight line through the origin.

(*2*) On the basis of the plotted data, it seems plausible that

$$\sigma(Y_1) = \sigma(Y_2) = \ldots = \sigma(Y_n) =, \text{say, } \sigma \,,$$

i.e., that the standard deviation of Y is constant.

Point estimation of X_0 proceeds as follows: The estimated calibration curve is the line

$$Y = \hat{\beta} X \,,$$

where

$$\hat{\beta} = \frac{X_1 Y_1 + X_2 Y_2 + \ldots + X_n Y_n}{X_1^2 + X_2^2 + \ldots + X_n^2}$$

so that

$$\hat{X}_0 = Y_0 / \hat{\beta} \,.$$

The geometrical construction of a 95% confidence interval I for X_0 proceeds as follows (Fig. 6–2):

(*1*) Define

$$s = \left[\frac{Y_1^2 + Y_2^2 + \ldots + Y_n^2 - (\hat{\beta})(X_1 Y_1 + X_2 Y_2 + \ldots + X_n Y_n)}{(n - 1)} \right]^{1/2} \,.$$

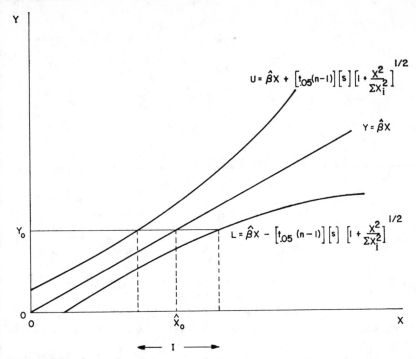

Fig. 6–2. Graphical construction of X_0-confidence-interval when standard deviation of Y is constant.

(2) Plot the estimated regression function $Y = \hat{\beta}X$.

(3) By adding and subtracting the function

$$[t_{.05}(n-1)][s]\left[1 + \frac{X^2}{\sum X_i^2}\right]^{1/2}$$

of X, respectively, to and from $Y = \hat{\beta}X$, plot U and L.

(4) The lower endpoint of I is the X-value on the curve U at level Y_0; the upper endpoint is the X-value on L at Y_0.

Alternatively, the upper and lower endpoints of I are given by the two roots (in X_0) of the following quadratic equation:

$$0 = X_0^2\left[\frac{t^2s^2}{\sum X_i^2} - \hat{\beta}^2\right] + 2X_0[\hat{\beta}Y_0] + (t^2s^2 - Y_0^2),$$

i.e., the upper and lower endpoints of I are given by

$$\frac{\hat{\beta}Y_0 \pm ts\left[\hat{\beta}^2 + \frac{Y_0^2 - t^2s^2}{\sum X_i^2}\right]^{1/2}}{\hat{\beta}^2 - \frac{t^2s^2}{\sum X_i^2}}.$$

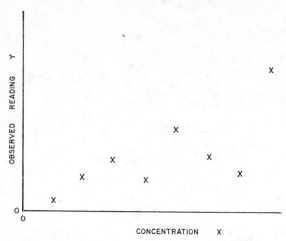

Fig. 6–3. Typical data plot when coefficient of variation of Y is constant.

6–3.2   Example 2

The critical features of the set of points $(X_1,Y_1),\ldots,(X_n,Y_n)$ in Fig. 6–3 are:

(*1*) It seems plausible that the true calibration curve is a straight line through the origin.

(*2*) On the basis of the plotted data, it seems plausible that

$$\frac{\sigma(Y_1)}{X_1} = \frac{\sigma(Y_2)}{X_2} = \ldots = \frac{\sigma(Y_n)}{X_n} =, \text{ say, } \delta$$

i.e., that the coefficient of variation of Y is constant.

Point estimation of X_0 now proceeds as follows: The estimated calibration curve is the line

$$Y = \hat{\beta}X$$

where

$$\hat{\beta} = \frac{\dfrac{Y_1}{X_1} + \dfrac{Y_2}{X_2} + \ldots + \dfrac{Y_n}{X_n}}{n}$$

so that

$$\hat{X}_0 = Y_0/\hat{\beta}\,.$$

The geometrical construction of a 95% confidence interval proceeds as follows (Fig. 6–4):

Define:

$$d = \left[\frac{\left(\dfrac{Y_1}{X_1}\right)^2 + \ldots + \left(\dfrac{Y_n}{X_n}\right)^2 - (\hat{\beta})\left(\dfrac{Y_1}{X_1} + \ldots + \dfrac{Y_n}{X_n}\right)}{(n-1)}\right]^{1/2}$$

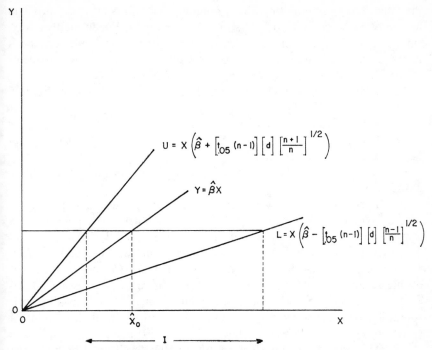

Fig. 6–4. Graphical construction of X_0-confidence-interval when coefficient of variation of Y is constant.

Then the confidence interval I for X_0 is given by the geometric construction in Fig. 6–4, which is analogous to the construction in Fig. 6–2. Alternatively the upper and lower endpoints of I are

$$\frac{Y_0}{\hat{\beta} + td\left[\dfrac{n+1}{n}\right]^{1/2}} \quad \text{and} \quad \frac{Y_0}{\hat{\beta} - td\left[\dfrac{n+1}{n}\right]^{1/2}}, \text{ respectively .}$$

6–3.3 Example 3

In the previous two examples, we have considered calibration curves that may be assumed linear and passing through the origin. In this example, we illustrate an approximate graphical technique[3] intended to cover those situations where the assumption of linearity is not quite met. The basic idea here is to make the data suggest a "transformation" of the abscissa, e.g.,

---

[3] A similar procedure has been advocated by C. E. Jensen in "Fitting a graphically developed algebraically unspecified form by least squares." U. S. Forest Research Note, CS-2, March 1963.

the logarithm or square-root transformation, that will convert the problem to one of those considered in the first two examples. Put in another way, suitable graphic analysis reveals that the calibration curve would have been a straight line through the origin, had one plotted not the standards themselves, but rather, say, the logarithms of the standards.

The details of application of this graphical method as shown in Fig. 6–5 are as follows:

(*1*) Plot all available data points.

(*2*) Using a French curve, plot by eye the smooth curve *C* that appears best to describe the plotted data.

(*3*) Draw a straight line *L* through the origin that lies near the curve *C* plotted in step *2*.

(*4*) Corresponding to every actual data point plotted in step *1*, compute a "synthetic" data point as follows: The synthetic data point has the same vertical coordinate (observed value) as the actual data point, but has an abscissa value (standard) constructed from that of the actual point by (*a*) passing a vertical line through the actual point, (*b*) noting the point of intersection *P* of this vertical line with the curve *C*, (*c*) passing a horizontal line through *P*, (*d*) noting the point of intersection *Q* of this horizontal line with the straight line *L*, and (*e*) recording the abscissa value of *Q*, which is the desired abscissa value of the synthetic point.

(*5*) The synthetic points should form a pattern well fitted by a straight line through the origin. Further, most such patterns will indicate one or the other of the two error structures considered in examples one and two to be

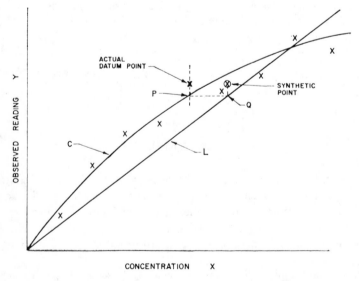

Fig. 6–5. Graphical computation of a "synthetic" data point from an actual data point.

relevant. Whichever of these two structures is decided upon, one proceeds with the synthetic data points, in combination with the unknown Y_0, as if these synthetic points were in fact actual points (indeed, the synthetic points are the data points that would have been obtained, had a fortunate choice of scale been made for the standards). One thus obtains the lower and upper endpoints Z_L and Z_U of the confidence interval for, and value $\hat{Z}_0$ of, the synthetic form of the estimated unknown corresponding to the observed Y_0.

(6) The final step is to transform Z_L and Z_U and $\hat{Z}_0$ back to their "actual" equivalents. The procedure is the same for all three, and is illustrated for Z_L: (a) Consider the vertical line at a distance Z_L from the vertical axis (in other words, the vertical line passing through the point $(Z_L, 0)$). (b) Note the point of intersection M of this vertical line with the line L. (c) Pass a horizontal line through M. (d) Note the point of intersection N of this horizontal straight line with the curve C. Record the abscissa value of the point N; this is the value X_L.

6-4 LITERATURE CITED

Eisenhart, C. 1939. The interpretation of certain regression methods and their use in biological and industrial research. Ann. Math. Statist. 10:162–186.

Lindley, D. V. 1947. Regression lines and the linear functional relationship. Supplement J. Roy. Soc. 9:218–244.

Snedecor, G. W. 1956. Statistical Methods. The Iowa State College Press, Ames, Iowa.

Williams, E. J. 1959. Regression Analysis. John Wiley and Sons, Inc., New York.

7 | Water Content

WALTER H. GARDNER
Washington State University
Pullman, Washington

7-1 GENERAL INTRODUCTION

Direct or indirect measures of soil water content are needed in practically every type of soil study. In the field, knowledge of the water available for plant growth requires a direct measure of water content or a measure of some index of water content. In the laboratory, determining and reporting many physical and chemical properties of soil necessitates knowledge of water content. In soils work, water content traditionally has been expressed as the ratio of the mass of water present in a sample to the mass of the sample after it has been dried to constant weight, or as the volume of water present in a unit volume of the sample. In either case the amount of water in the sample is needed. To determine this the water must be removed and measured, or the mass of the sample must be determined before and after removal of water. And, criteria must exist for deciding at what point the sample is "dry." For a great many purposes where high precision and reproducibility are not required, a precise definition of the term "dry" is not required. Where high precision does become important it should be recognized that "dry" is a subjective term and must be defined. Where high precision is implied in water content figures, such figures must be accompanied by the definition and a description of the procedure used to determine the water content. Traditionally, the most frequently used definition for a dry soil is the mass of a soil sample after it has come to constant weight in an oven at a temperature between $100°$ and $110°C$. The choice of this particular temperature range appears not to have been based upon scientific consideration of the drying characteristics of soil; and, in practice, samples are not always dried to constant weight.

Water content as usually used in soils work is either a dimensionless ratio of two masses or two volumes or is given as a mass per unit volume. When either of the dimensionless ratios is multiplied by 100, such values become percentages, and the basis (mass or volume) should be stated. Where no indication is given, the figure generally may be assumed to be on a mass basis because the determination usually involves getting mass-basis figures first and then converting them to volume-basis figures.

Occasionally the ratio of mass of water to that of the wet soil is used. Conversions from one basis to the other are easily made by use of the formulas,

$$\theta_{ww} = \theta_{dw}/(1 + \theta_{dw}), \qquad \theta_{dw} = \theta_{ww}/(1 - \theta_{ww}), \qquad [1]$$

where θ is the water content, and the subscripts dw and ww refer to dry-weight and wet-weight basis.

If water content is desired on a volume basis, the volume from which the sample was taken must be known. A sampling device which takes a known volume of soil (Richards and Stumpf, 1960) may be used; or, the bulk density of the soil (mass of soil per unit volume), as obtained from independent measurements in the same area, may be used. Where a bulk density is known or assumed, volume-basis water contents may be obtained from the mass-basis figures by use of the formula

$$\theta_{vb} = (D_b/D_w)\theta_{dw}, \qquad [2]$$

where D_b is the bulk density of the soil, D_w is the density of water (this usually may be taken as unity in the centimeter-gram-second system but must be present for dimensional consistency), and the subscripts vb and dw refer to volume basis and dry-weight basis. The accuracy of the inferred volume-basis water content depends upon the accuracy of the bulk density figure used as well as upon the accuracy of the dry-weight, water-content figure. Both depend upon the accuracy of the figure for the "dry" mass of the soil.

Computations of water content on a volume basis require a correct measure of the bulk density. Considering the variability of soil, even in an area as small as a few square feet, some error is nearly always involved. However, for many purposes where volume-basis water contents are needed, the error is probably no more important than the error involved in representing the water content at a particular depth in the field by a single number. Taylor (1955), working with Millville loam (which is a relatively uniform soil insofar as observable physical and chemical properties are concerned), reported coefficients of variation of 17 and 20% for gravimetric measurements of the water content of samples of soil from field plots under irrigation by furrow and sprinkler methods, respectively. Similar variation has been observed on apparently uniform areas of Palouse silt loam in the dryland areas of southeastern Washington. For precise work, statistically sound methods must be used for sampling and for reporting such measurements (see Cline, 1944, and section 5).

When water is applied to soil by irrigation or rainfall, the quantity applied is usually reported in the United States as "inches of water" (volume of water applied divided by the area, $L^3/L^2 = L$). Likewise, the water content of a soil or of a particular zone or depth of soil is reported in "inches." This refers to the depth of water which would be necessary to bring the soil to the particular water content in question. If water content of soil is known on a mass per unit dry-mass basis and if the bulk density is known or assumed, then water content can be obtained on a volume basis. And, by multiplying the volume-basis figure by the depth of the soil in question, a depth-of-water figure is obtained. This may be expressed as "inches per foot," or such figures may be summed to give "inches of water in the root zone," or in any desired depth increment. Water volume applied to a given soil area may be expressed as "acre-inches" or "acre-feet," which correspond to volumes of water the indicated number of inches or feet deep over a 1-acre area. Often water applied and water content are referred to as "acre-inches per acre" which reduces to "inches" or just the depth of the water.

7–2 DIRECT METHODS

7–2.1 General Principles

Determination of water content of soils may be accomplished by direct and indirect methods. Direct methods may be regarded as those methods wherein water is removed from a sample by evaporation, leaching, or chemical reaction, with the amount removed being determined. Determination of the amount removed may be by one or more of the following methods: (1) measurement of loss of weight of the sample, (2) collection by distillation or absorption in a desiccant and measurement of the amount of water removed, (3) extraction of the water with substances which will replace it in the sample and measurement of some physical or chemical property of the extracting material which is quantitatively affected by water content, or (4) quantitative measurement of reaction products displaced from a sample. In each of these methods the water and soil are somehow separated, with the amount of water removed being measured or inferred.

The key problem in water content determination in porous materials has to do with the definition of the dry state. Soil is made up of colloidal and noncolloidal mineral particles, organic materials, volatile liquids, water and chemical substances dissolved in water. Of the mineral fraction of the soil, the noncolloidal particles are probably the easiest with which to deal. At ordinary room temperatures and room humidities, such materials will have a small quantity of adsorbed water which is easily removed from their surfaces by heating. Only at elevated temperatures does water of crystallization associated with these minerals come off. The status of water in the colloidal particles of the mineral fraction is more complicated. Water present in the colloidal fraction may be considered in two categories, structural

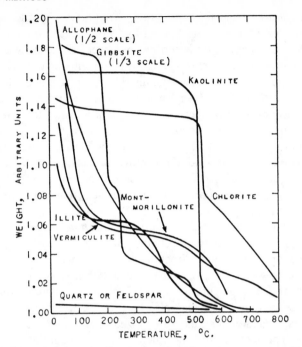

Fig. 7–1. Weight loss of clay minerals as a function of temperature. The weight of the sample at a temperature of 800°C. or greater is taken to be unity. Water content percentages on a mass basis may be obtained by subtracting 1 from the ordinate figure and multiplying by 100. (The numbers to the right of the decimal thus may be regarded as percentages.) (Nutting, 1943.)

water and adsorbed water, and it is often difficult to tell them apart.[1] Some representative thermal dehydration curves (after Nutting, 1943) are presented in Fig. 7–1.[2] These curves show the weight loss of samples that were initially at room temperature and in equilibrium with room humidity of approximately 60%, as the samples were heated to constant weight at various temperatures. The weight at a temperature of 800°C. or slightly higher is taken to be unity. It is not clear from the curves what part of the water is adsorbed water and what part is structural water. But it should be obvious from these curves that for colloidal minerals it is important to specify the

---

[1] The term "structural water" refers to water derived from components of the mineral lattice itself, whereas the term "adsorbed water" refers to water attached to the mineral lattice but which is not a structural component of the lattice. Some adsorbed water may be located with respect to the lattice in such a way that the difficulty of removal is comparable to that for structural water. (Difficulty here refers generally to the temperature required for removal and possibly to the fineness of the particles). The exact situation depends upon the nature of the particular mineral.

[2] It should be recognized that the character of the thermal dehydration curve depends upon the purity of the sample, so that it is unlikely that curves for the same type of minerals constructed by various workers would be identical.

exact temperature of drying if precision is required. Considering that the temperature control of ordinary laboratory ovens is not very good, precision water content measurements should not be expected except where extraordinary attention is given to temperature measurement and control.[3]

Insofar as most of the colloidal minerals are concerned, the temperature sensitivity of water content measurements would be materially reduced by selection of a temperature range where water loss changes with increasing temperature are smaller than they are from 100° to 110°C. Judging from the curves of Fig. 7–1, the range between 165° and 175°C. would be better than the traditional range of 100° to 110°C. However, excessive oxidation and decomposition of soil organic matter in this high temperature range would prevent its general adoption although in special cases it might be appropriate.

The problem of defining "dry conditions" in the organic fraction of the soil is even more difficult than defining such conditions for the colloidal mineral fraction. The organic fraction of soils consists of undecomposed plant fragments such as roots, and resistant decomposition products such as polysaccharides or polyuronides as well as intermediate products. Volatile liquids other than water may also be present. If subjected to too high temperatures, organic materials are oxidized or decomposed and lost from the sample. The temperature at which excessive oxidation occurs would be difficult to specify, but 50°C. seems to be a common temperature used to dry organic materials, and is thought by many investigators to be sufficiently low to avoid loss of organic matter by oxidation.

Little is said in the soils literature about weight changes due to oxidation and decomposition of the organic fraction in soil samples undergoing drying. However, many investigators readily admit that they often have observed weight changes in soils being dried over periods from many days to many weeks. In our own laboratory we have observed weight changes in samples during drying over periods as long as 15 days. A silt loam soil, containing about 3% organic matter, and with illite predominating in the clay fraction, lost weight which corresponded to 0.3% water content from the 2nd to the 10th day in a forced-draft oven at 100° to 110°C. Whether this represents water loss or oxidation and decomposition is difficult to tell.

---

[3] It is not possible to generalize on the precision of oven temperature control. However, it can be noted that, unless the temperature control of an oven has been checked, it is not safe to assume that control in the specified 100° to 110°C. range is achieved in ordinary laboratory ovens. Several ovens in Washintgon State University soils laboratories showed variations as large as ±15°C. over a period of a few weeks (without a sample load) and temperature differences within the ovens of as much as 40°C. This was true of forced-draft ovens as well as convection ovens. Temperature variation with elevation in the oven was found to be as great as 40°C. to 100°C. for several convection-type ovens at the Massachusetts Institute of Technology (Lambe, 1949). Since radiation heating could be a factor in some ovens, precision work requires that temperature measurements be made within the soil sample rather than in the oven atmosphere, as is done with conventional oven thermometers.

Extensive studies have been made on the drying of food products by food technologists interested in dehydration. Here efforts seem to be more in the direction of finding a drying technique which will yield reproducible results rather than of finding a method wherein the dry status is unequivocal. A reference method used by food technologists (Makower, 1950) involves drying ground vegetable material at room temperature in a vacuum over a desiccant that permits practically no water vapor pressure (magnesium perchlorate). Drying time is long (6 to 9 months). The assumption is made that with no air present decomposition and oxidation are negligible. Even as a reference standard, this method is painfully slow and other methods have been sought.

One modification which has reduced the drying time from months to days (Makower and Nielsen, 1948) involves lyophilization or freeze-drying. The fresh weight of the organic material is first obtained, and then water is added to the sample to cause it to swell. In the swollen state, the sample is then frozen, and most of the water is removed by sublimation. In this state the mechanical structure of the sample is essentially fixed, and evaporation can proceed much more rapidly than under conditions where the porosity of the sample is drastically reduced through shrinking. After most of the water has been removed, drying can be continued at higher temperatures. A redrying procedure involving drying at temperatures between 50° and 70°C. has also been developed by Makower et al. (1946) as a reference standard. They reported that considerable decomposition of vegetables takes place at temperatures above 70°C.

Since many soils contain only small amounts of organic material, much of which is fairly stable, inaccuracies introduced by uncertainties in drying of organic materials often may be negligible. However, since drying temperatures normally used for soils are well above those considered safe for organic materials, decomposition and oxidation should be expected and considered in the development of drying techniques and taken into account in reporting data. Where precise water content values are required, precautions must be taken to assure that minimum losses due to oxidation or decomposition occur and that all samples to be compared are dried to constant weight or to some arbitrary state of dryness which, by careful timing, can be reproduced. The measured water content of a soil which contains more than negligible quantities of organic material must be regarded as an arbitrary value, depending upon a state of dryness defined by the method used rather than upon a dry state which could be regarded as unequivocal.

In many salt-affected soils, considerable dissolved material exists in the soil solution. If water is leached out of the sample by some liquid such as alcohol, most of the dissolved materials would be removed along with the water. On the other hand, if the soil is dried in an oven only the volatile materials are lost. Depending upon the quantities of dissolved substances present, the method of water removal could make considerable difference. It is possible to have water content differences as great as several tenths of a percent, depending upon whether water was removed by leaching or by evaporation. It is a moot question whether or not the dissolved substance should be considered to be part of the "dry" soil. Most procedures in common use involve oven-drying or calibration against oven-drying data, so that dissolved salts are counted as part of the "dry" soil.

It appears from the literature that oven-drying methods often may have been accepted too readily as reference standards for water content measurement. The situation is complicated by lack of detail in the literature concerning oven-drying procedures used for the water content measurements which are reported. Drying time is rarely mentioned, and the specification of oven temperature appears to be perfunctory if mentioned at all. There usually is no evidence to suggest that an investigator has questioned oven-drying procedures. Scatter in many kinds of data based upon or related to water content measurements, by implication, fails to be associated with the water content measurement. In some cases, other methods for obtaining water content are compared to oven-drying methods, and any lack of reproducibility observed is ascribed automatically to the other method rather than to the oven-drying procedure. Accuracy itself is measured against oven-drying methods. As a consequence of this misplaced trust in oven-drying procedures, there may be good reason to re-evaluate some of the other methods for water content determination and possibly a few other type analytical procedures where water content determinations are critical.

Gravimetric water content measurements usually involve three independent measurements, the wet x and dry y weights of the sample and the tare weight t. These may be combined in this way

$$[(x - t)/(y - t)] - 1 = \theta \tag{3}$$

to provide water content θ. With each weighing, there is associated an error e, which is the balance error. The balance error is made up of two parts, a random error having to do with the reproducibility of a particular balance reading, and a bias which is the difference between an average reading and the true value. The bias is likely to be different at different weight values, but since a balance may be calibrated such bias may be eliminated to any desired degree of accuracy. A constant bias, such as might result from an improper adjustment of the zero on an automatic balance, introduces no error in the water content ratio provided it is the same for each weighing and the tare weight is not balanced out. This may be seen when such an error e is applied uniformly to each measurement appearing in equation [3]:

$$\frac{(x + e) - (t + e)}{(y + e) - (t + e)} - 1 = \theta . \tag{4}$$

The error term may be seen to cancel out.

The effect of random error may be evaluated by determining the variance V of the ratio, $(x - t)/(y - t)$, in equation [3]. The variance of this ratio with reasonable assumptions may be approximated by

$$V_{\frac{x-t}{y-t}} = \frac{1}{(y-t)^2}\left[V_{x-t} + \frac{(x-t)^2}{(y-t)^2}V_{y-t}\right].$$ [5]

The variances of the numerator and denominator are given as

$$V_{x-t} = V_x + V_t$$ [6]
$$V_{y-t} = V_y + V_t.$$ [7]

Substituting [6] and [7] into [5] gives

$$V_{\frac{x-t}{y-t}} = \frac{1}{(y-t)^2}\left[V_x + V_t + \frac{(x-t)^2}{(y-t)^2}(V_y + V_t)\right].$$ [8]

Since the variances due to the random error of all three weighings are likely to be nearly the same, equation [8] is approximated by

$$V_{\frac{x-t}{y-t}} = \frac{2V_{x,y,t}}{(y-t)^2}\left[1 + \frac{(x-t)^2}{(y-t)^2}\right].$$ [9]

Combining equation [3] with equation [9] and replacing $(y - t)$ by the dry mass of the soil z gives:

$$V_{\frac{x-t}{y-t}} = \frac{2V_{x,y,t}}{z^2}[1 + (\theta + 1)^2]$$

$$= \frac{2V_{x,y,t}}{z^2}(\theta^2 + 2\theta + 2).$$ [10]

For water contents and sample sizes ordinarily encountered in soils work, θ^2 is negligible so that equation [10] further reduces to

$$V_\theta = \frac{4V_{x,y,t}}{z^2}(\theta + 1)$$ [11]

where the subscript, $(x - t)/(y - t)$, is replaced by θ for water content. Written in terms of standard deviations $(V = \sigma^2)$, this becomes

$$\sigma_\theta = \frac{2\sigma_{x,y,t}}{z}\sqrt{\theta + 1}.$$ [12]

If a tare compensation device is used, so that each water content determination involves only two weighings, equation [5] becomes

$$V_{x/y} = \frac{1}{y^2}\left[V_x + \left(\frac{x}{y}\right)^2 V_y\right],$$ [13]

and equation [8] is not needed since the tare weight is not obtained independently. However, if the tare compensation involves a constant bias, this does affect the accuracy of the resulting water content figure. The effect on water content values of a constant bias e due to a tare error or other causes, which may be either positive or negative, may be obtained by solving explicitly for E in the equation

$$[(x + e)/(y + e)] - 1 = \theta + E \qquad [14]$$

which, when combined with $\theta = (x - y)/y$, reduces to

$$E = (-e\theta)/(e + y) \qquad [15]$$

or, when e is small compared to y, it reduces to

$$E = -(e/y)\theta. \qquad [16]$$

If the ratio e/y does not exceed 0.001 (e.g., 100 mg./100 g., 10 mg./10 g., or 1 mg./1 g.), the error will not exceed 0.1% water content up to water contents of 100%. If the ratio e/y does not exceed 0.0001, the error will not exceed 0.01% water content over a similar range. This applies to any constant bias of a balance as well.

The random error when tare compensation is used may be obtained from equation [13] using a similar development and with the same assumptions as used for equation [12]. The standard deviation is

$$\sigma_\theta = \frac{\sigma_{x,y}}{y} \sqrt{1 + (\theta + 1)^2} \qquad [17]$$

which, when θ^2 is regarded as negligible, reduces to

$$\sigma_\theta = \frac{\sqrt{2}\,\sigma_{x,y}}{y} \sqrt{\theta + 1} \qquad [18]$$

when tare compensation is used.

Balance precision and accuracy are reported in various ways by manufacturers, and the meaning of the terminology used is not always clear. Hence, it would be difficult to provide general instructions for using balance ratings as provided by the manufacturer to compute the variance or standard deviation in a water content measurement. However, the standard deviation for a particular balance at a specified load may be obtained experimentally with small effort.[4] Hence, water content measurement errors are given here in terms of standard deviations.

If the limit of precision in water content measurement E due only to random weighing errors is taken to be 3σ, then, from equation [12],

$$E = 3\sigma_\theta = \frac{6\sigma_{x,y,t}}{z} \sqrt{\theta + 1} \qquad [19]$$

where a tare weighing is involved. At 3σ, 99.7% of the measurements would be within $\pm E$, at 2σ, 95%, and at σ, 68%. If the dry weight z in equation [10] is replaced by the wet weight, $z' = z/(\theta + 1)$, then equation

---

[4] For statistical methods for computing standard deviations, consult an elementary book on statistical analyses or books on chemical analyses such as *Chemical Computations and Errors* by Crumpler and Yoe, 1946.

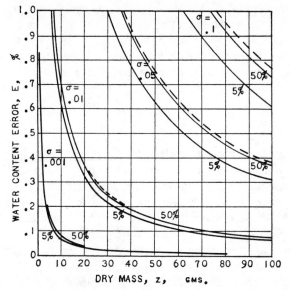

Fig. 7–2. Error in water content measurements as a function of the dry mass of the sample at various weighing precisions and for 5% and 50% water contents on a dry-mass basis (equation [19]). The value of E is $3\sigma_\theta$, and the weighing precision is the standard deviation σ for the balance in grams. When tare compensation is used E should be multiplied by $(2)^{1/2}/2$, and where n replicate determinations are made, by a factor of $1/(n)^{1/2}$. If z is taken as the wet mass of the sample the error E from the graph should be multiplied by $(\theta + 1)$, as can be seen from equation [20]. The dashed curves, for 50% water content, result when the θ^2 term in equations [10] and [17] is not ignored.

[19], again neglecting θ^2 and higher powers, becomes:

$$E = \frac{6\sigma_{x,y,t}(\theta + 1)}{z'} \sqrt{\theta + 1} = \frac{6\sigma_{x,y,t}}{z'} \sqrt{3\theta + 1}. \qquad [20]$$

Neglect of θ^2 and higher powers leads to E values which are slightly too small for large values of θ in equations [19] and [20]. However, the magnitude is correct, and the practical value of the expressions is enhanced by their simplicity. In cases where tare compensation is used, the equation corresponding to equation [19] is

$$E = 3\sigma_\theta = \frac{3\sqrt{2}\,\sigma_{x,y}}{y} \sqrt{\theta + 1} = \frac{4.24\sigma_{x,y}}{y} \sqrt{\theta + 1}. \qquad [21]$$

A balance should be read to $\pm\sigma$.[5] The precision measurement may be

---

[5] The precision of some balances is reported as $\pm e$ where e is taken to be 3σ. The Metler K-7 is of this type, the precision being given as ± 0.03 g. The standard deviation at loads of approximately 100 g. was found experimentally to be about 0.01 g. on 4 different balances of this type. The bias of each balance was $< \pm.01$ g. at the same loading.

improved by a factor of $1/(n)^{1/2}$ by making n replicate determinations. Values of E for various balance standard deviations $\sigma_{x,y,t}$, sample dry masses y, and water contents θ are shown in Fig. 7–2. When tare compensation is used the value of E should be multiplied by $(2)^{1/2}/2$, and where n replicate determinations are to be made, by a factor of $1/(n)^{1/2}$.

7–2.2 Gravimetry With Oven Drying

7–2.2.1 INTRODUCTION

Water content measurements by gravimetric methods involve weighing the wet sample, removing the water, and reweighing the sample to determine the amount of water removed. Water content is then obtained by dividing the difference between wet and dry masses by the mass of the dry sample to obtain the ratio of the mass of water to the mass of the dry soil. When multiplied by 100, this becomes the percentage of water in the sample on a dry-mass (or, as often expressed, on a dry-weight) basis. Water content may be described in other ways as indicated in section 7–1. Water may be removed from the sample in any of a number of ways, the principal method in common use being the oven-drying method described here. Accuracy and reproducibility of water content measurements, assuming that weighing precision is consistent with desired precision of water content measurement, depend upon the drying technique and the care with which it is used. (See discussion in section 7–2.1.)

7–2.2.2 METHOD

7–2.2.2.1 Special Apparatus. Apparatus required for gravimetric determination of water content may be used in many different forms, and so exact specifications are not needed. Requirements include an auger or sampling tube or some other suitable device to take a soil sample, soil containers with tight-fitting lids, an oven with means for controlling the temperature to 100° to 110°C., a desiccator with active desiccant, and a balance for weighing the samples. In the field, if soil samples are taken under conditions where evaporation losses may be of sufficient magnitude to affect the desired accuracy of measurement, special equipment for weighing the samples immediately or reducing evaporative loss must be used. Both convective and forced-draft ovens are used, and for precise work a vacuum oven is of particular value. Balances used range all the way from analytical balances to rough platform scales, depending upon the size of the sample to be taken, and the precision of measurement desired.

7–2.2.2.2 Procedure. The procedure to be used must vary with the circumstances of measurement and the equipment. Since these vary widely it is impossible to specify a detailed standard procedure which will fit all of the many uses made of water content measurements. The procedure given here is intended for use in routine work where moderate precision (say, measurements having a precision of ±0.5% water content) is desired. Replication must depend upon the nature of the sample and soil system for which water content is desired, but it is suggested that samples be run in duplicate as a minimum.

Place samples of 1 to 100 g. of soil in weighing bottles or metal cans with tight-fitting lids. Weigh the samples immediately, or store them in such a way that evaporation is negligible. Refer to Fig. 7–2 to find the required weighing precision. (The balance need not be read to a precision greatly exceeding the standard deviation for the balance.) Place the sample in a drying oven with the lid off, and dry it to constant weight. Remove the sample from the oven, replacing the cover, and place it in a desiccator containing active desiccant (e.g., magnesium perchlorate or calcium sulfate) until cool. Weigh it again, and also determine the tare weight of the sample container. Compute the water content by one of the following formulas:

$$\theta_{dw} = \frac{(\text{weight of wet soil} + \text{tare}) - (\text{weight of dry soil} + \text{tare})}{(\text{weight of dry soil} + \text{tare}) - (\text{tare})} \quad [22]$$

$$= \frac{(\text{weight of wet soil} + \text{tare}) - (\text{tare})}{(\text{weight of dry soil} + \text{tare}) - (\text{tare})} - 1 \quad [23]$$

$$= \frac{\text{weight of wet soil}}{\text{weight of dry soil}} - 1 \quad [24]$$

The third of these equations is useful where standardized cans are used and the tare weight is balanced out in the weighing process so that the sample weight is obtained directly. Multiplication by 100 gives the percentage of water in the sample on a dry-mass basis.

7–2.2.2.3   Comments.   The time necessary to reach constant weight (the term being loosely used here since constant weight is rarely obtained except for very sandy soils containing little or no organic matter) will depend upon the type of oven used, the size or depth of the sample, and the nature of the soil. If a forced draft oven is used, 10 hours is usually considered sufficient. If a convection oven is used, samples should be dried for at least 24 hours, and precautions should be taken to avoid adding wet samples during the last half of the drying period. Also, additional time should be added if the oven is heavily loaded. Water contents for samples which are to be compared should be determined using precisely the same method for each measurement. For more precise work, other considerations are involved which are discussed below.

An alternative method may be used for drying soil. Radiation-drying using an infrared or ordinary heat lamp, often in association with a built-in balance,[6] can be used for soil water content measurements where low pre-

---

[6] Several such instruments containing a built-in infrared heat lamp, a torsion or analytic-type chain balance, and a scale for direct reading of wet-mass basis water contents are available from scientific supply houses under the name of "moisture determination balance."

cision is adequate. The uncertainty of the drying temperature makes radiation-drying methods less accurate than those using closely controlled constant-temperature drying ovens. However, the method is rapid, requiring only a few minutes to dry the soil; and, when the built-in balance is used, wet-mass basis water content values may ordinarily be read directly from a scale. These may be converted to dry-mass figures by equation [1]. When using radiation-drying, care should be taken to avoid excessive heating of the sample.

Water content values for stony or gravelly soils, both on a mass and volume basis, can be grossly misleading. This arises from the fact that a large rock can occupy appreciable volume in a soil sample and contribute appreciably to the mass without making a commensurate contribution to the porosity or water capacity of the soil. Mass-basis water content figures are lower than corresponding values for a soil on a rock-free basis because of the excessive contribution to the dry mass made by a rock which may have a bulk density of about 2.6 g. per cm.³ compared to that of the finer soil material, which will usually range from 1.0 to 1.6 g. per cm.³ A mass-basis water content figure of 10% based upon the dry mass of a gravelly or stony soil having a bulk density of 2.0 g. per cm.³ would represent a water content of 20% if based upon the dry mass of the finer fraction with a bulk density of 1.6 g. per cm.³ It is important when presenting water content data on gravelly or stony soils to specify the basis of measurement —particularly the size fraction on which it is made.

The two types of water content figures of greatest interest are water content per unit bulk volume and water content per unit mass of the fine fraction. The volume-basis figure makes it possible to compute the volume of water per unit area in, say, a root zone. The mass-basis figure for the fine fraction is usually the figure obtained from gravimetric analyses or from a wilting-point or water-tension determination, and is the figure which would ordinarily be used to compare water conditions from place to place in a soil. The relationship between these two types of water content values is

$$\theta_{vb} = (\theta_{dmf} D_b / D_w)/(1 + M_{stone}/M_{fines}) \tag{25}$$

where θ_{vb} is the volume of water in unit volume of the whole soil, θ_{dmf} is the water content on a dry-mass basis for the fine fraction, D_b and D_w are the bulk densities of the whole soil (including stones) and of water, and M_{stone} and M_{fines} are the dry masses of the stone and fine fractions.

Water content on a volume basis or bulk density may be determined by taking a sample of known volume, oven-drying it according to procedures already described, and dividing the difference between wet and oven-dry mass by the volume to give water content, or dividing the oven-dry mass by the volume to give bulk density. The heterogeneity of gravelly and stony soils and the variability which usually exists from point to point in the soil make for low precision. Because of this low precision, it is possible to discard large stones prior to oven-drying without affecting the precision. Rocks and stones to be discarded are carefully and quickly brushed to avoid soil loss and to reduce evaporation loss, and then are weighed.

Conventional cylindrical tube samplers may be used in some gravelly and stony soils. However, as the number or size of stones increases, the utility of such sampling devices diminishes. In these kinds of soils it is important to determine the volume sampled each time a water content determination is to be made. Where core-type samplers can be used this is not difficult. However, where large rocks and stones interfere seriously, other methods must be used. One useful method involves sampling with a spade or shovel and determining the volume of the hole which is dug. The volume may be measured by placing a rubber or plastic membrane in the hole and filling it with water from a container filled to a known volume. The quantity of water used in filling the hole is easily determined. Grain millet or dry sand which flow easily and pack easily to constant bulk density may also be used to fill the hole; and, if the material is to be discarded, the rubber or plastic membrane is not needed. A detailed description of the method is given in section 30–3. No simple, inexpensive methods have as yet been developed for sampling beyond shallow depths without digging an access hole.

Certain general requirements must be met in the development of a procedure for obtaining accurate and reproducible water content measurements. Foremost of these is the requirement that the sample be dried at a specified temperature to constant weight with nothing being lost but water. This is rarely possible with a colloidal material like soil, particularly if it contains any appreciable organic matter. Weight losses during drying at 100° to 110°C. for periods as long as 15 days have been observed in soils ranging from fine sands to silty clay loams. Because of this it is important to specify the details of the drying procedure used in reporting water contents where precise values are needed.

Since accuracy in water content determinations hinges upon existence of a definable dry condition which, with soil, can only be based upon subjective judgment, it is more appropriate to refer to reproducibility than to accuracy. Reproducibility in water content measurements can be achieved in two ways: (1) treating every sample of a set to be compared exactly the same way in terms of such things as sample size and depth in the container, drying temperature, and drying time; or (2) following techniques which lead to equilibria which are as nearly independent of such variables as is possible. From the latter point of view, the nature of the thermal dehydration curves (Fig. 7–1) suggests the desirability of choosing a drying temperature in a region where the weight change of the colloidal constituents with temperature is at a minimum. Where the nature of the mineral colloids in a sample is unknown, the best temperature, as inferred from the curves of Fig. 7–1, is probably between 165° and 175°C. However, at such temperatures, organic matter oxidation and decomposition is likely to be excessive. Temperatures below about 50°C. appear to be required if oxidation of the organic fraction is to be avoided. Hence, for a soil sample containing organic matter, it is necessary to compromise unless elaborate methods of determination are used.

Vacuum drying at relatively low temperature, with the temperature being carefully controlled and specified when reporting, probably provides the most reproducible drying data. To assure perfectly dry conditions, the usual practice is to include a desiccant such as magnesium perchlorate in the oven. This is necessary since ordinary vacuum drying ovens are not constructed to be leak-proof, and some air is pulled continuously into the drying chamber. Drying times are considerably shortened by use of vacuum techniques. When a vacuum oven and careful techniques are substituted for the ordinary oven, considerable improvement in reproducibility is possible.

7–2.3   Gravimetry with Drying by Burning Alcohol

7–2.3.1   INTRODUCTION

Soil drying may be materially speeded through partial removal of water from soil samples with ethyl, methyl, or propyl alcohol followed by evaporation of the water with heat provided through burning the alcohol. Evaporation takes place both in the leachate and in the soil, and it is possible to remove water equivalent to that removed by oven-drying through repeating the leaching and burning process several times. A complete determination ordinarily can be made in as little as 20 minutes, and if a number of samples are handled concurrently, the time per sample is about 5 minutes. Except that the drying procedure and temperatures are different, the method is the same as that described in section 7–2.2. The precision of the method with reasonable care is from ±0.5% to ±1% water content, which is almost as good as oven-drying under conditions where elaborate precautions on temperature control and drying time are not taken. The precision decreases with increasing organic matter as was noted by Bouyoucos (1931, 1937, 1938) in his original description, where he indicated that the method was not accurate for organic matter contents >11%. Since Bouyoucos first proposed the method, it has been studied and recommended as a rapid method requiring a minimum of equipment by a number of investigators, particularly in foreign literature (e.g., Voskresenskii and Levina, 1939; Oganesyan, 1958; Kohler, 1951; Carter, 1938; and Kazo, 1951).

7–2.3.2   METHOD [7]

7–2.3.2.1   Special Apparatus.   For ordinary work use an aluminum can approximately 65 mm. in diameter and 45 mm. high (larger cans can

---

[7] Bouyoucos (1938), Oganesyan (1958), and unpublished work of the author.

be used for larger samples and increased precision). Prepare a tripod which fits inside the lid to support a 140-mesh screen (a screen with approximately 0.1-mm. openings, preferably made of stainless steel). Make the tripod just high enough to leave a 1-cm. opening above the lip of the lid to admit air to the burning alcohol under the screen. Make the diameter of the base of the tripod several millimeters smaller than the diameter of the can, thus permitting the can to function as a lid to cover the screen, tripod, and sample during cooling and weighing. For weighing, use a balance, preferably of direct-reading type, with a capacity of approximately 100 g. or more and a precision of ± 0.03 g. (standard deviation 0.01 g.) or less.

7–2.3.2.2 Reagent. Ethyl, methyl or propyl alcohol, technical grade.

7–2.3.2.3 Procedure. Place the screen and supporting tripod in the open lid of the can, and weigh this and the bottom of the can (which now forms a lid) together to obtain a tare weight. Spread about 10 g. of the wet sample uniformly over the screen, quickly replace the cover, and weigh the apparatus and sample together. Then drip alcohol onto the sample with a medicine dropper until the sample is saturated and alcohol begins to drip into the bottom cup. (Approximately 1/2 to 1 ml. of alcohol is required per gram of sample.) After saturation of the sample, ignite the alcohol and allow it to burn itself out. After a short cooling period (unless high precision is desired the apparatus need not be completely cooled), weigh the apparatus and soil again. Then apply additional alcohol as at first, with precaution to avoid vapor "explosions" which may occur if the sample is too hot. These may blow soil out of the container. Repeat the burning and weighing process until constant weight is achieved. In many tests of the method, only two burnings have been required to achieve the desired precision of measurement. Compute the water content by standard gravimetric methods described in section 7–2.2.

7–2.3.2.4 Comments. The major difference between this method and ordinary methods using oven-drying lies in the temperature used to remove the water. Bouyoucos (1937) reported finding temperatures of about 130°C. in the center of the sample and of about 160°C. near the edge. Oganesyan (1958) reported temperatures of about 120° to 130°C. in the surface of the soil and 90° to 100°C. at the center, increasing to from 110° to 120°C. for the last few seconds of the burning. From the dehydration curves of Fig. 7–1, it is obvious that the soil will not have dried uniformly. Likewise at such high temperatures, some organic matter is certain to have been oxidized. However, such temperatures frequently are encountered in drying ovens. Hence, the method can be expected to be no worse than oven-drying methods under conditions where precise oven temperatures are not maintained. A great many data reported in the literature show that the method produces results close to those of oven drying.

Although Bouyoucos (1938) regarded 11% organic matter as the upper limit for use of the method, other investigators have successfully used this method at higher organic matter contents. For example, Voskresenskii and Levina (1939) used the method on peat. However, they did mix in a weighed amount of dry sand, which seemed to reduce burning of the organic matter.

7–3 INDIRECT METHODS

7–3.1 Introduction

Certain physical and physical-chemical properties of soil vary with water content. However, the relationship between such properties and water content is usually complicated. Both the pore structure and constituents of the soil solution are involved. Also, some of these properties, even under conditions where all other factors are held constant, are not uniquely determined by water content. The wetting history of the soil is a factor in many instances. Despite many limitations some of these properties, with appropriate calibration, can be useful in characterizing soil with respect to its water content.

Wetting history often must be considered because water content of soil for a given energy status (temperature being constant) will be greater if the soil has reached a given water content by drying than by wetting. This phenomenon, known as hysteresis, is discussed in more detail in section 9–2. For purposes here, it is sufficient to point out that whether or not a pore becomes water-filled during a wetting process depends upon the size of the pore itself, whereas in a drying process the emptying of the pore depends upon the size of the channels connecting it with other pores in the system.[8] It is possible, therefore, to have two soil samples with identical porosities but different water contents at equilibrium with each other or at identical energy status if their wetting histories have been different.

Other factors sometimes included as part of the hysteresis phenomenon are changes in the sizes and shapes of pores as a soil is wetted and dried. Such changes usually are not completely reversible.

Indirect methods involve measurement of some property of the soil which is affected by soil water content or measurement of a property of some object placed in the soil, usually a porous absorber, which comes to water equilibrium with the soil. The water content of a porous absorber at equilibrium depends upon the energy status of the water rather than upon the water content of the soil with which it is in contact. For example, a soil with fine pores will contain more water than a soil with coarse pores at equal water tension. Hence, if the properties of the porous absorber are to provide an indication of water content, calibration against the water content of a sample of the soil in which the absorber is to be used is re-

---

[8] This statement about hysteresis must not be taken as a full explanation about what is really a more complicated phenomenon.

quired. Electrical or thermal properties of the absorber or weight changes in the absorber are indications of its water content. Methods involving weighing the absorber (Richards and Weaver, 1943) have not become widely used, probably because of technical complications associated with the weighing process.

Neutron-scattering and neutron and gamma ray absorption are affected by water content of a porous material and may be adapted to water content measurement. Although generally requiring calibration and therefore considered to be indirect methods, under some conditions radiation measurements can be converted directly to water content on the basis of theoretical considerations. Hence, such methods might be considered to be direct methods. In any event, there are conditions where radiation water content measurements are subject to less error than gravimetric measurements.

The need for indirect methods for obtaining water content or indexes of water content is evident when the time and labor involved in gravimetric sampling are considered. In addition to requiring a waiting time for oven-drying, such determinations are destructive, and therefore each sample must be taken at a different place in the soil system under study. Destructive sampling may disturb an experiment and may increase the possibility that a change in water content with position in a sampling area may be interpreted falsely as a change in water content with time at a particular location. Many of the indirect methods permit frequent or continuous measurements in the same place and, after equipment is installed, with only small expenditure of time. Thus, if a suitable calibration curve is available, changes in water content with time can be approximated.

Although this chapter is concerned primarily with measurement of water content or inferences of water content from other measurements, it should be pointed out that for many purposes water content is less useful than certain other properties of the soil-water system which depend upon water content. For example, in studies involving plant growth, water tension in the soil has greater meaning provided that, in soils containing more than small quantities of soluble salts, a term taking into account osmotic pressures is added. It is common practice to calibrate some of the indirect methods for evaluating water conditions in soil in terms of water tension rather than water content. The subject of water tension is discussed in greater detail and methods for its measurement are given in section 9.

7–3.2 Electrical Conductivity and Capacitance

7–3.2.1 PRINCIPLES

Electrical and thermal conductivity and electrical capacitance of porous materials vary with water content. Such properties of materials can ordinarily be measured with great precision; and, if a reliable correlation with water content existed, methods based upon measurement of these properties would have considerable utility. Unfortunately, such measurements made directly in soil have not resulted in unique correlations with water content and have not come into general use. The most thoroughly tested of the methods has involved measurement of electrical resistance (e.g., Edlefsen and Anderson, 1941; Kirkham and Taylor, 1950). Uncertain electrical contact between electrodes and soil, and soil heterogeneity, which prevents uniform flow of current in the soil mass, seem to be the major obstacles to successful use of direct electrical resistance methods.

Many of the problems involved in measurement of electrical and thermal conductivity and electrical capacitance in soil are avoided by use of porous blocks containing suitable electrodes and imbedded in the soil. When these blocks reach equilibrium; i.e., when water ceases to flow into or out of the blocks, their electrical or thermal properties are often regarded as an index of soil water content. However, the associated water content must be obtained from a calibration curve made using soil from the site where the block is used because the equilibrium between a block and soil is a water-tension equilibrium and not a water-content equilibrium. Different soils have different water-content water-tension curves, variations among soils often being as much as several hundred percent; e.g., a fine sandy loam may have a water content of 5% at 15 bars tension, whereas a clay loam may have a water content of, let us say, 13% at the same tension. As a consequence, calibration of a porous block against water tension often may be considered more reasonable and more useful than calibration against water content.

Hysteresis enters into the problem of inferring water content from measurements made on porous blocks even though a calibration curve for a particular soil is available. The water content of both soil and block depends in part upon wetting history. Ideally, two calibration curves are needed, one for drying, extending from very wet to very dry, and one for wetting, where the starting point is in the very dry range. These two curves are considered to close at the end points and to provide an envelope which would contain all possible intermediate curves. However, because it is difficult to wet a soil only part way the wetting curve is not usually made. In many practical situations the starting point is unknown. Hence, the curve traced out as the soil wets or dries is unknown, and water content can be known only to lie at some point between the limiting wetting and drying curves. Resulting errors in water content inferences depend upon the nature of the soil in question and its wetting or drying history but can easily be 20% or more (Taylor et al., 1961). Nevertheless, blocks often are used to indicate water content of soil even though the precision in such use is rather low. However, the popular use of porous blocks likely stems from their utility as indicators of water conditions favorable or unfavorable to plant growth (water tension as opposed to water content), rather than from their ability to indicate soil water content.

Thermal conductivity and electrical capacitance measurements in porous blocks, although favorably reported on from time to time in the literature, have not come into general use (see Fletcher, 1939; Shaw and Baver, 1940; Anderson and Edlefsen, 1942; de Plater, 1955; and Bloodworth and Page, 1957). This probably results from the fact that electrical conductivity is so easily measured and porous blocks for such use are so easily constructed. Since the most serious limitation in use of blocks does not seem to be the measurement of the water content of the block itself, the pressure for change to other types of measurement has not been great. The most common porous-block technique, therefore, involves measurement of electrical conductivity. The porous-block method which follows is for such measurements.

7–3.2.2 METHOD

7–3.2.2.1 Special Apparatus.

1. Wheatstone Bridge for measuring resistance: Bridges in common use are of the alternating current type (usually 1,000 cycle) to avoid polarization at the electrodes in the porous block. Both null-point and deflection-type instruments are used. Because of ease of reading, deflection-type bridges, involving measurement of bridge unbalance, are probably the most common. Resistances to be measured range from a few hundred ohms to 200,000 or more ohms, a single calibration curve often covering as much as 100,000 ohms.

2. Porous blocks: Blocks now available[9] are made of a variety of porous materials ranging from nylon cloth (Bouyoucos, 1949) and fiberglas (Colman and Hendrix, 1949) to casting plasters (Bouyoucos and Mick, 1940; Perrier and Marsh, 1958; and numerous others), the most common being some form of gypsum. Various grades and kinds of casting plaster are mixed with different amounts of water and in a variety of ways, including in some instances pouring the mix into the mold in a partial vacuum. In some instances resin is added to the mix, which changes the electrical characteristics and decomposition rate in the soil (Bouyoucos, 1953). The method of preparation as well as the mix governs the porosity of the block and the resulting response curve. Some types of gypsum last longer in soil than others, Hydrocal B11 (manufactured by U. S. Gypsum Co.) being the most resistant of current plasters used.

---

[9] Several types of commercial blocks are available from such companies as the W. R. Ames Co., Milpitas, Calif.; Delmhorst Instruments Co., Boonton, New Jersey; Soilmoisture Equipment Co., Santa Barbara, Calif.; and Industrial Instruments Inc., Cedar Grove, New Jersey. Beckman Instruments, Berkeley Instruments Division, Richmond, Calif., supplies fiberglas units which also contain a thermistor for temperature measurement. These companies also handle resistance bridges for use with the blocks.

Several different electrode systems are in common use. The simplest consists of two tinned wires about 35 mm. long (made using ordinary twin-conductor, rubber-insulated lamp cord). These are imbedded 1 or 2 cm. apart in a rectangular porous block roughly 1 by 3 by 5 cm. in size. Cylindrical blocks also are in use. These consist of a cylindrical screen (usually made of stainless steel) surrounding a central post or in some instances a second, smaller cylindrical screen. Such blocks are 2 to 3 cm. in diameter and about 3 cm. long. A parallel-screen system, using rectangular blocks, has been used by several investigators and is reported to have less lag in coming to equilibrium than other types of blocks.

3. Calibration container: Prepare a small screen box (window screen or hardware cloth soldered together), open at one end, and of suitable dimensions to contain the block and a layer of soil at least 2-cm. thick around the block (Kelley, 1944).

4. Equipment for determining a reference water content of the soil used in the calibration (section 7–2.2.2.1 or 7–2.3.2.1).

7–3.2.2.2 Procedure. Calibrate each block in soil typical of the site in which it is to be used, and with packing to about the same bulk density. To carry out the calibration, saturate the block with water, preferably with vacuum soaking, and weigh the wet block, its attached leads and the screen box together to obtain a tare weight. Moisten the soil to be used to a state where it can be packed around the block to approximately its field density, mix the soil thoroughly, and take a sample for water content determination. Then pack the soil around the block in the screen box, and weigh the entire apparatus. Using the water content determined independently by gravimetric methods (see section 7–2.2.2.1 or 7–2.3.2.1), compute the dry mass of the soil in the box. This will be:

$$\text{dry mass of soil} = \frac{(\text{mass of moist soil} + \text{tare}) - (\text{tare})}{\%\ \text{water content}/100 + 1}, \qquad [26]$$

where the water content figure is on a dry-mass basis. At all subsequent calibration points the water content percentage will be

$$\text{water content, dry-mass basis} = \frac{100[(\text{mass of tare} + \text{wet soil}) - (\text{mass of tare} + \text{dry soil})]}{\text{mass of dry soil}}. \qquad [27]$$

Wet the soil in the screen box to near saturation, weigh the entire assembly, and then measure the block resistance to determine the first calibration point. Allow water to evaporate from the apparatus in the air until the desired weight for the next calibration point is reached. After the desired weight is reached, place the entire apparatus in a closed container (such as a desiccator without desiccant) in the dark at uniform temperature overnight, or longer, to permit the water to equilibrate in the block and soil.

Then measure the resistance. Plot the resistance as a function of water content (3-cycle semilogarithmic paper is convenient).

To install a block in the field, form a hole vertically from the surface or horizontally in the side of a trench. Wet the block thoroughly, place it in the hole, and then pack soil around it to assure good contact with the surrounding soil. Bring the leads to the surface, running them horizontally for a short distance beneath the surface to assure that no continuous channel exists along the leads for passage of free water. After equilibrium is reached, usually overnight, make resistance measurements as desired, and convert them to water content values with a calibration curve.

7–3.2.2.3 Comments. In calibration as well as under field conditions, true water content equilibria are rarely reached, particularly in the dry range. However, the uncertainty of the water content inference, at best, does not justify an elaborate and time-consuming calibration. Under practical conditions when the resistance reading approaches a constant value, equilibrium may be assumed to be close. In the wet range, for most porous blocks, the resistance change with changing water content is small and the precision is low. Precision is also affected by changes in the calibration curve over successive wetting and drying cycles (Cannell, 1958). Blocks have not proved satisfactory in sandy soils or in soils which shrink or swell considerably.

It is common practice to place blocks into uniform groups according to their resistance at saturation and to calibrate only selected blocks from each group (Tanner, et al., 1949). This practice does not completely ensure obtaining groups of blocks with like calibration curves. But, considering the low precision of the method when it is used for water content determination, it is probably an adequate procedure.

The calibration procedure described is for desorption. The procedure cannot be reversed easily to provide a sorption curve because of difficulties associated with partially wetting a soil mass. However, a tedious procedure, involving condensation of water in a soil sample in a humidity chamber, can be used for obtaining a sorption curve.

Calibration is often carried out in the field by obtaining water content values gravimetrically and plotting them against resistance readings. Or, blocks are placed in pots containing growing plants and the water content determined by weighing the pot, with an estimate of plant weight being subtracted (Cannell, 1958).

Electrical conductivity of a porous block depends upon the electrolyte concentration of the conducting fluid as well as upon the cross section of this fluid or water content. In a porous block made from an inert material, the electrolyte which carries the current comes from the soil solution. Even a small change in electrolyte concentration of the soil will influence the resistance under such circumstances. In blocks made from gypsum the electrolyte concentration corresponds primarily to that of a saturated solution of calcium sulfate. Variations in the soil solution due to fertilization have relatively small influence upon the electrolyte concentration in such blocks and therefore relatively small influence on resistance. Such blocks also may be used without serious difficulty in slightly saline soils (where soil extract conductivities are less than approximately 2 mmho. per cm.[2] (Taylor, 1955).

Blocks made from gypsum compounds do gradually deteriorate in soil, particularly in sodic soils and in soil where the water table frequently is at high levels. However, those made from hydrocal have lasted for upwards of 6 years in some soils. Blocks made from ordinary plaster of paris have been known to deteriorate in a single season beyond the point where they can be used.

It would be difficult to specify an expected precision for water content measurements using electrical conductivity blocks because of the many sources of error involved. The precision depends not only upon the care used in manufacture, selection, and calibration of blocks but also upon factors of hysteresis which are out of the control of the operator. However, it appears that precision better than $\pm 2\%$ water content should not be expected and that errors as great as 100% are easily possible. On-the-site checking as the blocks are used appears necessary if confidence is to be developed in water content inferences to be made. On the other hand, where porous blocks are used as a measure of water tension rather than water content, considerably better performance is possible. Calibration against water tension may be carried out using porous-plate and pressure-membrane equipment (section 8) with special pass-through electrical contacts.

7–3.3 Neutron Thermalization

7–3.3.1 PRINCIPLES

Hydrogen nuclei have a marked property for scattering and slowing neutrons. This property is exploited in the neutron method for measuring water content. High-energy neutrons (0.1 to 10 Mev.) emitted from a radioactive substance such as a radium-beryllium or americium-beryllium neutron source are slowed and changed in direction by elastic collisions with atomic nuclei. This process is called "thermalization," the neutrons being reduced in energy to about the thermal energy of atoms in a substance at room temperature.

The two major factors involved in scattering and slowing of neutrons are the transfer of energy at each collision and the statistical probability of collision.

The average energy transfer at collision of a neutron with other nuclei depends largely upon the mass number of the nuclei encountered. The average number of collisions required to slow a neutron from 2 Mev. to thermal energies is 18 for hydrogen, 67 for lithium, 86 for beryllium, 114 for carbon, 150 for oxygen and $9A + 6$ for nuclei with large mass numbers A (Weinberg and Wigner, 1958, Table 10.1).

The statistical probability of collision is dealt with using the concept of "scattering cross section" [10] which is a statistically derived, cross sectional area measured in barns which is proportional to the probability of collision, in this case, between neutrons and other nuclei. This scattering cross section depends upon the nature of the nuclei encountered and the energy of the neutron. The scattering cross section for hydrogen varies from about 1 barn at 10 Mev. to about 13 barns at 0.1 Mev. The cross section varies considerably as the neutron continues to lose energy but is somewhat higher in the thermal energy range. Other elements found in soil with appreciable scattering cross sections (2 to 5 barns) are beryllium, carbon, nitrogen, oxygen, and fluorine.

Considering both energy transfer and scattering cross section, it is evident that hydrogen, having a nucleus of about the same size and mass as the neutron, has a much greater thermalizing effect on fast neutrons than any other element. In addition, when both hydrogen and oxygen are considered, water has a marked effect on slowing or thermalizing neutrons. This is particularly true in the thermal range.

The quantity of hydrogen in the soil ranges from near zero for dry coarse sand to as much as 8% of the mass of a fine-textured soil with 50% water content when structural water (see footnote 1) is included in the computation. Most of the hydrogen in soil is associated with water, and lesser amounts with organic matter.

As fast neutrons lose energy and become thermalized, another nuclear-matter interaction becomes increasingly important—neutron capture with the release of other nuclear particles or energy. Of the elements usually present in soil in quantities of 1% or greater, the capture cross section for thermal neutrons is greatest for iron (2.53 barns) and potassium (2.07 barns). The other most common elements in the soil, silicon, aluminum, hydrogen, carbon and oxygen, have capture cross sections of 0.16, 0.23, 0.33, 0.003, 0.0002 barns. Several elements present in soil in small, or even minute, quantities such as cadmium with an absorption cross section of 2,450 barns, boron with 755 barns, lithium with 71 barns, or chlorine with 34 barns, can have an appreciable effect on neutron capture.

---

[10] Neutrons interact with matter in two general ways, namely, by elastic and inelastic scattering and by interactions leading to capture with a consequent emission of energy or of other nuclear particles. The probability of any particular interaction depends upon neutron energy and characteristics of the nuclei encountered. These characteristics are described generally by the nuclear cross section, measured using a unit of area called the "barn" which is 10^{-24} cm.^{2}—the larger the probability of a particular interaction the larger the nuclear cross section.

When a fast neutron source is placed in moist soil it becomes immediately surrounded by a cloud of thermal neutrons. The density of this cloud represents an equilibrium between the rate of emission of fast neutrons, their thermalization by nuclei such as those of hydrogen, and their capture by absorbing nuclei, as determined by their concentration and capture cross section.

The scattering cross section and the concentration of hydrogen nuclei determine the distance from the source a fast neutron must travel before making a sufficient number of collisions to become thermalized. The farther a neutron travels from the source the larger the volume which will be occupied by thermal neutrons and the lower their density. With the numbers of slow neutrons involved, the absorption capacity of the soil for neutron capture is essentially infinite, and the rate of capture depends only upon thermal neutron concentration and the combined capture cross section of the elements in the soil. If the capture cross section, except for that due to water, remains constant (i.e., chemical composition constant), then the thermal neutron density may be calibrated against water concentration on a volume basis. Thermal neutron density is easily measured with a detector, insensitive to fast neutrons, which is placed in the vicinity of the fast neutron source to form a special probe. The source is usually placed at the bottom of the detector tube or against the side. This probe can be lowered through an access hole into the soil and measurements obtained for conversion to water content (Belcher et al., 1950; Gardner and Kirkham, 1952).

The nature of the neutron-scattering and thermalization process imposes an important restriction on the resolution of water content measurements. The volume of soil involved in the measurement will depend upon the concentration of scattering nuclei, hence, largely upon water content, and upon the energies of the emitted fast neutrons. The strength of the neutron source affects the thermal neutron density and is involved in the counting statistics but does not affect the range of the fast neutrons. Experimental work with radium-beryllium sources indicates that the practical resolution at best is about 15 cm., i.e., the soil volume most greatly affecting the slow-neutron count rate is a sphere, 15 cm. in diameter (Van Bavel, 1958). The diameter of this sphere increases with decreasing water content. Actually at low water contents the neutron density is affected by soil at distances as great as 60 cm. from the source (Van Bavel et al., 1961; Van Bavel et al., 1956). Lack of high resolution makes it impossible to detect accurately any discontinuity or sharp change in water content gradient in a soil profile (McHenry, 1963). In particular, measurements close to the soil surface are unreliable because of the soil-air discontinuity; and measurements are usually not made with well-type equipment any closer than about 18 cm. from the surface. (A probe designed for surface use is described below.) Therefore, water-content distribution curves for soil profiles containing steep water-content gradients will be rounded and inaccurate in detail; however, they are likely to be of sufficient accuracy for many practical uses in terms of overall water content.

Surface probes, where the slow-neutron detector is laid horizontally on the surface of the soil with the fast-neutron source beside it, make it possible to obtain water content measurements in the surface where the well-type unit is inadequate. Most surface probes involve use of a moderator rich in hydrogen (such as paraffin or polyethylene) over the top of source and detector to compensate partially for the soil-air discontinuity. Experimental work with surface units indicates a sensitive depth of from 15 to 35 cm. with precision comparable to well-type units for uniform soil water content (Van Bavel, 1961; de Vries and King, 1961; Phillips et al., 1960). Where water content of the surface soil is not uniform, say under conditions of rapid surface evaporation or superficial wetting by low rainfall, or where the surface of the soil is rough, precision falls off materially (Van Bavel, 1961).

Practical limitations make calibration essential for use of neutron water-content measuring equipment. Fortunately, a calibration curve for a particular instrument usually is adequate for a wide range of soils—particularly where high precision is not required. The shape of the calibration curve appears to depend largely upon the geometry of the probe and its neutron source and slow-neutron detector (Van Bavel et al., 1961). With appropriate geometry it appears possible to secure a nearly linear curve over most of the water-content range of interest in soil. Source strength and counter efficiency influence the count-rate, water-content curve. But, if the ratio of count rate in soil to the count rate in a standard absorber is used, these are eliminated. The calibration curve supplied by the manufacturer usually may be used, provided the specifications for soil access tubing are followed. However, for high precision or under conditions where a soil is suspected to deviate from the normal, special calibration may be required. See Van Bavel et al. (1961), Holmes and Jenkinson (1959), Stolzy and Cahoon (1957), and Holmes (1956) for discussions of calibration.

The hydrogen content of soil, apart from easily removable water, differs appreciably from soil to soil, and it is surprising that the same calibration curve is adequate for so many different soils. A definitive explanation is not yet available in the literature but it is apparent that certain fortuitous compensating factors are involved.

The quantity of hydrogen in soil, apart from absorbed water, depends upon organic matter content and the nature of the mineralogical components. Certain clay minerals contain appreciable structural water (see footnote 1), which is not removed by oven-drying at 100 to 110°C. For several minerals (Fig. 7–2) as much as 20% additional water can be removed by heating to about 800°C. On the other hand, coarse sands composed of quartz or feldspars have almost no water associated with them at 100° to 110°C. It is significant that the construction of many calibration curves for neutron water-content equipment has involved use of sand to provide some water contents and loams and clays for other water contents without apparent difficulty.

The explanation for this apparent anomaly possibly involves a nearly perfect balance between increased scattering due to hydrogen in organic matter or in the structural hydrogen of clays, which tends to increase thermal neutron density, and increased neutron capture associated with a different chemical composition, which tends to decrease thermal neutron density. Clay materials which retain large amounts of structural water also are known to contain higher concentrations of such elements as boron, lithium, chlorine, and iron which are good neutron absorbers compared to the elements composing sands. Evidence that small quantities of good neutron absorbers can affect a calibration curve has been obtained by Holmes and Jenkinson (1959). They added boron to a soil at rates of 65, 156, and 245 ppm. Increasing boron concentration decreased the slope of the counting-rate, water-content curve. It is evident that the right amounts of neutron absorbers could compensate for increased neutron-scattering due to organic or structural hydrogen in a soil. It is also evident that a soil containing uncommon excesses of such elements as boron, chlorine, or iron could have a different calibration curve.

An additional fact which must be recognized as being involved in the calibration problem is that tightly bound hydrogen nuclei interact differently with neutrons than do hydrogen nuclei of water. How this is involved in the calibration is currently unknown.

7–3.3.2 METHOD

7–3.3.2.1 Special Apparatus.

1. Small fast-neutron source such as radium- or americium-beryllium: Such sources are good indefinitely because of their long half-lives.
2. Shield for storage of the neutron source between readings and when the unit is not in use: The shield may also serve as a standard absorber for checking the equipment or for providing the standard count when data are computed on a count to count-in-standard ratio basis. The shield must protect the user against both neutrons and gamma rays—particularly with use of a Ra-Be source, which has a relatively high gamma emission. Shielding commonly used consists of lead and paraffin or polyethylene in a cylindrical shaped unit with a cylindrical hole through the axis to accommodate the probe. A lead sphere (with cylindrical hole) approximately 13 cm. in diameter immediately surrounds the probe at the location of the neutron source, and the balance of the cylinder is filled with paraffin or polyethylene. The outer diameter is approximately 30 cm. The unit is made so that it can be set over the

soil access hole and the probe lowered through the bottom of the shield into the hole. The soil between the source and the operator provides adequate protection when the probe is in use.

3. Detector of slow neutrons: There are several types, but the one used most commonly for water-content measurement is a BF_3-enriched proportional counter mounted in a cylindrical arrangement with a transistorized preamplifier mounted in the cable end. The neutron source is mounted in a lead shield at the bottom of the gas-filled detector tube in some probes, and in others in a lead shield on the side of the case at the center of the sensitive volume of the gas-filled detector.[11] In the second type the diameter of the probe is sufficiently greater than the diameter of the gas-filled detector to accommodate the source and lead shielding. This detector, when operated properly, is insensitive to fast neutrons and to gamma radiation given off by the source. The detector is filled with BF_3 gas, ordinarily at a pressure of about 20 cm. of Hg, and a high positive voltage is imposed on a wire running axially through the tube center. When a thermalized neutron encounters a B^{10} nucleus and is absorbed, an alpha particle (the helium nucleus) is emitted. The alpha particle moves to the charged wire, creating an electrical pulse. This minute pulse is amplified by a preamplifier contained in the probe and picked up by a conventional scaler, and the number of events over a measured time interval is counted. Alternatively the pulse can be picked up on a count-rate meter. A B^{10} atom is lost each time a neutron is absorbed, but the number of B^{10} atoms in the detector tube is sufficiently large that the detector will last for many years.

4. Portable scaler or rate meter: A number of suitable scalers or scaler-rate meter combinations are available from commercial suppliers such as Troxler Laboratories or Nuclear-Chicago. A scaler should have at least 5 decades for about 10^6 counts and an accurate timer. Counting times of $\frac{1}{2}$, 1, and 2 minutes are desirable. These units are operated by

---

[11] Troxler Laboratories (P.O. Box 5997, Raleigh, North Carolina 27607) supplies probes of the first type in two different probe diameters, 1.865 and 1.5 inches, and using either a 3-mc. radium-beryllium or a 100-mc. americium-beryllium fast-neutron source located on the radial axis at the bottom of the detector tube. These probes are designed and calibrated for use in a 1.9 or 1.555 inch i.d. aluminum irrigation tubing. They may be calibrated for other types of tubing. Nuclear-Chicago (333 East Howard Avenue, Des Plaines, Ill. 60018) supplies probes of the second type with either an americium-beryllium or radium-beryllium neutron source at the approximate center, lengthwise, of a 1-inch detector tube contained in a 1.5-inch cylindrical housing. This probe is designed for use in 1.555 inch i.d. aluminum or steel tubing. Use of americium permits high neutron flux with low gamma flux, thus simplifying the shielding problem.

Surface probes are commercially available from both Troxler and Nuclear-Chicago. By use of a special kit, the Troxler depth probe may be converted to a surface probe. Both companies supply several different models, some of which are combination moisture and density units.

rechargeable batteries with built-in or associated chargers. The greater precision possible with a scaler, which permits counting over periods from seconds to many minutes, has led to their greater use. However, for some purposes a rate meter, which permits conventional recording, has some advantages. Van Bavel (1962a) has recently published information regarding an improved portable rate meter which, for a probe with a linear calibration curve, can be calibrated directly in terms of water content. Increased use of such rate meters is likely.

Cables for connecting the probe and scaler are usually marked so that the depth of the probe may be measured easily. Cables usually supplied with commercial well-type instruments are 20 to 25 feet in length. However, much longer lengths can be supplied.

5. Access tubing and soil auger: Steel or aluminum access tubing is most commonly used, but other materials such as plastic have been used. Two sizes of access tubing are in common use: 20-gauge steel or aluminum tubing 1.625 inches o.d. and 2-inch o.d., 1.9-inch i.d. aluminum irrigation tubing. A soil auger slightly smaller than the tubing should be available for drilling the access hole. Access-hole drill guides also are available along with dummy probes for checking and removing dents from access tubing. Moisture probes should be calibrated for the particular material and size of access tubing to be used.

7–3.3.2.2 Procedure. To assure that the hole will be straight and without air pockets around the access tube, drill the access hole through the tubing. Insert the tubing in steps by advancing the auger several inches beyond the end of the tube and then forcing the tube to the drilled depth. To avoid bending of aluminum pipe that sometimes occurs where the tube can be forced downward only with difficulty, use first a piece of steel tubing of the same size in preparation of the hole, and then insert the aluminum tubing later. Leave several inches of the tubing above the soil surface, and cover it with an inverted can to prevent entrance of trash. If free water is expected to occur at any time within the depth of the access tubing, close the pipe at the bottom with a rubber stopper or with a metal or plastic plug.

To make a measurement, turn on the scaler or rate meter a few minutes ahead of time to warm up (transistorized units require no warm-up). Make several standardization counts with the probe in the shield, making sure that it is in precisely the same position each time. The normal counting time is 1 minute, but for greater precision 2- or 3-minute counts are often made and reduced to a 1-minute basis. After determining the standard count, take readings at successive depth intervals, starting at least 7 to 10 inches from the soil surface when a well-type probe is used. Six-inch intervals are ordinarily used. With probes described above, this provides for a small overlap of readings. Make a standard count occasionally as determined necessary by experience with particular equipment. It is often convenient to make a standard count at the start and end of a series of readings in each access hole. Keep a record of the standard count to provide an index of equipment condition.

Divide readings by the standard reading to obtain a count-ratio (referred to variously as "relative count," "ratio to standard," "percent of standard," etc.) and refer to the instrument calibration curve to obtain water content. The calibration curve supplied with the instrument usually may be used. But, since wide differences in soils are known to exist, calibration checks should be made for each soil type as guided by experience in an area. To check the calibration, make a series of readings in a test hole, and then, at a minimum of 4 positions within 6 inches of the test hole, take gravimetric samples at 3-inch intervals for both bulk density (see section 30) and water content determination (see section 7–2.2). Convert mass-basis water content values to volume-basis figures, determine the average of the 4 determinations, and plot a curve of water content against soil depth. Plot the similar curve as inferred from neutron instrument readings using the calibration curve provided with the instrument, and compare the curves. If a consistent difference exists between the two curves which is larger than should be expected when the precision of the gravimetric water content and bulk-density determinations is considered, it may be desirable to shift the calibration curve. However, pronounced changes in the soil profile must also be taken into account.

Procedure for use of a surface probe is substantially the same as for the well-type probe.

7–3.3.2.3 Comments. With reasonable attention to safety rules supplied by the manufacturer, the health hazard involved in using the equipment is small. The important precautions are the following: (*1*) Keep the probe in its shield at all times except when it is lowered into the soil for measurement. (*2*) Reduce exposure to the small radiation escaping the shield by keeping several feet away except when changing the position of the probe and by keeping the open end of the probe and shield pointed away from personnel. (*3*) Carry the probe in the field on a cart or on a sling between two persons if more than a few minutes is involved in getting the equipment to a using position. (*4*) Transport the probe in the back of a truck, a car trunk, or for short periods in the unoccupied rear seat. (*5*) Have operators wear a film badge at waist level. (*6*) When the probe is not in use, lock it in a storage room. Label the container plainly to indicate radioactive content. (*7*) Have a semiannual leak test performed on the source by a competent safety officer (the manufacturer can advise on this). (*8*) See that probe maintenance is performed only by personnel trained in servicing radioactive equipment.

For most practical uses of the neutron equipment, the manufacturer's calibration curve is adequate. However, calibration may be required if a soil has unusual neutron-absorption characteristics or if the access tubing is of different size or material from that in which the probe was calibrated. For maximum reproducibility of water content measurements, the probe should fit the access tubing as closely as practical.

The field calibration check may be used for detecting large differences in calibration due to unusual soil conditions. However, field calibration should not be relied upon for precision work because of the inaccuracies associated with the determination of the volume-basis water content values required. These inaccuracies arise from errors in measurement of both the mass-basis water content (see section 7–2.2) and the bulk density. Field variation in both water content and bulk density, which can occur over a relatively short distance, particularly in a heterogeneous soil, introduces an additional confounding factor. For these reasons, unless the calibration curve is considerably in error, water content inferences from the neutron measurements may well be better than those obtained by direct sampling.

Accurate calibration curves require the use of large homogeneous bodies of soil with carefully regulated water content. Some useful checking can be done with substitute neutron absorbers (such as $CdCl_2$-water solutions) in smaller containers. However, techniques are sufficiently complicated that persons attempting calibration should consult original literature sources such as Van Bavel et al. (1961), Holmes (1956), and Holmes and Jenkinson (1959).

Although the resolution of neutron water content measurements is low, the precision of measurement for large samples is good. There are three sources of error associated with such measurements: (1) random variation in count rate due to random variation in fast-neutron emission from the source, (2) errors associated with the counting equipment, including the timer, and (3) errors associated with the calibration curve. If the calibration curve has been prepared with care using long counting times, then the third error primarily involves differences between field conditions and calibration conditions, and the accuracy of the water content determination used in the calibration (see section 7–2.2). Differences in soil composition, soil bulk density, and geometry of the calibration arrangement can all influence the reliability of the calibration curve.

With equipment available commercially at the present time, instrumentation errors usually may be reduced to a small value, particularly when data are handled on a count-ratio basis. The size of the error depends upon characteristics of particular equipment. However, it is common practice to multiply the standard deviation due to random emission by a factor of 1.5 to 2 to account for instrument error. For 10,000 counts per minute the standard deviation for scattering and absorption would be 100 counts per minute. For common equipment, deviation of the order of 200 counts per minute should be expected. Calibration-curve errors must be considered subjectively since they can be large or small, depending upon care taken in the calibration process and the degree to which field conditions are comparable to calibration conditions. In common practice unless contrary evidence exists, such errors are regarded to be less than those arising from field variability where access tubes are the same as those used in calibration. The error due to random emission of the source can be dealt with statistically.

For a linear count-ratio, water-content curve (or for linear portions of such curves), the water content is given by the formula

$$\theta = (1/S)(N/N_{std}) \qquad [28]$$

where S is the slope,

$$\Delta(N/N_{std})/\Delta\theta .$$

Where N_{std} has been measured over a time interval several times that over which N is measured, so that the variance of N_{std} is negligible compared to the variance of N, the variance of θ due only to random emission errors is

$$V_{\theta_e} = \frac{1}{S^2 N_{std}^2} V_N , \qquad [29]$$

and the standard deviation due only to random emission errors is

$$\sigma_{\theta_e} = (1/S^2 N_{std}^2)^{1/2} \sigma_N . \qquad [30]$$

The standard deviation of a counting rate is $\sigma_N = (N/t)^{1/2}$, where t is the counting time, so that equation [30], with the aid of equation [28], becomes

$$\sigma_{\theta_e} = \sqrt{\frac{N/t}{S^2 N_{std}^2}} = \sqrt{\frac{\theta}{S N_{std} t}} . \qquad [31]$$

If the limit of precision due to random emission errors only is taken as $3\sigma_{\theta_e}$ as was done for equation [19] earlier, then the water content error due to random counting errors only is

$$E_{\theta_e} = 3 \sqrt{\frac{\theta}{S N_{std} t}} . \qquad [32]$$

In a typical situation—where the slope of the count-ratio, water-content curve is taken to be 1.5, the standard count N_{std} 10,000 cpm., the counting time 1 minute, and the water content conservatively considered to be 0.40 (40% water on a volume basis)—the error due to random source emission for 99.7% certainty (3σ) is

$$E_{\theta_e} = 3 \sqrt{\frac{.40}{1.5 \times 10^4 \times 1}} = 0.0155 \qquad [33]$$

or $\pm 1.6\%$ water content. (For 95% certainty the error would be $\pm 1\%$ and for 68%, $\pm 0.5\%$.) The error due solely to random source emission may be reduced to any desired value by increasing the counting time or increasing the count rate through increasing the source strength. A useful statistical guide for choosing an appropriate counting time has been published by Merriam (1962).

The size of random counting error to be tolerated should depend upon the size of the error anticipated due to field variability. This can vary widely. Stone et al. (1960) obtained coefficients of variation of 1.5% to 2.5%, with an average difference in water content between gravimetric and neutron values of <0.1 inch of water per 6-inch depth of soil, or in volume percent, 1.67. These differences were believed to be due more to limitations of bulk density determination than to the neutron water-content determination. At 40% water content, standard deviations corresponding to 1.5% and 2.5% coefficients of variation would be 0.6% and 1.0% water content, or in terms of E_θ (99.7% certainty), 1.8% and 3.0%. Van Bavel (1962b) suggested that experience indicates a standard deviation of 0.01 volume fraction (θ as used here) in the calibration relation found experimentally compared to the true relation between count rate and water content. This would correspond to an E_θ value of 0.03 or 3% water content. On this basis he concluded that a Ra-Be neutron source strength between 1 and 2 mc. is more nearly compatible with the precision of the normal calibration than is the usual 2 to 5 mc. source, and that lower cost and the reduced health hazard would be advantageous for general applications of the neutron method.

One additional factor relating to use of the neutron method for field water-content measurement should be considered. The presence of a metal tube in the soil can have an effect upon soil temperature because of the greater heat conductivity of metal compared to soil. Average temperature differences between soil adjacent to an aluminum access tube and the surrounding soil within the surface 2 feet did not exceed 3°F. during August and May, and the largest average temperature gradient was 0.7°F. per inch in work reported by Hanks and Bowers (1960). This work was done in a silty clay loam, and no measurable influence on water content in soil surrounding the access tube was observed. Unless temperature conditions of extraordinary nature are encountered, the influence of the access tube on water content due to temperature gradients probably is minor.

7–3.4 Gamma Ray or Neutron Attenuation

7–3.4.1 PRINCIPLES

Principles of absorption by matter of both gamma rays and neutrons are well known (see section 7–3.3). The degree to which a beam of monoenergetic gamma rays is attenuated or reduced in intensity in passing through a soil column depends upon the overall density of the column. If the density of the soil less its water content is constant, then changes in the attenuation represent changes in water content. The attenuation equation, neglecting air, is

$$N_m/N_o = \exp\left[-S(\mu_s\rho_s + \mu_w\theta) - 2S'\mu_c\rho_c\right] \qquad [34]$$

where N_m/N_o is the ratio of the transmitted to incident flux for the moist soil, μ_c, μ_s and μ_w are the mass attenuation coefficients for the container material, soil and water, θ is mass of water per unit bulk volume of soil, ρ_c is the density and S' is the thickness of the container walls, ρ_s is the density of the soil and S is the thickness of the column. The intensity of the incident monoenergetic gamma beam is proportional to the intensity at the source and inversely proportional to the square of the distance from the source.[12] The corresponding equation for a dry soil is

$$N_d/N_o = \exp\left(-S\mu_s\rho_s - 2S'\mu_c\rho_c\right). \qquad [35]$$

Division of equation [34] by equation [35] yields

$$N_m/N_d = \exp\left(-\mu_w\theta S\right) \qquad [36]$$

or

$$\theta = \frac{\ln\left(N_m/N_d\right)}{-\mu_w S} = \frac{\log\left(N_m/N_d\right)}{-0.4343\mu_w S}. \qquad [37]$$

If a perfectly collimated gamma beam of uniform energy were used, and if all scattered and secondary radiation were eliminated, the established value of μ_w, available from independent work, could be used. However, satisfactory calibration curves can be obtained experimentally, usually with greater practicality.

Low-energy gamma rays, such as the 0.661 Mev. gamma rays of Cs^{137}, are more easily absorbed by water than high-energy rays, and they are also easily counted. For these reasons, Cs^{137} is generally used as the source of gamma radiation.

Water-content measurement techniques using neutron attenuation are similar to those using gamma rays, but more specific to water. Although neutrons are scattered and absorbed in some degree by all kinds of nuclei in the soil, hydrogen is by far the most effective. Hence, attenuation change is relatively sensitive to water-content change. (See section 7–3.3.) Although bulk density is a minor factor when neutrons are used to measure water content, neutron attenuation can be used, nevertheless, to measure bulk density of dry soil by making long counts. This has some practical importance in water flow studies where data on bulk density of experimental columns are required.

---

[12] Since gamma ray sources are of various sizes and dimensions, some deviation from the inverse square of distance rule is possible. This rule holds strictly only for uniform radiation from an infinitely small source. However, for a Cs^{137} source, believed to have an active projected area of at least several square millimeters, the fall-off was closely proportional to the inverse square of the distance in the range of from 30 to 90 cm. as measured using a 12 cm. long by 0.33 cm. by 1.2 cm. collimator against the source and a 10 cm. long by 0.1 cm. by 1.0 cm. collimator against the scintillation crystal. A correction for air absorption was made.

The equations relating attenuation to water content using neutrons are identical in form to those for gamma rays. However, the terms corresponding to mass attenuation coefficients for gamma rays are not single mass functions, but are composite values which depend upon both scattering and capture cross sections of nuclei of the various elements making up the soil. The equations for neutrons corresponding to [34], [35], [36], and [37] for gamma rays are

$$N_m/N_o = \exp\left[-S(\sigma_s\rho + \sigma_w\theta) - 2S'\mu_c\rho_c\right] \qquad [38]$$

and

$$N_d/N_o = \exp\left(-\sigma_s S\rho - 2S'\mu_c\rho_c\right) \qquad [39]$$

which, combined, give

$$N_m/N_d = \exp\left(-\sigma_w S\theta\right) \qquad [40]$$

or

$$\theta = \frac{\ln\left(N_m/N_d\right)}{-\sigma_w S} = \frac{\log\left(N_m/N_d\right)}{-0.4343\sigma_w S} \qquad [41]$$

where N_m/N_d is the ratio of the count-rate through moist soil to that through the dry soil, σ_w is the attenuation coefficient through water, and S is the thickness of the sample. The value of σ_w is best obtained by calibration.

The application of neutron attenuation to water-content measurement at the present time is limited to locations where very high neutron fluxes are available such as at a reactor.[13] With a neutron counting rate (N_d) of 10,000 counts per second in dry soil columns 1.5 cm. thick, Stewart[13] achieved a resolution of 1 × 10 mm. The precision in water content measurements, assuming adequate calibration, is limited by the random nature of neutron emission. The standard deviation in water content measurement due to this cause for 2-second counting is about ±0.002 to 0.005 g. per cm.³ and for 20-second counting ±0.0007 to 0.0015 g. per cm.³ with the higher values being for high water content. Under the experimental conditions the optimum column thickness for maximum precision ranges from about 1 cm. in wet soil to about 3 cm. in dry soil.

Because of the current impracticality of the neutron-attenuation method for general use, the method will not be described here in detail, and the reader is referred to Stewart's[13] thesis for further information. Use of the method of gamma ray attenuation, however, is not restricted to special laboratories. Although the equipment is relatively expensive ($1,500 to $6,000, depending upon sophistication), once set up it provides a method for precise nondestructive water content determination for use with soil

[13] The method has been successfully used at the 100 kw. nuclear reactor at Washington State University where fast and thermal neutron fluxes available at beam ports are 4 × 10¹² and 1.2 × 10¹² neutrons per cm.² per second (Stewart, G. L., 1962. Water content measurement by neutron attenuation and applications to unsaturated flow of water in soil. Unpublished Ph.D. Thesis, Washington State University).

at constant bulk density in the laboratory which is unequaled except for the neutron method. The gamma ray method has been successfully used to follow rapid water content change in soil columns undergoing wetting (Gurr and Marshall, 1960; Ferguson and Gardner, 1962; Gurr, 1962; Rawlins and Gardner, 1963) and to monitor water content change in the root zone of growing plants (Ashton, 1956; Hsieh[14]).

7–3.4.2 METHOD

7–3.4.2.1 Special Apparatus.

1. Source of gamma radiation: Cs^{137}, which emits gamma rays at 0.661 Mev. and has a half-life of 30 years, is well suited for water-content measurements. The size of the source required depends upon the use to be made of the equipment. Sources of 20 or 25 mc. have been satisfactorily used. However, where rapidly changing water content is to be followed, so that counting times of only a few seconds are required, or where resolution of the order of a millimeter or less is required, much larger sources are desirable. Sources from 100 to 500 mc. have proved satisfactory under these more stringent conditions. Lead shielding required for safe operation, of course, increases with increasing source size.

2. Lead shield and collimator: The source is housed in a lead shield with a suitable collimating hole or slit. With a protective plug for the collimating slit, the shield serves also as a storage container. Ideally the collimating hole should be drilled appropriately to serve for gross measurements and to accept lead plugs with smaller collimating holes or slits for measurements where greater resolution is desired. A hole about 3 cm. in diameter will accommodate a collimating plug containing a 1- by 20-mm. slit or any number of other slits or holes that might be desired. The collimating plug should have the form of a bolt with a large head to cover the space between the bolt and lead block and should be 5 to 10 cm. long.

The dimensions of the block depend upon the source strength; but, for greatest convenience where weight is not an important factor, the block should be thick enough to reduce radiation in its vicinity to values only slightly above natural background so that special precautions required in the vicinity of such radiation hazards may be minimized. Normal background varies from 0.01 to 0.03 mR. (milliröntgen) per hour. One milliröntgen in air is about 5% less than 1 mrad. (the rad. is the unit of physical radiation dose) in tissue so that for practical considerations they may be regarded as equivalent.

In the design of shielding and collimators, it is necessary to determine

---

[14] Hsieh, J. J. C. 1962. A technique for controlling soil water content in the vicinity of root hairs and its application to soil-water-plant studies. Unpublished Ph.D. Thesis, Washington State University, Pullman.

the dose rate in terms of source strength, shielding thickness, and distance from the source. This may be determined by the following formula. The dose rate in mrad. per hour at a distance R in cm. from a point-source of gamma radiation at strength A in mc. and energy E_o in Mev. and with shielding of thickness t in cm. of a material with a linear attenuation coefficient μ in cm.$^{-1}$ is (as inferred from equations [2], [3] and [4] of Blizard (1958)

$$D(R,t) = 2.134 \times 10^6 B(\mu,t) \frac{\mu_a}{\rho} E_o \frac{A \exp(-\mu t)}{4\pi R^2} \qquad [42]$$

where $B(\mu,t)$ is the build-up factor, μ_a/ρ in cm.^{2} per g. is the energy-absorption mass-attenuation coefficient for the source energy and the material in which the dose is to be calculated (ρ is the density) and where the numerical constant has units of (g. $\times$ rad./Mev. $\times$ mc. $\times$ hr.).[15] For 0.661 Mev. gamma radiation from a Cs^{137} source, μ_a/ρ, measured in tissue, is about 0.0323 cm.^{2} per g. (Evans, 1968). For 0.661 Mev. gamma radiation μ is 0.717 cm.$^{-1}$, and the build-up factor $B(\mu,t)$ for lead thicknesses from 2 to 15 cm. is approximated by $1.4 + 0.21t$ (a dimensionless factor) so that equation [42] (inferred from data in Tables 1 and 4, Blizard, 1958, and Evans, 1968) is:

$$D(R,t) = (5.1 + 0.76t)10^3 \frac{A}{R^2} \exp(-0.717t) \text{ mrad./hr.} \qquad [43]$$

For a 100-mc. Cs^{137} source with 11.6 cm. of lead shielding, the radiation at the surface of the lead is about 2.5 mrad. per hour, and at 1 m. from the surface it is about 0.03 mrad. per hour or the equivalent of background radiation.

On the average, the A.E.C. dosage limitations are 100 mrem. per week or 5 rem. per year (the rem. is the "radiation equivalent, man") for persons 18 years of age or older. For gamma radiation, 1 rem. is the equivalent of 1 rad., so that 0.03 to 2.5 mrad. per hr. is well within A.E.C. regulations.[16]

3. Gamma-sensitive probe: Scintillation-type gamma-sensitive probes are the most satisfactory. A 2-inch phototube probe containing a preamplifier and equipped with a 1-inch thallium-activated sodium iodide crystal is adequate for many measurements. However, the crystal size may be increased for greater sensitivity. A second lead collimator about 5 cm. long and containing a thin slit or hole is aligned with the source collimator and with an intervening space large enough to accommodate the soil container. The scintillation crystal, with a surrounding lead

---

[15] For gamma sources with more than one peak in an energy range which would contribute significantly to the dose rate, equation [42] must be applied to each peak and the dose rates summed.

[16] For a more complete description of A.E.C. regulations see Part 20—*Standards for Protection Against Radiation* (Chapter I, Title 10, Code of Federal regulations).

shield of approximately the same thickness as used around the source, is placed against the collimator.

4. Soil container and mechanism for orienting soil in beam: Specifications for the soil container depend upon the nature of an experiment. However, two factors should be considered for optimum water content measurement. First, the container walls through which the beam will pass should be as thin as practical, of low density, and should not absorb water. Where a small source is to be used so that counting rate is limiting, it is often desirable to arrange holes in the container at desired counting positions, covering them with Mylar film. Second, the thickness of the soil through which the beam is to pass should be about 14 to 19 cm. for ordinary soil density and where Cs^{137} is used as a gamma source. (Equation [58] in section 7–3.4.2.3 can be used to compute optimum soil column thickness.) The mechanism for positioning the soil container in the beam can take many forms, depending upon the nature of an experiment. In some cases, because of the weight of the lead shielding, it is easiest to move the soil container in the beam. A rack- and pinion-operated sliding table or elevator works well.

5. Scaler or rate meter: A number of different types of scalers or rate meters can be used. A scaler with a built-in adjustable amplifier-dis- criminator and a resolving time of 10 μsec. or less and a preset timer is desirable.[17] In some specialized applications, a pulse-height analyzer may be helpful; and, to permit recording, a rate meter is often desir- able.

7–3.4.2.2 Procedure. Before it is possible to infer water content from gamma ray measurements it is necessary to evaluate μ_w and N_d in equation [37]. The value of S may be obtained directly by measurement. The value of the gamma absorption coefficient for water μ_w can be obtained from tables for particular gamma ray energies.[18] However, unless counting equipment capable of precision discrimination is used so that the measured gamma energy is confined to a small range, it is preferable to obtain an empirical value for μ_w. To obtain this value, set up the counting equipment the way it is to be used during measurement, with particular attention being paid to discriminator settings if discrimination is to be used. Turn equip- ment on, and allow time for instrument warm-up (several hours is desir- able). Position the empty soil container in the beam, and make a minimum of five 1-minute counts (or count for a minimum of 5 minutes) to give a base count N_c through the container walls only. Then fill the container with water and make a similar count N_w for the water and container walls. The

---

[17] Preset count also may be convenient where constancy of the standard deviation due to random emission is more important than constancy of the observation time. Print-out capability also has considerable utility.

[18] The mass absorption coefficients for water at 0.5, 0.6 and 0.8 Mev. are given as 0.0966, 0.0896 and 0.0786 cm.² per g. in Rockwell (1956).

equation for μ_w, derived in a similar fashion as was equation [37], is

$$\mu_w = \frac{\ln (N_w/N_c)}{-\theta S} = \frac{\log (N_w/N_c)}{-0.4343\theta S} \tag{44}$$

where the gamma mass absorption coefficient μ_w is in cm.[2] per g., water content θ in g. per cm.[3] (unity in this case), and the internal width of the container S in cm.

Under most experimental conditions, it is probable that soil bulk density will differ from point to point in a soil column. Where water content is to be measured at more than one position, the value of N_d (the count through the container and dry soil) must be determined at each measuring position and used in subsequent computations of water content with equation [37]. If N_d is measured using oven-dry soil, equation [37], with appropriate values for μ_w and S, can be used directly to obtain water content. Or, a graph of the count ratio as a function of water content on semilogarithmic paper may be used. If air-dry soil or soil at a uniform water content other than oven-dry is used, a correction must be made. Where the initial water content of the soil, determined gravimetrically, is θ_{ad} (e.g., air-dry) and the count through this soil is N_{ad} the attenuation equation corresponding to equation [36] and derived in a similar manner is

$$N_m/N_{ad} = \exp\left[-\mu_w S(\theta - \theta_{ad})\right], \tag{45}$$

and the equation comparable to equation [37] becomes

$$\theta = \theta_{ad} - \frac{\ln (N_m/N_{ad})}{\mu_w S} = \theta_{ad} - \frac{\log (N_m/N_{ad})}{0.4343\mu_w S} \tag{46}$$

where μ_w is in cm.[2] per g., S in cm., θ and θ_{ad} in g. per cm.[3], and N_m and N_{ad} are the number of counts taken at equal time intervals or reduced to an equivalent time interval basis. If water contents are desired on the basis of mass per unit mass of soil, water content values must be multiplied by the ratio of the density of water ρ_w (usually taken as unity in the cgs. system) to the bulk density of the soil ρ_s. Bulk-density values may be obtained from gamma measurements using the following formula

$$\rho_s = \frac{-\mu_w}{\mu_s}\theta_{ad} - \frac{\ln (N_{ad}/N_c)}{\mu_s S} = \frac{-\mu_w}{\mu_s}\theta_{ad} - \frac{\log (N_{ad}/N_c)}{0.4343\mu_s S}, \tag{47}$$

where N_{ad} is the count through air-dry soil, N_c the count through the empty soil container, θ_{ad} the initial water content in g. per cm.[3], S is the thickness of the soil in cm., and μ_w and μ_s are the gamma absorption coefficients for water and for soil in cm.[2] per g. The value of μ_s is obtained in the same manner as is μ_w, using oven-dry soil in place of water and computing the value with equation [44] with ρ_s replacing θ.

7–3.4.2.3 Comments. Since bulk density often changes when a soil is wetted, it is sometimes desirable to measure the bulk density gravimetrically at the end of an experiment and, if necessary, to recompute water contents using a corrected N_d. If bulk density changes during an experiment, subjective judgment must be used in deciding what bulk density value to use. The correct N'_d value corresponding to a different bulk density ρ' is given by the equation

$$\log N'_d = \frac{\rho'}{\rho} \log N_d/N_o + \log N_o, \qquad [48]$$

where ρ is the old density corresponding to the old N_d, and N_o is the count for the empty soil container. The error in water content inferences is significantly reduced if errors in N_d and N_o are negligible. Since N_d and N_o are counted infrequently compared to N_m, it is usually possible to count for a much longer time, reducing the count to the equivalent counting time as used to obtain N_m. If the counting times for N_d and N_o are 5 to 10 times that for N_m, the error in water content will be affected $<10\%$.

Dead-times of the counting equipment of the order of 1 to 10 μsec per count are common with typical equipment. For 10^6, 5×10^5, 3×10^5, 2×10^5 and 1×10^5 counts per minute using Cs^{137} in 15 cm. of dry soil and for a water content of 0.30 g. per cm.^{3}, the error being largest in wet soil, water content measurements will be too low by approximately $4.1 \times 10^3 d_t$, $2.1 \times 10^3 d_t$, $1.2 \times 10^3 d_t$, $0.82 \times 10^3 d_t$, and $0.42 \times 10^3 d_t$ g./cm.^{3}, where d_t is the dead-time in seconds.[19]

The precision of the method varies with the thickness and density of the soil column, the adsorption characteristics of the soil, and the size of counts N_m and N_d. To involve the counting time explicitly, the gamma ray intensity I as counts per unit time is introduced, so that $I_m t = N_m$ and $I_d t = N_d$, where t is the counting interval. Equation [37] becomes

$$\theta = \frac{\ln (I_m t/I_d t)}{-\mu_w S} \qquad [50]$$

and the variance, with reasonable assumptions, becomes

$$V_\theta = \frac{1}{\mu_w^2 S^2} V_{\ln (I_m t/I_d t)} \qquad [51]$$

so that the standard deviation is

$$\sigma_\theta = \frac{1}{\mu_w S} \sigma_{\ln (I_m t/I_d t)}. \qquad [52]$$

---

[19] During a short time interval as a pulse builds up, referred to as "dead-time," a counter is insensitive to additional pulses. Correcting for dead-time involves multiplying the dead-time per count by the number of counts to obtain total dead-time and subtracting this from the measured counting interval. Or, a corrected count can be obtained by multiplying the observed count by the ratio of the total counting time to the total minus dead-time. Applied to the count ratio used in equation [37] where the additional subscript "o" is used to denote "observed," t_t to denote the counting interval and d_t the dead-time per count, the corrected ratio becomes

$$\frac{N_m}{N_d} = \frac{N_{mo}}{N_{do}} \frac{t_t - N_{do} d_t}{t_t - N_{mo} d_t} \qquad [49]$$

To reduce the error, the counting time for $I_d t$, which is measured infrequently and usually under conditions where time is not pressing, is increased by a factor of 3 or 4 over that for $I_m t$. However, the computation requires that t be the same for both $I_m t$ and $I_d t$, and so the longer count $I_d t'$ is reduced to comparable size through division by n where $n = t'/t$. Thus $I_d t'/n$ is the time-equivalent count to $I_d t$ and may replace it in equations [51] and [52].

The standard deviation of $\ln(I_m t / I_d t'/n)$ is

$$\sigma_{\ln (I_m t / I_d t'/n)} = \frac{I_d t'/n}{I_m t} \sigma_{(I_m t / I_d t'/n)} = \frac{I_d t'/n}{I_m t} \frac{1}{I_d t'/n} \sqrt{\sigma^2_{I_m t} + \frac{(I_m t)^2}{(I_d t'/n)^2} \sigma^2_{(I_d t'/n)}} \; . \quad [53]$$

Using equation [53] with

$$\sigma_{I_m t} = \sqrt{I_m t} \text{ and } \sigma_{(I_d t'/n)} = \frac{1}{n} \sqrt{I_d t'}$$

equation [52] becomes

$$\sigma_\theta = \frac{1}{\mu_w S \sqrt{I_m t}} \sqrt{1 + \frac{I_m t}{I_d t'}} = \frac{1}{\mu_w S \sqrt{I_m t}} \sqrt{1 + \frac{I_m t}{n I_d t}} \; . \quad [54]$$

Where n is 3 or 4, the second term under the radical may be neglected with only small effect on σ_θ (*ca.* 10%) so that equation [54] becomes

$$\sigma_\theta = \frac{1}{\mu_w S \sqrt{I_m t}} = \frac{1}{\mu_w S \sqrt{N_m}} \quad [55]$$

or, substituting N_m from equation [38],

$$\sigma_\theta = \frac{\exp [S/2(\mu_s \rho_s + \mu_w \theta) + S' \mu_c \rho_c]}{\mu_w S \sqrt{N_o}} \; . \quad [56]$$

The optimum value of soil column thickness S may be obtained by equating $d\sigma_\theta/dS$, obtained by differentiation of equation [56], to zero; thus

$$\frac{d\sigma_\theta}{ds} = \frac{\exp [S/2(\mu_s \rho_s + \mu_w \theta)] \exp (S' \mu_c \rho_c)}{\mu_w S \sqrt{N_o}} [1/2(\mu_s \rho_s + \mu_w \theta) - (1/S)] = 0 \quad [57]$$

and

$$S = 2/(\mu_s \rho_s + \mu_w \theta) \; . \quad [58]$$

For $\mu_s = 0.07785$ and $\mu_w = 0.08559$ as determined by Gurr (1962), using a 25-mc. Cs^{137} source emitting 0.661 Mev. gamma rays, and with the discriminator set at 0.55 Mev. and for a bulk density of 1.3 g. per cm.^{3}, the optimum sample thickness ranged from 19 cm. at low water content to 14 cm. at high water content.

The basic gamma count rate I_o with only air between the source and scintillation crystal, and hence the precision and resolution possible in water content measurement, depends upon the strength of the gamma source, the range of gamma energies counted, the geometry of the equipment, and the efficiency with which gamma radiation is measured. The source emits gamma rays in all directions, with the intensity of the gamma field decreasing with the square of the distance from the source (neglecting the absorption of air in the path and assuming a point source).[20] Under these conditions, the fraction of the radiation reaching the face of the scintillation crystal depends upon the degree of collimation and the distance from the source. With an absorber in the beam, some scattered and secondary radiation reaches the crystal so that the inverse square law no longer holds. However, if a discriminator is used, so that only gamma rays of the maximum energy which are emitted from the source are counted, the effect of scattered and secondary radiation is eliminated.

In practice if a discriminator is not used, primary, secondary, and scattered radiation is counted, and the equations describing the attenuation do not hold if used with absorption coefficients which have been determined for particular energy values. However, equation [50], with μ_w determined empirically, does hold reasonably well over the range of water contents of interest, plotting as a straight line in θ and $\ln(I_m t/I_d t)$, or $\log(I_m t/I_d t)$.

The chief value to counting only particular gamma energies through use of a discriminator circuit in the counter lies in the improvement of resolution. Scattered and secondary radiation can come from regions outside the narrow collimated beam path, hence decreasing the resolution. For this reason some discrimination is desirable. However, it must be recognized that excessive discrimination can reduce the count rate to a point where precision, as affected by random source emission, is severely reduced. Gurr (1962), with a 25-mc. Cs^{137} source, successfully used a discriminator set to count energies from 0.50 to 0.66 Mev. It is obvious that with larger sources discrimination is practical.

With discrimination such that an approximately monoenergetic gamma beam may be assumed, the resolution possible for given precision, source strength and experimental arrangement can be computed. If the area of the collimator at the face of the crystal is a (assuming this to be the minimum collimator restriction), and the distance from the crystal face is r, then the fraction of the total radiation reaching the crystal, neglecting the absorption of air in the path, is $a/(4\pi r^2)$. The count rate I_o is proportional to the product of this fraction and the strength of the source Z; thus,

$$I_o = k(a/4\pi r^2)Z \qquad [59]$$

where the proportionality factor k absorbs all other factors relating to the intensity of the gamma beam as it reaches the crystal face and is absorbed and counted, and to characteristics of the electronic circuits involved in counting. If the source strength is too high, so that simultaneous pulses occur (coincidence losses), this effect too is absorbed in the k. The range of gamma energies counted is an important component of this constant.

---

[20] See section 7–3.3.2.1, number 3, footnote 11.

Several other factors are involved, the most important being the efficiency of the scintillation crystal, which is related to its size, particularly its depth in this case, since the collimated beam can be made small enough to fit on the face of most crystals which are used. The size of a scintillation crystal is generally given as the diameter of the face. However, the thickness is usually about equal to the diameter. If the source strength Z is in mc., the distance from the source to scintillation crystal face r in cm., the collimator area at the face of the crystal a in cm.[2] and I_o is in counts per minute, the units of k will be counts per min. per mc. A value of k, determined experimentally for a 1.75-cm. diameter, 2.5-cm.-thick thallium-activated sodium iodide crystal with the discriminator set to accept pulses only above 0.55 Mev., is 3.62×10^8 (inferred from data of Gurr, 1962). In this laboratory a value of 7.98×10^8 for k was determined for a Harshaw[21] 2-inch diameter, 2-inch thick thallium-activated sodium iodide crystal operating with the discriminator set to accept only pulses above 0.53 Mev. and with R.I.D.L. equipment.[22]

Replacing the count N_o in equation [56] by its equivalent $I_o t$, substituting this into equation [59] and solving explicitly for the source strength, leads to

$$Z = \frac{4\pi r^2}{ka} \frac{\exp\left[S(\mu_s\rho_s + \mu_w\theta) + 2S'\mu_c\rho_c\right]}{\mu_w^2 S^2 \sigma_\theta^2 t}. \qquad [60]$$

At high water content, say 40% ($\theta = 0.4$) where the error is largest, for soil at 1.3 g. per cm.[3] bulk density, held in a plastic container with 0.62-cm.-thick walls, 1.19 g. per cm.[3] density, and an absorption coefficient of 0.08747 cm.[2] per g. and with absorption coefficients for soil and water of 0.07785 and 0.08559 cm.[2] per g. as used by Gurr (1962), equation [60] can be reduced to

$$Z = 1.95 \times 10^3 \frac{r^2 \exp(0.1356S)}{kaS^2\sigma_\theta^2 t}. \qquad [61]$$

For a typical situation where r is 36 cm., S is 16 cm., a is 0.4 cm.[2], and k is taken to be 7.98×10^8, and where counting is done for 1 min. with a desired precision of $\pm 0.5\%$ water content ($3\sigma_\theta = 0.005$) due only to errors associated with random emission, the required source strength Z is 94 mc. Counting for 5 minutes would reduce the required source strength to 19 mc., or leaving the source strength at 94 mc. and counting for 5 minutes would bring the precision to approximately $\pm 0.2\%$ water content ($3\sigma_{\theta\text{improved}} = 3\sigma_\theta/(t)^{1/2} = 0.0022$).

---

[21] Harshaw Chemical Co., Cleveland, Ohio.

[22] Model 10-17 scintillation preamplifier, Model 40-B high-voltage power supply, Model 30-19 linear amplifier and discriminator and a Model 35-7 linear/log count rate meter, Radiation Instrument Development Lab., Div. of Nuclear-Chicago, 4501 West North Ave., Melrose Park, Ill.

Equation [61], solved explicitly for σ_θ,

$$\sigma_\theta = \frac{44.2r\exp{(0.0678S)}}{S\sqrt{kaZt}}, \qquad [62]$$

often is more useful than equations [55] or [56] for approximating the size of the standard deviation in water content due to the random emission of a Cs^{137} source used under typical conditions. For the geometry and source strength used by Gurr (1962) and a k-value inferred from his data, the standard deviation computed is 0.0011 g. per cm.^{3} (0.0011/1.444 = 0.00076 g. per g.), which is comparable to the value, 0.0007 g. per g., which he gives as the expected error due to the counting process.

If long counting times are practicable in an experiment, high precision is possible with relatively small sources and at high resolution. However, if rapid measurement is important, then either the resolution must be low or the source strength high. In such cases, since k increases with increasing crystal size, large scintillation crystals are desirable. If resolution and counting time are not important factors, as in an experiment involving measurement of gross water content in a container of soil with growing plants, source strengths of the order of 20 mc. are usually adequate. Also, small crystals are considerably less expensive than large ones, and crystals of the order of 1 inch or less may often be adequate under such conditions.

7-4 LITERATURE CITED

Anderson, A. B. C., and Edlefsen, N. E. 1942. Electrical capacity of the 2-electrode plaster of Paris block as an indicator of soil moisture content. Soil Sci. 54:35–46.

Ashton, F. M. 1956. Effects of a series of cycles of alternating low and high soil water contents on the rate of apparent photosynthesis in sugar cane. Plant Phys. 31:266–274.

Belcher, D. J., Cuykendall, T. R., and Sack, H. S. 1950. The measurement of soil moisture and density by neutron and gamma ray scattering. Civil Aeron. Admin. Tech. Develop. Rpt. No. 127.

Blizard, E. P. 1958. Nuclear radiation shielding. *In* H. Etherington, ed. Nuclear Engineering Handbook. McGraw-Hill, New York. Sec. 7–3.

Bloodworth, M. E., and Page, J. B. 1957. Use of thermistors for the measurement of soil moisture and temperature. Soil Sci. Soc. Am. Proc. 21:11–15.

Bouyoucos, G. J. 1931. The alcohol method for determining moisture content of soils. Soil Sci. 32:173–179.

Bouyoucos, G. J. 1937. Evaporating the water with burning alcohol as a rapid means of determining moisture content of soils. Soil Sci. 44:377–383.

Bouyoucos, G. J. 1938. A field outfit for determining the moisture content of soils. Soil Sci. 46:107–111.

Bouyoucos, G. J., and Mick, A. H. 1940. An electrical resistance method for the continuous measurement of soil moisture under field conditions. Michigan Agr. Exp. Sta. Tech. Bul. 172.

Bouyoucos, G. J. 1949. Nylon electrical resistance unit for continuous measurement of soil moisture in the field. Soil Sci. 67:319–330.

Bouyoucos, G. J. 1953. More durable plaster of paris moisture blocks. Soil Sci. 76:447–451.

Cannell, Glen H. 1958. Effect of drying cycles on changes in resistance of soil moisture units. Soil Sci. Soc. Am. Proc. 22:379–382.

Carter, C. E. 1938. Field method for determining soil moisture. Australian Forestry. 3:15–16. (CA 33, 1854).

Cline, Marlin G. 1944. Principles of soil sampling. Soil Sci. 58:275–288.

Colman, E. A., and Hendrix, T. M. 1949. Fiberglas electrical soil-moisture instrument. Soil Sci. 67:425–438.

Crumpler, T. B., and Yoe, J. H. 1946. Chemical Computations and Errors. John Wiley and Sons, Inc., New York.

Edlefsen, N. E., and Anderson, A. B. C. 1941. The four-electrode resistance method for measuring soil moisture content under field conditions. Soil Sci. 51:367–376.

Evans, Robley D. 1968. X-ray and γ-ray interactions, Chapt. 3. *In* F. H. Attix and W. C. Roesch (ed.) Radiation dosimetry, Vol. 1, Fundamentals. 2nd ed. Academic Press, New York.

Ferguson, Hayden, and Gardner, W. H. 1962. Water content measurement in soil columns by gamma ray absorption. Soil Sci. Soc. Am. Proc. 26:11–14.

Fletcher, J. E. 1939. A dielectric method for determining soil moisture. Soil Sci. Soc. Am. Proc. 4:84–88.

Gardner, Wilford, and Kirkham, Don. 1952. Determination of soil moisture by neutron scattering. Soil Sci. 73:391–401.

Gurr, C. G. 1962. Use of gamma rays in measuring water content and permeability in unsaturated columns of soil. Soil Sci. 94:224–229.

Gurr, C. G., and Marshall, T. J. 1960. Unsaturated permeability—its measurement and its estimation from other properties of the material. Trans. Intern. Congr. Soil Sci. 7th Madison. 1:306–310.

Hanks, R. J., and Bowers, S. A. 1960. Neutron meter access tube influences soil temperature. Soil Sci. Soc. Am. Proc. 24:62–63.

Holmes, J. W. 1956. Calibration and field use of the neutron scattering method of measuring soil water content. Australian J. Appl. Sci. 7:45–58.

Holmes, J. W., and Jenkinson, A. F. 1959. Techniques for using the neutron moisture meter. J. Agr. Eng. Res. 4:100–109.

Kazo, Bela. 1951. Determination of moisture content of soils by alcoholic combustion. Agrokemis es Talajtan. 1:235–240. (CA 50, 4442).

Kelley, O. J. 1944. A rapid method for calibration of various instruments for measuring soil moisture *in situ*. Soil Sci. 58:433–440.

Kirkham, Don, and Taylor, G. S. 1950. Some tests of a four-electrode probe for soil moisture measurement. Soil Sci. Soc. Am. Proc. (1949) 14:42–46.

Köhler, Richard. 1951. A field method for the determination of the natural water content of soils. Abhandl. geol. Dienstes Berlin 220:18–23. (CA 48, 11696g).

Lambe, T. W. 1949. How dry is a dry soil? Proc. 29th Annual Meeting, Highway Research Board 29:491–496.

Makower, Benjamin. 1950. Determination of water in some dehydrated foods. Adv. Chem. 3:37–54.

Makower, Benjamin, and Nielsen, Elisabeth. 1948. Use of lyophilization in determination of moisture content of dehydrated vegetables. Anal. Chem. 20:856–858.

Makower, Benjamin, Chastain, S. M., and Nielsen, E. 1946. Moisture determination in dehydrated vegetables. Vacuum-oven method. Ind. Eng. Chem. 38:725–731.

Merriam, R. A. 1962. Useful statistical guides and graphs for neutron probe soil moisture sampling. Intermountain Forest and Range Exp. Sta. Res. Paper 62.

McHenry, J. R. 1963. Theory and application of neutron scattering in the measurement of soil moisture. Soil Sci. 95:294–307.

Nutting, P. G. 1943. Some standard thermal dehydration curves of minerals. U. S. Geol. Survey, Profess. Paper 197-E.

Oganesyan, A. P. 1958. A simplified method for determining soil moisture. Soviet Soil Sci. 4:446–449. (Translation of Pochvovedeniye, by AIBS.)

Perrier, E. R., and Marsh, A. W. 1958. Performance characteristics of various electrical resistance units and gypsum materials. Soil Sci. 86:140–147.

Phillips, R. E., Jensen, C. R., and Kirkham, Don. 1960. Use of radiation equipment for plow-layer density and moisture. Soil Sci. 89:2–7.

Plater, C. V., de. 1955. A portable capacitance-type soil moisture meter. Soil Sci. 80:391–395.

Rawlins, S. L., and Gardner, W. H. 1963. A test of the validity of the diffusion equation for unsaturated flow of soil water. Soil Sci. Soc. Am. Proc. 27:507–511.

Richards, L. A., and Stumpf, H. T. 1960. Volumetric soil sampler. Soil Sci. 89:108–110.

Richards, L. A., and Weaver, L. R. 1943. The sorption-block soil moisture meter and hysteresis effects related to its operation. J. Am. Soc. Agron. 35:1002–1011.

Rockwell, Theodore III, ed. 1956. Reactor Shielding Design Manual. D. Van Nostrand Co., New York.

Shaw, Byron, and Baver, L. D. 1940. An electrothermal method for following moisture changes in soil in situ. Soil Sci. Soc. Am. Proc. (1939) 4:78–83.

Stolzy, L. H., and Cahoon, G. A. 1957. A field-calibrated portable neutron rate meter for measuring soil moisture in citrus orchards. Soil Sci. Soc. Am. Proc. 21:571–575.

Stone, J. F., Shaw, R. H., and Kirkham, Don. 1960. Statistical parameters and reproducibility of the neutron method of measuring soil moisture. Soil Sci. Soc. Am. Proc. 24:435–438.

Tanner, C. B., Abrams, E., and Zubriski, J. C. 1949. Gypsum moisture-block calibration based on electrical conductivity in distilled water. Soil Sci. Soc. Am. Proc. (1948) 13:62–65.

Taylor, S. A. 1955. Field determinations of soil moisture. Agr. Eng. 36:654–659.

Taylor, S. A., Evans, D. D., and Kemper, W. D. 1961. Evaluating soil water. Utah Agr. Exp. Sta. Bull. 426.

Van Bavel, C. H. M. 1958. Measurement of soil moisture content by the neutron method. Agr. Res. Serv., ARS 41–24.

Van Bavel, C. H. M. 1961. Neutron measurement of surface soil moisture. J. Geophysical Res. 66:4193–4198.

Van Bavel, C. H. M. 1962a. Light-weight rate meter for neutron soil moisture measurement. Soil Sci. 94:418–419.

Van Bavel, C. H. M. 1962b. Accuracy and source strength in soil moisture neutron probes. Soil Sci. Soc. Am. Proc. 26:405.

Van Bavel, C. H. M., Underwood, N., and Swanson, R. W. 1956. Soil moisture measurement by neutron moderation. Soil Sci. 82:29–41.

Van Bavel, C. H. M., Nielsen, D. R., and Davidson, J. M. 1961. Calibration and characteristics of two neutron moisture probes. Soil Sci. Soc. Am. Proc. 25:329–334.

Vries, J., de, and King, K. M. 1961. Note on the volume of influence of a neutron surface moisture probe. Can. J. Soil Sci. 41:253–257.

Voskresenskii, M., and Levina, S. 1939. A rapid method of determining soil moisture. Pedology (U.S.S.R.) 12:87–89. (CA 35, 4892).

Weinberg, A. M., and Wigner, E. P. 1958. The Physical Theory of Neutron Chain Reactors. Univ. of Chicago Press, Chicago.

8 | Physical Condition of Water in Soil[1]

L. A. RICHARDS
United States Salinity Laboratory
Riverside, California

8-1 GENERAL INTRODUCTION

Soil is composed of three reasonably distinguishable phases: solid, liquid, and gas. The solid phase may be called the "matrix" because this phase usually controls the form or distribution in space of the other two phases. The solid structures of the plant might be similarly designated, because there is much interdependence in the soil-plant-water system, and a terminology suitable for use in both could be advantageous.

It seems likely that over most of the wetness range in which plant roots normally function, all the water in soil is more or less constrained by, and has its properties altered by, forces associated with the matrix. It may be that only in the larger pores of coarse soils that are relatively wet is there water present that is beyond the influence of the matrix and has the properties of water in bulk. An attempt to identify the properties of liquid water in bulk with the liquid or film phase in soil is a considerable step that must be cautiously approached if confusion is to be avoided. Take for example the concept of hydrostatic pressure that is so useful for water in bulk. So far as the writer knows, this property has never been measured for film water, where, near the matrix, the quantity may have a high positive value.

Figure 8-1 may help to clarify the principles involved in several of the soil-water measuring methods described in this chapter. At *A* in the figure an idealized micro-micro syringe is shown withdrawing water from the film phase. The needle connects bulk water in the syringe with the soil water. When water transfer ceases, the temptation to say that the pressures at the two ends of the needle are the same should be resisted. It can only be said that the attraction of film water by matric forces is counteracted by the pressure reduction that is registered in the example by the deflection

[1] Contribution from the U. S. Salinity Laboratory, Soil and Water Conservation Research Division, ARS, USDA, Riverside, Calif. in cooperation with 17 Western states and Hawaii.

of the elastic diaphragm that is shown attached to the syringe to serve as a pressure gauge.

Neglecting solute effects, the work required to extract unit amount of water from soil was called the capillary potential by Buckingham (1907). When expressed as work per unit volume, this has the physical dimensions of pressure and was identified by Gardner et al. (1922) with the pressure difference registered by the diaphragm in the figure.

This equivalent pressure, when measured with reference to the atmosphere, is negative and for convenience has long been called soil-moisture tension or soil suction. Since it arises from water binding by forces anchored to the matrix, it could appropriately be called matric suction.

A more realistic mechanism for extracting water from soil is illustrated at the right in Fig. 8–1, where the soil-water system is shown in contact with a membrane that is permeable to soil solution, i.e., water and solute, but not to the matrix. The water films on the soil matrix make contact through the pores in the membrane with bulk water beneath the membrane. Here again, the deflection of an elastic diaphragm is used to indicate the matric suction, i.e., the pressure difference between the gas phase in the soil and the bulk water on the opposite side of the membrane. This is the pressure difference that is registered by the vacuum gauge of a tensiometer.

Measurements made with the structures shown in the figure are little affected by solute in the soil-water system. However, when water is lost from soil by vaporization, or when water having a different solute content is extracted from the soil by plant root action, osmotic effects become operative, and water binding by solute should be taken into account. This water binding will here be designated by the term solute suction, which is a physical property numerically equal to osmotic pressure, but which has

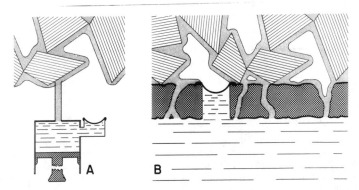

Fig. 8–1. Idealized mechanisms for visualizing the physical condition of water in soil. At A an idealized micro-micro syringe is shown connecting water in the film phase of the soil with water in bulk in the syringe. This is a "one-pore" equivalent of the permeable membrane shown at B. The deflection of the elastic diaphragm indicates that in each case the hydrostatic pressure of the bulk water is less than the pressure of the gas phase in the pore space of the soil.

opposite algebraic sense and therefore is directly additive and consistent with matric suction. The sum of matric suction and solute suction has been called total suction and has many of the advantages of a potential for expressing the energy condition of water in the soil-plant system without the disadvantage of the negative sign, which is inconvenient for some purposes.

For purposes of definition of these suction terms, consider the membrane system shown in Fig. 8–2, which is assumed to be at thermodynamic equilibrium under isothermal conditions. A chamber of wet soil at atmospheric pressure is shown in contact with "bulk" phases of water and soil solution through appropriate membranes. Matric suction is indicated by the middle manometer. In this case the soil, the permeable membrane, and the closed water system connected to a pressure indicator comprise a soil-water tensiometer. The reading of this instrument is little affected if the bulk solution in the instrument differs from the equilibrium dialyzate of the soil.

The left-hand (differential) manometer indicates solute suction, which is the equilibrium pressure difference across a semipermeable membrane separating soil solution (equilibrium dialyzate) from pure water. Solute suction is numerically equal to the osmotic pressure of the soil solution.

The right-hand manometer indicates the total suction of the solution in the soil. This is shown to be equal to the solute suction plus the matric

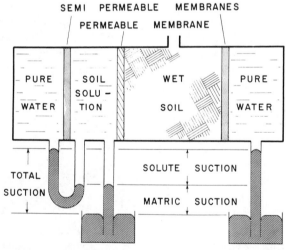

Fig. 8–2. In an isothermal equilibrium system, matric suction is the pressure difference across a membrane separating soil solution (equilibrium dialyzate) in bulk from soil containing the solution, the membrane being permeable to solution, but not to matrix or to mass flow of gas; solute suction is the pressure difference across a semipermeable membrane separating bulk phases of pure water and the soil solution; total suction is the sum of the matric suction and the solute suction and is the pressure difference across a semipermeable membrane separating pure water and soil that contains solution. An ideal semipermeable membrane is permeable to water only.

suction, and is the equilibrium pressure difference across a semipermeable membrane separating the solution in the soil from pure water.

Satisfactory membranes permeable to the soil solution are available and are commonly used for measuring or controlling matric suction, but the use of membranes to measure the solute and total suction of water in soil has not yet been successfully accomplished. Freezing-point depression measurements have long been used for evaluating solute suction (osmotic pressure) of bulk solutions, but uncertainties connected with the under-cooling correction have made questionable the use of this measurement for evaluating the total suction of water in soil. It is possible now, however, by making use of another colligative property, the vapor-pressure depression, to measure matric, solute, and total suction of water in soil at any water content. For this measurement, the gaseous phase acts, in a way, like a membrane that is permeable to water but not to solute.

By use of thermocouple psychrometers, Richards and Ogata (1961, 1962) have shown, as predicted by theory, that a unit of matric suction produces the same vapor-pressure depression as a unit of solute suction. They showed also that thermodynamic equilibrium is readily attainable for soil samples on conventional pressure membranes. Saturated paste samples of soil at different salinity levels were brought to known matric suction values on pressure plates, and the total suction was then measured by the thermocouple psychrometer method. They found that for each sample, the total suction value was substantially equal to the sum of the matric suction plus the solute suction of the solution extracted from the saturated paste.

Methods are given in this chapter for evaluating the physical condition of water in soil by membrane, freezing-point depression, and vapor-pressure depression procedures.

8–2 WATER RETENTIVITY OF SOIL AT SPECIFIED VALUES OF MATRIC SUCTION

8–2.1 Introduction

The terms sorption and desorption, as applied to soil, usually refer to the processes of uptake and release of water. Sorption usually refers to a monotonically increasing water-content change, while desorption refers to the reverse process. Sorption and desorption data usually consist of equilibrium or steady-state values of water content of soil as related to some controlled physical property such as vapor pressure or matric suction. Expressed in terms of water content, the lagging of sorption values below desorption values is referred to as hysteresis.

Measurements of the sorption of gases and of the vapor of liquids on soil have yielded very useful information, and are the basis for specific surface measurements, which are described in section 42. Measurement of soil hygroscopicity by sorption of water vapor was once popular; but, near the field wetness range, extreme care is required if this type of measurement is to be an index of a soil property that is independent of apparatus and procedure. The present section will deal with membrane measuring methods where matric suction is controlled.

8–2.2 Principles

The range of matric suction covered by membrane apparatus is limited to about 0.8 bar if the pressure in the soil air is atmospheric pressure and the pressure difference across the membrane is controlled by vacuum. This limitation is removed if means are provided for increasing the pressure of the gas phase of the soil as was done by S. J. Richards (1939). A pressure chamber containing a porous membrane, which in this case is a ceramic plate with a sheet-rubber backing, is shown at A in Fig. 8–3. A metal screen provides space under the plate for bulk water, which is kept at atmospheric pressure by the tabular connection to the outside. Another form of pressure membrane is shown at B in Fig. 8–3. Here, a cellulose acetate membrane is supported on a screen base that provides contact with bulk water at atmospheric pressure. When considerable shrinkage accompanies a decrease in the wetness of the soil, contact of the sample with the membrane can be maintained by an overlying diaphragm as shown.

The range of matric suction for pressure membranes is determined by

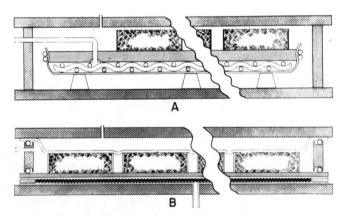

Fig. 8–3. *A*. Pressure plate apparatus in which the suction control "membrane" is a porous ceramic plate with a metal screen and sheet neoprene backing arranged to keep the lower side of the plate in contact with water at atmospheric pressure. (Not drawn to scale.) *B*. Pressure membrane apparatus with a typical arrangement for supporting a cellulose acetate membrane on a screen base. An overlying diaphragm may be used to hold the samples against the membrane. (Not drawn to scale.)

the safe working pressure of the chamber and the pressure difference the membrane will tolerate without allowing air to bubble through the pores. The bubbling pressure for some cellulose acetate membranes is about 150 bars, and ceramic membranes are available for use up to at least 15 bars. In addition to the bubbling-pressure requirement, the membrane must be permeable to water and to solutes in the soil, but not to matrix. Either organic or ceramic membranes may be used.

The hydraulic conductivity and hydraulic conductance of the membrane can be specified in terms of the conventional flow equation $v = ki$ (Richards, 1952) used for soil. Substituting $v = Q/TA$, $k = KL/A$, and $i = H/L$ gives $Q/T = KH$, where Q is the volume of water passing through a membrane of area A and thickness L in time T, H is the difference in hydraulic head of bulk water on the two sides of the membrane, and k and K are, respectively, the hydraulic conductivity and conductance of the membrane. For a pressure membrane with both sides in contact with bulk water and a pressure difference of P bars, we have for centimeter-gram-second (cgs.) units, $K = Q/1023\ TP$. Often the centimeters of water head per bar (1,023) is omitted, and the membrane conductance is expressed as cc. min.$^{-1}$ bar^{-1}.

The apparatus, procedures and terminology relating the sorption and desorption of water by soil are far from stabilized. The wetness of soil at specified matric suction has been called retentivity. The temperature and air pressure at which the measurement was made, as well as some information on the structure or history of the sample, should be given whenever retentivity data are formally presented. The maximum-desorption curve, which starts at saturation and shows retentivity at progressively increasing suction values, is often called a water-retention curve. It seems likely that desorption processes in the field, especially under irrigation, are of longer duration than sorption processes. Possibly for this reason, retention curves are most often measured.

Sintered-glass filter funnels and specially mounted clay plates with controlled vacuum were used for early retention measurements. Some retention data have been obtained at low suctions by use of tension tables that are suitable for handling a considerable number of samples (Jamison and Reed, 1949). Unfortunately, few retentivity measurements have been published for soil samples with field structure. Measurements made with samples that have been dried, screened, and artificially packed should be applied with caution to field situations, especially at the wet end of the soil moisture range. Some retentivity data have been obtained by placing the cores directly in contact with the suction-control surface (Jamison, 1958). Ceramic, bottom-retainer plates have been proposed for this type of measurement (Richards, 1956). Special apparatus design is required to keep one side of the membrane in contact with bulk water if water uptake measurements are to be made (Tanner and Elrick, 1958).

The pore-space system of soil dominates water retention at low suctions. The dependence of pore space on bulk density and structure therefore emphasizes the need for samples with field structure if the wet end of the retention curve is of particular interest. Nevertheless, numerous retentivity values for air-dried and screened samples of soil have been measured at suctions of 0.1 and 0.33 bar because these measurements are easy to make, and correlations with other soil-water measurements were found (Richards and Weaver, 1944). The usefulness of these correlations, however, should be carefully scrutinized (Richards, 1960).

Toward the dry end of the wetness range found in the root zone of crops in the field, water retention is determined largely by the specific surface of the soil. Consequently, the preservation of field structure in water-retention samples is of relatively little concern at matric suction values above 1 or 2 bars. In the absence of direct methods for measuring soil suction above the tensiometer range, retentivity data have provided useful information. The 15-bar retentivity value, for example, has a reasonably close linear correlation with the permanent wilting percentage (Lehane and Staple, 1960).

8–2.3   Method [2]

8–2.3.1   SPECIAL APPARATUS

1. Membrane apparatus: Pressure-plate and pressure-membrane apparatus like those shown in Fig. 8–3 are commercially available and are usually about 28 cm. in diameter. Soil on the membrane is contained in rings of approximately 1-cm. height and 6-cm. diameter that hold about 25 g. of sample. Rubber rings must be used on acetate membranes.
2. Source of regulated air pressure: A source of compressed air at adjustable regulated pressure is required, such as that supplied by Soilmoisture Equipment Co., Santa Barbara, Calif.

8–2.3.2   PROCEDURE FOR TESTING APPARATUS

To check ceramic pressure-plate apparatus for defects, install the plates in the chamber, cover the plates with water, close the chamber, and apply the maximum appropriate air pressure. Measure the outflow rate as soon as the outflow becomes relatively free of air bubbles. Since this is a qualitative test, do not wait for a steady outflow rate. Commercial plates of approximately 28-cm. diameter, with 1- and 2-bar bubbling pressure, have a conductance of about 15 cc. min.$^{-1}$ bar^{-1}, while plates with 15-bar bubbling pressure have a conductance in the range of 0.5 to 2 cc. min.$^{-1}$ bar^{-1}. Plate conductance is not critical except for retentivity measurements at low suction values. In this case, higher conductance gives appreciably faster results.

---

[2] U. S. Salinity Laboratory Staff (1954).

Next check the plates for bubbling pressure. This is the pressure difference that will cause streaming of air through a wet plate. Release the air pressure, empty excess water from the chamber, and apply the maximum air pressure to be used in the retentivity measurements. After a few minutes, the outflow of water will cease, and there should ideally be no bubbling of air. Actually a bubbling rate as high as 2 or 3 cc. of air per minute can be tolerated. Air bubbling at the outflow tube can come through the plate, but it can also come from leaks in the mounting or from joints in the outflow tube that are inside the chamber.

After observing air bubbling at the outflow tube, submerge the chamber in water, or observe air pressure change in the chamber with the supply source shut off, to make sure the chamber is air-tight. Air leaks from the chamber may produce evaporative losses that will dry the samples below the equilibrium value that would otherwise have been attained by membrane suction.

8-2.3.3 PROCEDURE FOR RETENTIVITY MEASUREMENTS

It is convenient to have 75 to 100 g. of air-dried soil. Reduce all aggregates to <2-mm. diameter by rubbing the soil through a 2-mm. round-hole sieve with a rubber stopper. Place the sieved fraction on a mixing cloth, and pull the cloth in such a way as to produce mixing. (Some pulling operations will produce segregation instead of mixing, and special care must be exercised to obtain a homogeneous sample.) Flatten the sample until the pile is 2 to 4 cm. deep.

For water retentivity, two or three representative subsamples having a fairly definite volume are required. Use a separate paper cup for each subsample. Mark with a pencil line around the inside of the cup the height of soil needed to give the desired volume of subsample. This volume should be somewhat less than the volume of soil required to make the soil-retainer ring on the membrane level full. Use a thin teaspoon or scoop (not a knife or spatula), and lift small amounts of soil from the pile. Place successive spoonfuls in successive cups, and progress around the pile until the cups are filled to the desired level. Transfer a small enough quantity of soil in each operation to keep the larger particles from rolling off the spoon or scoop. Roll-off should be avoided because it makes the extracted subsample nonrepresentative. Place the sample-retainer rings on the porous plate. To avoid particle-size segregation, dump *all* the subsample from each container into a ring, and level the soil without spilling any outside the ring. A wide-mouth powder funnel, used as a tremie, is convenient for this sample transfer operation. Allow the samples to stand at least 16 hours with an excess of water on the membrane. Close the pressure chamber, and apply pressure. Connect the outflow tube from the pressure chamber to the bottom of a 25- or 50-ml. buret.

For a pressure chamber with an acetate membrane and a rubber diaphragm for holding the samples against the membrane, proceed as follows: Apply the air pressure first to the soil chamber. After a short time, usually 1 or 2 hours, the water outflow rate falls off markedly. By this time, the wet samples acquire some bearing strength. Then apply an excess of pressure of about 1/4 bar to the diaphragm chamber in accordance with the manufacturer's instructions.

Samples 1-cm. high can be removed any time after 48 hours from initiating the extraction or when readings on the outflow buret indicate that liquid water outflow has ceased from all samples on each membrane. Some soils will approach equilibrium in 18 to 20 hours. Before releasing the air pressure in the chamber, put a pinch clamp on the outflow tube. This reduces backflow of water to the samples after the pressure is released. To avoid changes in the water content of the samples after opening the chamber, transfer the samples quickly to metal boxes for drying. Determine the water content by drying the samples to constant weight at 105°C. Express the water content in terms of percentage on a dry-weight basis. Retentivity data should be accompanied by information on the temperature and ambient air pressure of the soil while on the membrane. Information on the structure and history of the sample should also be given.

8–2.3.4 COMMENTS

For some purposes, the ratio R of the weight of the coarse separate (>2 mm.) to the weight of the fine separate (≤2 mm.) should be recorded. Mineral soil material >2-mm. diameter complicates retentivity measurements and retains a negligible amount of water. When desired, the retentivity of the whole soil P_W can be calculated from the retentivity of the fine separate P_F by the equation, $P_W = P_F[1/(1 + R)]$.

Some air transfer always occurs through wet pressure membranes. According to Henry's law, the solubility of air in water is proportional to the pressure. Consequently, the concentration of dissolved air in the membrane water on the soil side is always higher than on the outflow side. This air moves through the membrane during liquid outflow and appears as bubbles in the outflow buret. When liquid outflow ceases, dissolved air moves through the membrane by molecular diffusion, and air bubbles will continue to appear in the outflow system, but at a reduced rate. This may amount to several cubic centimeters per minute for Visking cellulose membranes, 28 cm. in diameter, at a pressure of 15 bars. The maximum possible error from this air transfer can be calculated by assuming that all the water required to humidify these air bubbles comes from the soil samples.

The time required for soil samples to attain hydraulic equilibrium with a membrane increases approximately with the square of the height of the sample. This should be taken into consideration if it is planned to put core samples on a membrane.

Ceramic plates with rubber backing for use in pressure chambers up to

15 bars are less troublesome to use than cellulose membranes. Microbial action in some soils, iron rust from the chamber, sand grains near the gasket seal, and other things can cause disabling leaks in cellulose membranes. Pressure chambers for acetate membranes, however, do have the diaphragm for pressing the sample against the membrane to prevent loss of contact that might be caused by shrinkage of fine-textured samples.

Principal errors in retentivity measurements come from nonrepresentative subsamples; evaporative loss from samples during approach to equilibrium, as occurs on tension tables, or as caused by air leaks from pressure chambers; pressure or temperature fluctuations causing hysteresis effects; failure to attain outflow equilibrium; inadequate prewetting of samples; wetting of samples from backflow; or drying by evaporation during removal of the samples from the membrane. With skill, a coefficient of variation of 1 or 2% is attainable, and the measured value is independent of the type of apparatus or membrane.

8-3 FREEZING POINT OF WATER IN SOIL

8-3.1 Introduction

The freezing point of liquids is commonly measured for determining osmotic pressure and for determining the molecular weight of solutes. Crysocopic measurements of water in soil (Bouyoucos and McCool, 1915; Bouyoucos, 1917), using both temperature measurements of freezing-point depression and dilatometer measurements of volume changes accompanying ice formation, have been made for many years.

The interpretation of freezing-point measurements is reasonably straightforward for solutions because corrections for the change in the concentration of the solution during the formation of ice crystals, which generally are assumed to contain no solute, can be readily made. The usual procedure is to cool the liquid below the freezing point, to observe the rise in temperature during freezing, and to record the steady temperature after equilibrium is established between the ice and the solution. The change in solution concentration produced by ice formation can be estimated from the temperature rise during freezing, which is referred to as undercooling. The amount of ice formed per unit volume of solution is related in a simple manner to the thermal capacity of the various constituents and the heat of fusion of water.

The interpretation of freezing-point measurements for water in soil, however, is very much more complicated because water binding, both by solute and by the adsorptive force field of the matrix, is involved; and satisfactory means for making undercooling corrections have not as yet been worked out. Progressive improvements in techniques for freezing-point measurements of water in soil have been made (Evans et al., 1958). However, the major disadvantages and uncertainties of the freezing-point method for soil water, as outlined by Edlefsen and Anderson (1943, p. 220), have not been overcome. Recent authors (Bolt and Miller, 1958) seem to agree with the writer that we do not yet have a satisfactory theoretical method for interpreting freezing-point data for water in soil. Some of these uncertainties apply also to the dilatometer measuring method (Anderson and Edlefsen, 1942; Buehrer and Aldrich, 1946).

Both freezing-point depression and vapor-pressure depression are related to the energy condition of water in soil. Since vapor-pressure-depression measuring methods are now available which have sufficient accuracy and precision, it appears that some of the questions that have hung over the freezing-point-depression measuring method can now be answered, at least experimentally. Investigational work along this line, however, still awaits doing.

8–3.2   Principles

Schofield (1935) pointed out the relation between freezing-point depression and the free energy of water in soil. Day (1942) clarified the derivation of this relation and proposed the term "moisture potential" for the free energy of water in soil. The moisture potential has been defined as the chemical potential of water in ergs per gram. It is identical with the partial molal free energy of water in all respects except for the unit of mass involved.

The partial molal free energy of water at the ice point is related to the freezing-point depression ΔT by the equation $\mu = (L/T_0) \Delta T$, where L is the latent heat of fusion and T_0 is the freezing point of water. The units of μ are the same as those selected for L; and, in cgs. units, $L/T_0 = -12.21 \times 10^6$ erg g.$^{-1}$ [3] for each degree of freezing-point depression.

8–3.3   Method

8-3.3.1   SPECIAL APPARATUS

1. Thermistor thermometer mounted in a hypodermic needle to limit structural disturbance of the sample. Mounts of this kind are available from Yellow Springs Instrument Co., Inc., Yellow Springs, Ohio. Other thermistor mounts have been used by Richards and Campbell (1948) and Evans et al. (1958).
2. Bath controllable to $\pm 0.01\,°C$. in the range $0°$ to $-10°C$.

[3] While units of work (energy) per unit mass are traditional, work per unit volume could also be used. If the density of water ρ is taken as 1 g. cm.$^{-3}$, dividing by ρ gives $L/T_0\rho = -12.21 \times 10^6$ erg cm.$^{-3} = -12.21 \times 10^6$ dynes cm.$^{-2}$. This is the equivalent negative pressure which corresponds to the value of μ/ρ for $\Delta T = 1$ and may be identified with total suction TS. Thus $TS = 12.21\Delta T$ bars at $0°C$.

3. Direct current bridge for measuring thermistor resistance.

4. Soil sampling tube and core-sample containers as described in section 8–4.3.1. Glass test tubes (approximately 2.2 by 17.5 cm.) with cork spacer sleeves to fit inside air-jacketing glass test tubes (approximately 2.9 by 20 cm.) can be used for supporting the samples in the bath. The lid for the bath should have holes for both tube sizes.

8–3.3.2 PROCEDURE

Fill the sample containers with soil cores as described for the vapor-pressure measurement (section 8–4.3.4). In the laboratory, remove the solid cap from one end of the container, and substitute a plastic end-cap with a hole to admit the thermistor. Cover the hole with cellophane tape, place the sample container in the smaller glass tube, and install the tube in the bath. Insert the thermistor in one of the samples in the bath.

Set the bath temperature to give the minimum undercooling that will allow satisfactory freezing of the sample. When the soil temperature becomes steady and equal to bath temperature, transfer the soil tubes to the air-jacket tubes that are in the bath. Initiate freezing by inserting or rotating the thermistor probe in the sample. As a possible aid in the process, transfer the probe quickly from a frozen sample, thereby introducing ice crystals into the new sample.

Observe and record the maximum temperature attained after freezing is initiated. The difference between this temperature and the ice point is the observed, uncorrected freezing-point depression of the sample.

8–3.3.3 COMMENTS

Evans et al. (1958) have described a slow-freezing technique in which heat is extracted from the sample at a low, known rate, so that sample temperature can be related to the unfrozen water in the sample. This makes it possible to get a complete curve showing the freezing point as a function of the liquid-water content of the soil from a single freezing operation. Freezing-point values thus found were converted to tension (matric suction) values and compared with membrane data for the same soil. Correction factors were required to bring data from the two measuring methods into approximate agreement. It is not known to what extent the need for this correction is due to soil structure differences for the samples used in the comparison (Richards and Ogata, 1961), or to other uncertainties mentioned above for the freezing method.

Values of free energy or total suction at the freezing temperature can be calculated from freezing-point measurements, but the effect of change of temperature on these values must be taken into account before comparisons can be made with free-energy or total-suction values obtained at other temperatures by other methods, such as membrane or vapor methods.

8-4   VAPOR PRESSURE OF WATER IN SOIL

8-4.1   Introduction

It has long been recognized that vapor measurements of water in soil would provide useful and scientifically significant information. Early measurements (Thomas, 1921) clearly indicated that in the wetness range of the plant root zone, the equilibrium vapor pressure of water in soil is high and approaches saturation. It is only recently that accurate and convenient methods for measurements in wet soils have been developed by Monteith and Owen (1958), Korven and Taylor (1959), and Richards and Ogata (1958). These methods employ thermocouple psychrometers made of fine wires that are inserted into small chambers containing the sample. The methods described in the first two of the cited papers make use of the Peltier-effect to cool one junction below the dew point. When the Peltier current is stopped, the thermocouple is connected to a galvanometer, and the psychrometric reading is based on the evaporative cooling of the dew. This procedure has the advantage that the chamber does not need to be opened to wet the junction; and, therefore, repeated readings can be made with a minimum of disturbance to the system. The third reference describes a thermocouple with a silver ring at one of the junctions. A droplet of water is placed on the ring just before the thermocouple is inserted into the sample chamber. The measuring method described below is based on the third reference because the published data indicate that this method has good accuracy and stability of calibration.

8-4.2   Principles

The condition of water vapor in air or the degree of saturation of air by water vapor can be expressed in terms of relative pressure p/p_0, where p is the partial pressure of water vapor in the air mixture, and p_0 is the equilibrium partial pressure at saturation. Relative pressure multiplied by 100 is called percent relative humidity. Relative pressure depression, $1 - p/p_0$, has special significance in physical chemistry and thermodynamics because it is a colligative property of solutions that is proportional to freezing-point depression, boiling-point elevation, and osmotic pressure. Critical tables and handbooks give values of osmotic pressure for different aqueous solutions.

Relative vapor-pressure depression is related to osmotic pressure by the equation $1 - p/p_0 = (\bar{v}/RT)\pi$. The symbols $\bar{v}$, R, T, and π represent, respectively, partial molar volume of water, gas constant, absolute temperature, and osmotic pressure at temperature T. Specifically, $1 - p/p_0 = (7.3 \times 10^{-4})\pi$ at 25°C.

The appropriate temperature is always indicated for handbook data relating osmotic pressure to solution concentration. Since osmotic pressure may be taken as proportional to absolute temperature, conversion of handbook data to any desired temperature can be easily made. The standard atmosphere is ordinarily used as the unit of pressure in physical chemistry literature; but, for the numerical values in the above equation, the value of the gas content was selected for the case where π is expressed in bars. For example, if it is desired to use the equation to calculate the relative humidity of the equilibrium vapor of a solution of which the osmotic pressure is 10 bars at 25°C., we may write $1 - p/p_0 = 7.3 \times 10^{-4} \times 10 = 0.0073$ and $p/p_0 = 0.9927$. Multiplying by 100 gives relative humidity equal to 99.27%.

The principle of operation of the thermocouple psychrometer is illustrated in Fig. 8–4. A thermocouple is made of dissimilar metals. The thermal electromotive force is proportional to the temperature difference between junctions A and B as shown at the left. Copper wires leading to a potentiometer can be inserted at A without affecting the voltage output if A_1 and A_2 are at the same temperature. Likewise, as shown on the right in Fig. 8–4, a silver ring can be inserted at B to hold a droplet of water. The evaporative cooling of junction B below the temperature of junction A is related to the vapor-pressure depression. The thermocouple and sample-container arrangement are shown in Fig. 8–5.

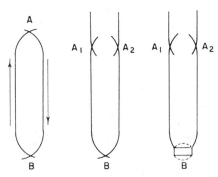

Fig. 8–4. Diagrams of thermocouples for relating the psychrometric reading to the thermal electromotive force. See text.

8–4.3   Method [1]

8–4.3.1   SPECIAL APPARATUS

1. Thermocouple psychrometer: In Fig. 8–5, A is the assembly as installed in the thermostat, and B is an enlarged view of the thermocouple. The insulating cover (1) helps to maintain the samples at constant temperature in the liquid bath (2). The masonite cover (3) supports a number of thin-walled brass test tubes (4), made from stock tubing of 13/16-inch o.d. (outside diameter) by 22 Stubs-gauge wall. The thermocouple mount accurately guides the couple into the sample container and makes it possible conveniently to shift the couple from one sample to another.

[1] Richards and Ogata (1958).

The mount consists of a cylinder of thin-walled brass (5), ¾-inch o.d. by 24 Stubs-gauge wall, closed at the lower end with a disc of copper (8) and a copper tube (7) assembled with soft solder. The tube sizes specified give only a narrow clearance of the psychrometer mount in the supporting brass test tube. The handle (6) is made of rigid plastic. The lead wires (11) have seven strands of 36-gauge untinned copper and have vinyl insulation of 0.1-cm. o.d. The two lead wires make a tight fit in the tube (7). The twisted strands extend a short distance (12) below the vinyl and are reduced to a single strand for an additional distance (13). Soft solder is used to join the bare Chromel P (14) and Constantan (15) wires[5] to the copper wires (13), and to attach the silver ring (16), which has an outside diameter of 0.185 cm., a wall thickness of 0.018 cm., and a height of 0.051 cm. The resistance of the thermocouple is about 20 ohms.

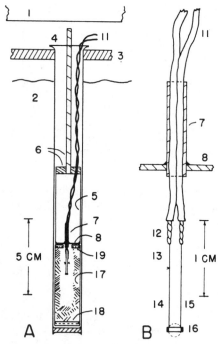

A stainless-steel-type flux is used to solder the thermojunction wire. This flux is a strong electrolyte and must be used in such a way that the couple can be washed free of flux after soldering.

In the foregoing design, the dry junction is thermally connected to the bath temperature through the mount. This arrangement provides a short response time, but makes the thermocouple respond adversely to a vertical temperature gradient in the supporting brass tube. Little trouble is experienced if the top of the bath is insulated and if the bath is operated at room temperature. For vapor measurements over a range of temperatures, Klute and Richards (1962) found it necessary to provide a flange for an "O" ring gasket on the brass test tube and to attach a brass closure plate with a polyethylene tube for enclosing the electrical leads. With this

Fig. 8–5. Construction details for the thermocouple psychrometer, and arrangement of the sample in the bath. See text.

arrangement the psychrometer-sample system can be submerged, and the vertical gradient effect can be avoided.

[5] The thermocouple wire, 0.001 inch diameter, may be obtained from Sigmund Cohn, Mount Vernon, New York.

2. Sample containers: These (17) are made from stainless steel tubing, ¾-inch o.d. by 20 B W gauge wall. Two end-caps (18) for each container are turned from rigid acrylic plastic and are ¾-inch diameter by 1/16-inch thick. The caps have a square shoulder recess to fit the inside diameter of the stainless steel tube and are prepared for use by dipping them in hot universal wax. The fillet of wax left in the shoulder recess provides a good vapor seal.

One end-cap with a 0.9-cm. axial hole is required to hold the soil in place during the process of scratching out a cavity in the soil core to accommodate the thermocouple. A cap (19) with a 0.6-cm. hole is required for each sample container for use in the bath during readings.

3. Soil sampling tube: A thin-walled tube with a sharp cutting edge is required for cutting core samples to fit the soil sample container. The following design has been in use for many years at the U. S. Salinity Laboratory, but details of construction have not previously been published. A·brass tube, ¾-inch o.d. by 0.700-inch i.d. (inside diameter) by 23 Stubs-gauge wall, is counterbored for ⅛ inch to an inside diameter of 0.720 inch. A piece of steel clock-spring ribbon ⅜-inch wide by 0.020-inch thick is coiled to approximately ¾-inch diameter, and a piece is cut to give a close fit in the counterbore in the brass tube. The ends of the spring steel should be ground to give a smooth butt joint. The steel is then soft-soldered into the brass without annealing the spring-tempered steel. The outside of the joint between brass and steel is then smoothed, and the edge of the steel is sharpened. This gives a thin, tough cutting edge followed by dimensional relief to allow cores to slide easily in the brass tube. A ⅝-inch wooden rod can be used to push cores through the tube into the sample containers.

4. Core-boring tool: This is used for scratching out a hole in the soil core 0.9-cm. diameter by 1.7-cm. deep to admit the thermocouple. Fig. 8–6 clarifies construction. If a thin tungsten carbide needle is used for the scratching tool, it will stay sharp and will cause a minimum of troweling action with attendant disturbance of soil structure. A type of boring tool that has been used is shown in Fig. 8–6 and makes use of the following materials: (a) wooden block 4 inch by 4 inch by 6 inch; (b) brass tubing 5/16-inch o.d. by 0.256-inch i.d.

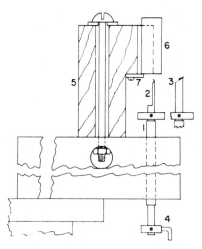

Fig. 8–6. Tool for making a hole for the thermocouple in core samples of soil. For legend, see text.

by 22 Stubs-gauge wall by 5 inches long; (c) brass tubing ¼-inch o.d. by 18 Stubs-gauge wall by 7 inches long; (d) two brass collars 1-inch o.d. by ¼-inch i.d. by ¼-inch long with set screws; and (d) tungsten carbide needle ground from a tool bit, ¼ to 5/16 inch in length, with a 5° to 10° angle at the point.

Drill a hole, and press the large tube (1) into the wooden block as shown in Fig. 8–6. Cut the small tube parallel to the axis, and remove about half of the tube (2) for a distance of 1 inch. Cut the top (3) at an angle of about 60° to the axis, and attach the tungsten carbide needle with silver solder. Grind the needle so that its point rotates on a circle of 0.9-cm. diameter. Install a crank arm in the lower collar (4). An

Table 8–1. Apparatus components: Description and sources (products equivalent to those of manufacturers mentioned may, of course, be used).

Galvanometer: (For thermistor bridge)--2430-e, 0.001 μv./mm., T = 3 sec., R = 175 ohm, CDRX = 5,000 to 8,000 ohms. Leeds and Northrup Co., Philadelphia, Pa.

Thermistor: No. 32 A 38, Glass rod 1 in. long, 2,000 ohm ± 20% at 25° C. Victory Engineering Corp., P.O. Box 373, Union, New Jersey.

Stirrer: Drum (squirrel cage) rotor, 3-in. diameter by 2 1/2-in. high, on 5/16-in. shaft mounted on ball-bearing quill. Speed approximately 375 rpm. Belt, Gates "Speed Flex" No. 95, 1/2-in. by 30-in. Induction motor, 1/20th hp., 1,590 rpm.

Bath liquid: Odorless kerosene or paint thinner having the following characteristics: for temperatures of 5°, 25°, and 40° C., the densities (g./cc.) and viscosities (centipoise) are, respectively, 0.791, 0.778, and 0.769; and 2.475, 1.596, and 1.214. Must be an electrical nonconductor because bare heater wires are used.

Cooling coil: 5 turns of 3/8-in. copper tubing soft-soldered to the outside of the copper baffle.

Refrigeration: Tecumseh sealed unit, Model No. C4414 HTK; 1/4 hp. Tecumseh Products Co., Marion, Ohio.

Expansion valve: Automatic type, Model 672, adjustable range 25 in. Hg vacuum to 25 psi. Detroit Lubricator Controls, 5900 Trumbull Avenue, Detroit 8, Mich.

Heaters: Two sections, one of 24 ohms and one of 48 ohms. Constructed of Chromel-A flat-ribbon heater wire, 1.39 ohms/foot. Wound on 6 lucite legs with notches to maintain spacing of turns. Hoskins Manufacturing Co., Detroit, Mich.

Control unit: Precision Temperature Controller, Model 103. Bayley Instrument Co., Box 538, Danville, Calif.

Voltage regulator: Model 20-13-125 B070, Type CV-1, Prim. 95-130 V., 250 VA, 60 cycle, Sec. 118V, 2.12 amp. Sola Electric Co., Chicago, Ill.

Amplifier: Direct current, Microvolt Ammeter, Model 150 A. Keithley Instruments, Inc., Cleveland 6, Ohio.

Recorder: Potentiometer recorder G11A. Varian Associates, Palo Alto, Calif.

adjustable "V" block (5), shown in section, holds the sample container (6) vertical and concentric with the axis of the needle. The collars are adjusted to limit the length of the hole in the soil to 1.7 cm. when the sample container is held against the stop (7).

5. Constant-temperature bath: Good temperature control for the sample during vapor pressure measurement is a critical requirement and constitutes the major apparatus difficulty of the method. Equipment for measuring and controlling the bath temperature has been described by Klute and Richards (1962),[6] and the following is a brief description of this equipment.

Temperature is measured with a thermistor bridge like that described by Richards and Campbell (1948), except that the bridge arms are 2,000 ohms; a bridge voltage of 1.034 is supplied by a single mercury cell, and a reversing switch is used in the galvanometer circuit. A 2,000-ohm glass-rod-type thermistor (Table 8–1) is mounted in a copper jacket with a Teflon tube attached as shown (A) in Fig. 8–7. The sectional view at the top shows the copper jacket, which is 0.187 inches o.d. by 0.10 inches i.d. by 2 inches long. A brass nipple is soft-soldered into one end. The Teflon tubing has a squeeze fit on the nipple and is secured by a snugly fitting brass slip-on ferrule as illustrated (Fig. 8–7). The two electrical leads for the thermistor are each composed of 7 strands of 36-gauge copper wire with a vinyl coating, the outside diameter of which is 0.04 inches. After attachment of the Teflon tube, the thermistor is centrally located in the copper jacket, the jacket is filled with Epoxy,

---

[6] More recent publications by L. A. Richards describe bath improvements.

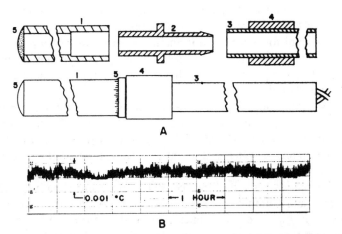

Fig. 8–7. (A) Components and method of assembly for the thermistor jacket: (1) copper tubing; (2) brass attachment nipple; (3) Teflon tubing; (4) brass keeper ferrule; and (5) soft solder. (B) Record of bath temperature fluctuations for a 5-hour period at 40°C.

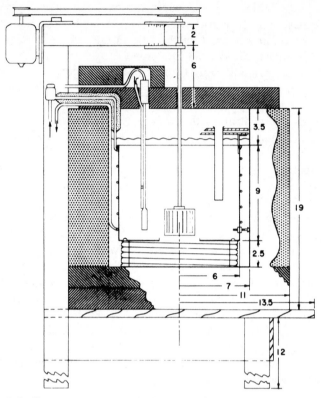

Fig. 8–8. Constant-temperature bath (see Table 8–1 and text for details).

and the free end is closed with soft solder. The lower sketch (*A*, Fig. 8–7) shows the assembled temperature probe.

The thermistor is mounted in the metal jacket to increase the dissipation constant, thus minimizing self-heating and attendant anemometer effects. This temperature probe has a response time of about 5 seconds in the bath liquid.

A portable lamp and scale galvanometer and a 6-decade resistance box makes it possible to balance the bridge to 0.02 ohm. This corresponds to 2×10^{-4}°C. at 25°C. The thermistor is calibrated against the triple-point of water and a National Bureau of Standards calibrated thermometer at total immersion.

An improved version of the "constant-temperature" bath described by Richards and Campbell (1948)[7] is suitable. A partially sectional view is shown in Fig. 8–8, with dimensions given in inches. The walls of the cylindrical tank are 4 inches thick and are made of 24-gauge sheet metal,

---

[7] Ibid.

stainless steel inside, and galvanized iron outside. The bottom is insulated with Styrofoam and the sides with rock wool. All seams are double-rolled and soft-soldered. An inset metal baffle, made from 16-ounce sheet copper, channels the circulation and supports the heating and cooling coils. Bath liquid is drawn through a 4-inch-diameter hole in the bottom of the baffle by a drum-type impeller.

The tank rests on a circle of plywood supported by three legs at the periphery. One leg extends vertically to support the stirrer. Various components are described in Table 8–1. The bath cover is a 2-inch slab of Styrofoam, which supports the resistance probe of the controller and the thermistor thermometer as shown in Fig. 8–2.

The sensing probe of a controller, such as that listed in Table 8–1, connects to an input bridge circuit, the output of which is amplified and used to control the current in one of the heater coils in the bath. To match the resistance of this heater to the characteristics of the controller, the following procedure may be used. The temperature of the controller probe is held constant by placing it in a Dewar flask filled with water at room temperature; and a decade resistance box, adjustable in 0.01-ohm steps, is inserted in series with the "fine" temperature dial of the controller. A curve is then plotted showing I^2R power in the heater as a function of the inserted resistance value read from the decade box. This is done for several heater-resistance values lying in the safe operating range of the controller. It is desirable to use the heater resistance that gives the largest change of heat input to the bath per unit change of inserted resistance. Stability of operation and the cooling rate of the bath are other factors to be considered.

Unfortunately, the controller listed is considerably affected by change-of-tube characteristics. This is true especially for the gas triode output tubes, which are not easy to check with a tube tester. Once the resistance value of the power-proportioning heater has been selected by the process just outlined, then, with the controller probe in a Dewar flask, the shape of the curve relating heater current to the decade-box input-resistance values can be used to check the performance of the controller at any later time, and thus aid in trouble-shooting and in the replacement of tubes when necessary.

The bath temperature can be precisely monitored with the resistance thermometer described above. It is often convenient to amplify and record (Table 8–1) the unbalance voltage of the bridge, and it is relatively simple to get a chart range of 2 or 3 cm. for 0.001°C. change of bath temperature. The chart shown as B in Fig. 8–7 indicates the degree of temperature control attainable with the equipment described. In the temperature range from 5° to 40°C., it is usually possible, without operator attention, to keep the peak-to-peak temperature variation less than 0.001°C. for hours at a time. To attain this control, the bath is operated in a room controlled to $\pm 0.5°C$., and both the constant heat and the controller are supplied with a-c. power from a voltage-regulating transformer.

6. Microvolt potentiometer: The Teele and Schuhmann (1939) potentiometer, when used with a sensitive galvanometer (such as Leeds and Northrup Company, Philadelphia, Pa., Model HS 2284-b, with a 2-m. scale distance), gives an accuracy of 0.01 μv. A potentiometer with almost this accuracy can be built using the same circuit but with inexpensive components. A conventional pushbutton leaf switch such as used in commercial electronic circuits (Switchcraft Inc., Chicago, Ill., No. 4006) can be used with a length of fine copper wire for the thermally guarded resistor. These can be mounted in a relatively small block of aluminum or copper that is surrounded by thermal insulation. Direct current amplifiers are also available that are adequately stable and sensitive and make it possible to read and to record the output of thermocouple psychrometers (Table 8–1).

8–4.3.2 STANDARD SOLUTIONS

Use reagent-grade KCl, and make up standard solutions having known osmotic pressure from data such as given in Table 8–2. The osmotic pressure at $0°C$., π_o, may be calculated from the freezing-point depression, using the relation $\pi_o = 12.21 \; \Delta T$ bars. For conditions when the gas law $[(P_1 V_1/T_1) = (P_2 V_2/T_2)]$ may be applied, the osmotic pressure π_K of a solution at Kelvin temperature K may be calculated from π_o by the relation $\pi_K = (K/273.2)\pi_o$.

Table 8–2. Molar freezing-point depression for different concentrations of KCl, and corresponding calculated values for freezing-point depression and osmotic pressure at $0°C$.

Molar concentration of KCl, N	Molar freezing-point depression,* $\Delta T/N$	Freezing-point depression, ΔT †	Osmotic pressure at $0°$ C., π_o ‡
		° C.	bar
0.01	3.610	0.03610	0.4408
0.02	3.566	0.07132	0.8708
0.10	3.451	0.3451	4.214
0.20	3.394	0.6788	8.288
0.50	3.314	1.657	20.23
1.00	3.250	3.250	39.68
1.50	3.22	4.83	58.97
2.00	3.22	6.44	78.63

* National Research Council of the U.S.A. (1928).
† $\Delta T = (\Delta T/N_W)N_W$.   ‡ $\pi_o = 12.21 \; \Delta T$.

8–4.3.3 PROCEDURE FOR PSYCHROMETER CALIBRATION

Fit a number of sample containers (equal to the number of psychrometers to be calibrated) with Lucite cylinders that have an inside diameter of 1 cm. Line the cylinders with filter paper, and add the osmotic solution to give an air-cavity depth of 1.7 cm. (These dimensions provide for calibration an air-filled cavity of about the same size as that used for measurement in soil samples.) After loading a sample container with a layer of filter paper and the standard solution, transfer it to the bath, and immediately insert the psychrometer after putting a water droplet on the silver ring. Add the droplet by submerging the ring in distilled water and then rapidly lowering the vessel containing the water.

Read the electrical output of the psychrometer periodically, and record the steady-state voltage output. To prepare a calibration curve, plot the steady-state voltage obtained with the various standard solutions against the corresponding relative-pressure depression calculated from the relationship given in section 8–4.2.

8–4.3.4 PROCEDURE FOR SAMPLE HANDLING AND MEASUREMENT

Take a core sample approximately 6 cm. long with the soil tube. Push the core through the sampler and into a cylindrical sample container. Trim the ends of the core with a knife, and attach solid plastic end-caps that have been waxed to make a tight seal. Protect the sample containers from rapid change of temperature and temperature gradients to limit dew formation inside the container.

In the laboratory, substitute an end-cap with a 0.9-cm. hole, and scratch out the cavity 0.9 cm. in diameter by 1.7 cm. in length for the psychrometer. Install an end-cap with a 0.6-cm. hole, and place the sample container in the bath. Place a droplet of distilled water on the silver ring of the psychrometer, and slowly insert the psychrometer into the sample. Read the electrical output of the psychrometer periodically to determine when the steady-state value is attained. Convert this steady-state value to relative-pressure depression by means of the calibration data previously obtained for the psychrometer (section 8–4.3.3).

8–4.3.5 COMMENTS

A thermocouple psychrometer which is calibrated in terms of osmotic pressure can also be called a thermocouple osmometer. This calibration serves directly for reading the solute suction of solutions and for reading the total suction of water in soil. Richards and Ogata (1960) have checked experimentally the fact that a unit of solute suction produces the same relative-pressure depression as a unit of matric suction. They (Richards and Ogata, 1961) also have shown that vapor-pressure measurements are in harmony with membrane measuring methods for soil.

The response of the psychrometer illustrated in Fig. 8–5 is slightly dependent on the geometry of the sample chamber, apparently because of thermal convection effects. Consequently, when the calibration is done with standard osmotic solutions on filter paper, the air cavity should be approximately the same size as in the sample later to be measured.

In the osmotic pressure range from 5 to 60 bars, the psychrometer output is proportional to π. Steady output readings may be expected in 15 to 30 minutes after installation of the sample and thermocouple in the bath if the vapor condition of the sample is steady. Longer equilibrium time is required as the solution concentration approaches zero. Also, the psychrometer sensitivity, defined as microvolts per bar, $\mu v./\pi$, increases slightly as π gets less than 1 or 2 bars. For accurate work in this range, a calibration curve should be used. Richards and Ogata (1958) have reported that, for calibration data in the 5- to 60-bar range, the average coefficient of variability of the output voltage for 100 readings (4 couples, 5 osmotic pressure values, and 5 replicates) was 0.5%. Thermocouple psychrometers have been used for 6 months and longer without measurable changes of calibration. Accidental bending of the wires may cause changes in calibration, perhaps because of changes in wet-junction location with respect to the surface of the sample. For this reason, the clearance between the thermocouple mounting tube and the brass test tube supporting the sample in the bath, as specified above, is kept small so as to provide accurate psychrometer alignment. The sensitivity of thermocouple psychrometers of the type described above usually lies in the range from 0.55 to 0.65 $\mu v.$ per bar.

The calibration of a psychrometer that makes use of evaporative cooling depends both on temperature and on atmospheric pressure.[8] For a given osmotic solution in the sample chamber of the couples here described, the rate of change of sensitivity with change in atmospheric pressure is constant but increases as the osmotic pressure of the sample is increased. The increase in sensitivity for a 10-millibar decrease in barometric pressure is 0.00145, 0.00155, and 0.00160 $\mu v.$ per bar of osmotic pressure, for standard osmotic solutions of 5, 10, and 20 bars, respectively. Correction for change of atmospheric pressure from the value at calibration will be needed only when maximum accuracy is required.

Psychrometer readings are much more exacting for soil samples than for solution on filter paper. Soil samples are more susceptible to disturbance and usually require longer for steady readings. If the soil samples have been stored at constant temperature in the bath, soil readings in the 10- to 20-bar range may approach the response time for solutions on filter paper. The length of time required for steady-state readings with soil samples is related to the amount of disturbance to which the soil sample has been subjected.

---

[8] Richards, L. A. 1964. A thermocouple psychrometer for measuring the relative vapor pressure of water in liquids and porous materials. Proc. Intern. Symp. on Humidity and Moisture, Wash., D. C. Reinhold Publishing Corp., New York.

A redistribution of water in the sample caused by subjecting it to rapid temperature changes or to temperature gradients across the sample may increase the time required to get a reliable psychrometric reading. Disturbance of the structure in taking the core or making the hole for the psychrometer likewise may increase the time required for a steady reading.

It is not difficult in routine work to attain a standard deviation of ±0.1 bar for replicate samples of solution on filter paper. As yet, however, it is difficult to evaluate the accuracy of measurement of the vapor condition for soil samples because it is not possible to prepare replicate soil samples. Using membrane equilibrium techniques, Richards and Ogata (1961) got standard deviation values of approximately ±0.5 bar for supposedly replicate soil samples, but this variation is thought to be caused mainly by variation in sample condition. In an experiment set up for reading the vapor pressure at the wall of a tensiometer cup, Richards and Ogata (1960) found that the accuracy of the psychrometer appeared to be of the same order as the accuracy of the electric measurement, which was 0.01 μv. This corresponds to ±0.015 bar, or 1 or 2 parts per 100,000 of relative pressure near saturation.

During normal use, the silver ring of the psychrometer comes in contact only with distilled water; but, even so, a white coating that is hard to wet tends to accumulate. This can be removed as needed by coating the ring for a short time with a thin water paste of disodium dihydrogen ethylenediamine tetraacetate.

8-5   LITERATURE CITED

Anderson, A. B. C., and Edlefsen, N. E. 1942. Volume-freezing-point relations observed with new dilatometer technique. Soil Sci. 54:221–232.

Bolt, G. H., and Miller, R. D. 1958. Calculation of total and component potentials of water in soil. Trans. Am. Geophys. Union 39:917–928.

Bouyoucos, G. J. 1917. Classification and measurement of the different forms of water in the soil by means of the dilatometer method. Michigan Agr. Exp. Sta. Tech. Bull. 36.

Bouyoucos, G. J., and McCool, M. M. 1915. The freezing-point method as a new means of measuring the concentration of the soil solution directly in the soil. Michigan Agr. Exp. Sta. Tech. Bull. 24.

Buckingham, E. 1907. Studies on the movement of soil moisture. U. S. Dept. Agr. Bur. of Soils, Bull. 38.

Buehrer, T. F., and Aldrich, D. G., Jr. 1946. Studies of soil structure. VI. Water bound by individual soil constituents as influenced by puddling. Arizona Agr. Exp. Sta. Tech. Bull. 110.

Day, P. R. 1942. The moisture potential of soil. Soil Sci. 54:391–400.

Edlefsen, N. E., and Anderson, A. B. C. 1943. Thermodynamics of soil moisture. Hilgardia 15:31–298.

Evans, D. D., Harrigan, J. A., and Chinn, C. E. 1958. Temperature-time curves as soil freezes related to moisture-stress curves. Soil Sci. Soc. Am. Proc. 22:375–378.

Gardner, W., Israelsen, O. W., Edlefsen, N. E., and Clyde, H. 1922. The capillary potential function and its relation to irrigation practice. Physical Review, Series 2, 20:196.

Jamison, V. C. 1958. Sand-silt suction column for determination of moisture retention. Soil Sci. Soc. Am. Proc. 22:82–83.

Jamison, V. C., and Reed, I. F. 1949. Durable asbestos tension tables. Soil Sci. 67:311–318.

Klute, A., and Richards, L. A. 1962. Effect of temperature on relative vapor pressure of water in soil: Apparatus and preliminary measurements. Soil Sci. 93:391–396.

Korven, H. C., and Taylor, S. A. 1959. The Peltier effect and its use for determining relative activity of soil water. Can. J. Soil Sci. 39:76–85.

Lehane, J. J., and Staple, W. J. 1960. Relationship of the permanent wilting percentage and the soil moisture content at harvest to the 15-atmosphere percentage. Can. J. Soil Sci. 40:264–269.

Monteith, J. L., and Owen, P. C. 1958. A thermocouple method for measuring relative humidity in the range 95–100%. J. Sci. Inst. 35:443–446.

National Research Council of the U.S.A. 1928. International Critical Tables of Numerical Data, Physics, Chemistry and Technology. Vol. 4, p. 259. McGraw-Hill Book Co., New York.

Richards, L. A. 1952. Report of the Subcommittee on Permeability and Infiltration, Committee on Terminology. Soil Sci. Soc. Am. Proc. 16:85–88.

Richards, L. A. 1956. Sample retainers for measuring water retention by soil. Soil Sci. Soc. Am. Proc. 20:301–303.

Richards, L. A. 1960. Advances in soil physics. Trans. Intern. Congr. Soil Sci. 7th Madison. 1:67–79.

Richards, L. A., and Campbell, R. B. 1948. Use of thermistors for measuring the freezing point of solutions and soils. Soil Sci. 65:429–436.

Richards, L. A., and Campbell, R. B. 1949. The freezing point of moisture in soil cores. Soil Sci. Soc. Am. Proc. (1948) 13:70–74.

Richards, L. A., and Ogata, Gen. 1958. A thermocouple for vapor pressure measurement in biological and soil systems at high humidity. Science 128:1084–1090.

Richards, L. A., and Ogata, Gen. 1960. Vapor pressure depression at a tensiometer cup. Trans. Intern. Congr. Soil Sci. 7th Madison 1:279–283.

Richards, L. A., and Ogata, Gen. 1961. Psychrometric measurements of soil samples equilibrated on pressure membranes. Soil Sci. Soc. Am. Proc. 25:456–459.

Richards, L. A., and Weaver, L. R. 1944. Moisture retention by some irrigated soils as related to soil moisture tension. J. Agr. Res. 69:215–235.

Richards, S. J. 1939. Soil moisture content calculations from capillary tension records. Soil Sci. Soc. Am. Proc. (1938) 3:57–64.

Schofield, R. K. 1935. The pF of water in soil. Trans. Intern. Congr. Soil Sci. 3rd Oxford. 2:37–48.

Tanner, C. B., and Elrick, D. E. 1958. Volumetric porous (pressure) plate apparatus for moisture hysteresis measurements. Soil Sci. Soc. Am. Proc. 22:575–576.

Teele, R. P., and Schuhmann, S. 1939. A potentiometer for measuring voltages of 10 microvolts to an accuracy of 0.01 microvolt. U. S. Natl. Bur. Stds. J. Res. 22:431–439.

Thomas, M. D. 1921. Aqueous vapor pressure of soils. Soil Sci. 11:409–434.

U. S. Salinity Laboratory Staff. 1954. Diagnosis and improvement of saline and alkali soils. U. S. Dept. Agr. Handbook 60.

9 Soil Suction Measurements with Tensiometers

S. J. RICHARDS
University of California
Riverside, California

9–1 INTRODUCTION

Soil water studies have long been carried out in terms of water content measurements. To evaluate relative wetness for the many soil types involved, it has been necessary to relate water content values to rheological or water retention properties. By determining the water content at the lower plastic limit, for example, this becomes a reference point for relative wetness when the water content of a given soil is at or near this amount. However, for studying agricultural soils as dynamic systems into which water moves and is stored and later delivered to root systems, an index to soil wetness is now available which is based on a direct measurement of a thermodynamic property of water films as they occur in soil.

Such an index was first proposed as a potential function (Buckingham, 1907). As conceived by Buckingham, this index was evaluated only for a vertical soil column with the soil water in equilibrium with a water table near the lower end of the column. For increasing elevations above the water table, the proposed "capillary potential function" would have decreasing values, since the well-known gravitational potential function increased with height. For a system in equilibrium, a change in the former must compensate for an equivalent change in the latter. Later, it was proposed (Gardner et al., 1922) that a pressure measurement on the water films using porous, ceramic-wall equipment is an equivalent means of measuring the "capillary" or "pressure" potential function. No fewer than three authors (Richards, 1928; Heck, 1934; and Rogers, 1935) published papers independently which suggested the use of porous ceramic cups, placed in field soils with connections to manometers or vacuum gauges, to follow pressure changes on the water inside the cup resulting from pressure changes associated with film water in the soil.

When commonly used conventions are applied, the pressure on water in unsaturated soils is negative. To avoid the use of negative numbers, terms have been used which are defined as negative pressures. Capillary or soil moisture tension is such a term, and it is from this term that the name for the instrument, tensiometer, was derived. Suction is a term used extensively to characterize the "action" of water retention by soils (Russell, 1950). Since suction is unique to soils literature and does not imply some of the ambiguities of other terminology, it is proposed that soil suction be used as the term to specify the property of soil water measured with tensiometers. Matric suction (Marshall, 1959) is also proposed as an additional characterization of this soil water property, since much of the action or force field which accounts for the measured index is associated with the surface areas of the solid or matrix portion of the soil.

9–2 PRINCIPLES

The accompanying Fig. 9–1 shows the essential parts of a tensiometer. A porous ceramic cup is positioned in the soil where information regarding soil water is desired. The cup, the connecting tube, and the sensing element of a vacuum indicator are all filled with water. Film water in the soil near the cup is in hydraulic contact with bulk water inside the cup through pores in the cup wall. Flow, in or out through the cup wall, tends to bring the cup

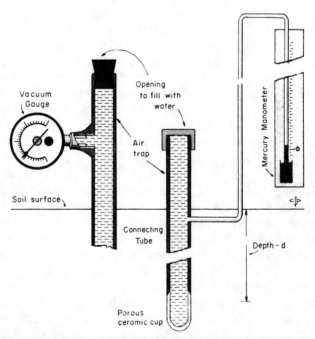

Fig. 9–1. Schematic diagram showing the essential parts of a tensiometer. Either the vacuum gauge or mercury manometer may be used.

water into hydraulic equilibrium with the soil water. As soil water is depleted by root action, or replenished by rainfall or irrigation, corresponding changes in readings on the tensiometer gauges occur. Tensiometer readings plotted as a function of time provide a useful record of soil water conditions in the neighborhood of the cup.

Experience has demonstrated that for many of the soil and water conditions under which commercial crops are grown, readings on tensiometers follow changes occurring in the water system of the root zone within acceptable limits. In laboratory experiments where better precision is desired, null-type tensiometers have been devised (Miller, 1951; Leonard and Low, 1962) which require no interchange of water to follow changes in the soil-water system.

Tensiometers do have a definite limitation in the range of values they can measure. The vacuum gauge or manometer indicates partial-vacuum relative to the atmosphere; hence, the highest reading theoretically possible is equivalent to atmospheric pressure. The practical limit is about 0.8 of this range.

Many of the publications dealing with tensiometers show calibration data relating soil suction to water content values for specific soils. It was found that the relation between these variables was not single-valued but was influenced by structure and compaction; and, even when all other variables were controlled, the drying and wetting curves were not the same, indicating a so-called hysteresis effect. It is now becoming more generally accepted that soil suction is a variable which need not be interpreted in terms of water content. For example, if tensiometer readings were taken in two blocks of soil, and then the blocks were placed in contact with each other, water would tend to flow from the block having the lower reading into the block having the higher reading, irrespective of the texture, structure, compaction, or water content of either soil involved. If readings on two tensiometers are equal, then the soils in which they are located are equally "wet" as far as a tendency for water flow is concerned.

A reading of zero suction on a tensiometer indicates a condition of "free water" in the soil. That is, if a hole were made at the depth of the cup, then water would flow into the hole. At the other extreme, as a soil is dried by root action, the readings on a tensiometer increase, corresponding to the amount of water withdrawn, until the limit mentioned above is reached. Then, even though the withdrawal of water is continued, the readings no longer increase. At this point, the readings should be discontinued until irrigation or rainfall brings the water condition in the soil back into the range of the tensiometer. By use of laboratory pressure-plate techniques, it has been well established that, as a soil is dried, soil suction continues to increase even though the tensiometer fails to measure it. For studies where a wider range in soil water conditions is desired, it is recommended that resistance blocks or electrothermal units be calibrated by pressure-plate equipment to indicate soil suction. Data from the various types of instruments may then be readily correlated.

The limitation in range of a tensiometer would appear to be a serious restriction on the use of such instruments in dealing with plant response. Their use is not to be recommended for experiments dealing with soil water conditions which are limiting to plant growth. Correlating soil suction with the available water depletion (Richards and Marsh, 1961) has shown that from 25 to 75% of available water depletion is covered by the range of the tensiometer, depending on whether the soil is fine or coarse textured. However, more often than not, soil water management is directed toward favorable growing conditions of plants. For this purpose, tensiometers are finding continuously wider application.

The metric unit for measuring pressure (suction) is the bar (1 bar = 0.987 atmospheres). Tensiometers are commonly calibrated in centibars except when measuring hydraulic head. While the use of tensiometers is widespread, the name for the soil-water property they measure is not universally agreed upon. Tension, pressure, suction, pressure head, suction head, potential, partial free energy are all more or less equivalent terms and may be used interchangeably when consistent units and reference conventions are observed.

Some of the early reports of tensiometer measurements (Richards and Neal, 1937) showed consistent diurnal changes where recording vacuum gauges were used. From these early observations, it was not possible to separate the influence of soil temperature on soil suction from a possible effect on the measuring technique. It was demonstrated later (Haise and Kelley, 1950) that temperature effects on soil suction can account for measurable amounts of water flow. Controlled laboratory results are now available (Taylor et al. 1961) to show the magnitude of the change in soil suction with temperature.

Tensiometers are not sensitive to the osmotic effects of dissolved salts in the soil solution. Techniques for evaluating osmotic concentrations are described in other sections of this monograph. In terms of energy relations, the commonly used osmotic pressure might well be called osmotic suction and, when expressed in equivalent units, should be directly additive to soil suction for characterizing water availability to plant roots.

9–3   METHOD

9–3.1   Tensiometer Design

The drawing in Fig. 9–1 was made to show the essential parts of a tensiometer. Figure 9–2 shows various models which are being manufactured and sold commercially. It is to be expected that many future innovations

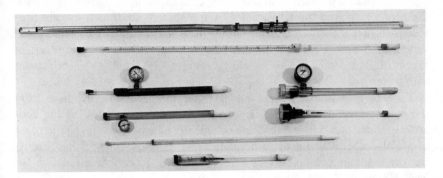

Fig. 9–2. Various models of tensiometers which are being sold commercially. The long instruments on the top have mercury manometers; the center four use Bourdon vacuum gauges; and the two on the bottom employ closed-arm manometers to indicate suction.

will be introduced as the use of tensiometers becomes more widespread and as they are adapted to a wider range of crop and soil conditions. With one exception, the models shown in Fig. 9–2 are for a 30-cm. depth of installation. The gauge-type instruments shown may be set at a more shallow depth by inserting them into the soil at an angle. Instruments for various depths are available on specification.

The following list of suppliers of tensiometers does not include possible sources in eastern United States or from outside the United States: Irrigation Engineering Corp., 335 Genoa St., Monrovia, Calif.; Irrometer Company (Formerly T. W. Prosser Co.), P. O. Box 2424, Riverside, Calif.; Lark Instruments, P. O. Box 424, Riverside, Calif.; L. A. Pennington, 2012 Main Street, Santa Monica, Calif.; Randolph Matson, 1954 Camino Loma Verde, Vista, Calif.; Soilmoisture Equipment Co., 3005 De La Vina, Santa Barbara, Calif.; and Perma-Rain Irrigation Systems, P. O. Box 880, Lindsay, Calif.

To perform satisfactorily, a tensiometer must fulfill certain requirements. The materials used for construction should be durable under a wide range of out-of-door conditions. All joints and materials, except the ceramic cup, must be impermeable to both air and water. The ceramic wall of the cup, when thoroughly wetted, must withstand an air pressure in excess of 1 bar (15 pounds per square inch) without bubbles showing when the cup is immersed in water. The cup conductance to water should be in excess of 1 ml. per minute when 1 bar of hydraulic pressure is applied across the cup wall. The sensing gauge should require only a small volume displacement. One milliliter per bar change in reading has been found satisfactory for most uses. A smaller displacement may be necessary for studying transient flow conditions.

Even under optimum conditions for operation, there is always a slow diffusion of air into the tensiometer. A transparent air trap is usually provided, so that the volume of air within the tensiometer can be readily observed each time a reading is taken. If the trap shows a volume of air in excess of 2 or 3 ml., the air should be removed by refilling the instrument with water.

To take into account the head of water in the connecting tube from the soil surface down to the depth of the cup, a correction to the zero setting of the scale is made for each depth of installation. The zeroing of a dial gauge, which is often hermetically sealed, cannot be done readily, but the readings can be corrected by subtracting 1 centibar of suction for each 10 cm. of depth. The accuracy of dial gauges usually does not justify applying this correction unless the depth of installation exceeds 50 cm. The zeroing of the scale of the mercury manometer can be carried out by filling the instrument with mercury and water in advance of installation. With the instrument supported in the same orientation that it will have in the field, and with the cup immersed to one-half its depth in a container of water, the position that the mercury level attains in the manometer is then marked as the zero setting for the scale. A scale 68 cm. long will read in centibars when divided into 85 divisions; such a scale is also equivalent to the numbered scale on a dial vacuum gauge which shows a scale of 0 to 100.

9–3.2 Testing and Installation

Prior to installation, each tensiometer should be tested. Add mercury to the mercury well, in the case of the manometer-type instrument, and then fill the instrument with water. Use a rubber bulb to apply pressure, so that water is forced through the manometer tubing until all bubbles are swept from the tube. The water added normally contains dissolved air, which can be removed by applying a vacuum to the system. With the instrument reading held at 80 to 85 by a vacuum pump, very fine bubbles of air will rise into the trap. Refilling the air trap with water and applying the vacuum several times will gradually exhaust this air. It will also de-air the ceramic cup wall and ensure that the sensing element in the dial gauge is filled with water. When the system is full of water, close the opening, and allow water to evaporate from the ceramic cup wall. After several hours, the evaporation will result in a reading of 70 or more. If very little air has accumulated in the air trap, this is evidence of no leaks.

While the instrument shows a reading of 70 or higher, submerge the ceramic cup in water. The reading should respond downward within a few seconds and should approach zero reading within 3 to 5 minutes. This test assures that the cup conductance is adequate. Occasionally, a dial gauge will not return to zero with the cup submerged in water. If the reading is not zero after applying the indicated correction for the water head in the connecting tube, the gauge is faulty and should be recalibrated or replaced.

For field installation, a hole is made in the soil using a thin-walled metal tube of the same outside diameter as the cup. Where the soil is hard or contains stones, a solid iron pin may be driven to the depth of installation. Before inserting the tensiometer, a small handful of loose friable soil is dropped into the hole; and, unless the soil is one that puddles easily, a small amount of water is poured into the hole. Then the tensiometer cup is firmed into the bottom of the hole with a firm twisting downward motion applied to the connecting tube.

Successful installations have been made in soils having many large stones which make it difficult to drive a tube or pin. A hole is excavated with a trenching spade by removing stones as needed to attain the desired depth. The cup is placed in firm contact with a side of the hole where no stones are observed, and the initial backfill to cover the depth of the cup is made with soil from which the stones are screened. The remaining hole is refilled with the material excavated.

Innovations in materials and design are continually improving the quality and reliability of tensiometers. When placed in the field, however, tensiometers usually require some degree of protection against damage by traffic or by animals. Tensiometers must be insulated against frost damage or removed from the field in advance of freezing temperatures.

Some degree of care and attention is required to maintain tensiometers. Periodic checking and refilling with water are necessary, and occasional tests should be made to assure that the gauge is accurate and that the cup conductance is within the recommended range of values.

Further details of tensiometer measurements and historical references are given by L. A. Richards (1949).

9–3.3 Comments

Before planning to use tensiometers, it should be recognized that there are two types of information relating to the study of soil water. For many engineering investigations, the water content of a soil is needed and is obtained by gravimetric sampling or by use of neutron-moderating equipment, which responds to the volume fraction of water in the soil. For other purposes, the evaluation of the energy status of soil water (soil suction) is important. Whichever type of information is desired, a procedure should be used to evaluate that property directly. To measure soil suction and obtain water content from calibration curves on typical soil samples, or vice versa, has been shown to be an unreliable procedure (Stolzy et al., 1959).

The use of soil suction as an index for evaluating soil-water relations recognizes that the soil water is a dynamic system. Water moves into and through the soil because of energy differences within the system. Tensiometer readings at various locations in a soil may be used to evaluate the direction and intensity of the water-moving factors. To evaluate the combined effects of gravity and suction gradients, a theory involving either potential functions or hydraulic gradients must be applied. The latter is more often used, and a method for computing the hydraulic gradient will be given in a later section. Water movement from the soil into the plant roots is also a flow process. The energy status of the water in the root zone of plants is one of the important factors which determines water availability to plants. Other factors such as water retention and conductivity of soils are not readily evaluated *in situ*.

9–4   APPLICATIONS

9–4.1   Rooting Zone and Soil Properties

Depth of rooting and soil profile characteristics are important subjects for investigation. Installing tensiometers at several depths and following the readings as they change with time provides useful information. If the soil is relatively uniform with depth, then the rate of increase in soil suction at any given depth can be related to the density of the active roots. Where profile differentiation occurs, the depths of installation should be chosen to correspond with the natural horizons. Relative root action in the various horizons is indicated by the relative changes in the instruments.

The rate of change of soil suction with time under field conditions is influenced by climatic factors, by the species and vigor of the crop involved, and by the water retention of the soil. If tensiometer stations are placed at several locations in a field where climatic and plant factors can be assumed to be uniform, then the relative rates of change of the soil suction readings are a good evaluation of the retention properties of the soil at each location. Where irrigation management can be adapted to local conditions by irrigating according to suction records, the characteristics of the soil are taken into account better than if they were measured explicitly.

9–4.2   Field Irrigation Based on Tensiometers

The use of tensiometers for guiding irrigation practice has been proposed by Richards and Marsh (1961). Briefly stated, it is considered time to irrigate when tensiometer readings reach a prescribed value for a soil depth where feeder root concentration is greatest. The duration of an irrigation is judged by instruments reading soil suction at a second or greater depth. If readings at this second depth are low, an irrigation of short duration is indicated; conversely, if they are high, irrigation water should be allowed to run until the readings following the irrigation respond downward. When such a program is carried out, irrigation is adapted to soil, climate, and crop requirements.

More research is needed before suction values for timing irrigations can be specified for each combination of conditions under the wide ranges in crops, soils, and climates, but considerable progress has been achieved in guiding irrigation under a number of commercial practices. Crops such as citrus, avocado, strawberries, celery, and tomatoes have shown favorable production when irrigation programs have maintained soil suction within the range measured with tensiometers.

In connection with the teaching program of the Agricultural Extension Service in California, it has been found that many growers have been induced to modify their irrigation programs after their former practices had been evaluated using tensiometers.

9-4.3 Irrigation of Potted Plants and Greenhouse Beds

The use of tensiometers for the irrigation of container-grown plants and greenhouse beds is not greatly different from their use under field conditions. The soil depth is usually shallow, and so the second depth of installation is not used. Irrigations are applied when readings reach a prescribed value. When sufficient water is applied to achieve some outflow of water from the container or bed, readings on a tensiometer fall to zero. When an amount of water less than that needed to produce outflow is added, instrument readings will respond downward, but usually will not go to zero. By adjusting the volume of applied water per irrigation, an irrigation program can be carried out such that soil suction values are maintained between an upper and a lower bound. A useful and concise designation of an irrigation practice is achieved by specifying these boundary values which are maintained by the irrigation program.

9-4.4 Water-Table Designation Using Tensiometers

For water-table measurements, the scale of a mercury manometer tensiometer must be carefully zeroed by the method described in section 9-3.2, and the scale above and below the zero mark must also be calibrated to read in millibars. When a reading on such a tensiometer in the field is below zero, this is evidence that a water table occurs above the depth of the cup. The negative reading in millibars is equivalent to the distance in centimeters from the water table to the cup depth.

Conventionally, a piezometer tube is used for establishing the location of a water table. A tensiometer may have greater usefulness in dealing with a fluctuating water table. To be useful, a piezometer tube must extend below the depth of the water table. A tensiometer cup may be installed at any depth in a soil profile. When the water table is above this depth of installation, a negative suction or positive pressure head is indicated. When the water table falls below this depth, readings on the instrument will rise above zero, and water under suction will be indicated. In reporting one of the earliest field installations of tensiometers, Richards and Lamb (1937) indicated that tensiometers showed the occurrence of a temporary or perched water table.

9–4.5 Hydraulic Gradient Measurements

In arid-zone agriculture, irrigation usually is practiced not only to provide a favorable water environment for crop roots, but also to leach excess salts from the root zone. Water flow through a profile is not easily measured, but useful information may be deduced from measurements of the hydraulic gradient as described by L. A. Richards (1955). For this purpose, tensiometer installations for several depths must be made. Where $S_1, S_2, S_3, \ldots$ are the soil suction values in millibars at depths $d_1, d_2, d_3,$ $\ldots$ measured in centimeters, the average hydraulic gradient between depths d_n and d_{n+1} is given by

$$i = [(S_{n+1} + d_{n+1}) - (S_n + d_n)]/(d_{n+1} - d_n).$$

Under these conditions, suction in millibars is equivalent to suction head expressed in centimeters of water, and $(S_n + d_n)$ is the hydraulic head at depth d_n with respect to the soil surface. Under the conventions assumed for these calculations, hydraulic head is positive when measured downward from the soil surface, and when values of i are positive, the flow is downward. Conversely when i is negative, the flow is upward. These calculations are valid even when a water table is involved, provided that readings of S below zero on the tensiometer are substituted as negative values in the equation for hydraulic gradient.

While it is recognized that evaluations of the water conductivity k for field soils are not sufficiently precise to estimate the flow v from the equation $v = ki$, it appears that when soils are such that leaching is difficult to carry out, irrigation management, in order to maintain a downward hydraulic gradient for long time intervals, goes as far as any means now available for managing a leaching program while crops occupy the land.

The foregoing assumes that hydraulic gradients and flow are vertical—upward or downward. Where the flow pattern is not known, as for example in the case of furrow irrigation, then numerous tensiometers are needed to measure hydraulic head values on a grid pattern over a surface at right angles to the furrow. From hydraulic head values over such a grid, by interpolating between points on the grid, lines of equal hydraulic head may be constructed and a set of orthogonal flow lines established. The approximate value of i along any flow line is given by the difference in hydraulic head at two points on a given line divided by the distance between the points.

9–5 LITERATURE CITED

Buckingham, E. 1907. Studies on the movement of soil moisture. U. S. Dept. Agr. Bur. Soils Bull. 38.

Gardner, W., Israelsen, O. W., Edlefsen, N. E., and Clyde, D. 1922. The capillary potential function and its relation to irrigation practice. Phys. Rev. 20:196. (Abstract)

Haise, H. R., and Kelley, O. J. 1950. Cause of diurnal fluctuations in tensiometers. Soil Sci. 70:301–313.

Heck, A. F. 1934. A soil hygrometer for irrigated cane lands of Hawaii. J. Am. Soc. Agron. 26:274–278.

Leonard, R. A., and Low, P. F. 1962. A self-adjusting, null-point tensiometer. Soil Sci. Soc. Am. Proc. 26:123–125.

Marshall, T. J. 1959. Relations between water and soil. Commonwealth Bur. Soils, Tech. Commun. No. 50.

Miller, R. D. 1951. A technique for measuring tensions in rapidly changing systems. Soil Sci. 72:291–301.

Richards, L. A. 1928. The usefulness of capillary potential to soil moisture and plant investigators. J. Agr. Res. 37:719–742.

Richards, L. A. 1949. Methods of measuring soil moisture tension. Soil Sci. 68:95–112.

Richards, L. A. 1955. Retention and transmission of water in soil. U. S. Dept. Agr. Yearbook Agr. 1955:144–151.

Richards, L. A., and Neal, O. R. 1937. Some field observations with tensiometers. Soil Sci. Soc. Am. Proc. (1936) 1:71–91.

Richards, S. J., and Lamb, J., Jr. 1937. Field measurements of capillary tension. J. Am. Soc. Agron. 29:772–780.

Richards, S. J., and Marsh, A. W. 1961. Irrigation based on soil suction measurements. Soil Sci. Soc. Am. Proc. 25:65–69.

Rogers, W. S. 1935. A soil moisture meter depending on the capillary pull of the soil. J. Agr. Sci. 25:326–343.

Russell, Sir E. John. 1950. Soil Conditions and Plant Growth. Longmans, Green and Co., London.

Stolzy, L. H., Weeks, L. V., Szuszkiewicz, T. E., and Cahoon, G. A. 1959. Use of neutron equipment for estimating soil suction. Soil Sci. 88:313–316.

Taylor, S. A., Evans, D. D., and Kemper, W. D. 1961. Evaluating soil water. Utah Agr. Exp. Sta. Bull. 426:1–67.

10 Heat of Immersion

D. M. ANDERSON

*U. S. Army Cold Regions Research & Engineering Lab.
Hanover, New Hampshire*

10–1 INTRODUCTION

Measurement of the heat of wetting (immersion) was first applied to the study of soils by Mitscherlich (1899), who apparently hoped by this means to characterize the colloidal fraction. Janert (1934) later offered an improved apparatus and procedure, and contributed a number of measurements. Since that time many others have measured heats of wetting of soils and soil constituents, but the characterization of soils on this basis has not been widely adopted, principally because it offers no clear-cut advantage over other more firmly established criteria.

In contrast with other fields in which calorimetry has been fruitful, the necessary supplemental and complementary work has not been advanced sufficiently in soil science to permit realization of the full potential of calorimetric studies of soils. This situation is changing rapidly, however. Among the areas where the determination of heats of immersion may be expected to be particularly revealing are in studies of the following: the energetics of ion-exchange phenomena, thermodynamics of soil-water systems, wettability and surface reactivity of soils, energetics of soil-water-air interfaces, and the polarizability and topography of surface-active sites of the individual soil constituents. This is in addition to the tabulation of the integral and differential heats of immersion of various soils and their constituents.

Since the heat of immersion is only one of several possible calorimetric measurements in the thermochemical study of soils, it is necessary to distinguish among several heat effects. The most common is the integral heat of immersion, more widely known as the heat of wetting. It is simply the heat evolved on immersing a soil, at a known initial water content (usually oven-dry), in a large volume of water. The differential heat of immersion is more useful in the detailed study of surfaces and interfaces than is the integral heat of immersion. The differential heat of immersion is defined as the ratio of the increment of heat evolved ∂q to the increment of water

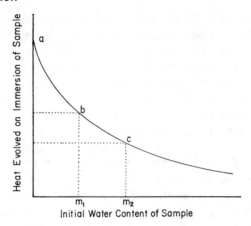

Fig. 10–1. Integral heat of immersion of soil in water as a function of initial water content. The ordinate at *a* gives the heat evolved on immersing and thoroughly dispersing a perfectly dry sample in a large container of water. Points *b* and *c* on the ordinate give the heat evolved when samples having initial water contents m_1 and m_2, respectively, are similarly immersed. The difference in ordinates corresponding to *b* and *c* gives the heat evolved in changing the water content of the soil from m_1 to m_2.

∂m added and uniformly distributed at constant temperature throughout an amount of soil sufficiently large that the added water does not change the soil water content appreciably. This concept is identical with that of partial molar and partial specific quantities developed in chemical thermodynamics. Therefore, the differential heat of immersion may also be called the partial molar or partial specific heat of immersion; it is symbolized by $(\partial q/\partial m)_T$ and is expressed in units of energy per unit mass of water. The physical significance of the differential heat of immersion is best comprehended by studying the diagram in Fig. 10–1. From the definition and the diagram, it is apparent that the differential heat of immersion at any given water content is simply the slope, at that point, of the line resulting from a plot of the integral heat of immersion as a function of the initial water content of the sample. A fuller discussion has been given by Edlefsen and Anderson (1943).

There are two other heat effects analogous to the integral and differential heats of immersion; they are the integral and differential heats of adsorption. In principle, they may be regarded simply as the sum of the heat of condensation and the appropriate heat of immersion (Edlefsen and Anderson, 1943; Brunauer, 1945). The integral heat of adsorption usually is obtained, by means of the Clausius-Clapeyron equation, from adsorption isotherms. When obtained in this way, it is called the isosteric heat of adsorption. In this context, the term isosteric means equal surface coverage and refers to the fact that the isosteric heat of adsorption is evaluated by comparing points at equal amounts of water adsorbed on two isotherms obtained at different temperatures. Several different definitions have been adopted for the differential heat of adsorption, however; and since there is not unanimity on this point, each investigator should give due consideration to possible choices (Brunauer, 1945; Hill, 1948; Adamson, 1960).

Sample preparation is of critical importance in determining the heat of immersion. Attempts to utilize the heat of immersion as a general criterion for characterizing soils have been complicated greatly by this fact. But dependence of heats of immersion on sample condition and preparation should be regarded as a hitherto neglected asset that can be of value in obtaining information more specific than a mere characterization. The heat of immersion evidently is sensitive to, and therefore reveals, properties of the sample which are not as yet understood, or completely interpretable, but may be of considerable importance. Strict attention to the chemical and physical state of the sample, as it is prepared and introduced into the calorimeter, is therefore necessary if the measurement is to be utilized fully. Details of sample preparation must, however, be left to the individual investigator since they depend largely upon the purpose of the investigation.

10–2 PRINCIPLES

Most calorimetric studies require special procedures and techniques determined largely by the purpose of a particular investigation, but three features are common to all. To be meaningful, any thermochemical study must include (1) a determination of an amount of energy, usually but not always inferred from an observed heat effect; (2) a specification of the process to which the energy is attributed; and (3) a determination of the extent of the process associated with the measured energy (Rossini, 1956). In a heat-of-immersion measurement, the energy is determined by inference from the measurement of a heat effect. The second requirement is met by so arranging the experiment that the heat of immersion can be distinguished from any other heat effects present. The last requirement is met by controlling the weight, water content, and the physical and chemical condition of the soil sample before and during the process. In determining the heat of immersion, all this may conveniently be done in a water-filled calorimeter surrounded by a jacket of constant, uniform temperature.

The calorimetric part of the investigation consists of measuring the temperature of the calorimeter and its contents before and after immersing the soil. The amount of electrical energy which, when transformed into heat inside the calorimeter, produces exactly the same temperature change is then determined and is regarded as equivalent to the energy released on immersion of the sample.

The essential parts of the calorimeter are: (1) The calorimeter vessel; (2) a thermometer; (3) an electrical resistance heater; (4) a thermostated surrounding jacket; and (5) a stirrer for the calorimeter contents.

The calorimeter must contain the water in which the soil is immersed; it must provide a means for introducing the sample and, in addition, must thermally insulate its contents. Provision must be made for stirring the contents to ensure thorough dispersion and wetting of the sample and to maintain a uniform temperature distribution. And last, means must be provided for the determination of an energy input by electrical resistance heating to determine the "energy equivalent" of the calorimeter. A widemouth, silvered Dewar flask has been found satisfactorily adaptable as a calorimeter vessel in fulfilling all these requirements.

The thermometer must be sensitive and stable. The development of thermistors has recently led to their use as calorimeter thermometers, since they possess the required sensitivity and have been proven to be sufficiently stable for this purpose. As a result, thermistor thermometers may in time replace the conventional thermopile and resistance thermometers in most ordinary calorimeters.

The energy equivalent of the calorimeter may be determined by passing an electrical current through a small coil of constantan, manganin, or other resistance wire having a low temperature coefficient and suitable diameter and length. The resistance of this coil must be accurately known. Then when an accurately known, constant potential drop is maintained across the coil for an accurately measured interval of time, the energy input, E, is given by

$$E = V^2t/R \qquad [1]$$

where V is the electric potential drop across the heater coil, R is the resistance of the heater coil, and t is the time interval during which the potential is maintained across the heater.

The calorimeter vessel should be surrounded by a thermostated fluid, so that all thermal leaks in the calorimeter can be reliably controlled. Immersion of the calorimeter and attendant apparatus in a water bath often has been employed with success but with considerable inconvenience. A satisfactory thermostated air-bath is almost as easy to assemble and is certainly to be preferred because of the convenience afforded.

The calorimeter contents must be stirred to effect rapid and complete wetting of the sample and to ensure a uniform temperature throughout. Stirring, however, unavoidably introduces energy into the calorimeter that must be accounted for. The best stirring device, therefore, will efficiently mix the calorimeter contents with the least uncertainty in energy input. A three- or four-bladed screw propeller turning inside a tube mounted vertically in the calorimeter vessel is a good stirring device (White, 1928). The tube length and diameter should be adjusted to provide the most effective stirring, and the propeller should be powered by a constant-speed motor external to the calorimeter.

The calorimeter gains heat because of stirring and will either gain or lose heat, as the case may be, because of thermal leaks. For this reason a correction usually must be made to the temperature rises accompanying both the heat of immersion and the input of electrical energy used to calibrate the calorimeter. The corrected temperature rise may be obtained either graphically or analytically. Most soil scientists, in determining heats of immersion, seem to have preferred to obtain it graphically from a plot of the temperature-time data. The plot consists of an initial portion and a final portion, during which the rate of temperature change is nearly constant, separated by the portion during which the heat of immersion is evolved. Lines extending the initial and final portions of the curve may be drawn, and the vertical distance separating them may be measured at a point on the abscissa judged to yield the best estimate for the corrected temperature rise. Usually the point chosen is where the calorimeter temperature has reached about two-thirds of the temperature change attributable to the heat of immersion. This method of correcting for extraneous heat effects often may be judged to be adequate, but for the most accurate determinations an analytical method of correction is to be preferred. Obtaining the corrected temperature rise analytically and formally not only is more accurate, but serves also to accent the operational features of each individual calorimetric study and, therefore, forces a consideration of possible errors which might otherwise be overlooked.

Figures 10–2 and 10–3 show two typical temperature-time plots of data obtained on immersion of a clay. They help clarify a discussion of the corrections for the heat of stirring and thermal leakage referred to in section 10–3.2. In both figures the symbols have identical meanings; θ_i and θ_f are the temperatures of the calorimeter contents when the sample is immersed and when all the heat of immersion has been evolved, respectively. θ_j is the temperature of the thermostated enclosure containing the calorimeter, and θ_∞ is the temperature the calorimeter contents would eventually reach if stirring were continued indefinitely and all other conditions were kept constant. The plots are conveniently divided into three portions. Portions ab and cd are characterized by a rate of temperature change that is nearly constant. During the intervening period, bc, when the heat of immersion is being evolved, θ is seen to be a more complicated function of time. In Fig. 10–2, because the determination was begun at a temperature sufficiently lower than θ_∞, it is seen that during all three periods the calorimeter was heating. In Fig. 10–3, however, the temperature at the beginning of the determination was slightly above θ_∞, so that during periods ab and cd the calorimeter was cooling and only during a part of period bc was it heating. In the discussions that follow, one should keep in mind that it is usually convenient to express temperature in terms of an increase or de-

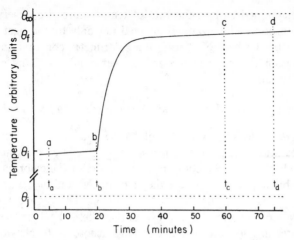

Fig. 10–2. A typical temperature-time curve for the heat of immersion of a clay soil. In this case, the soil sample was immersed at a temperature θ_i which is below θ_∞, the temperature which the calorimeter contents would reach in infinite time if stirring and all other conditions were kept constant; θ_f, the temperature after evolution of the heat of immersion, was also lower than θ_∞.

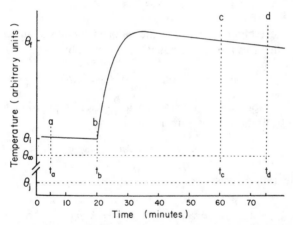

Fig. 10–3. A typical temperature-time curve for the heat of immersion of a clay soil. In this case, the soil was immersed at a temperature θ_i which was higher than θ_∞, the temperature which the calorimeter contents would reach in infinite time if stirring and all other conditions were kept constant. θ_f, the temperature after evolution of the heat of immersion, was higher than θ_∞.

crease in thermistor resistance or out-of-balance bridge voltage. And, since the calorimeter energy-equivalent is determined under conditions as nearly identical as possible to those existing when the heat of immersion is determined and in identical terms, conversion of the data to temperatures in degrees is not necessary.

As was mentioned earlier, the rate of temperature rise observed during the immersion of a soil in water is affected not only by the heat of immersion but also by the heat of stirring the calorimeter contents and the heat transfer between the calorimeter and its surroundings. This can be expressed mathematically as

$$d\theta_{\mathrm{obs}}/dt = u + k(\theta_j - \theta) + (d\theta_{\mathrm{imm}}/dt) \qquad [2]$$

where $d\theta_{\mathrm{obs}}/dt$ is the observed rate of temperature rise, u is the constant rate of temperature rise from the heat of stirring, k is a constant called the "leakage modulus," θ_j is the constant temperature of the calorimeter jacket, θ is the variable temperature inside the calorimeter, and $d\theta_{\mathrm{imm}}/dt$ is the rate of temperature rise from the heat of immersion. The second term on the right-hand side of equation [2] represents the rate of heat transfer between the calorimeter interior and its surroundings according to Newton's law of cooling. This term is positive or negative, depending upon whether heat is transferred into or out of the calorimeter.

When an "infinite" amount of time has elapsed after a heat-of-immersion measurement, it is to be expected that

$$u = k(\theta_\infty - \theta_j) \qquad [3]$$

where θ_∞ is the temperature inside the calorimeter after "infinite" elapsed time. Substituting this result into equation [2], one obtains

$$d\theta_{\mathrm{obs}}/dt = k(\theta_\infty - \theta) + (d\theta_{\mathrm{imm}}/dt) . \qquad [4]$$

The above equation can be rearranged to give an expression for the temperature rise from the heat of immersion:

$$d\theta_{\mathrm{imm}} = d\theta_{\mathrm{obs}} + k\theta \, dt - k\theta_\infty \, dt \qquad [5]$$

which on integration gives

$$\Delta\theta_{\mathrm{imm}} = \Delta\theta_{\mathrm{obs}} + k \int_{t_b}^{t_c} \theta \, dt - k\theta_\infty(t_c - t_b) \qquad [6]$$

where t_b and t_c are, respectively, the time when the heat-of-immersion measurement begins and when it ends, giving an observed temperature rise $\Delta\theta_{\mathrm{obs}}$. The integral term in equation [6] usually cannot be evaluated analytically, but must be evaluated by graphically integrating the observed heat-of-immersion curve.

An expression for k, the leakage modulus, may be derived by considering the heat-balance equation [4] before the heat-of-immersion measurement is made:

$$d\theta_{\mathrm{obs}}/dt = k(\theta_\infty - \theta) . \qquad [7]$$

The solution of this differential equation is

$$\ln\left[(\theta_\infty - \theta)/(\theta_\infty - \theta_i)\right] = -kt \tag{8}$$

where θ equals θ_i when t equals zero. Since this equation is linear in t, a plot of the left-hand side against time enables one to calculate k.

Each determination of the heat of immersion should be accompanied by a measurement of the energy equivalent of the calorimeter found by introducing a known amount of heat into the calorimeter by an electrical resistance heater and observing the resultant temperature rise. The corrected temperature rise for this determination is calculated by means of an equation exactly like equation [6] and then is divided into the electrical input to get the energy equivalent of the calorimeter. All the information required is now obtainable and may be introduced into the relation

$$Q_{\mathrm{imm}} = \Delta\theta_{\mathrm{imm}}(Q_E/\Delta\theta_E) \tag{9}$$

to actually compute the heat of immersion Q_{imm} for a particular sample. In equation [9] $\Delta\theta_E$ is the corrected temperature rise corresponding to a measured input of electrical energy, Q_E.

To obtain and evaluate equation [6], it was first necessary to regard the rate of temperature change due to thermal leaks as a linear function of the calorimeter temperature. Each experimenter is obliged to verify the validity of this assumption for his calorimeter whenever this method of correction is used; it will usually be found valid over the very small temperature range normally encountered, provided the heat of stirring is kept constant. Perhaps the best way to determine the extent to which a given stirring arrangement meets this requirement is, first, to check the constancy of the stirring speed. But, because of the change in viscosity of the calorimeter liquid on immersing the sample, and because of the numerous collisions between the propeller of the stirrer and large soil particles and glass from the broken sample vial, a constant rate of stirring may not result in a sufficiently constant heat of stirring during the determination. Therefore, it may be deemed desirable in some instances to try to evaluate the extent to which the heat of stirring is changed on immersion of the sample. Perhaps a good way to assess it is to make several determinations in which k and θ_∞ are carefully measured both before and after the heat of immersion is obtained. The difference in k and θ_∞ before and after immersing the sample, in conjunction with equation [3], will provide a means of evaluating the change in the heat of stirring occurring during the determination. If an appreciable difference is found, a method of correcting for it should be sought or else the sample size, etc., should be adjusted so that the difference is reduced to the point that it may be neglected.

10–3   METHOD [1]

10–3.1   Special Apparatus

10–3.1.1   CALORIMETER

A relatively simple and inexpensive calorimeter adequate for measuring heats of immersion of soils and soil constituents is shown in Fig. 10–4. It consists of a wide-mouth, 500-ml., silvered Dewar flask. A cover cut from a machinable plastic such as melamine, bakelite, or Plexiglass is provided to prevent evaporation of the calorimeter contents. A ring cut from the same material can be cemented to the Dewar flask to provide a means of fastening on the cover with bolts or screws. A good adhesive for this purpose is one of the epoxy adhesives, for example, one of the Armstrong series (sold by Armstrong Products Company, Warsaw, Ind.). It should be applied so that there are only three or four points of contact between ring and flask; otherwise excessive strains may develop during the curing of the adhesive that would result in an easily broken calorimeter. An "O"-ring groove should be cut in the cover to coincide with the lip of the flask to provide a means of ensuring a vapor-proof calorimeter cover.

The cover should contain openings and be provided with fittings to accommodate the stirring shaft, the sample holder supports, a sample-breaking rod, the heater, and the thermistor leads. The stirring shaft may be made of bakelite, fiberglas, or some other poorly conducting, machinable material that is, at the same time, rigid and strong. A stirrer tube made from thin copper or stainless steel tubing can be supported from the calorimeter cover by the two brass rods shown in Fig. 10–4. If the stirrer tube is fastened to the rods by an epoxy resin or some other suitable nonconducting substance in such a way that no electrical connection exists between them, the two brass rods can also serve as electrical leads to the resistance heater. The stirrer tube should have a diameter of about 3 cm. and a length of about 5 cm. For a tube of this size, a three-bladed propeller 1.8 to 2.0 cm. in diameter located near the center of the stirring tube will provide nearly optimum stirring, provided that the water level and position of the stirring tube and propeller are properly adjusted in the calorimeter. This adjustment is best made by trial until it is satisfactory for the particular Dewar flask used.

The stirrer shaft must be brought through the calorimeter cover in such a way that the shaft will turn easily without permitting evaporation of the calorimeter contents. Zettlemoyer et al. (1953) used a vacuum-seal stirrer. Another good solution offered by White (1928) consists of an oil seal

---

[1] This procedure is patterned after that of Zettlemoyer et al. (1953), although it corresponds in most respects to that of many other investigators before and since. It has been modified on the basis of the author's experience to fit what he judges to be the general circumstances of soils laboratories where this measurement might be utilized.

made by an upside-down cup soldered or glued to the shaft; the upside-down cup is positioned so that it rotates in an oil-filled, circular moat in the calorimeter cover. Figure 10–4 shows another arrangement that has proved satisfactory. The two bearings[2] are press-fitted or glued into the housing and to the stirrer shaft. The stirrer shaft may be connected to a constant-speed motor either directly or by a belt or pulley. A direct coupling, consisting of a short length of thick-walled, rubber tubing having an inside diameter slightly smaller than both the motor and the stirrer shafts, has proved satisfactory; it permits mounting the motor outside the thermo-stated enclosure housing the calorimeter, and it can be connected easily and simply.

Electrical connections can be made in many ways. A good method is to drill the necessary holes in the cover, to pass the leads through, and to seal them in the cover with epoxy resin. Of course, sealing glands, plugs, and other devices may be used but with hardly any advantage. Both

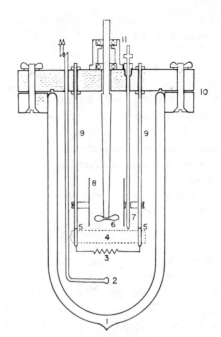

Fig. 10–4. Calorimeter consisting of
1. 500-ml., silvered Dewar flask.
2. Thermistor thermometer.
3. Resistance-wire heater.
4. Glass sample vial.
5. Sample vial holders.
6. Stirrer.
7. Sample-breaker rod.
8. Stirrer tube, fastened by two insulated "ears" to sample-holder supports.
9. Supports for sample holder and electrical conductors for the resistance heater.
10. Plexiglass top.
11. Bearing assembly for stirrer.

thermistor and resistance heater should be located near the bottom of the propeller tube and positioned securely. This, too, may be accomplished in various ways. The brass rods which support the stirring tube may be used to position the thermistor and also may be used as leads and supports for the heater. A clamping device to secure the glass sample vial at each end may also be attached to these rods as shown in Fig. 10–4. A third rod is brought into the calorimeter through a packing gland positioned so that by dropping or tapping it sharply it can be used to break the glass vial

---

[2] Two FaFrir FS160B-C1-Sw ball bearings carefully cleaned and reoiled with a light, varnish-free oil have proved satisfactory.

containing the sample. Provision should be made to limit its excursion, so that no danger to the calorimeter will exist.

The heater may be made by first wrapping bare resistance wire of about 24 gauge around a glass tube 10 to 12 mm. in diameter, heating it to incandescence to anneal it by passing an electric current through it while it is still tightly wrapped around the tube, and then cutting it to a length which will have a resistance of about 10 ohms, after which it may be connected to the brass rods, previously referred to, with solder or screws. It should be positioned so that it does not interfere with the sample breaking rod and so that relatively little abrasion from soil and broken glass will occur.

The thermistor which is to serve as an electrical thermometer may be any one of a large variety now on the market. Because such a large choice is possible and since final performance is the best indication of a good choice, only the essential requirements will be mentioned here. The thermistor should have a high temperature coefficient in the $10°$ to $50°C$. range for maximum sensitivity. It should be small in size to keep its thermal lag low; it and its leads should be well insulated; and it should be stable and dependable. Finally, the resistance of the thermistor at its normal operating temperature should be chosen to fit the resistance bridge or potentiometer to be used in conjunction with it. Resistance ranging from 100 ohms to about 50,000 ohms may be appropriate for various situations, so that a considerable latitude of choice exists. Thermistors sealed in plastic may be satisfactory but have not yet been tested sufficiently to be recommended. Those hermetically sealed in glass or metal are, therefore, to be preferred. It is now possible to buy thermistor assemblies which consist of a thermistor sealed in a tiny metal probe with its insulated leads brought out through a packing gland.[3] An assembly such as this offers a convenient means of positioning and housing the thermistor.

10–3.1.2 AUXILIARY ELECTRICAL DEVICES

The precision and sensitivity of the calorimeter depend to a great extent on the instrument used to measure the change in resistance of the thermistor; the highest sensitivity, therefore, will be achieved with a resistance bridge of high sensitivity. A Mueller bridge capable of detecting 0.0001-ohm resistance change was used by Zettlemoyer et al. (1953), and they reported being able to detect temperature changes of $0.00002°C$. reliably. An ordinary potentiometer with a good galvanometer or one of the electronic null-point indicators (such as the Hewlett-Packard Model 425A micro-voltmeter) has proved satisfactory in detecting temperature changes of $0.0001°C$. The author uses a Leeds and Northrup Type K-3 Universal

---

[3] Available from Fenwall Electronics, Inc., Framingham, Mass.; Gulton Industries, Inc., Metuchen, New Jersey; Cole-Parmer Instrument and Equipment Co., 224 W. Illinois Street, Chicago 10, Ill.; and many others.

Potentiometer and has obtained a calorimeter sensitivity of about 1 cal. per 1,000.

The resistance heater is also a most vital part of the calorimeter. With it, one determines the absolute amount of heat energy corresponding to a measured temperature rise. This quantity of heat is calculated from a knowledge of the electrical current passed through the heater, the electrical potential drop across that portion of the heater circuit inside the calorimeter, and the length of time this potential is applied. All these must therefore be measured accurately.

A suitable circuit for supplying and measuring electrical energy added to the calorimeter and its contents is shown in Fig. 10–5.[4] It consists of a standard resistor, a voltage divider, two double-pole, double-throw switches, a ballast resistor, a storage battery, and a potentiometer with standard cell. Current from the storage battery flows through the ballast resistor, R_1, or the heater, R_2, depending upon the position of switch A. The resistance of R_1 should be made as nearly equal to that of R_2 as possible, so that the current drawn from the storage battery will be nearly the same when switch A is in either position. The ballast resistor is provided to stabilize the storage battery output by allowing current to be drawn from the storage battery for an hour or so before switching to the heater. In utilizing the circuit shown in Fig. 10–5, V_2, the potential drop across the calorimeter heater, is compared to V_3, the potential drop across the standard resistor R_3. The electrical power input to the calorimeter is then V_2V_3/R_3. To facilitate making alternate measurements of V_2 and V_3, the voltage-divider ratio and the resistances of the heater coil and the standard resistor should be adjusted so that the potentiometer reading is nearly the same in each case. Otherwise, to make the measurements as rapidly as is required, it may be necessary to employ two potentiometers.

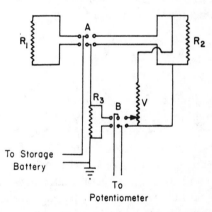

Fig. 10–5. Circuit for determining the electrical energy equivalent of the calorimeter. The circuit elements are: R_1, ballast resistor; R_2, calorimeter heater; R_3, standard resistor; V, voltage divider; A and B, double-pole, double-throw switches.

When the investigation warrants it, the electrical power source may be arranged to minimize the effect of the rapid change in the heater resistance at the beginning of the heating period; a method has been suggested by

---

[4] This circuit is shown and discussed by J. Coops et al. (1956, pp. 48–49). A similar one is given by White (1928, p. 135).

Skinner et al. (1962, pp. 211–214). Care should be taken in wiring the circuit to ensure that the leads from the heater are in intimate thermal contact with the calorimeter and its thermostated surroundings. Whenever possible, wires should be arranged so as to reduce heat flux by conduction. In some applications, simpler, less sensitive circuits and procedures may be more appropriate; this the experimenter should determine himself.

The measurement of time during calibration of the calorimeter may be accomplished satisfactorily with a stopwatch and manual operation of the heater switch. If one aims for an accuracy of better than 1 part in 1,000, however, it becomes necessary to use some means of coupling between switch and timer. Skinner describes one way in which this may be done and refers to other methods (Skinner et al., 1962, p. 181).

10–3.1.3 THERMOSTATED ENCLOSURE

A satisfactory constant-temperature air bath can be constructed easily from a sensitive mercury thermoregulator and matching relay,[5] a 10- to 50-watt resistance-wire heater, a small fan, and a wooden box lined with alternating layers of aluminum foil and Styrofoam. The motor powering the fan is best mounted outside the box with its shaft passing into the box through a small opening or bearing. Temperature control with fluctuations and drift of the order of $\pm 0.01 °C$. is not difficult to achieve.

10–3.2 Procedure

Prepare an accurately weighed, 4- to 5-g. soil sample, and seal it watertight in a glass ampule of a size and shape determined by the construction of the calorimeter. Fasten the filled sample vial into place in the calorimeter beneath the breaker rod. Fill the calorimeter with a measured amount (about 400 cc.) of distilled water at about the temperature that is to be maintained in the thermostated enclosure surrounding the calorimeter. Attach the calorimeter cover, engage the stirrer, connect the electrical leads, mount the assembly in a thermostated enclosure, and begin stirring.

Begin taking readings of the thermistor resistance, noting accurately the time each reading was taken. By means of the electric heater add energy in small increments, raising the calorimeter temperature until the rate of temperature change in the calorimeter is constant and small enough (a few ten-thousandths of a degree centigrade per minute) to permit subsequent correction of the results for the heat of stirring and thermal leakage. Break the sample vial with the breaker rod, and continue recording the thermistor resistance every 10 to 15 seconds. When it becomes evident that the heat of immersion has been evolved completely, introduce an accurately measured

---

[5] For example, one described recently by Anderson and Jones (1961).

amount of electrical energy through the resistance heater; continue recording the thermistor resistance every 10 to 15 seconds until it is evident that the thermistor response to the heat evolved has been complete.

Plot the thermistor resistance versus time on a large sheet of coordinate paper. The plots will have characteristic shapes such as those of Fig. 10–2 and 10–3. From a comparison of the resistance-time data accompanying the sample immersion with that accompanying the input of electrical energy, determine the uncorrected temperature rises resulting from the heat of immersion and the electrical heating. Correct the observed temperature rises for the heat flux due to thermal leakage and the heat of stirring.

When the corrected temperature rise accompanying the input of a measured quantity of electrical energy has been determined, it is referred to as the electrical equivalent of the calorimeter. From the electrical energy equivalent of the calorimeter, and from a knowledge of the weight of the sample immersed, calculate the heat of immersion from equation [9] described in section 10–2. Subtract the temperature rise due to breaking the glass sample vial. (Several blank determinations using a sealed vial containing 4 to 5 g. of large glass beads but otherwise identical with that normally employed will yield a relationship between sample weight and the heat of breaking from which an acceptable correction for each determination can be obtained.) Express the results as calories per gram of sample (dry-weight basis). In addition, record clearly the initial water content of the sample and other details of its physical and chemical state as well as the temperature of the determination.

10–3.3 Comments

In selecting a calorimeter design, the rate of the process, the size of the anticipated heat effect, the accuracy of the result desired, and whether or not other measurements or operations are to be made must be considered. For soils, one may expect the heat effect to be observed in 2 to 15 minutes after the sample is immersed and to amount to from 2 to 30 cal. per g. of soil. An accuracy of measurement of 1 cal. per 1,000 is more than sufficient for all but the most elaborate and demanding studies.

Neutraglas Ampuls No. 12011-L (Kimball Glass Co., a subsidiary of Owens-Illinois, Toledo 1, Ohio) have been found to be ideal for sample containers. A water-tight seal may be made by fusing the end in a flame.

The amount of water used in the calorimeter is not actually critical, but it should be known and reported since the observed integral heat of immersion depends in part on the final state of dilution of the soil-water system. Whereas the heat evolved on dilution of a soil suspension may be extremely small, it is nonetheless real and in some rare cases may have to be taken into account in comparing data from different investigations.

Stirring at about 3,500 revolutions per minute with a constant-speed motor provides sufficient agitation to break up and uniformly distribute the soil sample on immersion. This is a high stirring rate and produces enough heat in the calorimeter to maintain its temperature several degrees above that of the thermostated enclosure. According to White (1928), a high heat of stirring is very undesirable because it adds considerable uncertainty to the result. Unfortunately, because of the difficulty in thoroughly dispersing some soils, there seems to be no way to avoid a rather high heat of stirring in this determination. The heat of stirring is most conveniently accounted for if it is constant. It is necessary, therefore, that the stirring rate be actually controlled and held constant. When it is possible to reduce the stirring rate, as in the case of easily dispersed soils, this should certainly be done. The heat of immersion usually will be evolved within 2 to 15 minutes after breaking the sample free, depending upon the texture and consistency of the soil, unless the sample is not adequately dispersed by the stirrer.

The temperature of the sample and water must be known at the time the heat of immersion is measured. It may be obtained from the thermistor calibration when the data of the determination are being analyzed. The total temperature rise usually will be only a few hundredths of a degree, and at the most a few tenths of a degree, so that there is no serious problem in assigning a temperature to the process. For a discussion of this point, however, see Rossini (1956, pp. 16–20).

Care should be taken to eliminate all sources of error or uncertainty in determining the exact amount of heat imparted to the calorimeter and its contents. This requires a very careful analysis of the heating and measurement circuit as it actually exists when all connections are finally made. Alternate measurements of the potential drop across the heater and the standard resistor permit calculation and a check, by Ohm's law, of the electrical energy input, provided that all the circuit elements are known. By adjusting the heater current and the heating period, one should try to obtain nearly the same total temperature rise and nearly the same rate of change of temperature as when the heat of immersion was evolved. Errors then tend to become self-compensating.

The temperature rise due to breaking the sample free is an important correction in precision calorimetry. On breaking the vial, the calorimeter liquid does PV work that is converted into heat by the viscous or locally turbulent collapse of liquid into the void space. It has been found (Gunderjahn et al. 1958) that for empty glass and metal bulbs the heat evolved on breaking the bulb varied linearly with the void volume according to the equation

$$H = PV + 0.03 \pm 0.07 \text{ joule.} \tag{10}$$

This result is regarded as justification for the procedure given in the foregoing section. In the more precise investigations this correction should be measured with accuracy for each determination.

In addition to reporting all relevant details of sample preparation and experimental procedure, the accuracy and precision of the results should be estimated. The former must be estimated from the principles of the measurement and the accuracy with which the measurements were made. Investigators are obliged to furnish such an estimate when calorimetric data are reported. The latter may be best expressed by reporting at least (*1*) the number of observations made under supposedly identical circumstances, (*2*) the mean of the observed values, and (*3*) the standard deviation, when the complete data are found to be too bulky for publication (Rossini, 1956).

10-4   LITERATURE CITED

Adamson, A. W. 1960. Physical Chemistry of Surfaces. Interscience Publishers, Inc., New York.

Anderson, D. M., and Jones, R. C. 1961. An inexpensive control circuit for mercury thermoregulators. Soil Sci. Soc. Am. Proc. 25:416–417.

Brunauer, Stephen. 1945. The Adsorption of Gases and Vapors: I. Physical Adsorption. Princeton University Press.

Coops, J., Jessup, R. S., and van Ness, K. 1956. Reactions in a bomb at constant volume. *In* F. D. Rossini, ed. Experimental Thermochemistry, Chapter 3. Interscience Publishers, Inc., New York.

Edlefsen, N. E., and Anderson, A. B. C. 1943. Thermodynamics of soil moisture. Hilgardia 15:31–298.

Guderjahn, C. A., Paynter, D. A., Berghausen, P. E., and Good, R. J. 1958. Heat of bulb breaking in heat of immersion calorimetry. J. Chem. Phys. 28:520–521.

Hill, T. L. 1948. Statistical mechanics of adsorption: V. Thermodynamics and heat of adsorption. J. Chem. Phys. 17:520–535.

Janert, H. 1934. The application of heat of wetting measurements to soil research problems. J. Agr. Sci. 24:136–150.

Mitscherlich, E. A. 1899. Dissertation, Kiel. (Cited by H. Janert. J. Agr. Sci. 24:136.)

Rossini, F. D. 1956. Experimental Thermochemistry. Interscience Publishers, Inc. New York.

Rossini, F. D. 1956. Assignment of uncertainties. *In* F. D. Rossini, ed. Experimental Thermochemistry, Chapt. 4. Interscience Publishers, Inc., New York.

Skinner, H. A., Sturtevant, J. M., and Sunner, S. 1962. The design and operation of reaction calorimeters. *In* H. A. Skinner, ed. Experimental Thermochemistry II, Chapt. 9. Interscience Publishers, Inc., New York.

White, W. P. 1928. The Modern Calorimeter. Am. Chem. Soc. Monograph.

Zettlemoyer, A. C., Young, G. J., Chessick, J. J., and Healey, F. H. 1953. A thermistor calorimeter for heats of wetting: Entropies from heats of wetting and adsorption data. J. Am. Chem. Soc. 57:649–652.

11 | Hydraulic Head

R. C. REEVE

United States Salinity Laboratory
Riverside, California

11–1 INTRODUCTION

"Hydraulic head" is a concept of fluid mechanics that pertains to the energy status of water in water flow systems. It is useful for describing flow not only in conduits and other hydraulic structures, but also in soils and other porous media as well. It is a concept that simplifies the description of some liquid flow phenomena and often is relatively easy to measure. "Hydraulic head" in water flow systems is analogous to "potential" or "voltage" in electrical flow problems and to "temperature" where heat flow is involved. Hydraulic-head measurements are particularly useful in determining the direction of flow of water in soils. Evaluating the space rate of change of hydraulic head is required for applying the Darcy equation for the solution of various flow problems (see sections 13–2 and 16–2). Both the Darcy flow equation and hydraulic head measurements are used extensively in hydrology, hydraulics, irrigation, drainage, and other fields of science where flow of water in the liquid state is involved.

The methods described herein pertain particularly to the measurement of hydraulic head in soils. Methods are described for measuring hydraulic head both above and below a water table. While the interpretation of hydraulic-head readings is much the same for both cases, the equipment and procedures are quite different. In general, the measurement of hydraulic head above a water table, where an equivalent pressure that is less than atmospheric pressure is measured, is more difficult than below a water table where hydrostatic pressure in bulk water is usually involved. Two procedures are described for installing piezometers.

Section 9 should be consulted for directions and information on the use of tensiometers. Soil-suction and hydraulic-head measurements are discussed therein; however, hydraulic-head measurements are treated here in somewhat greater detail. An attempt is made to relate hydraulic-head measurements made with piezometers to those made with tensiometers in order that water flow in a given system involving both saturated and unsaturated flow can be evaluated. The method of installing tensiometers is the same whether suction values are desired or whether hydraulic head is to be measured. The principal difference is in the setting of the scales.

11–2 PRINCIPLES

The defining equation for hydraulic head comes from a consideration of the law of conservation of energy as applied to a liquid system by Bernoulli in 1738. This subject is treated in standard textbooks on fluid mechanics such as Dodge and Thompson (1937).

The Bernoulli equation describes the energy status of a flowing liquid in terms of kinetic, potential, and pressure energies. When the energy is expressed as energy per unit weight of water, it has the physical dimensions of length (L). This length, which is a vertical distance, i.e., parallel to the gravity force field, is termed "head."

For unit weight of water located at a point where the pressure is p, the velocity is v, and the elevation above a reference level is z, the "hydraulic head" h at the point in question in a steady flow system is as follows:

$$h = (v^2/2g) + (p/w) + z \qquad [1]$$

where g = the acceleration due to gravity, and w = specific weight of water $(w = \rho g$, where ρ = density of water). The individual components of the equation are termed "velocity head" $(v^2/2g)$, "pressure head" (p/w) and "position head" (z) representing the kinetic, pressure-potential, and position-potential energies, respectively. For flow of water in soils or other porous media, flow velocities are usually very low; and, for all practical purposes, the velocity head can be neglected. The hydraulic-head equation then becomes

$$h = p/w + z . \qquad [2]$$

The quantities of equation [2] are illustrated in Fig. 11–1 for (A) saturated conditions and (B) unsaturated conditions. Piezometers are used for measuring hydraulic head for the saturated case. The piezometer pipe makes connection with the soil water through the open end of the pipe as shown at point A, Fig. 11–1A. The pressure head is the length of the water column in the pipe above point A and in this case is positive. In accordance with equation [2] the hydraulic head at point A is equal to the sum of the pressure head p_A/w and the position head z_A; or, in other words, it is the height the water level stands in an open pipe above the reference elevation.

For the unsaturated case, a porous membrane, which is usually a ceramic body (Richards, 1942), is required for hydraulic connection between the liquid water in the soil and that in the tensiometer. The negative pressure in the tensiometer is measured with a mercury manometer, or a Bourdon vacuum gauge, or other vacuum-sensing device. The ceramic body or cup is required to restrict the entry of air into the tensiometer, where the pressure in the water is less than atmospheric, and at the same time allow free movement of water to and from the tensiometer to attain hydraulic equilibrium with the soil water. Specifications for ceramic cups and other tensiometer parts, together with procedures for the proper use of tensiometers, are given in section 9.

A reference elevation is required as a base for hydraulic-head measurements in any given flow system. It is convenient to select a reference elevation at some depth below the lowest hydraulic-head value in the system. Mean sea level is often used for this purpose, but any arbitrary reference elevation that is convenient will do. Hydraulic head increases in a positive direction upward from this reference elevation.

Tensiometers have been used for many years to read soil suction. To avoid negative numbers, it has become customary to consider the soil suction as a positive value. This convention is quite satisfactory for many purposes; but, for evaluating the energy status of water in a flow system for the purpose of determining direction of flow and evaluating driving forces or hydraulic gradients in a gravity field, it is necessary to consider this value in relation to the position-potential energy component z_B, which by convention increases in an upward direction opposite to the direction of the gravity force. With z_B positive in an upward direction, the soil suction or pressure head in unsaturated soil is a negative value as is illustrated in

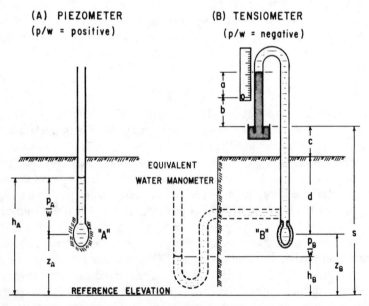

Fig. 11–1. Measurement of hydraulic head with a piezometer (A), and a tensiometer (B).

Fig. 11–1B by the phantom water manometer shown in dashed lines. Note that the water surface in the phantom manometer is below the point of measurement, thus indicating that the equivalent pressure in the soil water is less than atmospheric; i.e. the pressure-head value is negative. The hydraulic head h_B is the algebraic sum of the pressure head p_B/w and the position head z_B in accordance with equation [2].

It is impractical to use a water manometer, such as illustrated in Fig. 11–1B, to measure this negative pressure head because to do so would require that the measurement be made below the soil surface. In practice, a manometer with a fluid of density greater than that of water, such as mercury, is used to measure remotely either the hydraulic head or the negative pressure head at some depth in the soil from a position above the soil surface.

Whether the tensiometer reads the negative pressure-head component or the hydraulic head, depends upon the initial positioning of the tensiometer scale. The scale may be positioned to read zero opposite the mercury level of the manometer when any desired reference pressure or hydraulic head occurs at the cup. To read only the negative pressure-head component, the reference elevation is taken at the center of the cup. For hydraulic-head readings, the scale zero is set to correspond to zero hydraulic head at some convenient elevation, such as the soil surface, and all tensiometers in a given system are zeroed to the same elevation.

If s is the distance from the reference elevation to the surface of the mercury in the mercury reservoir (Fig. 11–1), ρ_m = density of mercury, and ρ_w = density of water, then the height of the scale zero above the mercury surface b is given by the equation

$$b = s(\rho_w)/(\rho_m - \rho_w).$$ [3]

In the derivation of this equation, it is assumed that the mercury level in the mercury pot remains constant. If the surface area of the mercury pot is large compared to the area of the mercury manometer, the correction required because of the change in level of the mercury in the mercury reservoir is small, and for many purposes can be neglected. There is also a depression of the mercury column as a result of surface tension forces in the manometer tube. A correction for this effect may also be made, but it is also negligible for most purposes and is not included in equation [3]. For additional information on this subject, the paper by Richards (1949) may be consulted.

If the reference elevation is to be set at the center of the tensiometer cup, s is taken equal to $(c + d)$, and equation [3] becomes

$$b = (c + d)(\rho_w)/(\rho_m - \rho_w).$$ [4]

When a mercury tensiometer is used to measure hydraulic head, a scale calibrated to read in length units should be specified. The centimeter is the unit most commonly used; however, any desired length unit may be selected. For reading soil suction values, manometer scales are commonly calibrated in millibars (1 bar = 1×10^6 dynes per cm.^{2} = 10^3 millibars). For all practical purposes, the millibar scale may be used as a centimeter scale (1 millibar = 1.0227 cm. of water at 21°C.). When properly zeroed, such a scale may be used to read hydraulic head directly. The ratio of scale length to head is

$$a/h_B = (\rho_w)/(\rho_m - \rho_w) \qquad [5]$$

where a = height of the mercury column above the scale zero (Fig. 11–1B). Thus for a mercury manometer, ρ_m = 13.5 g. per cm.^{3}, ρ_w = 1 g. per cm.^{3}, and a/h_B = 1/12.5.

The working range for tensiometers is from zero to about ⅔ of the negative pressure required for complete vacuum, or from zero to about 700 cm. of water. Since the zero setting of the tensiometer scale (length b, Fig. 11–1B) utilizes a part of the working range of the tensiometer scale, it is desirable to keep b relatively small to maintain the usable scale range as large as possible. For this reason, it is helpful to select a reference elevation that is not far distant from the elevation of the mercury reservoir. The ground surface is often used for this purpose. All tensiometers in a given system should be referenced to the same elevation. Hydraulic-head readings referred to one elevation can be transferred to another reference elevation by adding or subtracting the elevation difference as the case may be.

Tensiometers and piezometers have a response time that is not zero because of the volume of water that must move into or out of the piezometer or tensiometer to register a pressure change that occurs in the soil water. In the case of the tensiometer, this response time depends primarily upon the sensitivity of the manometer, the conductance of the porous cup, and the hydraulic conductivity of the soil in which the tensiometer is placed. For piezometers, the diameter of the pipe, the size and shape of the cavity at the base of the pipe, and the hydraulic conductivity of the soil are the major factors. For static-hydraulic-head conditions in the soil, the time required for the instrument to register the hydraulic pressure of the soil, following a head displacement within the instrument, depends upon this response rate. Where hydraulic head in the soil changes with time, there will be a time-lag in instrument readings which also is related to this response rate, and for which proper correction should be made. It is beyond the scope of this paper to provide the details required for this correction. The aim here is merely to call this source of error to the attention of the reader. Additional information can be obtained on this subject by consulting the papers by Klute and Gardner (1962) for tensiometers, and Hvorslev (1951) for piezometers. Null-type tensiometers that eliminate the response-time problem have been designed and used in special research studies (Miller, 1951; Leonard and Low, 1962).

Piezometers are installed both by driving and jetting. In general, the driving method is limited to relatively shallow depths (up to 25 or 30 feet), whereas piezometers may be jetted to depths of 100 to 150 feet or greater. A qualitative log of subsoil materials penetrated is obtained in the process of jetting piezometers, which is not possible by the driving method. The choice of method of installation will, therefore, depend primarily upon the nature of the problem under study and the information that is desired. The equipment needed and the procedures required are different for these two methods. Therefore, both methods are described in the following sections, and the choice of method is left to the operator. For additional information, the papers by Christiansen (1943), Reeve and Jensen (1949), Reger et al. (1950), Donnan and Bradshaw (1952), U. S. Salinity Laboratory Staff (1954), and Mickelson et al. (1961) should be consulted.

11–3 METHOD OF INSTALLING PIEZOMETERS BY DRIVING

11–3.1 Special Apparatus (Fig. 11–2)

1. Driving hammer, fence-post type.
2. Driving head.
3. Punch-out rod.

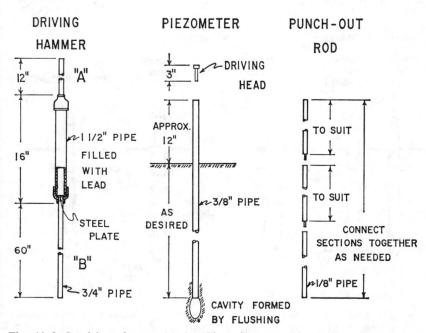

Fig. 11–2. Special equipment for installing piezometers by driving (Christiansen, 1943).

4. Rivets, ⅜-inch diameter by 1-inch length (2 needed per piezometer).
5. Piezometer pipe, black or galvanized iron, ⅜-inch nominal inside diameter, lengths as needed. (The actual inside diameter is slightly greater than ½ inch.)

11–3.2 Procedure

Cut the pipe into desired lengths (10.5-foot lengths are convenient), and mark the pipe in 1-foot intervals. Place a rivet in the lower end of the pipe, and insert the driving head in the upper end. Using the drive hammer first with the long end of the hammer (end *B*, Fig. 11–2) over the piezometer pipe, and lastly with the short end of the hammer over the piezometer pipe (end *A*, Fig. 11–2), drive the pipe to the desired depth in the soil.

11–3.3 Comments

Pipe lengths up to 12 feet can be started easily and driven in the manner described in the procedure. Greater pipe lengths can be started by use of a stepladder. Additional lengths can be added with standard pipe couplings as driving progresses until the pipe reaches the desired depth in the soil.

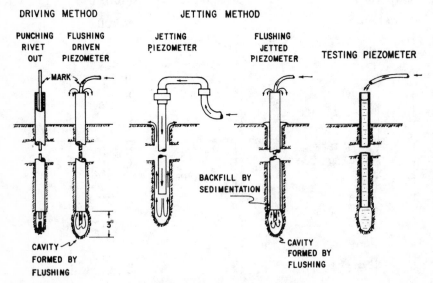

Fig. 11–3. Installing, flushing, and testing piezometers. Piezometers may be installed by driving or by jetting. A cavity is formed at the base of the piezometer by flushing, and the piezometer is tested for responsiveness by filling it with water and observing the rate of recession of the water level.

The pipe should be left extending approximately 1 foot above ground surface. A stake driven alongside the piezometer will serve as a protection against damage and as a location marker. If hydraulic-head readings are desired at several depths at a given location, drive pipes of different lengths into the soil, spacing the pipes laterally, with a separation of about 1 foot or more. It is convenient for recording and interpreting hydraulic-head readings to set the tops of all piezometers at a given location to the same elevation. This can be done with a carpenter's level, or with a transit or surveyor's level. With a transit or surveyor's level, an adhesive marker placed on the upper end of the driving hammer at such a position as to give the desired piezometer elevation is an easy way to set the tops of several piezometers to the same elevation, especially where the piezometers are separated by more than a few feet.

In some soils, the rivet in the end may not be necessary. When a piezometer is driven without a rivet, a soil plug of about 3 to 6 inches in length may lodge in the lower end of the pipe. In many soils, this plug can be flushed out in the flushing operation in less time than is required to punch the rivet out.

11–4 METHOD OF INSTALLING PIEZOMETERS BY JETTING

11–4.1 Special Apparatus

1. Commercial spray rig with tank and high-pressure pump:
   Pressure ≥ 400 psi.
   Tank capacity $= 200$ to 300 gallons.
   Flow capacity $= 5$ to 20 gallons per minute.
2. High-pressure hose, ¾-inch diameter, 25 feet or more, as needed.
3. Swivel joint, ⅜-inch diameter (swivel joint, Style No. 20. Chiksan Company, Brea, Calif.).

11–4.2 Procedure

Connect the upper end of the piezometer pipe to the swivel joint, which in turn is connected to the hose leading from the pump, as shown in Fig. 11–3. If a jetting rig with a frame for hoisting and handling the pipe is used (Reger et al., 1950), read and record the depth of penetration as jetting progresses directly from the adjustable measuring tape that is suspended from the frame alongside the piezometer pipe. If the pipe is installed by hand, mark the pipe at 1-foot intervals before starting, so that depth of penetration can be read directly from the pipe. Start the pump, and direct the jet of water issuing from the lower end of the pipe into the soil. As the pipe penetrates the soil behind the jetting stream, oscillate the pipe up and down a distance of from 1 to 2 feet to assist the pipe in penetrating the soil. Estimate and record the texture and consolidation of the material penetrated as installation progresses.

11–4.3 Comments

The jetting method makes use of the eroding and lubricating properties of a stream of water issuing from the end of the pipe for opening a passage into the soil. The movement of the pipe up and down helps to penetrate resistant materials. Logging of the soil materials penetrated provides helpful information for better understanding of ground-water movement and interpreting hydraulic-head readings. It also helps in the selection of subsequent termination points for additional piezometers.

If the pressure developed by the pump is less than about 200 pounds per square inch, the end of the pipe can become plugged with sediment from the driving action, especially when penetrating clays.

Logging subsurface layers by jetting requires experience that can be gained and checked by jetting in soils for which data on stratigraphy are available from independent logging procedures. An estimate of texture and consolidation of the material is made from (1) the nature of the vibrations transmitted from the material penetrated through the pipe to the hands of the operator, (2) the rate of downward progress, (3) examination of sediments carried by the effluent, and (4) observation of color changes of the effluent.

Return flow may be lost and penetration may stop in permeable sands and gravels. A driller's mud added to the water is effective for maintaining return flow in coarse materials. Approximately 10 pounds of driller's mud per 100 gallons of water has been found suitable for most conditions. It is necessary to add this preparation to the water supply slowly and to agitate it thoroughly as it is added.

Where several hydraulic-head measurements are desired at different depths, the deepest pipe is usually installed first. The log from the first pipe serves for selecting depths at which additional pipes are terminated. It is often desirable to terminate piezometers in sandy lenses to increase the rate at which they respond to hydraulic-head changes in the soil.

The sealing of the soil around the pipe at the base of the piezometer requires careful attention. Jetting should be stopped immediately as each pipe reaches the desired depth, so that excessive washing of material from around the pipe will not occur. The material in suspension settles back around the pipe and usually provides a satisfactory seal. When this precaution is not taken, leakage may occur along the pipe or from one pipe to another, causing invalid readings.

The size of the jetting stream is important. In general, the smallest stream-size that will maintain a return flow of water to the ground surface should be used to conserve water. A flow of 7 gallons per minute (gpm.) has been found to be satisfactory in many soils. Where deep sandy soils are involved, flows up to 20 gpm. have been required. Because the flow capacity must be determined at the outset when the pump is selected, it is important that advance consideration be given to the kind of soils likely to be encountered.

Other pipe sizes may be used quite satisfactorily for piezometers; however, the flow capacities suggested herein are for 3/8-inch pipe. If pipe size is greatly increased, water flow rates must also be increased to give equal jetting velocities. High flow rates also mean that a greater water storage capacity will be required. Pipe sizes smaller than 3/8-inch diameter are not recommended because of inadequate rigidity for driving or jetting, and because the bore is too small for the convenient measurement of water elevations.

11–5 METHOD OF FLUSHING AND TESTING PIEZOMETERS

11–5.1 Special Apparatus

1. Plastic tubing (Saran or nylon), 5/16-inch outside diameter by 1/32-inch wall, 20 feet or more, as needed.
2. Bucket pump, hand operated.

11–5.2 Procedure

After the piezometer is driven or jetted into place and the rivet is punched from the end of the pipe (where a rivet is used), flush the soil material out from the base of the pipe to form a cavity about 3 to 4 inches long, as shown in Fig. 11–3. To do this, push the plastic tubing (which has been previously marked with paint or tape to indicate the pipe length) to the bottom of the pipe, and pump water through the tube. As the flushing proceeds, move the tube up and down to help loosen the soil. Soil material and water will return and overflow the top of the pipe through the annular space between the tubing and pipe. After the cavity at the base of the pipe is formed, test the piezometer for response rate by filling it with water and observing the rate at which the water level drops (see Fig. 11–3). In sands and gravels, the rate of entry of water may be so great that no overflow can be obtained during flushing, whereas, in clays, the rate of drop may be so slow that it is hardly noticeable. If the level of the water in the pipe does not drop, repeat the flushing operation, without unduly extending the plastic tube below the end of the pipe, until the rate of change of the water level in the pipe, after filling, is perceptible. Allow the water level in the piezometer to come to equilibrium with the ground water.

Cap the piezometer to prevent the entry of insects and/or the filling of the piezometer by children or vandals. Attach a standard pipe coupling to the top of the piezometer, and insert a rivet, as shown in Fig. 11–4. Remove the rivet with a magnet to make water-level readings.

11–5.3   Comments

Because of the time lag involved in piezometer measurements, the above test of responsiveness of the piezometer is important. The time required for the water level in the piezometer to come to equilibrium with the ground water, after being displaced, is inversely proportional to the permeability of the soil.

From a practical standpoint, the time-lag difficulty can best be met by terminating piezometers in sandy lenses whenever this is possible, as described under procedure for the jetting method. When this is not practical, the difficulty can sometimes be overcome by enlarging the cavity by flushing. In any event, a measurement of the responsiveness of the piezometer should be made as a basis for interpretation of water-level readings. Because of the sealing and plugging of piezometers that may occur with time, it is good practice to reflush and retest piezometers periodically.

11–6   METHOD OF MEASURING WATER LEVELS IN PIEZOMETERS

11–6.1   Special Apparatus (Fig. 11–4)

1. Bell sounder.
2. Steel measuring tape, ¼-inch wide x 25 feet long.
3. Magnet.

11–6.2   Procedure

Remove the rivet from the top end of the piezometer with the magnet, as shown in Fig. 11–4. Attach the bell sounder to the end of the measuring tape, and lower it into the piezometer pipe. Ascertain the reading on the tape at the top of the piezometer pipe when the bell sounder impacts the water level. The impact is denoted by the sound produced as the "bell" strikes the water. First obtain an approximate reading for the impact point, and then refine the reading by subsequent short vertical strokes of the tape and sounder. Begin the vertical strokes with the bell a short distance above the water surface; and while stroking, gradually lower the bell until contact is made.

11–6.3 Comments

Inasmuch as the commercial steel tape is graduated to begin at zero at the end of the tape, it is necessary to make a correction for the additional length of chain used to attach the bell. It is convenient to use an even 1-foot length, as shown in Fig. 11–4.

Other types of sounders are also satisfactory. An electrical sounder may work well, but it is more complex and subject to difficulties, such as loss of power, shorting, improper contact, and other problems associated with electrical circuits.

The air-tube method is a simple alternative. A length of plastic tubing (Saran or nylon), with length graduations marked on the outside, is inserted and lowered into the piezometer pipe until it contacts the water level. The contact of the end of the tube with the water surface is discerned

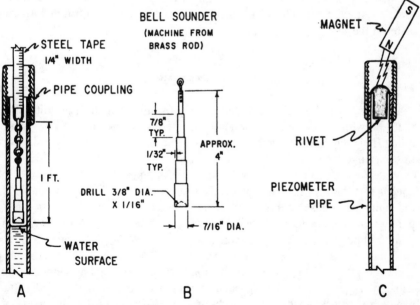

Fig. 11–4. Method for measuring depth to water level and for capping piezometers. (*A*) The "bell sounder," lowered on a ¼-inch steel tape into the piezometer, makes a sound when contact is made with the water. (*B*) The "bell sounder" is made by machining and drilling a solid brass rod. (*C*) A rivet placed in the top of the piezometer within a standard pipe coupling serves as a vented cap. The rivet is removed with a magnet for readings.

by blowing through the tube and listening for the bubbling sound of air through the water.

Other caps can be used for capping piezometers, such as a standard ⅜-inch pipe cap; but, whatever cap is used, it must be vented to admit air.

11–7 METHOD OF INSTALLING TENSIOMETERS

11–7.1 Procedure

This subject is covered in detail in section 9, where special apparatus and materials are listed. The following statement of procedure gives only the general requirements. The reader is referred to the above section for detailed directions and information for this test. Make a hole to the desired depth in the soil, using a soil tube or an auger of such size as to give a close fit for the ceramic cup of the tensiometer. Insert the soil tube into the hole, and fill the tube and the hole with water. Withdraw the soil tube and place the tensiometer by pushing it to the bottom of the hole. Fill the tensiometer with air-free water by injecting water into the manometer system through the air-trap vent. Force water into the system until it overflows the mercury cup to remove the free air in the manometer system. Stopper the air-trap vent, and allow the tensiometer to come to equilibrium with the water in the soil.

11–7.2 Comments

In some soils, the walls of the hole are not stable enough to permit filling the hole with water, and the soil tube is used as a liner in the hole while filling. It is important that the ceramic cup be in contact with the soil. For this reason, oversize holes should be avoided.

Water can be freed of air by boiling it. The water should be allowed to cool before filling the tensiometer. Tensiometer readings are unreliable if the units are not substantially filled with water. Tensiometers with transparent manometer lines are preferable to nontransparent ones for the reason that air bubbles can be easily detected.

Tensiometers are also subject to errors from temperature changes, especially those from heat conduction through the main stem of the tensiometer from the above-ground portion to the cup in the soil. This problem is satisfactorily overcome by use of tensiometers that are made of materials such as plastics that are poor conductors of heat.

Before a tensiometer is installed, the scale should be positioned to give the desired reference-level reading. With the manometer system filled with air-free water, the tensiometer should be stood on end in water so that the water level is at the desired reference-level position with respect to the center of the cup. The zero mark of the tensiometer scale then should be positioned opposite the mercury level of the manometer. When the reference level is set at the center of the cup, tensiometer readings will equal the negative-pressure-head component or soil suction. If the reference level is set at the ground surface line (or other desired reference level), the reading will include both the negative-pressure and the position-head components. Where several tensiometers are installed, each to a different depth for the purpose of measuring hydraulic head, it is advantageous to select a common reference level such as the soil surface. Moreover, it is helpful to mount the manometer tubes of the several tensiometers so as to be read from a single scale and to insert them into a common mercury reservoir. An unusually large scale displacement (value b, equation [3]) is avoided by selecting a reference level not far distant from the mercury level in the reservoir. The scale displacement b can be calculated by use of equation [3]; however, for greater precision it is advisable to set the scale as outlined above. The calculated value is most useful for detecting gross errors in scale position.

11–8 INTERPRETATION OF HYDRAULIC-HEAD READINGS

Figure 11–5 (Richards, 1952) shows hydraulic-head readings for both tensiometers and piezometers for A the static case, B downward flow from ponded water on the soil surface, and C upward flow from a pressure aquifer below. Points of measurement for the three cases shown in the figure are indicated by open circles for tensiometers and by shaded circles for piezometers. The measurement points are positioned in a vertical line downward through the profile. The line that connects from each circle to an equivalent or hypothetical water manometer in the case of tensiometers (open circles), and to the open end of a pipe for piezometers (shaded circles), represents a water line which provides hydraulic attachment from the manometer or piezometer to the point in question. A tensiometer is sketched for the first depth, Case A, to illustrate the fact that tensiometer hydraulic-head readings in all cases are actually made with the tensiometer scale above the soil surface. The equivalent or hypothetical manometers are diagrammatic only as an aid in interpretation of hydraulic-head readings.

From thermodynamics, it is well known that flow is in the direction of decreasing energy level. Since hydraulic head is a measure of energy per unit weight of water, flow is also in the direction of decreasing hydraulic head. For Case A, the hydraulic head is the same at all depths in the soil as indicated by equal water levels in all tubes. In this case there is no flow. For Case B, the hydraulic head at the soil surface is equal to the elevation of the ponded water; and, as can be seen by the levels in the open tubes, it decreases downward in the soil at each succeeding point of measurement. Flow in this case is downward. The reverse is true for Case C where the hydraulic head decreases from the pressure aquifer to the soil surface, indicating that in this case flow is upward.

Where there is no vertical flow component (Case A), the equal hydraulic-head values read in all tubes represents the position of the water table. The water table is defined as the loci of points in the soil where the soil water is at atmospheric pressure. Under conditions of vertical flow of water (Cases B and C), the hydraulic-head value, for either a tensiometer or piezometer, coincides with the water table only if the end of the pipe or the center of the cup is located at the water table elevation (see Case B). That is to say, when the piezometer terminates, or the tensiometer cup is located at the water table elevation, the pressure head p/w equals zero.

Hydraulic head is a point function in three dimensional space. Procedures and methods from standard textbooks that are used for the analysis of other physical flow processes, such as flow of heat and electricity, are applicable to the analysis of water flow in permeable media. An example of

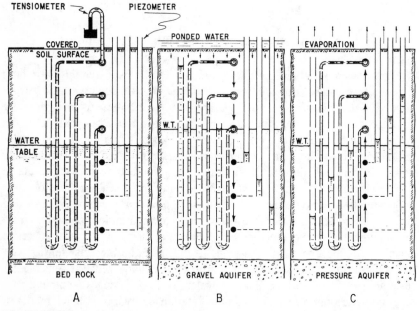

Fig. 11–5. Distribution of hydraulic head for several flow systems. (Case A) Static equilibrium under gravity—no flow. (Case B) Downward flow to a gravel aquifer from water ponded on the soil surface. (Case C) Upward flow from an aquifer under pressure to the soil surface where water is evaporated. Lines connecting from the point of measurement for tensiometers (open circles) and for piezometers (shaded circles) represent water lines for hydraulic attachment to equivalent or hypothetical manometers in the case of tensiometers, or open-end pipes in the case of piezometers (Richards, 1952).

the use of equal-hydraulic-head lines to represent the hydraulic-head distribution in a plane or profile for two-dimensional flow of water into an
open drain is shown in Fig. 11-6. Here the hydraulic-head values are
plotted on a cross-sectional drawing; and, by the procedures of interpolation and extrapolation, equal-hydraulic-head lines are constructed. Convenient hydraulic-head intervals may be selected, extending over the range
of measured values for hydraulic head. Usually an interval is selected
that allows a number of equal-hydraulic-head lines to be sketched on the
same profile. The component of flow in the plane of the profile is normal
to lines of equal-hydraulic-head, if the profile is plotted to a 1:1 scale.
For profiles where the scales are equal, flow lines can be sketched in at
right angles to the equal-hydraulic-head lines, with arrows to show the
direction of flow. If the vertical scale is exaggerated, the relation between
stream lines and equal-hydraulic-head lines on the plotted profile is no
longer orthogonal. Where the vertical and horizontal scales are not equal,
the hydraulic-head distribution may be properly plotted, but flow lines
should not be indicated. While Fig. 11-6 shows only hydraulic-head values
obtained by the use of piezometers below a water table, the lines of equal
hydraulic head in the unsaturated region above the water table can be
constructed in a similar manner by use of tensiometer readings. In this case,
they would be essentially horizontal lines above the water table with a
downward dip near the open drain, showing flow toward the soil surfaces
where evaporation takes place.

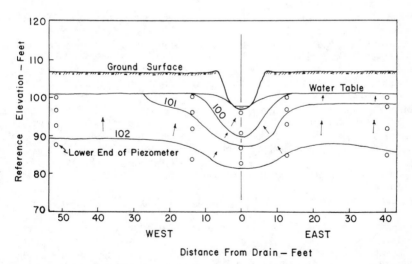

Fig. 11-6. Equal hydraulic-head lines below a water table on a profile section in the
vicinity of an open drain. Example from Delta area, Utah. The direction of the
hydraulic gradient is represented by arrows and indicates upward movement from
an underlying source.

Hydraulic-gradient values for use in the Darcy flow equation are obtained by determining the change in hydraulic head per unit flow distance in the soil. The usual practice is to use average gradient values, which are obtained by dividing the difference in hydraulic head at two points by the distance between points. If the two points in question happen to lie along a stream path, the result will represent the true average hydraulic gradient. Frequently, hydraulic-head measurements are made in a selected plane in three-dimensional space which may or may not coincide with the true flow direction. Where such measurements are used, the results represent only some space component of the true hydraulic gradient. Vector analysis is applicable for determining true flow direction or true hydraulic gradients in three-dimensional space. For flow of water in isotropic soils, the gradient vector coincides in direction with the velocity vector.

11–9 LITERATURE CITED

Christiansen, J. E. 1943. Ground water studies in relation to drainage. Agr. Eng. 24:339–342.

Dodge, R. A., and Thompson, M. J. 1937. Fluid Mechanics. McGraw-Hill Book Company, Inc., New York and London.

Donnan, W. W., and Bradshaw, George B. 1952. Drainage investigation methods for irrigated areas in Western United States. U. S. Dept. Agr. Tech. Bull. 1065.

Hvorslev, M. J. 1951. Time lag and soil permeability in ground-water observations. Waterways Experiment Station, Corps of Engineers, U. S. Army, Vicksburg, Mississippi. Bul. 36.

Klute, A., and Gardner, W. R. 1962. Tensiometer response time. Soil Sci. 93:204–207.

Leonard, R. A., and Low, P. F. 1962. A self-adjusting null-point tensiometer. Soil Sci. Soc. Am. Proc. 26:123–125.

Mickelson, R. H., Benz, L. C., Carlson, C. W., and Sandoval, F. M. 1961. Jetting equipment and techniques in a drainage and salinity study. Trans. Am. Soc. Agr. Eng. 4:222–223, 225, 228.

Miller, R. D. 1951. A technique for measuring tensions in rapidly changing systems. Soil Sci. 72:291–301.

Reeve, R. C., and Jensen, Max C. 1949. Piezometers for ground-water flow studies and measurement of subsoil permeability. Agr. Eng. 30:435–438.

Reger, J. S., Pillsbury, A. F., Reeve, R. C., and Petersen, R. K. 1950. Techniques for drainage investigations in the Coachella Valley, California. Agr. Eng. 31:559–564.

Richards, L. A. 1942. Soil moisture tensiometer materials and construction. Soil Sci. 53:241–248.

Richards, L. A. 1949. Methods of measuring soil moisture tension. Soil Sci. 68:95–112.

Richards, L. A. 1952. Water conducting and retaining properties of soils in relation to irrigation. In Proc. Internat. Symp. Desert Res. Research Council of Israel in cooperation with UNESCO. pp. 523–546.

U. S. Salinity Laboratory Staff. 1954. Diagnosis and improvement of saline and alkali soils. U. S. Dept. Agr. Handbook 60.

12 Rate of Water Intake in the Field[1]

ANSON R. BERTRAND

Agricultural Research Service, USDA
Watkinsville, Georgia

12–1 GENERAL INTRODUCTION

In recent years many methods have been employed to measure the rate of intake of water by soils. These methods may be classified in various ways, according to the manner in which the water is added, the manner in which the area for measurements is delimited, and the manner in which the measurements are made. Water may be added by natural rainfall, artificial rainfall, or flooding. The area on which the measurement is to be made may be defined by natural slope, in the case of watersheds, or by some sort of border, in the case of small areas. The border may be an impermeable barrier inserted in the soil, or it may be a dike or the edge of a furrow. The measurement of water intake may be made by determining the difference between water applied and water lost by runoff, or by determining the quantity of water needed to maintain a constant head of water on the soil.

Because the rate of water intake is so greatly influenced by the water content and surface condition of the soil, knowledge of these conditions is important to interpretation of the results obtained. The water content of the soil should always be measured before the water is applied. The physical state of the soil surface should be described, undue disturbance of the soil incident to the measurements should be avoided, and changes in the physical state of the soil surface that occur during the measurement should be evaluated.

Numerous papers have been published on the subject of water intake by soils. Davidson (1940) compiled a bibliography of over 200 references. In most instances the methods have been developed to meet specific needs and are not widely adaptable. A review of infiltration equipment by Parr and Bertrand (1960) showed the great diversity of methods and brought out the fact that no one method yet developed meets all needs.

[1] Contribution from the Southern Branch, Soil and Water Conservation Research Division, ARS, USDA, Watkinsville, Ga., and the Georgia Agr. Exp. Stations.

197

12–2   METHOD OF ARTIFICIAL RAINFALL

12–2.1   Introduction

A satisfactory method for measuring rate of intake of water from artificial rainfall in the field must have the following characteristics: (*1*) The distribution of drop sizes must be uniform over the plot area. (*2*) The artificial rainfall must be similar to the natural rainfall being simulated in respect of drop size, drop velocity, intensity range, and total energy value. (*3*) The plot area must be large enough to sample the population and give reproducible results (approximately 12 square feet for most soil conditions). (*4*) The artificial rainfall must be applied not only to the plot but also to an adequate buffer area around the plot. These qualities of the ideal method are approached more closely by the sprinkling infiltrometers used by Diebold (1951), Meyer and McCune (1958), and Bertrand and Parr (1961) than by other infiltrometers currently available.

The difference between the rates of application and runoff is usually taken as the rate of water intake. The rate of application is often measured continuously by a rain gauge in the plot area, or by a small trough across the plot to collect rainfall and carry it to a recording device. Alternatively, the rate of application may be measured in a separate trial in which all or part of the plot is covered by a collecting pan, and the quantity of water collected in a known length of time under conditions similar to the regular run is determined.

12–2.2   Method

12–2.2.1   SPECIAL APPARATUS

Because no single type of apparatus is entirely suitable for all circumstances, various types will be described in general terms with reference to the original descriptions. The reader can then make further study of the papers that describe apparatus adaptable for his purpose.

In 1936, a group of scientists at the Hydraulics Laboratory of the National Bureau of Standards began the development of a series of artificial rainfall devices. During a 3-year period, they developed six devices, known successively as types A through F. The type F and a later modification, type FA, were widely accepted and used. The type F nozzle produces drops ranging in size from 3.2 to 5.0 mm. in diameter and is usually used on a plot 6 by 12 feet in size, with a border 3 feet in width. The type FA nozzle is used with a plot 1 by 2.5 feet in size with a border 1.5 feet in width. Higher infiltration values are usually obtained with the latter apparatus, probably because of relatively greater lateral subsurface movement of water in the soil.

Most of the infiltrometers employing the type F nozzle have inclined the nozzle at an angle toward the plot, so that the artificial rainfall is applied in an arch-like pattern. In these infiltrometers the drops do not reach a constant terminal velocity, and accurate rainfall energy values are difficult to obtain. There have been several attempts to direct the spray from type F nozzles in a downward direction to reduce wind interference and to increase the kinetic energy of the drops. Where this is done, however, the angle of the spray pattern is so narrow that the artificial rainfall covers only a very small area of soil.

The "Rocky Mountain infiltrometer" described by Wilm (1943) uses three type F nozzles to apply artificial rainfall in an arching pattern onto a plot 2 by 4 feet in area. The rate of application is determined by a rain gauge that samples 1% of the plot area. Runoff is collected and measured. This equipment was described further, after several modifications, by Dortignac (1951). In his modification the nozzles are pointed upward, and the artificial rain falls on a plot 12 by 30 inches in area.

Another infiltrometer using four type F nozzles pointing upward was described by Diebold (1951). The nozzles are mounted in an aluminum shelter 5 feet in height, 8 feet in width, and 9 feet in length. The shelter is riveted to an angle-iron frame and is transported on a special trailer.

A movable-carriage, boom-type sprinkling device was described by Myers (1952). The carriage mechanism supports a boom on which are placed 10 nozzles that discharge water in a fan pattern. The boom is moved back and forth across a 16- by 24-foot plot by a continuous chain drive.

Meyer and McCune (1958) used the movable-carriage principle in the design of a rainfall simulator for soil erosion studies. This rainfall simulator is capable of covering standard-size runoff plots with artificial storms of approximately the kinetic energy of natural rainfall of similar intensity. The Veejet nozzle used in this apparatus (Veejet Nozzle No. U80100, manufactured by Spray Systems Co., Bellwood, Ill.) produces artificial rainfall in which the size distribution, velocity, and energy of drops are similar to those of raindrops in natural storms. Runoff is recorded by a standard water-stage recorder attached to the runoff flume.

A portable sprinkling-type infiltrometer was designed and described by Bertrand and Parr (1961). This instrument employs a single full-cone nozzle, spraying downward from a height of 9 feet. The nozzle is supported by a collapsible aluminum tower, which serves also to support a canvas screen that protects the spray pattern from distortion by wind. The plot is 3.81 feet square and is bounded by a metal frame driven 2 inches into the soil. The downhill side of the frame is slotted to allow runoff water to leave the plot and enter a special flume. A circulating runoff-accumulation system collects the runoff in an above-ground tank, where the rate of accumulation is measured by a water-stage recorder. The drop size, drop distribution, and kinetic energy of artificial rainfall produced by this apparatus compare favorably with values for natural rainfall.

Drip screens and drip towers have been widely used. One such apparatus (Ellison et al., 1944, 1945; Ellison, 1947) consists of a tank with holes drilled on 4-inch centers to supply the water to a drip screen positioned under it. The screen consists of 1-inch mesh chicken wire with cheesecloth spread loosely over it and pressed into each wire mesh. A short piece of yarn is hung from each pocket to form the drops. Different sizes of yarn are used to produce a variety of drop sizes. Drop sizes usually range from 3.5 mm. to 5.1 mm. in diameter. Drop velocity is controlled by varying the height of the apparatus. Intensity is controlled by varying the head of water or by varying the size of the holes in the supply tank. The drip screen is oscillated to distribute drops evenly over the plot.

An infiltrometer using a drip tower and drip screen was developed by Barnes and Costal (1957). In their apparatus, artificial rainfall ranging in intensity from 1 to 6 inches per hour is provided by selected nozzles that spray on a drip screen with yarn threads. The area around the 12- by 18-inch plot receives simulated rainfall in equal intensity and hence provides a buffer area. Runoff is collected at the downhill end of the plot by a suction apparatus that deposits the water in a Friez recording rain gauge. A calibration of rainfall intensity is obtained by placing a collecting pan over the plot for a known length of time before and after the run. The entire unit may be transported on a ½-ton pickup truck.

Adams et al. (1957) described a portable rainfall simulator and infiltration cylinder. In this apparatus, the artificial rain drops are formed at the bottom of glass capillary tubes protruding through the base of the water supply tank. A variety of drop sizes may be produced by varying the size of the capillary tubes and the diameter of the wire inserted in each tube. The rate of artificial rainfall is controlled by the head of water in the supply tank. The diameter of this instrument is only 5¾ inches, and drops do not reach constant terminal velocity.

Developmental work on the use of hypodermic needles to produce a variety of drop sizes is being conducted at several locations.

In the usual field application, the plot is delimited by a metal frame. The frame should have a width of about 6 inches. No. 14-gauge galvanized steel or cold-rolled steel are satisfactory for the purpose. The frame is driven into the soil to a depth of about 2 inches with a heavy hammer. Where runoff is to be measured, as is usually the case, a plot of rectangular shape is preferable to one with circular or other shape. The downhill side is slotted, and a covered collection flume is then attached to the slotted side of the frame to conduct the runoff water to a collection or metering device.

The most satisfactory method of measuring runoff rate is probably to use a calibrated runoff accumulation tank and an automatic recording device.

The portable water-stage recorder most suitable for this use is Model 5-FW-1 (manufactured by the Instrument Corp., Bellfort Meteorological Observatory, Baltimore, Md.). The recorder is used with a gear ratio to give a chart speed that will result in easy determination of water level versus time. The pen points of the recorder should be maintained in good condition. A light ink line, obtained by limiting the amount of ink in the pen, is desirable. Too much ink results in a broad line that is difficult to read precisely.

12–2.2.2 PROCEDURE

The operations to be described here pertain to measurements of rate of water intake made with portable apparatus in which a plot is established temporarily in an area in the field.

Give attention first to selection of an area that represents the condition for which measurements are desired. If replicated measurements are to be made, as is usually the case, make sure that a sufficiently uniform area large enough to accommodate the several measurements is available, taking into account not only the actual area that receives the artificial rainfall but also the additional area that will be disturbed by the necessary operations. (The usual practice is to make successive runs within 12 to 15 feet of each other.) The soil surface in the different areas to be used as replicates should not have unusual microdepressions, cracks, or other irregularities that will have a differential effect on the results. The density of vegetation should be approximately the same.

Position the plot frame with the slotted side downhill, and drive it 2 inches into the ground using a heavy hammer. Under row-crop conditions, orient the plot frame in a uniform fashion with each successive run to include the same number of rows, wheel tracks, and crop plants. While installing the plot frame, take care to avoid disturbing the soil inside of the frame and in the buffer area outside of the frame. Allow an undisturbed buffer width of at least 1 foot outside of the plot frame.

Apply the artificial rainfall from the spray nozzle or other drop-making device to the plot area plus the buffer area around the plot, and measure the quantity of water accumulated. Alternatively, collect the artificial rainfall from a small known portion of the plot by a trough or other device during the regular run. Measure the rate of accumulation of runoff by a portable water-stage recorder operating in a calibrated collection tank or by other suitable means.

To calculate the rate of water intake, subtract the rate of runoff accumulation from the rate of water application. To obtain a relatively smooth curve for the runoff data, divide the total time into periods of suitable length, and plot the average rate of runoff accumulation during individual periods against the time at the midpoint of each period.

12–3 METHOD OF FLOODING

12–3.1 Introduction

In the method of flooding, the plot area is bounded by a wall of soil or of some impermeable material that permits impounding of water within. The rate of fall of the surface of water ponded on the soil, or the rate of use of water from a supply source that keeps a constant head of water on the surface, is taken as the rate of water intake. Under most conditions the rate of intake is so much greater than the rate of evaporation that the error from evaporation can be neglected.

Cylinder-type infiltrometers employing metal plot borders are used most commonly. These are of various types, including single cylinders, multiple cylinders, weighing lysimeters, and drainage lysimeters. The metal cylinders are driven into the soil to depths up to several feet. For temporary installations, which are used most frequently, the cylinders are driven into the soil only a few inches and are then removed after the measurement has been made. The method to be described below is of this type.

Where the cylinders are not driven into the soil to a considerable depth, and where the diameter is small enough to be convenient for experimental use, the rate of water intake per unit area varies markedly with the size of the cylinder, decreasing asymptotically with increasing diameter of the cylinder (Marshall and Stirk, 1950). To control the lateral movement of water through the soil under the cylinder, which is the cause of the unrealistically high values obtained with the small cylinders, most researchers use two concentric cylinders and keep ponded water in both of them, while making the measurement of water intake in only the center cylinder.

Swartzendruber and Olson (1961a, 1961b) studied the double-cylinder infiltration technique using a sand model and found that the infiltration velocity increased sharply as the wall of the outer cylinder was approached. Under otherwise equal conditions, the rate of water intake at the center of the ring was found to increase if the diameter of the ring was reduced to 12 inches or less. In further studies involving uniform material, restricting layers, impermeable layers, different textures, and different depths of wetting, they found that rather successful results were obtained with an inner cylinder 40 inches in diameter and an outer cylinder 48 inches in diameter. With such cylinders, the rate of water intake in the central cylinder may be expected to approximate closely the rate of water intake in an infinitely large area of similar nature, provided that the depth of wetting does not exceed 24 inches, and provided further that extreme soil layering does not exist within the zone of water movement.

Disturbance of the soil incident to placing cylinder infiltrometers in position for measurement may have a significant effect on the results obtained. Some shattering or compaction of soil adjacent to the border is inevitable when cylinders are driven into position. Errors from this source may be reduced by allowing the cylinder to remain in place for an extended period prior to measuring the rate of water intake.

Entrapment of air in the soil column below the advancing water front likewise may have a significant effect on the results obtained. The effect of entrapped air may be expected to vary with the size of the cylinders employed and with the depth to which the cylinders are placed in the soil.

Basin methods and furrow methods have the advantage that requirements for specialized equipment are small. Large basins have the disadvantage of requiring level topography, and both large basins and large furrows require large volumes of water.

The same general principles described above for cylinder infiltrometers apply also to basin and furrow infiltrometers. With both basin and furrow infiltrometers, it is important to have a flooded buffer area outside of the area in which the measurement is made. With basin infiltrometers the entire border area is inundated, and the rate of water intake can easily be obtained from measurements on the inner area. With the furrow technique there is only partial inundation, and the rate of water intake found applies specifically to the conditions of furrow application under which the measurement is made, and not to the condition where the entire area is flooded. The degree of inundation is usually expressed by the stream width between rows because depths encountered in border or furrow measurements do not greatly affect the rate of intake (Philip, 1958a, 1958b). A technique for obtaining the rate of intake as a function of stream width and time was developed by Bondurant (1957). Use of the measured rate of advance of a stream of given dimensions in a furrow to calculate the rate of water intake by soil was proposed by Christiansen et al. (1959). However, the most accurate method of determining the rate of intake of water in furrows is measurement of inflow and outflow.

12–3.2 Method [2]

12–3.2.1 SPECIAL APPARATUS

1. Metal cylinders: Prepare three to preferably five cylinders for use in a single test, using smooth, cold-rolled steel or galvanized steel of thickness not to exceed 0.08 inch (approximately 14 gauge) unless a sharpened cutting edge is provided. Make the length at least 10 inches and preferably 12 to 14 inches. Make the inside diameter at least 12 inches and preferably more, making the diameters such that the cylinders will nest inside each other if desired. Butt-weld the longitudinal seams, and grind them to a reasonably smooth finish. If a set of buffer cylinders is to be

[2] Haise et al. (1956).

used instead of an earthen dam to provide a buffer compartment, make these cylinders in the manner described above; but use 10-gauge or heavier metal, use a length of 8 inches, use a diameter at least 8 inches larger than the measuring cylinders, and weld a reinforcing strip around the top.

2. Driving plate: Use a piece of steel plate at least ½-inch thick and from 2 to 4 inches larger than the diameter of the largest measuring cylinder. Weld lugs to the lower face to keep the plate approximately centered on the cylinders. If desired for greater ease in carrying the plate, weld a handle of steel rod ½ inch in diameter to one edge.

3. Driving hammer: A 16-pound sledge hammer, used with a tamping blow rather than a swinging blow, is adequate for many soils. To make a heavier and better hammer, attach a handle to one edge of a steel block weighing about 30 pounds (this weight is provided by a block having dimensions about 8 by 6 by 2 inches). Alternatively, attach a 1¼-inch by 3-inch, banded, malleable-iron reducer to a 4-foot length of standard 1¼-inch galvanized pipe, and fill the reducer and pipe with 15 to 20 pounds of lead.

4. Water supply: Use 50-gallon steel drums, 10-gallon milk cans, or other suitable containers for transporting water to the site of the measurements. Use one or more buckets of 10- to 12-quart capacity to convey water to the cylinder. Employ water suitable for irrigation.

5. Puddling protection device: Use a piece of folded burlap, cloth, heavy paper, or loosely fitting ¼-inch board inside the central cylinder to protect the soil surface from puddling when water is first applied.

6. Timing device: Use a watch or other timepiece that can be read to 1 minute or less.

7. Hook gauge: Grind a 16-inch length of welding rod to a fine point in one end, and bend this end through 180° to form a hook in which the pointed end is parallel with the long axis of the rod. Solder a flat piece of brass about ¾ by ¼ by 1/16 inch in size to the welding rod about 3 inches from the end opposite the hook, placing the long dimension of the brass piece perpendicular to the axis of the welding rod. Use this assembly in connection with a triangular engineer's scale to measure the distance of the water surface in the cylinder below a reference point. Alternatively, use the manometer described below in 8 or the constant-head device in 9.

8. Manometer: As an alternative to the hook gauge for measuring the level of water inside the central cylinder, prepare a manometer in the following manner. Secure a graduated pipette of perhaps 30 cm. length and several millimeters inside diameter, and cut off the lower restricted end. Then cut a piece of 2- by 12-inch board in the shape of a right triangle with one angle of about 30° and with the hypotenuse of a length slightly greater than that of the graduated pipette. Fasten the pipette to the edge

of the triangle that forms the hypotenuse, and fasten the side that forms the other leg of the 30° angle to a triangular piece of ¼-inch steel plate that is set on three leveling pins and is placed outside the infiltrometer. Before each use, carefully level the platform. Before adding water to start the infiltration run, attach one end of a piece of flexible tubing to the bottom of the pipette, and lead the other end over the top of the two cylinders to the bottom of the inner cylinder. Immediately following addition of water to the inner cylinder, suck on the top of the pipette to cause water to fill the flexible tube. Then read the position of the meniscus on the pipette scale, and multiply the values by the appropriate factor to obtain readings of vertical movements of the water surface in inches or centimeters as desired. The conversion factor will remain the same as long as the platform is accurately leveled.

9. Constant-head device: If a constant head is to be maintained in the cylinder, connect the main water supply tank to a float valve attached to the side of the measuring cylinder (or to a stake if the furrow or basin method is used). Use a siphon tube of sufficient size (usually ½-inch diameter) to make the connection. As a special adaptation of this device, Daniel (1952) used a measuring cylinder 8 inches in diameter in connection with a standard recording rain gauge for the water supply tank. The level of water in the measuring cylinder was controlled by á carburetor float connected to the bucket of the recording rain gauge by a siphon hose. The rate of water intake could then be read directly from the rain gauge chart because the diameters of the infiltrometer and the water supply tank in the rain gauge were both 8 inches.

12-3.2.2 PROCEDURE

Select a general area that is representative for the purpose of the measurement. Examine and describe the soil profile conditions of texture, structure, water content, and adsorbed sodium, with particular reference to the first foot. Secure samples for measuring the adsorbed sodium content (where sodium may be a problem) and the water content. Record the kind of crop and the stage of growth, and describe any surface litter or mulch and the condition of the soil surface—freshly cultivated, cloddy, crusted, cracked, etc. Make note of any other condition observed that might have an influence on rate of water intake.

To provide for concurrent measurements on three or more sites, select the exact sites for the measurements within a limited area, normally ½ acre or less. Unless the objective is to make measurements of special conditions, avoid areas that may be affected by unusual surface disturbance, animal burrows, stones that might damage the cylinder, animal traffic, or machine traffic.

Set a cylinder in place, and press it firmly into the soil. For cylinders less than 24 inches in diameter, place the driving plate on the cylinder, stand on the plate, and drive the cylinder into the soil by tamping the plate with the driving hammer. Drive the cylinder in vertically, using a carpenter's level as needed. Do not drive the cylinder into the soil irregularly, so that first one side and then the other goes down. This procedure produces a poor bond between the cylinder wall and the soil, and it disturbs the soil core within the cylinder. If the cylinder should enter the soil at an angle, remove it, and reset it in another location. Drive the cylinder into the soil to a depth of approximately 4 inches.

Around the measuring cylinder place a buffer cylinder having a diameter at least 8 inches greater. Drive this cylinder into the soil to a depth of 2 to 4 inches by tamping it around the circumference with the driving hammer. Strictly vertical movement of this cylinder into the soil is not particularly important. As an alternative to the buffer cylinder, construct a buffer pond by throwing up a low (3 to 6 inches) dike around the cylinder, avoiding disturbance of the soil inside the dike, and keeping the inside toe of the dike at least 6 inches from the cylinder.

Place burlap or other puddling protection device on the soil within the central cylinder. Then fill the buffer pond on the outside with water to a depth of about 2 inches, and maintain approximately the same depth throughout the period of observation. (The depth of water in the buffer pond is not critical as long as a supply of water is always available for infiltration into the soil.) Immediately after adding water to the buffer pond, fill the central cylinder with water to the desired depth (usually 1 to 3 inches), remove the puddling protection device, and make a measurement of the water surface elevation by a hook gauge (or manometer if desired). Use the cylinder edge for the reference level, and mark the cylinder so that all subsequent measurements can be made at the same point on the cylinder. Alternatively, if the basin or furrow method is used, employ a stake to provide a reference level. Record the hook-gauge reading and the time at which the observation was made. Carry out these operations quickly, so that errors from intake during the operations will be small.

Make additional hook-gauge measurements at intervals, and record the water level and the time. For most soils, observations at the end of 1, 3, 5, 10, 20, 30, 45, 60, 90 and 120 minutes, and hourly thereafter, will provide adequate information. Make observations more frequently as needed on soils having a high rate of intake. As a general rule, the intake between measurements should not exceed 1 inch. Continue measurements until the rate of intake is almost constant.

When the water level has dropped 1 or 2 inches in the cylinder, add sufficient water to return the water surface approximately to its initial elevation. Record the level and time just before filling and the level after filling. Keep the interval between these two readings as short as possible to avoid errors caused by intake during the refilling period. (In analyzing the results, the assumption is made that the refilling is instantaneous.)

If a constant water level in the cylinder or basin is maintained by a float valve, measure the rate of depletion of water in the supply tank by a hook gauge, manometer, or automatic water-stage recorder.

12-3.2.3 COMMENTS

Tests with double-ring and single-ring infiltrometers have shown that the number of measurements needed to characterize an area may be relatively large. With single rings on an extremely uniform soil, Burgy and Luthin (1957) found that each of six separate measurements came within 30% of the general mean. Slater (1957) found that 15 measurements with 4.25-inch rings were necessary to ensure a standard error within 20% of the mean.

12-4 METHOD OF WATERSHED HYDROGRAPHS

Where the area of a watershed and the total rainfall and runoff during a given storm are known, it is possible to calculate the total infiltration, neglecting evaporation. At any given moment during the rainfall, of course, some of the water is detained in surface depressions in the watershed, and some is in the process of running off, as was noted by Sharp and Holton (1940). The portion that has not appeared as runoff but which has not yet been absorbed into the soil is difficult to estimate for a complex watershed. Hence, measurements that include the cumulative rainfall and runoff up to a given moment before the runoff has ceased are not related to infiltration in a manner as simple and direct as is true for measurements described in preceding sections.

Sharp and Holton (1940, 1942) proposed a graphical method for estimating rate of water intake by soil in the presence of detention of water on the soil, and this method was used by Bertoni et al. (1958) to estimate rates of water intake from plots of various lengths of slope where rainfall intensity and runoff rates were known.

Interpretation of hydrographic data from watersheds is a complex and highly specialized subject. For further information the reader is referred to the work of Zingg (1943), who worked through the problem of determining surface flow, surface storage, and infiltration rates from data on rainfall and runoff on a 7.5-acre watershed. In general, it may be said that infiltration rates derived from watershed hydrographs are of limited value for agronomic purposes, the reason being that the single over-all value obtained by measurement does not provide information on the many variations in conditions of slope, soil type, surface condition of soil, water content of soil, vegetation, and surface litter that modify the behavior of individual areas that constitute the whole.

12–5 ANALYSIS AND PRESENTATION OF DATA

Data on water intake may be recorded and presented in a variety of ways, depending on their intended use. With field-type sprinkling infiltrometers where the rate of application of water is known, the original measurements are ordinarily in the form of the cumulative volume of runoff obtained at successive times of measurement. The same is true of furrow-type or basin-type infiltrometers using the inflow-outflow principle. With cylinder-type infiltrometers, the measurements are in the form of the drop in head of water in the cylinder (or in the supply tank if constant-head equipment is used).

Measurements on inflow-outflow systems are usually plotted as rate of runoff against time. Enough data points should be plotted to obtain a reliable, smooth curve. The difference between runoff rate, in depth of water per unit time, and application rate, in similar units, is the infiltration rate at the given time.

With cylinder-type infiltrometers, a plot of cumulative water intake versus time should result in a smooth curve, the slope of which is equal to the rate of intake. Plotting the rate of intake against time results in a curve showing the change in tendency of the soil to absorb water with time. The area under the curve represents the capacity of the soil to absorb water up to the time in question. This "infiltration capacity" curve is normally the final result.

12–6 LITERATURE CITED

Adams, J. E., Kirkham, D., and Nielsen, D. R. 1957. A portable rainfall-simulator infiltrometer and physical measurements of soil in place. Soil Sci. Soc. Am. Proc. 21:473–477.

Barnes, O. K., and Costal, G. 1957. A mobile infiltrometer. Agron. J. 49:105–107.

Bertoni, Jose, Larson, W. E., and Shrader, W. D. 1958. Determination of infiltration rates on Marshall silt loam from runoff and rainfall records. Soil Sci. Soc. Am. Proc. 22:571–574.

Bertrand, A. R., and Parr, J. F. 1961. Design and operation of the Purdue Sprinkling Infiltrometer. Purdue Univ. Res. Bull. No. 723.

Bondurant, James A. 1957. Developing a furrow infiltrometer. Agr. Eng. 38:602–604.

Burgy, R. H., and Luthin, J. N. 1957. Discussion of a test of the single and double ring types of infiltrometers. Trans. Am. Geophys. Union 38:260–261.

Christiansen, J. E., Bishop, Alvin A., and Fok, Yu-Si. (In press) The intake rate related to the advance of water in surface irrigation. Presented at Winter Meeting Am. Soc. of Agr. Eng., Paper #59-713, Dec. 1959. (Submitted for publication to Agr. Eng.)

Daniel, Harley A. 1952. Recording concentric ring infiltrometer. Agron. J. 44:451.

Davidson, J. M. 1940. Infiltration of water into soil. USDA Soil Conservation Service Bibliography, No. 3.

Diebold, C. H. 1951. Soil layers causing runoff from hard-land wheat fields in Colorado and New Mexico. J. Soil Water Conserv. 6:202–209.

Dortignac, E. J. 1951. Design and operation of Rocky Mountain Infiltrometer. USDA Forest Serv., Rocky Mt. Forest & Range Expt. Sta., Sta. Paper No. 5.

Ellison, W. D. 1947. Soil erosion studies—Part II. Agr. Eng. 28:197–201.

Ellison, W. D., and Pomerene, W. H. 1944. A rainfall applicator. Agr. Eng. 25:220.

Ellison, W. D., and Slater, C. S. 1945. Factors that affect surface sealing and infiltration of exposed soil surfaces. Agr. Eng. 26:156–157.

Haise, H. R. et al. 1956. The use of cylinder infiltrometers to determine the intake characteristics of irrigated soils. USDA-ARS Res. Rept. 41–7.

Marshall, T. J., and Stirk, G. B. 1950. The effect of lateral movement of water in soil on infiltration measurements. Australian J. Agr. Res. 1:253–265.

Meyer, L. Donald, and McCune, D. L. 1958. Rainfall simulator for runoff plots. Agr. Eng. 39:644–648.

Myers, Earl A. 1952. A field plot irrigator. Pennsylvania State Progress Report No. 83.

Parr, J. F., and Bertrand, A. R. 1960. Water infiltration into soils. Adv. Agron. 12:311–363.

Philip, J. R. 1958(a). The theory of infiltration: VI. Effect of water depth over soil. Soil Sci. 85:278–286.

Philip, J. R. 1958(b). The theory of infiltration: VII. Soil Sci. 333–337.

Sharp, A. L., and Holton, H. N. 1940. A graphical method of analysis of sprinkled-plot hydrographs. Trans. Am. Geophys. Union 21:558–570.

Sharp, A. L., and Holton, H. N. 1942. Extension of graphic methods of analysis of sprinkled-plot hydrographs to the analysis of hydrographs of control-plots and small homogeneous watersheds. Trans. Am. Geophys. Union 23:578–593.

Slater, C. S. 1957. Cylinder infiltrometers for determining rates of irrigation. Soil Sci. Soc. Am. Proc. 21:457–460.

Swartzendruber, D., and Olson, T. C. 1961(a). Sand-model study of buffer effects in the double-ring infiltrometer. Soil Sci. Soc. Am. Proc. 25:5–8.

Swartzendruber, D., and Olson, T. C. 1961(b). Model study of the double-ring infiltrometer as affected by depth of wetting and particle size. Soil Sci. 92:219–225.

Wilm, H. G. 1943. The application and measurement of artificial rainfall on types FA and F infiltrometers. Trans. Am. Geophys. Union 24:480–487.

Zingg, A. W. 1943. The determination of infiltration rates on small agricultural watersheds. Trans. Am. Geophys. Union 24:475–480.

13

Laboratory Measurement of Hydraulic Conductivity of Saturated Soil

A. KLUTE

University of Illinois
Urbana, Illinois

13–1 INTRODUCTION

The rate of movement of water through soil is of considerable importance in many aspects of agricultural and urban life. The entry of water into soil, the movement of water to plant roots, the flow of water to drains and wells, and the evaporation of water from the surface of soil are but a few of the obvious situations in which the rate of movement plays an important role. An important soil property involved in the behavior of soil water flow systems is the conductivity of the soil to water. Qualitatively, the conductivity is the ability of the soil to transmit water. Measurements of conductivity of saturated soil have long been made. The data are of use in analysis of any saturated-soil water-flow system. These include drainage of soils for agricultural as well as engineering purposes. Drainage of highways, airports, and construction sites, and seepage below dams are among the latter. The data also provide indirect information about the structure and structural stability of soils.

13–2 PRINCIPLES

Water moves through a soil in response to the various forces acting upon it. Among these are the pressure-gradient, gravitational, adsorptive, and osmotic forces. In addition, thermal and electrical gradients may impose forces upon the water in soil and cause its movement under certain circumstances (Hutcheson, 1958). In this discussion we shall deal only with isothermal movement of soil water, and we shall be primarily concerned with liquid-phase movement.

One of the basic physical relationships used to describe the flow of water in soils is a flux equation, Darcy's law, relating the flux of water v to the driving force:

$$v = -(k\rho/\eta)\nabla\Phi \qquad [1]$$

where k is the permeability of the soil or porous medium, ρ is the fluid density, η is the fluid viscosity, and $\nabla\Phi$ is the driving force per unit mass of water. The soil water potential Φ is the work per unit mass of water required to transfer the water reversibly from a reference state to the point in question in the soil. In this paper, the potential gradient $\nabla\Phi$ will be considered to be composed of a gravitational potential gradient and a "capillary" potential gradient. The capillary potential includes the combined effect of hydrostatic pressure in the water and the adsorption forces.

Darcy's law may also be written in terms of the hydraulic gradient:

$$v = -K\nabla H. \qquad [2]$$

In this equation, v is the volume flux of water, i.e., the volume of water passing through unit cross sectional area of soil per unit time, ∇H is the hydraulic gradient or the space rate of change of hydraulic head H in the direction of flow, and K is the conductivity of the soil to water. The water-moving force is expressed as the negative gradient of a hydraulic head composed of gravitational and pressure head, i.e.,

$$H = h + Z \qquad [3]$$

where h is the pressure head and Z is the gravitational head. The relationships between the two components are shown in Fig. 13–1. The pressure

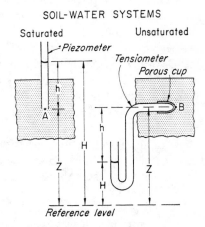

SOIL-WATER SYSTEMS

Fig. 13–1. A diagram of the relationships between hydraulic head H, pressure head h, and gravitational head Z. The pressure head is measured from the level of termination of the piezometer or tensiometer in the soil to the water level in the manometer and is negative in unsaturated soil.

head is numerically equal to the soil water tension or suction (Richards, 1952), but of opposite sign when the soil water tension is expressed in units of length of a column of water. The pressure head should not be interpreted as the actual pressure in the soil water, but as an equivalent pressure, i.e., the pressure in a body of water which is in hydraulic equilibrium with the soil water. The body of water may be in a piezometer tube at its termination in the soil, or it may be the water inside a tensiometer cup.

The permeability and conductivity are measures of the ability of the soil to conduct water. The permeability is ideally a property of the porous medium alone; and, in those media which do not interact with the fluid in such a way as to change the properties of the fluid or the porous medium, the same value of the permeability will be obtained with different fluids. This ideal situation is seldom if ever realized in soils, and changes in fluid properties such as density and viscosity will affect the permeability in a manner not predicted by equation [1].

The conversion from conductivity to permeability can be made by the use of the equation:

$$k = K\eta/\rho g .$$ [4]

The conductivity has the dimensions of a velocity, while the permeability has the dimensions of a length squared. A practical unit for expressing permeability of soils is the square micron, μ^2. Since one $\mu = 10^{-4}$ cm. one $\mu^2 = 10^{-8}$ cm.^{2}

The fact that conductivity appears as a proportionality factor in Darcy's law does not necessarily mean that it is or must be a constant. Because of various chemical, physical and biological processes that take place in the soil, changes of conductivity may occur when water is passed through a soil. A change in the exchangeable ion status of a soil may greatly affect the ability of the soil to conduct water. Such changes in exchangeable ions can be imposed upon a sample by the introduction of water having a different concentration of solute species than was originally present in the soil (Reeve et al., 1954; Quirk, et al., 1955; Brooks, 1956). The conductivity tends to be higher when the concentration of solutes in the water is relatively high. The conductivity may change with electrolyte concentration of the water because of other incompletely understood phenomena such as viscosity changes in the vicinity of the solid surfaces (Low, 1960). Physical transfer of the smaller particles in the soil sample as a result of flow of the water may occur with resultant changes in conductivity. Microbial activity within the sample may affect the conductivity, particularly when water is passed through the sample for long periods of time or when

Table 13-1. Permeability classes for saturated subsoils, and the corresponding ranges of hydraulic conductivity and permeability (O'Neal, 1952).

Class	Hydraulic conductivity		Permeability
	inches/hour	cm. /hour	cm.^{2}
Very slow	< 0.05	< 0.125	< 3×10^{-10}
Slow	0.05- 0.2	0.125- 0.5	3×10^{-10}- 15×10^{-10}
Moderately slow	0.2 - 0.8	0.5 - 2.0	15×10^{-10}- 60×10^{-10}
Moderate	0.8 - 2.5	2.0 - 6.25	60×10^{-10}-170×10^{-10}
Moderately rapid	2.5 - 5.0	6.25 -12.5	170×10^{-10}-350×10^{-10}
Rapid	5.0 -10.0	12.5 -25.0	350×10^{-10}-700×10^{-10}
Very rapid	> 10.0	> 25.0	> 700×10^{-10}

the sample has been submerged for a long time in water. The techniques used for wetting the samples usually result in some air entrapment. When the water used for the conductivity determination is passed through the sample, gas may go into solution or come out of solution, depending upon the degree of gas saturation of the incoming water. The change in volume of the gaseous phase will result in a change of conductivity. Reeve's (1957) discussion of the various factors affecting the conductivity should be consulted for further information.

A wide range of conductivity values will be encountered in soils. To give the reader some appreciation and feeling for the magnitudes of conductivity and permeability to be encountered, the permeability classes of O'Neal (1952) are given in Table 13–1.

Darcy's law is not universally valid for all liquid flow through all porous media. Analysis of the various forces acting upon the water passing through a porous medium shows that Darcy's law is applicable under conditions such that inertial forces are negligible compared to viscous forces (Hubbert, 1957). As a practical matter, such a condition will prevail in silts and finer materials for any commonly occurring hydraulic gradient found in nature. In sands, especially the coarser sands, it will be necessary to restrict the hydraulic gradient to values <0.5 to 1.0 to apply Darcy's law.

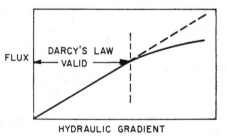

Fig. 13–2. A diagram showing the deviation from Darcy's law at high flux.

The range of validity of Darcy's law can be demonstrated by measuring the flux of water resulting from a series of applied hydraulic gradients. The result should be a linear relation between the flux and the hydraulic gradient. If the applied hydraulic gradient is too large, the resulting flux will be less than predicted by Darcy's law (see Fig. 13–2).

13–3 METHODS

13–3.1 Samples

Soil samples with either disturbed or undisturbed structure are usually held in metal or plastic cylinders, so that one-dimensional flow can be obtained. Relatively undisturbed samples can be obtained in a number of ways (Uhland, 1950; Lutz, 1947; Kelley, 1948; Smith and Stallman, 1954). Thin-walled cylinders or cans may be pressed into the soil to obtain samples, or soil cores may be obtained in metal cylinders that fit into a sampling tube. After the samples have been taken, the cylinders serve as retainers for the soil in the conductivity determination. The Uhland sampler is an example of this type. Because of the great number of variations of sampling techniques for undisturbed samples, no specific directions for the sampling technique will be given. The reader is referred to the reviews by Reeve (1957a, 1957b) and to the literature cited for specific directions.

13–3.2 Constant-Head Method

13–3.2.1 SPECIAL APPARATUS

A simple apparatus for measurement of conductivity of saturated samples by the constant-head method is shown in Fig. 13–3 in cross section. The apparatus may be arranged to hold a number of soil cores in a row.

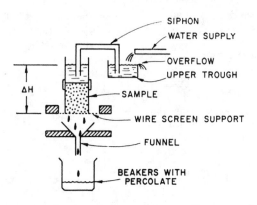

ΔH = Hydraulic head difference across sample

Fig. 13–3. Diagram of the constant-head system for conductivity measurement.

13–3.2.2 PROCEDURE

Cover one end of each sample with a circular piece of cloth held in place with a rubber band. Place the samples, cloth-covered ends down, in a tray filled with water to a depth just below the top of the samples. Allow them to soak at least 16 hours or longer if they are not completely saturated.

Turn on the water supply to the upper trough. Connect an empty cylindrical sample holder to the top of each sample, using a large rubber band or waterproof tape. Leave the lower part of the sample in the water while this is being done. Place a small piece of blotting paper on the top of the sample. Slowly pour water into the upper cylinder until it is ⅔ to ¾ full.

Quickly transfer the sample to the rack, and start one of the siphons to maintain a constant head of water on the sample. *Do not allow the water to drain from the top of the sample.*

After the water level on top of the sample has become stabilized, collect the percolate in a beaker or other suitable container. Measure the volume of water Q that passes through the sample in a known time t. Measure the hydraulic head difference ΔH and the temperature of the water.

13–3.2.3 CALCULATIONS

Calculate the hydraulic conductivity by the use of

$$K = (Q/At)(L/\Delta H) \qquad [5]$$

where A is the cross sectional area of the sample, and L is the length of the sample. The other symbols have been defined previously.

The conductivity has the dimensions of a velocity. The permeability is calculated from the conductivity by means of equation [4]. The convenient unit to be used for permeability will depend upon the range of values commonly encountered. In the lower range of values of permeability, the square micron is a reasonable unit.

13–3.3 Falling-Head Method

13–3.3.1 SPECIAL APPARATUS

A schematic diagram of the apparatus for the falling-head method is shown in Fig. 13–4. The actual form of the apparatus may be varied. Provision must be made to change the standpipe to the sample and to provide

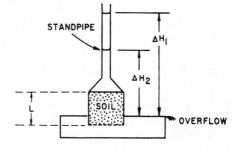

Fig. 13–4. Diagram of the falling-head system for conductivity measurement.

support for the sample. One such arrangement is shown in Fig. 13–6. The diameter of the standpipe should be chosen such that an easily measurable change in head will occur in a few hours or less. The tubing connections to the inflow side of the sample should have rigid walls. The end-caps can be made of aluminum or plastic. They are held on the sample by small bolts passing through the edges of both end-caps. The porous plates should be very permeable. Porous stones, such as are used in consolidation tests, or a very coarse-grade ceramic plate may be used (porosity XF or XFF, Selas Corp. of America, Dresher, Pa.).

13–3.3.2 *PROCEDURE*

Soak the sample in the manner described in section 13–3.2.2. Connect the sample to the end-caps, fill the standpipe with water to a height greater than H_1, and measure the time for the hydraulic head difference to fall from H_1 to H_2. Measure the cross sectional area of the standpipe, the temperature of the water, and the sample length and diameter.

13–3.3.3 *CALCULATIONS*

Calculate the conductivity from

$$K = (al/At) \ln (H_1/H_2) \quad\quad [6]$$

where a is the area of cross section of the standpipe, l is the length of the sample, A is the cross sectional area of the sample, and t is the time for the hydraulic head difference to decrease from H_1 to H_2.

13–3.4   Comments

The experimental arrangement for the measurement of conductivity is subject to considerable variation. The flow must be unidirectional, and the arrangement such that the hydraulic gradient and the resulting flux can be determined. The constant-head system is best suited to samples with conductivities greater than approximately 0.01 cm. per minute, while the falling-head system is best suited to samples with lower conductivity.

Apparatus more elaborate than that described here may be used for conductivity determinations. Lambe (1951) describes variants of both the constant-head and falling-head systems. The simple permeameter described here is not suited to soils of low permeability because of the error introduced by evaporation. Lambe describes a modification that greatly decreases the evaporation error. Soils that are low in permeability may have to be held between porous plates in a sealed cylinder, so that an increased hydraulic gradient can be applied to the sample. The fixed-ring type of consolidation apparatus (Lambe, 1951) can be used for conductivity determinations on disturbed samples.

The choice of a system for the measurement of conductivity involves several factors. Among these are (1) the accuracy required and (2) the amount of effort that can be expended to obtain the data on each sample. It is the author's opinion that elaborate painstaking methods are not generally required for conductivity determinations on field samples of undisturbed structure. The variability among samples is large enough that precise determination of the conductivity of a given sample is not required. On the other hand, for some research purpose in connection with fluid flow studies, it may be very profitable and necessary to use all possible refinements of technique to obtain highest possible precision and accuracy. The reader interested in details of technique with more elaborate equipment should consult Lambe (1951), Scheidegger (1960), and Smith and Stallman (1954). Constant-head control can be obtained by the use of a Mariotte bottle or by an overflow system. A Mariotte bottle may take on various forms, two of which are shown in Fig. 13–5. The hydraulic gradient may be obtained from direct observations of the water levels applied to the ends of the sample as described above, or it may be obtained from measurements with piezometers inserted into the side of the sample.

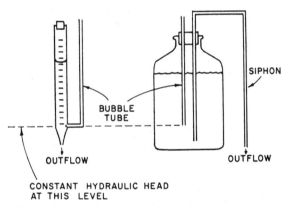

SIPHON

BUBBLE TUBE

OUTFLOW

OUTFLOW

CONSTANT HYDRAULIC HEAD AT THIS LEVEL

Fig. 13–5. The Mariotte flask for constant head control.

The soil sample may be supported at its lower end by any porous material that will prevent the loss of soil and that will not introduce an appreciable hydraulic head loss into the flow system. Cloth, fine wire screen, and coarse porous ceramic and glass plates are some of the materials that may be used.

If it is desired to determine the conductivity with other than tap water, it will be necessary to provide a constant-head source of water with sufficient capacity to permit the determinations to be completed. Large carboys fitted as Mariotte flasks can often be used for this purpose.

The method of wetting the samples described above will not necessarily lead to complete saturation. If it is desired to attain complete saturation, consideration should be given to one of the possible techniques for air removal. Among these are vacuum wetting, fluctuating external gas pressure, and preliminary flushing of the pores with carbon dioxide followed by passage of air-free water (Reeve, 1957a). Gas bubbles entrapped in the pores may produce erratic results. If the water used is relatively saturated with dissolved gas, the amount of entrapped gas may increase. This often is the case when tap water is used. On the other hand, if the water is relatively gas free, the entrapped gas may slowly be dissolved. In general, the use of air-free water is to be preferred. A system for the removal of air from fairly large quantities of water is described by Smith and Stallman (1954). Small quantities of water may be de-aerated by boiling or by vacuum.

The concentration and chemical nature of the solution used for the conductivity measurement are of extreme importance. This topic has been discussed and studied by several authors (Reeve, 1957a; Smith and Stallman, 1954; Foster, 1954). If possible, water containing the same amount and kinds of chemical species as the naturally occurring water should be used. Distilled water should seldom be used except for special purposes, such as a case in which structural breakdown is desired. Even tap water can produce large changes in the conductivity of the sample if it does not happen to be similar in concentration and composition to the soil water.

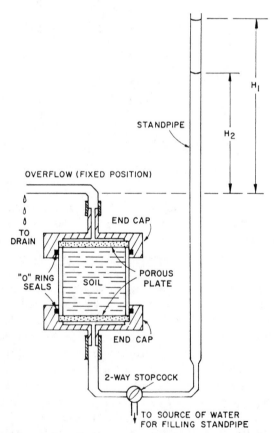

Fig. 13–6. Suggested experimental arrangement for a falling-head conductivity measurement.

The effects of the concentration and composition of the test solution are caused by ion-exchange phenomena of the colloidal fraction of the soil, with resultant variation in the swelling and flocculation of the colloids, and possibly with some effects on the water itself within the pores.

Because of swelling of clays and slaking of aggregates, soil that has been air dried will undergo changes in structure when it is rewetted. To prevent such changes, core samples should not be allowed to dry.

Biological activity in the samples may cause plugging of the pores by growth of microorganisms or by production of polysaccharides or other organic gummy materials. If it is desired to control such effects, dinitrophenol or some other disinfectant may be used.

The various effects mentioned above, viz., entrapped air, biological activity, swelling, and slaking will interact to produce a resultant variation in the conductivity with time. Allison (1947) has studied these effects. The reader is referred to the review by Reeve (1957a) for additional discussion of these phenomena and for sources of additional literature.

Leakage along the interfaces between the soil core and the sample retainer may be a source of error which can be eliminated or controlled by sealing the sample in the container. Sealing techniques have been described using a bentonite slurry (Reeve, 1957a) and paraffin (Smith et al., 1944).

The conductivity will be affected by the temperature of the water. The results may be corrected to a standard temperature by the use of the relation

$$K_{ST} = K_T(N_T/N_{ST}) \qquad [7]$$

where K and N are the conductivity and viscosity, respectively, and the subscripts T and ST denote the temperature of measurement and the standard temperature, respectively. The viscosity of water as a function of temperature is usually taken from standard tables.

When using the constant-head method, it is not necessary to standardize the time or the volume of water that is passed through the sample. It is suggested that about 100 cc. of water be passed through the sample, provided that this does not take longer than 15 to 30 minutes. If the volume is < 100 cc., the volume measurement should be made in such a way that three significant figures are obtained in the data.

Cracks and worm holes in core samples are an additional problem. These structural phenomena are present in the field and affect the flow in different ways, depending on the condition of flow. If the pressure head is positive, and if the cracks or holes have access to the soil surface, they will run full of water and will contribute greatly to the observed flux. If the pressure head in the water is negative, such structures will be drained if they have access to the soil surface and will cause a decrease in the flux of water. The streaming of water through a crack or hole in a laboratory sample may not be representative of the behavior of the soil in the field. If fragmented and repacked samples are used, such structures are eliminated. It has been recommended (Smith and Browning, 1947) that samples with obvious cracks and holes be discarded for purposes of evaluation of subsoil conductivity.

Fragmented samples are useful in comparative studies and in dealing with soils where structure is of relatively little importance. The results should not be regarded as absolute values that may be applied in the field unless the field soil is essentially a fragmented soil. This may be the case in the surface horizon and in soil that has been used for earth fill. Procedures for use of fragmented samples are given by Fireman (1944) and by the U. S. Salinity Laboratory Staff (1954).

Table 13–2. Confidence limits for hydraulic conductivity as a function of number of samples and the mean conductivity.

Number of samples	Confidence limit ΔK
2	2.00 $\overline{K}$
3	1.90 $\overline{K}$
5	1.45 $\overline{K}$
8	1.11 $\overline{K}$
16	0.76 $\overline{K}$

The sampling error in conductivity measurements has been studied by Mason et al. (1957). Analysis of variance was carried out on the logarithm of 100 times the conductivity in inches per hour. The sampling error variance component $\sigma_\mu{}^2$ attributed to variation in laboratory technique and to local soil variation within a given pit or site ranged from 0.10 to 0.18. Confidence limits in terms of the hydraulic conductivity were computed using $\sigma_\mu{}^2$ as 0.10 and a "Students" t value appropriate to a 95% confidence level. The results are shown in Table 13–2. The confidence interval ΔK depends upon the number of samples n and upon the mean value of the conductivity $\overline{K}$.

13–4   LITERATURE CITED

Allison, L. E. 1947. Effect of microorganisms on permeability of soil under prolonged submergence. Soil Sci. 63:439–450.

Brooks, R. H., Bower, C. A., and Reeve, R. C. 1956. The effect of various exchangeable cations upon the physical condition of soils. Soil Sci. Soc. Am. Proc. 20:325–327.

Fireman, M. 1944. Permeability measurements on disturbed soil samples. Soil Sci. 58:337–353.

Foster, Margaret D. 1954. Discussion of factors affecting permeability. Am. Soc. Test. Materials Spec. Tech. Publ. 163:117–121.

Hubbert, M. King. 1957. Darcy's law and the field equations of the flow of underground fluids. Bull. de l'Assoc. Intern. d'Hydrologie Scientifique No. 5:24–59. Also in Trans. Am. Inst. of Mining, Metallurgical and Petroleum Engineers 207:222–239, 1956.

Hutcheson, W. L. 1958. Moisture flow induced by thermal gradients within unsaturated soils. Highway Res. Board. Spec. Rept. 40:113–133.

Kelley, O. J., Hardman, J. A., and Jennings, D. S. 1948. A soil sampling machine for obtaining 2-, 3-, and 4-inch diameter cores of undisturbed soil to a depth of 6 feet. Soil Sci. Soc. Am. Proc. (1947) 12:85–87.

Lambe, T. W. 1951. Soil Testing for Engineers. John Wiley & Sons, New York.

Low, P. F. 1960. Viscosity of water in clay systems. Conference on Clays and Clay Minerals Proc. 8:170–182.

Lutz, J. F., Nelson, W. L., Brady, N. C., and Scarsbrook, C. E. 1947. Effects of cover crops on pore-size distribution in a coastal plain soil. Soil Sci. Soc. Am. Proc. (1946) 11:43–46.

Mason, D. D., Lutz, J. F., and Petersen, R. G. 1957. Hydraulic conductivity as related to certain soil properties in a number of great soil groups—sampling errors involved. Soil Sci. Soc. Am. Proc. 21:554–561.

Muskat, M. 1946. The Flow of Homogeneous Fluids Through Porous Media. J. W. Edwards, Inc., Ann Arbor, Mich.

O'Neal, A. M. 1952. A key for evaluating soil permeability by means of certain field clues. Soil Sci. Soc. Am. Proc.16:312–315.

Quirk, J. P., and Schofield, R. K. 1955. The effect of electrolyte concentration on soil permeability. J. Soil Sci. 6:163–178.

Richards, L. A. (Chairman). 1952. Report of the subcommittee on permeability and infiltration, committee on terminology, Soil Science Society of America. Soil Sci. Soc. Am. Proc. 16:85–88.

Reeve, R. C. 1957a. The measurement of permeability in the laboratory. Agron. 7:414–419.

Reeve, R. C. 1957b. Drainage of irrigated lands. Soil Conserv. 23:12–15.

Reeve, R. C. 1957c. Factors which affect permeability. Agron. 7:404–414.

Reeve, R. C., Bower, C. A., Brooks, R. H., and Gschwend, F. B. 1954. A comparison of the effects of exchangeable sodium and potassium upon the physical condition of soils. Soil Sci. Soc. Am. Proc. 18:130–132.

Scheidegger, A. E. 1960. The Physics of Flow Through Porous Media. The Macmillan Company, New York.

Smith, R. M., and Browning, D. R. 1947. Some suggested laboratory standards of subsoil permeability. Soil Sci. Soc. Am. Proc. (1946) 11:21–26.

Smith, R. M., Browning, D. R., and Pohlman, G. G. 1944. Laboratory percolation through undisturbed soil samples in relation to pore size distribution. Soil Sci. 57:197–213.

Smith, W. O., and Stallman, R. W. 1954. Measurement of permeabilities in ground water investigations. In Symposium on Permeability of Soils. Am. Soc. Test. Materials Spec. Tech. Publ. 143:98–114.

Uhland, R. E. 1950. Physical properties of soils as modified by crops and management. Soil Sci. Soc. Am. Proc. (1949) 14:361–366.

U. S. Salinity Laboratory Staff. 1954. Diagnosis and improvement of saline and alkali soils. U. S. Dept. Agr. Handbook 60.

14 Field Measurement of Hydraulic Conductivity Below a Water Table

L. BOERSMA

Oregon State University
Corvallis, Oregon

14-1 INTRODUCTION

The hydraulic conductivity of saturated soil is the constant which, for a given soil, relates the rate of water transport in that soil to the hydraulic gradient or driving force causing water to move. The significance of this parameter is discussed in section 13, in which laboratory methods are outlined for its measurement.

A mathematical relationship was first postulated by Darcy in 1856. It is most commonly expressed as follows:

$$v = -K\nabla H$$

where v is the volume of water passing unit cross sectional area per unit time (cm. per sec.), ∇H is the hydraulic gradient (cm. per cm.) and K is the hydraulic conductivity of the soil (cm. per sec.).

In the section on laboratory methods, it was shown how this relationship may be used to determine the value of K by laboratory arrangements such that the quantities v and ∇H can be measured and K remains as the unknown to be calculated. Field methods for the measurement of hydraulic conductivity are based on similar principles. Again, experimental arrangements are used such that measurements of v and ∇H can be made, with K remaining as the unknown to be calculated.

Several methods have been developed for the measurement of hydraulic conductivity in the field for conditions where the soil is saturated. Obviously, these methods can only be used when a water table is present in or above the soil layer of which the conductivity is to be determined. The auger-hole method and the piezometer method belong to this group. The methods have the advantage that the water present in the soil is used for the measurement. Diserens (1934) first developed a technique using auger holes for the measurement of hydraulic conductivity. Improvements and modifications were later introduced by Hooghoudt (1936), Ernst (1950), Kirkham and Van Bavel (1949) and Van Bavel and Kirkham (1949). The piezometer method was first introduced by Kirkham (1946). The method was developed by Luthin and Kirkham (1949) and Reeve and Kirkham (1951).

14–2 AUGER-HOLE METHOD

14–2.1 Principles

The auger-hole method used for the determination of hydraulic conductivity in saturated soils involves the construction of a cavity below the water table with a minimum of soil disturbance. The cavity is allowed to fill with water and is subsequently pumped out several times until any puddling effects caused by augering out the cavity have been eliminated by the inseeping water. The measurement then proceeds in the following manner. After the elevation of the water table is first determined by allowing the water surface in the hole to attain equilibrium with the water table, the hole is again pumped out to a new water level elevation. The rate of rise of the water level in the cavity is then measured and from it the hydraulic conductivity is subsequently calculated. The similarity with the laboratory methods is easily recognized. The rate of rise of the water level in the hole is a measure of the rate of flow v, and the hydraulic gradient is determined by the difference between the water level in the hole and the water table. Contrary to the conditions of the laboratory methods, however, no simple equation can be written which gives the hydraulic conductivity as a function of the rate of rise and the hydraulic gradient. First of all, the flow system is "three dimensional" rather than "one dimensional." Secondly, the boundary conditions of the flow system are more complex. Water enters the cavity from the bottom and all sides. Flow takes place in both the horizontal and vertical directions, and the hydraulic conductivity in two different directions is not necessarily the same. Finally, soils change in characteristics with depth. The same cavity may penetrate several layers with different hydraulic conductivity, each contributing to the total flow at a different rate.

Several variations of the auger-hole method have been developed, all designed to circumvent one or more of the problems mentioned above. Also, different methods have been developed to calculate the hydraulic conductivity from the measurement of the experimental variables. A mathematical treatment of the theory of water flow into cavities is beyond the scope of this discussion. The equations used in the various methods have been summarized and reviewed by J. N. Luthin (1957). The hydraulic conductivity calculated with the data of an auger-hole test reflects primarily the horizontal conductivity of the layers penetrated by the hole below the water table. However, the result is dominated by the more permeable layers.

To calculate the hydraulic conductivity, the following equation may be used (Johnson et al., 1952).

$$K = \frac{\pi R^2}{A[(L_2 + L_1)/2 - E]} \frac{\Delta h}{\Delta t} \text{ cm. per sec .}$$

The symbols are defined in the insert diagram in Fig. 14–1 and as follows:

K = hydraulic conductivity (cm. per sec.),

$\Delta h = L_1 - L_2$ = increment of rise of water level in the hole (cm.),

$\Delta t = t_2 - t_1$ = increment of time (sec.) required for increment of rise Δh,

R = radius of the hole (cm.),

$(L_2 + L_1)/2 - E$ = average distance H (cm.) of water level in the hole below the water table during time of measurement, and

A = geometry factor (cm.) which is a constant depending on $R, d, h,$ and s where s is the distance of the impermeable layer below the bottom of the hole, h is the average depth of water in the hole during the measurement interval and d is the depth of the hole below the water table.

Since the result is dominated by more permeable horizons in nonuniform stratified material, the method is of most value in unstratified soil. However, a method has been developed to use the auger-hole method in stratified soil to obtain the hydraulic conductivity of each layer. If the profile consists of two layers differing appreciably in hydraulic conductivity, the value for each layer can be determined if the water table lies well within the upper layer. Ernst (1950) has proposed that the hydraulic conductivity of each layer can be calculated from the measurements obtained from two holes of different depth. The hydraulic conductivity of the first layer is determined from the measurements made in a shallow hole, the bottom of which should be at least 10 to 15 cm. above the lower layer. A mean value of the hydraulic conductivity for the two layers is determined from the measurements made in a deep hole penetrating well into the lower layer. If a third layer is present, the bottom of the deep hole should stay above that layer.

14–2.2   Method [1]

14–2.2.1   SPECIAL APPARATUS

1. Auger: Choose a closed-type post-hole auger for coarse-textured soils and an open-blade-type auger for fine-textured soils. Because the diameter of the hole is a variable involved in the final analysis of the

---

[1] Diserens (1934), Hooghoudt (1936), Kirkham and Van Bavel (1949).

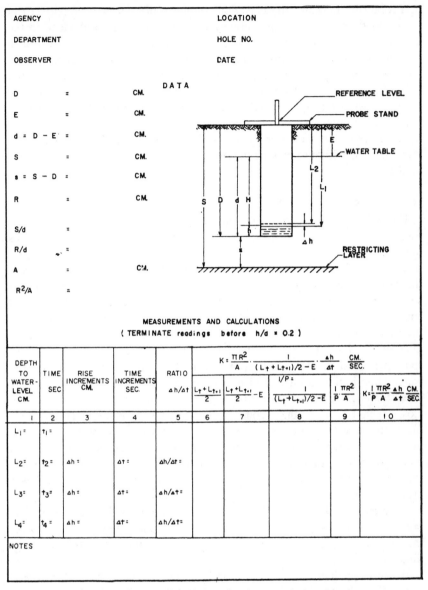

Fig. 14–1. Suggested field sheet for the auger-hole method.

results, choose a diameter that will be applicable for use with any nomographs that may be used as an aid in obtaining the hydraulic conductivity.

2. Bailer or pump: Use a bailer or pump to remove seepage water from the hole. Construct the bailer of thin-walled tubing, with a diameter smaller than that of the hole, and with a check-valve at the lower end.

3. Probe: To measure the elevations of the water surface, prepare a rod of wood or other nonconducting material, with a wire imbedded in the center. Allow the wire to project from both ends. Graduate the rod in centimeters from the tip of the wire extending from the bottom. To the wire extending from the top, attach in series a limiting resistor of about 7,000 ohms, a milliammeter (Shurite, 0 to 5 ma.) and one terminal of a 33-v. hearing-aid battery. Attach the other terminal of the battery to a metal pipe driven into the soil to the depth of the water table. Alternatively, use a measuring tape attached to a float of size to fit in the auger hole without touching the sides.
4. Stop watch.

14–2.2.2 PROCEDURE

For efficient operation in the field, prepare a set of data sheets such as Fig. 14–1, which includes as an insert a diagram defining the measurements to be recorded.

To make the measurement, first remove sod, trash, and loose soil from the selected location. Then auger out the hole to the desired depth. If the soil is uniform for some depth below the water table, extend the hole at least 30 cm. below the water table. The depth is limited by the A-factor as presented in Fig. 14–2. If the soil is nonuniform, and if an average conductivity is desired for soil extending from the water level downward to some particular depth, auger out the soil to that depth. If the soil below the water table is nonuniform, and if a separate figure for conductivity is desired for each of two layers, first auger out a hole in the first layer, not closer than 10 cm. to the second (to be suitable for making the measurement, the hole should extend at least 30 cm. below the water table), and make the measurements described below. Then auger out the soil to a greater depth so that the bottom of the hole is as far as possible below the bottom of the first layer but at least 10 cm. above the top of a lower layer, and make the measurements described below.

Decrease or eliminate puddling effects by removing the water from the hole several times. To permit selection of suitable time or depth increments to be used later, estimate during this operation the order of magnitude of the rate of rise of water in the hole.

Record the depth D of the auger hole below the surface. Record the depth E of the water table below the soil surface when the water level in the hole has reached equilibrium with the water table in the soil. Record the distance S between the soil surface and a restricting layer, and calculate the distance s between the bottom of the hole and the restricting layer. Remove the water from the hole, and measure the time Δt required for the water level to rise through the distance Δh. If the time permits, make four such pairs of readings as the water rises. Complete all measurements before

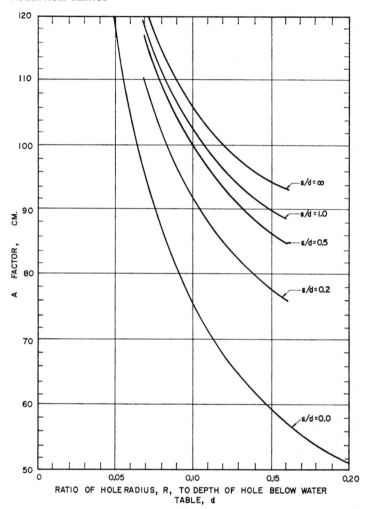

Fig. 14–2. Nomograph for determination of the A-factor used in the computation of the hydraulic conductivity from data obtained by the auger-hole method. The nomograph is valid only for measurements completed before the water level rises to the elevation where $h/d = 0.2$.

the water level has risen to the level $h/d = 0.2$, where h is the average depth of water in the hole during the measurement, and d is the depth of the hole below the water table. Repeat the measurements on the same hole after the water level in the hole has risen to the level of the water table. If values of $\Delta h/\Delta t$ obtained in the second series of measurements are not consistent with those of the first, repeat the process until consistent results are obtained.

14-2.2.3 CALCULATIONS

Determine the A-factor from Fig. 14–2, and record this value on the data sheet. The A-factor is shown as a function of the ratios s/d and R/d. The A-factor is also a function of the average depth h of water in the hole during the time of measurement. The graph is valid only for measurements completed before the water level rises to the elevation where $h/d = 0.2$. Complete columns 3 through 10.

To calculate the hydraulic conductivity of individual layers, where measurements have been made in each, make the calculations described above for each set of measurements. Then use the following equation to estimate the hydraulic conductivity of the lower layer:

$$K_2 = (Kd_2 - K_1d_1)/(d_2 - d_1)$$

where K_2 is the hydraulic conductivity of the lower layer, K_1 is the hydraulic conductivity of the first layer as calculated from the rate of rise of water in the shallow hole, K is the composite hydraulic conductivity of the two layers as calculated from the rate of rise of water in the deep hole, and d_1 and d_2 are the depths of the shallow and deep holes below the water table.

14-2.2.4 COMMENTS

The validity of measurements of hydraulic conductivity obtained by the auger-hole method may be questioned on the basis that values may differ as much as 100% between holes only a few feet apart in soil classified as a single type. After comparing the results of several thousand measurements with observed drainage behavior of soils, however, Maasland and Haskew (1957) concluded that the auger-hole method yields accurate results.

Because of the great difference among holes, approximate values on a number of holes are more valuable for practical drainage problems than are precise measurements on one or two holes. Differences in hydraulic conductivity among soil types may be of the order of a thousand fold, and so a soil map is a useful adjunct in selecting sites for measurement and in expressing the results.

It must be realized that appreciable errors arise when the reported equations are used beyond their range of validity. When dimensions are used other than those recommended, the cited literature must be consulted to obtain the appropriate equations. The conditions not covered by the recommended procedure are, however, seldom encountered. Under certain conditions the auger-hole method is difficult to use or gives unreliable results. The auger-hole method is difficult to use in rocky soil or coarse gravel material, in soils with very high permeability rates, and under conditions where the water table is at or above the ground surface. Unreliable results are obtained under artesian conditions and under conditions where the profile contains sand lenses between less permeable layers.

The equation for estimating the hydraulic conductivity of two layers of soil from the hydraulic conductivity of the upper layer and a composite value for the upper and lower layers was proposed by Ernst (1950). Ernst estimated that the error resulting from the simplifying assumptions used in the derivation does not exceed about $\pm 10\%$. According to Luthin (1957), the equation gives fairly reliable results if $K_2 > K_1$.

14-3   PIEZOMETER METHOD

14-3.1   Principles

The auger-hole method is based on the measurement of flow into an unlined cavity, and the hydraulic conductivity calculated from the results of this test is an average value of primarily the horizontal conductivity of the layers below the water table penetrated by the hole. The piezometer method is based on the measurement of flow into an unlined cavity at the lower end of a lined hole. Because the vertical dimension of the unlined cavity is smaller with the piezometer method than with the auger-hole method, the former method is superior to the latter for measuring the hydraulic conductivity of individual layers. The conditions and symbols employed with the piezometer method are shown in Fig. 14–3. Water entering the unlined cavity and rising in the lined hole is removed several times by pumping or bailing to flush the soil pores along the cavity wall. After flushing is completed, the water is allowed to come to equilibrium with the water table. After the water has been pumped out again, the rate of rise is recorded. To calculate the hydraulic conductivity the following equation may be used (Johnson et al. 1952):

$$K = \frac{\pi R^2}{A \Delta t} \, \ln \frac{L_1 - E}{L_2 - E} \text{ cm. per sec.}$$

The symbols are defined in the insert diagram in Fig. 14–3 and as follows:

K = hydraulic conductivity (cm. per sec.),
R = inside radius of the liner (cm.),
E = distance from top of liner to the water table (cm.),
L_1 = distance (cm.) from top of liner to water level in liner at time t_1,
L_2 = distance (cm.) from top of liner to water level in liner at time t_2,
$\Delta t = t_2 - t_1$, time increment for water to rise from L_1 to L_2 (sec.), and
A = geometry factor (cm.) which is a function of R, the distance d from the water table to the bottom of the liner, the distance W from the bottom of the liner to the bottom of the hole, and the distance s from the bottom of the hole to a restricting layer.

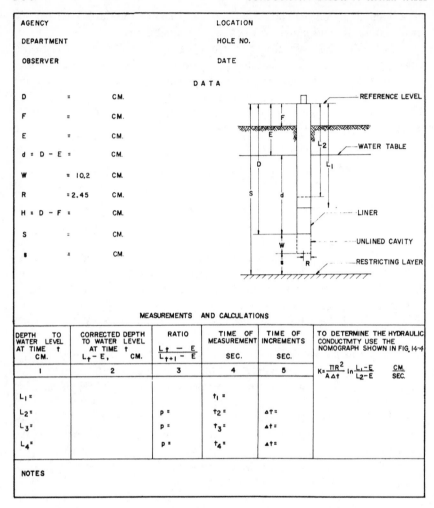

Fig. 14–3. Suggested field sheet for the piezometer method.

14–3.2 Method [2]

14–3.2.1 SPECIAL APPARATUS

1. Items 1, 2, 3, and 4 described in section 14–1.3.1.
2. Liner: Use a section of pipe of diameter that will fit tightly in the auger hole and of a length sufficient to extend from the bottom of the hole to a height 15 cm. or more above the surface of the soil. Electrical conduit with an inside diameter of 5.08 cm., sharpened at the bottom, is convenient for use in connection with an auger 4.9 cm. in diameter.

---

[2] Kirkham (1946), Luthin and Kirkham (1949).

14-3.2.2 PROCEDURE

For efficient operation in the field, prepare a set of data sheets such as Fig. 14–3, which contains as an insert a diagram defining the measurements to be recorded.

Remove surface sod, trash, and loose soil from the location of the hole. Make a hole to a depth of 10 cm. with an auger 4.9 cm. in diameter. Remove the auger, and tap the sharpened end of the liner into the hole to the depth of the opening. Insert the auger into the liner, bore the hole 15 cm. deeper, and tap the liner down to the bottom of the hole. Repeat this process until the bottom of the liner is at the desired depth below the water table. Then carefully auger out a cavity 10.2 cm. in length and 4.9 cm. in diameter below the end of the liner. Remove the water from the hole several times to reduce or eliminate puddling effects. Estimate the order of magnitude of the rate of rise for selection of the increments of rise or time to be used in the measurements.

Record the following measurements as defined in the insert of Fig. 14–3: length of piezometer D, depth of water table E, cavity dimensions W and R, depth of measurement $(D - F)$ and depth of water table $(E - F)$. Remove the water from the pipe, and measure the time Δt required for the water level to rise through the distance Δh. If time permits, make three or more such pairs of measurements as the water rises. Make no measurements after the water has risen to a level 20 cm. below the water table. Repeat the measurements of rate of rise of the water level in the same hole after the water level in the hole has risen to the level of the water table. If values of $\Delta h/\Delta t$ obtained in the second series of measurements are not consistent with those of the first, repeat the process until consistent results are obtained.

Determine the hydraulic conductivity of deeper layers by lowering the hole and liner and by making another series of measurements.

14-3.2.3 CALCULATIONS

Use the value of 43.2 cm. for the A-factor for a cavity 10.2 cm. in length and 4.9 cm. in diameter if s and d are greater than 20 cm. An error less than $\pm 8\%$ is introduced by assuming $A = 43.2$ cm. as long as $d \geqslant W$ and $s \geqslant (1/2)W$. Since these limiting conditions are rarely encountered, the A-factor is assumed to be constant and equal to 43.2 cm. A nomograph has been prepared showing the solutions of the equation of section 14–3.1 for various values of $\ln [(L_1 - E)/(L_2 - E)]$ and Δt. To calculate the hydraulic conductivity, complete columns 2, 3 and 5 on the data sheet. Then use the nomograph of Fig. 14–4 to find the hydraulic conductivity.

14-3.2.4 COMMENTS

The piezometer method is best suited for determination of the hydraulic conductivity of homogeneous layers in stratified soil. If the diameter of the

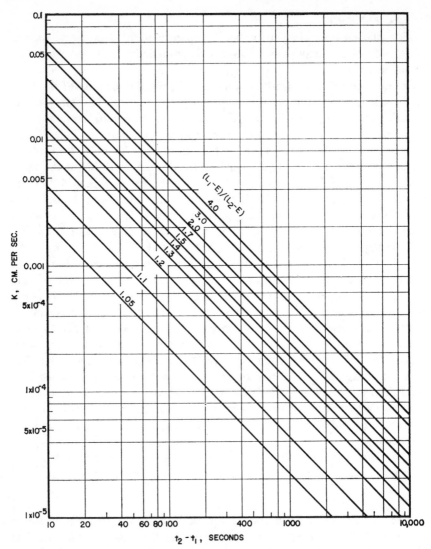

Fig. 14–4. Nomograph for the determination of the hydraulic conductivity from data obtained by the piezometer method. The nomograph is valid only for conditions where the length of the cavity is 10.2 cm. and the diameter is 4.9 cm.

cavity is small (3 to 5 cm.) and the length of the cavity is several times its diameter, the horizontal permeability is measured. The wider the hole and the shorter the length of the cavity left unlined, the more nearly the measurement becomes one of vertical permeability. The tube method developed by Frevert and Kirkham (1948) is a modification of the piezometer method designed to measure vertical permeability. A liner penetrates to the bottom of a hole 20 cm. in diameter, and water can enter only through the bottom of the hole.

The piezometer method gives accurate results if the conditions stated in section 14–1.4.3 for use of the graphs are met. Measurements near an impermeable layer result in considerable error, however, unless appropriate corrections are made in the A-factor used. The method is difficult to use in rocky soils. Even when the tube can be installed in these soils, it is difficult to do so without leaving channels along the outside of the tube. Also it is difficult to establish cavities of the correct dimensions. The diameter of the cavity is very important in the calculation of the hydraulic conductivity, so that a stable cavity is mandatory for reproducible results.

14-4 LITERATURE CITED

American Society of Agricultural Engineers. 1961. Measuring saturated hydraulic conductivity of soils. Am. Soc. Agr. Eng. Spec. Publ. SP-SW-0262.

Diserens, E. 1934. Beitrag zur Bestimmung der Durchlässigkeit des Bodens in Natürlicher Bodenlagerung. Schweiz. Landw. Monatshefte. 12:188–198, 204–212.

Ernst, L. F. 1950. Een nieuwe formule voor de berekening van de doorlaatfactor met de boorgatenmethode. Rap. Landbouwproefsta. en Bodemkundig Inst. T.N.O. Groningen, The Netherlands (mimeo).

Frevert, R. K., and Kirkham, Don. 1948. A field method for measuring the permeability of soil below a water table. Proc. Highway Res. Board 28:433–442.

Hooghoudt, S. B. 1936. Bydragen tot de kennis van eenige natuurkundige grootheden van den grond, 6. Versl. Landb. Ond. 43:461–676. Algemene Landsdrukkerÿ, The Hague.

Johnson, H. P., Frevert, R. K., and Evans, D. D. 1952. Simplified procedure for the measurement and computation of soil permeability below the water table. Agr. Eng. 33:283–289.

Kirkham, Don. 1946. Proposed method for field measurement of permeability of soil below the water table. Soil Sci. Soc. Am. Proc. (1945) 10:58–68.

Kirkham, Don, and Van Bavel, C. H. M. 1949. Theory of seepage into auger holes. Soil Sci. Soc. Am. Proc. (1948) 13:75–89.

Luthin, J. N., and Kirkham, Don. 1949. A piezometer method for measuring permeability of soil in sites below a water table. Soil Sci. 68:349–358.

Luthin, J. N., ed. 1957. Drainage of agricultural lands. Agron. 7.

Maasland, M., and Haskew, H. C. 1957. The auger hole method of measuring the hydraulic conductivity of soil and its application to the drainage design. Proc. 3rd Intern. Congr. Irrigation Drainage Questions 8:69–114.

Marshall, T. J. 1959. Relations between water and soil. Commonwealth Bur. Soils, Tech. Commun. 80.

Reeve, R. C., and Kirkham, Don. 1951. Soil anisotropy and some field methods for measuring permeability. Am. Geophys. Union Trans. 32:582–596.

Van Bavel, C. H. M., and Kirkham, Don. 1949. Field measurement of soil permeability using auger holes. Soil Sci. Soc. Am. Proc. (1948) 13:90–96.

Van Beers, W. F. J. 1958. The auger hole method. International Institute for Land Reclamation and Improvement. Bul. 1.

15

Field Measurement of Hydraulic Conductivity Above a Water Table

L. BOERSMA

Oregon State University
Corvallis, Oregon

15–1 INTRODUCTION

Field methods for the measurement of hydraulic conductivity discussed in section 14 have the distinct disadvantage that a water table must be present. These methods cannot be used in the many regions where a water table is only infrequently or never present in the layers the hydraulic conductivity of which must be determined. Other methods have been developed for use in such areas.

Field methods applicable where no water table is present consist basically of measuring the rate of flow of water from a lined or unlined auger hole. Since the flow system is unconfined, large quantities of water are required. As a result the methods are more involved than the methods used below a water table. More equipment is required, and the methods are much more time-consuming because it takes longer to saturate the soil and establish equilibrium conditions.

15–2 DOUBLE-TUBE METHOD

15–2.1 Principles

The principle of the operation of the double-tube method is shown in Fig. 15–1. An auger hole is excavated to the depth at which a measurement of the hydraulic conductivity is desired. An undisturbed soil surface is obtained at the bottom of the hole with a specially designed hole cleaner. This surface is protected with a thin layer of coarse sand. The two concentric cylinders are carefully installed so that they penetrate the undisturbed soil surface approximately 2 cm. Water is continuously supplied to both tubes simultaneously. During this operation, care is exercised to keep the water level the same in both standpipes. With time, a wet zone with positive pressures builds up. It is essential that complete saturation of the soil in this

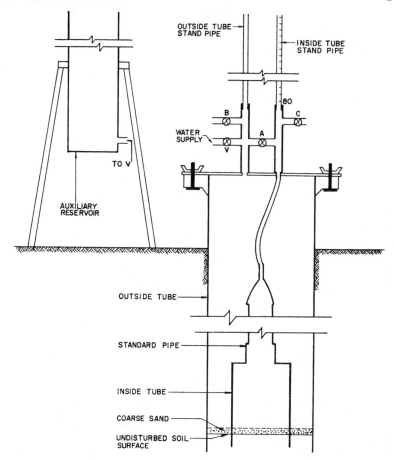

Fig. 15–1. Schematic diagram of equipment for the double-tube method in place.

zone is obtained. When complete saturation is obtained the measurements can be made. To calculate the hydraulic conductivity, two sets of data are required. First, the water level in the inside tube is allowed to change while the level in the outside tube is kept constant. The rate of fall of the water level in the inside tube is recorded. Next, the water levels are brought back to the same starting point and, by waiting a suitable length of time (10 times the time required to obtain the first set of data), initial equilibrium conditions are again established. The water supply to the inside tube is then cut off. As the water level in the inside tube falls, the water level in the outside tube is kept equal to that in the inside tube by manipulation of a valve. The rate of fall of the water level in the inside tube is recorded. The results of the two sets of measurements are plotted on linear graph paper

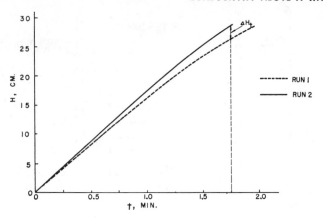

Fig. 15–2. Graph showing the results of the observations necessary to calculate the hydraulic conductivity obtained by the double-tube method.

with time t as the abscissa and the corresponding drop in water level H as the ordinate, as shown in Fig. 15–2.

The hydraulic conductivity K is determined from the relation

$$K = \left(\frac{R_v^2}{FR_c}\right)\left(\frac{\Delta H_t}{\int_0^t Hdt}\right) \text{ cm. per min.}$$

where R_v is the radius of the inside-tube standpipe, R_c is the radius of the inside tube, F is a dimensionless quantity describing the geometry of the flow system, ΔH_t is the vertical difference at time t between the two curves of t versus H plotted from the data of the two sets of measurements (Fig. 15–2) and $\int_0^t Hdt$ is the area under the curve of t versus H plotted from the data of the set of readings with the water level in the outside tube kept constant up to the time at which ΔH_t is measured.

The dimensionless quantity F describing the flow system is analogous to the A-factor used in the methods of section 14. The value of F can be determined with the nomographs of Fig. 15–3 and 15–4. Two nomographs are shown. Figure 15–3 is to be used when the material of which the hydraulic conductivity is to be determined is underlain by impermeable material, and Fig. 15–4 is to be used when the material of which the hydraulic conductivity is to be determined is underlain by highly permeable material. The symbols used in Fig. 15–3 and 15–4 are defined in the insert diagram in Fig. 15–5 and as follows: d is the depth of penetration of the inside tube into the undisturbed soil, D is the depth of a restricting layer below the bottom of the hole, and D_p is the depth of a highly permeable layer below the bottom of the hole.

15-2.2 Method [1]

15-2.2.1 SPECIAL APPARATUS

1. Double-tube installation:[2] A schematic diagram of apparatus for a double-tube installation is shown in Fig. 15–1. Prepare the outer tube and the lower section of the inner tube of thin-walled steel pipe, hardened, and with a sharp beveled edge at the bottom. Use stock having a diameter of 12.7 cm. or more for the inner tube, and maintain the ratio of diameters of the outer and inner tubes at 1.7 or more. Make the outer tube long enough to extend above the surface of the soil when the bottom is imbedded in the layer for which measurements are to be made. Connect a length of galvanized pipe 5 cm. in diameter to the top of the inner tube using couplings, and connect a bell reducer to the top of the galvanized pipe. Weld spacer vanes to the lower coupling and to the bell reducer to assure that the inner tube is centered in the outer tube. Prepare a rigid metal top-plate for the outer tube, and weld two short pieces of metal pipe with 2.5-cm. inside diameter vertically over two holes in the plate. Arrange for connection A between the pipes, for inlets C and V to the pipes, and for outlet B from the pipe connecting to the outer tube, as shown in Fig. 15–1. In the top of each pipe, seal a piece of plexiglas tubing 2.54 cm. in diameter and approximately 50 cm. in length. Make the inside tube standpipe 3 cm. longer than the outside tube standpipe. Graduate the inside tube standpipe in centimeters, adjusting the scale so that the zero level is at the top of the outside tube standpipe. Attach a piece of nonkinking flexible tubing to the top of the bell reducer and the bottom of the top plate with Swagelok fittings. Seal the top plate to the outer tube by bolting the plate down over a rubber gasket to a flange on the outside tube.

2. Auger: Use a posthole auger equipped with blades to give a hole of diameter equal to or greater than that of the outer tube.

3. Hole cleaner: Assemble a series of thin stainless steel blades with plywood spacers 1.2 cm. in thickness. Make the tops of the blades flush with the tops of the plywood spacers, and allow the blades to extend 1.8 cm. below the spacers. Make the assembly small enough to fit in the auger hole and slightly larger than the inside diameter of the outer tube. Bolt the blades and spacers together, and attach an extendable handle to the side opposite the protruding blades.

4. Energy breaker, consisting of a piece of metal pipe with the lower end

---

[1] Bouwer (1961, 1962).

[2] Since the writing of this manuscript the double-tube installation, as described here, has become commercially available from Soiltest, Inc., 2205 Lee Street, Evanston, Ill.

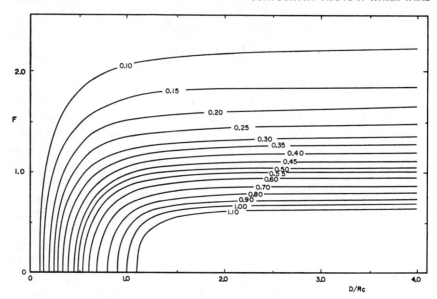

Fig. 15–3. Nomograph for determination of the dimensionless flow-factor F to be used in computation of the hydraulic conductivity from data obtained by the double-tube method. F is shown as a function of depth to an impermeable layer, expressed as the ratio D/R_c for various values of d/R_c.

welded to a perforated disk having a diameter about 0.5 cm. smaller than the inside diameter of the outer tube of the double-tube assembly.

5. Water supply, consisting of a 500-liter tank with fittings and tubing to connect to the pipes leading to the outer and inner tubes of the double-tube installation.

6. Stop watch.

15–2.2.2 PROCEDURE

Prepare a set of data sheets such as shown in Fig. 15–5 for recording measurements and for calculations.

Auger out the hole to the desired depth. Force the cleaner down into the soil at the bottom, and pull upward vertically to produce a clean surface. In carrying out this operation, do not force the hole cleaner beyond the depth required to fill the openings between the blades, and avoid turning the cleaner. If the soil is too hard to permit ready entry of the cleaner, do not force it in by hammering, but first soften the soil by adding a few centimeters of water and allowing the water to drain. Pour a 1 cm. layer of coarse dry sand over the cleaned surface.

Place the outside tube in the hole, and force it down through the sand to the original surface. Insert the energy breaker in the tube, and allow

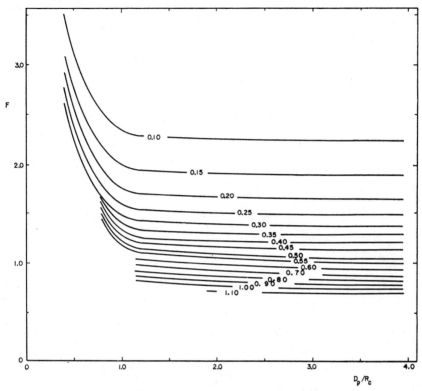

Fig. 15–4. Nomograph for the determination of the dimensionless flow-factor F to be used in the computation of the hydraulic conductivity from data obtained by the double-tube method. F is shown as a function of depth to a highly permeable layer, expressed as the ratio D_p/R_c for various values of d/R_c.

the perforated disk to rest on the sand. Fill the outside tube with water, and remove the energy breaker while maintaining the water level. Force the outside tube down about 5 cm. to obtain a seal so that water does not rise on the outside of the tube. (If a good seal cannot be obtained and leakage still occurs, make sure that the water level outside the tube does not fluctuate during measurements.) Wait until the soil has come close to saturation. The waiting time is about 1 hour for fine-textured soils, less for coarser soils. Then lower the inside tube inside the outer tube, and force it down until it penetrates the soil surface about 2 cm. in a fine-textured soil and 3 cm. in a coarser soil. Control the depth of penetration by choosing an appropriate bench mark. Connect one end of the flexible tubing to the bell reducer of the inside tube.

The following steps are designed to fill both tubes simultaneously, so that excessive pressure differences between the two tubes are avoided. Hold the top plate above the hole, with the water supply temporarily connected

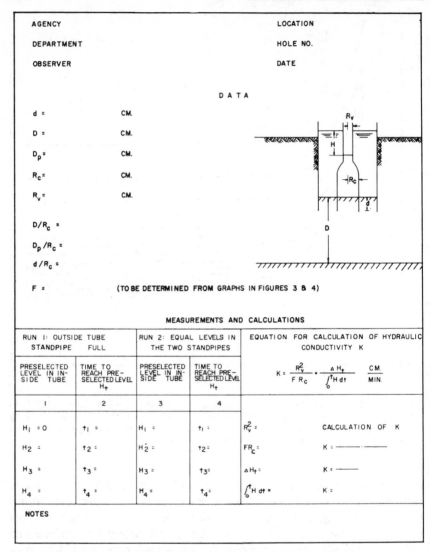

Fig. 15–5. Suggested field sheet for use with the double-tube method.

to inlet C on the inner-tube standpipe, and with valve A open and valves B and V closed. With water flowing from both standpipes, connect the upper end of the flexible tubing to the inner-tube standpipe. Then bolt the top plate to the outer tube. When the outer-tube standpipe overflows, change the water supply from C to V with valve A still open.

Adjust the flow rate so that the water level in the inner-tube standpipe is maintained at the zero mark and the outer-tube standpipe is overflowing slightly. To obtain data for calculating the hydraulic conductivity K, two sets of readings are necessary, as follows.

To make the first measurements, close valve A while the water level in the outer-tube standpipe is maintained to overflowing. Add a little water to the inner-tube standpipe to raise the level above the zero mark. Then start a stopwatch when the water level passes the zero mark. Record the time required for the water level to drop through increments of 5 cm. or some other preselected distance to a total of 30 cm. Then immediately add water to the inner-tube standpipe to restore the water level to the zero mark, and open valve A to return to the initial equilibrium condition. Before starting the second measurements, keep the water at the equilibrium level for a period at least ten times as long as that required to make the first series of measurements.

To make the second measurements, start a stopwatch at the time valves A and V are closed, and manipulate valve B so that the rate of fall of the water level in the outer-tube standpipe is equal to that in the inner-tube standpipe. Record the time required for the water level to drop through increments of 5 cm. or some other preselected distance to a total of 30 cm. Then close valve B, open valves A and V, and allow the water to rise in both standpipes to restore the initial equilibrium condition.

Keep the water at the equilibrium level for a period at least ten times that required to make the second series of measurements. Then repeat both series of measurements. If values in the second run are not consistent with those in the first, repeat the measurements a third time.

15–2.2.3 CALCULATIONS

Calculate the ratio d/R_c and the ratio D/R_c if the zone of measurement is underlain by an impervious or slowly permeable layer or the ratio D_p/R_c if the zone of measurement is underlain by a highly permeable layer. Determine the value of F from Fig. 15–3 or Fig. 15–4. Plot the H versus t curves of the two series of measurements. An example of the use of these curves is shown as Fig. 15–2. From the plotted curves determine ΔH_t and $\int_0^t H dt$. ΔH_t is the vertical distance between the two curves at time t, and the integral is the area under the curve of the set of measurements with the outside tube standpipe full (run 1). Choose time t such that the water level in the inside standpipe has fallen at least ⅔ the length of the scale. Complete the calculation of the hydraulic conductivity on the data sheet as shown in Fig. 15–5.

15–2.2.4 COMMENTS

The double-tube method (Bouwer 1961, 1962) permits the measurement of hydraulic conductivity of a well-defined sample area in absence of a water table. The method of calculating the hydraulic conductivity is free of simplifying assumptions, and the geometry of the flow systems is taken into account. Results from the double-tube method in the field compare favorably with hydraulic conductivity values obtained in the laboratory from soil samples taken at the bottom of the auger hole after completion of the field tests.

15–3   SHALLOW-WELL PUMP-IN METHOD

15–3.1   Principles

Hydraulic conductivity of soil in which no water table is present can be determined in place by measuring the rate of flow of water from a lined or unlined auger hole when a constant height of water is maintained in the hole. This method is known as the shallow-well pump-in method, the well-piezometer method, or the dry-auger-hole method.

An auger hole is dug as shown in Fig. 15–6, taking care to limit or avoid possible sealing and compaction of the sides. Water is supplied to the hole from a supply tank, and the water level in the hole is maintained at a constant level by a constant-level float valve. The sides of the hole are prevented from caving in by a perforated liner or by filling the hole with coarse sand. The daily rate of water use is determined until a steady state is obtained. The hydraulic conductivity is calculated from equations or determined from nomographs shown in Fig. 15–8 and 15–9. Two conditions are possible, and a different equation or nomograph must be used for each one. These conditions are shown in the insert of Fig. 15–7. For conditions where the distance T_u between the water level in the hole and the restricting layer is equal to or greater than three times the distance h between the water level in the hole and the bottom of the hole, the equation to be used is as follows:

$$K = \frac{\left[\ln \left(\frac{h}{r} + \sqrt{\left(\frac{h}{r} \right)^2 - 1} \right) - 1 \right] Q}{2\pi h^2} \text{ cm. per hour}$$

where K is the hydraulic conductivity (cm. per hour), h is the depth of water maintained in the hole as measured from the bottom of the hole (cm.), r is the radius of the hole (cm.), and Q is the rate at which water is flowing into the soil (cc. per hour). T_u is the depth of the water table or the depth of a restricting layer measured from the level at which the water is maintained in the hole (cm.).

For conditions where the distance T_u between the water level in the hole and the restricting layer is equal to or smaller than three times the distance h between the water level and the bottom of the hole but greater than the distance h itself ($3h > T_u \geqslant h$), the equation to be used is as follows:

$$K = \left[\frac{3 \ln \frac{h}{r} Q}{\pi h (h + 2T_u)} \right] \text{ cm. per hour}$$

where the symbols are defined as before. The nomographs shown in Fig. 15–8 and 15–9 are solutions of the above equations. The water temperature must be recorded to correct flow rates for viscosity changes. The position of the water table and depth of an impermeable layer below the test hole must be recorded to enable selection of the proper nomograph.

The rate of outflow is determined primarily by the hydraulic conductivity in the horizontal directions. The hydraulic conductivity determined by this method is a composite rate for the full depth of the hole being tested, but reflects primarily the permeability of the more permeable layers.

15–3.2 Method[3]

15–3.2.1 SPECIAL APPARATUS

A schematic diagram of the apparatus for a shallow-well pump-in installation is shown in Fig. 15–6.

1. Head tank: Use a 200-liter tank, calibrated in cubic centimeters with zero marking at the top, and with fittings so that two tanks can be connected when required.
2. Wooden platform to keep head tank off the ground to prevent rusting.
3. Steel pipe, 2.5 cm. in diameter and 125 cm. long, to be driven into the ground to keep the tank secured in position.
4. Constant-level float-valve which must fit inside the hole. For this an old cut-down carburetor float-valve can be used.
5. Tubing: Use rubber tubing with an inside diameter of 1.0 cm. to connect the head tank to the constant-level float-valve.
6. Rod used to regulate the depth to which the float-valve is lowered into the hole.
7. Casing: Use commercial well screen if available (manufacturers listed in yearbook Am. Soc. Agr. Eng.). If no commercial well screen is available, construct a liner using 6 uniformly spaced perforations per 10 cm., each 0.3 cm. wide by 2.5 cm. long.
8. Sand to be used in lieu of casing: Use clean sand passing a No. 15 sieve and retained on a No. 28 sieve. Fill the hole with the sand to within 15 cm. of the level at which the water surface will be controlled. Use a casing with the lower 15 cm. perforated between the soil surface and the top of the sand. This casing is essential to keep fine material from dropping onto the sand and sealing the surface.
9. Plexiglas cover: 30 cm. by 30 cm. by 0.5 cm., with a hole in the center for the rod to hold the constant-level float-valve in place, and with two other holes, one for rubber tubing and one for measuring the water temperature.

---

[3] Winger (1960).

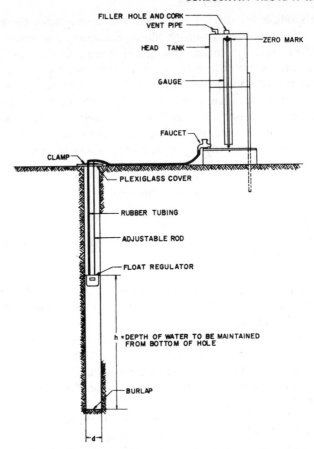

Fig. 15–6. Schematic diagram of equipment for the shallow-well pump-in method in place.

10. Water-supply tank truck of at least 1,500-liter capacity with gas-powered water pump to pump water to the head tank if gravity feed is not possible.
11. Ten meters of 2.0-cm. garden hose for rapid filling of the head tank from the water-supply tank.
12. Orchard-type soil auger.
13. Tiling spade.
14. Steel tape.
15. Watch.
16. Thermometer which can be lowered into the hole.
17. Brush for cleaning the walls of the hole. A floor scrub-brush cut in two and bolted together around a 1-cm. pipe coupling is recommended.
18. Burlap to be placed in the bottom of the hole where perforated casing is used.

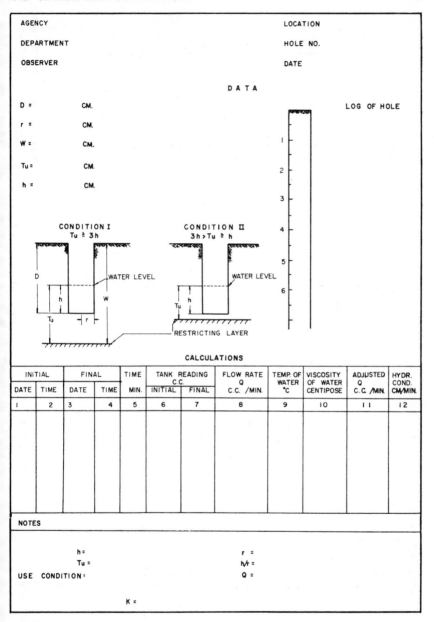

Fig. 15–7. Suggested field sheet for use with the shallow-well pump-in method.

15–3.2.2 PROCEDURE

Prepare a set of data sheets such as shown in Fig. 15–7 for recording measurements and for calculations.

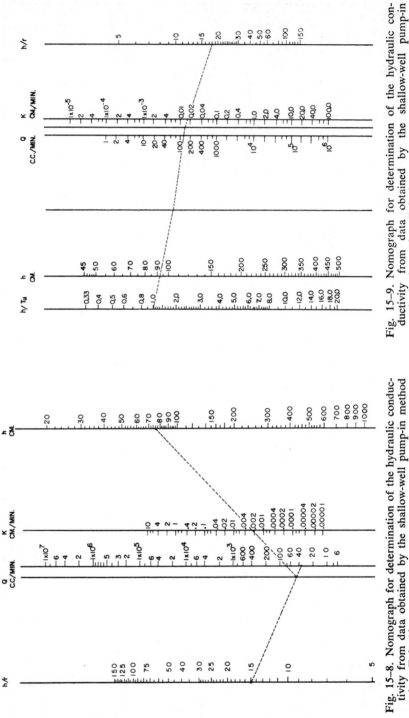

Fig. 15-9. Nomograph for determination of the hydraulic conductivity from data obtained by the shallow-well pump-in method where $3h > T_u \geqslant h$.

Fig. 15-8. Nomograph for determination of the hydraulic conductivity from data obtained by the shallow-well pump-in method where $T_u \geqslant 3h$.

Auger out the hole to the desired depth with as little disturbance as possible to the sides. While performing this operation, obtain a complete log of the hole, and record this information on the field sheet in the space provided. Brush the sides of the hole to remove possible compaction or sealing caused by the auger. In finer textured soils at field capacity it may be necessary to construct and use a round wooden scratcher with small nails protruding about 0.3 cm.

Put the calibrated supply tank in place, and anchor it securely; then install the thin-walled well casing. Perforations should extend from the bottom up to the predetermined controlled water level. If sand is used, fill the hole to within 15 cm. of the predetermined controlled water level. In the latter case, install the well casing with the lower 15 cm. perforated.

Install and approximately position the constant-level float-valve, and connect the float-valve to the calibrated supply tank. Fill the hole with water to approximately the bottom of the constant-level float-valve, open the valve of the supply tank and adjust the height of the float-valve so that the water level will be maintained at the desired depth.

Record the time and the reading on the supply-tank gauge on the data sheet. Check the water level in the tank regularly, and refill the tank when necessary. Continue the test by recording the time, supply-tank gauge reading, amount of water added and water temperature at regular intervals. The intervals should be short enough so that the supply tank never runs dry.

Compute the flow rate each time the site is visited. Compute all flow rates for a temperature of 20°C. Make corrections for viscosity effects by multiplying the calculated flow rate by the ratio of the viscosity of water at the temperature during the period of measurement to the viscosity of water at 20°C.

Determine the hydraulic conductivity from the appropriate nomograph (Fig. 15–8 or 15–9) when the flow rate has become constant over a 24-hour period.

15–3.2.3 COMMENTS

The shallow-well pump-in method permits the measurement of an average hydraulic conductivity for the full depth of the hole being tested. The final value, however, reflects primarily the permeability of the more permeable layers.

Limitations of the method are that large quantities of water are needed, considerable equipment is required, and the procedure is time consuming. A further limitation is that it may sometimes be difficult to obtain test water having about the same chemical composition as the irrigation water to be used.

Values of hydraulic conductivity obtained with the shallow-well pump-in method are usually lower than values obtained with the auger-hole test.

The ratio of the hydraulic conductivity determined by the shallow-well pump-in method to the value obtained with the auger-hole method was estimated to be on the order of 0.50 by Talsma (1960) and 0.85 by Winger (1960) and was found to vary over a range from 0.72 to 1.97 by Sillanpää (1956).

15–4 PERMEAMETER METHOD

15–4.1 Principles

The permeameter method, also referred to as the cylinder permeameter method, is based on the measurement of the rate of outflow of water supplied to an auger hole above the water table.

A hole of large diameter is dug as shown in Fig. 15–10. At the center of the hole is placed a cylindrical sleeve 45 cm. in diameter. The sleeve is made to penetrate the soil 15.24 cm. below the bottom of the hole. The same water level is maintained inside and outside the cylinder, and the rate of water intake from the inside cylinder is measured. The hydraulic conductivity in the vertical direction can be calculated if the pressure near the bottom edge of the cylinder is known. The pressure near the bottom edge of the cylinder is measured with tensiometers. When the tensiometers indicate zero tension, saturation is assumed. Build-up of positive pressures is registered by the tensiometers. No measurements should be made after positive pressures have developed. Hydraulic conductivity is calculated with Darcy's law: $K = QL/HA$, where Q is the rate of flow, H is the pressure difference across the soil column inside the cylinder, L is the height of the soil column inside the cylinder, and A is the cross sectional area of the soil column inside the cylinder.

15–4.2 Method [‡]

15–4.2.1 SPECIAL APPARATUS

A schematic diagram of apparatus for a permeameter test installation is shown in Fig. 15–10.

1. Head tank: Use a 200-liter tank calibrated in cubic centimeters, with zero marking at the top.
2. Wooden platform to keep head tank off the ground to prevent rusting.
3. Steel pipe, 2.5 cm. in diameter and 125 cm. long to be driven into the ground to keep the tank secured in place.

[‡] Winger (1960).

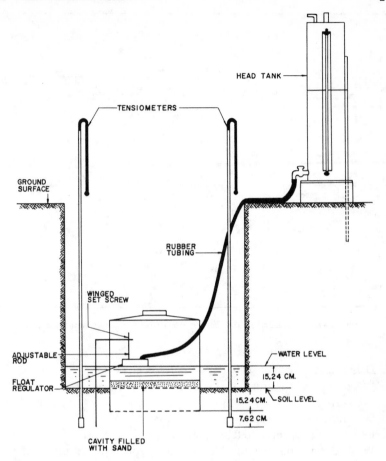

HEAD TANK

TENSIOMETERS

GROUND SURFACE

RUBBER TUBING

WINGED SET SCREW

ADJUSTABLE ROD

FLOAT REGULATOR

WATER LEVEL

15.24 CM.

15.24 CM. SOIL LEVEL

7.62 CM.

CAVITY FILLED WITH SAND

Fig. 15–10. Schematic diagram of equipment for the permeameter method in place.

4. Cylinder: 14-gauge steel with an inside diameter of 45 cm. and a height of 50 cm. with a reinforced band on top and a sharpened edge on the bottom, and with the welded seam ground down flush.

5. Constant-level float-valve made from old cut-down carburetor.

6. Tubing: Use rubber tubing with an inside diameter of 1 cm. to connect the head tank to the constant-level float-valve.

7. Adjustable rod to hold the constant-level float-valve at the desired elevation.

8. Threaded bolt which fastens to the steel cylinder and supports the adjustable rod to hold the float-valve at the desired elevation.

9. Tensiometers: Use four mercury tensiometers with a length of 50 cm. and an inside diameter of 1 cm. and with construction such that positive as well as negative pressures can be registered.

AGENCY
DEPARTMENT
OBSERVER

LOCATION
HOLE NO.
DATE

DATA AND CALCULATIONS

INITIAL		FINAL		TIME	TANK READING C.C.		VOLUME	Q	TEMP OF	VISCOSITY OF WATER	ADJUSTED Q	HYDRAULIC CONDUCTIVITY	TENSIOMETERS			
DATE	TIME	DATE	TIME	HRS.	INITIAL	FINAL	C.C.	C.C./HR	WATER°C	CENTIPOISES	C.C./HR.	CM./HR.	1	2	3	4
1	2	3	4	5	6	7	8	9	10	11	12	13	14	15	16	17

NOTES

$K = (Q/A) \times (L/H)$

Q =   CC./HR.

A = CM^2

T =   HRS.

L =   CM.

H =   CM.

K =   CM./HR.

Fig. 15–11. Suggested field sheet for use with the permeameter method.

10. Driving equipment for cylinder and piezometers.
11. Water-supply tank truck of at least 1,500-liter capacity.
12. Tiling spade.
13. Steel tape.
14. Bentonite to seal around tensiometers.
15. Washed sand passing the No. 14 sieve and retained on the No. 28 sieve.
16. Carpenter level.

15–4.2.2 PROCEDURE

Prepare a set of data sheets such as shown in Fig. 15–11 for recording measurements and for calculations.

Excavate a hole 1 m. square to the layer to be tested, and level an area 45 cm. square in the center of the hole. Check the level with a carpenter level, and be sure not to walk in this area. Drive the test cylinder 15 cm. into the soil of the leveled area. Keep the cylinder level during the operation, and direct the blows straight down to avoid disturbance of the natural profile. Tamp the soil against the cylinder wall on the inside as well as on the outside to avoid channeling of the water along the sides. Against the inside wall, tamp the soil only lightly and only close to the wall. Spread about 2 cm. of uniform coarse sand over the area inside the cylinder to avoid puddling of the soil surface during the test.

Space the four calibrated tensiometers at equal intervals around the outside cylinder, each 10 cm. outside the cylinder and 23 cm. below the level of the soil inside the cylinder. Make sure that good contact is obtained between the porous cup and the soil. Tamp a 50:50 bentonite-soil mixture around the tensiometer to avoid channeling of water along the sides. Install the constant-level float-valve in the cylinder, and adjust it to maintain a constant 15-cm. head. Put the calibrated supply tank in place, anchor it securely, and connect it to the constant-level float-valve; then fill the cylinder with water 15 cm. deep, and open the float-valve. Fill the hole outside the cylinder with water to a depth of 15 cm., and maintain the water level at approximately this depth during the test period.

Record the time and the reading on the supply-tank gauge. Also record the readings on the tensiometers. Continue the test by recording the time, supply-tank gauge reading, tensiometer readings, amount of water added and water temperature at regular intervals. The intervals should be short enough so that the supply tank never runs dry. Terminate the test when the tensiometers indicate zero tension, and the water is moving through the 15-cm. test layer at a constant rate. At this time it is assumed that the requirements for the use of Darcy's law are met.

Compute the flow rate each time the site is visited. Compute all flow rates for a temperature of 20°C., making corrections for viscosity effects by multiplying the calculated flow rate by the ratio of the viscosity of water at the temperature during the period of measurement to the viscosity of water at 20°C. Calculate the hydraulic conductivity from Darcy's law, $K = QL/AH$, where K is hydraulic conductivity, Q is the flow rate, A is the cross-sectional area of the cylinder, L is the length of the soil column inside the cylinder, and H is the height of the water level inside the cylinder above the base. Calculations can be performed on the data sheet shown in Fig. 15–11.

15–4.2.3 COMMENTS

The cylinder permeameter method permits measurement of the vertical component of hydraulic conductivity of restricting or slowly permeable layers that obstruct percolation and cause perched water tables.

A limitation of the method is that positive pressures may develop when the horizon being tested is underlain by a layer of lower hydraulic conductivity or is close to a water table. In the presence of positive pressures indicated by the tensiometers, the test will no longer give a true value of the hydraulic conductivity. Winger (1960) suggested that it might be possible to discharge the positive pressure by augering a number of holes around the outside of the cylinder approximately 10 inches away from it. Another situation under which conditions necessary for the calculation of the hydraulic conductivity are difficult to meet arises when the test zone is above a deep, very permeable material. A steady flow rate can be obtained, but the tensiometers will never indicate zero tension below the test zone.

A further limitation is that the method cannot be used in rocky or coarse gravel material.

The method, although relatively easy to use, requires large quantities of water, is time consuming, and requires a great deal of specialized equipment.

15–5 LITERATURE CITED

Bouwer, H. 1961. A double tube method for measuring hydraulic conductivity of soil in sites above a water table. Soil Sci. Soc. Am. Proc. 25:334–342.

Bouwer, H. 1961. Application of the double tube method for field measurements of hydraulic conductivity of soil above the water table. Paper presented at winter meetings, Am. Soc. Agr. Eng. Chicago, Ill. Paper No. 61–709 (mimeo).

Bouwer, H. 1962. Field determination of hydraulic conductivity above a water table with the double-tube method. Soil Sci. Soc. Am. Proc. 26:330–335.

Sillanpää, Mikko. 1956. Studies on the hydraulic conductivity of soils and its measurement. Acta Agr. Fenn. 87.

Talsma, T. 1960. Comparison of field methods of measuring hydraulic conductivity. Trans. Congr. Irrigation Drainage IV (6): C 145–C 156.

Winger, R. J. 1960. In-place permeability tests and their use in subsurface drainage. Treatise prepared for the International Commission on Irrigation and Drainage-Fourth Congress-Madrid, Spain. Office of Drainage and Ground Water Engineering, Commissioner's Office, Bureau of Reclamation, Denver, Colo.

16

Laboratory Measurement of Hydraulic Conductivity of Unsaturated Soil

A. KLUTE

University of Illinois
Urbana, Illinois

16–1 INTRODUCTION

Unsaturated soils have the ability to transmit water, but not to the same degree as saturated soils. The ability of an unsaturated soil to transmit water is measured by its conductivity. The term "capillary conductivity" is often used in reference to unsaturated soil. In this discussion we shall assume that the fluid in the pores is water and shall use the term "conductivity" in place of "capillary conductivity" or "hydraulic conductivity" of unsaturated soil.

The principles of measurement of the hydraulic conductivity of unsaturated soil have long been known. The techniques, however, are difficult and subject to improvement in many ways. The description of procedure given below is to be regarded as tentative.

The conductivity of unsaturated soil may be measured by two types of techniques, steady-state and unsteady-state. The steady-state method involves the establishment of a flow system in which the water content, tension, and flux are not changing with time. In the unsteady-state method, these quantities vary with time. In this section, a steady-state method based on the use of cylindrical core samples will be described. The unsteady-state outflow system described for the determination of soil water diffusivity (section 17) may also be used to determine the conductivity.

Several agriculturally important water-flow processes involve unsaturated flow. Infiltration, evaporation, and the flow of water to plant roots are among these. An analysis and understanding of these flow systems requires knowledge of the conductivity of unsaturated soil.

16–2 PRINCIPLES

The conductivity of unsaturated soil depends upon the geometry of the water within the framework of the soil. As the water content decreases from saturation, the large pores are the first to drain. There may also be an increase in the tortuosity of the path of flow, and changes in the properties

253

of the water. These and perhaps other factors contribute to a rapid decrease in conductivity with a decrease in water content. The conductivity may decrease to as little as 1/100 or 1/1,000 of its value at saturation, when the water content has been reduced to the ⅓-atmo. percentage.

The flux of water at a certain point in an unsaturated soil may be considered to be given by the product of the conductivity at that point and the driving force. That is:

$$v = -K(\theta)\nabla H \qquad [1]$$

where v is the volume flux of water, or flow velocity. It is the volume of water passing through unit cross sectional area of soil in unit time. The conductivity $K(\theta)$ is regarded as a function of the water content θ. The driving force is expressed as the negative of the gradient of the hydraulic head H. The hydraulic head of water in an unsaturated soil is the elevation of a free-water surface in the open arm of the V-tube water manometer. The other arm of the manometer is connected to a porous permeable cup in contact with the soil (see Fig. 13–1). Equation [1] is an extension of Darcy's law to unsaturated soil. It is to be regarded as a reasonable first approximation to the flux. There is evidence for its validity in soils, and there is also evidence that it is not valid in certain instances. Until something better is developed, equation [1] may be used as a working equation.

The conductivity is measured by applying a constant hydraulic head difference across the sample and measuring the resulting steady-state flux of water. The soil sample is brought to an unsaturated condition in either of two ways. The sample may be placed in a pressure chamber between porous plates or membranes that are permeable to water. A constant-head water supply system is connected to one porous plate, and a constant-head removal system is connected to the other. By adjustment and control of the gas-phase pressure in the chamber, the sample may be brought to various levels of water content. Alternatively, hanging water columns may be connected to the ends of the sample through the porous plates, and the water content of the sample may be adjusted by the suction applied.

At each level of water content and mean pressure head, a flow is set up by imposing a hydraulic gradient across the sample. The conductivity value obtained is considered to be valid at the mean water content in the sample. To obtain the conductivity function $K(\theta)$, the measurements of flux and gradient are repeated at a series of values of average water content.

The pressure head of water in unsaturated soil is the gauge pressure of the water inside a porous tensiometer cup expressed in units of length of a column of water (see Fig. 13–1). The water content of the soil is a function of the pressure head H. Consequently, the conductivity may be regarded as a function of the pressure head. The determination of the conductivity function then involves measurements of a sufficient number of paired values of K and h to delineate the function.

In general, the water-content, pressure-head relationship exhibits hysteresis. There will also be hysteresis in the function $K(h)$, and perhaps also in $K(\theta)$. The intended use for the data will aid in determining the range and sequence of pressure heads at which measurements of K will be made. Normally, measurements are made starting at or near saturation and proceeding toward lower water content values. Data obtained on the desorption leg of the water-content, pressure-head relation in this way are valid in the analysis of flow systems that involve desorption from saturation only. A more complete determination of the hysteresis behavior of the conductivity function would involve measurements of the conductivity along an absorption leg of the water-content, pressure-head curve and perhaps also on some of the scanning curves (Poulovassilis, 1962).

16–3 METHOD

16–3.1 Special Apparatus

The following description of apparatus is to be regarded as suggestive of possible constructions that may be used. Richards and Moore (1952), Nielsen and Biggar (1961), Moore (1939), Childs (1945), Croney et al. (1958) and Corey (1957) have given descriptions of steady-state methods of determining conductivity. The development of apparatus and techniques is a continuing process and much remains to be learned in this field.

The essential features of the experimental system are shown in Fig. 16–1. Water at hydraulic head H_1 is supplied to the top of porous plate P_1. Flow occurs through the plate, the soil sample, and the porous plate P_2. Water is maintained at a constant hydraulic head H_2, in the space below plate P_2, by the location of the drip point.

The soil sample is subjected to a controlled gas-phase pressure which is greater than atmospheric by an amount proportional to the height of the fluid column m in the manometer M. Gas-phase pressure control can be achieved by commercially available pressure regulators (e.g., the Model 40 series, Moore Products Co., Philadelphia, Pa.), or by a bubble-column unit (Richards, 1949). The porous plates may be ceramic (Selas Corp., Dresher, Pa., or Coors Porcelain Co., Golden, Colo.), fritted glass (Corning Glass Co., Elmira, N. Y.), or fritted glass-bead plates (Nielsen and Phillips, 1958).

The system may be operated as a hanging-water-column type of apparatus by using atmospheric gas pressure in the cell and by lowering the drip point and the constant-head supply below the level of the sample. Flow is maintained in the downward direction by keeping $H_1 > H_2$. Such an arrangement is limited by vaporization of water to pressure heads larger than -850 cm. of water, and by practical considerations to approximately the

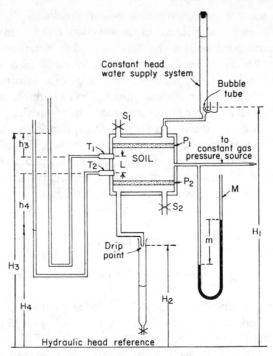

Fig. 16–1. Diagram of apparatus for steady-state method of measurement of conductivity of unsaturated soil. The meaning of the symbols is explained in the text.

range −200 cm. to 0 cm. of water. The pressure-cell arrangement is not subject to this limitation.

If it is desired to determine the conductivity of undisturbed samples, such samples may be taken in metal or plastic cylinders. An experimental arrangement which can accommodate such samples is shown in Fig. 16–2. The sandwich consisting of the soil cylinder between two porous plates is enclosed in a pressure chamber. In this system gas-tight seals are not required at the junction of the sample cylinder and the end caps, and between the sample cylinder and the tensiometers. Only mechanical support is needed. The sample cylinders must be pre-drilled to receive the tensiometer assembly. Pressure seals are required at all points where the connections to the tensiometer manometers and water supply and removal lines cross the wall of the pressure chamber. Commercially available pressure cookers can be used as pressure chambers.

Two methods of mounting the porous plates are shown in Figures 16–3 and 16–4. Porous ceramic or fritted-glass plates may be cemented to the end cap, or may be clamped in place with "O" ring seals. The double "O" ring seal shown in Fig. 16–3 is convenient for replacement of the porous

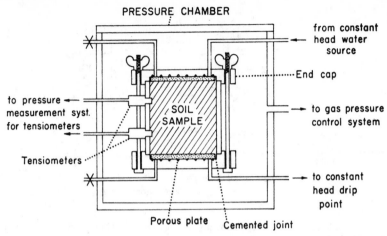

Fig. 16–2. An alternative method of construction of the apparatus in which the sample holder is enclosed within a pressure chamber.

plate. The outer "O" ring is necessary to prevent loss of water from the edge of the plate.

The arrangement shown in Fig. 16–3, in which there is a cavity in the end cap ⅛ to ¼ inch deep and with a diameter slightly less than that of the porous plate, is satisfactory up to a cell pressure of about 1 atm. At higher pressures, the plates must be supported so that they can withstand the pressure differential across them. The arrangement shown in Fig. 16–4 is suitable for higher cell pressures. The plate rests upon a surface into which interconnected grooves are machined. The plate may be cemented[1] at the edges as shown, or the double "O" ring arrangement of Fig. 16–3 may be used. Careful fitting of the plate will be necessary to obtain a seal. Hand lapping of the plate upon a sheet of abrasive supported on a flat surface has been found useful in fitting the plates, provided that the plates are not too hard.

The sample retainer can also serve as the wall of the pressure cell. In this case, there must be a gas-tight seal between the sample retainer and the end caps, and between the sample retainer and the tensiometers. The arrangements shown in Figs. 16–3 and 16–4 are suggested. In Fig. 16–3, the sample retainer is fastened to the end cap by a flange with an "O" ring seal. Figure 16–4 shows an alternative method of obtaining the necessary gas-tight seal.

When disturbed, artificially packed samples are used, the tensiometers may be fastened to the sample retainer with a permanent gas-tight seal,

---

[1] Epoxy resins such as those obtainable from Armstrong Products Co., Warsaw, Ind., have been found suitable. A rubber-base cement such as "Goo," manufactured by Walther Specialties, Milwaukee, Wis., may also be found useful.

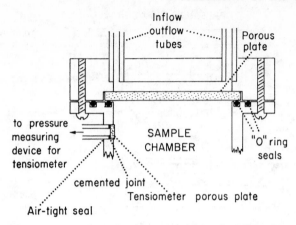

Fig. 16–3. End-cap construction showing a method of sealing the porous plates with "O" rings.

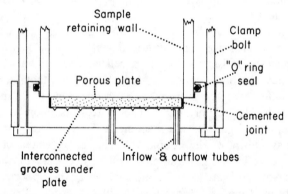

Fig. 16–4. End-cap construction with the porous plate cemented in place.

either by cement, or with "O" rings. Small porous ceramic discs cemented [2] to the end of the tube leading to the manometer are suitable for tensiometer "cups." It is recommended that the surface of these porous discs project about 1 mm. beyond the inner wall of the sample holder.

The end caps and sample retainers may be made from plastics such as Lucite, or from metals such as brass or stainless steel. Because of the low flow rates that must often be measured, the water loss that can occur through Lucite must be kept in mind when designing the cell. Such a loss will not ordinarily be of concern, but when measurements are to be made at low water contents, it is probably best to use metal to construct the cell.

---

[2] Ibid.

Separate water manometers are indicated on the tensiometers. When low gradients are to be determined, a differential manometer is more suitable. Corey (1957) described a version of such a manometer. The two tensiometers may be connected by an inverted U-tube filled with a fluid of lower density than water and immiscible with it.

16–3.2 Procedure

It will be assumed that samples are at hand and that it is desired to determine the conductivity as a function of pressure head starting at or near zero pressure head and proceeding toward lower pressure-head values. Only general steps in the procedure will be indicated because the various modifications of apparatus may require certain procedures that cannot be anticipated here.

Fill the tensiometers, water-supply and water-removal systems with de-aerated water by filling them under vacuum or by flushing them followed by prolonged soaking. Clamp the sample between the end caps and install the tensiometers. With the outflow tubing clamped off, apply water to wet the sample at or near zero pressure head. When the sample has been wetted, establish a hydraulic gradient across the sample at a mean pressure-head near zero.

Maintain a constant hydraulic head until steady flow is attained. The criteria of steady state are (1) time-invariant readings of the tensiometers and (2) equality of inflow and outflow rates.

Record the volume of flow Q which occurs in time t. Record the height of the fluid column in manometer M, the hydraulic heads H_3 and H_4, and the pressure heads h_3 and h_4. Note that the hydraulic heads are measured from an arbitrary reference to the free-water levels in the tensiometer manometers; that the pressure heads are measured from the level of the tensiometer "cup" to the free-water surface in the manometers; and that m, the height of the fluid column in manometer M, is measured from the level of fluid in the open arm of the manometer to the level of fluid in the arm connected to the pressure chamber. Take measurements to obtain the distance L between the tensiometers and to obtain the cross sectional area A of the soil cylinder.

Decrease the water content of the sample by increasing the gas pressure in the cell, or by reducing the mean value of H_1 and H_2.

Repeat the series of operations in the preceding three paragraphs as needed to obtain data for calculation of the conductivity at a series of decreasing pressure heads and water contents.

Keep a complete record of the volumes of inflow and outflow, as well as the volume of water involved in changes in the readings of the tensiometers.

After the last conductivity determination has been made, determine the amount of water in the entire sample by gravimetric means. Calculate the water content at each mean pressure head from the final water content and the volumes of inflow and outflow.

Calculate the conductivity at each mean pressure head and water content from:

$$K = [Q/At][L/(H_3 - H_4)] . \tag{2}$$

Calculate the mean pressure head $\bar{h}$ corresponding to the above conductivity value from:

$$\bar{h} = (\rho_1 m/\rho) + (h_3 + h_4)/2 \tag{3}$$

where m is the gauge pressure in the cell expressed as a column of fluid of length m, ρ_1 is the density of the manometer fluid, and ρ is the density of water.

16–3.3   Comments

If the apparatus is operated with a cell gas pressure greater than atmospheric, air will go into solution in the water in the soil, and will diffuse in solution through the porous plate. When the concentration of dissolved gas in the water behind the plate becomes sufficiently large, gas bubbles will accumulate, causing an error in the volume measurement. This gas can be removed by a flushing procedure, and stopcocks S_1 and S_2 are for this purpose. Kunze and Kirkham (1962), and Tanner and Elrick (1958) describe a roller pump arrangement for removal of air which may be found useful. Air may also accumulate in the tensiometers. A concentric-tube flushing arrangement for tensiometers described by Luthin and Worstell (1957) may be used to permit frequent air removal from the tensiometers.

The low flow rates increase the difficulty of obtaining accurate volume measurements. Burettes, as shown, are suitable so long as three significant figures can be obtained in the volume measurement. It may be necessary to use more sensitive techniques to obtain the necessary number of significant figures. The movement of a meniscus in a horizontal capillary (Croney et al., 1958), or a drop-counting mechanism (Richards and Richards, 1962) are possibilities that should be considered.

The comments about the effect of solute concentration and composition on the conductivity of saturated soil (section 13) also apply to the conductivity of unsaturated soil. It may be possible to reuse the water from the outflow burette to reduce the structural changes caused by continuous leaching.

The conductivity of the porous plates should be high enough so that the head loss across them does not prevent the establishment of an easily measurable hydraulic gradient in the sample. The bubbling pressure of the plates and tensiometer cups should be slightly higher than the highest cell gas pressure to be applied.

The length of the sample will strongly influence the time required to proceed from one steady state to another, and the sample should be as short as feasible, perhaps on the order of 1 to 5 cm. Another consideration is the accuracy of measurement of the separation of the tensiometers and the errors introduced in the estimate of the gradient when the tensiometers are very close together. Longer samples can be used at pressure heads near zero, or at water contents near saturation.

The variability of results from this procedure will be as large or larger than those from the measurement of conductivity of saturated soil (section 13). As far as is known to the author, no statistical analysis of conductivity data for unsaturated soils has been made.

16–4 LITERATURE CITED

Childs, E. C. 1945. The water table, equipotentials and streamlines in drained lands. Soil Sci. 59:405–415.

Corey, A. T. 1957. Measurement of air and water permeability in unsaturated soil. Soil Sci. Soc. Am. Proc. 21:7–11.

Croney, D., Coleman, J. D., and Black, W. P. M. 1958. Movement and distribution of water in soil in relation to highway design and performance. Highway Res. Board Spec. Rept. 40:226–252.

Kunze, R. J., and Kirkham, Don. 1962. Simplified accounting for membrane impedance in capillary conductivity determinations. Soil Sci. Soc. Am. Proc. 26:421–426.

Luthin, J. N., and Worstell, R. V. 1957. The falling water table in tile drainage—a laboratory study. Soil Sci. Soc. Am. Proc. 21:580–584.

Moore, R. E. 1939. Water conduction from shallow water tables. Hilgardia 12:383–426.

Nielsen, D. R., and Biggar, J. W. 1961. Measuring capillary conductivity. Soil Sci. 92:192–193.

Nielsen, D. R., and Phillips, R. E. 1958. Small fritted glass bead plates for determination of moisture retention. Soil Sci. Soc. Am. Proc. 22:574–575.

Poulovassilis, A. 1962. Hysteresis of pore water, an application of the concept of independent domains. Soil Sci. 94:405–412.

Richards, L. A. 1949. Methods of measuring soil moisture tension. Soil Sci. 68:95–112.

Richards, L. A., and Moore, D. C. 1952. Influence of capillary conductivity and depth of wetting on moisture retention in soil. Trans. Am. Geophys. Union. 33:531–540.

Richards, L. A., and Richards, P. L. 1962. Radial-flow cell for soil-water measurements. Soil Sci. Soc. Am. Proc. 26:515–518.

Tanner, C. B., and Elrick, D. E. 1958. Volumetric porous pressure plate apparatus for moisture hysteresis measurements. Soil Sci. Soc. Am. Proc. 22:575–576.

17 Water Diffusivity

A. KLUTE

University of Illinois
Urbana, Illinois

17-1 INTRODUCTION

Several techniques have been described for the measurement of soil water diffusivity (Bruce and Klute, 1956; Gardner, 1956 and 1960; Miller and Elrick, 1958; Kunze and Kirkham, 1962). These procedures should be regarded as tentative and subject to improvement. The outflow method for diffusivity measurement, which will be described below, has been studied and developed more than any other technique. Other techniques may be more suitable in particular instances, and the selection of the outflow method for description here does not imply that other methods are unsatisfactory.

Water diffusivity, as a function of water content or pressure head, occurs in the equations of flow for water in unsaturated soil. The diffusivity function is sometimes required in the analysis of unsaturated unsteady-state flow systems. The recent increased application of computer techniques to the solution of water-flow problems has emphasized the need for diffusivity data for various soils.

17-2 PRINCIPLES

The concept of soil-water diffusivity was originally suggested in a paper by Childs and Collis-George (1950), and arises out of combination of Darcy's law with the equation of continuity for the conservation of matter. The resulting equation is

$$\partial\theta/\partial t = \nabla\cdot[K(\theta)\nabla H] \qquad [1]$$

where θ is the volume water content, t is time, H is the hydraulic head, and $K(\theta)$ is the conductivity function. Equation [1] can be written in the form

$$\frac{\partial\theta}{\partial t} = \nabla\cdot[K(\theta)\,\nabla h] + \frac{\partial K(\theta)}{\partial Z} \qquad [2]$$

where h is the pressure head, and z is the vertical axis of the Cartesian coordinate system. Assumption of a single-valued functional relationship between h and θ allows one to write equation [2] as

$$\frac{\partial \theta}{\partial t} = \nabla \cdot [D(\theta)\,\nabla \theta] + \frac{\partial K(\theta)}{\partial Z} \tag{3}$$

where the soil-water diffusivity function $D(\theta)$ has been defined as

$$D(\theta) = K(\theta)\frac{dh}{d\theta} = \frac{K(\theta)}{C(\theta)}. \tag{4}$$

The function $C(\theta)$ or $d\theta/dh$ is the specific water capacity. The ratio of the conductivity to the specific water capacity is called the soil water diffusivity by analogy with the corresponding terms in the equations of heat flow. The diffusivity has dimensions of length squared per unit time, and the specific water capacity has dimensions of volume of water per unit volume of soil per unit pressure head.

The outflow method is based on the measurement of the volume of water outflow as a function of time from a sample in a pressure cell (Gardner, 1956). A slab of soil on a porous plate or membrane is brought to equilibrium with a given gas-phase pressure in the cell. The pressure is raised by a small increment, and the volume of water outflow versus time is recorded. The diffusivity is obtained from an analysis of the volume-outflow versus time curve.

If the effect of gravity is neglected, and the flow is in one dimension only, equation [3] becomes

$$\frac{\partial \theta}{\partial t} = \frac{\partial}{\partial X}\left[D(\theta)\frac{\partial \theta}{\partial X}\right] \tag{5}$$

If it is assumed that the conductivity $K(\theta)$ and the specific water capacity $C(\theta)$ are constant in the range of water content change which occurs during a given outflow run, then the flow equation can be written

$$\partial h/\partial t = D(\partial^2 h/\partial X^2) \tag{6}$$

which is the linear form of the diffusion equation. The boundary conditions appropriate for the flow system in the outflow procedure are as follows:

$$h = \Delta h, \qquad 0 < x < L, \qquad t = 0 \tag{7}$$

$$h = 0 \qquad X = 0 \qquad t > 0 \tag{8}$$

$$\partial h/\partial X = 0 \qquad X = L \qquad t > 0 \tag{9}$$

where Δh is the pressure-head equivalent of the increase in gas pressure in the pressure cell, and L is the sample length. If the porous plate upon which the sample rests offers negligible resistance to the flow, boundary condition [8] will be met. The solution of equation [6], subject to [7], [8], and [9], is given in standard texts on diffusion and heat-flow theory

(Carslaw and Jaeger, 1959). The solution gives the pressure-head h as a function of x and t. An equation for the cumulative outflow volume Q can be derived from this solution of equation [6]. A convenient form of the cumulative outflow function for analysis purposes is:

$$1 - \frac{Q(t)}{Q(\infty)} = \frac{8}{\pi^2} \sum_{m=0}^{\infty} \frac{1}{(2m+1)^2} \exp\left[\frac{-(2m+1)^2\pi^2\,Dt}{4L^2}\right] \qquad [10]$$

where $Q(t)$ is the volume of outflow at time t, and $Q(\infty)$ is the total volume of outflow that occurs because of the applied pressure increment. The use of equation [10] for the analysis of data will be described below.

Other methods are available for the determination of the diffusivity. The conductivity can be measured by the steady-state method described in section 13–3.2, and the specific water capacity can be obtained from measurement of the water-content, pressure-head relationship. The conductivity and specific water capacity can then be combined using equation [4] to obtain the diffusivity. A method of calculating the diffusivity from measurements of the water content distribution at a fixed time in a semi-infinite horizontal-infiltration flow system has been described by Bruce and Klute (1956). Methods for the measurement of diffusivity and conductivity continue to be a subject of research.

17–3   METHOD

17–3.1   Special Apparatus

The essential parts of the equipment are (*1*) a pressure cell with a porous plate or membrane, (*2*) an outflow-volume-measurement system, (*3*) a system for control of the gas-phase pressure in the cell, (*4*) a system for removal of gas bubbles from beneath the porous plate or membrane, and (*5*) a timer. A diagram of the apparatus is shown in Fig. 17–1. The description of apparatus given here is intended to be suggestive of the kind of equipment required to determine the diffusivity. The details of the apparatus and consequent details of procedure may be varied in many ways.

The walls and end caps of the pressure cell may be constructed of metal or plastic. Lucite plastic is suitable for measurements up to about 1 or 2 atm. of cell pressure. When the outflow rates are small, the slow loss of water which occurs through lucite may introduce error into the measurements. The author has observed losses on the order of 1×10^{-4} cm.^{3} per cm.^{2} per day through lucite which was ¼ inch thick. If losses of this magnitude will interfere seriously with the determination of volume outflow, the cell should be built of metal such as brass or stainless steel.

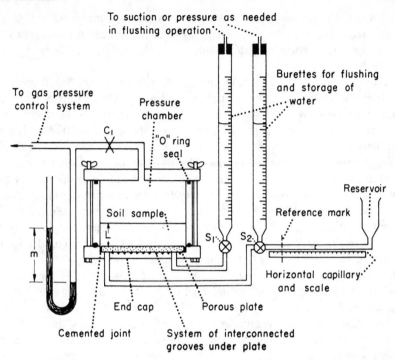

Fig. 17–1. Diagram of apparatus for the outflow method of soil water diffusivity determination.

The porous plate may be sealed into the lower end cap with a cement (Epoxy resins, such as types A-2 and A-4 available from Armstrong Products Co., Warsaw, Ind., have been found suitable) or with "O" ring seals. Construction details are shown in Figs. 16–3 and 16–4.

If samples with undisturbed structure are to be used, the sample in its retaining cylinder may be placed within the pressure chamber, or the apparatus may be designed so that the sample retainer functions as the wall of the pressure chamber. If disturbed samples are to be used, the sample material must be packed into place upon the porous plate, either in a separate retaining ring or in the bottom of the pressure chamber as shown in Fig. 17–1.

Gas pressure control may be achieved with standard pressure regulators (e.g., Model 40 pressure regulators from Moore Products Company, Philadelphia, Pa.). Alternative pressure control systems are described by Richards (1949) and Hanks et al. (1953). Pressure control to approximately 1 part in 100 or 200 is desirable.

The volume of outflow can be determined by observations of the position of an air-water interface in a horizontal glass tube. The diameter and length of the tube should be chosen to contain the volume of water that will result from the pressure increment applied. A vertical meniscus can be maintained in a horizontal tube with an inside diameter as large as 4 or 5 mm.

The reservoir at the end of the horizontal tube has been found useful in flushing the system free of gas bubbles, and is a safety feature in the event that an excess of water flows out of the sample. It may also be desirable to incorporate a ball and socket joint between stopcock S_2 and the horizontal capillary. The capillary can then be removed for cleaning without dismantling the rest of the apparatus. The burette connected to stopcock S_2 is used for storage of the cumulative outflow from all the outflow runs that may be made on a given sample. The actual measurements of water volume may be made in this burette, or they may be made by calibrating the capillary tube. The volume outflow from large diameter samples may be great enough that it can be measured in a standard burette. The drip-point arrangement shown in Fig. 16–1 may be used in this case. Other methods of volume measurement that may be used are (a) weighing of the outflow, (b) drop counting (Richards and Richards, 1962), and (c) weighing of the cell with its contents (Reginato and Van Bavel, 1962). Regardless of the method chosen for volume measurement, it is necessary that the pressure head in the water at the porous plate remain constant during the outflow process.

The porous plate must have a bubbling pressure slightly higher than the highest cell pressure which will be applied. It is also desirable that the plate be as permeable as possible to minimize the pressure drop across the plate during the outflow.

The two burettes shown in Fig. 17–1 are used for removal of air from beneath the porous plate. A roller pump arrangement described by Kunze and Kirkham (1962) may also be used for this purpose. In the range of cell pressures up to approximately 1 atm., ceramic plates are usually strong enough so that a cavity about ⅛ to ¼ inch deep and with a diameter slightly less than that of the plate may be left beneath the plate for the collection of gas bubbles. This cavity can then be swept free of gas at a convenient stage in the procedure.

It is highly desirable that the measurements be made in a constant-temperature environment. Even when the apparatus is operated in a constant-temperature room or cabinet with control to ±0.5°C., condensation of water upon the walls of the pressure chamber usually occurs. This is a loss of water from the sample that is not accounted for in the volume outflow measurements. Condensation upon the walls can be prevented by winding an electric heater wire upon the outer surface of the pressure chamber and applying sufficient voltage to prevent the deposition of water. Care should be taken that no more than the minimum amount of heating required to prevent condensation is used. Excess heating will cause loss of water from the sample through the porous plate.

17–3.2 Procedure

Saturate the porous plate by wetting it under vacuum or by soaking it for a long time in de-aerated water.

Assemble the lower end-cap and the system for measuring the volume of outflow. Remove all gas bubbles from the outflow system.

Place the sample upon the porous plate, and assemble the cell. Saturate the sample by soaking it in water. Use the burettes as a source of water for wetting the sample.

When it is considered that the sample is saturated, close the cell, and apply the lowest gas-phase pressure desired. When outflow equilibrium has been reached, carry out the flushing operation to remove air from beneath the plate, and check again for equilibrium. Equilibrium is indicated when the meniscus in the horizontal tube does not move.

Adjust the position of the meniscus in the horizontal tube to the starting mark (see Fig. 17–1). Record the burette readings.

Close the clamp C_1 on the air pressure line, and raise the pressure in the line by the desired amount. Record the initial and final pressures.

Simultaneously open the clamp on the pressure line, and start the timer. Record the position of the meniscus as a function of time. Take frequent readings in the beginning of outflow and fewer toward the end.

Continue to record the outflow until equilibrium is attained. Make the necessary measurements to obtain the total volume of water $Q(\infty)$ removed from the sample as a result of the increase in pressure. Flush any gas from beneath the plate before the final volume readings are taken.

Repeat the operations in paragraphs 4 through 8 of this section (17–3.2) at as many levels of gas pressure as desired. The number of steps will be determined by the range of soil water content to be covered, by the amount of time available for the measurements, and the desired delineation of the diffusivity function.

Determine by gravimetric means the amount of water in the entire sample after the last equilibrium has been attained.

17–3.3 Analysis of Data

There are several methods of obtaining a diffusivity value from the outflow data (Gardner, 1956; Kunze and Kirkham, 1962; Miller and Elrick, 1958; Rijtema, 1959). If, as has been assumed here, the resistance to flow in the plate is negligible, the following method of analysis is suggested:

(1) Construct a theoretical plot of the quantities log $[1 - Q(t)/Q(\infty)]$ versus log $(Dt/4L^2)$ from equation [10]. This plot will be referred to as the overlay or theoretical curve. The data for the construction of the overlay are given in Table 17–1.

(2) From the experimentally determined volume-outflow data, calculate the quantity $1 - Q(t)/Q(\infty)$. If it was possible to hold in the horizontal tube all the outflow due to a given pressure increment, use the scale readings for the position of the meniscus to calculate the outflow ratio. Absolute values of volume are not needed because the units of quantity cancel. It will be necessary to use the cross sectional area of the tube when calculations of the water content of the sample are to be made.

(3) On another sheet of the same lot of log-log graph paper used for the overlay, construct a plot of log $[1 - Q(t)/Q(\infty)]$ versus log t, using the experimental data.

(4) Place the theoretical curve over the experimental curve, match the log $[1 - Q(t)/Q(\infty)]$ scales; and, by translation along the log $(Dt/4L^2)$ axis only, bring the theoretical and experimental curves into coincidence.

Select any convenient value of $Dt/4L^2$ from the overlay, and read the corresponding value of t from the experimental curve. If the chosen value of $Dt/4L^2$ is represented as w then the diffusivity is given by

$$D = w4L^2/t \qquad [11]$$

where t is the experimental value of time corresponding to the chosen value of w.

The water-content, pressure-head curve can be calculated from the final water content of the sample, and from the outflow volumes corresponding to each pressure increment. If the volume of the sample is V, the specific water capacity C is given by

$$C = Q(\infty)/V \, \Delta h \, . \qquad [12]$$

The conductivity is given by

$$K = DC \, . \qquad [13]$$

Table 17–1. Reduced diffusivity Dt/L^2 versus $1 - Q(t)/Q(\infty)$ for construction of the overlay.

Dt/L^2	$1-Q(t)/Q(\infty)$	Dt/L^2	$1-Q(t)/Q(\infty)$
0	1.0000	0.040	0.7743
0.001	0.9643	0.070	0.7014
0.002	0.9495	0.100	0.6433
0.004	0.9286	0.200	0.4959
0.007	0.9056	0.400	0.3022
0.010	0.8872	0.700	0.1390
0.020	0.8404	1.000	0.0690
		1.4185	0.0245

The values of conductivity, diffusivity, and specific water capacity obtained by these calculations may be considered to apply at a mean pressure head $\bar{h}$ given by

$$\bar{h} = -\left(m + \frac{\Delta m}{2}\right)\frac{\rho_1}{\rho} \qquad [14]$$

where m is the initial cell pressure and Δm is the change in cell pressure expressed as a length of a column of fluid of density ρ_1, and ρ is the density of water. The pressure-head values for unsaturated soil are negative. The mean soil water tension is the negative of the pressure head. Both tension and pressure head may conveniently be expressed in centimeters of water.

17–3.4 Comments

If disturbed samples are used, it is desirable to pack the sample, wet it, and drain it to the lowest water content that will be imposed and then re-saturate the sample. This procedure will stabilize the packing and reduce the magnitude of the changes in packing that can and do occur during the outflow procedure.

The assumption of a negligible head loss due to the flow through the porous plate is not always valid, especially when the sample has a water content approaching saturation. Porous plates which have a sufficiently high bubbling pressure may have a conductance that is low enough so that the head loss across the plate during the flow is appreciable. Under these conditions the pressure head at the soil-plate boundary will not be zero, and boundary condition [8] is not valid. Rijtema (1959) and Miller and Elrick (1958) have developed solutions of equation [6] in which the resistance to flow in the porous plate is considered. Kunze (1962) describes a modification of the Miller and Elrick procedure, which appears to be satisfactory. These analyses are of necessity more complex than the one described here. It is the opinion of the author that an attempt should be made to design the apparatus in such a way that the plate impedance is negligible. This will not always be possible, but by proper choice of porous plate one can make the head loss across the plate relatively small. The reader is referred to the papers by Kunze and Kirkham (1962) and Miller and Elrick (1958) for a description of their procedure. In the procedure given by Kunze and Kirkham, the initial stages of the outflow are given greatest weight in the analysis to obtain the diffusivity. Difficulties with gas accumulation, changes in the sample, etc., are made relatively small. A separate measurement of plate impedance is not required, and contact resistance between the sample and the plate is automatically considered.

The air line leading to the cell must not have restrictions which will interfere with the rapid change of gas pressure in the cell at time zero. Tubing with an inside diameter of $\frac{3}{8}$ inch or more, a short direct run from the pressure regulator to the cell, and a pinch clamp at C_1 rather than a stopcock should be used.

The time required for equilibrium is proportional to the square of the length of the sample, and inversely proportional to the magnitude of the diffusivity. Since D varies widely in a given sample, perhaps over a thousand-fold range, it will be difficult to use one sample length and one porous plate for the entire range. It is desirable to construct the cell so that samples of various lengths can be used, and so that porous plates of various porosities can be used. An equation for the time required for 0.99 of the outflow to occur can be derived from equation [10]. It is

$$t_{0.99} = 1.68L^2/D . \qquad [15]$$

This equation can be used to help select an appropriate sample length or to estimate the time for equilibrium if some idea of the magnitude of D is available. The diffusivity will probably be in the range 1×10^{-5} to 1×10^{-1} cm.^{2} per second. Practical sample lengths appear to be in the range 1 to 10 cm., with the shorter length appropriate for lower diffusivity values and higher tensions. The sample length should be chosen so that there will be sufficient time to make the necessary measurements during an outflow run, and so that an appreciable back pressure will not develop because of the flow in the volume measuring device. Economy of time and use of equipment should also be considered.

The concentration and nature of the solutes in the water used for the diffusivity measurement will affect the results. In general, the comments made in section 13–3.4 with regard to solute effects will apply here. Gardner et al. (1959) have studied the effect of the exchangeable sodium percentage and electrolyte concentration upon the diffusivity. The horizontal-infiltration technique with measurement of the water content distribution in the infiltration column was used for the measurement of the diffusivity. It was found that when the exchangeable sodium percentage was above about 25 the diffusivity was reduced about 1,000-fold if the electrolyte concentration was reduced from 300 to 3 me. per liter. Most of the decrease in diffusivity occurred in the higher water content range.

No attempt has been made to specify the nature of the sample for the measurement of the diffusivity. Whether one uses disturbed samples or undisturbed samples depends upon considerations that are in general beyond the scope of this article. Structure probably has a very pronounced effect upon the diffusivity function. If one is interested in the behavior of soil in a given structural condition, the use of undisturbed samples is indicated. On the other hand, disturbed samples are appropriate for many purposes in the study of soil water movement theory. The reader will have to decide for himself what type of samples are to be used.

A decision will have to be made concerning the required range of pressure-head values in which D will be determined. This decision will be influenced by the intended use of the data. The data are used in analysis of flow-system behavior. The range of pressure heads expected in the flow system to be analyzed will be the range of h in which D must be measured. The data may also be used in studying the effect of given management practices upon soil water relationships. The most pronounced effect of structure upon the diffusivity function will probably be in the range of pressure heads $-1,000$ to 0 cm. of water.

In the procedure as described, it is assumed that the diffusivity will be determined by starting at or near saturation and proceeding toward lower and lower water contents. Hysteresis will be present in the diffusivity function, and the functions for increasing and decreasing water content will not in general be the same. The hysteretic behavior of the diffusivity function is rather complex and not entirely understood. For some purposes, it may be necessary to know the diffusivity function for increasing water content. The outflow apparatus can also be used as an inflow apparatus, and the diffusivity function corresponding to increasing water content obtained. The procedure is the same except that incremental decreases of gas-phase pressure are used, and the meniscus is pre-set at a starting point with the horizontal tube filled with water. The analysis of the data is carried out in the same manner.

The choice of the pressure increment involves two conflicting requirements. The change in the water content should be small enough that the diffusivity does not change significantly during a given outflow run. The pressure increment must be large enough to remove a volume of water from the sample that can easily be measured. As a rule of thumb, it would appear that the pressure increment should not be larger than about 10% of the applied pressure, and preferably it should be smaller.

Some difficulty may be experienced with loss of water by vapor transfer through the air line. This can be prevented by connecting a cell or flask in the air line close to the pressure cell in which a nearly saturated atmosphere is maintained. Tanner and Elrick (1958) describe such an arrangement.

When carrying out the curve-matching procedure in the analysis to obtain the diffusivity corresponding to the conditions of a given run, it may be found that the experimental and theoretical curves are not of the appropriate shape so that they can be matched. The strict interpretation of this is that the boundary conditions, or the flow equation, or some assumption inherent in the procedure was not valid. If deviations from behavior predicted by equation [10] are encountered, the user of the method will have to make his own decision about the matter. These deviations have been observed and are the subject of continuing research.

17–4 LITERATURE CITED

Bruce, R. R., and Klute, A. 1956. The measurement of soil water diffusivity. Soil Sci. Soc. Am. Proc. 20:458–462.

Carslaw, H. S., and Jaeger, J. C. 1959. Conduction of Heat in Solids, pp. 99–102. Oxford Univ. Press, London.

Childs, E. C., and Collis-George, N. 1950. The permeability of porous materials. Proc. Royal Soc. London 201A:392–405.

Gardner, W. R. 1956. Calculation of capillary conductivity from pressure plate outflow data. Soil Sci. Soc. Am. Proc. 20:317–320.

Gardner, W. R. 1960. Measurement of capillary conductivity and diffusivity with a tensiometer. Trans. Intern. Congr. Soil Sci. 7th Madison. 1:300–305.

Gardner, W. R., Mayhugh, M. S., Goertzen, J. O., and Bower, C. A. 1959. Effect of electrolyte concentration and exchangeable sodium percentage on diffusivity of water in soils. Soil Sci. 88:270–274.

Hanks, R. J., Miller, E. E., and Tanner, C. B. 1953. Float valve pressure control for porous plate apparatus. Soil Sci. Soc. Am. Proc. 17:318–320.

Kunze, Raymond J., and Kirkham, Don. 1962. Simplified accounting for membrane impedance in capillary conductivity determinations. Soil Sci. Soc. Am. Proc. 26:421–426.

Miller, E. E., and Elrick, D. E. 1958. Dynamic determination of capillary conductivity extended for non-negligible membrane impedance. Soil Sci. Soc. Am. Proc. 22:483–486.

Reginato, R. J., and Van Bavel, C. H. M. 1962. Pressure cell for soil cores. Soil Sci. Soc. Am. Proc. 26:1–3.

Richards, L. A. 1949. Methods of measuring soil moisture tension. Soil Sci. 68:95–112.

Richards, L. A., and Richards, P. L. 1962. Radial-flow cell for soil-water measurements. Soil Sci. Soc. Am. Proc. 26:515–518.

Rijtema, P. E. 1959. Calculation of capillary conductivity from pressure plate outflow data with non-negligible membrane impedance. Netherlands J. Agr. Sci. 7:209–215.

Tanner, C. B., and Elrick, D. E. 1958. Volumetric porous pressure plate apparatus for moisture hysteresis measurements. Soil Sci. Soc. Am. Proc. 22:575–576.

18 | Water Capacity

A. KLUTE
University of Illinois
Urbana, Illinois

18–1 INTRODUCTION

The differential equation for water flow in unsaturated soil, which results from the combination of Darcy's law and the conservation of matter principle, may be written in the form

$$C(h)(\partial h/\partial t) = \nabla \cdot [K(h) \nabla H] \tag{1}$$

where h is the pressure head, t is the time, ∇H is the hydraulic gradient, and $K(h)$ is the conductivity function. The water capacity $C(h)$ is the change in water content of the soil per unit pressure-head change, i.e., $d\theta/dh$, where θ is the volume water content.

If equation [1] is valid, the flow pattern in a given soil will be described by a solution of the equation. The appropriate solution of equation [1] is determined by the boundary and initial conditions that apply to the flow system under study and by the properties of the soil as expressed in the conductivity and the water-capacity functions. Analysis of the behavior of soil water movement requires a knowledge of these functions. The recently increased use of numerical techniques to solve equation [1] has emphasized the need for conductivity and water capacity data. These functions should reflect the effects of various treatments upon the ability of soils to conduct and store water. The use of the water-retention curve $\theta(h)$ in evaluating soil structure has been suggested by a number of workers (Bradfield and Jamison, 1939; Childs, 1940; Donat, 1937; Lutz et al., 1947; Leamer and Shaw, 1941). The water capacity is the first derivative of the $\theta(h)$ function and is closely related to a "pore-size" distribution which may be derived from water-retention data (Donat, 1937; Childs and Collis-George, 1950).

Water capacity data may be obtained as a byproduct of other determinations. For example, any determination of the water-content, pressure-head function is, in effect, a method for determining the water capacity. The water capacity is also obtained when measurements of the soil water diffusivity are made by the outflow-cell procedure (section 17–3). The basic measurements required are water content and pressure head. The standard types of apparatus for these determinations include pressure-membrane cells (section 8–2.3.1) and tension apparatus (section 9–3.1).

A weighable pressure cell similar to that used by Reginato and Van Bavel (1962) will be described in this section. The principles of operations are the same as for the pressure-membrane apparatus (section 8–2.2; Richards, 1948). A sample of wet soil rests upon a saturated porous plate and is enclosed in a pressure chamber. An outflow tube is connected to the bottom of the porous plate. The gas pressure in the cell is raised above that upon the water in the outflow tube. The hydraulic head of the soil water is thereby made larger than that of the water on the opposite side of the plate, and outflow occurs. The water content of the soil is reduced, and equilibrium is established when the hydraulic head of the soil water and the water beneath the plate are equal. If the pressure on the water beneath the plate is atmospheric, the cell pressure is equivalent to the soil water tension, and the pressure head is the negative of the cell pressure.

The standard pressure-membrane procedure in which the sample is removed from the chamber for weighing is not well suited to precise determination of the $\theta(h)$ function on a given sample, because of the difficulty of reestablishing hydraulic contact between the sample and the porous plate. The weighable cell, in which the water content at equilibrium is determined by the relatively precise operation of weighing, and which does not require separation of the sample from the plate, is better suited to the determination of the water capacity. Evaporative losses from the sample are greatly reduced compared to the standard pressure-membrane technique.

The type of cell described in section 17–3.1 in which the volume outflow is measured in a horizontal capillary and burette system, may also be used to determine the water-content, pressure-head relationship, and the water-capacity function.

18–2 METHOD [1]

18–2.1 Special Apparatus

1. Pressure cell and sample retainers: Figure 18–1A shows the construction details of the pressure cell with a porous ceramic plate (Porosity grade 015, Selas Corp., Dresher, Pa.). Figure 18–1B shows a modification of the cell for use with a membrane (Superstrength process polypore, Type 1120, Gelman Instrument Co., Chelsea, Mich.).

   The dimensions given are appropriate for brass sample retainers 1.50 inches high, and 2.00 inches outside diameter (o.d.). For other sizes of sample retainers the proper dimensions have to be worked out. The side wall of the cell is made from a piece of 3-inch o.d. lucite tubing

---

[1] The procedure is similar to that described by Reginato and Van Bavel (1962).

with a ¼-inch wall thickness. The upper end-cap is a 3.2-inch-square piece of ¼-inch lucite sheet, and is cemented to the side wall with ethylene dichloride. The lower end-cap is a 3.2-inch-square piece of ½-inch lucite with a circular recess for the plate and a 0.1-inch-deep cavity under the plate. The four 10-24 clamping screws are set in the corners of the end caps and are long enough to act as legs for the cell. The outflow tube is a piece of ¼-inch o.d. lucite tubing bent into an L shape and cemented into the lower end-cap with ethylene dichloride. A 35-ohm heater made of No. 28 nickel chrome resistance wire is wound on the outer surface of the cell wall and on top of the upper cap, and is held in place with Duco cement and plastic insulating tape. The heater terminals are two 6-32 screws set in the edge of the upper cap. A ring of ¼-inch o.d. gum rubber tubing is cemented in the top of the sample compartment and holds the sample in firm contact with the porous plate. The heater is operated at 3 or 4 volts by a step-down transformer or autotransformer connected to a 110 volt a-c source.

The 2.45-inch-diameter by ¼-inch-thick porous plate is cemented to the end cap with an epoxy resin (Type A-2 or A-4, Armstrong Products Co., Warsaw, Ind.). "O" ring seals may also be used as shown by Reginato and Van Bavel (1962), or as shown in Fig. 16–3. The bub-

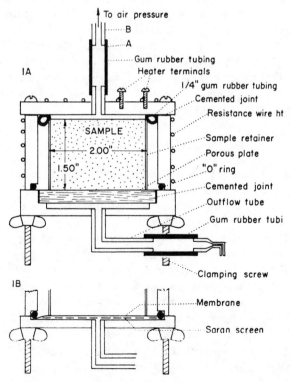

Fig. 18–1. Construction details of the weighable cell.

bling pressure of the plate or membrane material should be slightly higher than the highest cell pressure to be used. Measurements of the type considered here are probably most useful in the range of zero to 1 atm. tension. Hence plates with a bubbling pressure of about 1 atm. are generally satisfactory. Porous ceramic plates may be cut to the correct diameter with a carbide tool on a lathe. The thickness of the plate may be adjusted by hand lapping upon a sheet of abrasive paper on a flat surface.

2. Pressure regulator: The gas pressure in the cell should be controlled within a few millimeters of water in the range of less than 30 cm. of water, and to about 3 or 4 parts per hundred in the range above 30 cm. Regulators are available from commercial sources that are quite satisfactory (Models 40-2, 40-15, Moore Products Co., Philadelphia, Pa.). Systems for pressure control have also been described by Hanks et al. (1953), and Richards (1949). It is recommended that a small supply of water be kept in the regulated pressure line to prevent loss of water from the sample by back diffusion. A group of pressure cells may be operated from one pressure regulator by connecting each cell to a manifold through a valve, so that the air pressure to any cell may be shut off.

3. Balance: A balance with sufficient sensitivity and capacity to weigh the cells will be needed. The total weight of the cell with a sample is about 500 g. The required balance sensitivity may be estimated from $\Delta\theta V$, where V is the sample volume, and $\Delta\theta$ is the smallest change in water content that it is desired to detect. For a sample volume of 70 cc., a balance with a sensitivity of ±0.01 g. will allow one to measure θ to $\pm1.4 \times 10^{-4}$ which is quite adequate. Reginato and Van Bavel (1962) used a Mettler automatic direct-reading balance with a capacity of 800 g. and a sensitivity of 0.03 g.

18–2.2 Procedure

Measure the contained volume and the weight of the sample retainers. Obtain samples in the sample retainers. Saturate the porous plates by soaking them for 16 to 24 hours or by wetting them under vacuum with de-aerated water. Connect a leveling bulb filled with de-aerated water to the outflow tube, and adjust the water level to the top of the porous plate. Place the sample in its retainer upon the porous plate, and clamp the top of the cell in place. Raise the water level in the leveling bulb to a few millimeters below the top of the sample, and allow the sample to absorb water. When the sample is saturated, disconnect the leveling bulb from the outflow tube, and apply the lowest air pressure desired.

When outflow appears to have ceased, place a hose clamp at point A on the air line (Fig. 18–1), close the valve in the air line, and disconnect the air line at point B. Be sure that the cavity under the plate and the outflow tube are free of gas bubbles. If bubbles are present, remove them by tip-ping the cell and injecting water through the gum rubber tubing with a hypodermic syringe and needle. Handle the cell as gently as possible.

Weigh the cell and reconnect it to the air line. Weigh the cell periodi-cally (at intervals of 4 to 16 hours) until constant weight is attained. Re-cord the gross weight of the cell and its contents W_i, and the gas pressure in the cell P_i.

Raise the cell gas pressure to the next desired value, and repeat the operations in the preceding paragraph until the highest desired pressure, corresponding to the highest tension, is reached. Remove the entire sample from the cell, and determine the oven-dry weight of the soil. Weigh the cell without a sample and sample retainer, with the plate saturated with water, and with a pressure of about 10 cm. of water in the cell.

18–2.3 Calculations

Calculate the volume water content θ_i at each cell pressure P_i from

$$\theta_i = M_i/\rho V \qquad [2]$$
$$= [W_i - (W_1 + W_2) - W_d]/\rho V \qquad [3]$$

where M_i is the mass of water in the sample, ρ is the density of water, V is the sample volume, W_i is the mass of cell plus the wet sample in its retainer, W_1 is the mass of the sample retainer, W_2 is the mass of the empty cell with wetted porous plate, and W_d is the mass of oven-dry soil in the sample. Construct a graph of θ versus h by plotting θ_i versus $-P_i$, with P_i expressed in centimeters of water. The soil water tension is equal to the cell pressure, and the pressure head is the negative of the soil water tension. Differentiate the $\theta(h)$ function to obtain the water capacity $C(h)$.

18–2.4 Comments

Before differentiation of the $\theta(h)$ function, it may be desirable to smooth the primary $\theta(h)$ data by appropriate curve-fitting techniques. Curve fit-ting by eye may be sufficient. The differentiation may be done numerically by taking first differences from the smoothed data, or by graphical means. Tangents to the curve may be constructed with the aid of a tangent meter having a totally reflecting prism which is rotated until the image of the curve appears to be a continuation of the curve. Standard texts on numerical treatment of data should be constructed for further details of the differentia-tion procedure (Milne, 1949).

The soaking time required for the samples is somewhat uncertain. Com-mon practice is to soak the samples about 24 hours. However, there is reason to believe that a longer time of soaking may be required for air-dry samples to rehydrate the soil colloids and bring the sample to equilibrium at or near zero tension. It is probably better to keep undisturbed core samples moist from the time they are taken until the determination can be carried out. If the sample is not at equilibrium at the end of the soaking period, it may continue to absorb water when the first or even subsequent steps of cell pressure are applied. Water will be drawn from the outflow tube, and since the outflow tube is filled with water before each weighing, the cell weight will increase.

The $\theta(h)$ and $C(h)$ functions will exhibit hysteresis behavior. The usual procedure is to start at or near zero cell pressure and obtain equilibrium at a series of increasing pressures and thus determine a desorption curve. Absorption curves may also be determined by connecting a constant-head source of water to the outlet tube of the cell and progressively decreasing the pressure to obtain a series of points on a wetting curve.

The time for equilibrium is directly proportional to the square of the sample length and inversely proportional to the soil water diffusivity. To keep the equilibrium times within reasonable limits, the sample should not be longer than about 3 cm. and probably should be shorter.

The resistance wire heater is designed to prevent condensation of vapor upon the interior walls of the cell. Only enough heat should be used to prevent condensation. With a 35-ohm resistance heater on the cells as shown, about 3 or 4 volts has been found sufficient to prevent condensation. This amount of heating does not cause a perceptible rise in the temperature of the sample.

18-3 LITERATURE CITED

Bradfield, R., and Jamison, V. E. 1939. Soil structure—attempts at its quantitative characterization. Soil Sci. Soc. Am. Proc. (1938) 3:70–76.

Childs, E. C. 1940. The use of soil moisture characteristics in soil studies. Soil Sci. 50:239–252.

Childs, E. C., and Collis-George, N. 1950. The control of soil water. Adv. Agron. 2:233–272.

Donat, J. 1937. Das Gefuge des Bodens und dessen Kennzeichnung. Trans. 6th Comm. Intern. Soc. Soil Sci., Vol. B:423–429.

Hanks, R. J., Miller, E. E., and Tanner, C. B. 1953. Float valve pressure control for porous plate apparatus. Soil Sci. Soc. Am. Proc. 17:318–320.

Leamer, R. W., and Shaw, B. 1941. A simple apparatus for measuring non-capillary porosity on an extensive scale. J. Am. Soc. Agron. 33:1003–1008.

Lutz, J. F., Nelson, W. L., Brady, N. C., and Scarsbrook, C. E. 1947. Effect of cover crops on pore-size distribution in a coastal plain soil. Soil Sci. Soc. Am. Proc. (1946) 11:43–46.

Milne, W. E. 1949. Numerical Calculus. Princeton Univ. Press. Princeton, N. J.

Reginato, R. J., and Van Bavel, C. H. M. 1962. Pressure cell for soil cores. Soil Sci. Soc. Am. Proc. 26:1–3.

Richards, L. A. 1948. Porous plate apparatus for measuring moisture retention and transmission by soil. Soil Sci. 66:105–110.

Richards, L. A. 1949. Methods of measuring soil moisture tension. Soil Sci. 68:95–112.

19 | Water Availability

D. B. PETERS

Agricultural Research Service, USDA, and
University of Illinois
Urbana, Illinois

19–1 GENERAL INTRODUCTION

The capacity of soils to absorb and retain water provides a reservoir from which water may be withdrawn by plants during periods between rainfalls and/or irrigations. The water retention properties of soils and the extraction of water from soils by plants have been intensively studied, and various soil-water constants have been defined and used as an index of the water-holding capacity of soils. Of these, the properties defining the range of plant-available water have been the most universally used. The moist end of the range is defined by the field capacity; the dry end, by the wilting point.

19–2 FIELD CAPACITY

19–2.1 Introduction

Veihmeyer and Hendrickson (1931) have defined the field capacity as "the amount of water held in the soil after the excess gravitational water has drained away and after the rate of downward movement of water has materially decreased." Thus field capacity is supposed to represent the water content of soil at a certain location in the profile at a certain time after wetting. The determination of field capacity is therefore accomplished by use of a dynamic flow process. Theoretically the moisture content at a particular time and location could be analytically determined by solution of the flow equation for vertical infiltration and subsequent redistribution. The particular water content, in space and time, would be determined by the initial and boundary conditions. Specifically, the flux density at a location in the profile is equal to the product of the capillary conductivity and hydraulic gradient. The capillary conductivity is an intrinsic physical property (but by no means constant in space and time during a flow process); however, the hydraulic gradient is largely determined by hydraulic conditions elsewhere in the profile. Consequently, to obtain unique values at a particular position in the profile at a particular time would require that each determination for a particular soil be made with identical initial and boundary conditions. This, however, would be difficult to achieve in a practical way, inasmuch as the determination ideally must be made under field conditions.

The original intent in defining "field capacity" was to devise a procedure which would enable determination of the upper limit of available water. In ideal situations, such as deep permeable soils, initially dry, the values obtained do approximate the upper limit of available water. However, there are many soil conditions which alter the upper limit from that prescribed by the field-capacity definition. Any soil condition which would impede drainage would cause misleading results. Soil conditions which are effective in the formation of perched water tables should be carefully evaluated. Sand lenses are especially effective in producing perched water tables; therefore, where sand lenses are present the amount of water added should be regulated either to penetrate the lens completely or not to reach it.

Field observations indicate there is no sudden change in the profile drainage rate for many soils. Consequently it is not possible in general to designate a time after which soil water movement is negligible. Therefore it is necessary that the operator study each soil, and determination, to ensure that the results obtained are realistic in terms of the problem for which the data are to be used.

The nature of the field-capacity definition implies that there is a unique water retention value, opposing the force of gravity, which could be used to specify the upper limit of available water. The unique water retention value would also specify the soil water retention at which capillary conductivity rapidly approaches zero. Certain retentivity values do, in fact, have a useful correlation with the upper limit of field water contents for certain soils. The ⅓-bar percentage has been found to be closely correlated to field capacity for many soils (see section 8–2.2). However, such correlations must be verified by field measurements; consequently, the method described herein is specific for field determination.

In humid regions it is often difficult to evaluate the upper limit of available water by the procedure defined by field capacity. Frequently in humid regions the upper limit of available water is specified, in the absence of evaporation, by a true equilibrium water content, specifically by static equilibrium water content. Under these conditions, the actual water content values are dependent on the kind of soil and depth to the water table. In many instances the upper limit of available water can be determined by measurement of the soil water content when tile flow ceases.

For further reading on field capacity, the papers of Nielsen et al. (1959), Richards (1955), and Youngs (1957) may be consulted.

19–2.2 Method

19–2.2.1 PROCEDURE

Select a field site of the soil to be measured. Attempt to make the determination when the soil is in its normal driest condition. Place a raised border (a simple earth dike is sufficient) around an area at least 8 feet by 8 feet, and add sufficient water (by flooding on level terrain and sprinkling if the terrain is not sufficiently level) to wet the soil of the entire sampling area to the depth of interest (for example, to the expected root depth). Cover the area with polyethylene plastic, or some similar material, to prevent evaporation. Allow the soil to drain for approximately 2 days, remove the protective cover and take soil samplings (or use some equivalent technique, such as nuclear scattering) to determine the water percentage. Sample near the center of the plot, and take samples, by successive increments, to the depth of wetting. Make at least five separate borings if a gravimetric procedure is used. The water percentage at the time of sampling is defined as the field capacity.

19–2.2.2 COMMENTS

Since the procedure is laborious, the usual procedure is to measure at one sample site for a well-defined soil. However, where greater precision is required, or soil variability is known to be large, it will be necessary to increase the number of sample sites (see section 5). For practical use, the bulk density of the soil should be determined concurrently with the field capacity to convert the water percentage on an oven-dry basis to the more practical water percentage per unit volume basis, as follows:

$$P_v = P_w(\rho_B)(1/\rho_w)$$

where

P_v = water percent per unit volume,
P_w = water percent per unit oven dry weight,
ρ_B = bulk density, and
ρ_w = density of water.

Then the number of inches of water in a given depth is determined by

$$\text{Inches } H_2O = (P_v)(\text{depth}) .$$

19–3   WILTING POINT

19–3.1   Introduction

The evaluation of the water content of soils after permanent wilting of plants grown in them is one of the oldest techniques used in the determination of the lower limit of available water. Briggs and Shantz (1911) introduced the concept of the wilting point, but the use of biological methods to determine the lower limit of available water dates back even beyond their classical work.

The permanent wilting point is defined as the water percentage of a soil when plants growing in that soil are first reduced to a wilted condition from which they cannot recover in an approximately saturated atmosphere.

There is a considerable range of water content between the inception and end point of permanent wilting. Consequently, techniques have been devised to measure the wilting range, that is, the water content of the soil at the inception of permanent wilting and the water content at permanent wilting. The water content difference between the two wilting points, incipient wilting and permanent wilting, defines the wilting range.

The incipient wilting point is defined as the water content in the soil at which the lowest pair of true leaves of a particular kind of plant at a particular stage of growth wilts and fails to recover in a saturated atmosphere. The elongation of plants ceases at about the same time that incipient wilting occurs. The concept of incipient wilting was first elucidated by Furr and Reeve (1945), and the procedure described below is essentially the procedure they used originally. The determination of the incipient wilting point and the permanent wilting point can be made simultaneously; consequently, the procedures are given in sequence below.

Although the wilting points are good, reproducible indicators of the lower limits of available water, there is ample evidence to indicate that the wilting points are not true constants or intrinsic soil properties. The values obtained in practice are affected by the technique and plant indicator used. There is no unique soil water retentivity value at which the uptake of water by plants suddenly ceases. The wilting points refer to the soil water content at which soil cannot supply water at a sufficient rate to maintain turgor. Thus the point at which plants wilt is controlled by rate factors, both supply and demand, and not by a unique retention value. However, at high values of soil water retention the rate of water movement becomes so slow as to give an apparent retention value controlling wilting. Also the method uses a technique to set the water demand rate to a very low value. Consequently, a retention value should approximate the wilting point. In this regard the 15-bar percentage (see section 8–2.2) has been found to be closely correlated with the permanent wilting point (Richards and Weaver,

1943). In many cases, especially in medium-textured soils, the 15-bar percentage will sufficiently describe the permanent wilting point to be of practical use.

19–3.2 Method [1]

19–3.2.1 PROCEDURE FOR INCIPIENT WILTING POINT

Place a weighed quantity of about 600 g. of air-dried, 2-mm. soil in a weighed, No. 2, friction-top can or similar watertight container. (Make a water-content determination on a separate sample, so that the oven-dry weight of the soil is known.) Add nitrogen and other nutrients as needed to produce good plant growth without pronounced nutrient deficiencies. Plant several seeds of dwarf sunflower (*Helianthus annuus,* large-seeded variety).

Moisten the soil to a water content suitable for plant growth, and re-weigh the container. The water content corresponding to the ⅓-bar per-centage forms a convenient starting point. Each time the soil is watered, bring the average water content back to the starting point.

After the seeds have germinated, cut off all but the best seedling at soil level, and discard the plants. Lead the remaining seedling out through a hole in the lid of the can. Grow the plant in a greenhouse or under a cloth shade until the third pair of leaves is fully developed. Repeatedly check the soil water content to ensure an adequate supply of water during the plant development period. Never allow the plants to remain in an environ-ment where daily wilting occurs at high water contents. At the same time, exercise care to prevent waterlogging. Adjust the aerial environment of the plants to a condition where normal plant development occurs but where the environmental demand for water is low.

After the third pair of leaves has developed, irrigate the soil with enough water to bring the water content to the moist starting value. Fill the space between the stem and the sides of the hole in the lid with cotton to reduce soil evaporation to a low level.

When the lowest one or two pairs of true leaves wilt, transfer the con-tainer and plant to a dark, humid chamber. If the leaves regain turgidity during an overnight period (14 to 16 hours), return the experimental sam-ple to the growth location. Repeat the process of wilting and humidification until the lowest pair of true leaves fails to recover in the humid chamber. (The remaining leaves at this stage should regain turgor during the humidi-fication period.)

When this stage of wilting has been reached, cut off the plant at soil level, and discard the plant. Then weigh the container and soil, and calcu-late the water content on the oven-dry basis. Alternatively, determine the

---

[1] Furr and Reeve (1945); Veihmeyer and Hendrickson (1949).

water content of the soil by oven-drying a sample after removing the plant top and as many roots as can be taken out conveniently. The water percentage of the soil at this stage of wilting is defined as the incipient wilting point.

19–3.2.2 PROCEDURE FOR PERMANENT WILTING POINT

Repeat the procedure as described in section 19–3.2.1 up to the point where wilting begins. Then follow the described procedure of alternating the experimental samples between the dark, humid chamber and the growth area until all leaves are wilted beyond recovery. Determine the water percentage in the soil as described in section 19–3.2.1.

19–3.2.3 COMMENTS

In the last stages of the wilting-point measurements, the use of cotton is preferable to impermeable materials for the plug in the hole in the top of the can. A cotton plug reduces evaporation from the soil to a low level without at the same time preventing adequate soil aeration. Any technique which will control evaporation and still allow air exchange to occur can be used. Polyethylene plastic can be used if care is taken to prevent the condensation of water on the soil side of the plastic.

The determination of the water content of the soil after wilting points are reached is most precise if the roots are removed from the soil before analysis for water content. However, the error introduced by including the roots in the larger soil mass is in most cases negligible.

The water content is usually expressed as a weight percentage based on the oven-dry weight (drying at 110°C.). The computation procedure is as follows:

$$P_w = \left(\frac{\text{wet weight} - \text{oven-dry weight}}{\text{oven-dry weight} - \text{tare weight}} \right) \times 100$$

where

P_w = water percentage on weight basis,

wet weight = weight of container and contents after wilting,

oven-dry weight = weight of container and contents after drying in an oven at 110°C., and

tare weight = weight of container.

If the containers are standardized to a standard weight, then one of the containers may be used on the weighing device to balance out the tare weight. If this procedure is followed, the computation is as follows:

$$P_w = \left(\frac{\text{wet soil weight}}{\text{oven-dry soil weight}} - 1 \right) \times 100 \, .$$

At least three separate determinations should be made for each wilting-point value.

The incipient wilting point is closely correlated with cessation of growth. As an auxiliary measurement, a continuous record of plant height as the plants are wilting gives a good measure of when incipient wilting, as defined, begins to occur.

19-4 AVAILABLE WATER

The available water in a soil is the amount of water that can be used or removed from the soil in the support of the life of higher plants. The available water content is estimated by the difference between the water content at field capacity and the water content at the permanent wilting point. The accuracy of the available water content is therefore dependent upon the reliability of the field capacity and permanent wilting point to estimate, respectively, the upper and lower limits of available water.

Available water can be expressed either as the difference between the water percentages at the upper and lower limit, or if bulk density is known, the percentage values can be converted to inches of water, as follows:

$$\text{Inches of water per inch of soil} = (P_w)(\rho_B)(1/\rho_w)$$

where

P_w = percent H_2O on oven-dry weight basis,

ρ_B = bulk density, and

ρ_w = density of water.

19-5 LITERATURE CITED

Briggs, L. J., and Shantz, H. L. 1911. A wax seal method for determining the lower limit of available soil moisture. Botan. Gaz. 51:210–220.

Furr, J. R., and Reeve, J. O. 1945. Range of soil moisture percentages through which plants undergo permanent wilting in some soils from semiarid irrigated areas. J. Agr. Res. 71:149–170.

Nielsen, D. R., Kirkham, Don, and van Wijk, W. R. 1959. Measuring water stored temporarily above field moisture capacity. Soil Sci. Soc. Am. Proc. 23:408–412.

Richards, L. A. 1955. Water content changes following the wetting of bare soil in the field. Soil Sci. Soc. Florida Proc. 15:142–148.

Richards, L. A., and Weaver, L. R. 1943. Fifteen-atmosphere percentage as related to the permanent wilting percentage. Soil Sci. 56:331–340.

Veihmeyer, F. J., and Hendrickson, A. H. 1931. The moisture equivalent as a measure of the field capacity of soils. Soil Sci. 32:181–194.

Veihmeyer, F. J., and Hendrickson, A. H. 1949. Methods of measuring field capacity and permanent wilting percentage of soils. Soil Sci. 68:75–95.

Youngs, E. G. 1957. Moisture profiles during vertical infiltration. Soil Sci. 84:283–290.

20 | Evapotranspiration[1]

J. S. ROBINS

Agricultural Research Service, USDA
Boise, Idaho

20–1 GENERAL INTRODUCTION

Evapotranspiration as used here is defined as the sum of water lost by the combined processes of evaporation and transpiration from a particular area in a specified time. This definition differs slightly from that of Aldrich et al. (1956) which uses the phrase "removed by vegetation" in place of "transpiration." Since a part of the water "removed by vegetation" is retained in the plant and not transpired, the author prefers to use the term "transpiration" in reference to the water lost through the plant.

Evapotranspiration is not really a measurement of a soil property but rather a quantity arrived at through soil or other measurements. Therefore, the reader may note that the organization and method of treatment used in this section differs from that generally used in the monograph. Many of the measurements required are described in other sections and are referred to rather than described in this section.

An estimation or prediction of the quantity and rate of evapotranspiration from vegetated land surfaces is important in designing irrigation projects and systems, and in determining when to irrigate and the proper quantity of water to apply. Other practical applications include prediction of water supplies, estimation of drought incidence, forecasting of crop yields, and estimation of soil moisture conditions connected with military operations. Each use necessitates a different degree of accuracy in estimation, and a number of methods are available.

Methods used can be classed in two general types: (*1*) Those that involve an assessment of water loss from the soil or other medium in a finite time interval; and (*2*) those that involve measurement of climatic or other factors which either correlate with or cause evapotranspiration. The former will be referred to here as "indirect measurements" and the latter as "estimation methods."

---

[1] Contribution from the Soil and Water Conservation Research Division, ARS, USDA, Boise, Idaho.

20–2 INDIRECT MEASUREMENTS

20–2.1 Methods

These methods are based on periodic assessment of the quantity of water in a given soil mass, either by direct or indirect soil moisture measurement, or by total weight or water volume determination in lysimeters. In the absence of water intake by the soil, the difference in soil water content at any two times of measurement represents the evapotranspiration for the interval. Increments of evapotranspiration for short periods can be added to arrive at evapotranspiration for longer periods, or can be divided by the time interval involved to determine average evapotranspiration rate for the period of determination. A necessary assumption is that the observed water loss occurs to the atmosphere.

Periodic measurements of water content in field soils can be made by any method such as those described in section 7. Precision, accuracy, and cost vary widely for the many available methods, and the method selected must be fitted to the desired accuracy, physical system and resources available.

Gravimetric, electric and heat conductance, and certain other water content measurement techniques usually require a knowledge of bulk density to convert water content data to a volume basis. This creates a source of error in the water content estimation which is often serious. A major advantage of the neutron moderation technique lies in the calibration of the count of slowed neutrons directly with moisture content on a volume basis.

Where large amounts of rainfall occur during a period of measurement, some uncertainty is associated with possible loss of water beyond the sampling zone. If this occurs, a resampling for water content should be made as soon as feasible after the rain in order (1) to judge whether or not water was lost by deep percolation, so that possible adjustment of the data for the interval can be made on the basis of estimated water content when rain occurred and the quantity of rainfall; and (2) to establish a new initial water content value upon which to base calculations of subsequent changes. Small showers (1.25 cm. or less) have often been ignored in measuring evapotranspiration. Currently, however, evidence indicates that all rainfall, regardless of the quantity in a given storm, should be added so long as runoff does not occur. Where runoff is common, plots should be leveled and diked, or runoff should be measured to adjust for this water loss.

Gravimetric water content determinations generally cannot be made when soils are very wet following irrigation or rainfall. Thus, there is a period of unmeasured evapotranspiration between the pre-irrigation and post-irrigation sampling which may be as much as 5 days or more on slowly permeable soils. Evapotranspiration for this period is determined by making a linear extrapolation of the plots of water content versus time before and after irrigation to the time of irrigation. Some error is involved, but if determined rates before and after the unmeasured interval are reliable and if weather remains about the same, such errors are small.

An alternative method sometimes used is to take samples only before each irrigation and to add a precisely measured quantity of water to a plot of known size. The water content prior to an irrigation plus the quantity of water added less the water content at the first sampling after the irrigation represents evapotranspiration for the interval between samplings. Possible deep percolation losses are ignored. Thus, the estimate of water needed to refill the profile and the measurement of water added must be accurate to avoid serious errors.

Water content changes can be assessed with great precision in weighing lysimeters (Van Bavel, 1961). Both direct weighing (Pruitt and Angus, 1960) and floating (King et al. 1956) types can be used. Precision of determination is limited mainly by the sensitivity of the weighing apparatus. Reasonably accurate loss records for intervals of 1 hour or less are possible with this technique.

Replacement (percolation) lysimeters are satisfactory for measuring evapotranspiration for periods of several days (Van Bavel, 1961). In these systems, a measured volume of water, in excess of that which will be retained, is added to a confined lysimeter equipped with facilities for free drainage or for creating a specified tension at the bottom. After drainage has ceased, evapotranspiration is permitted for a suitable time period after which a measured excess quantity of water is again applied. When drainage again ceases, recorded drainage effluent is subtracted from the latter quantity of water applied. The difference represents a measure of evapotranspiration for the interval between times of cessation of drainage. It is reasonably assumed that moisture content distribution at cessation of drainage is unique for a given system. The method is satisfactory provided sufficient depth is present (usually about 2 m.) to avoid confounding results of temporary water table development. For evapotranspiration measurements in the presence of a water table, constant water table lysimeters can be used (Van Bavel, 1961). Water can be added at the surface as described above, or loss from the water table can be measured volumetrically.

20–2.2 Comments

The primary limitations in precision of evapotranspiration measurements in the field are differences among replicate observations of water content resulting from soil variability (see section 5). Reliability of the water content measurement can be improved by increasing the number of determinations. With measurement methods which utilize small soil volumes (gravimetric, tensiometric, electrical and thermal conductivity, etc.), 8 to 12 samples usually give reasonable precision (standard deviation <0.015 cm. per cm. depth of soil) unless soil variability is excessive. Increased precision per additional sample beyond that possible with 12 samples is small. Methods such as neutron moderation which measure a larger soil volume give similar precision with fewer samples. Four to eight samples by such methods are generally adequate. Inhomogeneity in moisture and structural properties varies widely from soil to soil; thus the standard deviation with a given number of samples may be 0.005 cm. per cm. for one soil and 0.035 cm. per cm. for another. It is advisable to determine the necessary number of samples required for the desired degree of precision. A method for such determination is given in section 5. In most field soils, variability is such that evapotranspiration values obtained by current methods are of questionable value for time intervals less than about 4 or 5 days.

In periodic water content measurement in field soils, it is essential that the entire soil zone from which evapotranspiration occurs be sampled. When plants are small and root depth is restricted, appreciable quantities of water may move upward from depths of 1 m. or more to replace that evaporated or transpired. With mature annuals, rooting depth is often 2 to 3 m., and mature alfalfa or tree crops commonly extract water from depths of 6 or 8 m. Unless the entire supplying zone is measured, observed losses will be in error.

Another source of error is use of water from a water table. If roots penetrate within 1 or 1.5 m. of a water table, serious errors in measurement may result since it is impossible to assess the amount of water consumed from the water table.

One final source of error in unconfined systems is movement of water out of the sampling zone during the interval between samplings. Such losses result in overestimation of evapotranspiration and have been shown to cause appreciable errors (Robins et al. 1954; Nixon and Lawless, 1960). Solutions to this problem include the following: (1) use of a confined system such as a lysimeter or natural water-flow barrier such as bedrock; (2) very precise control of water application to avoid movement beyond the sampling depth; (3) sampling sufficiently deep into soil layers which are considerably drier than field capacity to measure accretion at lower depths; and (4) determination and use of drainage functions for the soil in question. The first two methods are most practical.

Soil variability can be reduced and precision of most types of moisture measurement improved for specialized studies by homogenization of the soil as is often done in lysimeter studies. Such disturbance of the profile alters soil nutrient mineralization, aeration, water retention and movement and other factors which affect both root and top growth behavior of plants and evaporation of water. Therefore, possible effects of such procedures on observed evapotranspiration must be taken into account in interpreting data obtained.

In use of lysimeters, the soil system is usually artificially prepared and the comments above on soil homogenization are pertinent. In addition, the lysimeter must be large enough to avoid severe confinement of the root system. Development of a water table in such confined systems can also confound results. Containers <1 m. in diameter and of depth insufficient to accommodate a well-developed root system of the crop in question should be avoided. A depth of 1 m. is sufficient for some short-season annuals, but a depth of 2 m. or more is usually required for deep-rooted annuals or perennials. The lysimeter rim and the uncropped area at the border of the lysimeter should be as small as possible to reduce edge effects. More detailed information on lysimetric measurements may be found in papers by Van Bavel (1961) and Pruitt and Angus (1960).

One final problem in deriving evapotranspiration data that can be applied to field situations with reliability is maintenance of suitable surroundings. Plots or lysimeters must be surrounded by a considerable area of the same crop, or horizontal divergence in energy for evapotranspiration will seriously affect the observations. Uniformity in height, density, row direction, aspect, moisture condition, etc., is required as well as avoiding upwind obstructions such as trees, buildings, roadways, etc. (Halstead and Covey, 1957; Lemon et al., 1957; Tanner, 1960). Effects of such changes in geometry on evapotranspiration are most serious in dry areas, but appreciable errors can be made in subhumid or humid regions as well. For representative measurements, uniformity should be maintained downwind for a distance of 40 to 50 times the height of any sizable geometry change. Changes in evapotranspiration due to abrupt differences in moisture condition also may be reflected measurably for considerable distances. A sizable border (15 m. or more) usually will reduce such effects to a negligible level.

The above comments and precautions must be observed to obtain a measurement of evapotranspiration which is representative of a large field or area of a given kind of soil and crop. It should be pointed out that measured evapotranspiration approaches the potential for a given physical environment only when adequate water and a complete canopy of the crop in question is present. It should be noted that where moisture is limiting, as often occurs in non-irrigated areas or on inadequately irrigated crops, measured evapotranspiration may be far less than if adequate water were present. This in no way negates the measurement but seriously limits use of such data in predicting evapotranspiration for the same crop in another area, season, or moisture environment. Further elaboration on methods of measuring evapotranspiration and difficulties associated therewith in arid and semiarid areas can be found elsewhere (Robins and Haise, 1961).

20-3 ESTIMATION METHODS

20-3.1 Introduction

A wide variety of methods for indirectly estimating evapotranspiration have been developed and used with varying degrees of success. Methods described in detail here will be limited (*1*) to those that have been sufficiently tested and evaluated to permit specification of their limitations and applicability to the problem, and (*2*) to those that are sufficiently straight-forward and for which data are readily available or obtainable to permit general utilization. Brief reference will be made to certain less known or more complex methods for those interested in pursuing them further.

20-3.2 Blaney-Criddle Method [2]

This method utilizes an empirical expression

$$u = kf = k(t \times p)/100$$

where u is consumptive use (evapotranspiration) in inches for any period by any crop, k is an empirical consumptive-use coefficient, f is the climatic consumptive-use factor for the period, and t and p are mean temperature in degrees Fahrenheit and percent of annual daylight hours occurring during the period, respectively. An estimate of evapotranspiration for extended periods can be computed (*1*) by using appropriate f and k values for the entire period; (*2*) by computing f and selecting k values as appropriate for short intervals, usually 1 month, and summing the computed values of u; or (*3*) by summing short interval f values and using a constant k value for the entire period. Expressed mathematically

$$u = kf,$$
$$u = [k_1f_1 + k_2f_2 + \cdots + k_nf_n] ,$$

or

$$u = k [f_1 + f_2 + \cdots + f_n] .$$

Values of u can thus be calculated for seasonal or annual periods, either directly or by summation of computed values for shorter intervals.

Values of k for individual crops are determined empirically based on measured evapotranspiration. Values vary from crop to crop, from one geo-graphic area to another, and from month to month for a given crop and area. This coefficient partially compensates for advected energy as well as crop and climatic differences. For generalized predictions, however, k values for a given crop can be transposed with reasonable assurance from

[2] Blaney and Criddle (1950); Blaney et al. (1952).

one area to another so long as the general climatic situation is not greatly different. Values of f vary markedly with latitude and season. Daylight duration has been tabulated by latitudes by the U. S. Weather Bureau (1905).

This method is most useful for predicting long-term average seasonal or annual evapotranspiration for areas where necessary climatic records and empirical consumptive-use coefficients are available. Predicted monthly values are usually reliable but for short periods (less than about 2 weeks) errors may be large (Pruitt, 1960; Van Wijk and De Vries, 1954). Therefore, use of this method for estimating irrigation need is hazardous.

20–3.3 Thornthwaite Method [3]

This method utilizes the empirical expression

$$e = 1.6(10t/I)^a$$

in which e is monthly evapotranspiration in centimeters, t is mean monthly temperature (centigrade), I is the heat index obtained by summation of 12 monthly values of heat index i obtained by the expression

$$i = (t/5)^{1.514}$$

and a is derived from I by the relationship

$$a = 6.75 \times 10^{-7} I^3 - 7.71 \times 10^{-5} I^2 + 0.01792\, I + 0.49239 .$$

The value so obtained for potential evapotranspiration is further adjusted for mean possible duration of sunlight for the station and time of year by a correction table given in the original paper of Thornthwaite (1948). Nomographs and tables relating i to t, a to I and e to t can be constructed to facilitate computations. In absence of such materials, automatic data processing is required for expedient computation by the method.

Values for periods <1 month are generally of limited reliability in estimating evapotranspiration by this method but can be computed by multiplying the constant 1.6 by the fraction of 1 month involved to reflect the shorter period. Values for periods >1 month are computed by summation of monthly values.

Thornthwaite claims the expression reflects the maximum evapotranspiration possible for a given area. Mean temperature and a latitudinal adjustment for potential sunshine as given in the original paper (Thornthwaite, 1948) are used as a measure of available energy similar to the Blaney-Criddle product of temperature and day length. No crop coefficient is used; thus, differences between crops and stage of crop development are ignored.

---

[3] Thornthwaite (1948).

Advected energy is compensated for only in the temperature measurement rather than in temperature plus empirical adjustment in the crop factor for a given area and season as in the Blaney-Criddle method. The method is generally less satisfactory than the Blaney-Criddle procedure in dry areas (Pruitt, 1960) but gives values of similar accuracy in subhumid and humid climates. Its prime advantage is permitting general estimates in areas where climatic records and evapotranspiration data are limited.

20-3.4 Evaporative Devices

Use of evaporative devices (evaporation pans, atmometers, etc.) to estimate evapotranspiration has been proposed by Blaney et al. (1933); Bouwer (1959); Gray et al. (1955); Halkias et al. (1955); Pruitt (1960); and Pruitt and Jensen (1955). Such methods are based on the supposed ability of such instruments to integrate effects of climatic factors on evaporation which, in turn, is presumed to correlate with evapotranspiration by well-watered vegetation. Proper use of evaporimeter data to estimate evapotranspiration requires knowledge of the empirical relationship between evapotranspiration and evaporimeter measurements under conditions similar to those that prevail experimentally.

No attempt will be made here to describe specific procedures in detail. Estimates of seasonal or annual values made by evaporative devices are generally as accurate as those derived by methods involving use of simple climatic measurements, particularly in dry areas. Short-term estimates (2 weeks or less) are probably more accurate than those derived from simple climatic measurements, provided proper environmental conditions are maintained and empirical factors are well established. Most evaporative devices are simple to operate, and computations are routine. A major disadvantage is that such devices become inoperative at temperatures below freezing. This results in incomplete records in many areas.

20-3.5 Energy-Balance Method

This method is based on disposition of energy at the land surface (Halstead and Covey, 1957; Levine, 1959; Tanner, 1960). Net incident radiant energy is partitioned as to mechanism of consumption or loss from the surface as follows:

$$R_N = S + A + P + E$$

where R_N represents net incident radiation (sometimes symbolized as H), S is soil heat flux, A is air heat flux, P is energy consumption in photosynthesis, and E is evapotranspiration, all expressed in common units.

Net incident radiation can be assessed directly by a variety of commercial instruments, usually in heat units (Tanner, 1960), or can be computed by the following equation:

$$R_N = R_A[1 - r][0.18 + 0.55(n/N)]$$
$$- \sigma T_a^4[0.56 - 0.092(e_d)^{1/2}][0.10 + 0.90(n/N)]$$

where R_N is the net incident radiation and R_A is mean extraterrestrial radiation expressed in terms of equivalent evaporation in millimeters per day; r is the radiation reflection coefficient usually taken as 0.05 as for a water surface (values of 0.15 to 0.25 have sometimes been used for cropped surfaces); n/N is the ratio of observed hours of sunshine to the maximum possible for the latitude and dates involved; σ is the Stefan-Boltzman constant $= 2.01 \times 10^{-9}$ mm. per day equivalent evaporation; T_a is the absolute temperature (°Kelvin); and e_d is actual vapor pressure of the air in millimeters of Hg. Methods of measurement of the radiation reflection coefficient are described in section 27. Where short-term values for correlation with measured evapotranspiration or estimated evapotranspiration for specific short periods are desired, it is preferable to use directly measured R_N values.

Soil heat flux can be measured by means of flux plates of various types (Tanner, 1960). It can be approximated for longer periods by recording soil temperature (section 24) and water content (section 7), determining soil heat capacity (section 25), and converting to heat units from the product of temperature change and heat capacity. Heating of the soil is sometimes ignored for computation of evapotranspiration for individual days, an assumption which may lead to significant errors unless the vegetative canopy is very dense and day to day weather is stable. For periods <1 day, soil heat storage cannot be ignored.

Energy consumption in photosynthesis is generally of the order of 2 to 5% for a 24-hour period and can generally be neglected or arbitrarily estimated if daily or longer periods are considered. For short periods, especially for a few hours after sunrise, up to 30% or more of the net radiation may be stored by this mechanism, a fraction which cannot be ignored. Assessment of this value is complex and beyond the scope of this discussion. A discussion of this subject and description of methods is given by Lemon (1960).

Partitioning of sensible heat (convective heating of the air) and latent heat (evaporation of water) requires application of turbulent-transfer aerodynamic theory referred to at a later point in this section. Without certain simplifying assumptions, such methods generally are excessively laborious and have such complex and precise instrumentation requirements that their use is limited to highly detailed experiments. Discussions of this subject and methods of measurement are given by Halstead and Covey (1957),

Lemon et al. (1957), Rider (1954), and Tanner (1960). The energy-balance method is useful even without detailed measurements of sensible and latent heat components. With simplifying assumptions, such as employed by Penman (1948, 1956) and described subsequently in this section, reliable evapotranspiration estimates can be made. Generalized estimates are also possible based solely on net radiation measurement or computation in humid areas (negligible advected energy), since evapotranspiration cannot exceed net radiation. Where water is readily available for evapotranspiration and good crop cover exists, 70 to 80% of the net radiant energy generally is consumed in evapotranspiration, and the remainder goes to photosynthesis and heating of the soil and air. Therefore, from reliable net radiation measurements or computations, an estimate of evapotranspiration can be computed which generally will be in error by no more than about 10%. For many purposes, errors of this magnitude are not serious. Computations for periods <1 day should be avoided since assumptions are based on consideration of the daily energy balance. Daily estimates may be seriously in error also if day-to-day weather differences are appreciable. In arid and semiarid areas, such methods should not be used since advected energy often causes evapotranspiration to exceed net radiation, and errors of 100% or more may be incurred.

20–3.6 Penman Method

Penman (1948, 1956) has developed a simplified and widely accepted method for approximating the latent heat component. He uses the Bowen ratio for this purpose and by use of simplified aerodynamics computes potential evaporation based on wind movement and vapor content of the air at a single height. The following is Penman's equation:

$$E_o = (\Delta H + \gamma E_a)/(\Delta + \gamma)$$

where E_o is potential evaporation (maximum evaporation from a large water surface) in millimeters per day; H is net radiation (R_N) in millimeters per day; γ is the hygrometer constant in millimeters of Hg per degree temperature change (0.27 in °F. or 0.49 in °C.); Δ is the slope of the vapor pressure, temperature relationship at observed air temperature at 2-m. height; and E_a is an auxiliary quantity computed by the expression

$$E_a = 0.35(e_a - e_d)(0.5 + 0.54U_2)$$

in which e_a and e_d are saturation and observed vapor pressure of the air in millimeters of Hg and U_2 is wind movement in meters per second, all observed at 2-m. height. (Penman originally used the term $(1 + 0.54\,U_2)$ as the wind component but later revised the equation to the form given). Wind speed U_2 at 2 m. can be computed from measurements at any other height U_h by the formula

$$U_2 = U_h \times \frac{\ln\left[(2.0 - d)/Z_o\right]}{\ln\left[(h - d)/Z_o\right]}$$

in which h is the height of measurement in meters, d is the displacement in meters of the zero plane (plane at which wind speed is zero) and Z_o is the roughness parameter. For short turf, d can usually be neglected without serious error, but for many crop plants, the displacement is appreciable in comparison to normal heights of measurement. Values of Z_o have not been well established, since they vary with height and density of crop cover and possibly with wind speed. A value of 0.025 m. is normally used for turf.

The computed E_o is converted to potential evapotranspiration E_t (maximum evapotranspiration from a large, well-watered, densely vegetated land area) by multiplying by an empirical reduction factor of 0.6 to 0.8 depending on the crop and season of the year. A factor of 0.7 is most commonly used. This factor presumably compensates for many possible errors in the procedure, probably including soil heat flux, photosynthetic consumption of energy, sensible heat loss and others, since such measurements are not generally made in use of the procedure.

Mean wind speed, temperature and vapor pressure for the period of consideration are used. Recent information indicates that separate computations for daylight and dark periods are advisable due to temperature inversions and small vapor density gradients at night (Tanner, 1960).

This method gives reliable evapotranspiration estimates for daily or longer periods in relatively humid areas where horizontal heat divergence is negligible and good vegetative cover and ample water are present. Serious discrepancies occur, however, in dry areas where advected heat accounts for a significant proportion of the actual evapotranspiration. Pruitt (1960), for example, has observed need for a reduction factor of 0.97 in central Washington. Under such conditions, it appears that locally determined empirical reduction factors may be used successfully.

For precise estimates of short duration (intervals <24 hours), it is advisable to make frequent measurements of wind, temperature, and vapor density profiles and to measure the soil heat flux, because the component is appreciable for short periods. Photosynthetic consumption may ultimately be subject to estimation or direct assessment but at present must be either ignored or arbitrarily approximated (Lemon, 1960).

Tanner (1960) has described in detail instrumentation and methods of precise short-term measurement. Work of Van Bavel (1956) illustrates use of the Penman method for long-term estimates.

Numerous other methods containing some aspects of the energy balance approach have been proposed. These vary from empirically adjusted net radiation as discussed earlier to more complex relationships of Makkink

(1957) and others. They generally involve empirical correlations with measured evapotranspiration and have generally been insufficiently tested to judge their merit. However, as is the case with correlation methods described earlier, such procedures are capable of reasonable precision where empiricisms are well established. Space does not permit elaboration here on such procedures.

20–3.7 Turbulent Vapor-Transfer Theory

This approach is based on turbulent vapor-transfer theory developed in description of aerodynamic phenomena. With adequate instrumentation and adherence to boundary conditions, it is capable of precise evaluation of the most complex situations. Specific methods have been advanced by Thornthwaite and Holzman (1942) and others. Both sensitivity of instruments and adherence to boundary conditions are generally more critical in these methods than in the energy-balance approach. These stringent requirements generally place the methods beyond possibility for other than very specialized measurements, and detailed procedures will not be described here. Description and limitations of such methods are given by Halstead and Covey (1957), Rider and Robinson (1951), Rider (1954), Tanner (1960), and Thornthwaite and Holzman (1942).

20–4 LITERATURE CITED

Aldrich, D. G., Lutz, J. F., Retzer, J. L., Rogers, H. T., Smith, F. B., and Taylor, S. A. 1956. Report of definitions approved by the committee on terminology. Soil Sci. Soc. Am. Proc. 20:430–440.

Blaney, H. F., and Criddle, W. D. 1950. Determining water requirements in irrigated areas from climatological and irrigation data. U. S. Dept. Agr. Soil Conserv. Serv. Tech. Paper 96.

Blaney, H. F., Rich, L. F., Criddle, W. D., Gleason, G. B., and Lowry, R. L. 1952. Consumptive use of water. Am. Soc. Civ. Eng. Trans. 117:948–1023.

Blaney, H. F., Taylor, C. A., Nickle, H. G., and Young, A. A. 1933. Water losses under natural conditions from wet areas in southern California. California State Dept. Public Works, Div. Water Res. Bull. 44.

Bouwer, H. 1959. Integrating rainfall-evaporation recorder. Agr. Eng. 40:278–279.

Gray, H. E., Levine, G., and Kennedy, W. K. 1955. Use of water by pasture crops. Agr. Eng. 36:529–531.

Halkias, N. A., Veihmeyer, F. J., and Hendrickson, A. H. 1955. Determining water needs for crops from climatic data. Hilgardia. 24:207–233.

Halstead, M. H., and Covey, W. 1957. Some meteorological aspects of evapotranspiration. Soil Sci. Soc. Am. Proc. 21:461–464.

King, K. M., Tanner, C. B., and Suomi, V. E. 1956. A floating lysimeter and its evaporation recorder. Trans. Am. Geophys. Union 37:738–742.

Lemon, E. R. 1960. Photosynthesis under field conditions. II. An aerodynamic method for determining the turbulent carbon dioxide exchange between the atmosphere and a corn field. Agron. J. 52:697–703.

Lemon, E. R., Glaser, A. H., and Satterwhite, L. E. 1957. Some aspects of the relationship of soil, plant, and meteorological factors to evapotranspiration. Soil Sci. Soc. Am. Proc. 21:464–468.

Levine, G. 1959. Methods of estimating evaporation. Trans. Am. Soc. Agr. Eng. 2:32–34.

Makkink, G. F. 1957. Ekzameno de la formjlo de Penman. Netherlands J. Agr. Sci. 5:290–305.

Nixon, Paul R., and Lawless, G. Paul. 1960. Translocation of moisture with time in unsaturated profiles. J. Geophys. Res. 65:655–661.

Penman, H. L. 1948. Natural evaporation from open water, bare soil, and grass. Proc. Roy. Soc. London, Series A. 193:120–146.

Penman, H. L. 1956. Estimating evaporation. Trans. Am. Geophys. Union. 37:43–46.

Pruitt, W. O. 1960. Relation of consumptive use of water to climate. Trans. Am. Soc. Agr. Eng. 3(1):9–13.

Pruitt, W. O., and Angus, D. E. 1960. Large weighing lysimeter for measuring evapotranspiration. Trans. Am. Soc. Agr. Eng. 3(2):13–15.

Pruitt, W. O., and Jensen, M. C. 1955. Determining when to irrigate. Agr. Eng. 36:389–393.

Rider, N. E., and Robinson, G. D. 1951. A study of the transfer of heat and water vapor above the surface of short grass. Quart. Jr. Roy. Meteorol. Soc. 77:375–401.

Rider, N. E. 1954. Eddy diffusion of momentum, water vapor and heat near the ground. Phil. Trans. Roy. Soc. London, Series A. 246:481–501.

Robins, J. S., and Haise, H. R. 1961. Determination of consumptive use of water by irrigated crops in the Western United States. Soil Sci. Soc. Am. Proc. 25:150–154.

Robins, J. S., Pruitt, W. O., and Gardner, W. H. 1954. Unsaturated flow of water in field soils and its effect on soil moisture investigations. Soil Sci. Soc. Am. Proc. 18:344–347.

Tanner, C. B. 1960. Energy balance approach to evapotranspiration from crops. Soil Sci. Soc. Am. Proc. 24:1–9.

Thornthwaite, C. W. 1948. An approach toward a rational classification of climate. Geograph. Rev. 38:55–94.

Thornthwaite, C. W., and Holzman, B. 1942. Measurement of evaporation from land and water surfaces. U. S. Dept. Agr. Tech. Bull. 817.

U. S. Weather Bureau. 1905. Sunshine tables. U. S. Weather Bureau Bull. 805.

Van Bavel, C. H. M. 1956. Agricultural drought in North Carolina. North Carolina Agr. Exp. Sta. Tech. Bull. 122.

Van Bavel, C. H. M. 1961. Lysimetric measurements of evapotranspiration rates in the Eastern United States. Soil Sci. Soc. Am. Proc. 25:138–141.

Van Wijk, W. R., and De Vries, D. A. 1954. Evapotranspiration. Netherlands J. Agr. Sci. 2:105–119.

21 | Porosity

JAMES A. VOMOCIL

University of California
Davis, California

21–1 INTRODUCTION

The geometry of the pore system of soil is just as complex as that of the solid phase. Just as soil particles vary in size, shape, regularity, and swelling tendencies, so the pores differ greatly from one another in shape, lateral dimensions, length, tortuosity, continuity, and other characteristics. Descriptions of the pore system, however, tend to be in relatively simple terms such as total porosity, volume percentage of large pores, or pore-size distribution, the latter two characterizations being based on a capillary-tube model with which the experimental observations may be identified. The methods currently employed have long been used for describing the soil pore system. They yield results that are quantitative in nature, but they must be thoroughly understood to be employed effectively because the configuration of soil pore systems does not correspond to the capillary model.

Characterizations of the pore system are important in investigations of the storage and movement of water and gases, in studies of the development of root systems by plants, in problems concerned with the flow and retention of heat, and in investigations of soil strength. For such purposes, the simple measurement of total porosity provides information of only limited utility. It is usually preferable to measure the pore-size distribution or the volume occupied by the larger pores.

The principle on which the methods are based is very simple: the bulk volume occupied by a given mass of soil can be divided into various "kinds" of space. Consider first a bulk volume of soil dried in an oven to constant weight at 105°C. The mass in grams of a volume of 1 cc. can be taken as its bulk density (section 30). The bulk density thus obtained is always considerably lower than the average particle density (section 29). This means that only part of the bulk volume is occupied by solid particles; the remainder is occupied by a lighter material, air.

21–2 TOTAL POROSITY [1]

21–2.1 Principles

Determinations of total porosity yield the simplest partial characterization of the soil pore system. Calculating porosity from density measurements simply involves converting data from densities to volumes. Since bulk density (D_b) is defined as M_s/V_b, in which M_s is the mass of soil (oven dry) in bulk volume (V_b), then

$$V_b = M_s/D_b .$$

Similarly, from the definition of ρ_p, the particle density, one obtains the relationship $V_p = M_s/\rho_p$, in which V_p is the collective volume occupied by solid particles having total mass M_s. But V_b is the whole volume of the space to be partitioned, and consequently V_p/V_b is the fraction of the volume occupied by solid particles. From the above definitions, it follows that this fraction equals D_b/ρ_p. Total porosity S_t is defined as the percentage of the bulk volume not occupied by solids, that is,

$$S_t = 100[1 - (D_b/\rho_p)] = 100[(\rho_p - D_b)/\rho_p] . \qquad [1]$$

21–2.2 Method

21–2.2.1 PROCEDURE

Determine the bulk density and particle density with the procedures described in sections 30 and 29. Insert values into equation [1] above, and calculate porosity. In cases where great accuracy is not required, use the assumed value of 2.65 g. cm.$^{-3}$ for particle density of mineral soils.

21–2.2.2 COMMENTS

Because of the swelling and shrinkage of soils with changes in water content, a decision must be made whether to use the dry volume or "moist" volume of soil. The problems relating to the influence of soil shrinkage are such that decisions relative to these matters must be left to individuals concerned with particular cases. For considerations of plant growth and water movement, many investigators prefer to use a "moist" volume.

21–3 PORE-SIZE DISTRIBUTION

21–3.1 Principles

Current use of pore-size distribution as a soil characteristic depends on acceptance of the capillary model as representing soil pore space. Imagine

---

[1] See also section 21–4.

a bundle of capillary tubes, all of the same short length but varying in diameter from one to another and varying in the number of tubes of a particular diameter present in the bundle. Imagine further that each capillary in the bundle has a very slight constriction exactly at one end. Consider the tubes to be immersed in water with the constricted ends upward and filled. Then, if all the tubes were small enough, the bundle could be lifted out of the water, and the tubes would remain filled. Now imagine that means are available at the bottom of the bundle to apply a controlled variable negative pressure, or suction. As the suction is increased, water will drain out of those tubes in which the pressure drop across the air-water interface at the upper end exceeds the pressure drop across a meniscus with a radius of curvature less than the radius of the slightly constricted portion of the tubes in question. The concept of the slight constriction is used to obtain a model in which each tube will be either completely filled or completely drained at each suction level rather than introducing the possibility of partially drained tubes.

The behavior just described may be stated mathematically by the law of capillary rise:

$$h = 2\gamma \cos \theta / \rho g r$$

where h is the height to which a liquid will rise in a clean capillary tube of radius r, γ is the surface tension of the liquid, ρ is its density, and g is acceleration due to gravity. For water, let us assume that the air-water interface is hemispherical and that the contact angle θ between water and the material composing the tubes is zero. The pressure drop across an air-water interface that can be sustained by surface forces in a capillary of radius r is $\rho g h$. Since ρ is a constant for water at a given temperature, h will represent the suction necessary to drain a tube of given radius. In soil porosity work, pressures and suctions are often reported in centimeters of water.

If water is extracted from an initially saturated sample of soil by a given suction h, the volume of water extracted is equal to the volume of pores having an effective radius greater than the r corresponding to the selected value of h in the capillary equation.

Obviously, soil pore systems are not simply a bundle of straight, uniform-bore capillary tubes. Nevertheless, if capillary theory can be assumed valid in the pore system, the radius calculated with the equation will at least represent the minimum size of pore neck through which an air-water interface must move during drainage. Hence, this procedure will yield descriptive information about the soil pore system.

The key component of the apparatus for measuring pore-size distribution is a membrane that conducts water at a reasonable rate, but when wet is impermeable to air (or other gases virtually insoluble in water) over the pressure range in which it is used. To fit these conditions, present procedures designate different membranes for various portions of the suction range of interest (0 to 15,000 cm. of water). Relatively coarse-grained membranes such as asbestos boards or sheets with a low binder content (Jamison and Reed, 1949), hard blotting paper, fritted glass discs, and fritted glass-bead plates (Nielsen, 1958) have been used for membrane materials in the suction range 0 to 100 cm. of water. Fritted and sintered glass plates can be obtained that have air-entry pressure as high as 300 to 400 cm. of water. Ceramic plates (Richards, 1949) have been prepared and used for the suction range of 100 to 2,000 cm. of water. Obviously, these plates could be used in the range of 0 to 100 cm. of water suction, but their pores are of such size that water movement through them is very slow at these small pressure differences. For pressure differentials >2,000 cm. of water across the membrane, special ceramic plates or heavy cellophane or cellulose sausage casing is used.

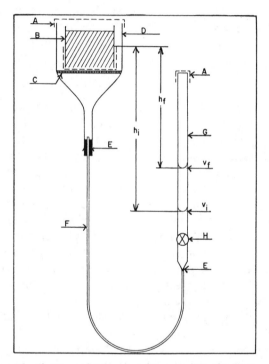

Fig. 21–1. Schematic diagram of apparatus for pore-size distribution determination:

A = Aluminum foil covers.
B = Sample in cylinder with cheesecloth bottom. Volume, V_b. (Omit cheesecloth for suctions >150 cm. of water.)
C = Fritted glass porous plate (part of D).
D = Büchner funnel with porous plate.
E = Joints must be secure.

F = Flexible tubing.
G = Burette, least division not more than 0.1% sample volume.
H = Stopcock of burette.
h_i = cm. of water suction, initial.
h_f = cm. of water suction, final.
v_i = Burette reading, initial.
v_f = Burette reading, final.

Once a suitable membrane has been selected, the other features of the apparatus consist of an arrangement for applying the selected pressure (positive or negative) and an arrangement for tracking changes in the water content of samples as a function of applied pressure.

In studies of soil air relations or drainage, the larger pores are of primary importance. Measurements with negative pressure corresponding to the range 0 to 300 cm. of water, obtainable across fritted glass plates with nominal maximum pore diameter of 5μ, will provide information sufficient for many purposes. Arrangements and the necessary apparatus for pressure differentials > 100 cm. of water are described in section 8–2.3.

A number of experimental setups could be used, but only one is described here. The hanging-water-column method is presented because it employs an accurate method for producing small pressure differentials and employs a minimum of special apparatus.

Mechanical null-point vacuum regulators, which are commercially available, are suitable for use in combination with water columns to obtain the negative pressures required. By this means, the length of the water column necessary can be greatly shortened.

If sensitive and accurate pressure regulation apparatus is available, positive pressures on the sample side of the plate can be used in place of negative pressure on the opposite side to accomplish the extraction of water. The common pressure-plate apparatus, however, is rarely used at pressures < 100 cm. of water because of the resistance of the plate to water movement.

21–3.2 Method

21–3.2.1 SPECIAL APPARATUS

Prepare the apparatus as shown in Fig. 21–1. It consists of a fritted-glass Büchner funnel connected to a burette with stopcock by means of flexible tubing. The funnel should be of sufficient diameter to accept the sample, and the plate in the funnel should be of sufficiently fine porosity to preclude air entry over the range of negative pressures of concern. Funnels (Fig. 21–1D) having plates (Fig. 21–1C) with a nominal maximum pore diameter of 5μ are commercially available in a variety of diameters and are suitable for this test.

Select the flexible tubing (Fig. 21–1F) of transparent, moderately rigid material (Mayon is recommended) to make air bubbles visible and to avoid undue collapse under the negative pressures to be employed. As an aid to preventing collapse of the tubing and to preparing air-tight connections, select stock having an inside diameter as small as feasible, and soften the tubing temporarily in boiling water to make it stretch more easily during attachment to the funnel and burette.

Select a burette (Fig. 21–1*G*) having a capacity of at least 30% and calibration in units not more than 0.1% of the volume of the sample. For example, if the sample volume is 100 ml., a 50-ml. burette calibrated to 0.1 ml. would be appropriate.

21–3.2.2 PROCEDURE

To remove the air from the porous plate, the space below the plate in the funnel, and the tubing leading to the burette, submerge the assembly in cooled, boiled water, allow it to remain overnight, and then pump the air out and water in through the plate with an aspirator or vacuum pump attached to the plastic tubing. Support the plate funnel upright, and support the burette vertically in such a way that the flexible tube will form a "U" tube (Fig. 21–1). Adjust the quantity of water in the system to allow the water level in the burette to stand within the calibrated volume but near its bottom end when free water has drained from the surface of the porous plate.

Calibrate the system for collapse of the flexing tubing and for plate drainage by positioning the burette so that its water level is 3 to 5 cm. below the porous plate. Record the volume reading in the burette when drainage of the plate has ceased, and then lower the burette so that its water level is 10 cm. below the plate. Tubing collapse and plate drainage will increase the volume of water in the burette. Record the burette reading, and continue in this manner stepwise to the maximum suction desired. Calculate and record the volume of tubing collapse and plate drainage for each step. Return the system to zero negative pressure at the plate by raising the burette (or lowering the plate funnel) until the water in the burette is level with the plate.

Where the device is used with an undisturbed sample obtained with a core sampler, trim the ends of the sample, and place it directly on the porous plate, taking care to ensure good contact between soil and plate. (Cheesecloth or other retainer may be used safely across the bottom of the sample only if the maximum suction to be employed is less than the equivalent of 150 cm. of water.) Where the device is used with a disturbed sample, place the material on the plate in a cylinder having a diameter at least twice its height, with a height less than the inside height of the funnel, and with provision to measure the sample volume after equilibration. Where the device is used with a precompacted sample, make sure that the lower surface of the sample is flat and that good continuity of water will occur through the interface between sample and plate.

With the sample in place, close the burette stopcock, and add water to the funnel until free water stands around the sample to the soil surface. Allow the soil to stand immersed for 24 hours. Add more water as needed during this period. Then hold the sample cylinder firmly in place, and pour the excess water out of the funnel. To reduce evaporation, loosely cover the funnel and the open end of the burette (Fig. 21–1A). Position the burette water level at 1 to 2 cm. below the plate to drain free water from the plate and sample container and to obtain an initial volume of water in the burette. Lower the burette during drainage of free water as needed to maintain a pressure differential. When flow ceases, record the burette reading (V_i, Fig. 21–1), and lower the burette so that its water level is 22 or 24 cm. (h_i) below the center of the sample. Allow drainage to proceed until it can no longer be detected. This may require 8 to 24 hours, depending on the sample. When the volume of water in the burette remains constant or decreases (evaporation or temperature change) during a period of 6 hours, record the burette reading (V_f, Fig. 21–1) and the vertical distance (h_f) from the surface of water in the burette to the center of the soil sample. Proceed to the next desired suction level (e.g., 40 cm. of water), and repeat the steps as above. Note that as suction increases, the time allowed for drainage will probably have to be increased. Because of the nature of pore-size distributions in soils, make the suction increments relatively small at low suctions, and increase the increment with increasing suctions. For example, a sequence such as 20, 40, 60, 100, 150, 200, and 300 cm. of water would be appropriate for many cases.

On completion of an appropriate series of drainage steps, determine the sample volume (V_b), and the sample weight. Use the entire sample for water-content determination if a subsample is not required for other purposes.

21–3.2.3 CALCULATION OF RESULTS

Calculate the results in the following way: From the drained volume of the sample (V_b), oven-dry weight of the sample (W), and an assumed or determined particle density, calculate total porosity S_t (see section 21–2.1). Convert the volume of water lost during the oven-drying step into a volume percentage P_v by dividing this volume by V_b, the volume of the sample, and multiplying the result by 100. Then $S_t - P_v$ is the percentage of the sample volume that has been drained free of water by the highest applied suction. Designate $S_t - P_v$ as S_n, in which n is the number of centimeters of water suction applied during the water extraction procedure. S_n is the percentage of the soil volume occupied by air space at the highest suction employed. Correct the volume of water drained from the sample during the last drainage step ($V_i - V_f$) for tube collapse and plate drainage, and divide the corrected value V' by V_b. The quantity $100\ (V'/V_b)$ is the change in P_v (water content, volume basis) during the last drainage step in the sequence. Putting it another way, $100\ (V'/V_b)$ is the difference between the water content in apparent equilibrium with the highest suction employed and the water content in apparent equilibrium with the next lower suction. Subtract $100\ (V'/V_b)$ from S_n to obtain $S_{n-\Delta n}$, the volume percentage of drained pore space at the second highest suction, where Δn is the difference in suction (centimeters of water) between the highest and second highest suction employed in the sequence. Continue these calculations in sequence from the highest suction to the lowest until all drainage steps have been accounted for.

Alternatively, calculate the results by assuming that the sample is initially saturated. Divide the corrected volume of drainage (V') during the first step by V_b, and multiply the result by 100 to get S_n, which is the percentage of the soil volume consisting of pores that are drained by the minimum suction n in centimeters of water (note the difference of meaning of S_n between this and the preceding method of calculation). Divide the volume of drainage during the second step by V_b, multiply the quotient by 100, and add the result to S_n to obtain $S_{n+\Delta n}$. Continue these calculations until all drainage steps are accounted for. Calculations are simpler by the second method than by the first, but the second method does not provide the check for errors available from the first.

Plot an accumulation curve of S as a function of suction. In both methods of calculation, take the value of h_f at the time when no further drainage is detectable as the equilibrium pressure (n). Do not use the value h_i manually established at the beginning of the step for this purpose.

21–3.2.4 COMMENTS

Complete saturation can be obtained only by vacuum wetting or displacement of air by carbon dioxide. For many purposes, however, wetting the sample by soaking it in water, as described in the procedure, will suffice.

Several sources of error are inherent in the method described. By the first method of calculation, S should be zero when h_f is zero. However, there are several reasons why this check may fail: (1) the sample may not have been saturated originally; (2) the suction used to obtain the burette volume reading at sample saturation may have been too great; (3) excessive evaporation losses may have occurred during the drainage steps; or (4) the assumed particle density (if used) may have been inaccurate. Sample volume decrease during drainage can result in the finding that the volume of water drained could not be accommodated in the final air-space volume of the sample. The assumption can be made that all of the sample volume decrease occurs during the first drainage step, and prior to that step the sample volume was the final volume plus the volume of excess water.

Because of hysteresis in relationships of water content versus suction, initial setting of the system at a given suction to allow equilibration at a lower suction, and using the final suction as a datum point, introduces some error. As the size of suction intervals is reduced, this error is reduced. Temperature changes likewise have effects.

Discontinuity of water in the region between the sample and the porous plate will make portions of the "interface" region nonconductive and must be avoided. A common cause of discontinuity is poor sample preparation in which the lower surface of the sample is uneven. Another cause is excess evaporation of water from the plate. Evaporation losses can be controlled by completing each step as rapidly as is consistent with satisfactory equilibration.

The slow movement of water in unsaturated soils will prevent attainment of equilibrium, particularly at higher values of suction. An arbitrary decision must be made as to when a given drainage step shall be considered complete. Apparently satisfactory as the final limit is the selection of that time after which no change in burette reading is detectable in 6 hours, or after which evaporation losses, in spite of control, cause the volume of water in the measuring burette to decrease.

Depending on the quality of apparatus components used and the maximum level of suction desired, calibration of the apparatus for plate drainage and tubing collapse may prove unnecessary. In any event, a single calibration should suffice for a number of determinations with the apparatus. It is suggested that in all cases the calibration procedure should be followed at least initially, as it provides an excellent means for checking the apparatus for leaks and performance.

Where a mechanical null-point vacuum regulator is used in combination with a water column to obtain the desired negative pressure, the vacuum regulator should be connected through a suction flask to a mercury manometer and to the top of the burette (Fig. 21–1G). The manometer and the burette should be in parallel, not in series. With an arrangement of this sort, the procedure is the same as that described in section 21–3.2.2. To obtain the total negative pressure applied, however, the product of (1) the difference in height on the two sides of the mercury manometer and (2) the specific gravity of mercury is added to the height of the water column (h_f). It is recommended that use of mechanical regulators be limited to suctions >100 cm. of water.

21–4 AIR-FILLED PORES

21–4.1 Principles

When one determines pore-size distribution as described above, one is essentially determining the volume percentage of air-filled pores at a series of soil water contents. To report air-filled pore space meaningfully, one must specify the negative pressure, or suction, with which the water content of the soil is in apparent equilibrium. Alternatively, for "field samples" an indication that drainage after wetting is virtually complete is employed to characterize the water status. Soil porosity has been described in terms of air-filled pore space at soil water suctions equivalent to 40, 50, 60, or 100 cm. of water or at "field water content." For some purposes, the investigator may be interested only in the physical quantity of air space at the time of sampling. In this case, no determination of either the amount of water present or the suction with which it is in apparent equilibrium would be necessary.

Air-filled pore space in samples of any water content can also be determined by means of an air-space pycnometer. This procedure takes advantage of Boyle's law, $P_1V_1 = P_2V_2$, in which P and V are gas pressure and volume, respectively. The volume of air space in a sample is measured by observing the resulting pressure when a known volume of gas at known pressure expands into a larger volume that includes the air space in the sample.

Let V_a be the volume of a chamber containing a sample of volume V_b and air at atmospheric pressure P_a. Let V_r be the volume of a chamber containing air at pressure P_r. If S is the percent air space in the sample of soil, then $V_b(1 - S/100)$ is the volume of that portion of the sample not occupied by air. The total amount (number of moles or grams) of air in the two chambers would then be proportional to $P_a[V_a - V_b(1 - S/100)] + P_rV_r$. Let P be the pressure resulting when the two chambers are connected and air flow has equalized the pressure throughout the system. Then

$$P_a[V_a - V_b(1 - S/100)] + P_rV_r = P[V_a - V_b(1 - S/100) + V_r] \quad [2]$$

can be written. If P_r and P are P_a plus the gauge pressures of the reservoir initially and the system after equilibration, respectively, gauge pressures can be used throughout. By doing so, the first term of equation [2] becomes zero and considerable simplification is possible. Finally, one can write

$$S/100 = k + (k'/P_g) \quad [3]$$

where k is $(V_b - V_a - V_r)/V_b$ and k' is $(P_{r,g}V_r)/V_b$. The gauge pressure of the reservoir is $P_{r,g}$ before pressure equalization, and P_g is the gauge pressure of air in the system after the pressure is the same throughout. V_b is an apparatus constant if cores of the same size are always used, which is usually the case. V_a, V_r, and $P_{r,g}$ are fixed by the design of the apparatus and procedure.

21–4.2 Difference Method

21–4.2.1 PROCEDURE

Determine the bulk density (section 30) of the soil and the water content on an oven-dry weight basis. Calculate porosity from the bulk density as shown in section 21–2.1, and calculate water content on a volume basis using the equation

$$P_c = 100 \times \frac{\text{volume of water lost on oven drying}}{\text{volume of sample}}$$

or, assuming that the density of water is 1.00 g. per cm.$^{-3}$, a satisfactory assumption for this purpose,

$$P_v = P_w D_b$$

in which P_v is the water content on a volume basis, P_w is the water content on an oven-dry weight basis, and D_b is the soil bulk density in centimeter-gram-second units. Then calculate the air-filled pore space S by the equation

$$S = S_t - P_v . \qquad [4]$$

21–4.2.2. COMMENTS

The determination of air-filled pore space through measurement of bulk density and water content of field samples involves the assumption that the particular water content selected for sampling has some special significance compared to other water contents. In aeration and drainage studies, "field capacity" (section 19–2; Richards and Wadleigh, 1952) might be considered to be such a water content. The definition of field capacity, however, and the problem of obtaining a number of samples at this water content should be kept in mind. In the calculation of either P_v or S_n, volume data must be used that introduce the problem of the volume changes that occur in soils on wetting and drying. As mentioned before, a decision to consider bulk density as the ratio of dry weight to moist volume seems reasonable.

21–4.3 Air-Space-Pycnometer Method [2]

21–4.3.1 SPECIAL APPARATUS

Required are two air-tight chambers connected to one another through a valve. One chamber contains the sample, and the other is empty. The latter is a reservoir used to provide a volume of air under pressure.

Make the sample chamber of a size and shape that will just contain the sample cylinder to be used. Arrange the closure to provide both an air-tight seal and a reproducible internal volume. Make the reservoir with a smaller volme, say 20% of the volume of the sample chamber. Optimum sensitivity, with respect to relative volumes of the two chambers, is attained where the volume of the reservoir is equal to the total volume of air space in the sample chamber (including soil pores) in the presence of a sample. Maximum sensitivity, with respect to the relative volumes of sample and sample chamber, is approached as the sample volume approaches the total volume of the sample chamber.

---

[2] Page (1948).

Equip the reservoir with a manometer or sensitive pressure gauge, a valved port for inflating it above atmospheric pressure, and a bleeder valve for venting excess pressure to the atmosphere. Connect the reservoir to the sample chamber with small-bore tubing fitted with a stopcock. Keep the connecting passage at the minimum feasible volume that is consistent with rapid flow.

21–4.3.2 PROCEDURE

First calibrate the air-space pycnometer. To make the calibration, insert into the sample chamber the sample cylinder containing enough metal plates to occupy 50% of its volume. Inflate the reservoir to 5 pounds per square inch (psi.) on the gauge. Open the connecting valve, and record the pressure when flow has stopped. Repeat the above steps when various portions from 50 to 100% of the sample volume are occupied by metal discs. Then prepare a graph or table relating final pressure to volume of air space in the sample cylinder.

Alternatively, calculate the calibration curve from careful measurements of the volume of the sample chamber and the reservoir, in each case including the appropriate portion of the connecting arrangement and the pressure-measuring device.

The apparatus is then ready for use in laboratory or field. Insert the sample, inflate the reservoir to 5 psi., open the connecting valve, and record the final pressure. Use the calibration curve to convert this reading to percent air space.

21–4.3.3 COMMENTS

In the use of an air-space pycnometer, the fact that this instrument can act as a gas-filled thermometer must be recognized. Therefore, precautions such as rapid reading and shading are recommended in its field use.

The principles of operation of the pycnometer make it clear that it will measure the volume of "entrapped" or isolated air bodies only to the extent of their compression. That is, if one imagines an isolated pocket of air surrounded by water and the supporting soil particles, the volume of the isolated body of air will not be measured at all unless the increased air pressure outside the enclosing water forces some of the water to occupy part of the space of the isolated pocket by compressing the air initially present. Whether or not this will happen depends on the geometry of the pore system containing the enclosing water and on the applied pressure. The occurrence and extent of compression is, in most cases, impossible to predict.

The sensitivity of an air-space pycnometer is determined by the sensitivity of the pressure gauge, the ratio $(V_a + V_r)/V_r$, and the ratio V_b/V_a. Larger values of $(V_a + V_r)/V_r$ make an instrument that is sensitive at low air-space contents, where sensitivity is more critical, and less sensitive at large air spaces.

A combination of a bellows with a dial displacement indicator has proved to be a satisfactory pressure gauge (Page, 1948).

It is possible to use air space S_n with the weight and volume of the sample at the water content at which air space is measured to calculate water content, bulk density, and total porosity. Therefore, the use of the pycnometer enables one to obtain all this information immediately without drying the sample. Bulk density is given by

$$D_b = k_1 W_w - k_2[(100 - S_n)/100]$$

in which W_w is the weight of the sample at the water content of measurements, S_n is the measured air-filled pore space, $k_1 = \rho_p/[V_b(\rho_p - \rho)]$, and $k_2 = (\rho_p \rho)/(\rho_p - \rho)$. The symbol ρ_p is the solid phase density and the symbol ρ is the density of water. Water content on a volume basis is given by

$$P_{v/100} = k_2/\rho[(100 - S_n)/100] - (k_1/\rho_p)W_w .$$

From these values, S_t and P_w can be calculated as described in sections 21–2.1, and 21–4.2.

21–4.4 Tension-Table Method [3]

21–4.4.1 SPECIAL APPARATUS

Construct a tension table using asbestos board as the porous membrane. The product sold in 42- by 48-inch pieces of ⅛-inch thickness by the Central Scientific Co., Chicago, Ill., under Cat. No. 10140C has been found satisfactory. This material has been found to admit air at a suction of 250 cm. of water. The following description is in terms of a table 16 by 21 inches in size, but other sizes may be constructed as desired.

Construct a tray of sheet plastic ½ inch in thickness by cutting a piece 16 by 21 inches in size and cementing narrow strips of the same material around the outside to form a tray with an inside depth of ¾ inch or more. Drill a hole about 4 inches diagonally inside of one corner, and tap it for a ⅛-inch pipe fitting. Insert a high-pressure fitting for 1/16-inch copper tubing, and seal the fitting to the plastic using caulking compound. Grind the fitting smooth on the surface inside the tray. Cut four strips of the same plastic 1 inch in width and having a length such that they can be used to border the edge of the tray on the bottom. Cement these strips to the bottom of the tray in such a way that the thickness of the outside bottom of the tray is doubled and the outside of the strips is flush with the

[3] Leamer and Shaw (1941); Jamison and Reed (1949).

outside of the rim of the tray. Cut an additional group of four strips of the same plastic ½ inch in width and of length such that they will fit loosely inside the rim of the tray. Cut a piece of asbestos board to fit loosely inside the tray. Then with the asbestos board in place in the bottom of the tray and the loose plastic strips in position on the surface of the asbestos board, drill holes at approximately 3-inch intervals around the edge of the tray ¼ inch inside of the rim. Insert enough bolts to hold the various units in place while the drilling is proceeding. Then remove the bolts and the asbestos board, and lay a flat piece of copper or brass screen 15 by 20 inches in size in the center of the bottom of the tray. Coat the outside edges of the asbestos board with caulking compound. Then place the asbestos board in the tray without disturbing the screen, and apply additional caulking compound as needed to seal the asbestos board to the inside of the rim of the tray. Then coat the inside of the holes around the edge with caulking compound, place the plastic strips on the surface of the asbestos board, and pass bolts through the holes. Tighten the bolts to produce a good seal. If cracks appear in the asbestos board, seal them with plaster of paris or portland cement paste after the board has been wetted.

To put the tension table in operating condition, first immerse it in water. To the outlet hole, attach a piece of rubber tubing having a short glass tubing insert. Then raise the corner of the unit containing the outlet hole, and apply suction to the tubing. When the water flowing from the unit is free of air bubbles, clamp the end of the tubing that is attached to the source of suction, and remove the unit from the water. Set the unit in a level position with the asbestos surface up, and add water to the surface to prevent air entry until the tube is connected to a water source.

Prepare a constant-level water source from a carbon filter funnel. Seal a glass side-arm to the funnel 1½ inches below the top. This side-arm is the overflow tube. Attach a piece of flexible tubing that leads from the side arm to a drain. To the bottom of the filter funnel, attach the tubing leading from the tension-table unit. In the top of the funnel, place a two-hole rubber stopper, in one hole of which has been inserted a piece of glass tubing that protrudes slightly from the bottom of the stopper but does not extend downward as far as the side arm. Attach a source of tap water to the end of the glass tubing that extends from the top of the rubber stopper.

Adjust the flow rate of the tap water so that the level of water in the funnel remains even with the side arm, and so that only a little overflow takes place through the side arm. Position the constant-level water source so that the surface of the water in it is the desired distance below the center of the soil samples when the samples are in place on the asbestos-board membrane.

If the capacity of the single unit described here is insufficient, construct a single larger unit or additional smaller units. Mount additional units above each other in an angle-iron rack or other convenient arrangement.

21–4.4.2 PROCEDURE

Presoak the soil samples in cylinders (which have cheesecloth held in place by a rubber band over the lower end) for 24 hours in water standing 1 cm. below the surface of the soil. Clamp the drain tube on the tension table, and add water to just cover the asbestos. Remove the samples from soaking, allow them to drain for 1 or 2 minutes, blot the outside of the cylinder lightly, and weigh the assembly. Place each sample on the tension table with the cheesecloth cover next the asbestos. When the table is loaded, cover it with a piece of thin polyethylene sheeting to reduce evaporation from the table and samples, remove the clamp from the table drain tube, and allow drainage to proceed for 24 hours or until flow is insignificant. Remove the samples from the table, weigh them, and determine the sample volume. Oven-dry the samples at 105°C., weigh them again, and subtract the tare weight of cylinder, cheesecloth, and rubber band.

21–4.4.3 CALCULATION OF RESULTS

Calculate the results according to one of the following equations. In the first equation the volume of drained pores is calculated directly from the weight of water lost during the period on the tension table:

$$S_n = \frac{\left(\dfrac{W_1 - W_t}{\rho}\right) \times 100}{V_b} = \frac{100}{V_b \rho}(W_1 - W_t)$$

where

S_n = percentage of soil volume drained under a suction of n cm. of water,
V_b = bulk volume of the sample in milliliters before drying,
W_1 = weight of sample in grams after soaking and before drainage on the tension table,
W_t = weight of sample in grams after drainage on the tension table, and
ρ = density of water in g. cm.$^{-3}$ (1.00 can be used).

In the second equation, the volume of drained pores is calculated indirectly as the difference between the volume of the sample and the volume that the water and solids are calculated to occupy after drainage on the tension table:

$$S_n = \frac{100}{V_b}\left(V_b - \frac{W}{\rho_p} - \frac{W_t - W}{\rho}\right)$$

where

W = oven-dry weight of sample in grams,
ρ_p = density of soil particles in g. cm.$^{-3}$ (2.65 can be used for mineral soils), and where the other symbols have the same meaning as before.

21–4.4.4 COMMENTS

In calculations with tension-table data, using the first method described involves the assumption that soaking saturates the soil sample with water.

Air entrapment is likely to make this assumption invalid. An additional difficulty is that the weight of the saturated sample is difficult to obtain because of the judgment factor in the blotting step and the fact that most samples will consolidate slightly and drain "free" (up to, say 5 cm. suction) water for some time after removal from soaking. The extent and rate of this drainage depend on sample length and permeability. Therefore, the second method of calculation has points to recommend it in spite of the necessity of a determination or assumption of particle density and in spite of the longer, more tedious calculation.

21–5 LITERATURE CITED

Jamison, V. C., and Reed, I. F. 1949. Durable asbestos tension tables. Soil Sci. 67:311–318.

Leamer, R. W., and Shaw, B. 1941. A simple apparatus for measuring noncapillary porosity on an extensive scale. J. Am. Soc. Agron. 33:1003–1008.

Nielsen, D. R. 1958. Small fritted glass bead plates for determination of moisture retention. Soil Sci. Soc. Am. Proc. 22:574–575.

Page, J. B. 1948. Advantages of the pressure pycnometer for measuring the pore space in soils. Soil Sci. Soc. Am. Proc. (1947) 12:81–84.

Richards, L. A. 1949. Methods of mounting porous plates used in soil moisture measurements. Agron. J. 41:489–490.

Richards, L. A., and Wadleigh, C. H. 1952. Soil water and plant growth. Agron. 2:73–251.

22

Composition of Soil Atmosphere[1]

C. H. M. VAN BAVEL

United States Water Conservation Laboratory
Tempe, Arizona

22–1   INTRODUCTION

Agronomic and ecological studies require methods for typifying the soil environment, including the composition of the gaseous phase. Such measurements are generally required under field conditions, so that gas samples must be brought into the laboratory for analysis, or the analysis must be carried out on the spot with portable apparatus. Since *in situ* methods have not been developed, it is necessary in either case that a sample of the soil atmosphere is obtained.

There are two methods to obtain a sample of the soil atmosphere for analysis. The first method involves mass flow of air through the soil. This method of obtaining samples is objectionable where any significant volume of air is removed because one does not know the exact depth from which the sample originated. Mass flow takes place preferentially through the largest soil pores. It is possible that much of the air withdrawn at a certain depth originated from a location at a remote distance because of a large, connecting channel or crack. This statement applies in particular when the soil is dense and moist. A second method, not subject to the foregoing objection, is dependent upon gaseous diffusion. In this method, the sample container is connected directly and permanently to the location of interest. Given sufficient time, the sampler will contain a gas mixture of a composition the same as that in the soil at the point where the sampling tube is open to the soil.

Nitrogen, argon, oxygen, and carbon dioxide are the principal components of the gaseous phase. The proportion of nitrogen plus argon is usually found to be equal to that in the atmosphere, that is, 79% by volume. Oxygen and carbon dioxide vary in complementary proportions to make up the remaining 21%. Since small deviations from atmospheric composition are never found to be of ecological significance, the precision required of a

---

[1] Contribution from the Soil and Water Conservation Research Division, ARS, USDA, Tempe, Ariz.

method of measurement is not extreme, and a knowledge of the oxygen and carbon dioxide content of the soil air to the nearest 0.5% by volume is adequate.

Generally, aeration studies are concerned only with the presence of carbon dioxide and oxygen. To measure the carbon dioxide and oxygen content of soil air, indirect methods are used since they are simple and rapid.

22–2   METHOD

22–2.1   Special Apparatus

1. A small, diaphragm-type air pump with minimum internal volume, as "Dynapump" (Fisher No. 1-092-5) or similar.
2. Gas sampling tubes of 125-ml. capacity, as Corning No. 7800 (Pyrex) or similar.
3. Portable oxygen analyzer with 0 to 20% by volume range, utilizing the paramagnetism of oxygen, as Model D, A. D. Beckman, Inc., or similar.
4. Portable carbon dioxide analyzer with 0 to 25% by volume range, utilizing the thermal conductivity principle, as Model 120H, Cambridge Instruments Company, or similar.
5. Direct current-alternating current inverter (200-watt rating) to obtain 110 volts a-c. from car battery. The inverter is needed to operate the pump if analyses are to be made in the field.

22–2.2   Compressed Gases

1. Pure nitrogen.
2. 25% CO_2 in air, composition verified by chemical analysis.

22–2.3   Procedure

22–2.3.1   SAMPLING BY MASS FLOW

Push a veterinary-type hypodermic needle of sufficient length and strength to the desired depth, and extract a sample of soil air. For repeated measurements, install a suitable tube, closed at the top, and draw soil air through the tube when a sample is needed. Obtain at least 125 cm.[3] of gas, and transfer the sample to a gas sampling tube by displacement of water. Analyze the sample as described in section 22–2.3.3.

22–2.3.2   SAMPLING BY DIFFUSION

As indicated in Fig. 22–1, install a length of thin-walled, electrical conduit, 1 inch outside diameter, to the depth of measurement so as to protrude about an inch from the surface. Close the tube with a neoprene stopper with two holes. Install through each hole a length of ⅛-inch copper tubing, one to go just through the rubber stopper, the other to terminate about ½ inch above the bottom of the test well. Both copper tubes should protrude about ½ inch above the stopper. When the test well is in place, connect the exposed ends of the two copper tubes with a short piece of neoprene tubing of 3/16-inch inside diameter and 1/16-inch wall thickness.

Obtain a sample of the air in the test well as follows: Connect a small, diaphragm-type air pump and a 125-cm.³ gas sample tube with two stopcocks by means of neoprene tubing (see above) to the copper tubes A and B, as shown in Fig. 22–1, right-hand side. Make the neoprene connections as short as possible.

Next, let the pump circulate the gas through the system for a period of time sufficient for 10 complete air changes. Following circulation, close the sample collecting tube with the stopcocks, and take the sample in for analysis.

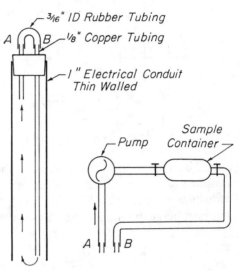

Fig. 22–1. Diagram of sampling well and pumping arrangement.

Evidently, the soil gas will be diluted by the air in the remainder of the apparatus during sampling. To obtain the dilution factor appropriate for the particular equipment in use, conduct blank experiments, in which the soil well is filled with pure nitrogen before the gas is circulated through the pump and analyzers.

If one is able to measure the composition of the gas directly in the field, omit the sampling bulb, and replace it by the test cell of the gas analysis apparatus. In this case also, determine the proper dilution factor.

22–2.3.3 GAS ANALYSIS

Verify both oxygen analyzer and carbon dioxide analyzer before each use. Standardize the oxygen meter with atmospheric air and compressed, pure nitrogen. Verify the carbon dioxide analyzer with atmospheric air and compressed 25% CO_2 in air that has been analyzed chemically.

Carry out the analysis as follows. Connect the sample tube, air pump, carbon dioxide, and oxygen analyzer in series (see Fig. 22–2) with neoprene tubing, making the connections as short as possible. Circulate the gas mixture for 1 or 2 minutes, and read the analyzers while the pump is

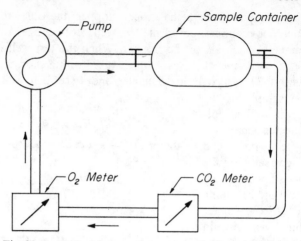

Fig. 22–2. Method for pumping gas sample through analyzers.

turned off and the system is opened to the atmosphere between pump and sampling tube. Determine the dilution factor using a sampling tube filled with pure nitrogen or 25% CO_2 from compressed gas bottles. Between analyses, purge the entire apparatus with atmospheric air.

22–2.4 Comments

The standard error of the analytical procedure as given above is about 0.1% by volume and is sufficient for soil aeration or related work. Sources of error other than instrumental errors are slight changes in the volume of the connecting tubing, and leakage or diffusion at the bottom of the test well. Raney (1950) designed a well that can be closed with a valve, but data obtained by Van Bavel (1954) show that the error owing to an open-ended arrangement is insignificant.

As already indicated, preference is given to obtaining a sample by diffusion. For incidental observations or measurements at considerable depth, withdrawing a sample by suction may be the only feasible method. One precaution to observe with diffusion wells is to allow sufficient time for equilibration. This time varies from about 1 hour for a well 4 inches deep to about 6 hours for a well 16 inches deep.

22–3 LITERATURE CITED

Raney, W. A. 1950. Field measurement of oxygen diffusion through soil. Soil Sci. Soc. Am. Proc. (1949) 14:61–65.

Van Bavel, C. H. M. 1954. Simple diffusion well for measuring soil specific diffusion impedance and soil air composition. Soil Sci. Soc. Am. Proc. 18:229–234.

23 | Gas Movement

D. D. EVANS
University of Arizona
Tuscon, Arizona

23-1 AIR PERMEABILITY

23-1.1 Introduction

The flow of gas through porous media is of concern to soil scientists and other scientists, particularly those in the field of petroleum development. Gaseous flow as a result of a difference in total pressure of the gas is commonly referred to as mass flow, signifying a transfer of mass from one point to another. In contrast, gaseous diffusion occurs as a result of a difference in concentration, or partial pressure, of components of a gaseous mixture with no difference in total pressure. Mass flow and diffusion may occur simultaneously when concentration and total pressure gradients exist in the same region concurrently. In the normal exchange of gas between the atmosphere and the soil, both processes operate, but diffusion is considered the primary mechanism. However, mass flow is important at times when differences in pressure develop because of changes in barometric pressure, temperature, or soil water content. The transfer of petroleum gases to wells from the earth is a mass-flow process of great economic importance.

The air permeability of a soil is a parameter which indicates the readiness of the soil to transmit gases when a difference in pressure exists. The percentage, size, and continuity of pores within the soil and occupied by air determine the permeability of the soil. To illustrate the importance of size of pores alone, consider the analogy of flow of a fluid through a capillary tube for which Poisseuille's law is valid. The quantity of fluid flowing through the tube per unit time is proportional to the fourth power of the radius; hence, if the radius of the tube is doubled, the quantity of flow is increased 16 times. A similar relationship is expected for soil material, but the configuration of the pores does not permit a simple mathematical expression. Since air permeability depends upon the porosity of the soil, which in turn depends upon the structure of the soil, air permeability has been used alone as an index of soil structure (Buehrer,

1932; Kirkham et al., 1958), or in combination with water permeability as an index of soil structure stability, as discussed in section 41 of this monograph. Air and water permeabilities are identical for a dry soil provided no structural change occurs during the act of measurement.[1] Obviously, air permeability decreases as soil water content increases since less area is available through which flow can take place.

The method to be described for measuring air permeability may be modified in many ways to fit particular needs, but the described method appears to be most suited for measurements on undisturbed soil samples.

23–1.2 Principles

The flow of gas through soil obeys, subject to some restrictions, the equation

$$q = -(k/\eta)(dp/dx) \qquad [1]$$

where q = volume of gas per unit time passing across a unit area taken perpendicular to the x axis; k = permeability of the soil; η = viscosity of the gas; and dp/dx = pressure gradient. The restrictions are as follows: (*1*) the flow is viscous or laminar, (*2*) steady-state conditions exist, and (*3*) the flow is horizontal, or else the gravity effect is negligible. In the method to be described, only steady-state conditions are employed, and only small pressure differences are used to ensure viscous flow. It has been shown by Kirkham (1947) that neglecting the effect of gravity will produce an error $<1\%$, which can be neglected for most purposes. Equation [1] may be used for the problem under consideration.

By restricting the pressure to ± 50 cm. of water from atmospheric pressure, Kirkham (1947) has shown that, for one-dimensional flow, equation [1] becomes after integration

$$Q = (k/\eta)[(P_2 - P_1)/L]At \qquad [2]$$

where k and η are as defined before, Q is the volume of flow in time t, $P_2 - P_1$ is the pressure difference across length L of the soil, and A is the cross-section area through which flow occurs. In the centimeter-gram-second (cgs.) system, the units for the various quantities are: $Q = $ cm.[3], $k = $ cm.[2], $\eta = $ dynes sec. per cm.[2] or poise, $P = $ dynes per cm.[2], $L = $ cm., $A = $ cm.[2], and $t = $ seconds. For convenience, k is usually expressed in units of square microns (1 $\mu^2 = 10^{-8}$ cm.[2]).

Equation [2] is solved for k and used in the calculation of air permeability for the laboratory procedure. For measurements in the field, the equation must be slightly modified. The factor A/L in equation [2] must be

---

[1] Aljibury, F. K. 1961. Saturated water permeability of soils as related to air permeability at different moisture tensions. Ph.D. Thesis, Oregon State University Library.

replaced by another factor F since the geometry of the soil sample in the field is different from that in the laboratory.

The viscosity of air depends upon the temperature and only slightly upon the relative humidity. In the method to be described, the relative humidity is close to constant and is taken as 95%. The viscosity of air with a relative humidity of 95% and a temperature of 25°C. is 1.84×10^{-4} poise (Tanner and Wengel, 1957). Deviations in temperature of ±10 degrees from 25°C. will cause an error <10%.

The device described for measuring the quantity of gas flowing into the soil Q is called a gasometer, the principle of which will be explained using Fig. 23–1. This type of gasometer has been developed by Grover (1955) and Tanner and Wengel (1957). The principle is very simple. A float, open at the bottom, is placed in a reservoir of water. A tube opening into the air space within the float leads to the soil sample to be analyzed. The weight of the float causes a pressure greater than atmospheric to develop within the float, thus causing air to flow through the tube into the soil. As flow occurs, the pressure stays nearly constant, and the downward displacement of the float is a measure of the quantity of flow through the soil. By knowing the pressure, the quantity of flow in a measured time, and a geometry factor for the soil sample, one may calculate k using a form of equation [2].

23–1.3 Method [2]

23–1.3.1 SPECIAL APPARATUS

1. Gasometer, constructed according to Fig. 23–1 or the detailed plans of Tanner and Wengel (1957). Provide a means to permit rapid leveling of the gasometer at each setting in the field.
2. Sample containers, prepared from 12-ounce, seamless cans manufactured by Crown Can Company, Eric Avenue at H Street, Philadelphia, Pa., or from other materials. The Crown cans have a diameter of 6.9 cm. and an effective length (the length driven into the soil) of 8 cm. To prepare the cans for use in the manner proposed by Steinbrenner (1959), remove the bottoms and the special seal ordinarily used at the top.
3. Driving tube: Prepare a piece of metal pipe 25 cm. in length, with an inside diameter just larger than the outside diameter of the sample container, and with three triangular-shaped legs with spikes in the bottoms to hold the tube in place and perpendicular to the soil surface.
4. Driving head: Construct a metal head with the lower surface hollowed out to fit the top of the sample container and with a rod about 1 cm. in diameter and 30 cm. in length extending vertically from the upper surface to use as a guide for the hammer.

---

[2] Grover (1955); Tanner and Wengel (1957).

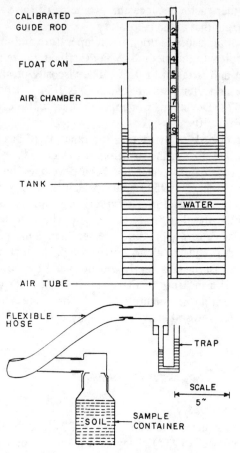

Fig. 23–1. Diagram of gasometer with attached sample container.

5. Hammer: Construct a weight of about 2,000 g. from a cylindrical piece of metal with a central hole large enough to permit free movement along the rod on the driving head.
6. Flexible tube for connecting the gasometer to the sample container. To reduce friction loss, use a tube with a large diameter. The type used on vacuum cleaners is satisfactory.
7. Stop watch.

23–1.3.2 PROCEDURE

For laboratory or field measurements, much of the procedure is the same. After the selection of a site to be sampled, insert the sample container into the soil with as little disturbance as possible. This can best be done by first removing any litter from the site and smoothing the surface. Then place the driving tube at the desired location, and push the spikes into the soil. Insert the sample container into the driving tube, and place the driving head on top of the sample container. With the hammer, drive the sample container to the desired depth. Remove the driving head and tube.

If the measurement is to be made in the field, connect the hose from the gasometer directly to the top of the sample container protruding from the soil. Then carry out the measurement as described later. If the measurements are to be made in the laboratory, remove the sample container and encased soil from the soil mass using a spade. Trim the bottom of the soil even with the bottom of the container. Seal both ends, and protect the container and contents from damage until time to make the air permeability measurement. At this time remove the seals and connect the hose from the gasometer to the top of the sample container.

After the hose is connected to the sample container, whether in the field or the laboratory, measure the quantity of flow through the sample in a measured period of time using the gasometer which has previously been leveled. Several readings may be made on the same sample to check the precision of measurement.

23–1.3.3 CALCULATION OF RESULTS

Use a form of equation [2] for calculating the air permeability. For laboratory measurement on the soil cores, the equation to use is

$$k = Q\eta L/PAt$$

where the symbols are defined as before, except P is now the gauge pressure within the float. P, L, and A are fixed by the apparatus used, and η is 1.84×10^{-4} poise at $25°C$.

For measurements made in the field with the container inserted into the soil, the appropriate equation is

$$k = Q\eta/PFt$$

where F is a factor which must be obtained from Fig. 23–2. As an example of the use of Fig. 23–2, consider that the diameter D of the sample cylinder is 6.9 cm., and the effective length L is 8 cm. Then D/L equals 0.82 and, from Fig. 23–2, F/L equals 0.50 or F equals 4 cm.

23–1.3.4 COMMENTS

It is usually more convenient to make measurements in the laboratory than in the field. Less time is spent in the field, with the result that the change in environmental conditions over the period of time the measurements are made may be reduced. It is also more convenient to operate the gasometer in the laboratory since leveling is not such a problem. It is possible to make other measurements such as bulk density or hydraulic conductivity on the same soil cores if they are taken to the laboratory.

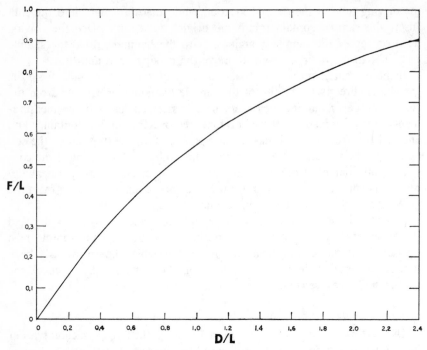

Fig. 23–2. Graph for determining F for field measurements as described in the text. From Grover (1955) as corrected by Kirkham (1958).

To measure the air permeability at depths below the surface, it is necessary to dig a pit and insert the sample container on a smoothed surface. Horizontal as well as vertical samples may be taken. As most soils become dry the penetrability decreases, and it may be difficult to insert the sample containers into the soil. The procedure operates best when the soil water content is near field capacity.

There are many adaptations of the above described procedure which may be more suitable under certain circumstances. For instance, the hose from the gasometer may be connected to a tube filled with disturbed soil which may be at any soil water content. Also, the flexible tube may be sealed directly to the soil surface with wax for *in situ* measurements (Evans and Kirkham, 1950; Grover, 1955). Other types of flow meters may be available and more practical for certain studies. However, the above described method appears to be the most feasible method for most cases.

23-2 APPARENT DIFFUSION COEFFICIENT

23-2.1 Introduction

Diffusion is considered to be the principal mechanism in the interchange of gases between the soil and the atmosphere. The interchange results from concentration gradients established within the soil by the respiration of microorganisms and plant roots. Oxygen normally diffuses into the soil while carbon dioxide diffuses out.

The rate of diffusion depends upon the concentration gradient, the temperature, the molecular weight of the diffusing gas, and the cross sectional area through which diffusion may occur. The parameter of importance in characterizing a soil for diffusivity is the apparent diffusion coefficient. (Apparent is used here to differentiate this parameter from the usual diffusion coefficient which applies to diffusion through regions with only gaseous constituents.)

The apparent diffusion coefficient may be considered as having the magnitude of the mass of a particular component of a gaseous mixture diffusing through a unit cross section of soil in unit time when the concentration gradient is unity. The magnitude will depend upon both the soil and the gases.

Since different gases have different rates of diffusion it is most desirable to measure the apparent diffusion coefficient using a gas of particular concern. Taylor (1950) proposed a method which involves the diffusion of oxygen in one direction and nitrogen in the opposite direction. Oxygen and nitrogen have close to the same molecular weight and, consequently, similar rates of diffusion. Taylor did not suggest calculating the apparent diffusion coefficient as such, but the method has been further explored and shown to be suitable for measuring diffusion coefficients. This is the method to be described.

Several adaptations of the method are possible and may be more suited for specific studies. However, the one method utilizing undisturbed cores has been chosen for detailed description.

23-2.2 Principles

The fundamental diffusion equation (Fick's Law) is

$$\partial q / \partial t = - D(\partial c / dx) \qquad [1]$$

in which $\partial q / \partial t$ is the time rate of transfer of mass per unit area taken perpendicular to the x axis, D is the diffusion coefficient, which for a porous medium is the apparent diffusion coefficient, and $\partial c/\partial x$ is the concentration gradient in the x direction. When the units of mass of q and c are the same and cgs. units are used elsewhere, D has the units of cm.^{2} sec.$^{-1}$.

It is common to express the gradient in terms of partial pressure p rather than concentration. Then equation [1] becomes

$$\partial q/\partial t = -(D/\beta)(\partial p/\partial x) \qquad [2]$$

where β is $\partial p/\partial c$. Under isothermal conditions, β is a constant.

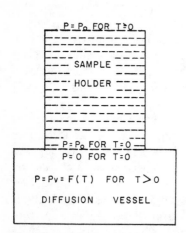

Fig. 23–3. Initial and boundary conditions of problem solved for calculating apparent diffusion coefficient.

To develop the equation for calculating the apparent diffusion coefficient, consider the problem depicted in Fig. 23–3 for diffusion of oxygen and nitrogen. The initial and boundary conditions for oxygen only are shown in the figure. At time equal zero, the partial pressures of oxygen and nitrogen in the soil are P_0 and P_n, respectively, while in the diffusion vessel they are zero and $P_n + P_0$, respectively. Immediately at time equal zero, diffusion starts, with oxygen diffusing in one direction and nitrogen in the opposite. The oxygen partial pressure increases in the diffusion vessel, while the nitrogen partial pressure decreases. At all times the partial pressures at the upper soil surface remain constant. The rate of change of the partial pressure of oxygen within the diffusion vessel depends on the apparent diffusion coefficient of the soil. If the partial pressure is measured at a particular time, it is possible to calculate the apparent diffusion coefficient.

Taylor (1950) made the following two assumptions in his theoretical analysis: (1) that the partial pressure gradient within the diffusion vessel is zero at all times, and (2) that the partial pressure gradient within the soil is constant throughout at any particular time. The first assumption is justified on consideration of the geometry of the diffusion regions, the relative rates of diffusion in soil and air, the possibilities of small air currents in the diffusion vessel, and observations and calculations made by Currie (1960). The second assumption can result in a sizable error in the calculated diffusion coefficient. The size of error depends upon the diffusion coefficient and the time over which diffusion is allowed to occur.

This problem has been solved without making assumption (2). The solution is more complicated than that presented by Taylor, but it is more accurate. Rather than present the equation for calculating the apparent

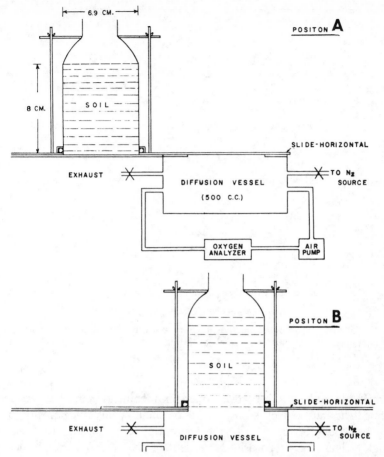

Fig. 23-4. Diagram of apparatus used for determining apparent diffusion coefficient.

diffusion coefficient as such, graphs (Figures 23–5 & 23–6) are presented from which the apparent diffusion coefficient may be directly obtained if the partial pressure in the diffusion vessel is known at either 30 minutes or 120 minutes after diffusion starts. The graphs apply only for 30 and 120 minutes and for the geometries shown in Fig. 23–4 for the soil container and diffusion vessel. For other times and geometries, further calculations are necessary. The times 30 and 120 minutes and the size of the diffusion vessel were selected as reasonable for routine laboratory analyses for the range of diffusion coefficients encountered for soils.

The apparent diffusion coefficient, as defined, depends upon the air

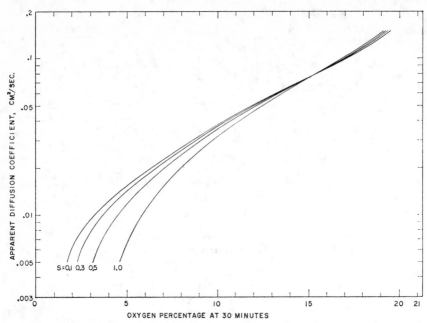

Fig. 23–5. Graph for obtaining the apparent diffusion coefficient from the oxygen percentage in the diffusion vessel at 30 minutes. S = volume fraction of soil occupied by air.

porosity. In addition, air porosity enters into the measurement as a capacity factor. The latter effect is only slight for small changes in porosity, but it may be accounted for by using the appropriate curve in Fig. 23–5. Only a rough estimate of air porosity is needed for the precision usually desired.

23–2.3   Method

23–2.3.1   SPECIAL APPARATUS AND MATERIALS

1. Sample containers, driving tube, driving head, and hammer, as described in items 2 through 5 in section 23–1.3.1.
2. Nitrogen gas: Commercially available compressed nitrogen gas in metal tanks is convenient and satisfactory.
3. Diffusion vessel with attached valve arrangements and connectors: Construct the apparatus according to the plan shown in Fig. 23–4. Carefully machine the sliding plate and base plate to give an air-tight seal when the sliding surface has a thin coating of a light lubricant. Seal the sample container to the sliding plate with an "O"-ring seal. Seal the diffusion vessel to the base plate. Make four holes in the diffusion vessel for connections to an oxygen analyzer, a nitrogen source, and an exhaust.

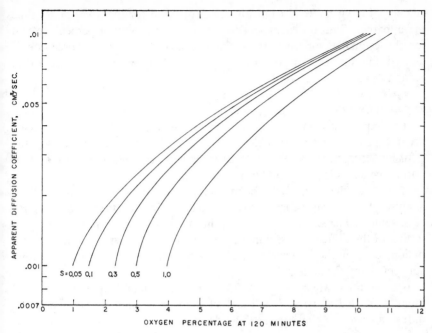

Fig. 23–6. Graph for obtaining the apparent diffusion coefficient from the oxygen percentage in the diffusion vessel at 120 minutes. S = volume fraction of soil occupied by air.

4. Oxygen analyzer, Beckman Model D, scale 0 to 25%.
5. Pump: Use a hypodermic syringe of 20-cm.³ capacity. Insert a one-directional valve into the line on each side of the pump, and attach the pump in series with the oxygen analyzer and the diffusion chamber.

23–2.3.2 PROCEDURE

Obtain undisturbed cores in the sample containers as described in section 23–1.3.2. Clamp each sample container in turn to the sliding plate, and move it to position A as shown in Fig. 23–4. Flow nitrogen through the diffusion vessel until gas pumped through the oxygen analyzer from the vessel reads zero oxygen percentage. Stop the flow of nitrogen, and close the valves on the inlet and outlet. Slide the sample to position B, and record the time.

If the estimated apparent diffusion coefficient is high, measure the oxygen partial pressure in the diffusion vessel after 30 minutes; or, if the estimated diffusion coefficient is low, measure the partial pressure at the end of 120 minutes for greater precision. To make the measurement, move the sample to position A, and then pump the gas within the diffusion vessel through the analyzer until a constant reading is obtained. Record the percentage of oxygen. Read from Fig. 23–5 or 23–6 for the appropriate time the apparent diffusion coefficient for the measured oxygen percentage and for the estimated air porosity of the sample. Where greater precision is desired, measure the air porosity of each sample by a method described in section 21–4.

23–2.3.3 COMMENTS

It is important to have precise temperature control when making measurements since temperature changes disrupt the diffusion process. Also, the diffusion coefficient is temperature dependent, and when results are reported the temperature should be stated.

More than one sample may be measured simultaneously with one oxygen analyzer, but it is necessary to have a separate diffusion vessel and slide for each sample. The small volume of gas in the analyzer system in comparison to that of the diffusion vessel makes only a very slight error in the determination, even if the analyzer contains pure nitrogen or normal air when connected into the system.

It is essential, when using Fig. 23–5 and 23–6, that a time of 30 or 120 minutes is used and the dimensions of the sample and the volume of the diffusion vessel are the same as those described.

23–3 LITERATURE CITED

Buehrer, T. F. 1932. The movement of gases through the soil as a criterion of soil structure. Arizona Agr. Exp. Sta. Tech. Bull. 39.

Currie, J. A. 1960. Gaseous diffusion in porous media: 1. A nonsteady state method. Brit. J. Appl. Phys. 11:314–317.

Evans, D. D., and Kirkham, Don. 1950. Measurement of air permeability of soil in situ. Soil Sci. Soc. Am. Proc. (1949) 14:65–73.

Grover, Ben L. 1955. Simplified air permeameters for soil in place. Soil Sci. Soc. Am. Proc. 19:414–418.

Kirkham, Don. 1947. Field methods for determination of air permeability of soil in its undisturbed state. Soil Sci. Soc. Am. Proc. (1946) 11:93–99.

Kirkham, Don, DeLeenheer, L., and DeBoodt, M. 1958. Physical measurements and yields on some loam and clay soils in Belgium. Proc. Intern. Symp. on Soil Structure. Ghent, May 29–31, 1958.

Steinbrenner, E. C. 1959. A portable air permeameter for forest soils. Soil Sci. Soc. Am. Proc. 23:478–481.

Tanner, C. B., and Wengel, R. W. 1957. An air permeameter for field and laboratory use. Soil Sci. Soc. Am. Proc. 21:663–664.

Taylor, Sterling A. 1950. Oxygen diffusion in porous media as a measure of soil aeration. Soil Sci. Soc. Am. Proc. (1949) 14:55–61.

24 | Temperature[1]

STERLING A. TAYLOR
Utah State University
Logan, Utah

RAY D. JACKSON
United States Water Conservation Laboratory
Tempe, Arizona

24–1 GENERAL INTRODUCTION

Temperature is a concept that is widely used to characterize the thermal properties of a system. The growth of biological systems is optimal within certain ranges of temperature and inhibited or prevented beyond such boundaries. The agricultural significance of temperature is readily ascertained when one considers that, in addition to plant growth, physical, chemical, and microbiological processes occurring in soil are strongly influenced by temperature. The influence of temperature on such processes has been, and will probably continue to be, intensively studied. Such studies require the measurement of temperature. Several means of making this measurement are described in this chapter.

Temperature cannot be measured directly. It can only be estimated by its influence on some property of matter that responds to variation in the intensity of heat in the body of matter. Changes in properties of matter listed in Table 24–1 have been found most useful for practical temperature measurements. Instruments built to take advantage of any of these properties of matter are called thermometers. In order that all of these properties will give the same indication of the temperature of a given body, calibration techniques have been established, and certain standard references have been agreed upon.

24–2 KINDS OF THERMOMETERS USED IN SOILS WORK

24–2.1 Introduction

There are numerous kinds of thermometers that can be used for measuring soil temperatures. Some of the commonly used types are mercury or

---
[1] Contribution from the Agronomy Dept., Utah State Univ., Logan, Utah, and the Southwest Water Conservation Laboratory, Soil & Water Conserv. Res. Div., ARS, USDA, Tempe, Ariz. Approved for publication by the Director of the Utah Agr. Exp. Sta.

liquid in glass, bimetallic, bourdon, and electrical resistance thermometers. The choice of a thermometer for a given application depends, among other things, upon availability, degree of required precision, accessibility to location of sensing element, and physical size of element. Proper calibration and installation are necessary if reliable results are to be expected.

24–2.2 Mercury or Liquid-in-Glass Thermometers

Instruments of this kind should be checked against a standard thermometer or at a reference point, such as the ice point, once each year to adjust for any change in calibration that might result from irreversible changes in volume of the glass bulb.

A correction must be made if the stem is subjected to a temperature different from that which the instrument was intended to indicate. If n degrees of the mercury column are out of a medium that is at temperature T, and if the mean temperature of the emergent stem is T_s, then the necessary correction to the reading of an immersion thermometer is

$$\Delta T = n(\gamma_h - \gamma_g)(T - T_s), \qquad [1]$$

where γ_h and γ_g are the cubical expansion coefficients of mercury and glass. For most glass, $\gamma_h - \gamma_g = 1/6200$ to a sufficient degree of accuracy if n is in centigrade degrees. It is difficult to measure T_s precisely.

Care must be exercised in reading any mercury or liquid-in-glass thermometer to see that the line of sight is in the plane through the end of the mercury and perpendicular to the plane of the thermometer.

24–2.3 Bimetallic Thermometers

These thermometers are made commercially by welding together two bars of different metals and rolling the resulting compound bar into a strip. The metals generally used are invar and brass or invar and steel. Because of the difference in linear expansion of the two metals, the strip bends in response to temperature changes. An indicating arm or pointer to indicate the amount of angular deformation is attached to a helical coil of the bimetallic strip. The angular deflection is calibrated in terms of tempera-

Table 24–1. Thermometric substances and their thermometric properties.

Thermometric substances	Thermometric property
Mercury or liquid in a glass capillary	Volume
Bimetal strip	Length
Platinum or other wires and thermistors	Electrical resistance
Thermocouples and thermels	Thermal EMF
Gas or vapor at constant volume	Pressure

ture. The instrument can be made with an adjustable zero by providing an adjusting screw at the place where the helix is attached to the frame. A pen can be attached to the indicating arm to make the instrument self-recording.

This kind of thermo-sensing element is used extensively in soils laboratories for regulating constant-temperature baths, environment chambers, and constant temperature rooms. Dial type thermometers based on this principle are used both in the laboratory and in the field.

The bimetal thermometers are generally less precise than the mercury-in-glass thermometers. The advantages responsible for their use are their lower lag and increased durability and the mechanical advantage which makes it possible for them to be made self-recording.

Precautions to avoid exposure to direct radiation must be taken if these thermometers are to give reliable measurements of temperature.

24-2.4 Bourdon Thermometers

This type of thermometer consists of a curved tube of elliptical cross section connected through a capillary to a bulb that is inserted into the soil. The system is completely filled with some organic liquid. The bulb is usually long and about 1 cm. in diameter. An increase in temperature causes the organic liquid to expand and increase the pressure inside the soil bulb and the curved capillary tube. This causes the curved tube to become slightly less curved, thus changing the position of the pointer attached to it. If a pen is attached to the pointer on the end of the bourdon element, a continuous record of the temperature can be made on a chart that is attached to a clock-operated drum. When properly placed horizontally in the soil, it will give a good indication of the temperature at that depth. If the bulb is placed vertically in the soil, an integrated or average temperature over a depth interval can be obtained.

The most troublesome problem of using this type of instrument is that the instrument and capillary tube are relatively sensitive to changes in temperature and are responsive to direct radiation heating. Radiant heating can be reduced by properly shielding the bourdon element from direct radiation and by burying at least 3 feet of the protected capillary tube at the same depth as the bulb.

24-2.5 Electrical Resistance Thermometers

There are two types of resistance thermometers in general use. One type depends upon the increase in resistance with an increase in temperature of a wire such as nichrome, copper, silver, or platinum. The temperature coefficient of resistance of platinum wire at 0°C. is about 0.35% per degree.

Resistance changes are measured with a bridge, or in some cases a potentiometer, and are related to temperature changes. Recording bridges or potentiometers yield a continuous record of resistance and hence of temperature.

The second type of resistance thermometer is a semiconductor called a thermistor. Thermistors have a high negative temperature coefficient of resistance, on the order of 4% per centigrade degree. This coefficient is opposite in sign and about 10 times larger than that of platinum resistance thermometers. Thermistors are available in various shapes, e.g., spheres, discs, and rods, all in various sizes, thus permitting great flexibility in application. Thermistors are, however, not all uniform; therefore, each unit must be separately calibrated.

Some thermistors have been found to change calibration with time; thus recalibration is required. In discussing this problem, Friedberg (1955) says:

"Thermistors undergo systematic resistance changes with time, generally becoming more stable after aging at elevated temperatures (100°C.) for several days or weeks, making preaging essential in most thermometric applications. In some instances, similar stabilization may be achieved by the passage of currents much larger than the usual measuring current through the material for shorter periods. Properly aged and electrically "formed" thermistors have been found to have resistance at 100°C. reproducible to within ±0.01°C. over periods of several months. Stability is less satisfactory when these thermometers are used up to 300°C."

Small bead-type thermistors mounted in glass probes, similar to VECO 32A1 (Western Electric Type 14-B), of the Victory Engineering Co., Union, New Jersey, are suitable for measurements of freezing-point depression, heat of wetting, heat capacity, and thermal conductivity. The thermistors may be used as glass rods or may be mounted in metallic shields as desired. If the thermistors are mounted in metallic shields, the heat capacity is increased, and the response time is modified accordingly. A direct-current Wheatstone bridge, capable of recording 9,999 ohms to the nearest ohm, and a galvanometer to indicate the null point are satisfactory for reading temperatures to about 0.003°C. (Richards and Campbell, 1948). More sensitive instruments and more precise laboratory techniques are necessary to achieve greater accuracy and precision. Care must also be taken to minimize self heating of the thermistor.

For some applications, thermistors are purposely self-heated. However, for precise temperature measurements, self-heating must be controlled. This is attained by applying a low voltage to the thermistor. To estimate the maximum voltage allowable, the dissipation constant for each type of thermistor must be known. This constant is usually given by the manufacturer for the thermistor immersed in a particular fluid; e.g., still air, moving air, still oil, or water. The dissipation constant is the power required to raise the temperature of the thermistor 1 centigrade degree when immersed in a specified fluid. For example, a VECO 32A8 bead thermistor has a dissipation constant given by the manufacturer of 0.7 mw. per centigrade degree in still air and a nominal resistance of 2,000 ohms at 25°C. If the required precision of the air temperature measurement is 0.01C.°, the allowable power is $(0.7)(0.01) = 0.007$ mw. $(7 \times 10^{-6}$ w.$)$. The maximum voltage that can be applied with negligible self-heating is $E = (7 \times 10^{-6} \times 2 \times 10^3)^{1/2} = 0.118$ v.

For measuring heat conductivity where the precise location of the temperature determination must be known, the VECO 34A1 thermistor of the Victory Engineering Company is satisfactory. It is the size of a very small sand grain and can be used to measure temperature with about the same precision as the 32 A1 which has similar characteristics. It can be placed at a point in the soil with little or no disturbance to the soil. With a sufficiently sensitive bridge and good circuits, temperature can be measured with a precision of 0.003C.° or better. This precision greatly exceeds the accuracy of most laboratory standard thermometers, but this fact does not preclude their use in measuring differences or variations in temperature with greater precision than standard thermometers, provided that the exact temperature on the international standard scale is not important.

Temperatures indicated by thermistors may be continuously recorded with a recording potentiometer by placing a small (1.3 v.) constant-voltage battery in series with a protective resistance large enough to reduce the voltage across the thermistor, low enough to prevent self heating. A recording potentiometer is placed across the thermistor to measure the voltage drop across it. The voltage drop varies with temperature.

The magnitude of the protective resistance R_p necessary to reduce the voltage drop V_T across the VECO 32A8 thermistor of the last example to 0.118 v., if a 1.3-v. mercury battery V_B is used, and if the resistance of the thermistor R_T is 2,000 ohms, is $R_p = (V_B/V_T)R_T = (1.3/0.118)(2,000) = 11,000$ ohms.

Bridge circuits can also be conveniently used for recording temperatures measured with thermistors. An appropriate recorder can be placed in the circuit in place of the galvanometer; and, with proper choice of resistance ratios and recorder sensitivity, a satisfactory range of temperatures can be recorded. Some suppliers of thermistors will provide tested circuit diagrams for various applications.

24–2.6 Thermocouples

Thermoelectric junctions, called thermocouples, are made by joining two dissimilar metals at two different places, to form two junctions. If the entire circuit is composed of only two metals, the total electromotive force in the circuit is proportional to the difference in temperature of the two junctions. One junction is called the measuring (or hot) junction, and the other, the reference (or cold) junction. For measurement of temperature, the reference junction is kept at a constant temperature, for example, in melting ice. The electrical potential produced is usually measured with a potentiometer when precise measurements are desired. Also, a galvanometer or millivoltmeter can be used. Some commercially available potentiometers have a built-in correction for the temperature of the reference junction, thus eliminating the need of an ice bath or other constant temperature source. These methods are also adaptable to recording equipment.

If several thermocouples are wired in series so that their hot and cold junctions are composed of several different couples, the emf. is increased and greater precision is possible. Such units are called thermels or thermopiles.

One great advantage of thermocouples and thermistors for measuring soil temperature, in addition to their adaptability to automatic recording, is their small size and almost instantaneous response to temperature changes. They have a low heat capacity, and the lead wires may be very small, so that there is little influence of the temperature outside the soil on the reading. They may be placed precisely and, therefore, indicate the temperature at a given point.

Thermocouples with an appropriate potentiometer and a suitable reference have numerous uses for measuring temperature in the soils laboratory. Differential thermal analysis of soil minerals, differences in temperature between moist soil and dry soil, the temperature rise that occurs upon wetting of soil, and the evaporative cooling are some of the applications. Properly calibrated galvanometers or recording potentiometers may be used for detecting and recording the difference in temperature between the two junctions.

Thermocouples have been used to measure the vapor pressure of soil water. These methods, however, require special precautions to remove all contact and junction potentials and require thermally shielded and guarded circuits and switches. At the time of this writing, the methods are not yet sufficiently well developed for adoption as routine laboratory procedures, although they can be used with confidence in specialized laboratories that have the necessary equipment and skilled personnel. Two general methods are being developed. One is based upon a measure of the temperature difference between a reference, which is usually the constant temperature bath, and the wet bulb temperature that is obtained by inserting a tiny thermal junction, containing a droplet of water, into the soil environment (Richards and Ogata, 1958). This method is described in section 8–4. The other method is based upon cooling one junction to the dew point while retaining the other at the temperature of the bath. The Peltier effect is utilized to cool the junction to the dew point (Korven and Taylor, 1959; Monteith and Owens, 1958).

Table 24–2. Fundamental fixed points and primary fixed points
of the International Temperature Scale under the standard
pressure of 1,013,250 dynes/cm.²

Fixed point	Value adopted	
	1927	1948
Temperature of equilibrium between liquid oxygen and its vapor (boiling point of oxygen)	-182. 97° C.	-182. 970° C.
Temperature of equilibrium between ice and air-saturated water (melting point of ice) (Fundamental fixed point)*	0. 000	0
Temperature of equilibrium between liquid water and its vapor (boiling point of water) (Fundamental fixed point)*	100. 00	100
Temperature of equilibrium between liquid sulfur and its vapor (boiling point of sulfur)	444. 60	444. 600
Temperature of equilibrium between solid and liquid silver (freezing point of silver)	960. 5	960. 8
Temperature of equilibrium between solid and liquid gold (freezing point of gold)	1,063	1,063. 0

* The freezing and boiling points of water under standard conditions are fundamental fixed points. The other points are given values as close to the Celsius temperature as possible and fixed by definition to the precision listed; these points are called primary fixed points and may change slightly as more precise methods are developed.

24–3 CALIBRATION OF THERMOMETERS

24–3.1 Introduction

Temperature is a fundamental physical property that can be measured using any method that has been correctly related to the accepted standard scale. A set of fundamental fixed points to which specified values have been assigned by international agreement is used as a basis for calibrating thermometers. These fixed points are the freezing and boiling points of the materials given in Table 24–2 (Hall, 1955).

24–3.2 Principles

In addition to the fixed points defined in Table 24–2, a continuous temperature scale requires that the means which are to be used for interpolation between the fixed points be specified. For this purpose, the scale has been divided into three regions. From −182.97° to 630.5°C., the scale is defined by the electrical resistance of a standard platinum resistance thermometer. For purposes of interpolation in the region of the scale between 0° and 630.5°C., use is made of the equation

$$R_T = R_o(1 + AT + BT^2),$$ [2]

where R_T is the resistance at temperature T, R_o is the resistance at 0°C., and A and B are constants that are determined by measurements at the melting point of ice, the boiling point of water, and the boiling point of sulfur. Below 0°C. a different equation,

$$R_T = R_o[1 + AT + BT^2 + C'(T - 100)T^3],$$ [3]

is used for interpolation purposes. The additional constant is determined by measurement of the boiling point of liquid oxygen (-182.97°C.).

From 630.5° to 1,063°C., the scale is defined by means of a 10% rhodium-platinum against pure platinum thermocouple using the equation

$$E = a + bt + ct^2.$$ [4]

The constants are determined by measurements at the freezing point of antimony (630.5°C.), silver, and gold. So that the scale will be continuous, it is prescribed that the freezing point of the actual sample of antimony which is used shall be determined by means of a platinum resistance thermometer, and that the value so determined shall be used in calculation of the thermocouple calibration. Alternatively, the thermocouple may be compared directly with the resistance thermometer at a temperature close to 630.5°C.

In soils work, it is unlikely that there will be concern with temperatures above 1,063°C.; consequently, that region is not considered.

In most soils laboratories, the standard instruments prescribed are not available for the purpose of comparing and checking instruments used for measuring soil temperature; consequently, secondary standards of sufficient accuracy for the intended purposes are used. A thermocouple of platinum with an alloy of platinum containing 10% rhodium can be read to ±0.01°C. with a precise potentiometer. This instrument can be calibrated either by the supplier or by the National Bureau of Standards to give a good secondary standard over the range of temperatures generally covered in soils work. Mercury-in-glass thermometers may also be calibrated to give a satisfactory secondary standard for most purposes.

24–3.3 Method

24–3.3.1 SPECIAL APPARATUS

1. Primary standard platinum resistance thermometer or a secondary standard thermometer
2. Dewar flask or thermos bottle.
3. Stirrer.

24–3.3.2 PROCEDURE

Begin by checking the ice point. (If the necessary equipment is available, a more stable point is the triple point of water which is 0.0100°C. above the ice point (Stimpson, 1955)). Suspend the standard thermometer and the thermometer to be checked near the center of a Dewar flask. Fill the Dewar flask with crushed ice made from distilled water (if ice from distilled water is not available, it may be made from regular tap water in a domestic freezing unit with errors <0.01°C.). Add liquid water to the crushed ice to displace all the air, and allow the system to establish temperature equilibrium. This temperature will give the ice point (0°C. or 32°F.).

Gradually add heat until all the ice melts. Place the stirrer in the Dewar flask, and stir the solution vigorously. Add hot water to the system to raise the temperature. When stable readings are attained, compare the reading of the standard thermometer to that of the instrument being checked or calibrated. Maintain the water at the proper level near the top of the Dewar flask by siphoning off the excess.

24–3.3.3 COMMENTS

If mercury-in-glass thermometers are being used or calibrated, care should be taken to see that the thermometer is immersed to the proper depth, depending on whether the thermometer is intended for total immersion or partial immersion. If electrical resistance or thermoelectric thermometers are being used, care should be taken to see that the leads do not conduct heat into the bath and to the sensing unit, thereby changing the temperature reading. This can be avoided by immersing 8 to 10 inches of electrically insulated lead in the same bath with the thermometer. Simultaneous readings should be taken on both the standard thermometer and the instrument being calibrated at approximately 10-degree intervals over the range from the freezing point to the boiling point of water.

A pressure correction for the melting point of ice will probably be unnecessary except for the most exacting work. If it is necessary to make a correction, it can be done by applying the Clapeyron equation

$$dT/dP = T(V_l - V_s)/\Delta H_s$$

where T is temperature, P is pressure, and V_l and V_s are the specific or molar volume of liquid water and ice, respectively, at the freezing point. For ice at 0°C., $T = 273.2°K.$, $(V_l - V_s) = -0.0906$ cm.^{3} g.$^{-1}$, and $\Delta H_v = 333.6$ joules g.$^{-1}$; hence $dT/dP = -0.00742°K./bar = -0.00752°K./atmosphere.$

The solubility of air in water at the freezing point under standard conditions is given by Dorsey (1940, p. 605) as 1.29×10^{-3} g. formula weight of air dissolved in 1 kg. of water at equilibrium. This causes a depression of the freezing point of 2.4×10^{-3} degrees. The solubility of gas increases by about 0.4% per atmosphere, which is entirely negligible for normal variations in atmospheric pressure, so that the correction of 2.4 × 10^{-3} degrees for solubility of air is adequate.

The boiling point of water is a fundamental fixed point at a standard pressure of 1.01325 bars (the standard atmosphere). If the pressure is different from the standard reference pressure, a correction must be made for the temperature of the boiling point. For precise work, the correct boiling point should be taken from tables (for example, Dorsey (1940, page 580)). However, the simple linear average of 0.39°C. reduction in boiling point per 10 mm. decrease in barometric pressure below the standard atmosphere is accurate to the nearest 0.1°C.

To read the correct temperature at the boiling point of water, the thermometer should be placed at a point far from the surface through which heat is supplied, the rate of heating should be low, mixing should be thorough, and the thermometer should be screened from direct radiation. The observed temperature will then be near to that of the true boiling point.

Precise calibration can only be justified for use in the laboratory where conditions can be carefully controlled. Under these conditions, the use of a "triple-point" apparatus would remove some of the sources of variation discussed above (Stimpson, 1955). In the field, installation errors and the continual fluctuation in temperatures with depth and time make precise determinations difficult; hence, any calibration needs to be only as accurate as the level of experimental error encountered in the field measurements.

24–4 FIELD MEASUREMENTS

24–4.1 Introduction

There are no single methods for measuring soil temperature that are recommended to the exclusion of others. The user should always be sure that the methods and instruments he is using are properly related to the standard scale.

The more commonly used methods for measuring the soil temperatures will now be described. There may be other methods and equipment that can be used to achieve the same purpose.

24–4.2 Methods

24–4.2.1 ONE-POINT

The thermometer most appropriate for the measurement desired should be selected. The sensing element should then be placed at the point (location and depth) for which the measurements of temperature are desired.

Care should be taken to ensure that the sensing element or thermometer bulb is in good thermal contact with the soil. The apparent temperature of the soil air is likely to be somewhat different from the temperature of the solid and liquid portions because of the low thermal conductivity of the air (Onchukov, 1957). Good thermal contact is particularly important if the thermometer has a large heat capacity.

Mercury-in-glass thermometers have a high heat capacity. At depths >1 foot in the field, specially constructed thermometers are used. One method is to hang the thermometers in a tube or pipe and pull them out for reading. In order that its temperature shall not change appreciably during the process, the bulb is surrounded by a mass of paraffin wax to give it a high lag coefficient. This is permissible only because the temperature at depths of more than a few inches changes very slowly; and, in most applications, it is probably not serious if the observed temperature represents the temperature that actually occurred in the soil a few minutes earlier. It has been observed, however, that in some of the thermometers at temperatures <5°C., appreciable error is caused by the thermal contraction of the wax and resultant thermometer bulb deformation (Garvitch and Probine, 1956). Consequently, thermometers of this kind should be checked frequently to see that they are indicating the correct temperature. It is possible to make a suitable wax that will not cause this contraction.

A more serious error is probably attributable to the thermal conductivity of the steel pipe that is usually used as a well. A mild steel pipe terminated in a sharp cone that can be driven into the soil without serious disturbance is usually provided. The pipe should be heavily painted to minimize its effect on the measured temperature. Convection of heat within the tube when the surface is colder than the deeper soil would also be expected to have an influence on the observed temperature.

Thermometers should be shielded from direct radiation of the sun. Electric thermometers should have 2 or 3 feet of lead wires buried at the same depth as the sensing element to avoid errors in reading that result from direct radiation.

When precise measurements of temperatures and temperature gradients are desired, one needs to use a thermometer with a very low heat capacity that will respond almost instantaneously to temperature changes. The location of the unit may also need to be known with accuracy. Thermistor units and thermocouples are ideally suited for these measurements since they are small and quick to respond. It is very important that they be installed properly in the soil. With sensitive units of this kind and with precision measuring equipment, one can readily detect a difference in temperature between the air space and the soil particles with the associated liquid if the temperature is changing rapidly, as it does during summer in the surface 5- to 10-cm. depths of soil (Onchukov, 1957).

24–4.2.2 TEMPERATURE DISTRIBUTION

In the past little attention has been given to depths of temperature measurement, and the data are reported for many different depths. It is desirable to have measurements at the same depths so that the data from place to place can be directly compared. It is suggested that, whenever possible, temperatures be measured at 10, 20, 50, 100, 150, and 300 cm. (4, 8, 20, 39, 59, and 118 inches) (Richards et al., 1952; Blanc, 1958). Temperatures may also be measured at 5 cm. (2 inches) and at the surface of the soil, but special precautions are necessary to achieve proper thermal contact and to avoid errors resulting from direct radiation when surface measurements are made.

Surface temperatures can be measured by using a sheet of conducting metal and a thermometer firmly attached to a piece of insulating board 1 to 2 cm. in thickness. Good thermal contact is made between the metal and the thermometer, and the two are attached to the insulating board with an epoxy resin or other suitable cement. Electrical thermometers are best suited for this kind of measurement, but mercury thermometers may also be used successfully. In use, the metal is placed in direct contact with the soil surface, and the 1- to 2-cm. board to which it is attached shields it from direct radiation. The board shield may be eliminated if the metal is covered with about 1 cm. or more of soil. A convenient size for the metallic conductor, and one that appears to give satisfactory readings of surface temperature, is 20 by 20 cm. Many other sizes have been used with satisfactory results. Whenever this method is used, one should report the size and dimensions of the metallic conductor and shield used. For semipermanent or seasonal installations, copper screens covered with a thin layer of soil might be substituted for metallic plates.

The type and amount of ground cover, as well as the soil moisture status, have a marked effect on soil temperatures. For this reason, it is recommended that, whenever possible, measurements be made under a uniform sod or in a bare soil plot (Newman et al. 1959). The sod should be clipped regularly so that the grass remains between 2 and 3 inches tall. The sod should not be irrigated. In arid regions where grass will not grow, measurements should be made under a vegetative cover that is as near to that of the native vegetation as possible. In irrigated regions, it may be necessary to irrigate the sod in a manner similar to that used in adjacent areas. Whenever it is convenient, it is suggested that temperatures be measured under bare plots maintained free of vegetation by herbicides or by scraping the soil surface with a hoe in order that there may be a universal comparison for all kinds of climatic zones.

24–4.2.3 INTEGRATED VALUES

Many applications of soil temperature data to biology require an integrated or average soil temperature. The simplest and probably the least desirable method for doing this is to take readings once or twice a day at various depths and make a simple average of all observations during the time interval and over the depth interval for which information is desired.

A somewhat better method, but still not completely satisfactory, is to average the maximum and minimum temperatures that are observed each day. This information can be obtained either from maximum- and minimum-registering thermometers or from thermographs of the temperature at the desired point. If results obtained by this method are compared with those calculated by hourly average temperatures, it is found that in the winter the median calculated from daily maximum and minimum temperatures is above the hourly average, while in the summer it is below. These variations, however, are often <1°C. and may be negligible.

There are several methods of continuously integrating the temperature variations so that one reading gives the integrated value. MacFayden (1956) has proposed a method for obtaining the weekly integrated temperature at a point in the soil. His method consists of using a thermistor connected in series with a silver voltameter. A voltage of 1.3 volts was supplied by means of a dry cell. A separate thermistor and voltameter is required for each position to be measured. The battery and any measuring or metering circuit can be common for all positions at a site.[2]

Thermistors with well-insulated leads are placed in the soil at the desired position. Since the resistance of the thermistor has a very marked temperature coefficient, the amount of current that will flow through it (at constant voltage) is a function of the temperature and time. The amount of current that flows through the voltameter in a week is determined by accurately weighing the amount of silver that is transferred from one electrode of the voltameter to the other during the period of observation. The amount of silver transferred must be calibrated with average temperature using a particular thermistor, since thermistors are not sufficiently uniform to permit use of a universal calibration curve.

A resistance thermometer for integrating temperatures over several soil locations and depth intervals has been proposed by Tanner (1958). Several resistance thermometers are wired in series and are attached to a specially designed Wheatstone bridge. For rapid measurements, a galvanometer is used. For the continuous record that is necessary for a time integration, a strip-chart recorder is used. Since the method depends on an unbalanced circuit, the battery must be of constant voltage such as provided by mer-

---

[2] An electrochemical device known as a solion two-terminal integrator type SV 150 has recently been made available from Self Organizing Systems, Inc., 6612 Denton Drive, Dallas 35, Texas. This device can be used in place of the silver voltameter in a circuit similar to the one described. The unit gives a voltage which can be calibrated to give the integrated temperature. The unit is disconnected from the thermistor circuit and taken into the laboratory where the voltage is measured with a potentiometer. A rough estimate of the reading may also be obtained by noting the color of the integrator solution through a window provided in the chamber.

cury or alkali cells. Precautions must be taken to see that the battery current is either very small or is applied for only short time periods to avoid undesirable self-heating of the thermometers.

If the units are placed vertically in the soil, they will integrate the temperature over the depth of the soil in which the unit is buried as well as over the several locations in which the units are placed. If placed horizontally in the soil, they will integrate temperatures over the several locations but at only one depth. In either method of installation, the leads should be buried for several feet to reduce the effect of thermal conductivity of the lead wires that are exposed to different temperatures.

24–5 LITERATURE CITED

Blanc, Milton L. 1958. The climatological investigation of soil temperature. World Meteorological Organization, Geneva, Switzerland, Technical Note 20.

Dorsey, N. E. 1940. Properties of Ordinary Water-Substance. American Chemical Society Monograph Series, No. 81. Reinhold Publishing Corp., New York.

Friedberg, S. A. 1955. Semiconductors as thermometers. In Temperature, Its Measurement and Control in Science and Industry. Vol. 2. pp. 359–382. Reinhold Publishing Corp., New York.

Garvitch, Z. S., and Probine, M. C. 1956. Soil thermometers. Nature 177:1245.

Hall, J. A. 1955. The international temperature scale. In Temperature, Its Measurement and Control in Science and Industry. Vol. 2. pp. 115–139. Reinhold Publishing Corp., New York.

Korven, H. C., and Taylor, S. A. 1959. The Peltier effect and its use for determining relative activity of soil water. Can. J. Soil Sci. 39:76–85.

MacDowell, J. 1957. Soil thermometers. Nature 179:328.

MacFayden, Amyan. 1956. The use of a temperature integrator in the study of soil temperature. Oikos 7:56–81.

Monteith, J. L., and Owen, P. C. 1958. A thermocouple method for measuring relative humidity in the range 95–100 percent. J. Sci. Inst. 35:443–446.

Newman, J. E., Shaw, R. H., and Suomi, V. E. 1959. The agricultural weather station. Wisconsin Agr. Exp. Sta. Bull. 537.

Onchukov, D. N. 1957. The phenomenon of heat and moisture transmission in soils and subsoil (in Russian). Moskov. Teknd. Inst. Pisheh. Promgsch. Trudy, 1957 (8):55–63.

Richards, L. A., and Campbell, R. B. 1948. Use of thermistors for measuring the freezing point of solutions and soils. Soil Sci. 65:429–436.

Richards, L. A., and Ogata, G. 1958. Thermocouple for vapor pressure measurement in biological and soil systems at high humidity. Science 128:1089.

Richards, S. J., Hagan, R. M., and McCalla, T. M. 1952. Soil temperature and plant growth. In Shaw, B. T., ed. Soil Physical Conditions and Plant Growth. Agronomy 2: 304–336.

Tanner, C. B. 1958. Soil thermometers giving the average temperature of several locations in a single reading. Agron. J. 50:384–387.

Stimpson, H. F. 1955. Precision resistance thermometry and fixed points. In Temperature, Its Measurement and Control in Science and Industry. Vol. 2. pp. 141–168. Reinhold Publishing Co., New York.

25 | Heat Capacity and Specific Heat[1]

STERLING A. TAYLOR
Utah State University
Logan, Utah

RAY D. JACKSON
United States Water Conservation Laboratory
Tempe, Arizona

25–1 INTRODUCTION

The rates of biological and chemical reactions and hence the rate of crop growth are influenced by the temperature of the soil. The temperature, in turn, depends directly upon the specific heat and heat capacity of the soil. The amount of temperature change in response to the absorption or release of heat is governed by the heat capacity. Temperature will increase faster in the spring, and the magnitude of the diurnal temperature changes will be greater in soil with lower heat capacity. In addition, heat transfer through soil depends upon the specific heat.

The heat capacity of natural soil is strongly dependent upon the soil porosity and water content, both of which are subject to rapid fluctuations. If the specific heat and amounts of each soil constituent and the water content are known, the heat capacity of the soil-water system can be calculated; hence it is desirable to have a reliable method for determining the specific heat of soil constituents. Baver (1956) gives the specific heat for some soil constituents and indicates the procedure used for calculating the heat capacity of a soil-water system.

25–2 PRINCIPLES

The heat capacity of a system at Kelvin temperature T is the limit of the ratio $\delta Q/\delta T$ as δT approaches zero, where δQ is the amount of heat that must be introduced into the system to increase its temperature from T to $T + \delta T$. There are two heat capacities that are used in thermodynamic

[1] Contribution from the Agronomy Department, Utah State University, Logan, Utah, and the Southwest Water Conservation Laboratory, Soil and Water Conserv. Res. Div., ARS, USDA, Tempe, Ariz. Approved for publication by the Director of the Utah Agr. Exp. Sta.

applications. One is the heat capacity at constant volume C_V, which is given by the equation

$$C_V = (\partial U/\partial T)_V \qquad [1]$$

where U is the total (sometimes called internal) energy of the system. The energy U is related to the heat content Q by the relation $Q = \Delta U + W$, where W is the work performed by the system. The work term can usually be expressed as the work of expansion or shrinking at some constant pressure P. That is, $W = P\Delta V$, where ΔV is the change in volume of the system. The heat content or the enthalpy H of the system at constant pressure is $U + PV$, and so the equation for the heat capacity of a system at constant pressure is

$$C_p = [\partial(U + PV)/\partial T]_p = (\partial H/\partial T)_p . \qquad [2]$$

The heat capacity, as defined above, is an extensive property and varies with the amount of material in the system. When expressed on the basis of a unit mass of substance, it becomes an intensive property that is independent of the size of the system. The term is then called the "specific heat." If the size of the unit is taken as a mole, rather than unit mass, the term is called the "molar heat."

The most useful term for soil science is the specific heat at constant pressure, since it is possible to calculate the enthalpy, entropy, and free energy of the systems from such data.

The heat capacity at constant pressure can be measured with sufficient accuracy for most purposes by calorimetric means. That is,

$$\tilde{C}_p = \frac{H_2 - H_1}{T_2 - T_1} \frac{\Delta Q}{\Delta T} . \qquad [3]$$

If the curve of C_p versus T is nearly linear between T_1 and T_2, and if ΔT is sufficiently small, the value of $\tilde{C}_p$ can be identified with C_p at $(T_1 + T_2)/2$. This approximation can be safely made in most cases if $T_2 - T_1$ does not exceed 5°C.

25–3   METHOD [2]

25–3.1   Special Apparatus

1. Calorimeter: Use a commercial calorimeter. Alternatively, improvise one by immersing a 1-pint Dewar flask in a constant-temperature bath or by placing it in an insulated box. Fit the flask with an insulated cover, and equip it with a stirrer and with a thermometer (such as a Beckman differential thermometer, a thermo-electric thermometer, or a resistance

---

[2] The origin of the method described has been lost; however, it is an adaptation of the method of mixtures (Estermann, 1959) modified to eliminate the heat of wetting.

thermometer) capable of indicating a temperature difference of 0.01°C. or less.

2. Accessory vessel: Use a commercial calorimeter. Alternatively, improvise an accessory vessel as described above (1.), omitting the constant temperature bath or insulated box if desired. Calibrate the thermometer in the same vessel with and at the same time as the thermometer in the calorimeter, so that the two thermometers give the same temperature readings.

25–3.2 Procedure

Add a known quantity of soil to the calorimeter, along with a measured amount of water, sufficient to form a dilute suspension. Stir the suspension slowly until thermal equilibrium is established. Record the temperature to the nearest 0.01°C.

From the accessory vessel, add a measured quantity of water at a higher known temperature such that the final temperature will be about 1 degree, but not more than 5 degrees, higher than the initial temperature in the calorimeter. Record the initial temperature of the calorimeter and the accessory water and the final temperature of the calorimeter to the nearest 0.01°C. Weigh or measure all soil samples and water additions to at least three significant figures.

Evaluate the heat capacity $\tilde{C}_p$ of the soil sample from the difference T_c between the initial and final temperatures of the calorimeter, the temperature T_a of the added water, the water equivalent C_c (or heat capacity) of the calorimeter, the mass M_s of soil, the mass M_c of water initially in the calorimeter, and the mass M_a of water added from the accessory vessel.

Determine the water equivalent or heat capacity of the calorimeter, including the thermometer, stirrer, and vessel, by measuring the temperature of the calorimeter containing a known amount of water, by placing a measured amount of water at a higher known temperature in the calorimeter, and by observing the final temperature. The equation for this calculation is

$$C_c = M_{wc}c_w - M_{wa}c_w(\Delta T_a/\Delta T_c) \qquad [4]$$

where M_{wc} and M_{wa} are the mass of water initially in the calorimeter and the mass added in grams, respectively, c_w is the specific heat of water at the mean temperature of the determination (1.00 at 15°C.) in calories per gram centigrade degree (cal. per g. C.°), and ΔT_a and ΔT_c are the temperature changes in centigrade degrees for the water added and that already in the calorimeter. Then the heat capacity of the calorimeter is given in calories per centigrade degree, and C_c is the mean heat capacity of the calorimeter over the temperature interval of the experiment.

When the heat capacity of the calorimeter is known, the average specific heat of the soil sample (cal. per g. C.°) may be determined by the formula

$$c_s = c_w(M_{wa}/M_s)(\Delta T_a/\Delta T_c) - (M_{wc}c_w + C_c)/M_s \qquad [5]$$

where M_s is the mass of soil used in the experiment and the other symbols are as previously defined. Example: Assume that 50.0 g. of soil were mixed with 100.0 g. of water and brought to a temperature of 14.00°C. Then 77.5 g. of water at 20.00°C. were introduced from the auxiliary vessel. The final temperature was 16.00°C. The heat capacity of the calorimeter at this temperature had been determined to be 42.00 cal. per degree. Near 15°C. the specific heat of water (c_w) is 1.00 cal. per g. C.°. From the data $M_{wa} = 77.5$ g., $M_s = 50.0$ g., $M_{wc} = 100.0$ g., and $C_c = 42.00$ cal. per C.°, $c_s = 1.00(77.5/50.0)(4.00/2.00) - (1/50.0)(100.0 \times 1.00) + 42.00 = 3.10 - 2.84 = 0.26$ cal. per C.° × g. of soil.

25–3.3 Comments

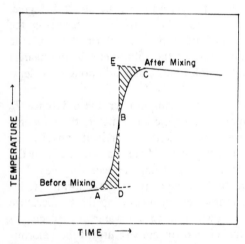

TIME ⟶

Fig. 25–1. Graphical correction for heat loss from the calorimeter during measurement of heat capacity and specific heat.

It is frequently necessary to correct for the thermal leakage of the calorimeter and to compensate for energy added by stirring. This is accomplished by correcting ΔT_c from a temperature versus time plot as shown in Fig. 25–1. In rough work, it is sometimes sufficient to extrapolate the initial and final linear portions of the temperature-time curve to a time midway between the end of the fore period and the maximum and to take the temperature difference at the point. A better approximation is to take the length of the vertical line DE so constructed as to make the areas ABD and BCE equal.

25–4 LITERATURE CITED

Baver, L. D. 1956. Soil Physics. Ed. 3, p. 370. John Wiley & Sons, Inc., New York.
Estermann, I. 1959. Methods of Experimental Physics. Vol. 1, Classical methods. pp. 260–269. Academic Press, Inc., New York.

26 | Heat Transfer[1]

RAY D. JACKSON
United States Water Conservation Laboratory
Tempe, Arizona

STERLING A. TAYLOR
Utah State University
Logan, Utah

26–1 GENERAL INTRODUCTION

The properties of soil which govern the flow of heat through it are of interest to several disciplines. Soil scientists, meteorologists, and agronomists are concerned with such problems as the temperature distribution in soil and lower air layers, the energy balance at the surface of the earth, the influence of temperature on water movement, and the measurement of soil water content by thermal methods. Engineers require information on heat conductance in soil in connection with buried cables, road construction, and heat transfer from heat pump coils.

The flow of heat through soil involves the simultaneous operation of several different transport mechanisms. Conduction is responsible for the flow of heat through the solid materials, while across the pores, three mechanisms, conduction, convection, and radiation, act in parallel. When water is present, latent heat of distillation is an additional factor involved in heat transfer.

Calculations of temperatures and quantities of heat flow within soil are usually made using equations derived to describe the conduction of heat in homogeneous, isotropic solids. The assumptions under which these equations were derived are not always met in soils. As an example, when heat is applied to a moist soil, mass transfer of water from hotter to colder areas carries heat with it. Within a pore, water may evaporate from the hot side and condense on the cold side, with the simultaneous transfer of a quantity of heat equal to the mass of water moved times the heat of vaporization of water.

The mathematics describing heat flow in porous materials such as soils which account for these additional factors are complicated and not fully

---

[1] Joint contribution from Soil and Water Conservation Research Division, ARS, USDA, Tempe, Ariz., and Utah State University, Logan.

developed. In many cases, if certain conditions are observed, mechanisms of heat transfer other than conduction may be neglected and the well-known, well-developed mathematics of heat conduction in homogeneous isotropic solids can be applied to the description of heat flow in soils. The assumptions underlying the mathematics of conduction will apply to the following discussion. The term "heat transfer" will refer only to heat transfer by conduction.

Conductive heat flow may be compared to the flow of electricity. Thermal resistivity is analogous to electrical resistivity. The reciprocal of the resistivity is the conductivity. The thermal conductivity is defined as the quantity of heat that flows through a unit area in a unit time under unit temperature gradient.

Another useful heat-transfer coefficient is the thermal diffusivity. Mathematically, the diffusivity is the ratio of the conductivity to the product of the specific heat and density. The diffusivity is a measure of the change of temperature which would be produced in a unit volume by the quantity of heat which flows through the volume in a unit time, when a unit temperature gradient is imposed across two opposite sides of the volume. The term "thermal diffusivity" was first used by Lord Kelvin.

There are many ways to measure the thermal diffusivity and conductivity. In some instances a method must be selected to meet special conditions. All methods are either a steady-state heat flow (temperature not a function of time) or transient heat flow (temperature changes with time). When a steady-state method is used to study heat transfer in moist, unsaturated soils, a moisture gradient as well as a temperature gradient results. When a constant temperature difference is applied across a moist soil column, the soil near the hot face becomes drier; that near the cold face becomes wetter. Smith (1940) measured the thermal conductivity of moist soils using a steady-state method and observed the moisture gradients. The meaningfulness of the thermal conductivity coefficient measured in such systems is questionable. Steady-state methods are, however, sufficiently accurate for measuring the diffusivity and conductivity of dry soils.

Methods using transient heat flow are generally considered to be most useful for soils work. The advantages of transient methods are that water movement in response to temperature gradients is minimized, and a long wait for thermal gradients to become constant is not required. Patten (1909) and De Vries (1950) discussed these points in detail and recommended using transient systems with small temperature gradients for measurements of thermal conductivity and diffusivity of soil.

A review of published works on thermal conductivity and diffusivity measurements in soil is given by Baver (1956), Crawford (1952), and Richards et al. (1952). A method of calculating theoretically the conductivity of granular materials of known composition is given by De Vries (1952a).

26–2 GENERAL PRINCIPLES

The general equation of heat conduction, which describes both transient and steady-state heat flow, is

$$\partial T/\partial t = k\nabla^2 T, \tag{1}$$

where T is temperature, t is time, k is the thermal diffusivity, and ∇^2 is the Laplacian operator.

For one-dimensional flow of heat in the direction of distance x, equation [1] becomes

$$\partial T/\partial t = k\partial^2 T/\partial x^2, \tag{2}$$

and for radial flow of heat in the direction of distance r from a line source

$$\partial T/\partial t = k[(\partial^2 T/\partial r^2) + (1/r)(\partial T/\partial r)]. \tag{3}$$

Derivation of the above equations is given in standard references on heat conduction, such as Carslaw and Jaeger (1959) and Jakob (1949). These references discuss the assumptions upon which the equations are based. Hence, the applicability of the equations for describing heat flow in soils may be ascertained.

The relation between the thermal conductivity K and the thermal diffusivity k is

$$K = kc_{sw}. \tag{4}$$

The term c_{sw} is the volumetric heat capacity. It is the product of the specific heat and the density. The centimeter-gram second (cgs.) units of c_{sw} are calories per cubic centimeter per degree centigrade.

The specific heat and density of both solids and water must be considered when calculating the volumetric heat capacity. For soils, the volumetric heat capacity is given by

$$c_{sw} = \rho_s(c_s + c_w\theta) \tag{5}$$

where ρ_s is the density of dry soil, c_s the specific heat of dry soil, c_w the specific heat of water, and θ the ratio of the mass of water to the mass of dry soil.

26–3 THERMAL CONDUCTIVITY

26–3.1 Introduction

Classically, the thermal conductivity has been determined using steady-state methods. As discussed at the beginning of this chapter, the results obtained by the use of steady-state methods on unsaturated soils are questionable because of the temperature-induced water movement. In addition, steady-state methods are almost entirely limited to the laboratory, whereas some transient-state methods are readily adaptable to both the laboratory and field.

The transient-state cylindrical-probe method at present offers one of the better means of measuring the thermal conductivity of soil *in situ*. The probe can be placed horizontally or vertically at various depths in the soil, and the method can be adapted for laboratory use.

The probe method, when used in unsaturated soils, is also affected by temperature-induced water movement, but to a lesser degree than steady-state methods. The over-all effect of the water movement on the measured conductivity is determined by the probe size, type of soil, water content of the soil, and many other factors. De Vries and Peck (1958b) analyzed theoretically the effects of water movement on thermal conductivity measurements and concluded that this effect is small. Their theory can be used to account for the water movement if a high degree of accuracy is desired.

The construction of the probe requires careful workmanship, especially if the diameter is small. A probe larger than the one discussed herein is described by Lachenbruch (1957). Woodside (1958) discussed the chronological development of the cylindrical probe method. His references to this method are fairly complete. Information on steady-state methods can be found in papers by Kersten (1949), Smith and Byers (1939), and Waddams (1944).

26–3.2 Principles

If an infinitely long line source of heat is embedded in an infinite, homogeneous, isotropic medium, then the flow of heat away from the source is described by equation [3]. For thermal conductivity measurements, the infinite line source is approximated by a long electrically heated wire enclosed in a cylindrical probe. The probe is introduced into the material, heating current is supplied to the wire, and the temperature rise is measured with a thermocouple placed next to the wire.

The temperature rise $(T - T_0)$ at a radial distance r from the source is represented by

$$(T - T_0) = [q/(4\pi K)][-Ei(-r^2/4kt)] , \qquad [6]$$

where q is the heat produced per unit time and unit length of the source, K the conductivity, k the diffusivity, t the time, T_0 the temperature at time $t = 0$, and

$$-Ei(-r^2/4kt) = \int_{r^2/4kt}^{\infty} (1/u) \exp(-u)\, du$$

$$= -\gamma - \ln(r^2/4kt) + (r^2/4kt) - (r^2/4kt)^2/4 + \dots ,$$

is the exponential integral.[2] In the exponential integral, γ is Euler's constant $(0.5772 \cdots)$, and u is a variable of integration.

For values of $r^2/4kt \ll 1$, all terms after the logarithmic term may be neglected. Thus

$$T - T_0 = q/(4\pi K)[-\gamma - \ln (r^2/4kt)]$$
$$= q/(4\pi K)[c + \ln t] . \qquad [7]$$

Errors caused by neglecting terms after the second in the exponential integral and those caused by the finite radius of the heat source are accounted for by introducing a time correction factor t_0 into equation [7]. For the heating period, the temperature rise is, to a good approximation,

$$T - T_0 = q/(4\pi K)[d + \ln (t + t_0)], \qquad \text{for } t < t_1, \qquad [8]$$

where d is a constant and t_1 is the time at the end of the heating period.

The temperature difference can also be obtained during the time of cooling. Thus for $t > t_1$

$$T - T_0 = q/(4\pi K)[d + \ln (t + t_0)] - q/(4\pi K)[d + \ln (t - t_1 + t_0)] . \qquad [9]$$

In equations [8] and [9], t_0 is a constant which depends upon the dimensions of the probe and the thermal properties of the probe and the medium. For probes of 0.1 cm. diameter or less and for $t > 60$ sec., t_0 may be neglected. For larger probes or smaller times, t_0 may be evaluated graphically. A plot is made of $T - T_0$ versus $\ln t$. For large values of t, a straight line results. This straight line is extrapolated to smaller values of t. A value of t_0 is chosen such that the adjusted experimental points fall on the extrapolated line. Thus a straight line ensues, the slope of which is used to determine the thermal conductivity K.

The conductivity K is calculated by equating the measured slope S to the theoretical slope $q/4\pi K$ as given by equations [8] and [9]. It is usually more convenient to use common instead of Naperian logarithms for plotting the temperature rise versus the logarithm of time data; consequently, the measured slope is

$$S = 2.303q/4\pi K . \qquad [10]$$

The heat produced q is obtained from current and resistance measurements; or, using Ohm's law, the voltage may be used in conjunction with the current or resistance. If I is the current in amperes and R the resistance in ohms per centimeter of probe, then I^2R is the watts of heat produced per centimeter (1w. = 1 joule sec.$^{-1}$ = 1/4.186 cal. sec.$^{-1}$).

Substituting I^2R for q and rearranging, equation [10] yields

$$K = 0.1834I^2R/S \text{ joules (cm. sec. C.}^\circ)^{-1}$$
$$= 0.0438I^2R/S \text{ cal. (cm. sec. C.}^\circ)^{-1} . \qquad [11]$$

---

[2] For numerical values see Jahnke and Emde (1945).

26–3.3   Method [3]

1. Galvanometer: A galvanometer of sensitivity of 2 μv. per mm. deflection on a galvanometer scale at 1 m. is a suitable instrument. Thermocouple potentiometers that indicate temperatures to 0.02°C. are suitable.
2. Dewar flask.
3. Sensitive Wheatstone bridge.
4. Stop watch.
5. Six-volt storage battery.
6. Cylindrical probe: The components to be used in the construction of the probe are as follows: enameled constantan heating wire, 0.01 cm. in diameter, of specific resistance about 0.63 ohms per cm., and about 20 cm. long; glass capillary tube of about 0.04 cm. outside diameter, 10 cm. long; fine monel gauze; enameled copper and constantan thermocouple wire of 0.01 cm. diameter; collodion for insulating; and paraffin wax.

Fold the heating wire once, and introduce it into the glass capillary. Roll one layer of gauze along a metal wire so that it forms a cylinder of about 0.14 cm. outer diameter. Because the individual wires of the gauze interlock closely at the seam, no soldering is necessary.

Make a thermocouple by soldering the copper and constantan wires, and insulate the junction with a thin layer of collodion. Place the thermocouple junction and the glass capillary containing the heating wire into the monel gauze cylinder. Locate the thermocouple junction adjacent to the glass capillary midway between the ends of the probe. Fill the space remaining in the gauze cylinder with paraffin wax.

Solder both ends of the heating wire to copper wires which lead to the power source. Place a plastic jacket over the end of the probe to protect the wires extending from the element.

Make a second thermocouple, insulate it, and connect the constantan lead to the constantan lead of the couple in the probe. Connect the copper thermocouple leads to a galvanometer. Make the leads of the second couple of sufficient length that it can be placed in the soil at the same depth as the probe, or in an insulated flask located on the soil surface.

Excavate the soil to the desired depth of measurement. For horizontal positioning, bore a hole of the same diameter as the probe into the side of the excavation. Insert the probe. Locate the thermocouple cold junction

---

[3] De Vries (1952b).

at the same depth but at a sufficient horizontal distance (≈ 15 cm.) away from the probe so that it will not be influenced by the heating of the probe. Alternatively, place the cold junction above the soil in a Dewar flask filled with melting ice. Replace the excavated soil.

Measure the resistance R of the heating wire with a sensitive Wheatstone bridge. Connect the heater lead wires through a switch to a 6-v. storage battery. Switch on the current, and measure the temperature rise $(T - T_0)$ with the galvanometer or portable thermocouple potentiometer. Read the time of each temperature measurement with a stop watch. After 3 minutes, switch off the heating current. Note the temperature decline as a function of time.

Plot the temperature rise $(T - T_0)$ as a function of time, and determine t_0 as previously described in section 26–3.2. Plot $(T - T_0)$ as a function of $\ln(t + t_0)$, and determine the slope of the line. For the cooling curve, plot $q/(4\pi K)[d + \ln(t + t_0)] - (T - T_0)$ as a function of $\ln(t - t_1 + t_0)$. Find the required value of $q/(4\pi K)[d + \ln(t + t_0)]$ for this plot by extrapolating the line obtained for $t \leq t_1$. Again determine the slope. For both the heating and the cooling periods, the plots should yield straight lines of slope $q/4\pi K$.

26–3.3.3 CALCULATIONS

Average the measured slopes for the heating and cooling curves. Calculate the thermal conductivity using equation [11]. As an example, if the measured resistance of the probe is 1.26 ohms per cm., the current 0.03 amp. and the slope of the temperature rise versus the common logarithm of time is 0.065°C., then

$$K = 0.0438(0.03)^2(1.26)/0.065$$
$$= 7.6 \times 10^{-4} \text{ cal. (cm. sec. C.°)}^{-1}.$$

26–3.3.4 COMMENTS

The construction of the probe requires careful workmanship. Although the monel gauze and the paraffin wax construction offer some rigidity, the probe is somewhat fragile. The advantages of having such a small probe are that it gives a good approximation of a line source of heat required by the theory, and that the dissipation of the heat is controlled largely by the soil and little by the probe. The metal of the gauze aids in providing a good thermal contact between the probe and the soil; however, care must be taken that the boring for the probe is not too large.

The possible contact resistance and the effect of the conductivity and heat capacity of the probe material were treated theoretically by De Vries and Peck (1958a). They concluded that in many cases the simple theory is sufficient.

The observed value of the time correction t_0 for this probe is about -2 seconds. Accuracy of the conductivity values obtained by this method is $\pm 5\%$.

26–4   THERMAL DIFFUSIVITY

26–4.1   Principles

Consider a sample of soil in a container having uniform cross section and insulated sides. The cross section is usually taken as cylindrical or rectangular, but it may be of irregular shape. The temperature of the sample is initially uniform at ambient temperature T_0. At time $t = 0$, one end of the sample is brought into contact with a heat source of constant temperature T_s. A solution of equation [1] which relates the temperature T occurring in a plane a distance x from the heat source to the time t is (Carslaw and Jaeger, 1959)

$$T - T_0 = (T_s - T_0)[1 - \text{erf } x/(4kt)^{1/2}] , \qquad [12]$$

where k is the thermal diffusivity of the soil and

$$\text{erf } x/(4kt)^{1/2} = 2\pi^{-1/2} \int_0^{x/(4kt)^{1/2}} \exp{(-u^2)} \, du .$$

The term erf is called the error function or the probability integral.

Equation [12] is applicable only if the soil sample is sufficiently long or if the time is sufficiently short that the temperature at the end of the sample opposite from the heated face is not changed during the experiment. This restriction is necessary because a semi-infinite medium is assumed in the derivation of the equation.

In practice T_s, T_0, and x are measured, heat is applied to one face of the sample, and the temperature T a distance x from the source is measured at one or more times. The term $1 - (T - T_0)/(T_s - T_0)$ is calculated for each time. The resulting numerical value is equal to the error function of argument $x/(4kt)^{1/2}$. A value of $x/(4kt)^{1/2}$ is obtained from tables of the error function in a manner similar to obtaining an antilogarithm from tables of logarithms. The diffusivity k can be calculated from this value since x and t are known. A table of the error function (probability integral), sufficiently complete for this method, is given by Larsen (1958). Tables of the *normal* probability integral are not the same as tables of the probability integral; hence, it is necessary to use a conversion factor if these are to be used.

26–4.2 Method [4]

26–4.2.1 SPECIAL APPARATUS

1. Stop watch.
2. Sample container and heat exchanger: Exact dimensions of component parts of the sample container and heat exchanger are not critical. The dimensions given below have proved satisfactory.

Construct the sample containers of plastic (a suitable plastic is poly-methylmethacrylate which is available under the trade names of Plexiglas and Lucite) or other material having a low thermal conductivity. Cut cylindrical containers at least 10 cm. long from plastic tubing 10 cm. in diameter. If rectangular containers are desired, make them at least 10 by 10 by 10 cm. Cut a plastic plate, fit a gasket to it, and bolt it on one end of the tubing. The gasket makes the joint watertight. Bolt the plate on the tubing in such a manner that it can be removed to replace the soil sample.

Construct the heat exchanger on the other end of the tubing in the following manner. Cut a 1.3-cm. piece of the 10-cm. tubing. Cement 6 plastic lugs to the outside of the 1.3-cm. piece and 6 lugs on the sample container. Align the lugs on the two pieces before cementing them in place. After the cement has hardened, drill a hole through the aligned lugs. This will allow the two pieces to be bolted together. Cut a thin copper plate and a plastic plate the same size as the container cross section. Install the copper plate between the sample container and the 1.3-cm. piece of tubing. Bolt the pieces together. Make the joints watertight by applying paraffin wax.

Drill two 1.3-cm. holes in the plastic plate—one in the center, the other near the outside edge. Cement two pieces of 1.3-cm. outside diameter plastic tubing about 5 cm. long in the holes. These form the inlet and outlet for the heat source (water at constant temperature). On the inside edge of the plate, construct a baffle using strips of 1.3-cm. plastic to form a spiral path from the center to the outside edge. Fit the completed plate on the 1.3-cm. piece of 10-cm. diameter tubing with the baffle on the inside touching the copper plate and with the small tubes protruding.

For the temperature-sensing device, drill two 0.25-cm. holes in the side of the sample container at distances 1 and 2 cm. from the copper plate. Install glass-coated thermistor rods 5 cm. long in the holes. Veco 32A1 thermistors, available from the Victory Engineering Co., Union, New Jersey, are suitable for this application. Seal the thermistors in the holes with paraffin wax. This construction lends rigidity to the ther-

---

[4] Jackson, R. D. 1960. The importance of convection as a heat transfer mechanism in two-phase porous materials. Unpublished Ph.D. dissertation, Colorado State University Library, Fort Collins, Colo.

mistors and makes a watertight seal. The sensing points of the thermistors thus installed are located approximately in the center of the cross section of the container and about 1 and 2 cm. from the copper plate.

3. Temperature-controlled water bath: Obtain a well-stirred, large-capacity (30- to 40-liter) water bath. Install a pump in the bath to provide a means of circulating water through the heat exchanger. Control the water bath temperature by use of a power-proportioning precision temperature controller. The "Electron-O-Therm Senior," available from the Bayley Instrument Co., P. O. Box 538, Danville, Calif., is a suitable instrument.

4. Temperature recorder: Record temperature with a recording bridge-type potentiometer. Endeavor to obtain precision of 0.01°C.

26–4.2.2 PROCEDURE

Measure the distance from the copper plate to each thermistor with a cathetometer. Remove the bottom of the sample container and fill the container with soil. Take care to avoid disturbance of the thermistors since the distance from the copper plate to the thermistors is critical. This distance may be checked upon completion of the measurement if care is exercised in removal of the soil.

After the soil has been packed into the container, insulate the sides with Styrofoam[5] or other insulating material. Connect 1-cm. inside diameter rubber tubing to the inlet and outlet of the heat exchanger. Connect the inlet tubing to the pump in the water bath, and put the outlet tubing in the bath for the return flow. Measure the initial temperature T_0 of the sample and the temperature T_s of the water bath. Refer to section 24 for a procedure for using and calibrating thermistors.

Begin a run by switching on the pump motor. Start a stop watch the instant the heat exchanger is filled with water. Let the water circulate through the heat exchanger continuously during the measurement. Record the temperature T of each thermistor, and note the time the temperature is measured. Take the first temperature and time readings about 1 minute after the pump motor is switched on. Take five readings of temperature and time for each thermistor at intervals of approximately 1 minute.

26–4.2.3 CALCULATIONS

Use the measured values of T_0, T_s, x, and T at a specific t, and calculate $1 - (T - T_0)/(T_s - T_0)$. This is the numerical value of erf $x/(4kt)^{1/2}$. Consult a table of the error function to obtain the numerical value of $x/(4kt)^{1/2}$. Denote this numerical value by y, and calculate the diffusivity using the expression

$$k = x^2/(4ty^2) .$$ [13]

---

[5] Styrofoam is a trade name for expanded polystyrene produced by the Dow Chemical Co. The thermal conductivity of Styrofoam is about 8.5×10^{-5} cal. cm.$^{-1}$ sec.$^{-1}$ C. deg.$^{-1}$.

Calculate k for each set of measurements of T and t for each thermistor. Average the values of k obtained.

As an example, let $T_s = 34.00°C.$, $T_0 = 24.00°C.$, $x = 1.00$ cm., $t = 300$ sec., and $T = 28.5°C$. From equation [12]

$$\text{erf } x/(4kt)^{1/2} = 1.00 - (28.50 - 24.00)/(34.00 - 24.00)$$
$$= 0.5500 .$$

In tables of the error function, the number 0.5500 lies between 0.54987 and 0.55071. Values of y corresponding to the latter two numbers are 0.534 and 0.535, respectively. Linear interpolation yields a value of $y = 0.5342$. The thermal diffusivity is, using equation [13],

$$k = (1)^2/[(4)(300)(0.5342)^2]$$
$$= 0.00292 \text{ cm.}^2 \text{ sec.}^{-1} .$$

26–4.2.4 COMMENTS

The sample container should be positioned in such a way that the best possible contact is maintained between the soil and the copper plate. This may be accomplished by placing the container so that heat flow is either horizontal or vertical with the heat exchanger on the bottom. If the heat flow is vertical, the heat flow direction should be downward; that is, the water bath temperature T_s is less than ambient temperature T_0. The terms $(T - T_0)$ and $(T_s - T_0)$ in equation [12] are therefore negative, but their ratio is positive, and the equation is not changed. Heat flow downward is preferred to reduce the effects of convection. In general, it is best to make the temperature-time determinations when the ratio $(T - T_0)/(T_s - T_0)$ is within the range of 0.1 to 0.6.

With adequate temperature-indicating equipment, using two thermistors, and making five determinations per thermistor, results can be obtained with a coefficient of variability $<3\%$ for dry soils. Greater variabilities are to be expected for moist soils.

The size of the sample is not critical. The cross section should be large enough that edge effects are negligible. Even with insulated sides, it is desirable to have the temperature-sensing devices at least twice as far from the edge as from the hot face. The container needs only to be sufficiently long that the temperature at the end does not change during the experiment.

If the copper plate used in the construction of the heat exchanger and the container is very thin, it may bend when water is turned into the heat exchanger. The bending can be reduced by soldering a bolt to the plate near its center and bringing the bolt out through the plastic cover plate.

For best results, the apparatus should be kept in a constant-temperature room.

26–5 LITERATURE CITED

Baver, L. D. 1956. Soil Physics. Ed. 3. pp. 370–379. John Wiley & Sons, Inc., New York.

Carslaw, H. S., and Jaeger, J. C. 1959. Conduction of Heat in Solids. Ed. 2. Oxford Univ. Press, London.

Crawford, C. B. 1952. Soil temperature, a review of published records. Highway Res. Board Spec. Rept. 2:19–41.

De Vries, D. A. 1950. Some remarks on heat transfer by vapour movement in soils. Trans. Intern. Congr. Soil Sci. 4th Amsterdam 2:38–41.

De Vries, D. A. 1952a. The thermal conductivity of granular materials. Inst. Intern. du Froid, Bul., Annexe 1952–1. pp. 115–131.

De Vries, D. A. 1952b. A nonstationary method for determining thermal conductivity of soil *in situ*. Soil Sci. 73:83–89.

De Vries, D. A., and Peck, A. J. 1958a. On the cylindrical probe method of measuring thermal conductivity with special references to soils: I. Extension of theory and discussion of probe characteristics. Australian J. Physics 11:255–271.

De Vries, D. A., and Peck, A. J. 1958b. On the cylindrical probe method of measuring thermal conductivity with special reference to soils: II. Analysis of moisture effects. Australian J. Physics 11:409–423.

Jahnke, E., and Emde, F. 1945. Tables of Functions. pp. 6–8. Dover Publications, New York.

Jakob, M. 1949. Heat Transfer. John Wiley & Sons, Inc., New York.

Kersten, M. S. 1949. Thermal properties of soils. Univ. of Minn. Eng. Exp. Sta. Bull. 28.

Lachenbruch, A. H. 1957. A probe for measurement of thermal conductivity of frozen soils in place. Trans. Am. Geophys. Union. 38:691–697.

Larsen, H. D. 1958. Rinehart Mathematical Tables, Formulas, and Curves. pp. 162–165. Rinehart and Co., Inc., New York.

Patten, H. E. 1909. Heat transference in soils. U. S. Depart. Agr. Bur. Soils Bull. 59.

Richards, S. J., Hagan, R. M., and McCalla, T. M. 1952. Soil temperature and plant growth. *In* Shaw, B. T., ed. Soil Physical Conditions and Plant Growth. Agronomy 2:304–336.

Smith, W. O. 1940. Thermal conductivities in moist soils. Soil Sci. Soc. Am. Proc. (1939) 4:32–40.

Smith, W. O., and Byers, H. G. 1939. The thermal conductivity of dry soils of certain of the great soil groups. Soil Sci. Soc. Am. Proc. (1938) 3:13–19.

Waddams, A. L. 1944. The flow of heat through granular material. J. Soc. Chem. Ind. 63:337–340.

Woodside, W. 1958. Probe for thermal conductivity measurement of dry and moist materials. Am. Soc. Heating and Air-Conditioning Eng. J. Sect., Heating, Piping and Air Conditioning. pp. 163–170. September issue.

27 | Reflectivity

TORRENCE H. MACDONALD
United States Weather Bureau
Washington, D. C.

27–1 INTRODUCTION

Soil reflectivity may be defined as the percentage of the solar radiation incident on the soil surface which is reflected away from that surface. Solar radiation may be defined as radiation of solar origin arriving at the soil directly from the solar beam and scattered downward from the solar beam by the atmosphere and its contents. Its power is almost entirely in the spectral range shorter than 4μ (Johnson, 1954), whereas "long-wave" radiation from sky and soil is almost entirely in the range 4 to 120μ (Berry et al., 1945).

As used here, the term "solar radiation" has dimensions of power per unit area in a horizontal plane near the soil surface. Units in wide use for this quantity are gram-calories per square centimeter per minute (g. cal. cm.$^{-2}$ min.$^{-1}$), or "langleys per minute," the langley being 1 g. cal. cm.$^{-2}$. Reflected solar radiation has the same dimensions and units, but is incident on the horizontal plane from beneath, after having undergone reflection by the soil.

The reflectivity is computed from two measurements carried out in the field: that of solar radiation, and that of reflected solar radiation. Reflectivity is computed from these measurements, and is 100 times the ratio of the reflected solar radiation to the solar radiation. In meteorology the term "albedo" has been used for this quantity for many years. An excellent bibliography on reflectivity or albedo was published under the editorship of Rigby (1957).

Reflectivity data are commonly used in heat-transfer and storage studies: the power per unit area entering the soil surface is [unity − (reflectivity/100)] multiplied by the solar radiation. Reflectivity is not a parameter measured extensively in the sense that temperature and precipitation are measured in climatological networks. Perhaps partly for this reason, techniques have not been established in detail for its determination, methods being determined generally by the equipment used, circumstances of the measurement, and judgment of the investigator. The technique described here is based on the equipment in use by the U. S. Weather Bureau in its solar-radiation network, namely, Eppley pyranometers and suitable high-impedance potentiometers. Because procedures for measuring reflectivity are not well established, the instructions given in section 27–3 should be viewed as a "point of departure."

27–2 PRINCIPLES

The pyranometer is an instrument for measuring solar radiation. The type used in the U. S. Weather Bureau network and elsewhere was invented by Kimball and Hobbs (1923), and is now known as the Eppley pyranometer after the manufacturer. Superficially, it resembles a light bulb. It consists essentially of a plane-surface receiver and support surrounded by a glass envelope which contains dry air at sea-level pressure, an arrangement for mounting and leveling, and two copper wires to which the read-out meter is attached. The receiving surface consists of two shallow annular disks, one blackened with a material of high absorptivity for solar radiation, and the other having a low absorptivity. The disks do not quite touch each other and are supported in place in a way that minimizes heat conduction between them. A thermopile is mounted beneath the receiver, with hot junctions in close thermal contact with (but insulated electrically from) the blackened surface, and with cold junctions similarly attached to the underside of the white surface. Temperature differences resulting from the differential absorption of solar radiation by the two surfaces result in an electromotive force (emf.) which is very closely proportional to the solar radiation incident on the receiver. Transmission properties of the glass envelope limit the spectral sensitivity to wavelengths shorter than about 5μ (MacDonald, 1951), considering the range of wavelengths of interest here.

The calibration factor of the instrument is the number of millivolts generated per langley per minute of solar radiation incident upon the instrument. Thus to convert the pyranometer millivolts to radiation units, the output in millivolts is divided by the calibration factor. The factor is not entirely independent of ambient temperature and angle of incidence of radiation (MacDonald, 1951).

The potentiometer used in measuring the emf. output can be either a portable type or a recorder. Such devices must have a "high impedance." When the device is balanced against the emf. being measured, "no" current must flow in the pyranometer leads; otherwise the calibration factor might be changed. If the reflectivity data are obtained under solar radiation of 1 langley per minute or more, 5-μv. resolution of the emf. output by the potentiometer should be sufficient. Instruments of this accuracy are available commercially, both as portable potentiometers and as recording potentiometers.

27–3 METHOD

27–3.1 Special Apparatus

1. Eppley pyranometers, two per installation. These instruments are available from the Eppley Laboratory, Inc., Newport, Rhode Island, and other sources.
2. Potentiometers, high-impedance type. See section 28–2.1.

27–3.2 Procedure

Obtain a stiff board or perhaps an aluminum girder 12 or 15 feet long; support it at either end by wooden posts or cinder blocks at a height of about 4 feet. Alternatively, to make the pyranometer equipment portable to some extent, use tripods to support the ends of the girder. Dimensions of these members will depend upon the area of the soil surface to be sampled. Mount a pyranometer on each side of a flat plate of minimum dimensions in such a way that the receiving surfaces of the pyranometers and the surface of the plate are in parallel planes. In these operations, take care not to expose the pyranometers to strong mechanical shock, as they are rather fragile and expensive. Mount the plate near the center of the board or girder; level the mounting plate and secure it to the girder. Shade the downward-facing pyranometer by a cylindrical shield 8 or 10 inches in diameter, painted with matte black on the inside and aluminum paint on the outside, and mounted to be concentric with the receiving surface of the pyranometer. Align the lower edge of the shield with the plane of the receiver of the lower pyranometer. Leave the shield open at the top in such a way as to permit ventilation without admitting direct radiation from above. This arrangement will tend to suppress possible error from direct solar radiation reflection from the glass hemisphere. Solder flexible, insulated copper lead-in wires to the pyranometer, and extend the leads to the point where the emf. of the pyranometers is to be measured (perhaps 50 feet or more). If a portable potentiometer is used, use a double-pole, double-throw thermocouple switch for rapidly switching the portable potentiometer input terminals from one pyranometer to the other. Take measurements in rapid succession until a statistically adequate set of data is obtained.

It may be desirable to record the data continuously. If so, extend the leads from the two pyranometers (possibly 500 feet or more) to suitable recording potentiometers.

27–3.3 Comments

Instrumental errors include those arising from the pyranometer, the potentiometer, and "stray" potentials arising in the leads from the pyranometer to the potentiometer. The last is not ordinarily a problem, but to suppress possible induced potentials it is prudent to use shielded leads. If trouble occurs, expert advice should be obtained from a physicist, electrical engineer, or another reliable source.

The pyranometer calibration repeatability is within 1%, to judge from Weather Bureau experience (MacDonald, 1954). It is important, of course, that the two pyranometers give the same reading when exposed to the same solar radiation. This should be established by exposing the two pyranometers side-by-side, both facing upward, and obtaining a statistically adequate set of comparative readings whereby to make any adjustments in either calibration constant needed to bring the radiation measurements into agreement within 1%. (The *absolute* calibration of the pyranometers is not important in making the reflectivity observations, so that either calibration value can be changed to obtain the necessary agreement in indicated radiation level. *Absolute* calibration requires special equipment; if such calibration is required for any reason, the manufacturer can be consulted.)

Pyranometers are obtainable with calibration factor of about 2 and 6 mv. per langley per minute. The down-facing pyranometer should be the latter type; the up-facing pyranometer can be either type.

As already mentioned, the emf. output of the two pyranometers should be read within about 5 μv.

It is desirable to obtain field measurements with the sun obscured, but with high solar radiation levels. (These two demands are antithetical to some extent, since the highest solar radiation values are in general obtained with the sun unobscured.) High radiation levels will tend to suppress the error component in the reflectivity attributable to measurement of emf. output, but measurements with strong direct radiation should be avoided. This is especially important if the unobscured sun is <15 or 20 degrees elevation above the horizontal. Under such conditions, the "cosine response" error of the pyranometer—i.e., change of calibration factor with change in angle of incidence of radiation—may become significant (MacDonald, 1951). Ideally, the measurements should be made under a thin, uniform, overcast sky, which is associated with diffuse solar radiation and slow time-rate-of-change of solar radiation level.

Precautions to be observed in making measurements include the following:

(*1*) The pyranometer receivers should be in a horizontal plane. It is assumed that the soil surface is in a horizontal plane. A level is attached to the base of the pyranometer by the manufacturer for normal use—with the instrument facing upward. (The plane of the receiver may not be parallel to the plane of the base.) If the pyranometer is inverted, the level is of course useless, and suitable means must be taken to assure that its receiver is in a horizontal plane when the measurements are made.

(2) The vertical supports of the pyranometer field mount will necessarily constitute part of the "field of view" of the downward-facing pyranometer, and hence will influence the measurement to some extent. Precautions should be taken to make the resulting error negligible. The error diminishes with increasing distance of the vertical support from the pyranometer (i.e., with diminishing solid angle of support as measured from the pyranometer), with diminishing dimensions of the support, and with closeness of the match of reflectivity of the supports to that of the soil surface. The effect of the support posts on the readings can be checked qualitatively by changing the reflectivity of their surfaces over a range which brackets the reflectivity of the surface being measured, and noting the effects on the measured reflectivity. This can be done by draping the post alternately with black velvety cloth and white cloth.

(3) If measurements of the reflected solar radiation are made in direct sunlight, an error may be introduced by the shadow of the pyranometer and supports. The error will depend on the geometry of the supports and sun position, diminishing with reduction of solid angle of shadow as measured from the pyranometer and with the approach of the shadow to the edge of the field of view of the pyranometer. The importance of these elements of error should be evaluated, and precautions should be taken to keep the errors to a tolerable level in practical installations that deviate from the one described in section 27–3.2.

It should be possible to obtain reflectivity or albedo values accurate to within 5% or better, considering only instrumental and observational sources of error. Sampling errors should be appraised by the investigator.

27–4 LITERATURE CITED

Berry, F. A., Bollay, E., and Beers, Norman R. 1945. Handbook of Meteorology. p. 297. McGraw-Hill Book Co., Inc. New York.

Johnson, Francis S. 1954. The solar constant. J. Meteorol. 11:431–439.

Kimball, H. H., and Hobbs, Hermann E. 1923. A new form of thermoelectric recording pyrheliometer. Monthly Weather Rev. 51:239–242.

MacDonald, T. H. 1951. Some characteristics of the Eppley pyrheliometer. Monthly Weather Rev. 79:153–159.

MacDonald, T. H., and Foster, Norman B. 1954. Pyrheliometer calibration program of the U. S. Weather Bureau. Monthly Weather Rev. 82:219–227.

Rigby, Malcolm. (Editor.) 1957. Meteorological Abstracts and Bibliography, Vol. 7. American Meteorological Society, 45 Beacon Street, Boston 8, Mass.

28 | Long-Wave Radiation

TORRENCE H. MACDONALD
United States Weather Bureau
Washington, D. C.

28-1 INTRODUCTION

Long-wave radiation from the sky and soil is so-called to distinguish it from solar radiation. The former is associated almost entirely with wavelengths in the range 4 to 120μ, while solar radiation occurs mainly at shorter wavelengths (Berry et al., 1945). A second conspicuous difference between long-wave and solar radiation is that the former originates in the atmosphere and at the soil surface. For all substances radiating at a given temperature, there is an upper limit to the power per unit area leaving the bounding surface. This upper limit is known as "black-body" radiation, and tables showing its values as a function of temperature are readily available (List, 1951, pp. 411–413). In general, substances emit only a fraction of the black-body radiation, the fraction being known as "emissivity." Many of the materials of the earth surface have emissivity close to unity in the range of temperatures they undergo from natural processes (Berry et al., 1945). Also, a cloud of sufficient thickness is approximately a black-body radiator (Berry et al., 1945).

Long-wave radiation is of great importance in studies of the thermal behavior of soils. Such investigations may require data simply of the "net radiation"—the difference between the power per unit area incident on and leaving a horizontal surface. At night the incident radiation is long-wave radiation from the atmosphere, including clouds and other aerosols, while that leaving the soil is long-wave radiation emitted by and reflected from the soil surface. During the day the incident radiation is long-wave atmospheric radiation and solar radiation; that leaving the soil is long-wave radiation and reflected solar radiation. (Radiation sources relatively trivial from the energy standpoint are not considered here. Such sources are starlight, moonlight, aurora, etc.) Net radiation is measured with a net radiometer. A hemispherical radiometer can be used to measure the radiation from either hemisphere separately.

If it is necessary to distinguish between long-wave and solar radiation components, pyranometers can be used as described in the section on reflectivity. In such a case, it is important that the pyranometers be accurately calibrated in the absolute sense, whereas in the reflectivity measurements this requirement is not necessary, relative calibration then being sufficient.

If soil surface temperature and emissivity are known, long-wave radiation from the soil surface can be computed by multiplying emissivity by the black-body radiation corresponding to the soil temperature. A difficulty sometimes arises in determining soil temperature if the surface is poorly defined, as for example in the case of a recently plowed field. Additional uncertainty is introduced by possible differences between the assumed and actual values of soil emissivity.

Radiometers for measuring long-wave radiation from sky and ground began to come into prominent use with the invention of the pyrgeometer by Angstrom (1905) about 1905. In 1922, Aldrich and Abbot (Aldrich, 1922) invented the melikeron, a device similar in principle to the pyrgeometer but differing in some essential details. Neither instrument in its original form was suitable for continuously recording long-wave radiation. Both are "compensation" or "null" devices, the radiation being determined by a measurement of electric power needed to produce thermal effects equal to those produced by the radiation. The pyrgeometer is still being used to some extent (Annals of IGY, 1958, p. 438). Gier and Dunkle (1951) described an instrument suitable for continuously recording long-wave radiation. This device is known as a "ventilated radiometer" and is available commercially. A modification of this device has been described by Suomi et al. (1954). An instrument using a radiation thermopile covered with a synthetic plastic is described by Schulze (1953). An inexpensive form of net radiometer of "moderate accuracy" has been described by Suomi and Kuhn (1958). Funk (1959, 1962) has made important advances in radiometer design. Instruments after Funk are available commercially from Middleton & Co., Ltd., 8–12 Eastern Road, South Melbourne, Australia. Fritschen and Van Wijk (1959) described an economical radiometer, an improved version of which is being manufactured by C. W. Thornthwaite Associates Laboratory of Climatology, Route 1, Centerton, Elmer, New Jersey. Eppley Laboratory, Inc., Newport, Rhode Island also manufactures radiometers for special purposes, including use on aircraft. More information on some of these instruments is available (Annals of IGY, 1958). Other radiometers have been used in the past and are still being used but will not be mentioned here individually for lack of space.

The radiometer in most common use currently in the United States seems to be the Gier and Dunkle (1951) type. This radiometer consists of a thermal transfer plate, a blower which directs a stream of air over both sides of the plate, a thermopile for measuring temperature gradient through the plate, and a thermocouple which serves to measure the plate temperature. The temperature gradient through the plate, and the thermal conductivity of the plate are used to compute time-rate of flow of heat through the plate, which is exposed in a horizontal plane. Both surfaces of the plate are covered with a material having a high absorptivity for solar and long-wave radiation. The blower serves two purposes: (*1*) it reduces the temperature gradient through the plate (thus making more tenable the assumption of equal heat losses from the two surfaces due to conduction to the air), and (*2*) it reduces the effect of wind on the readings (though imperfectly in the case of high winds).[1] In the hemispherical radiometer, a radiation shield is placed over one side of the plate to eliminate all significant effect of radiation on that side. If the shielded side is facing up, the radiometer measures radiation from the soil surface. It is assumed that the radiation emitted from the soil and incident on the lower surface of the plate is equal to the radiation emitted from the lower surface of the plate plus heat transferred through the plate. Radiation from the lower plate surface is computed from black-body radiation tables, plate temperature as measured with the thermocouple, and the known value of emissivity of the plate surface.

In mounting the radiometer, principles to be observed are similar to those pertaining to pyranometer measurements: the plate should be level and exposed, insofar as feasible, to the entire sphere in the case of the net radiometer and the appropriate hemisphere in the case of the hemispherical radiometer. (The blower mounting limits achievement of this objective to some extent.) The solid angle subtended by the vertical supports as seen from the radiometer should be kept to a minimum. In addition it should be noted that the measurements are useless if the plate is wet or covered with snow or frost. The plate should be kept free of any foreign material.

In addition to the radiometers, it is, of course, necessary to employ supplementary apparatus to accomplish the temperature measurement of the plate and the output of the thermopile and to make proper connections between the thermocouple and the thermopile and the supplementary apparatus. Sample readings of temperature can be made by use of a reference junction and bath and a suitable portable potentiometer. A continuous record of temperature can be had by recording the output of the thermocouple arrangement just described by means of a recording potentiometer, or the reference bath can be omitted and a continuous record of temperature obtained by means of a temperature recorder with an automatic reference-junction compensator (Dike, 1954). Output of the thermopile can be measured by either a portable or recording potentiometer.

Details of field mounts are not well standardized and are mainly dependent on judgment of the observer. For this reason, the account given in the following method is rather general.

---

[1] Portman, Donald J., and Dias, Flemong. 1959. Influence of wind and angle of incident radiation on the performance of a Beckman and Whitley total hemispheric radiometer. The University of Michigan (Unpublished) final report to U. S. Weather Bureau. Copy in U. S. Weather Bureau Library.

28–2   METHOD

28–2.1   Special Apparatus

1. Radiometer of Gier and Dunkle (1951) type, in the net form or hemispherical form as desired: Radiometers are available from the following and other manufacturers: Beckman and Whitley, 985 San Carlos Ave., San Carlos, Calif.; Eppley Laboratory, Newport, Rhode Island; Middleton and Co., Ltd., 8–12 Eastern Road, South Melbourne, Australia; and Thornthwaite Associates Laboratory of Climatology, Route 1, Centerton, Elmer, New Jersey.
2. Potentiometer, high-impedance type: Automatic-recording potentiometers that provide a continuous record in the millivolt range are available from the following and other manufacturers: The Bristol Co., Waterbury 20, Conn.; Leeds and Northrup Co., 4907 Stanton Ave., Philadelphia 44, Pa.; and Minneapolis-Honeywell Regulator Co., Wayne and Windrim Ave., Philadelphia 44, Pa. Suitable portable potentiometers can be obtained from the following and other companies: Minneapolis-Honeywell Regulator Co., Wayne and Windrim Ave., Philadelphia 44, Pa. (the Rubicon Portable Potentiometer); and Leeds and Northrup Co., 4907 Stenton Ave., Philadelphia 44, Pa.

28–2.2   Procedure

Mount the radiometer above the soil surface with the plate in a horizontal plane about 4 feet above the soil surface (height above soil surface is determined by area of sample to be measured and other considerations peculiar to the problem under study). To keep the support from interfering unduly with the radiation, mount the radiometer on an arm extending several feet from a vertical support (which might, for example, be a 4-inch by 4-inch post set firmly into the ground), or use some other convenient arrangement. Attach insulated copper wires to the thermopile terminal posts. Attach appropriate thermocouple extension wires as specified by the radiometer manufacturer to the thermocouple. Extend the conductors to the site of the measuring apparatus, and complete the circuits. Run a suitable power-line pair from an appropriate source to the blower motor, and connect it to the motor leads. If a portable potentiometer is to be used to measure outputs of both the thermocouple apparatus and thermopile, it is convenient to use a double-pole, double-throw thermocouple switch for alternately connecting the portable potentiometer to the two devices. Follow the directions of the manufacturer in taking the required observations and in obtaining the calibration data needed for reducing the observational data to radiation units.

28–2.3　Comments

The consensus seems to be that, if properly used, the radiometer gives data of useful accuracy. A possible exception is daytime use of a combination of radiometers and pyranometers for obtaining daytime long-wave radiation (by subtracting solar radiation from the radiometer-indicated total of solar and long-wave radiation); anomalous data due possibly to instrumental aggregate errors can result (Anderson, 1954, pp. 38–40). In studying thermal behavior of soils, it may not be necessary to attempt such a resolution of the two radiation components.

If the operator is unfamiliar with precautions that should be observed in using thermocouples, a source of information such as the publication by Dike (1954) should be consulted.

For making random sample measurements over an area, and for equipment generally more portable, the Funk (1962) and Fritschen and Van Wijk (1959) devices seem promising. Research in radiometry is currently being carried out in a number of places, and improvements in instrumentation will almost surely be made within the next few years.

28–3　LITERATURE CITED

Aldrich, L. B. 1922. The Melikeron—an approximately black body receiver. Smithsonian Misc. Collections 72, No. 13.

Anderson, E. R. 1954. Water loss investigations: Lake Hefner studies. Technical report. U. S. Geol. Surv. Profess. Paper 269.

Angstrom, K. 1905. Ueber die Anwendung der elektrischen Kompensations-methode zur Bestimmung der nachtlichen Ausbestrahlung. Nova Acta Soc. Sci. Upsala (Ser. 4) 1, No. 2.

Annals of the International Geophysical Year, 1958. Vol. V, parts IV, V, and VI. Pergamon Press—Macmillan Co., New York.

Berry, F. A., Jr., Bollay, E., and Beers, Norman R. 1945. Handbook of Meteorology. p. 297. McGraw Hill Book Co., Inc., New York.

Dike, Paul H. 1954. Thermoelectric Thermometry. Ed. 2. Tech. Publ. EN-33A (1a), Leeds and Northrup Company, Philadelphia, Pa.

Fritschen, L. J., and Van Wijk, W. R. 1959. Use of an economical thermal transducer as a net radiometer. Bull. Am. Meteorol. Soc. 40:291–294.

Funk, J. P. 1959. Improved polythene-shielded net radiometer. J. Sci. Instr. 36:267.

Funk, J. P. 1962. A net radiometer designed for optimum sensitivity and a ribbon thermopile used in a miniaturized version. J. Geophys. Res. 67:2753–2760.

Gier, J. T., and Dunkle, R. V. 1951. Total hemispherical radiometers. Trans. Am. Inst. Elec. Eng. 70:332–343.

Johnson, F. S. 1954. The solar constant. J. Meteorol. 11:431–439.

List, R. J., ed. 1951. Smithsonian Meteorological Tables, 6th Revised Ed. The Smithsonian Institution, Washington, D. C.

Schulze, R. 1953. Über ein Strahlungsmessgerät mit ultrarotdurchlässiger Windschutzhaube am Meteorol. Observatorium Hamburg. Geofisica Pura e Applicata. 24:107.

Suomi, V. E., Frunsilla, M., and Islitzer, N. 1954. An improved net radiometer. J. Meteorol. 11:276–284.

Suomi, V. E., and Kuhn, P. M. 1958. An economical net radiometer. Tellus 10:160.

29 | Particle Density[1]

G. R. BLAKE
University of Minnesota
St. Paul, Minnesota

29–1 INTRODUCTION

Particle density of soils refers to the density of the solid particles collectively. It is expressed as the ratio of the total mass of the solid particles to their total volume, excluding pore spaces between particles. Units used are nearly always grams per cubic centimeter (g. cm.$^{-3}$).

Particle density is used in most mathematical expressions where volume or weight of a soil sample is being considered. Thus interrelationships of porosity, bulk density, and air space, and rates of sedimentation of particles in fluids depend on particle density. Particle-size analyses that employ sedimentation rate, as well as calculations involving particle movement by wind and water, require information on particle density.

29–2 PRINCIPLES

Particle density of a soil sample is calculated from two measured quantities, namely, mass of the sample and its volume. The mass is determined by weighing, the volume by calculation from the mass and density of water (or other fluid) displaced by the sample. This method has long been in use. It is simple, direct, and accurate if done carefully.

29–3 METHOD [2]

29–3.1 Special Apparatus

A pycnometer (specific-gravity flask) is employed. A pycnometer is a glass flask fitted with a ground glass stopper that is pierced lengthwise by

---

[1] Paper No. 4949 of the Scientific Journal Series, Minnesota Agr. Exp. Sta., St. Paul.
[2] Am. Soc. Testing Mater. (1958, p. 80) and U. S. Dept. Agr. (1954, p. 122).

a capillary opening. A thermometer is sometimes an integral part of the stopper, the glass-enclosed mercury reservoir being in contact with the fluid in the flask, and the stem extending above the ground joint.

A small volumetric flask (25, 50, or 100 ml.) may be used in place of a pycnometer where the sample is large enough to compensate for the decrease in precision of measuring fluid volume.

29–3.2 Procedure

Weigh a clean, dry pycnometer in air. Add about 10 g. of air-dry soil. If a 100-ml. volumetric flask is used, add 50 g. of soil. Clean the outside and neck of the pycnometer of any soil that may have spilled during transfer. Weigh the pycnometer, including stopper, and its contents. Determine the water content of a duplicate soil sample by drying it at 105°C.

Fill the pycnometer about one-half full with distilled water, washing into the flask any soil adhering to the inside of the neck. Remove entrapped air by gentle boiling of the water for several minutes with frequent gentle agitation of the contents to prevent loss of soil by foaming.

Cool the pycnometer and its contents to room temperature, and then add enough boiled, cooled, distilled water at room temperature to fill the pycnometer. Insert the stopper, and seat it carefully. Thoroughly dry and clean the outside of the flask with a dry cloth. Weigh the pycnometer and its contents, and determine the temperature of the contents.

Finally, remove the soil from the pycnometer. Fill the pycnometer with boiled, cooled distilled water at the same temperature as before, insert the stopper, thoroughly dry the outside with a cloth, weigh the pycnometer and contents, and measure the temperature.

Calculate the particle density as follows:

$$D_p = \frac{d_w(W_s - W_a)}{(W_s - W_a) - (W_{sw} - W_w)}$$

where

d_w = density of water in grams per cubic centimeter at temperature observed,

W_s = weight of pycnometer plus soil sample corrected to oven-dry condition,

W_a = weight of pycnometer filled with air,

W_{sw} = weight of pycnometer filled with soil and water, and

W_w = weight of pycnometer filled with water at temperature observed.

29–3.3 Comments

The method is very precise if volumes and weights are carefully measured. A weighing error of 1 mg. on a 10-g. soil sample gives an error in particle density of only 0.0003 g. cm.$^{-3}$. A weighing error of 10 mg. on a 30-g. sample gives a particle density error of 0.001 g. cm.$^{-3}$. Greater errors can result from lack of precision in the volume measurement. If W_{sw} is based on a volume that exceeds the volumetric flask marking by 0.2 ml. and W_w on a volume 0.2 ml. deficient of the marking, the compounded particle density error is 0.15 g. cc.$^{-3}$ on a 40-g. sample. The analyst should check the calibration marking on the flask, as well as his ability to measure a reproducible volume by making a number of weighings of water in the flask to be used preliminary to the analysis. In addition to weight and volume errors, one must assume some error due to nonrepresentative sampling.

It has long been observed that water gives higher density values for finely divided, active powders than do weakly adsorbed, i.e., nonpolar, liquids. One of the later papers with an excellent review of previous findings is that of Gradwell (1955). For soils, density values in water are greater by 0.01 to 0.03, but densities of clay fractions may be higher by 0.1 to 0.3 in water than in other liquids such as toluene, xylene, or carbon tetrachloride. The use of special liquids for determining particle density is probably necessary for highly accurate determinations on the more active clays or clay fractions. In fine-textured soils, the error is probably 1% or less and can be disregarded for most purposes.

This method for determining particle density does not give the average density of the particles because soils do not contain equal masses of particles of all densities represented. Rather, the values obtained are weighted with respect to the relative masses of the particles having the different densities. Day,[3] in pointing out this ambiguity, suggests that "harmonic mean particle density" might be a more specific designation than particle density.

The method is not suitable for determining the density of individual soil grains. Density of large particles, weighing at least 1 g., may be determined by weighing the suspended particle in air and when immersed in a fluid as described for bulk samples (section 30–4). Special balances, such as the Jolly balance or the Westphal balance, are designed for this purpose, and are widely used by geologists and mineralogists.

---

[3] Day, P. R. Personal communication.

29–4 LITERATURE CITED

American Society for Testing and Materials. 1958. Procedures for testing soils. Am. Soc. Testing Mater. Philadelphia.

Gradwell, M. W. 1955. The determination of specific gravities of soils as influenced by clay-mineral composition. N. Z. J. Sci. Tech. 37B:283–289.

U. S. Department of Agriculture. 1954. Diagnosis and improvement of saline and alkali soils. USDA Handbook 60.

30 | Bulk Density [1]

G. R. BLAKE

University of Minnesota
St. Paul, Minnesota

30–1 GENERAL INTRODUCTION

Soil bulk density D_b is the ratio of the mass to the bulk or macroscopic volume of soil particles plus pore spaces in a sample. The mass is determined after drying to constant weight at 105°C., and the volume is that of the sample as taken in the field.

Bulk density is a widely used value. It is needed for converting water percentage by weight to content by volume, for calculating porosity when the particle density is known, and for estimating the weight of a volume of soil too large to weigh conveniently, such as the weight of a furrow slice, or an acre-foot.

Bulk density is not an invariant quantity for a given soil. It varies with structural condition of the soil, particularly that related to packing. For this reason it is often used as a measure of soil structure.

The clod method, core method, and excavation method consist essentially of drying and weighing a known volume of soil. These methods differ principally in the way the sample of soil is obtained. A different principle is employed with the radiation method. Transmitted or scattered gamma radiation is measured; and, with suitable calibration, the density of the combined liquid-solid components of a soil mass is determined. Correction is then necessary to remove the component of density attributable to liquid that is present. The radiation method is an *in situ* method.

Clod and core methods have been used for many years. Excavation methods were developed in recent years, chiefly by soil engineers. Radiation methods are relatively new, having been developed since 1950.

In most agricultural soils work, bulk density is expressed in grams per cubic centimeter (g. cm.$^{-3}$). In these units volume weight is equal, and bulk specific gravity (or apparent specific gravity) is nearly equal, numerically, to bulk density. The term bulk density is preferred over the terms

[1] Paper No. 4433 of the Scientific Journal Series, Minnesota Agr. Exp. Sta., St. Paul.

volume weight, bulk specific gravity or apparent specific gravity. Because of its definition, in terms of mass rather than weight, it has universal applicability, and conforms more closely to accepted physical terminology than does volume weight. Specific gravity terms are relative terms, being the ratio of the mass of a dry bulk volume of soil to the mass of an equal volume of water. Since the mass of water per unit volume varies with temperature, bulk specific gravity varies numerically with the temperature at which the measurement is made.

In many engineering applications, bulk density is expressed in pounds per cubic foot. One may convert from g. cm.$^{-3}$ to lb. ft.$^{-3}$ by multiplying by 62.4, the mass, in pounds, of a cubic foot of water at the temperature of its maximum density, i.e., 4°C.

30–2 CORE METHOD

30–2.1 Introduction

With this method, a cylindrical metal sampler is pressed or driven into the soil to the desired depth and is carefully removed to preserve a known volume of sample as it existed *in situ*. The sample is dried to 105°C. and weighed. Bulk density is the oven-dried mass divided by the field volume of the sample.

The core method is usually unsatisfactory if more than an occasional stone is present in the soil.

30–2.2 Method [2]

30–2.2.1 SPECIAL APPARATUS

Core samplers vary in design from a thin-walled metal cylinder to a cylindrical sleeve with removable sample cylinders that fit inside. A widely used and very satisfactory sampler consists of two cylinders fitted one inside the other. The outer one extends above and below the inner to accept a hammer or press at the upper end and to form a cutting edge at the lower. The inside cylinder is the sample holder. The inside diameters of the two cylinders when nested are essentially the same at the lower end, the inner being fitted against a shoulder cut on the inner surface of the outside cylinder. Figure 30–1 shows such a sampler (available in slightly different design from the Utah Scientific Research Foundation, Utah State University Campus, Logan, Utah).

---

[2] U. S. Dept. Agr. (1950, p. 121), Russell (1949), and Am. Soc. Testing Mater. (1958, p. 442).

Fig. 30–1. Typical double-cylinder, hammer-driven core sampler for obtaining soil samples for bulk density.

Numerous samplers have been described in the literature. Some of the more recent and accessible ones are described by Lutz (1947), Jamison et al. (1950), Baver (1956, p. 181), and U. S. Dept. Agr. (1954, p. 159).

30–2.2.2 PROCEDURE

The exact procedure for obtaining the samples depends on the kind of sampler used. The following steps apply when the widely known double-cylinder sampler is used.

Drive or press the sampler into either a vertical or horizontal soil surface far enough to fill the sampler, but not so far as to compress the soil in the confined space of the sampler. Carefully remove the sampler and its contents so as to preserve the natural structure and packing of the soil as nearly as possible. A shovel, alongside and under the sampler, may be needed in some soils to remove the sample without disturbance. Separate the two cylinders, retaining the undisturbed soil in the inner cylinder. Trim the soil extending beyond each end of the sample holder (inner cylinder) flush with each end with a straight-edged knife or sharp spatula. The soil sample volume is thus established to be the same as the volume of the sample holder. In some sampler designs, the cutting edge of the sampler has an inside diameter slightly less than the sample holder, so as to reduce friction as the soil enters the holder. In these cases, determine the diameter of the cutting head and use this to calculate the sample holder volume. Transfer the soil to a container, place it in an oven at 105°C. until constant weight is reached, and weigh it. The bulk density is the oven-dry mass of the sample divided by the sample volume.

30–2.2.3 COMMENTS

It is often desired to make other measurements on the same samples taken for bulk density. Water content determinations, like bulk density, do not require that the soil be kept undisturbed during transport to the laboratory and drying. They do require a wet weight, however, so that the samples must be transported from field to laboratory in containers that do not permit loss of water. One-pint cylindrical waxed-paper cartons with lids will receive the 3-inch-diameter, 3-inch-long cylinders, and serve very well to transport the sample with almost no loss of water. Some studies, such as pore-size distribution, require that the sample be maintained as free of disturbance as possible.

Core samples should not be taken in wet or dry soils. In wet soils, friction along the sides of the sampler and vibrations due to hammering are likely to result in viscous flow of the soil and thus in compression of the sample. When this occurs the sample obtained is unrepresentative, being more dense than the body of the soil. Compression may occur even in dry soils if they are very loose. Whenever a sample is taken, one should carefully observe whether the soil elevation inside the sampler is the same as the undisturbed surface outside the sampler. One can only roughly estimate in this manner whether the density of the sample is changing because of sampling.

In dry or hard soils, another problem arises. Hammering the sampler into the soil often shatters the sample, and an actual loosening during sampling may occur. Samplers pressed into the soil usually avoid the vibration which causes this shattering. Close examination of the soil sample usually allows one to estimate whether serious shattering occurs. And, as in the case of wet soils, soil level inside and outside the sampler must remain the same if the sample is to be considered satisfactory.

30–3 EXCAVATION METHOD

30–3.1 Introduction

Bulk density is determined in this method by excavating a quantity of soil, drying and weighing the soil, and determining the volume of the excavation. The volume is determined, in the sand-funnel method, by filling the hole with sand, of which the volume per unit mass is known. The vol-

Fig. 30–2. Apparatus for sand-funnel technique of determining soil bulk density in place.

ume is determined, in the rubber-balloon method, by inserting a balloon into the excavation and by filling it with water, or other fluid, until the excavation is just full. The volume of the excavated soil sample is then equal to the volume of the fluid dispensed.

Excavation methods were developed by soil engineers who required a method suitable for use in gravelly soil. This is the chief advantage of the sand-funnel and rubber-balloon methods over the core method. Soil that is removed for drying is disturbed, precluding its use for other measurements, such as pore-size distribution, where undisturbed structure is necessary. Also, in contrast to the core method, determinations cannot be made vertically into the walls of a pit, as is sometimes desirable where anisotropy is to be measured.

30–3.2   Method [3]

30–3.2.1   SPECIAL APPARATUS

30–3.2.1.1   Sand-Funnel Apparatus[4] (see Fig. 30–2).

1. A metal funnel 15 to 18 cm. at its largest diameter, fitted with a valve on the stem. Attached to the stem, when the funnel is inverted, is a sand container.

---

[3] Am. Soc. Testing Mater. (1958, pp. 422–441).
[4] This apparatus can be purchased from Soiltest, Inc.. 2205 Lee Street, Evanston, Ill.

2. A standard sand that is clean, dry, and free-flowing. Particle size should be fairly uniform to avoid possible separation in the dispenser with consequent error in calibration. Sand particles passing a No. 20 and retained on a No. 60 sieve are recommended.

3. A template, consisting of a thin, flat, metal plate approximately 30-cm. square, with a hole 10 to 12 cm. in diameter in its center.

4. Scales to weigh to 5 g.

30–3.2.1.2 Rubber-Balloon Apparatus.

1. A thin-walled rubber balloon (may be purchased from Barr Rubber Co., Sandusky, Ohio, and the Anderson Rubber Co., Akron, Ohio).

2. A 1,000-cc. graduated cylinder, and a water container.

3. A template, described in 3 above.

Rubber-balloon density apparatus is available from several manufacturers supplying soil testing equipment (one supplier is Soiltest, Inc., 2205 Lee Street, Evanston, Ill.). The apparatus made commercially has the convenience of a volumetrically calibrated water container-dispenser, with suction facilities for returning the water to the container for re-use (see Fig. 30–3).

Fig. 30–3. Apparatus for determining soil bulk density in place by the rubber-balloon technique.

30–3.2.2 PROCEDURE

Level the soil surface, and remove loose soil at the test site. Place the template on the soil. Excavate a soil sample, through the center hole of the template, leaving a hole with a diameter of approximately 12 cm. and a depth of approximately 12 cm., or other value as desired. A large spoon is convenient for excavating. Recover all excavated soil in a container, being careful to include any loose soil that has fallen in from the sides of the excavation. Determine the oven-dry soil mass by drying it to 105°C. and weighing it.

Determine the volume of the test hole in one of two ways:

30–3.2.2.1   Sand-Funnel Procedure.   Fill the hole with the sand even with the bottom of the template. Level the sand at the bottom of the template with a spatula if necessary, but disturb it as little as possible to avoid packing the free-flowing sand. (Dispensing the sand through a funnel placed on the template, as is done with commercially available equipment, avoids the problem of leveling the sand. The excavation, as well as the funnel, is filled by free flow of sand, the predetermined weight required to fill the funnel being subtracted as a tare.)

Determine the weight of sand required to fill the test excavation by weighing it to the nearest 5 g. Precalibrate the mass to volume of sand with sand falling at a similar height and rate of flow as in the test procedure. Using the calibration curve, or values derived from it, determine the volume of the excavation from the measured mass of sand dispensed.

30–3.2.2.2   Rubber-Balloon Procedure.   Place the rubber balloon in the test hole, and fill the balloon with water to the bottom of the template. Determine the volume of water required to the nearest 2 cc. (A 1,000-cc. graduate has markings to 10 cc., but one can estimate to 2 cc. if the graduate is placed on a horizontal surface.)

Calculate bulk density from the oven-dry mass of the excavated sample and the volume of the test excavation.

30–3.2.3   Comments

Bulk density can be estimated accurately by excavation methods carried out carefully. The relatively large sample (a cylinder of 12-cm. diameter and of 12-cm. depth has a volume of 1,357 cc.) is at once an advantage and a disadvantage. The disadvantage is the lack of discrimination to a localized horizon. The advantage is that small errors in measuring water volumes or sand weights result in insignificant errors.

An error of 5 cc. in liquid volume will give an error of 0.005 in a sample having a bulk density of 1.36 g. cm.$^{-3}$. Though one determines the water dispensed to perhaps 2 cc., a much greater source of error in water measurement arises in determining when the water in the excavation is level with the bottom of the template. Extreme care and judgment are required in this. The volume of the balloon itself, being of the order of 2 cc., will give a considerably smaller error than the volume measurement, and can be neglected.

An error in weighing the sand of 7 g. gives an error of 0.005 if the bulk density is 1.36 g. cm.$^{-3}$. As in the balloon technique, greater error is likely to result in the precision with which one can determine the sand level at the bottom of the template. An error of 1 mm. in this level will result in an error of 0.01 in the bulk density. Extreme care is therefore required to obtain the sand level at the template bottom. The need for the dispensing funnel in reducing this error is obvious.

A comparison of the sand funnel and radiation methods was made by Mintzer (1961), and the results are summarized in Table 30–1.

30–4 CLOD METHOD

30–4.1 Introduction

The bulk density of clods, or coarse peds, can be calculated from their mass and volume. The volume may be determined by coating the clod with a water-repellent substance and by weighing it first in air, then again while immersed in a liquid of known density, making use of Archimedes' principle. The clod or ped must be sufficiently stable to cohere during coating, weighing and handling.

30–4.2 Method [5]

30–4.2.1 SPECIAL APPARATUS

1. A balance, modified to accept a container basket for the sample, the basket being attached to the balance lever arm by a thin wire to allow weighing a sample when it is immersed in a container of liquid.
2. A coarse-mesh wire pan or basket to contain the sample while it is being dipped in a water-repellent substance and while it is being weighed. Thin wire mesh, 1 to 2 meshes per inch, will keep the amount of repellent held by the basket to a low value, particularly along the line of contact with the clod. Attach the basket to the balance arm with a single strand of thin wire to keep at a small value the difference in container buoyancy in case of a slightly variable immersion depth from one sample to another.
3. Paraffin in a container kept at, or a few degrees above, 60°C. into which the soil sample contained in the wire basket can be dipped.

30–4.2.2 PROCEDURE

Air-dry the clod or ped on which measurements are to be made. Place it in the wire basket, and weigh it suspended in air. Dip the clod and container momentarily in melted paraffin, and allow the excess to drain. When the adhering paraffin solidifies, weigh the clod, paraffin, and container together. Suspend the system in water, and weigh it again. Determine the tare weight of the basket in air and in water, since its weight will, of course, differ in the two fluids. To obtain a correction for water content of the soil,

---

[5] Since the first printing of this Monograph, superior coating materials have been developed which, if used, will alter the method somewhat. See Brasher et al. (1966) and Abrol and Palta (1968).

break open the clod, remove a sample of soil, and weigh the sample before and after drying it at 105°C.

Calculate the oven-dry mass of the soil sample W_{ods} from the subsample that is removed from the clod after other weights are taken as follows:

$$W_{ods} = \frac{W_{sa}}{1 + (P/100)}$$

where

P = percent water, on an oven-dry basis, found in the subsample, and
W_{sa} = net weight of soil clod or ped in air.

Calculate bulk density as follows:

$$D_b = d_w W_{ods} / [W_{sa} - W_{spw} + W_{pa} - (W_{pa}d_w/d_p)]$$

where

d_w = density of water at temperature of determination,
W_{ods} = oven-dry weight of soil sample (clod or ped),
W_{spw} = net weight of soil sample plus paraffin in water,
W_{pa} = weight of paraffin coating in air, and
d_p = density of paraffin (approximately 0.9).

30–4.2.3 COMMENTS

The clod method usually gives higher bulk-density values than do other methods (see Tisdall, 1951). One reason is that the clod method does not take the inter-clod spaces into account. A second reason is that the soil volume is the air-dry volume, which is likely to be slightly less than the volume of a field-moist sample used in other methods.

Extreme care should be exercised to get naturally occurring masses of soil. Clods on or near the soil surface are likely to be unrepresentative, for these are often formed by packing with tillage implements. Natural soil masses, or coarse peds, that are more representative should be sought.

If bubbles appear on the paraffin when the sample is weighed in water, or if the weight in water increases with time, water is penetrating the clod, and the sample must be discarded.

Parafin is best used between 60° and 70°C., a few degrees above the melting point, when clods are dipped. At this temperature, it quickly solidifies upon removal of the clod and is less likely to penetrate the pores of the clod than at higher temperatures. Furthermore, at higher temperatures, pin-sized air leaks through the paraffin seal are more likely because of penetration of heat into the clod with consequent expansion of soil gases that continues after surface solidification of the paraffin.

Several other substances have been used as water seals, including collodion, wax mixtures, oils, and synthetic resins. The claimed advantage of these over paraffin is that a thin film that does not appreciably change the clod volume can be applied, thus avoiding the uncertainty of a correction (see Russell and Balcerek, 1944).

30–5 RADIATION METHODS

30–5.1 Introduction

The transmission of gamma radiation through soil or scattering within soil varies with soil properties, including bulk density. By suitable calibration, measurements of either transmission or scattering of gamma radiation can be used to estimate bulk density.

In the transmission technique, two probes at a fixed spacing are lowered into previously prepared openings in the soil. One probe contains a Geiger tube, which detects the radiation transmitted through the soil from the gamma source, located in the second probe. The scattering technique employs a single probe containing both gamma source and detector separated by shielding in the probe. It can be used either at the soil surface or placed in a hole, depending on design of the equipment.

Radiation methods have several advantages, among which are minimum disturbance of the soil, short time required for sampling, accessibility to subsoil measurement with minimum excavation, and the possibility of continuous or repeated measurements at the same point.

The transmission or double-probe technique has the advantage of confining the sample to a soil horizon a few centimeters in vertical dimension between the probes. The single probe used with the scattering technique sees a somewhat spherical sample varying from about 20 to 75 cm. in diameter, depending on characteristics of the sampler and the soil. Thus it is not well suited to many soils studies. The scattering technique also requires a greater source strength than the transmission technique in most prototype designs described in the literature.

Both techniques measure the bulk density of all phases combined. The densities of gaseous components are insignificant in comparison to those of the solid or liquid components, and can therefore be ignored. It is necessary, however, to determine the water content of the soil at sampling time and to apply a correction to obtain bulk density on a dry-soil basis.

30–5.2 Methods[6]

30–5.2.1 SPECIAL APPARATUS

30–5.2.1.1 Transmission Apparatus.[7]

1. Double-probe densitometer: The design may vary with the need. The

---

[6] Neville and Van Zelst (1961) and Vomocil (1954).

[7] This apparatus may be purchased from Troxler Laboratories, P.O. Box 5997, Raleigh, North Carolina.

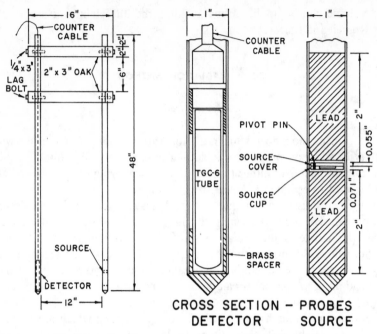

Fig. 30–4. Double-probe densitometer (Vomocil, 1954).

densitometer described by Vomocil (1954) is shown in Fig. 30–4 and is made as follows: Construct the probes using aluminum tubing with an outside diameter of 1 inch and with a wall thickness of 0.064 inch. Fasten the two probes together near one end by two 12-inch lengths of 2- by 3-inch oak wood.

As a source of radiation, use 1 millicurie of Co^{60} in the form of a length of 1-mm. wire contained in a hollow aluminum cylinder about 1.5 mm. in length and 2.1 mm. in diameter. As a lid, use a second cylinder about 0.5 mm. by 2.1 mm. attached to the first by an off-center rivet. Mount the source in one of the probes near the bottom between 2.5-inch plugs of lead. Provide shielding around the radiation source by placing the probe with the Co^{60} source through a hole bored through a lead sphere 5 inches in diameter. Fit the sphere so that it will slide along the probe when the probe is lowered into the soil. Place a stop at the bottom of the probe to prevent the lead sphere from being removed completely and to hold it in place over the Co^{60} when the densitometer is being transported.

In the other probe, mount a Geiger Mueller detector tube (a Tracerlab TGC-6 tube in a P-17 side-window shield has been found satisfactory) at the same height as the source of radiation in the first probe.

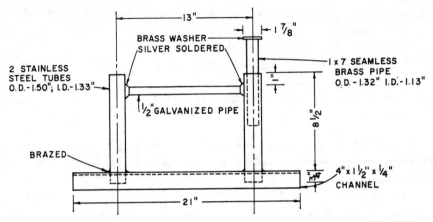

Fig. 30–5. Guide for making holes for double-probe densitometer (Vomocil, 1954).

Fit a brass spacer to the end of the side-window shield opposite the tube socket (Fig. 30–4) to provide a better fit in the probe. Attach a 10-foot length of coaxial cable to the detector tube, lead the cable out the top of the probe, and attach a fitting to the end for connection to the scaler.

2. Portable scaler.

3. Device for boring holes into soil: Prepare a guide frame as indicated in Fig. 30–5. The guide frame consists of two stainless steel tubes with a length of 10 inches, an inside diameter of 1.334 inch, and a wall thickness of 0.083 inch, welded into a piece of channel iron 4 by 1½ by ¼ by 21 inches in size. In the channel iron, bore two holes with a diameter just adequate to receive the steel tubes and with a distance of 13 inches between centers of the holes. Weld the guide tubes into these holes in such a way that the tubes are perpendicular to the surface of the channel iron and exactly parallel with each other. Allow about 1 inch of tubing to protrude in the concave side of the channel. At the ends opposite the channel iron, weld a length of ½-inch galvanized iron pipe between the tubes to aid in maintaining alignment and to serve as a carrying handle. Prepare a 7-inch piece of brass pipe with an outside diameter of 1.315 inches and an inside diameter of 1.063 inches. To the top of the pipe, solder a brass washer with an outside diameter of about 1⅞ inches and an inside diameter of 1.063 inches. This tubing fits inside of the stainless steel guide pipe and outside of the Veihmeyer soil sampling tube (available from Robert Mc-Nairn Machine Works, 1431 Second St., Sacramento, Calif.) and aids in keeping the sampling tube aligned with the guide.

4. Soil sample containers to remove samples to laboratory for water determination.

30–5.2.1.2 Scattering Apparatus.[8]

1. Single-probe, depth-density gauge, or surface-density gauge.
2. Access tube and hammer.
3. Items 2 and 4 described in section 30–5.2.1.1.

30–5.2.2 PROCEDURE

30–5.2.2.1 Transmission Procedure. Firm the parallel-guide device to the soil surface. With the Veihmeyer sampler, bore parallel holes to the desired depth in the soil. Retain a sample from 2 inches above to 2 inches below the sampling depth, and determine the water content by weight. Lower the source and detector tubes in the holes to the depth desired. Determine the count-rate. From the calibration curve prepared in the manner described in the following paragraph, convert count rate to wet bulk density D_{bw}, i.e., bulk density of liquid plus solid soil components. Convert wet bulk density to the commonly used dry bulk density, i.e., bulk density of soil on a dry weight basis, as follows:

$$D_b = D_{bw} - D_w \qquad [1]$$

where

D_{bw} = wet bulk density, and
D_w = bulk density of water in sample.

Now

$$D_w = d_w V_w / V_s, \text{ and}$$
$$P_w/100 = d_w V_w / D_b V_s.$$

Therefore,

$$D_w = P_w D_b / 100 \qquad [2]$$

where

d_w = density of water,
V_w and V_s = volume of water and bulk volume of soil, respectively, and
P_w = percent water by weight.

Substituting [2] into [1] and simplifying gives

$$D_b = D_{bw}/(1 + \text{percent } H_2O \text{ by weight}/100) .$$

To calibrate the instrument, determine the count-rate obtained with a number of soils selected to cover the range to be encountered in practice. Immediately after recording the count-rate, measure the wet bulk density of the soil between the source and the detector by means of the core method in section 30–2. Plot the logarithm of the count-rate against the wet bulk

---

[8] This apparatus may be purchased from Nuclear Chicago Corp., 333 East Howard St., Des Plaines, Ill., or from Troxler Laboratories, P.O. Box 5997, Raleigh, North Carolina.

density to obtain a calibration curve. Alternatively, make the calibration using the instrument in a large tank of soil that has been compacted artificially to a desired wet bulk density, and calculate the wet bulk density from the mass and volume of wet soil. Each such measurement provides one point on the calibration curve. If a calibration curve has been supplied with the instrument, check the validity of the calibration by one of the techniques described here.

30–5.2.2.2 Scattering Procedure. Put either the surface-density gauge or the single-probe depth gauge in operation according to the manufacturer's instructions.

If the surface gauge is used, remove the dried soil surface crust and smooth an area 16 by 16 inches. Place the gauge on the soil, twisting it gently to ensure intimate contact. Measure the count-rate on the scaler according to the manufacturer's instructions. Rotate the gauge 90 degrees, and take a second reading. Divide the average count-rate by the standard count-rate obtained according to the manufacturer's instructions. If no provision is made for obtaining a standard count-rate, prepare a standard such as a waterproofed 1-foot cube of wood, and measure the count-rate when the gauge is placed on it in a reproducible position. Make counts in the standard position as frequently as needed to provide the appropriate value for the standard count-rate. By means of a calibration curve described below, find the wet bulk density. To find the dry bulk density, measure the water percentage on a volume basis in the surface 6 inches of soil directly below the gauge. Then correct the wet bulk density to bulk density on a dry-soil basis as previously described in section 30–5.2.2.1 for the transmission procedure.

To prepare a calibration curve, make measurements as described in the preceding paragraph using selected soil materials compacted uniformly to a depth of 12 inches or more. Measure the wet bulk density of each material at the site of measurement using the sand-funnel method of section 30–3.2.2.1. Plot the ratio of the count-rate with the given soil material to the standard count-rate against the wet bulk density measured by the sand-funnel method. The points plotted in this way form the calibration curve.

When using the single-probe depth gauge, drive the access tube into the soil to the desired depth. Place the gauge in its carrying shield on top of the access tube. Lower the probe to the desired depth. Measure the count-rate according to the manufacturer's instructions. When measurements are complete, raise the gamma source into its carrying shield. Divide the count-rate by the standard count-rate obtained according to the manufacturer's instructions. If no instructions are given for obtaining a standard count-rate, use the count-rate obtained where the probe has been retracted into the carrying shield, unless this results in numerical values that differ by a factor of five or more from the count rate obtained with the probe in soil. Under the latter circumstances, prepare a standard source in the form of a cylinder of waterproofed wood about 1 foot in diameter and height. Provide an access pipe that will permit repeated positioning of the probe in precisely the same place in approximately the center of the cylinder. By means of a calibration curve described in the following paragraph, find the wet bulk density. To find the dry bulk density, measure the water percentage on a volume basis in the soil surrounding the site of measurement, and make the calculation as described in section 30–5.2.2.1.

To prepare a calibration curve, use soil materials that have been packed uniformly to the desired bulk density to a depth of 2 feet or more. Obtain preliminary counts with the probe at different depths to make certain that measurements will be taken within a zone that is uniform vertically, or use depths in natural soils where the bulk density remains essentially the same for distances of 4 inches or more above and below the source and detector in the probe. Then measure the count-rate with the probe located in the uniform portion. Following the counting, take say five core samples at the depth of the probe and at a distance 2 to 4 inches from the probe using the method of section 30–2. Weigh these samples in their initial moist condition and calculate the wet bulk density from the weight and volume of the cores. Average the values from all cores.

30–5.2.3 COMMENTS

There is radiation hazard with this method. Gamma photons are high-energy radiation. Some will pass through several centimeters of lead shielding. Commercially available equipment, as well as designs described in the literature, reduce the hazard to safe levels. But it is important to adhere strictly to time limits, distances, and other conditions described by the manufacturers. One should be equipped and knowledgeable in means of checking the equipment for radiation levels according to the way it is handled in actual sampling. If there is doubt, the equipment should be checked for safety by a competent testing laboratory. It is also recommended that film badges be worn regularly by users as an added safety check.

The user must be somewhat familiar with electronic equipment and factors that might affect its normal performance. Checking the calibration should be carried out at each sampling, or several times in a day if the equipment is in continuous use, according to instructions of the manufacturer.

The transmittancy method, using a double probe, is superior in profile discrimination, and is therefore more likely to be useful in most soils work. The method suffers, however, from lack of a supplier. There are numerous details to consider in design and selection of equipment for this method. These are discussed in a rather extensive literature, of which the most pertinent references are those by Goldberg et al. (1955), Van Bavel et al. (1957), and Vomocil (1954).

Table 30–1. Comparison of surface nuclear gauge and sand-cone method for determining soil bulk density (Mintzer, 1961).

Soil material	Number of comparisons	Mean difference	Extreme difference
		%*	%
Wet bulk density, D_{bw}			
Brown sand, trace silt	9	2.03	-0.25 to 4.28
Brown silt and clay	4	0.89	-0.64 to 1.87
Brown sand and gravel some silt, trace clay	6	1.01	-2.27 to 7.75
Brown till	4	-1.19	-3.97 to 1.60
Dry bulk density, D_b			
Brown sand, trace silt	9	2.05	-1.21 to 4.98
Brown silt and clay	4	7.21	5.51 to 9.27
Brown sand and gravel some silt, trace clay	6	1.48	-1.71 to 8.32
Brown till	4	-0.38	-4.53 to 3.21

* A positive value indicates nuclear method gave higher bulk density value.

Since radiation transmitted from a source to a detector is dependent on probe spacing, or sample thickness, care must be exercised with the two-probe sampler to assure that access holes are parallel and spaced exactly as in the calibration.

Ideally when radiation methods are used, soil water content will be determined with a neutron meter (see section 7–3.3), obviating the need to remove a sample for water. The neutron gauge is calibrated to percent water on a volume basis, however, and so the correction to bulk density on a dry soil basis is made a little differently:

Let

$$D_b = D_{bw} - D_w$$

where

D_{bw} = wet bulk density, and
D_w = bulk density of water in sample.
But,

$$D_w = d_w S_w$$

where

d_w = density of water at temperature of observation (assuming a density of 1 gives a negligible error at ordinary temperatures), and
S_w = fraction of soil volume occupied by water determined from a neutron count-rate and a calibration curve of count-rate versus volume-fraction of water.

Mintzer (1961) reported comparisons of the surface-density probe and the sand-cone method on four engineering projects. He reported his com-

parisons on both the wet and dry bulk-density bases. He used a surface
neutron meter for water content where the surface-density probe was used.
His results are summarized in Table 30–1.

30–6 LITERATURE CITED

Abrol, I. P., and Palta, J. P. 1968. Bulk density determination of soil clods using
rubber solution as a coating material. Soil Sci. 106:465–468.
American Society for Testing and Materials. 1958. Procedures for Testing Soils.
Am. Soc. Testing Mater., Philadelphia.
Baver, L. D. 1956. Soil Physics. Ed. 3. John Wiley and Sons, Inc., New York.
Brasher, B. R., Franzmeier, D. P., Valassis, V., and Davidson, S. E. 1966. Use of
Saran Resin to coat natural soil clods for bulk density and moisture retention
measurements. Soil Sci. 101:108.
Goldberg, I., Trescony, L. J., Campbell, J. S., Jr., and Whyte, G. J. 1955. Measure-
ment of moisture content and density of soil masses using radioactivity methods.
Natl. Conf. on Clays and Clay Minerals, Proc. 3:516–548.
Jamison, V. C., Weaver, H. H., and Reed, I. F. 1950. A hammer-driven soil core
sampler. Soil Sci. 69:487–496.
Lutz, J. F. 1947. Apparatus for collecting undisturbed soil samples. Soil Sci. 64:399–
401.
Mintzer, S. 1961. Comparison of nuclear and sand-cone methods of density and
moisture determinations for four New York State soils. *In* Symposium on nuclear
methods for measuring soil density and moisture. Am. Soc. Testing Mater., Spec.
Tech. Publ. 293:45–54.
Neville, O. K., and Van Zelst, T. W. 1961. Design and application of the Nuclear-
Chicago d/M-Gauge. *In* Symposium on nuclear methods for measuring soil density
and moisture. Am. Soc. Testing Mater., Spec. Tech. Publ. 293:3–8.
Russell, E. W., and Balcerek, W. 1944. The determination of the volume and air
space of soil clods. J. Agr. Sci. 34:123–132.
Russell, M. B. 1949. Methods of measuring soil structure and aeration. Soil Sci.
68:25–35.
Tisdall, A. L. 1951. Comparison of methods of determining apparent density of soils.
Australian J. Agr. Res. 2:349–354.
U. S. Department of Agriculture. 1954. Diagnosis and improvement of saline and
alkali soils. USDA Handbook 60.
Van Bavel, C. H. M., Underwood, N., and Ragar, S. R. 1957. Transmission of gamma
radiation by soils and soil densitometry. Soil Sci. Soc. Am. Proc. 21:588–591.
Vomocil, J. A. 1954. *In situ* measurement of soil bulk density. Agr. Eng. 35:651–
654.

31 Consistency

GEORGE F. SOWERS

Georgia Institute of Technology
Atlanta, Georgia

31–1 INTRODUCTION

The consistency limits, also termed the Atterberg limits, are indexes of the workability or firmness of artificial mixtures of soil and water as affected by the content of water in the mixture. The limits are defined by the water contents required to produce specified degrees of consistency that are measured in the laboratory.

The liquid limit or upper plastic limit is the point at which soil becomes semifluid, like softened butter. In operational terms, the liquid limit is defined as the water content at which a trapezoidal groove of specified shape cut in moist soil held in a special cup is closed after 25 taps on a hard rubber plate (Am. Soc. Test. Mater. Committee D-18, 1958). The soil in the cup is 1 cm. deep; the groove is 2 mm. wide at the bottom, and slopes outward at a 60-degree angle with the horizontal. The soil in the walls of the groove flows under the impact of the cup on the hard base, closing the groove. In reality, it is a crude shear test. Norman (1958) found strengths of from 0.11 to 0.32 pound per square inch for soils at the liquid limit. Other forms of shear tests have been employed for measuring the liquid limit. The cone penetration test (Sowers et al., 1960) defines the limit by means of a 30-degree cone weighing 75 g. that penetrates the soil a distance of 1 cm. The cone point is suspended in contact with the soil and then permitted to fall slowly so that its momentum does not affect the penetration. This method is simple and is not as sensitive to operator technique and equipment variations as the cup-and-groove method.

The plastic limit or lower plastic limit is defined as the water content at which soil begins to crumble on being rolled into a thread ⅛ inch or 3 mm. in diameter. It represents the lowest water content at which soil can be deformed readily without cracking. It does not imply a certain firmness or shear strength. Some soils are weak and spongy at the plastic limit while others are stiff.

The plastic index (which is the difference between the liquid and plastic limits) gives an indication of the "clayeyness" or plasticity of a clay and is widely employed in engineering classification systems for soils (Casagrande, 1948).

The sticky limit is the water content at which soil no longer sticks to a steel spatula drawn over its surface. The minimum value of the sticky limit occurs in fine sands containing no clay and is about 16, which is just sufficient water for saturation. The sticky limit and the liquid limit are often nearly the same.

These limits were first described by the Swedish soil scientist Atterberg (1911a, 1911b), who developed them to measure the plasticity of clays. Since that time they have found use in agriculture and engineering for measuring the water-holding properties of fine-grained soils. They are employed in most engineering classification systems for soils, and for describing quantitatively the plasticity of clays. They have also been found to be related to some of the important engineering properties of clays such as shrinking, swelling, compressibility, permeability, strength, and water content required for workability in construction. Although all the relationships which involve these limits are empirical, they are valuable in predicting soil behavior when more exacting data are not available. Further reading on this subject will be found in papers by Lambe (1953, 1958, 1959), Grim (1959), Rosenqvist (1959), Sowers (1961), and Seed et al. (1964).

31–2   PRINCIPLES

Current concepts of the status of water in soil provide some insight into the physical basis for soil consistency phenomena. Water in a soil may exist as "free" bulk water or as adsorbed water on the particle surfaces. The adsorbed water is attracted to the particle surfaces in one or more of several possible ways. A layer of water molecules may be hydrogen-bonded to the surface oxygens. This layer, in turn, may be hydrogen-bonded to a second layer and so forth until, by relayed action, a coherent water structure may be propagated outward from the surface. It is possible also that the water molecules, being dipolar in nature, have their positive ends directed toward the negative charge sites on the mineral surfaces to form bonds similar to ion-dipole bonds. Additional layers of water molecules may then be bonded to the first layer and to each other by dipole-dipole bonds. Or, the possibility exists that the successive layers of water molecules are attracted to the mineral surfaces by long-range van der Waals' forces.

Undoubtedly, the exchangeable ions play a role in water adsorption. When the soil is very dry these ions hydrate and, thereby, hold water in the vicinity of the particle surfaces. Then, as the soil becomes moist, the exchangeable ions dissociate somewhat and attract water osmotically; that is, the water tends to move into the region of the particle surfaces because the ionic concentration is greatest there. Highly dissociated cations such as sodium increase the liquid limit and, to some extent, the plastic limit. Less dissociated cations, such as calcium and some large organic cations, decrease them.

The adsorbed water in a soil has unusual physical properties. One of these is its great coherence or viscosity. Near the particle surfaces the viscosity of the water may be similar to that of ice. With increasing distance from these surfaces, the viscosity of the water decreases until it equals that of "free" bulk water. The distance over which this decrease occurs is unknown, but it is probably equal to many molecular diameters.

The highly viscous nature of the adsorbed water may play a role in soil plasticity. If the particles of a soil were in direct contact, the soil would be difficult to deform or shear. And, unless its yield point were exceeded, it would recover its original size and shape after a slight deformation. In other words, it would act like an elastic body. But a soil, especially one with a high clay content, is plastic above a certain water content; that is, it can be permanently deformed under stress without breaking or cracking. This fact suggests that the soil particles are separated by thin films of highly viscous water which creep or flow slowly under stress. However, it is not inferred that the strength of a soil is due entirely to the resistance of the adsorbed water to creep or flow. It is likely that attractive forces between the particles are involved also. These attractive forces would operate to prevent the relative movement of adjacent soil particles whether the particles be in direct contact or separated by water films.

The nature of the attractive forces is unknown. However, there is evidence which indicates that the edges of clay particles are positively charged. Therefore, Coulomb attraction could exist between the positive edges and the negative, planar surfaces of adjacent particles. Such an attraction would give rise to a card-house arrangement of particles. Another attractive force could be the Coulomb force between negative planar surfaces and intermediate cations. In other words, the cations may act as "bridges" which hold the negative surfaces together. Organic molecules bonded to each surface may also act as bridges. Finally, van der Waals' attractive forces may exist between the particles.

It was mentioned earlier that the viscosity of the adsorbed water decreases with distance from the mineral surfaces. Consequently, as the water content of a soil is increased and the water films separating the soil particles become thicker, the water should be less resistant to flow or creep. In addition, the attractive forces between the particles, which are inversely related to the distance of separation, should decrease. Thus, at low water contents the soil particles are in contact, and the soil tends to be elastic. As the water content increases, water is adsorbed between the particles, and the soil, especially one with a high clay content, becomes plastic. The water content at which plasticity becomes apparent is the plastic limit or lower plastic limit. When the water films are so thick that the outermost water layers have nearly normal viscosity and the interparticle attractive forces are negligible, the soil will flow under a slight stress. The water content at which this occurs is the liquid limit or upper plastic limit.

Several factors other than the clay minerals and their exchangeable ions influence the consistency limits. These include porous grains, organic matter, and drying. Porous grains increase all three limits by the amount of water absorbed. Fibrous organic particles absorb water and have the same effect as the porous grains. Drying affects all three limits, but particularly the liquid limit. In most clays, drying at 105°C. reduces both the liquid limit and plastic limit proportionally. In some clays, such as those containing halloysite or members of the montmorillonite group, drying has profound and often unpredictable effects on the consistency limits.

31–3   METHOD [1]

31–3.1   Special Apparatus

1. Mortar with rubber-covered pestle for grinding soil sample.
2. Liquid limit device (see Fig. 31–1).[2]

31–3.2   Sample Preparation

Obtain a representative sample of the soil weighing approximately 200 g. for all three tests. Preferably the sample should be at its natural water content. If the sample is to be dried before use, dry it slowly in air at a temperature no greater than 110°F. (43°C.). If the sample is moist, remove all particles larger than 1/16 inch by hand. If it is air-dried, pulverize the sample in a mortar with a rubber-covered pestle. Pass the pulverized soil through a No. 40 sieve to remove the coarse particles.

Mix the sample thoroughly with distilled water to form a stiff paste. If it was moist initially, it may be tested immediately. If the sample was dry initially, allow it to condition in a covered container for 12 hours or more before testing.

31–3.3   Liquid-Limit Procedure

(1) Clean the liquid-limit device so that the cup drops freely and so that no soil cushions the contact between the cup and the base. Raise the

---

[1] Am. Soc. Testing Mater. (1968).

[2] Detailed working drawings for this liquid limit device are available at a nominal cost from the American Society for Testing and Materials, 1916 Race St., Philadelphia 3, Pa.

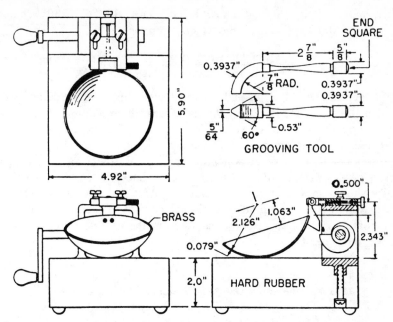

Fig. 31–1. Mechanical liquid-limit device (ASTM Committee D-18, 1958).

cup to its maximum height by rotating the cam. Insert a 1-cm. gauge block (usually the handle of the grooving tool) between the point of contact of the cup and the base. This contact point is not the lowest point of the cup, but instead is denoted by a bright, worn spot. Adjust the height to 1 cm. if necessary. Check this height regularly because it changes with wear and any abuse of the device.

(2) Mix about 100 g. of the stiff paste thoroughly with enough distilled water to give the sample the consistency of soft putty. Place about 30 ml. of soil in the cup, and smooth the surface level with the front of the cup to form a pat that is 1 cm. thick above the point of contact as shown in Fig. 31–2A. After cutting the groove, remove any soil along the walls of the groove more than 1 cm. above the cup bottom. The groove should be as shown in Fig. 31–2A and 31–2C (in some highly micaceous soils, it may be necessary to cut the groove with a sharp knife).

(3) Turn the crank at 2 revolutions per second. Record the number of taps of the cup required to cause the soil to flow together and obscure the bottom of the groove for a distance of ½ inch as shown in Fig. 31–2D.

(4) Remix the soil in the cup. Form a new groove, and repeat step 3. If the number of blows is within 1 or 2 of the value obtained previously, and is more than 12 and less than 38, consider the determination valid.

(5) Remove about 10 g. of the portion of the soil which flowed to-

gether, and weigh it to 0.01 g. Dry it in an oven at 110°C. (230°F.) and reweigh it to 0.01 g. Calculate the water percentage w by

$$w = \frac{\text{weight lost on drying}}{\text{weight of soil after drying}} \times 100 \,.$$

(6) Repeat steps 2, 3, 4, and 5 two or more times after adding more of either the stiff paste or water, so that at least three different determinations are obtained in the range of blows between 12 and 38, with some above and below the required 25 of the liquid limit.

(7) Plot a flow curve of water content against the logarithm of the number of blows. Draw the best-fitting straight line through the test points (which should show a decrease in water content with increasing blows).

(8) Report the liquid limit as the water content of the flow curve that corresponds to 25 blows. Report the value to the nearest whole number, omitting the percent sign.

31–3.4   Alternative One-Point Procedure for Liquid Limit

(1) Follow steps 1 through 5 as described in Section 31–3.3 for the liquid limit. The number of blows must lie between 18 and 32. Repeat the steps with the same soil. If the numbers of blows required do not differ by more than 1, the determination is valid; if the difference exceeds 1 blow, repeat the five steps until two consecutive tests yield blows within 1 of each other.

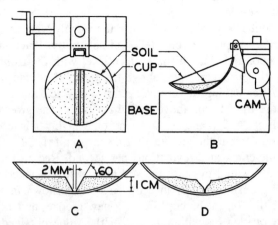

Fig. 31–2. Liquid-limit test: *A*. Plan view of device with groove cut in soil in cup. *B*. Cross section of device with soil in cup. *C*. Cross section of cup with soil and groove. *D*. Cross section of cup showing groove after closing.

Table 31–1. Values of $(N/25)^{0.12}$ corresponding to different values of N.

N	$(N/25)^{0.12}$	N	$(N/25)^{0.12}$
18	0.961	26	1.005
20	0.974	28	1.014
22	0.985	30	1.022
24	0.995	32	1.030
25	1.000		

(2) Estimate the water percentage at the liquid limit by the following relation:

$$LL = w_N(N/25)^{0.12}$$

where w_N is the water percentage corresponding to the number of blows N of the determination, and LL is the liquid limit (Table 31–1).

31–3.5 Plastic-Limit Procedure

(1) Knead 10 to 15 g. of the stiff soil paste into a ball.

(2) Roll out the soil on a glass plate or rubber floor tile with the fingers until a thread ⅛ inch (3 mm.) in diameter is formed. Remold the soil into a ball.

(3) Repeat step 2 until a thread is obtained which begins to crumble when it reaches a diameter of ⅛ inch.

(4) Weigh the crumbling soil to 0.01 g. Dry it in an oven at 110°C. (230°F.), and reweigh it. Compute the water percentage as for the liquid limit in section 31–3.3.

(5) Repeat steps 1 to 4 to obtain three determinations.

(6) The plastic limit is the average of the water percentages of the three determinations, reported to the nearest whole number and omitting the percent sign.

31–3.6 Sticky-Limit Procedure

(1) Place about 50 g. of the stiff soil paste on a glass plate.

(2) Add a small amount of distilled water, and work the soil into a uniform paste with a stainless steel spatula. (The original test of Atterberg specified a nickel spatula to avoid the variable effect of corrosion roughness of an ordinary steel spatula).

(3) Draw the clean spatula blade across the surface of the soil, exerting a firm pressure against the soil, to test for adherence.

(4) If the soil does not adhere to the spatula, repeat steps 2 and 3 until the water content is sufficient that adherence commences. This is the sticky limit or sticky point.

(5) Take 20 g. of the soil which just adheres to the steel and determine its water percentage as for the liquid limit in section 31–3.3.

(6) Repeat the procedure in steps 1 to 5. Consider the test valid if the water contents agree within 2%.

(7) Report the sticky limit as the average of the two water contents, to the nearest whole percent, omitting the percentage sign.

31–3.7 Comments

The most important source of error in all three tests is lack of uniformity of mixing the soil and water. This shows up readily in lack of agreement in the points of the flow line in the liquid-limit test and in differences among the three plastic-limit determinations. When there is more than a 5% variation in the results, the tests should be repeated.

The tests preferably are made on samples which have not been allowed to dry below their natural water content because of the changes in the limits which are produced by drying. When air-dried samples are used, this should be noted in the test report. Oven-dried samples should not be employed.

The liquid-limit test suffers from a number of variations in test equipment. The material used originally in the base of the device was hard rubber, which is still the standard in many specifications (ASTM, 1958). Plastics such as Micarta and Plexiglas (Casagrande, 1958), and even soft resilient rubber have been used. The difference between the results obtained with the hard rubber and the Micarta bases appears to be small (<5%).

Two different forms of grooving tools are in use. The ASTM tool is a curved wedge that forces the soil apart to form the groove shown in Fig. 31–2C. The flat tool, developed by Casagrande, pushes the soil ahead of itself to form a groove with the same 2-mm. bottom width and approximately the same angle, but with a depth of 8 mm. instead of 1 cm. The flat tool is easier to use in sticky clays than the wedge, but the wedge is more satisfactory in sandy clays. The liquid limit obtained by use of the flat tool is slightly higher than that obtained with the wedge, but the difference is usually less than 5%.

The consistency limits are susceptible to variations in operator technique (Casagrande, 1958; Sowers et al., 1958; Morris, 1958).

The one-point technique for the liquid limit should be used only by experienced personnel who have demonstrated their ability to secure consistent results by the regular method that employs the logarithmic graph.

Distilled water is recommended because the ions present in many public water supplies can change the results significantly. Where experience shows that the mineral content of the water is not great enough to have any effect, the tap water may be used.

Widely accepted procedures for the liquid and plastic limits have been published by Am. Soc. Testing Mater. Committee D18 (1958) and Lambe (1951).

31–4 LITERATURE CITED

American Society for Testing and Materials. 1968. Book of Standards, Part 11, p. 217–224. Am. Soc. Testing Mater., Philadelphia.

Atterberg, A. 1911a. Ueber die physikalische Bodenuntersuchung. Int. Mitt. Bodenkunde 1:7–9.

Atterberg, A. 1911b. Die Plastizität der Tone. Int. Mitt. Bodenk. 1:10–43.

Casagrande, A. 1948. Classification and identification of soils. Trans. Am. Soc. Civil Eng. 113:901–930.

Casagrande, A. 1958. Notes on the design of the liquid limit device. Geotechnique 8:84–91.

Grim, R. E. 1959. Physico-chemical properties of soils: clay minerals. Proc. Am. Soc. Civil Eng., J. Soil Mech. Found. Div., 85, No. SM2:1–17.

Lambe, T. W. 1951. Soil Testing for Engineers. John Wiley and Sons, New York.

Lambe, T. W. 1953. The structure of inorganic soil. Proc. Am. Soc. Civil Eng. 79, Separate 315.

Lambe, T. W. 1958. The structure of compacted clay. Proc. Am. Soc. Civil Eng., Soil Mech. Found. Div., 84, No. SM2, Paper 1654.

Lambe, T. W. 1959. Physico-chemical properties of soils: role of soil technology. Proc. Am. Soc. Civil Eng., J. Soil Mech. Found. Div., 85, No. SM2:55–70.

Morris, M. D., Ulp, R. B., and Spinna, R. J. 1960. Recommendations for changes in the liquid limit test. Am. Soc. Testing Mater. Spec. Tech. Publ. 254:203–211.

Norman, L. E. J. 1958. Comparison of values of liquid limit determined with apparatus having bases of different hardness. Geotechnique 8:79–83.

Rosenqvist, I. T. 1959. Physico-chemical properties of soils: Soil-water systems. Proc. Am. Soc. Civil Eng., J. Soil Mech. Found. Div., 85, No. SM2:31–53.

Seed, H. B., Woodward, R. J., and Lundgren, R. 1964. Fundamental aspects of the Atterberg limits. Proc. Am. Soc. Civil Eng., J. Soil Mech. Found. Div., 90, No. SM6.

Sowers, G. F., Vesíc, A., and Grandolfi, M. 1960. Penetration tests for liquid limit. Am. Soc. Testing Mater., Spec. Tech. Publ. 254:216–224.

Sowers, G. B., and Sowers, G. F. 1961. Introductory Soil Mechanics and Foundations. Ed. 2. pp. 17–21. Macmillan Company, New York.

Taylor, A. W. 1959. Physico-chemical properties of soils: Ion exchange phenomena. Proc. Am. Soc. Civil Eng., J. Soil Mech. Found. Div., 85, No. SM2:19–30.

32

Compactibility

EARL J. FELT

Portland Cement Association
Skokie, Illinois

32–1 INTRODUCTION

The strength characteristics and performance of a soil or soil material as a foundation for a building, highway, or airport runway depend greatly on the "density" (usually expressed, for engineering purposes, as pounds of oven-dry soil to 1 cubic foot of solids and associated voids) and water content. Proper control of these two characteristics develops in a soil its most favorable engineering properties. If the foundation is in an excavation, the density and water content of the soil can be changed only with considerable inconvenience. In the construction of roadway and runway bases, earth dams, and embankments, however, both the density and water content can be controlled readily, and the compactibility behavior of the soil employed is of great importance.

The density to which a given soil can be compacted varies with the water content of the soil and the force of compaction. If either factor is held constant, the maximum density varies with the other. Early in the 1930's, test procedures were developed to establish the relationship between the density of a soil, the water content, and the force of compaction. Data obtained with these procedures in the laboratory are used in the field for controlling the water content and density of soil during compaction. In the laboratory, the data and procedures are used for molding replicate test specimens that are employed in tests of permeability, shrinkage, swelling, and strength to aid in predicting future performance of the compacted soil.

The desired value of density varies with the degree of stability required in the construction. For example, a roadway fill of considerable depth need not be compacted as much as the upper few inches of base course for an airport runway. Specifications adequate for different purposes have been developed through experience. Cooperative work on methods of laboratory testing by the American Society for Testing and Materials, the American Association of State Highway Officials, and certain federal organizations has resulted in adoption of a standard method of testing. The method includes two procedures that differ in compactive force employed. The choice between procedures depends upon the degree of compaction required in the construction.

In the standard method of the American Society for Testing and Materials (ASTM), the soil is compacted in layers in a metal mold by a number of impacts from a free-falling rammer. This is the method described here. Two other methods have been suggested. In one, the soil is compressed in a mold under a static force (Stanton, 1938; Porter, 1949), and in the other, the soil is compacted by a kneading force (McRae and Rutledge, 1952; Hveem and Davis, 1950). These two methods have not been used extensively.

The impact-type compaction method described here is particularly satisfactory for cohesive soils and for well-graded sandy soils, and test data can be reproduced within practical limits. Frequently, however, the method is not suitable for coarse-textured, cohesionless soils. Accordingly, the ASTM, through committee activities, is now developing a more suitable method of compaction for such materials. Compaction characteristics of coarse-textured, cohesionless soils were discussed by Holtz and Lowitz (1957), and suggestions for compacting such soils by vibration were presented by Felt (1958). Coarse-textured materials usually develop greater densities by vibration than by impact-type compaction.

The compactibility relationships measured in the laboratory are generally assumed to apply to compaction in the field. As pointed out by McRae and Rutledge (1952) and Hveem and Davis (1950), however, compactibility relationships are not the same in the field as in the laboratory. In the field, compactibility relationships depend to some extent on the type of equipment used for compaction. Studies are being made to correlate field and laboratory data.

Equipment utilized in the field is of three principal types: (1) rollers, including sheepsfoot, smooth-wheel, and rubber-tired varieties, (2) vibrators, including plates and rollers, and (3) impact rammers, generally of the internal-combustion type. Clayey soils ordinarily are compacted in layers 6 or 8 inches in thickness by means of sheepsfoot rollers, although rubber-tired rollers are used occasionally with layers 2 or 3 inches in thickness. Sandy soils are compacted for the most part by smooth-wheel rollers or vibrators and occasionally by rubber-tired rollers. Impact rammers are used in areas of limited extent.

Field tests made by the U. S. Army Engineers (Corps of Engineers, 1956; Turnbull and Foster, 1960) and the Road Research Laboratory of England (Dept. Sci. Ind. Res., 1952, pp. 178–207) show that the density of soil compacted in the field depends not only on the water content and nature of the soil material but also on the type of compaction equipment, the number of passes made by the equipment, the total weight of the roller, the pressure per unit area on the feet of a sheepsfoot roller, the air pressure in the tires of a rubber-tired roller, and other factors.

In practice, principal attention must be directed to adjusting the water content of the soil to a value near the optimum for compaction and to testing the soil after compaction to find whether the density has been increased to the desired value. If the density is not high enough, an increase must be made in number of passes, total weight, or weight per unit area. As a final resort, the equipment must be replaced with something more effective.

32–2 PRINCIPLES

A pulverized, air-dry soil does not compact readily, nor does it compact to a high density. If a little water is added, the soil usually compacts more readily and to a greater density. If the process is repeated several times, the density after compaction usually is found to increase progressively with the water content of the soil up to a limit, called the optimum water content for compaction, and to decrease as the water content is increased further. If comparable samples are tested with different forces of compaction, the maximum density is found to increase and the optimum water content for compaction to decrease with increasing force of compaction. These relationships are illustrated in Fig. 32–1.

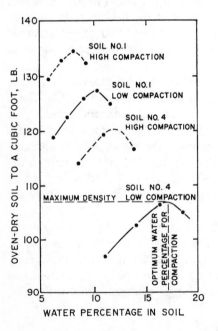

Fig. 32–1. Density of compacted soil versus water content during compaction of two soils by two procedures. The curves illustrate the characteristic displacement of the locus of maximum density.

Water plays several important roles in the compaction process. Films of water of increasing thickness around soil particles decrease the cohesion between adjacent particles and provide lubrication, thus permitting the particles to slide over each other with increasing facility to form a closer packing under pressure. Both soil particles and water are virtually incompressible, however. Hence where the water content is increased beyond the level required to occupy the voids at the maximum density, the excess water prevents full compaction of the soil particles. The cohesional, lubricational, and space-filling effects of water are present at all levels of water content, but the first two are of greater importance where the soil is relatively dry, and the last is of greater importance where the soil is relatively wet. With some fine-textured soils, the density after compaction first decreases as small quantities of water are added to the air-dry material. Soil 6 in Fig. 32–2 is an example. This behavior may be attributed to another effect of water, namely, that of producing swelling of individual aggregates. Aggregates of soil particles invariably swell upon being moistened, and the swelled aggregates are strong enough in some soils that they are not compacted readily. Thus it appears that in soils in which the aggregates are numerous enough and are strong enough after slight moistening, and where the aggregates swell enough upon moistening, the negative effect of swelling upon the density after compaction may be more important throughout part of the range of water content than the positive effect of water associated with cohesion and lubrication.

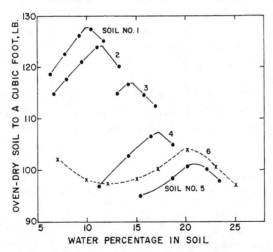

Fig. 32–2. Density of compacted soil versus water content during compaction of six soils differing in mechanical composition. The maximum density tends to decrease and to occur at a higher water percentage as the texture becomes finer. See Table 32–1 for the mechanical composition of the soils.

Table 32–1. Mechanical composition, liquid limit, and plasticity index of six soils.

Soil No.	Mechanical composition*			Liquid limit†	Plasticity index‡
	Sand 2 to 0.074 mm. diam.	Silt 0.074 to 0.005 mm. diam.	Clay, < 0.005 mm. diam.		
	%	%	%	%	%
1	81	13	6	Nonplastic	Nonplastic
2	81	11	8	26	4
3	8	80	12	26	7
4	40	25	35	37	18
5	41	31	28	39	14
6	21	30	49	58	36

* American Society for Testing and Materials (1958a).
† American Society for Testing and Materials (1958b).
‡ American Society for Testing and Materials (1958c).

The optimum water content of soil for compaction tends to increase as the texture becomes finer. The principal cause of this observation is probably the fact that the specific surface of soil increases with fineness of texture. If equal quantities of water are added to equal weights of soils differing in specific surface, the thickness of the water films produced around individual particles will decrease with increasing specific surface. At the same time, the maximum density of soil after compaction tends to decrease as the texture becomes finer. The principal cause of this observation appears to be that many small particles of irregular size cannot fit together as closely as they could if they constituted a single, large, solid particle. Hence, the percentage of the total volume occupied by pore space is greater in fine-textured soils than in coarse-textured soils. During compaction of the soil, the pore space is filled with water and air, both of which have a lower density than do the solid particles. A comparison of the figures for clay percentage in six soils in Table 32–1 with the locus of the maximum density after compaction for the same soils in Fig. 32–2 illustrates both the decrease in maximum density and the increase in optimum water content for compaction as the soil texture becomes finer.

Table 32–2. Specifications of compaction apparatus.

	Low-compaction procedure, ASTM D 698-58 T		High-compaction procedure, ASTM D 1557-58 T	
Diameter of metal mold, inches	4	6	4	6
Height of mold, inches	4.584	4.584	4.584	4.584
Volume of mold, cubic feet	0.0333	0.075	0.0333	0.075
Weight of rammer, pounds	5.5	5.5	10	10
Free fall of rammer, feet	1	1	1.5	1.5

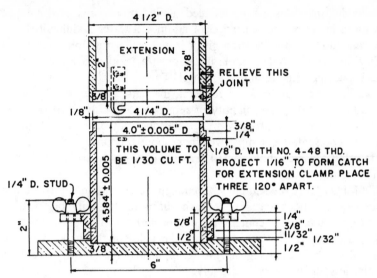

Fig. 32–3. Cylindrical 4-inch mold, extension collar, and base plate for compaction tests.

32–3   METHOD [1]

32–3.1   Special Apparatus[2]

Specifications of the compaction apparatus for the two different procedures are given in brief in Table 32–2. Two different mold sizes are specified for each procedure, but only one is needed (see comments, section 32–3.6). Specifications for a 4-inch mold and extension collar are shown in Fig. 32–3. Specifications for a 6-inch mold and extension are analogous but are not shown.

Construct the mold and collar assembly so that it can be fastened firmly to a detachable base plate. Construct the rammer of metal with a circular face having a diameter of 2 inches. Place the compaction apparatus on a uniform, rigid foundation, such as that provided by a block of concrete weighing 200 pounds or more.

32–3.2   Low-Compaction Procedure for Soil Materials Passing a No. 4 Sieve (ASTM D 698–58 T)

Use the procedure in the following paragraphs for soil materials that pass a No. 4 sieve (4.76-mm. openings), excepting those in which the size

---

[1] Am. Soc. Testing Mater. (1958d, 1958e).
[2] Commercially available from all except the third source listed in section 37–2.2.1.

of individual particles will be reduced significantly by repeated compaction and those in which incorporation of additional water is difficult. For such materials, use the modification given in the last paragraph of this section.

Dry the original bulk sample in air or at a temperature not over 60°C. until it becomes friable under a trowel. Then break up the soil aggregates in such a manner as to avoid reducing the natural size of individual particles. Pass an adequate quantity of representative pulverized soil through a No. 4 sieve and discard any gravel that does not pass through the sieve. Select a representative sample weighing about 6 pounds if the test is to be made using a 4-inch mold, or 14 pounds if the test is to be made using a 6-inch mold.

Thoroughly mix the sample with enough water to dampen it to an initial water content about 4 to 6% (on the basis of dry soil) below the estimated optimum water content for compaction. At this initial water content, plastic soils, tightly squeezed in the palm of the hand, will form a cast that will bear only slight pressure applied by the thumb and fingertips; nonplastic soils will bulk noticeably.

Place the moistened soil in a metal container, and compact it to a depth of about 2 inches using a 5.5-pound rammer falling through a distance of 12 inches. Cover the container and allow it to stand for 5 minutes or longer to permit more complete absorption of the water. After the curing period, break up the soil as before and pass it through a No. 4 sieve. Mix the sieved soil thoroughly.

Attach the collar to the mold and compact the sample in three equal layers to give a total depth of about 5 inches of soil after compaction. Apply 25 or 56 blows of the 5.5-pound rammer to each layer, according to whether the mold has an inside diameter of 4 inches or 6 inches, respectively. Distribute the blows uniformly over the surface. Adjust the rammer to provide a free fall from a height 12 inches above the surface of the soil during compaction.

Following compaction, remove the extension collar, and carefully trim the compacted soil even with the top of the mold using a steel straightedge having a beveled edge. Weigh the compacted soil in the mold. Subtract the weight of the mold. Then multiply the weight of compacted soil by 30 if the 4-inch mold is used, or by 13.33 if the 6-inch mold is used, and record the result as the wet weight of a cubic foot of compacted soil.

Remove the compacted material from the mold. Immediately take a representative sample of 100 g. or more, weigh the sample, and dry it in an oven at 110° ± 5°C. for at least 12 hours or to constant weight. Weigh the dried sample, and calculate the water percentage as indicated in section 32–3.5.

Break up the remainder of the compacted material and pass it through a No. 4 sieve. Add enough water to increase the water content of the sample by 1 or 2% on the basis of the dry soil. Mix the moistened sample. Then repeat the procedure outlined in paragraphs 4, 5, 6, and 7 of this section. Continue repeating the moistening, compaction, and analysis for water content until there is either a decrease or no change in the wet weight of 1 cubic foot of compacted soil.

Use a separate sample that has passed a No. 4 sieve for each compaction test made on (*1*) soil materials the particle size of which is reduced significantly by repeated compaction and (*2*) soil materials in which incorporation of additional water is difficult (certain fine-textured materials). With materials of type (*2*) mix individual samples with quantities of water required to cause the water content to increase by increments of about 2% on the basis of the dry soil and to bracket a water percentage equal to 0.8 of the plastic limit (see section 31–3.5). Allow the moistened soil to stand for 12 hours or longer in a covered container before carrying out the compaction and measuring the water content as described in paragraphs 5, 6, and 7 of this section.

32–3.3 Low-Compaction Procedure for Soil Materials Passing a 2-Inch Sieve (ASTM D 698–58 T)

Use the procedure in the following paragraphs for soil materials passing a sieve with 2-inch openings except those materials in which the size of individual particles will be reduced significantly by repeated compaction and those in which incorporation of additional water is difficult. For such materials, use the modification given in the last paragraph of section 32–3.2 in connection with the procedure in the following paragraphs.

Dry the original bulk sample in air or at a temperature not over 60°C. until it becomes friable under a trowel. Then break up the soil aggregates in such a manner as to avoid reducing the natural size of individual particles. Sieve a representative portion of the pulverized material using a nest of two sieves in which the openings are 2 inches in the upper and ¾ inch in the lower. Discard the gravel retained on the 2-inch sieve. Remove the gravel passing the 2-inch sieve and retained on the ¾-inch sieve, and replace it with an equal weight of gravel passing the ¾-inch sieve and retained on a No. 4 sieve (4.76-mm. openings). Take the material for replacement from a separate portion of the sample that is not to be used in the subsequent tests.

Select a representative sample of 10 or 22 pounds of the sieved and modified material, prepared in the manner described in the preceding paragraph, for use with the 4- or 6-inch mold, respectively. Mix the sample with enough water to moisten it to a water content about 4% (on the basis of the dry weight of soil) below the optimum water percentage for compaction. At this initial water content, plastic soils, tightly squeezed in the palm of the hand, will form a cast that will bear only slight pressure applied by the thumb and fingertips; nonplastic soils will bulk noticeably.

Attach the collar to the mold and compact the sample in three equal layers to give a total depth of about 5 inches of soil after compaction. Apply 25 or 56 blows of the 5.5-pound rammer to each layer, according to whether the mold has an inside diameter of 4 inches or 6 inches, respectively. Distribute the blows uniformly over the surface. Adjust the rammer to provide a free fall from a height 12 inches above the surface of the soil during compaction.

Remove the extension collar and carefully trim the compacted soil even with the top of the mold by means of a steel straightedge having a beveled edge. Use fine material to patch holes developed in the surface by removal of coarse material. Immediately weigh the mold and compacted soil. Subtract the weight of the mold, and multiply the weight of the moist, compacted soil by 30 if the 4-inch mold is used, or by 13.33 if the 6-inch mold is used. Record the result as the wet weight of compacted soil per 1 cubic foot. Remove the compacted material from the mold, take a representative sample of 500 g. or more, weigh the sample immediately, and dry it in an oven at $110° \pm 5°C$. for 12 hours or longer, or to constant weight, and weigh the dried sample. Carry out the calculations as indicated below in section 32–3.5.

Break up the remainder of the compacted material until all of it passes a ¾-inch sieve and 90% of the aggregates of fine material pass a No. 4 sieve, as judged by eye. Add enough water to increase the water content of the sample by 1 or 2% (on the basis of the dry weight of soil). Mix the moistened sample, and then repeat the procedure outlined in paragraphs 4 and 5 of this section. Continue repeating the moistening, compaction, and analysis for water content until there is either a decrease or no change in the wet weight of compacted soil per 1 cubic foot.

32–3.4   High-Compaction Procedure (ASTM D 1557–58 T)

Follow the procedure specified in section 32–3.2 or 32–3.3, whichever is applicable, with the following exceptions. Use a 10-pound rammer having a free-fall drop of 18 inches, and compact the sample in 5 layers.

32–3.5   Calculations and Representation of Data

Calculate the water percentage and the dry weight of compacted soil for each trial as follows:

$$w = [(A - B)/(B - C)] \times 100$$

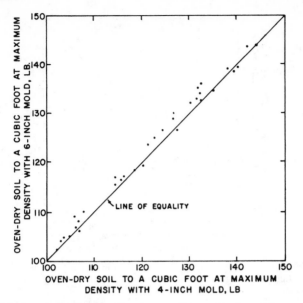

Fig. 32–4. Maximum density of soils compacted in a 6-inch mold versus maximum density of the same soils compacted in a 4-inch mold.

and

$$W = [W_1/(w + 100)] \times 100 \, ,$$

where

w = water percentage in specimen on the oven-dry basis,
A = weight of container and wet soil,
B = weight of container and dried soil,
C = weight of container,
W = dry weight of compacted soil in pounds per 1 cubic foot, and
W_1 = wet weight of compacted soil in pounds per 1 cubic foot.

Plot the oven-dry weights of soil per 1 cubic foot against the corresponding water percentages on cross section paper, and draw a smooth curve through the points, as in Figs. 32–1 and 32–2. Take the water percentage corresponding to the peak of the curve as the optimum water percentage of the soil for compaction; take the oven-dry weight of soil per 1 cubic foot at this water percentage as the maximum density with the particular compaction procedure employed.

32–3.6 Comments

The term "density" employed in connection with the foregoing compaction procedures is expressed in units of mass per volume, where the

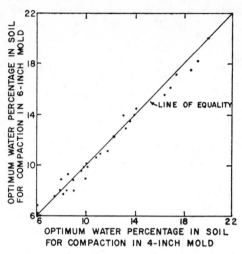

Fig. 32–5. Optimum water percentage for compaction of soils in a 6-inch mold versus optimum water percentage for compaction of the same soils in a 4-inch mold.

volume refers to the total volume of solids plus voids. This convention is customary in soil engineering work. In agricultural work, the convention is for the volume to refer to the total volume of solids only.

Figure 32–4 is a plot of maximum densities of a number of soils, as found by use of a 6-inch mold, against maximum densities of the same soils, as found by use of a 4-inch mold. Figure 32–5 is a plot of optimum water percentage of a number of soils for compaction in a 6-inch mold versus optimum water percentage of the same soils for compaction in a 4-inch mold. The close correspondence of all points to a 1:1 relationship indicates that the mold size has little effect on the results. A 6-inch mold is used most commonly where a specimen of this diameter is required for some special test, such as the California Bearing Ratio test (section 38–2), or where the soil contains significant quantities of gravel retained on a No. 4 sieve.

The energy expended in compaction of 1 cubic foot of soil is about 4.5 times as great with the high-compaction procedure as with the low-compaction procedure. Hence the maximum densities are higher, and the optimum water percentages for compaction are lower with the former procedure than with the latter. These relationships are shown for soils 1 and 4 in Fig. 32–1 and for many soils in Fig. 32–6 and 32–7. The data in Fig. 32–6 and 32–7, obtained from tests in the author's laboratory and from papers published by McRae (1958), Proctor (1948), Dawson (1959), and the Highway Research Board (1952), indicate that maximum densities obtained with the high-compaction procedure are greater than those obtained with the low-compaction procedure by about 13 pounds per cubic

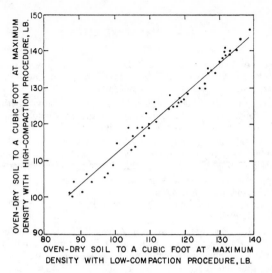

Fig. 32–6. Maximum density of soils with the high-compaction procedure versus maximum density of the same soils with the low-compaction procedure.

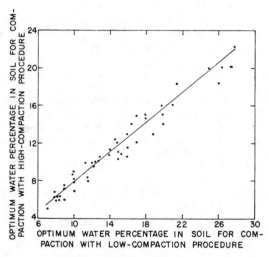

Fig. 32–7. Optimum water percentage for compaction of soils by the high-compaction procedure versus optimum water percentage for compaction of the same soils by the low-compaction procedure.

foot for fine-textured soils, and about 5 pounds per cubic foot for coarse-textured soils. The difference between optimum water percentages for compaction is about 2% with coarse-textured soils and 6% with fine-textured soils, the higher values being associated with the low-compaction procedure.

32–4   LITERATURE CITED

American Society for Testing and Materials. 1958a. Tentative method for grain-size analysis of soils. *In* 1958 Book of ASTM Standards Including Tentatives. Part 4: 1119–1129. Am. Soc. Testing Mater., Philadelphia.

American Society for Testing and Materials. 1958b. Tentative method of test for liquid limit of soils. *In* 1958 Book of ASTM Standards Including Tentatives. Part 4:1132–1136. Am. Soc. for Testing Mater., Philadelphia.

American Society for Testing and Materials. 1958c. Tentative methods of test for plastic limit and plasticity index of soils. *In* 1958 Book of ASTM Standards Including Tentatives. Part 4:1137–1139. Am. Soc. Testing Mater., Philadelphia.

American Society for Testing and Materials. 1958d. Tentative methods of test for moisture-density relations of soils, using 5.5 lb. rammer and 12-in. drop. *In* 1958 Book of ASTM Standards Including Tentatives. Part 4:1152–1157. Am. Soc. Testing Mater., Philadelphia.

American Society for Testing and Materials. 1958e. Tentative methods of test for moisture-density relations of soils, using a 10-lb. rammer and an 18-in. drop. *In* 1958 Book of ASTM Standards Including Tentatives. Part 4:1158–1163. Am. Soc. Testing Mater., Philadelphia.

Corps of Engineers, U. S. Army. 1956. Effect on soil compaction of tire pressure and number of passes of rubber-tired rollers and foot-contact pressure of sheepsfoot rollers. Waterways Exp. Sta. Tech. Memo. 3–271, Rept. 7.

Dawson, Raymond F. 1960. Some laboratory studies of the moisture-density relations of soils. Am. Soc. Testing Mater. Spec. Tech. Publ. 254:308–317.

Department of Scientific and Industrial Research, Road Research Laboratory. 1952. Soil Mechanics for Road Engineers. Her Majesty's Stationery Office, London.

Felt, Earl J. 1958. Laboratory methods of compacting granular soils. Am. Soc. Testing Mater. Spec. Tech. Publ. 239:89–108.

Highway Research Board. 1952. Compaction of embankments, subgrades, and bases. Highway Res. Board Bull. 58.

Holtz, Wesley G., and Lowitz, Clemith A. 1957. Compaction characteristics of gravelly soils. USDI, Bur. Reclamation, Earth Lab. Rept. EM-509.

Hveem, F. N., and Davis, Harmer E. 1950. Some concepts concerning triaxial compression testing of asphaltic paving mixtures and subgrade materials. Am. Soc. Testing Mater. Spec. Tech. Publ. 106:25–45.

McRae, J. L. 1958. Index of compaction characteristics. Am. Soc. Testing Mater. Spec. Tech. Publ. 239:119–123.

McRae, J. L., and Rutledge, P. C. 1952. Laboratory kneading of soil to simulate field compaction. Highway Res. Board Proc. 31:593–600.

Porter, O. J. 1949. Development of the original method for highway design. Proc. Am. Soc. Civil Eng. 75:11–17.

Proctor, R. R. 1948. Laboratory compaction methods, penetration resistance measurements, and indicated saturation penetration resistance. Proc. Second Intern. Conf. Soil Mech. Found. 5:242–245.

Stanton, T. E. 1938. Compaction of earth embankments. Highway Res. Board Proc., Part II, 18:151–157.

Turnbull, W. J., and Foster, C. R. 1960. Proof-rolling of subgrades. *In* Soil compaction and proof-rolling of subgrades. Natl. Res. Council, Highway Res. Board Bull. 254:12–21.

33 | Stress Distribution

EDWARD S. BARBER

Consulting Engineer
Arlington, Virginia

33-1 INTRODUCTION

When a load is applied to the surface of the ground, stresses (load per unit area) are transmitted throughout the ground. This is called stress distribution.

At any point there are stresses in all directions. For a given plane at a point the resultant stress may be divided into two components: (*1*) a normal stress (tension or compression) perpendicular to the plane, and (*2*) a shearing stress tangential to the plane. The transmitted normal stresses generally decrease with distance from the applied load and with distance from its line of action as shown in the upper part of Fig. 33–1, where stress distribution is shown by lines connecting points of equal magnitude of stress.

Knowledge of the distribution of stresses is used to determine areas which may be overstressed by shearing or tensile stresses and to determine compression stresses which cause reduction in volume. The stresses can be combined with the stress-strain properties of the ground to determine the displacement of any point.

For stresses much lower than the soil strength, the distribution of stresses may be calculated from the theory of elasticity (Terzaghi, 1943), which determines the effect of interaction of elements characterized by a modulus of elasticity E and a Poisson's ratio v. In a simple compression test, E is the ratio of stress to strain while v is the strain (change in length per unit length) perpendicular to the direction of applied stress divided by the strain in the direction of applied stress.

It is sometimes desirable to measure transmitted stresses to check on the applicability of the theory of elasticity, especially as the strength of the material is approached, and where calculation may be difficult because of lack of homogeneity in the soil or uncertainty of applied stresses.

Photoelastic tests on models (Coker and Filon, 1931) have been used to determine stresses experimentally from complex loadings. When the

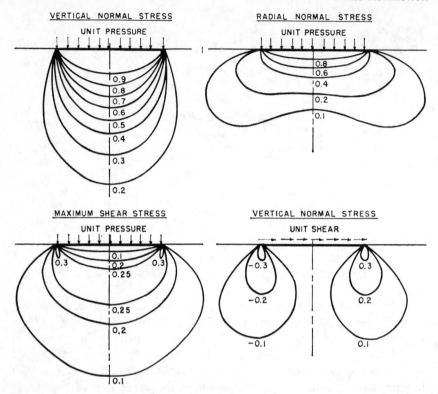

Fig. 33–1. Stress in elastic material from uniform stress over circular area at surface (Poisson's ratio = 0.5) (Barber, unpublished).

model is stressed, patterns are formed by the double refraction of polarized light passed through the special material of the model. This method is usually limited to two dimensions. As an example, such tests have shown tensile stresses at the top of soil slopes under gravity load.

Stress distribution has been inferred from displacement of or strains in boundaries such as stretching (Spangler, 1956) or bending (Spangler, 1948) of culverts under fills, bending of flexible walls (Moore and Shaw, 1951; Rowe, 1952), thrust on sheeting struts (Peck, 1943), and compression of piles (Mansur and Kaufman, 1958).

More direct measurements have been made of normal stresses at boundaries with friction tapes (Spangler and Mickle, 1956) and various pressure cells (Goldbeck, 1938; Housel, 1943; Trabbic et al., 1959). A use of pressure cells for making such measurements is described in section 33–3. Boundary shear stresses have also been measured (Bonse and Kuhn, 1959). Pressures in pore water have been determined by pressure gauges or

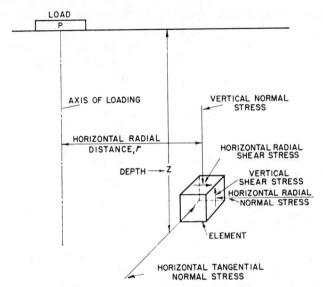

Fig. 33-2. Stresses on an element from pressure applied at the surface (Barber, unpublished).

small open tubes connected to a porous intake (Gould, 1949; Hvorslev, 1951).

Measurements of internal total soil stress have generally been limited to compressive stress on a thin disk with one pressure sensitive face. However, an internal shear cell has been developed (Ahlvin, 1954). Pore-water pressures can be measured by supporting a porous plate above the weighing face of a compression cell. Pressures are determined from strains in electrical resistance gauges or the frequency of a vibrating wire (Kallstenius and Bergan, 1956).

33-2 PRINCIPLES

Methods of calculating stresses will be described, and this description will be followed by the principles of pressure-cell installation.

In a homogeneous, semi-infinite mass with a horizontal surface and no external load, the vertical pressure at a depth Z is wZ where w is the unit weight of the material. The ratio of lateral to vertical pressure K depends on the lateral displacement; for no lateral movement, $K = \nu/(1 - \nu)$ which varies from zero for $\nu = 0$ (volume change with no lateral strain) to one for $\nu = 0.5$ (distortion with no volume change).

Stress distributions for various loads or restraints at the boundaries are calculated from differential equations representing equilibrium of stresses and compatibility of strains. For a vertical load P applied at a point to the horizontal surface of a semi-infinite, isotropic (equal properties in all directions), homogeneous elastic medium, Boussinesq (Westergaard, 1952) found the stresses as defined in Fig. 33–2 to be

$$\text{vertical normal stress} = \frac{3P}{2\pi}\frac{Z^3}{R^5}$$

$$\text{horizontal radial normal stress} = \frac{P}{2\pi}\left\{\frac{3Zr^2}{R^5} - \left[(1 - 2\nu)\left(\frac{1}{r^2} - \frac{Z}{r^2 R}\right)\right]\right\}$$

$$\text{horizontal tangential normal stress} = \frac{P}{2\pi}(1 - 2\nu)\left(\frac{1}{r^2} - \frac{Z}{r^2 R} - \frac{Z}{R^3}\right)$$

$$\text{horizontal radial shear stress} = \frac{3P}{2\pi}\frac{Z^2 r}{R^5}$$

where $R^2 = Z^2 + r^2$, $\nu =$ Poisson's ratio, and compression is positive.

All stresses are independent of the modulus of elasticity E, and the vertical normal (perpendicular) and shear stress are independent of ν.

Solutions for a horizontal point load by Cerruti and for a load applied below the surface by Mindlin are also available (Westergaard, 1952). For a load applied at great depth, the stresses are half those given by Boussinesq.

For the linear elasticity assumed, stresses from different loads, as from the soil weight and external loads, may be added. Using Boussinesq's formulas for the stress from a load on an infinitesimal area, stresses from loads distributed over various areas on the surface may be determined. Thus for a uniform load on a circular area, Table 33–1 is derived (Barber, 1946). Convenient graphs are available (Foster and Ahlvin, 1954). The vertical stress from a horizontally applied stress (shown in Fig. 33–1) is the same as the radial shear stress from a vertically applied stress. Except close to the applied load, Table 33–1 can also be used for stresses from a uniform pressure on a square of equal area (St. Venant's principle). Under pneumatic tires, inward acting shear stresses increase vertical pressures at shallow depths (Barber, 1946).

Stresses from a uniform vertical load over rectangular areas may be determined from Fig. 33–3 for vertical stress or from Fig. 33–4 for horizontal stress. Newmark (1942) devised influence charts such as Fig. 33–5 and 33–6 whereby the stress at a point can be determined from the area of the chart covered by the loaded area drawn to a scale depending on the depth. For a two-dimensional problem such as a long strip load, an influence chart for nonuniform load can be constructed as shown in Fig. 33–7. Other published solutions include loads on a slope (Holl, 1941); loads transmitted to culverts (Spangler and Hennessy, 1946); various strip loads

(Barber, 1952); and uniform (Newmark, 1935), triangular (Gray and Hooks, 1948), and horizontal (Baron, 1947) loads on a rectangular area.

Displacements may be calculated from the stresses and elastic constants. A uniform vertical pressure produces a bowl-shaped depression as shown in Table 33-2.

Westergaard calculated the stress distribution in a horizontally reinforced material (Taylor, 1948) which may simulate a varved material. For Poisson's ratio of zero, it gives vertical stresses similar to those found in a homogeneous material at 50% greater depth. Holl (1941) considered different moduli of elasticity in different directions.

Burmister (1956) calculated stresses in an elastic material underlain by a rigid boundary. For Poisson's ratio equal to 0.5, the vertical stress at the boundary is equal to that found in a homogeneous material at a depth about ¾ the depth of the boundary. When an elastic layer overlies another with a lower modulus of elasticity (Burmister, 1943), the vertical stress in the lower layer can be roughly approximated by substituting for the upper layer an equivalent thickness equal to its actual thickness multiplied by the cube root of the ratio of the moduli of elasticity (modulus of top layer ÷ modulus of under layer).

Stresses within embankments require special calculations (Dingwall and Scrivener, 1954). Inertia effects must be considered with vibrating (Quinlan, 1953) or impact loads. Some attention has been given to the effect of pore-water pressures (Biot, 1941). The effect of loading through elastic structures has been studied (Hetenyi, 1946).

Stresses are redistributed as soon as the elastic limit is exceeded (stress no longer proportional to strain). A rigid disc forced into an elastic material would theoretically produce infinite stress at the edge. Edge stresses equal to twice the average have been measured. A rigid footing on the surface of sand has a maximum reaction under the center because the unconfined sand at the edge has no strength (Barber and Sawyer, 1950). As load is increased, plastic areas increase until failure develops. Elastic-plastic stress distribution has been calculated for a few cases such as shafts, tunnels, and wedges (Terzaghi, 1943). When stresses exceed the elastic limit, residual stresses may remain after unloading. Completely plastic conditions are assumed in calculating earth pressure on walls and culverts due to soil weight (Spangler, 1951).

Formulas are sometimes empirically modified to adjust for unmeasured variable conditions. At a depth of one radius below a uniform pressure over a circular area, concentration factors of 4, 5, and 6 suggested by Froehlich (Soehne, 1958) correspond to multiplying the depth by 0.81, 0.68, and 0.58 respectively.

The measurement of stress distribution is usually a research project rather than a routine test. Several investigators have shown reasonable

Table 33–1. Stresses transmitted to a point in a semi-infinite mass from a surface load uniformly distributed over a circular area of radius a (Barber, 1946).

Depth of point ÷ radius	Horizontal radial distance ÷ radius, r/a								
	0	0.25	0.5	1.0	1.5	2.0	2.5	3.0	4.0
z/a	Vertical normal stress transmitted to point ÷ pressure applied at surface, p_z/p								
0.25	0.986	0.983	0.964	0.460	0.015	0.002	0.000	0.000	0.000
0.5	0.911	0.895	0.840	0.418	0.060	0.010	0.003	0.000	0.000
0.75	0.784	0.762	0.691	0.374	0.105	0.025	0.010	0.002	0.000
1.0	0.646	0.625	0.560	0.335	0.125	0.043	0.016	0.007	0.000
1.25	0.524	0.508	0.455	0.295	0.135	0.057	0.023	0.010	0.001
1.5	0.424	0.413	0.374	0.256	0.137	0.064	0.029	0.013	0.002
1.75	0.346	0.336	0.309	0.223	0.135	0.071	0.037	0.018	0.004
2.0	0.284	0.277	0.258	0.194	0.127	0.073	0.041	0.022	0.006
2.5	0.200	0.196	0.186	0.150	0.109	0.073	0.044	0.028	0.011
3	0.146	0.143	0.137	0.117	0.091	0.066	0.045	0.031	0.015
4	0.087	0.086	0.083	0.076	0.061	0.052	0.041	0.031	0.018
5	0.057	0.057	0.056	0.052	0.045	0.039	0.033	0.027	0.018
	Horizontal radial normal stress ÷ applied pressure (Poisson's ratio = 0.5) p_r/p								
0.25	0.643	0.626	0.565	0.385	0.144	0.058	0.028	0.014	0.004
0.5	0.374	0.360	0.325	0.286	0.196	0.098	0.050	0.027	0.008
0.75	0.208	0.204	0.196	0.209	0.175	0.112	0.064	0.044	0.012
1.0	0.116	0.118	0.123	0.149	0.146	0.104	0.069	0.045	0.022
1.25	0.067	0.072	0.080	0.107	0.116	0.096	0.069	0.047	0.026
1.5	0.040	0.046	0.055	0.078	0.091	0.082	0.064	0.047	0.026
1.75	0.025	0.028	0.035	0.056	0.070	0.068	0.058	0.046	0.027
2.0	0.016	0.019	0.024	0.041	0.053	0.057	0.052	0.042	0.027
2.5	0.008	0.009	0.013	0.023	0.033	0.038	0.038	0.035	0.025
3	0.004	0.006	0.008	0.014	0.021	0.026	0.028	0.026	0.022
4	0.001	0.002	0.003	0.006	0.009	0.012	0.015	0.016	0.016
5	0.001	0.001	0.002	0.003	0.005	0.007	0.008	0.009	0.010
	Horizontal tangential normal stress ÷ applied pressure (Poisson's ratio = 0.5) p_t/p								
0.25	0.643	0.628	0.580	0.243	0.019	0.005	0.001	0.000	0.000
0.5	0.374	0.359	0.317	0.141	0.028	0.007	0.003	0.001	0.000
0.75	0.208	0.197	0.170	0.085	0.025	0.008	0.003	0.001	0.000
1.0	0.116	0.109	0.096	0.054	0.021	0.008	0.003	0.001	0.000
1.25	0.067	0.063	0.056	0.035	0.016	0.007	0.003	0.001	0.000
1.5	0.040	0.037	0.034	0.023	0.012	0.006	0.003	0.001	0.000
1.75	0.025	0.024	0.022	0.015	0.009	0.005	0.003	0.001	0.000
2.0	0.016	0.015	0.014	0.011	0.007	0.004	0.002	0.001	0.000
2.5	0.008	0.007	0.007	0.006	0.004	0.003	0.002	0.001	0.000
3	0.004	0.004	0.003	0.003	0.002	0.002	0.001	0.001	0.000
4	0.001	0.001	0.001	0.001	0.001	0.001	0.000	0.000	0.000
5	0.001	0.001	0.000	0.000	0.000	0.000	0.000	0.000	0.000

(continued on next page)

Table 33–1. (continued).

Depth of point ÷ radius	Horizontal radial distance ÷ radius, r/a								
	0	0.25	0.5	1.0	1.5	2.0	2.5	3.0	4.0
z/a	Horizontal radial shear stress at point ÷ pressure applied at surface, s_r/p								
0.25	0.000	0.024	0.065	0.299	0.042	0.014	0.003	0.002	0.001
0.50	0.000	0.057	0.129	0.262	0.102	0.032	0.013	0.006	0.002
0.75	0.000	0.069	0.141	0.221	0.128	0.053	0.024	0.013	0.003
1.00	0.000	0.065	0.124	0.178	0.128	0.069	0.033	0.018	0.007
1.25	0.000	0.053	0.101	0.146	0.118	0.072	0.039	0.023	0.010
1.50	0.000	0.041	0.080	0.119	0.104	0.071	0.045	0.028	0.012
1.75	0.000	0.033	0.062	0.094	0.091	0.068	0.046	0.030	0.014
2.00	0.000	0.026	0.048	0.070	0.078	0.062	0.045	0.032	0.015
2.5	0.000	0.016	0.030	0.050	0.056	0.050	0.041	0.032	0.018
3	0.000	0.009	0.019	0.034	0.040	0.040	0.035	0.029	0.018
4	0.000	0.005	0.009	0.018	0.022	0.024	0.024	0.022	0.016
5	0.000	0.002	0.005	0.010	0.013	0.015	0.016	0.016	0.013
	Horizontal radial normal stress ÷ applied pressure (Poisson's ratio = 0) p_r/p								
0.25	0.265	0.248	0.199	0.082*	-0.026	-0.045	-0.061	-0.046	-0.026
0.50	0.098	0.087	0.063	0.075	0.056	-0.006	-0.016	-0.018	-0.017
0.75	0.008	0.008	0.009	0.055	0.067	0.033	0.009	0.000	-0.010
1.00	-0.030	-0.025	-0.015	0.033	0.058	0.041	0.021	0.008	0.000
1.25	-0.043	-0.036	-0.024	0.018	0.044	0.040	0.026	0.015	0.004
1.50	-0.044	-0.038	-0.028	0.007	0.032	0.035	0.027	0.019	0.006
1.75	-0.041	-0.036	-0.028	-0.001	0.022	0.028	0.025	0.019	0.009
2.00	-0.037	-0.033	-0.024	-0.006	0.013	0.022	0.022	0.019	0.010
2.5	-0.028	-0.026	-0.022	-0.010	0.004	0.012	0.016	0.016	0.011
3	-0.022	-0.020	-0.017	-0.010	-0.002	0.006	0.010	0.011	0.010
4	-0.014	-0.012	-0.011	-0.009	-0.004	-0.001	0.003	0.005	0.007
5	-0.009	-0.009	-0.008	-0.007	-0.004	-0.002	0.000	0.001	0.004
	Horizontal tangential normal stress ÷ applied pressure (Poisson's ratio = 0) p_t/p								
0.25	0.265	0.259	0.245	0.183	0.132	0.095	0.061	0.046	0.026
0.50	0.098	0.094	0.085	0.070	0.074	0.061	0.048	0.037	0.022
0.75	0.008	0.007	0.007	0.017	0.034	0.038	0.034	0.029	0.019
1.00	-0.030	-0.030	-0.025	-0.009	0.011	0.020	0.023	0.021	0.016
1.25	-0.043	-0.042	-0.037	-0.021	-0.002	0.009	0.014	0.015	0.013
1.50	-0.044	-0.043	-0.039	-0.025	-0.010	0.001	0.007	0.010	0.010
1.75	-0.041	-0.040	-0.037	-0.026	-0.013	-0.003	0.003	0.006	0.008
2.00	-0.037	-0.036	-0.033	-0.025	-0.015	-0.007	-0.001	0.003	0.006
2.50	-0.028	-0.028	-0.026	-0.022	-0.015	-0.010	-0.004	-0.001	0.002
3	-0.022	-0.021	-0.020	-0.018	-0.014	-0.010	-0.006	-0.004	0.000
4	-0.014	-0.014	-0.014	-0.012	-0.010	-0.008	-0.006	-0.005	-0.002
5	-0.009	-0.009	-0.009	-0.009	-0.008	-0.007	-0.006	-0.005	-0.002

* Minus sign indicates tensile stress.

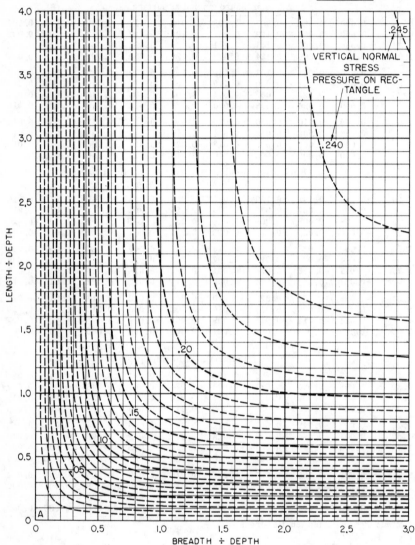

Fig. 33–3. Graph of vertical normal stress under corner of rectangle loaded with
unit pressure. For other points, the sketch above the graph (representing the graph
in miniature) shows where to read the stress ratios (Barber, unpublished).

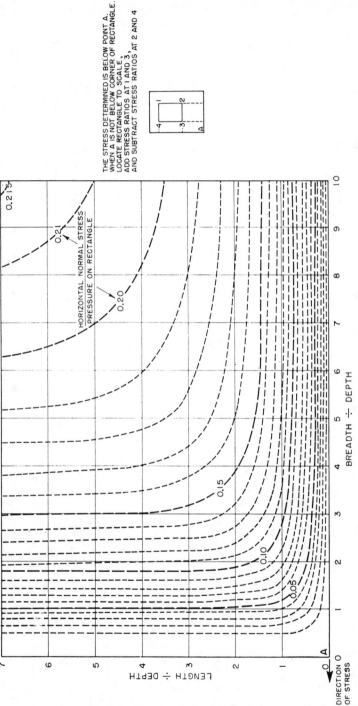

THE STRESS DETERMINED IS BELOW POINT A.
WHEN A IS NOT BELOW CORNER OF RECTANGLE.
LOCATE RECTANGLE TO SCALE,
ADD STRESS RATIOS AT 1 AND 3,
AND SUBTRACT STRESS RATIOS AT 2 AND 4

HORIZONTAL NORMAL STRESS
PRESSURE ON RECTANGLE

BREADTH ÷ DEPTH

LENGTH ÷ DEPTH

DIRECTION O
OF STRESS

Fig. 33–4. Graph of horizontal normal stress under corner of rectangle loaded with unit pressure. For other points, the sketch to right of the graph (representing the graph in miniature) shows where to read the stress ratios (Barber, unpublished).

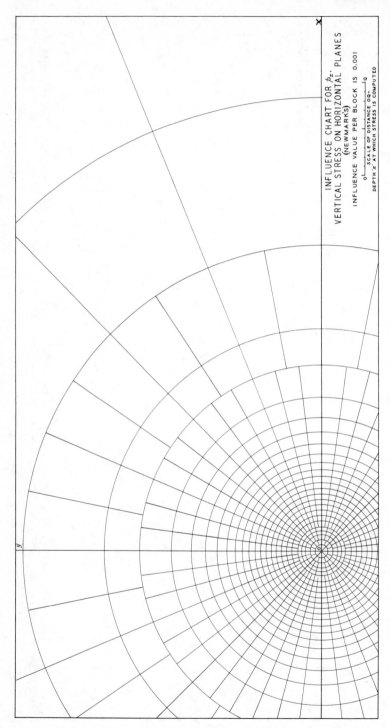

Fig. 33–5. Influence chart for vertical stress. To determine the stress below O from unit pressure, plot the loaded area in the plan on the graph to scale (OQ = depth of stress), count the number of blocks covered by the loaded area, and multiply the result by 0.001 (Newmark, 1942).

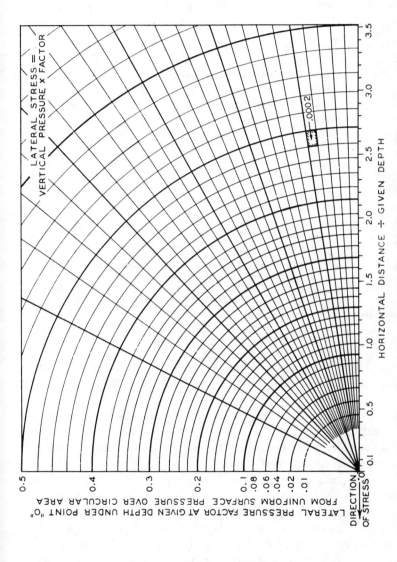

Fig. 33–6. Chart for computing lateral pressure at any point from finite surface load — Poisson's ratio = 0.5. To determine the stress below O from unit pressure, plot the loaded area in the plan on the graph to scale, count the number of blocks covered by the loaded area, and multiply the result by 0.0002 (Barber, unpublished).

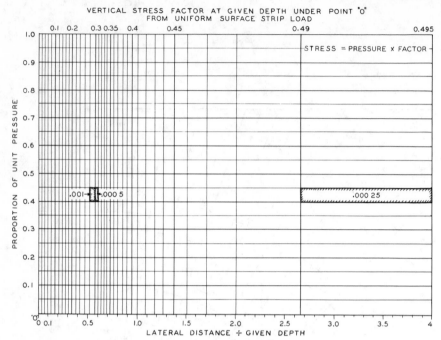

Fig. 33–7. Chart for computing vertical stress at any point from surface strip load. To determine the stress below O, plot the cross section of the load to scale shown on the left and bottom of the graph, count the blocks covered by the cross section, multiply by the appropriate factor (.001, .0005 or .00025), and add the resulting products (Barber, unpublished).

agreement between stresses measured with pressure cells and those computed from the theory of elasticity (Foster and Fergus, 1951; Cooper et al. 1957).

Cells may be oriented in several directions; for example, horizontal, vertical, and at 45 degrees. To measure a distribution, cells are usually placed at several depths; horizontal distribution is obtained by changing the location of the applied load.

Devices for measuring stresses in the soil should produce as little discontinuity as possible. At best, measurement is made of the pressure on a cell rather than in a continuous soil. Maintaining continuity of soil properties around the cell during installation is most important. Tests have shown that the cell diameter should be at least 5 times its thickness, and its compression should not be more than 0.0005 times its diameter (Taylor, 1947).

While there is no standard pressure measuring device, the following description of the U. S. Waterways Experiment Station pressure cell illustrates current practice (Woodman, 1955). A simpler cell has been used by agricultural engineers (Cooper and Nichols, 1959).

Table 33–2. Displacement factors for use in calculating displacements resulting from uniform pressure on a circular area. To calculate the displacement, use the formula, $S = (pa/E)F$, where $S =$ displacement, $p =$ pressure per unit area, $a =$ radius of area to which pressure is applied, $E =$ modulus of elasticity, and $F =$ displacement factor. (Barber, 1946).

Depth of point ÷ radius	Horizontal radial distance ÷ radius, r/a										
	0	0.25	0.5	0.75	1.0	1.25	1.5	2	2.5	3	4
z/a	Displacement factor for Poisson's ratio = 0.5, SE/pa										
0	1.50	1.48	1.40	1.25	0.95	0.66	0.54	0.39	0.30	0.26	0.18
0.5	1.34	1.31	1.23	1.09	0.89	0.68	0.55	0.40	0.31	0.27	0.19
1	1.06	1.05	0.98	0.89	0.78	0.66	0.56	0.41	0.32	0.27	0.19
1.5	0.83	0.83	0.79	0.73	0.67	0.60	0.52	0.40	0.32	0.28	0.20
2	0.67	0.67	0.65	0.62	0.57	0.53	0.48	0.39	0.32	0.28	0.20
3	0.47	0.47	0.46	0.45	0.43	0.41	0.38	0.34	0.30	0.27	0.21
4	0.36	0.36	0.35	0.35	0.34	0.33	0.32	0.30	0.28	0.25	0.20
5	0.29	0.29	0.29	0.29	0.29	0.28	0.28	0.25	0.24	0.23	0.19
	Displacement factor for Poisson's ratio = 0, SE/pa										
0	2.00	1.97	1.86	1.67	1.27	0.88	0.71	0.52	0.41	0.34	0.25
0.5	1.51	1.49	1.39	1.24	1.06	0.85	0.68	0.51	0.41	0.34	0.25
1	1.12	1.11	1.04	0.94	0.85	0.74	0.65	0.50	0.40	0.34	0.25
1.5	0.86	0.85	0.81	0.76	0.70	0.65	0.59	0.47	0.39	0.34	0.25
2	0.68	0.67	0.65	0.62	0.59	0.55	0.52	0.44	0.38	0.33	0.25
3	0.48	0.47	0.46	0.45	0.44	0.42	0.40	0.37	0.33	0.30	0.24
4	0.37	0.36	0.35	0.35	0.35	0.34	0.33	0.31	0.29	0.26	0.22
5	0.29	0.29	0.29	0.29	0.29	0.28	0.28	0.26	0.25	0.24	0.20

33–3 METHOD

33–3.1 Special Apparatus

Procure, or make from stainless steel, thin circular cells as shown in Figs. 33–8 and 33–9. The average total external pressure perpendicular to one face is transmitted through a layer of mercury to the internal weighing face to which are attached four active bonded-wire electrical resistance strain gauges (SR-4). Set the gauges in heat-cured Bakelite cement, as shown in Fig. 33–10, and waterproof them with Petrosene wax. Make electrical connections and balance circuits as shown in Fig. 33–11. Make joints by welding and soldering to eliminate gaskets, and anneal the whole device. Freeze and thaw the device to stabilize its dimensions. Make electrical connections through a strong, flexible, waterproof cable hermetically sealed to the cell which is filled with dry nitrogen gas. After evacuating the pressure-transfer cavity, completely fill it with mercury (see Fig. 33–8), and seal it by welding.

Make readings with a Baldwin-Southwark SR-4 Strain Indicator (Fig. 33–12). The use of four active gauges in the cell (two in tension and

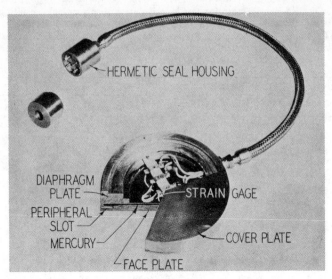

Fig. 33–8. U. S. Waterways Experiment Station earth pressure cell (Woodman, 1955).

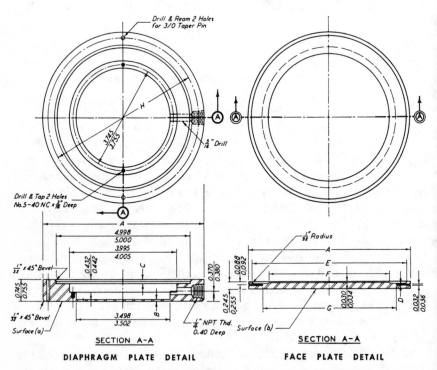

SECTION A-A

DIAPHRAGM PLATE DETAIL

SECTION A-A

FACE PLATE DETAIL

Fig. 33–9. Parts of earth pressure cell (Woodman, 1955).

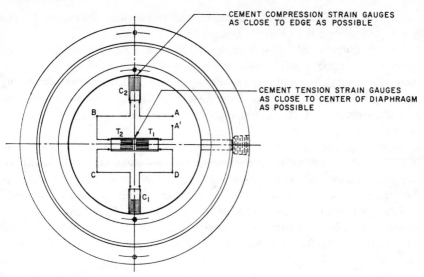

Fig. 33–10. Detail locations of gauges on diaphragm (Woodman, 1955).

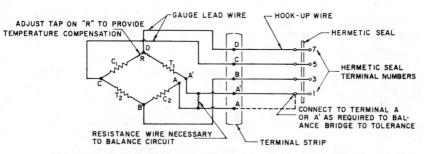

Fig. 33–11. Schematic diagram of gauge circuit (Woodman, 1955).

two in compression) provides temperature compensation, doubles the sensitivity, permits alternate readings, and eliminates the effect of variable resistance in connecting cables. Calibrate the cell by air pressure in a closed chamber with and without rubber membranes to eliminate pressure on the edges. Make readings at different temperatures while the cell is immersed in a stirred fluid.

33–3.2 Procedure

For readings at a rigid boundary such as a wall, seat the back of the cell uniformly against the wall with the weighing face preferably flush with the face of the wall. Carefully control the backfill to provide uniform conditions while preventing damage to the cell.

For readings within a soil mass, place each cell with an accurately known and stable position and orientation. Place cells at several depths and with several orientations, depending on the kind of distribution being investigated. Backfill the space around each cell taking care that the stress-strain characteristics of the soil around the cell are representative of the larger mass.

In a rolled fill, excavate 1 foot or more of soil with flat side slopes to prevent arching, seat cells on the bottom of the excavation, and recompact the soil, with the first layer sufficiently thick to protect the cell from damage by the roller. (Overcompaction is less detrimental than undercompaction.)

Check the operation and zero reading of the cells. Apply each type and magnitude of load at various locations, record all readings for each, and plot readings against coordinates to determine the pattern of stress distribution.

33–3.3 Comments

In backfilling an undisturbed soil after placing a pressure cell, maintaining the same water content and bulk density may not be sufficient, since the

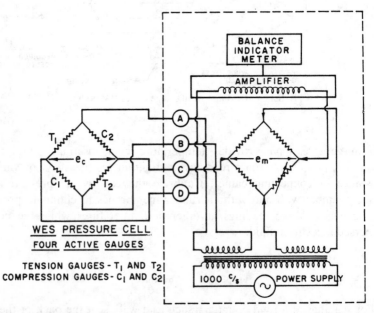

Fig. 33–12. Modified Baldwin-Southwark strain indicator showing connections to gauges in pressure cell (Woodman, 1955).

arrangement of soil particles has a marked effect on the stress-strain properties of the soil; a satisfactory placement method must be determined experimentally.

Cells currently in use are sensitive to eccentric loads; their compressibility is generally not the same as the soil. With time, the ratio of pressure to readings changes somewhat, and the reading for zero stress is not a constant.

Accuracy for 25 to 500 pounds per square inch is $\pm 10\%$ with residual stresses of $\pm \frac{1}{2}$ pound per square inch. For stresses near 25 pounds per square inch, comparable measurements in a uniform silt soil had a coefficient of variation of 10%.

33–4 LITERATURE CITED

Ahlvin, R. G. 1954. Direct measurement of shear stresses in soil mass. Proc. Highway Res. Board 33:471–474.

Barber, E. S. 1946. Application of triaxial compression test results to the calculation of flexible pavement thickness. Proc. Highway Res. Board 26:26–39.

Barber, E. S., and Sawyer, C. L. 1950. Application of triaxial compression test results to highway soil problems. Am. Soc. Testing Mater., Spec. Tech. Publ. 106:228–247.

Barber, E. S. 1952. Use of direct shear tests in highway design. Am. Soc. Testing Mater., Spec. Tech. Publ. 131:19–35.

Baron, F. 1947. A mathematical study of shearing stresses produced in a pavement by airplane. U. S. Civil Aeronautics Administration, Tech. Develop. Note 47.

Biot, M. A. 1941. Consolidation settlement under a rectangular load distribution. J. Appl. Phys. 12:426–430.

Bonse, R. P. H., and Kuhn, S. H. 1959. Dynamic forces exerted by moving vehicles on a road surface. Highway Res. Board Bull. 233.

Burmister, D. M. 1943. The theory of stresses and displacements in layered systems and application to the design of airport runways. Proc. Highway Res. Board 23:126–148.

Burmister, D. M. 1956. Stress and displacement characteristics of a two layer rigid base soil system: influence diagrams and practical applications. Proc. Highway Res. Board 35:773–814.

Coker, E. G., and Filon, L. N. G. 1931. A Treatise on Photo-Elasticity. Cambridge Univ. Press, Cambridge.

Cooper, A. W., VandenBerg, G. E., McColly H. F., and Erickson, A. E. 1957. Strain gage cell measures soil pressures. Agr. Eng. 38:232–235.

Cooper, A. W., and Nichols, M. L. 1959. Some observations on soil compaction tests. Agr. Eng. 40:264.

Dingwall, J. C., and Scrivener, F. H. 1954. Application of the elastic theory to highway embankments by use of difference equations. Proc. Highway Res. Board 33:474–482.

Foster, C. R., and Fergus, S. M. 1951. Stress distribution in a homogeneous soil. Highway Res. Board, Res. Rept. 12-F (Supplement, HRB Proc. 30:175).

Foster, C. R., and Ahlvin, R. G. 1954. Stresses and deflections induced by a uniform circular load. Proc. Highway Res. Board 33:467–470.

Goldbeck, A. T. 1938. The measurement of earth pressure on retaining walls. Proc. Highway Res. Board, Part II. pp. 66–80.

Gould, J. P. 1949. Analysis of pore pressure and settlement observations at Logan International Airport. Harvard Soil Mechanics Series No. 34. Cambridge.

Gray, H., and Hooks, I. J. 1948. Charts facilitate determination of stresses under loaded areas. Civil Eng. 18:373–375.

Hetenyi, M. 1946. Beams on Elastic Foundation. Univ. Michigan Press, Ann Arbor.

Holl, D. L. 1941. Plane-strain distribution of stress in elastic media. Iowa Eng. Exp. Sta. Bul. 148.

Housel, W. S. 1943. Earth pressure on tunnels. Trans. Am. Soc. Civil Eng. 108:1037–1058.

Hvorslev, J. J. 1951. Time lag and soil permeability in ground-water observations. U. S. Waterways Exp. Sta. Bul. 36.

Kallstenius, T., and Bergan, W. 1956. Investigation of soil pressure measuring by means of cells. Royal Swedish Geotech. Inst., Proc. No. 12.

Mansur, C. I., and Kaufman, R. I. 1958. Pile tests, low-sill structure, Old River, Louisiana. Trans. Am. Soc. Civil Eng. 123:715–748.

Moore, R. L., and Shaw, J. R. 1951. Pressures in a shallow rectangular bin. Proc. Am. Soc. Civil Eng. 77, Separate 82.

Newmark, N. M., 1935. Simplified computation of vertical pressures in elastic foundations. Univ. Illinois Eng. Exp. Sta. Circ. 24.

Newmark, N. M. 1942. Influence charts for computation of stresses in elastic foundations. Univ. Illinois Eng. Exp. Sta. Bul. 338.

Peck, R. B. 1943. Earth pressure measurements in open cuts, Chicago, (Ill.) Subway. Trans. Am. Soc. Civil Eng. 108:1008–1036.

Quinlan, P. M. 1953. The elastic theory of soil dynamics. Am. Soc. Testing Materials, Spec. Tech. Publ. 156:3–34.

Rowe, P. W. 1952. Anchored sheet-pile walls. Proc. Inst. of Civil Eng. London 1(1):27–70.

Soehne, W. 1958. Fundamentals of pressure distribution and soil compaction under tractor tires. Agr. Eng. 39:276–281.

Spangler, M. G., and Hennessy, R. L. 1946. A method of computing live loads transmitted to underground conduits. Proc. Highway Res. Board, 26:179–188.

Spangler, M. G. 1948. Stresses and deflections in flexible pipe culverts. Proc. Highway Res. Board, 28:249–259.

Spangler, M. G. 1951. Soil Engineering. International Textbook Co., Scranton, Pa.

Spangler, M. G. 1956. Influence of compression and shearing strains in soil foundations on structures under earth embankments. Highway Res. Board Bul. 125:70–177.

Spangler, M. G., and Mickle, J. L. 1956. Lateral pressures on retaining walls due to backfill surface loads. Highway Res. Board Bul. 141:1–18.

Taylor, D. W. 1947. Review of pressure distribution theories, earth pressure cell investigations and pressure distribution data. U. S. Waterways Exp. Sta. Progress Rept. pp. 211–236.

Taylor, D. W. 1948. Fundamentals of Soil Mechanics. pp. 258–261. John Wiley & Sons, Inc., New York.

Terzaghi, K. 1943. Theoretical Soil Mechanics. p. 367 and p. 407. John Wiley & Sons, Inc. New York.

Trabbic, G. W., Lask, K. V., and Buchele, W. F. 1959. Measurement of soil-tire interface pressures. Agr. Eng. 40:678–681.

Westergaard, H. M., 1952. Theory of Elasticity and Plasticity. Harvard Univ. Press.

Woodman, E. H., 1955. Pressure cells for field use. U. S. Waterways Exp. Sta. Bull. 40.

34 | Shear Strength

JOHN R. SALLBERG

*U. S. Dept. of Transportation, Bureau of Public Roads
Washington, D. C.*

34–1 GENERAL INTRODUCTION

In testing for shear strength, external forces are applied to the soil test specimen in such a way as to cause two adjoining parts of the specimen to slide relative to each other (see Fig. 34–1). The force developed within the soil, in opposition to sliding or shearing, is its shear resistance. The maximum shearing resistance developed in the soil is the shear strength of the soil.

The shear strength of soil is generally considered to be a function of cohesion between the soil particles and intergranular friction. This relationship can be represented as follows:

$$\text{Shear strength } (s) = c + fn \qquad [1]$$

in which

$s =$ shear strength (force per unit area),
$c =$ cohesion, or shear strength when normal stress (n) is zero, (force per unit area),
$f =$ coefficient of friction between the soil particles (dimensionless), and
$n =$ stress normal to the shear surface (force per unit area).

34–2 METHODS FOR MEASURING SHEAR STRENGTH

The shear strength of the soil can be measured either in place (in the field) or in the laboratory. In-place measurements include vane-shear, plate-load, and penetration tests.

The vane-shear test (American Soc. for Testing and Materials, 1956, 1968) consists of pushing the vane (a rod with four equally spaced vertical blades on the lower end) into the soil and measuring the torque required to rotate it slowly. The soil between the blades tends to turn with the device;

this soil shears from the surrounding soil on a cylindrical surface. The test is limited to soft materials into which the vane can be pushed.

The plate-load test (Sowers & Sowers, 1961, 1968) consists of applying steadily increasing vertical loads through a rigid plate to the surface of the soil and measuring the deformation under each load. After an initial settlement, the deformation versus applied load relationship is essentially linear until the ultimate bearing capacity is reached (when deformation increases rapidly) and shear failure occurs. The method for calculating shear strength from plate load tests depends upon whether the soil is cohesive or non-cohesive.

The penetration test (Am. Soc. Testing Mater., 1968; Hvorslev, 1949) consists of driving a 2-inch outside diameter split-barrel sampler into the ground with a 140-pound weight falling 30 inches. The number of blows required to force the sampler 12 inches into undisturbed soil is recorded. The method does not permit the calculation of shear strength, but is useful in foundation analysis. In sand and silt, the relative density can be estimated; in clay, the consistency or stiffness can be estimated.

Laboratory tests include miniature vane shear, direct shear, triaxial compression, and unconfined compression. The miniature vane-shear test (Skempton and Bishop, 1950; Testlab Corp., 1964) is similar to the field test described previously, and is useful in testing soft samples directly in the sampling tube. The vane is inserted through one end of the sampling tube into the soil, the vane is turned slowly, the torque is measured, and shear strength is calculated.

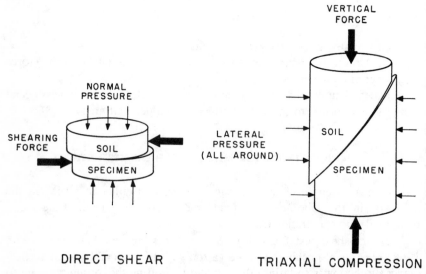

DIRECT SHEAR   TRIAXIAL COMPRESSION

Fig. 34–1. Basic features of the direct shear and triaxial compression test showing applied forces and shear surfaces.

The basic features of the direct-shear and triaxial-compression tests are shown in Fig. 34–1; the unconfined-compression test is similar to the triaxial test except that the lateral pressure is zero. In each of these three tests, the test specimen is sheared or compressed at a constant rate, and the forces necessary to cause this deformation are measured (shearing force for direct shear; vertical force for triaxial- and unconfined-compression tests) until the maximum resistance is developed. A constant or reducing resistance is evidence of failure. The maximum shearing resistance along the shearing surface can then be calculated. Methods for performing these three tests are described in the sections 34–4, 34–5, and 34–6.

The shear strength of soils is needed for the evaluation of the bearing capacity under foundations, the stability of earth slopes, earth pressures on retaining walls, and traction and support under vehicles. The type of shear test that should be made and the conditions of the test should be based upon the specific problem at hand.

34–3 FACTORS AFFECTING SHEAR-STRENGTH TEST RESULTS

Shear-strength test results are affected not only by the type of soil being tested, but also by (1) the soil conditions and (2) the test method.

The shear-strength of a soil is not a physical constant; it varies with stress history, structure, degree of disturbance, water content, and dry unit weight[1] of the soil. For example, clay soils are normally very strong when dry, but may be weak when wet. In soil strength tests, the condition of the soil specimen should represent as nearly as possible the condition of the soil material in the field. Undisturbed samples are used to represent soil as found in-place, and molded samples to represent soil to be compacted. Undisturbed samples may also be remolded at constant water content to determine the effect of disturbance on strength.

The test method may also affect the shear-strength values obtained. Consider a saturated specimen from which water is squeezed during a shear test. If drainage is prevented, pressure is developed in the pore water, and

---

[1] Dry unit weight is generally considered synonymous with bulk density. Dry unit weight is defined (Standard Definitions of Terms and Symbols Relating to Soil Mechanics, Am. Soc. Testing Mater. Designation: D 653–67) as follows: "The weight of soil solids per unit of total volume of soil mass." Bulk density is defined (Aldrich et al., 1956) as follows: "Mass per unit bulk volume of soil that has been dried to constant weight at 105°C." Basically, both definitions are the same; the dry unit weight or the bulk density of a soil sample is the ratio of its oven-dried weight to its volume before drying. In most soil mechanics laboratories, the samples are oven-dried at temperatures ranging from 105° to 115°C. The terms "mass" and "weight" are not synonymous, but for most practical purposes the units and the values are the same; a pound of mass weighs a pound (exactly true at 45 degrees latitude and at sea level).

the strength of the specimen is reduced. Shear strength is proportional to the pressure between the soil particles; this, in turn, equals the total pressure minus the pore pressure. Thus, for constant total pressure, increased pore pressure decreases strength. Shear-strength tests have not been standardized; considerable freedom in testing procedures is necessary to test soil samples properly to determine their behavior under field stress conditions. The test method should, as nearly as possible, reproduce the conditions imposed on the soil material in the field. There are three basic types of shear-strength test. These are (*1*) the unconsolidated-undrained shear test, in which *no consolidation* under the normal pressure (in a direct-shear test) or under the lateral or confining pressure (in the triaxial test) is permitted prior to shearing, and in which *no drainage* is permitted during shear; (*2*) the consolidated-undrained test; and (*3*) the consolidated-drained test.

In the following sections, specific methods currently used by the U. S. Bureau of Public Roads for performing direct-shear, triaxial-compression, and unconfined-compression tests are described. The method for direct shear provides for consolidation prior to shearing and permits drainage during shear. The triaxial-compression test described is an unconsolidated-undrained test, as is the unconfined-compression test. Apparatus and methods for performing consolidated-drained and consolidated-undrained triaxial compression tests are described elsewhere (Am. Soc. Testing Mater., 1964; Bishop and Henkel, 1964; Lambe, 1951).

34–4 DIRECT SHEAR

34–4.1 Introduction

This shear-strength test consists of four steps: (*1*) obtaining a soil test specimen (see Fig. 34–1 for general shape) either by trimming undisturbed samples or by molding disturbed samples; (2) placing the soil test specimen in a horizontally-split box (see Figures 34–2 and 34–3) with approximately half of the specimen in the upper frame and the remainder in the lower frame; (*3*) consolidating the specimen, as desired, under the appropriate normal load; and (*4*) shearing the specimen at a constant rate of shear. Drainage and immersion are provided through porous plates above and below the test specimen.

The direct-shear test is one of the oldest methods for determining the shear strength of soil materials. All types of soil can be tested by direct shear. The apparatus described herein is relatively small and is suitable only for fine-grained soils, but larger apparatus can be used satisfactorily to test gravels. Other direct-shear apparatus and test methods are presented elsewhere (Am. Soc. Testing Mater., 1964; Lambe, 1951).

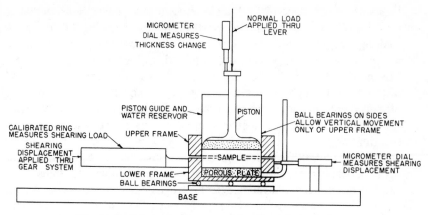

Fig. 34–2. Schematic diagram of the direct shear device.

The principal advantages of the direct-shear test are: (1) simplicity of operation, because the apparatus is mechanical, with very few adjustments required; (2) speed, because the test specimen is relatively thin, so that consolidation or swelling takes place rapidly, and testing time is short; and (3) ease in applying whatever normal stress is desired.

The principal disadvantages are: (1) the specimen is "forced" to fail on a specific plane, not necessarily the weakest plane; (2) progressive shear failure occurs, with shear starting at the edges and progressing toward the center of the specimen, the effect being development of less total resistance than if failure had occurred across all points on the shear surface simultaneously; (3) undrained tests cannot normally be performed because the apparatus is not watertight; and (4) stresses on planes other than the shear plane cannot be calculated.

The advantages noted above are the principal reasons why many soil laboratories doing routine testing continue to employ the direct-shear test; the disadvantages have caused many researchers to rely more heavily upon the triaxial compression test.

34–4.2   Method [2]

34-4.2.1   SPECIAL APPARATUS

1. Shear device (Fig. 34–2 and 34–3): The shear device consists of two frames, each with an inside diameter of 1-15/16 inches, arranged so that the upper frame can move vertically but not horizontally during the test, while the lower frame moves horizontally and rides on ball bear-

---

[2] Am. Soc. Testing Mater. (1964).

ings with a clearance of 0.01 inch between the frames. This clearance may be eliminated, except when shearing, by screwing together two wedges located under the lower frame. The lower frame contains a porous stone, leaving a space 0.250 inch deep for half of the specimen. The normal load is applied by weights through a lever and a guided piston with a rough porous face. Two retaining pins prevent shearing displacement until removed when the shearing test is started. The shearing and normal displacements are measured by micrometer dials. The shearing stress is measured by a 200-pound proof-ring which deflects approximately 0.0002 inch per pound. (Equivalent direct-shear apparatus is available from most manufacturers of soil testing apparatus. This specific equipment is available from Hogentogler & Co., Washington D. C.; shop drawings are available to instrument manufacturers from the U. S. Bureau of Public Roads.)

2. Motor; 1/20 horsepower, constant-speed, with gear box capable of applying shear displacement at a uniform rate of 0.002 inch per minute.
3. Cylindrical metal blank, 0.5 inch thick and 1-5/8 inches in diameter.

34–4.2.2 PROCEDURE

Eliminate the clearance between the boxes by tightening the wedges. Trim a soil specimen 0.5 inch thick and 1-15/16 inches in diameter, weigh it, and place it in the shear device. (Soil can also be placed in the device in loose or disturbed state and be compacted to the desired dry unit weight prior to testing.) Assemble the remainder of the device and determine the

Fig. 34–3. Direct shear apparatus.

initial thickness of the soil specimen from the vertical dial, which has been previously calibrated under the normal load with the blank substituted for the specimen.

Apply the desired normal load. Then either shear the specimen immediately, or allow it to come to equilibrium under the normal load, either in air or inundated by a head of water in the outlet tubes. When ready to shear the specimen, read the vertical dial to determine the thickness change, siphon off excess water, and loosen the wedges. Set the shear-displacement dial to zero, and remove the retaining pins. Reset the vertical dial to zero, so that vertical displacements during shear can be easily read. Place the spacers, with bearings attached, between the vertical attachments on the upper and lower frames, so that the upper frame can move vertically but not horizontally. Connect the motor to the shaft and start the motor. Record sufficient dial readings to define the relation between shearing displacement, vertical displacement, and shearing load. After the shearing stress stops increasing, stop testing, remove the specimen, and note its appearance. Weigh the specimen after drying it to constant weight at 110°C. (230°F.).

34–4.2.3 CALCULATIONS AND PLOTTING OF RESULTS

Include in the report all the basic test data, including normal pressure, shear displacements, and corresponding shear-resistance values and specimen thickness changes. In particular, show the maximum shearing resistance, the initial water content, the initial wet and dry unit weights, and the change in specimen thickness during pre-shear consolidation.

The maximum shearing resistance is equal to the applied shearing force divided by the area in shear (the initial cross sectional area of the specimen). The initial water content of the test specimen is equal to the difference between the initial wet weight and the oven-dry weight divided by the oven-dry weight. The initial wet unit weight in pounds per cubic feet equals the initial wet weight in pounds divided by the initial volume of the test specimen in cubic feet. The initial dry unit weight equals the oven-dry weight divided by the initial volume.

Next, plot the shearing resistances as ordinates against shear displacements as abscissas. If two or more identical specimens have been tested under different normal pressures, plot the maximum or otherwise designated shearing resistances as ordinates against corresponding normal stresses as abscissas to obtain the relationship between shear strength and normal stress. (See equation [1] section 34–1.)

34–4.2.4 COMMENTS

Direct-shear test results are affected by each step in preparing and testing the soil specimen. Generally, each disturbance will reduce the shear strength. Drying of the test specimen and friction within the shear box may, however, result in larger apparent strength values.

Reproducibility of results is reasonably good. For example, the coefficient of variation of the shear strength of a clay was about 7%. Twelve specimens of the same clay were molded at the same water content and dry unit weight, and were tested in two identical direct shear devices (6 in each device). The average shear-strength values, obtained in the two devices, were 0.98 and 0.97 ksf. (kips per square foot, where 1 kip = 1,000 pounds), and the coefficients of variation were 7.5 and 6.1%, respectively. Test results of undisturbed samples from one general location and soil type can be expected to vary much more than this because of the natural variations within soil deposits.

34–5 TRIAXIAL COMPRESSION

34–5.1 Introduction

The triaxial-compression test, as described herein, is an unconsolidated-undrained type of test; consolidated undrained and consolidated-drained type tests are described elsewhere (Am. Soc. Testing Mater., 1964; Bishop and Henkel, 1964).

This shear-strength test consists of four steps: (*1*) obtaining a soil test specimen (see Fig. 34–1 for general shape) by either trimming undisturbed soil samples or by molding disturbed soil samples; (*2*) placing the test specimen within a rubber sleeve or membrane inside the triaxial cell (Fig. 34–4); (*3*) applying a predetermined lateral pressure (chamber pressure) around the specimen, while keeping the axial loading piston fixed; and (*4*) testing for shear strength by increasing the axial (vertical) load until the maximum resistance is obtained.

This test method can be used with both saturated and unsaturated soil specimens and is a rapid procedure for determining the relation between the stress and strain in a specimen under various constant lateral pressures. Test specimens having dimensions other than those specified may be used, provided the length is equal to or greater than twice the diameter.

The triaxial-compression test (or cylindrical-compression test) has been used for about 30 years and is generally considered the best all-around soil shear test. Its principal advantages are: (*1*) tests can be performed on all types of soil except soft cohesive soils that will fail under their own weight; (*2*) all basic variations of shear test can be performed—unconsolidated-undrained, consolidated-undrained, and consolidated-drained; (*3*) the plane of failure is not restricted to one plane as in the direct-shear test; and (*4*) stresses on any particular plane (or on all planes) can be calculated within the soil specimen.

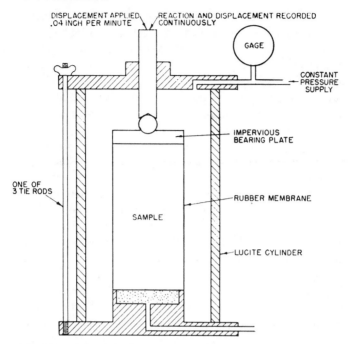

Fig. 34–4. Schematic diagram of the triaxial compression device.

The principal disadvantages of the triaxial-compression test are: (*1*) the equipment and testing procedures are complex, particularly when pore-water pressures are measured during undrained tests (such measurements are described by Bishop and Henkel [1964] and Lambe [1951]); (*2*) the time required for performing consolidated or drained tests may be excessive; (*3*) specimen volume changes are difficult to measure during the test; (*4*) vertical (or axial) pressures are difficult to determine because the end areas of the specimen change during deformation of the specimen; and (*5*) the applied axial loads may be affected by piston friction and resistance offered by the rubber membrane and filter strips (when used).

34–5.2 Method [3]

34–5.2.1 SPECIAL APPARATUS

1. Test-specimen cutter and guide: Figure 34–5 shows the general construction of a test-specimen cutter and guide. Construct the guide so that the specimen cutter may be moved vertically without horizontal deviation. Prepare the cutter in cylindrical form, sharpened at one end,

[3] Am. Soc. Testing Mater. (1964).

and of such dimensions that it will form a test specimen having a length greater than twice its diameter. Machine the cutter to have an inside diameter of 2.000 inches for approximately ⅛ inch at the cutting end and approximately 2.005 inches in the remaining length of approximately 6 inches.

2. Mold for test specimens of disturbed cohesive soils: Make the mold in cylindrical form, with an inside diameter of 2 inches and a length of approximately 10 inches. A split mold is preferable. Fit the mold with two plungers to secure compaction at the top and bottom of the test specimen. Make the diameter of the plungers 0.005 inch less than that of the mold.

3. Mold for test specimens of cohesionless soils: Make the mold cylindrical in shape, split lengthwise, with an inside diameter of 2.00 inches plus twice the thickness of the rubber sleeve, and with a length of 4.5 inches. Provide attachments which allow the mold to be fastened firmly to the base of the triaxial device, and provide a metal ring to hold the mold together.

4. Triaxial device: Prepare the apparatus in a manner similar to that indicated in Fig. 34–4, where the test specimen is shown enclosed in a thin rubber sleeve, placed between two disks (upper bearing plate and

Fig. 34–5. Apparatus for trimming and molding triaxial compression test specimens: 1. Piano-wire saw; 2. Specimen mold for disturbed cohesive soils; 3. Sample cutter and guide; 4. Specimen mold for cohesionless soils; 5. Rubber sleeve to retain specimen; 6. Beveled straightedge.

base), and subjected to a constant confining air pressure. Provide an outlet tube at the base of the device. Make the top of the device of brass, and equip it with a piston of hardened steel that is lapped into a bronze bushing loosely enough to slide under its own weight, but tightly enough to be airtight. Make the inner end of the piston concave to fit a steel sphere ½ inch in diameter. When assembled, with the test specimen in place and the tie rods drawn tight, the triaxial device forms an airtight chamber. (Similar devices are available from most manufacturers of soil-testing apparatus.)

5. Loading device: Prepare or obtain a compression-testing machine capable of applying a vertical force to the lapped piston and capable of displacing it at a rate of 2% of the sample length per minute. Measure the differential vertical load by a calibrated ring and measure the vertical displacement by a micrometer. (A loading device with a maximum capacity of 1,000 pounds will be satisfactory to test most soil specimens 2.0 inches in diameter. Suitable devices are available from most manufacturers of soil-testing apparatus.)

6. Rubber sleeve, 6 inches in length, 0.012 inch or less in thickness, and of diameter such that it will slip easily over a test specimen 2 inches in diameter.

7. Air supply from an air pressure line or reservoir, with a gauge pressure somewhat greater than the lateral pressure desired on the test specimen (50 pounds per square inch [psi.] should be adequate for most purposes), and with pressure reduction valves capable of maintaining the lateral pressure desired.

8. Vacuum system capable of maintaining approximately 7 psi. of vacuum.

9. Piano wire saw.

10. Micrometer dial gauge, 0.001-inch minimum reading, 0- to 1-inch range.

11. Miter box, 4 inches long.

12. Cylindrical metal blank, 2 inches in diameter and 4 inches in length.

13. Cylindrical metal sleeve, thin-walled, with an inside diameter of 2.15 inches and with a length of 5 inches.

14. Calipers, 0- to 6-inch range.

34–5.2.2 PREPARATION OF TEST SPECIMEN

34–5.2.2.1 Test Specimen from Undisturbed Sample. Obtain an original sample large enough to provide a trimmed specimen 2 inches in diameter and 4 inches in length. Trim the undisturbed sample so that one end is a plane surface, perpendicular to the direction in which the load is to be applied. Place the sample, with trimmed surface down, on the platform of the sample guide. Place the lightly greased sample cutter with cutting edge on the top surface of the sample; and force the cutter down lightly and gradually, as excess material is trimmed from the outside, to minimize the pressure required on the cutter. Make the trimming motions outward and downward from the cutter, leaving a column of soil slightly larger than the outside diameter of the cutting edge.

When more soil has entered the cutter than is required for the test specimen, remove the excess soil at the bottom with the piano wire saw. Remove the cutter from the support, force the specimen lightly from the cutter through the top or larger end, and place it in a miter box. Cut the specimen to the desired length and make the ends parallel by means of the piano wire saw and a beveled straightedge. Weigh the prepared specimen and record the weight as the initial wet weight.

34–5.2.2.2 Test Specimen from Disturbed Cohesive Soil. Assemble the mold for test specimens of disturbed cohesive soil, as shown in Fig. 34–5, except place the metal blank in the mold between the two plungers. Place the apparatus with the metal blank in place in the loading device, bring the compression head in contact with the top plunger, and record the reading of the dial gauge. (This reading corresponds to a specimen length of 4 inches.) Arrange the dial gauge so that it can be left in place during the compaction of the test specimen. Remove the top plunger and blank.

Take the exact weight of air-dry or wet soil that will result in the required dry unit weight when compacted in the mold to a length of 4 inches. Add to the soil the additional water required to give the desired water content and stir the mixture until it is uniform. Determine the total weight of soil and water, and add additional water to replace that lost by evaporation.

Add the wet soil gradually to the mold while tamping it with a light wooden rod to ensure uniform compaction. Replace the top plunger; and apply a load by means of the loading device, until the dial gauge indicates that the test specimen has been compacted to a length of 4.000 inches. Hold the load constant for 2 minutes; then remove the load and check the rebound of the specimen. Load the specimen again as needed to obtain the desired length. Remove the plungers, open the mold, and take out the test specimen.

34–5.2.2.3 Test Specimen from Cohesionless Soil. Place the metal blank, 2 inches in diameter and 4 inches in length, on the pedestal of the triaxial device, and place the top bearing plate on the blank. Place the apparatus in the loading device, bring the compression head into contact with the bearing plate, and record the reading of the dial gauge. (This reading corresponds with a specimen length of 4 inches.) Arrange the dial gauge so that it can be left in place during the compaction of the test specimen.

Clamp the rubber sleeve to the bottom pedestal of the base of the triaxial device to form an airtight joint. Attach the mold for test specimens of cohesionless soils to the base of the triaxial device, with the sleeve extended up through the top of the mold. Draw the sleeve tightly, so that it fits closely against the walls of the mold, and turn the end down over the mold. Weigh sufficient soil to give the desired dry unit weight when it is compacted. Place the soil in the rubber sleeve, rodding it firmly to make a uniform structure at the desired dry unit weight.

When all the material is compacted in the mold, place the bearing plate on the top of the specimen and read the dial gauge to determine the length. If the proper length has not been obtained, apply additional compaction, or recompact the entire specimen, adjusting the amount of rodding so that the desired length or dry unit weight is obtained. Draw up the top of the rubber sleeve from the mold and clamp it around the top bearing plate. Apply a vacuum of approximately 7 pounds per square inch to the specimen through the outlet in the base of the triaxial device. Carefully remove the split mold from the test specimen.

34–5.2.3 TEST PROCEDURE

Insert test specimens prepared from undisturbed or disturbed cohesive samples into the triaxial device, using the following procedure: Slip one end of the rubber sleeve over the lower disk of the triaxial device, and clamp it. Insert a thin metal sleeve, the inside diameter of which is slightly greater than the diameter of the test specimen, into the rubber sleeve, and place the metal sleeve on the lower disk. Insert the specimen into the metal sleeve and then remove the metal sleeve. If necessary, invert the triaxial device to insert a very weak test specimen.

After the test specimen has been inserted into the rubber sleeve or molded in the sleeve, place the top bearing plate on top of the specimen, clamp the rubber sleeve to the top bearing plate, and place the ½-inch ball in the socket of the plate. Place the lucite cylinder (other equivalent transparent, rigid plastics may also be used) in the grooves of the triaxial device, place the top plate of the device on the lucite cylinder, and attach it to the base. Place the lapped piston on the steel ball, place the calibrated ring and dial gauge on the piston, and adjust the head of the testing machine to make contact with the piston. If necessary, support the weight of the calibrated ring and the dial gauge by an attachment between them and the top plate of the device; leave the support in place until the lateral pressure is applied. Admit compressed air into the triaxial chamber until the required lateral pressure is indicated on the gauge. Select the lateral pressure applied to the test specimen on the basis of the conditions under which the material represented by the specimen will be used in the field. At this point, turn off the vacuum used in molding cohesionless soils. Test three specimens, each under a different lateral pressure. Adjust the micrometer dial in the calibrating ring to zero to allow for the air pressure under the piston.

Apply the load to the piston so that the displacement is at the rate of 2% of the length of the test specimen per minute. Note and record readings of the differential vertical load (load applied through piston) at selected increments of deformation. Apply the load until it becomes constant, or reduces, or until the specimen is shortened 20% of its length. Release the lateral pressure and disassemble the triaxial device.

If knowledge of the water content of the test specimen is desired, weigh the specimen, dry it in an oven at 110°C. (230°F.), and weigh it again.

34–5.2.4 CALCULATIONS AND PLOTTING OF RESULTS

Calculate the initial water content (if desired), initial wet and dry unit weights, strain, and vertical stress differences as follows:

$$\text{Water content (percent)} = [(W_i - W)/W] \times 100$$
$$\text{Initial wet unit weight} = W_i/V$$
$$\text{Initial dry unit weight} = W/V$$

where

W_i = initial weight of test specimen,

W = weight of test specimen, oven-dried, and

V = volume of test specimen prior to test.

Strain = $\Delta h/h$.

Vertical stress difference

$$(v - l) = [P/A][(h - \Delta h)/h]$$

where

Δh = reduction in length of specimen,

h = initial length of test specimen,

v = vertical pressure applied to specimen,

l = lateral pressure applied to specimen,

P = total vertical load measured on testing machine or proving ring gauge (does not include vertical force applied by air pressure within triaxial chamber),

A = average cross sectional area of test specimen prior to the test, and

$(h - \Delta h)/h$ = correction for increased cross sectional area of test specimen due to deformation during test. (This correction assumes constant volume and is generally applied in the absence of volume-change measurements.)

Plot the stress differences ($v - l$ values) as ordinates against the strains as abscissas. Use the maximum or otherwise designated stress difference derived from these curves, together with the lateral pressures, to determine a relation between normal and shear stresses by means of Mohr's circle diagrams. Use of Mohr's circle in graphical analysis of stress data from the triaxial test is described in most soil mechanics texts (for example, Sowers and Sowers, 1961).

34–5.2.5 COMMENTS

Test specimens may be molded by suitable impact methods that will produce specimens of the desired dimensions and dry unit weight. Apparatus for the purpose has been described by the U. S. Army Corps of Engineers (1946).

Triaxial-shear-test results are affected by each step in preparing and testing the soil specimen. Each disturbance will tend to weaken the soil.

On the other hand, friction between the loading piston and the top plate of the triaxial device, plus the resistance of the rubber sleeve to stretching when the specimen is deformed, may add 5% or more to the measured strength of the test specimen. Mounting the proof-ring within the chamber is used to eliminate the friction error.

Reproducibility of test results is somewhat better than for the direct-shear test. As an example, the coefficients of variation of the vertical stress difference $(v - l)$ of clay specimens, compacted to the same unit weight at the same water content and tested at 0, 2, and 4 ksf. lateral pressure, were 2, 2, and 4%, respectively. (Eight specimens were tested at each lateral pressure; the average $v - l$ values were 8.72, 9.68, and 10.31 ksf., respectively.)

Test results of undisturbed samples can be expected to vary within much wider limits than those above because of the natural variations within soil deposits.

34–6 UNCONFINED COMPRESSION

34–6.1 Introduction

The unconfined-compression test is a special case of the triaxial-compression test. The lateral or confining pressure is zero. It is unnecessary to use the triaxial device or to enclose the specimen in a rubber sleeve. The test is mainly suited for testing cohesive soils and consists of two steps: (*1*) obtaining a soil test specimen similar in shape to that used in the triaxial-compression test (see Fig. 34–1) by either trimming undisturbed samples or by molding disturbed samples, and (*2*) applying an increasing axial (vertical) load until the maximum resistance is obtained. The unconfined-compression test is the simplest form of the unconsolidated-undrained shear test. It is the quickest and most common strength test for cohesive soil materials. The test is most suited to measuring the strength of foundation soils before they are loaded or unloaded. The test is limited, however, to soils that have sufficient cohesion to provide test specimens that will not fail under their own weight. Also, the compressive strength of undisturbed samples may not equal the in-place strength unless the in-place confining pressures are replaced and maintained by capillary tensions within the sample.

34–6.2 Method [4]

34–6.2.1 SPECIAL APPARATUS

1. Loading device: Any standard compression-testing machine, as described in most catalogs for scientific apparatus, or an apparatus similar to the gear system and calibrated ring shown in Fig. 34–6 that has provision for applying strain at the rate of 2% of the sample length per minute and measuring the reaction. The counter shown in Fig. 34–6 gives the displacements of the loading piston.
2. Items 1, 2, 9, 10, 11, and 14 described for triaxial compression in section 34–5.2.1.

Fig. 34-6. Unconfined compression device.

34–6.2.2 PROCEDURE

Cut or mold the specimen to a right circular cylinder or a right prism with length equal to twice the lateral dimension.

Measure and record the length and the lateral dimensions of the specimen. Weigh the prepared specimen and record the weight as the initial wet weight.

Bring the bearing plate in contact with the specimen. Apply compressive strain at the rate of 2% of the specimen length per minute. Record the load and displacement until the load decreases or the specimen is shortened 20%. Note the appearance of the specimen.

34–6.2.3 CALCULATIONS

Calculate the initial water content, initial wet and dry unit weights, strain, and vertical stress (corrected for increase in end area of the test specimen resulting from deformation during test) as shown in section 34–5.2.4. Determine the maximum stress value if one is reached; otherwise, note the value at 20% strain. This stress value is the unconfined compressive strength.

---

[4] See also American Society for Testing and Materials (1968).

34–6.2.4 COMMENTS

Test specimens may be molded by suitable impact methods that will produce specimens of the desired dimensions and unit dry weight. Apparatus for this purpose has been described by the U. S. Corps of Engineers (1946).

Reproducibility of unconfined-compression test results is very good, provided the test specimens are identical. For example, the coefficient of variation of the unconfined compressive strength of two stiff clays ranged from 1.2 (average strength 5.8 ksf.) to 0.9% (average strength 12.1 ksf.). The two sets of test specimens were compacted from disturbed soil samples; eight specimens of the weaker clay and six specimens of the stronger clay were tested. Test results of undisturbed samples can be expected to vary within much wider limits than those above because of natural variations within soils.

34–7 LITERATURE CITED

Aldrich, D. G., Lutz, J. F., Retzer, J. L., Rogers, H. T., Smith, F. B., and Taylor, S. A. 1956. Report of definitions approved by the Committee on Terminology, Soil Science Society of America. Soil Sci. Soc. Am. Proc. 20:430–440.

American Society for Testing and Materials. 1956. Symposium on vane shear testing of soils. Spec. Tech. Publ. 193. Am. Soc. Testing Mater., Philadelphia.

American Society for Testing and Materials. 1964. Procedures for Testing Soils. Am. Soc. Testing Mater., Philadelphia.

American Society for Testing and Materials. 1964. Laboratory shear testing of soils. Spec. Tech. Publ. 361. Am. Soc. Testing Mater., Philadelphia.

American Society for Testing and Materials. 1968. ASTM Standards, Vol. 11. Am. Soc. Testing Mater., Philadelphia.

Bishop, A. W., and Henkel, D. J. 1964. The Measurement of Soil Properties in the Triaxial Test. Edward Arnold Publishers, Ltd., London.

Hvorslev, M. J. 1949. Subsurface Exploration and Sampling of Soils for Civil Engineering Purposes. Available through The Engineering Foundation, 29 West 39th Street, New York 18, N. Y.

Lambe, T. W. 1951. Soil Testing for Engineers. John Wiley and Sons, Inc., New York.

Skempton, A. W., and Bishop, A. W. 1950. The measurement of the shear strength of soils. Geotechnique. 2:90–108.

Sowers, G. B., and Sowers, G. F. 1961. Introductory Soil Mechanics and Foundations. The Macmillan Company, New York.

Testlab Corporation. 1964. General Catalog, Testing Apparatus and Laboratory Supplies for Soils, Concrete, Asphalt, Highway Foundations. Chicago.

U. S. Army Corps of Engineers. 1946. Resinous water repellents for soils. Tech. Mem. No. 217–1. Waterways Exp. Sta., Vicksburg, Miss.

35

Volume Change

W. G. HOLTZ
*United States Bureau of Reclamation
Denver, Colorado*

35–1 INTRODUCTION

These methods explain how to make consolidation and expansion tests on undisturbed or compacted soil samples which have no particle sizes greater than 3/16 inch (passing the No. 4 standard ASTM sieve). These methods conform closely to those most commonly used in the United States today (Casagrande and Fadum, 1940; Lambe, 1951; U. S. Bureau of Reclamation, 1960; Subcommittee 3 of U. S. National Committee, 1948; Terzaghi and Peck, 1948; Taylor, 1951; Holtz and Gibbs, 1956; Am. Soc. Test. Mater., 1968). The tests are made to determine (*1*) magnitude of volume change under load, (*2*) rate of volume change, (*3*) influence of wetting on volume change, and (*4*) axial permeability of laterally confined soil under axial load during consolidation or expansion. Drainage takes place axially. Permeant water is applied axially for determining the effect of saturation and permeability. The volume change of expansive soils in an unloaded condition can also be determined. The specimens prepared for these tests may also be used to determine the vertical or volume shrinkage as the water content decreases. Total volume change for expansive soils is determined from expansion plus shrinkage values for different ranges of water content.

Provided that natural conditions and operating conditions are duplicated, consolidation and expansion test data may be used to estimate the extent and rate of settlement or uplift in subgrades beneath structures or in structures formed from soils, and shrinkage tests may be used to estimate the volume changes which will occur in soils upon drying.

35–2 PRINCIPLES

The consolidation and expansion characteristics of a soil mass are influenced by a number of factors. Some of these are size and shape of the soil particles, water content, density, load history, and chemical properties.

Because of the difficulty in evaluating these individual factors, the volume-change properties cannot be predicted to any degree of accuracy unless laboratory tests are performed. When settlement or uplift problems are critical, it is important to test samples from the sites being considered. Volume-change theories (Terzaghi and Peck, 1948; Taylor, 1951; Holtz and Gibbs, 1956; Terzaghi, 1953; Gibbs, 1953) and experience are combined to translate test data into settlement or uplift predictions for a field problem. The consolidation theory most commonly used is that of Terzaghi (1953), which is based on several simplifying assumptions. These include the assumptions that the soil in the field is homogeneous, is saturated, and has one-dimensional drainage and compression. The actual structure loading most comparable to the laboratory test loading is that exerted over a large area on a fine-grained, saturated, compressible stratum, at considerable depth, which is bounded above and below by dense, permeable materials. Where the stratum is near the surface, and for small loaded areas, shear failure may be important. If settlement is caused principally by lateral movement from under the loaded area, the soil should be analyzed for shear strength (section 34), and the bearing capacity should be determined on this basis.

The laboratory tests described herein are primarily intended for the study of soils having no particles larger than the No. 4 standard sieve size (3/16 inch). If the test is made on the minus No. 4 fraction of soils containing gravel material (plus No. 4), some adjustment is required in the analysis. Gravel reduces volume change because it replaces compressible soil and interferes with consolidation. This latter effect is usually noticeable only when the gravel content exceeds about 25% (Gibbs, 1950).

35–3 METHOD FOR CONSOLIDATION [1]

35–3.1 Special Apparatus[2]

1. Consolidometer: Consolidometers most used in the United States are of the fixed-ring and floating-ring types, illustrated in Fig. 35–1 and 35–2, respectively. Either of these is suitable for consolidation testing. Both types are available commercially. In the fixed-ring container, all specimen movement relative to the container is downward during consolidation and upward during expansion. In the floating-ring container, movement of the soil sample is from the top and bottom toward the center of the container during consolidation and away from the center during expansion. The specimen containers for the fixed-ring consolidometer

---

[1] Holtz and Gibbs, 1958.
[2] Commercially available from all except the third source listed in section 37–2.2.1.

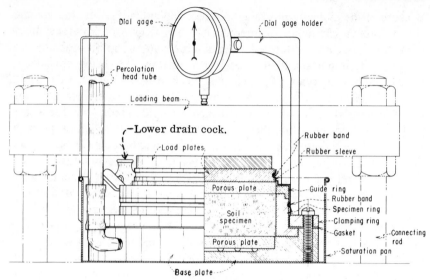

Fig. 35–1. Fixed-ring consolidometer.

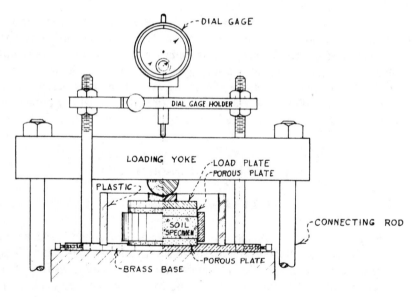

Fig. 35–2. Floating-ring consolidometer.

and the floating-ring consolidometer consist of brass or plastic rings, and other component parts as shown. Sizes of container rings most commonly used vary between 4-¼-inch diameter by 1-¼ inches deep and 2-½-inch diameter by ¾ inch deep, although other sizes are used. However, the diameter should be not less than 2 inches and the depth

Fig. 35–3. Platform scale loading device.

not greater than three-tenths of the diameter, except that the depth must not be less than ¾ inch for specimens of small diameter. Lesser depths introduce errors caused by the magnitude of surface disturbance, while large depths cause excessive side friction (Van Zelst, 1948). In a test using the floating-ring apparatus, the friction between the soil specimen and container is smaller than with the fixed-ring apparatus. On the other hand, the fixed-ring apparatus is more suitable for saturation purposes and when permeability data are required. Porous stones are required at the top and bottom of the specimen to allow axial drainage and/or application of water. The apparatus must allow vertical movement of the top porous stone for fixed-ring consolidometers, or vertical movement for top and bottom porous stones for floating-ring consolidometers, as consolidation or expansion takes place. A ring gauge machined to the height of the ring container to an accuracy of 0.001 inch is required; thus, the ring gauge for 1¼-inch-high specimens will have a height of 1.250 inches. Measure the diameter of the specimen container ring to 0.001 inch.

2. Loading device: A suitable device for applying vertical load to the specimen is required. The loading device may be platform scales of 1,000- to 3,000-pound capacity mounted on a stand as shown in Fig. 35–3. The scale is equipped with a screw-jack attached underneath the frame. The jack operates a yoke which extends up through the scale platform and over the specimen container resting on the platform. The yoke is forced up or down by operating the jack, thus applying or releasing load to the soil specimen. The desired applied pressure, which

Fig. 35–4. Lever system loading device.

is measured on the scale beam, becomes fully effective when the beam is balanced.

Another satisfactory loading device utilizes weights and a system of levers. Figure 35–4 shows a device of this type with multiple units for

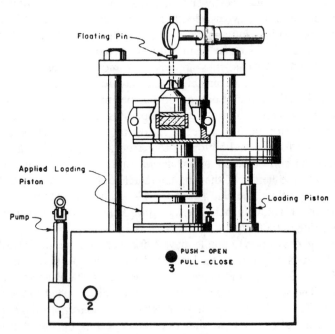

Fig. 35–5. Hydraulic loading device.

handling several tests simultaneously. Hydraulic-piston or bellows-type loading apparatus are also commonly used. One such device is shown by Fig. 35–5. These are satisfactory if they have adequate capacity, accuracy, and sensitivity for the work being performed.

3. Device for cutting undisturbed specimens: This apparatus consists of a cutting bit of the same diameter as the ring container of the consolidometer, a cutting stand with bit guide, and knives for trimming the soil. Figure 35–6 shows this apparatus. Wire saws or trimming lathes may be used if a uniform tight fit of the specimen to the container is obtained.

4. Device for preparation of remolded specimens: Compacted soil specimens are prepared in the consolidometer ring container. In addition to the container, the apparatus consists of an extension collar about 4 inches in depth and of the same diameter as the container. A compaction hammer of the same type required in ASTM. Method A of Test for Moisture Density Relations of Soils (Designation 698–66T) is required (Am. Soc. Testing Mater., 1968).

35–3.2 Procedure

35–3.2.1 PREPARATION OF UNDISTURBED SPECIMENS

Perform the tests on hand-cut cube samples or core samples of a size which will allow the cutting of approximately ½ inch of material from the sides of the consolidometer specimen. (Alternatively, obtain a core of a diameter exactly the same as the diameter of the consolidometer specimen container, and extrude the core directly into the container. This procedure is satisfactory provided that the sampling has been done without any side-wall disturbance and provided that the core specimen exactly fits the container.)

Place the undisturbed soil block or core on the cutting platform, fasten the cutting bit to the ring container, and place the assembly on the sample in alignment with the guide arms, as shown in Fig. 35–6. With the cutting stand guiding the bit, trim the excess material with a knife close to the cutting edge of the bit, leaving very little material for the bit to shave off as it is pressed gently downward. (Other suitable procedures to accommodate guides for wire saws, trimming lathes, or extrusion devices may be used in conformance with the use of alternative apparatus and samples.) In trimming the sample, be careful to minimize disturbance of the soil specimen and to assure an exact fit of the specimen to the consolidometer container.

When sufficient specimen has been prepared so that it protrudes through the container ring, trim it flush with the surface of the container ring with

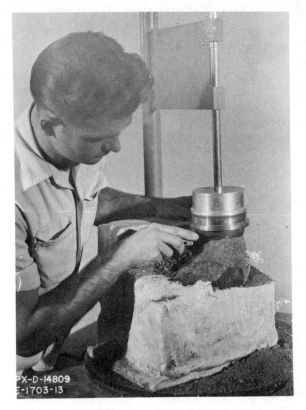

Fig. 35–6. Apparatus for cutting undisturbed soil specimens.

a straightedge cutting tool. Place a glass plate on the smooth, flat, cut surface of the specimen, and turn the container over. Remove the cutting bit, trim the specimen flush with the surface of the container ring, and cover it with a second glass plate to control evaporation until it is placed in the loading device.

35–3.2.2 PREPARATION OF REMOLDED SPECIMENS

Use about 2 pounds of representative soil which has been properly moistened and processed free from lumps and from which particles or aggregations of particles retained by a 3/16-inch (No. 4) sieve have been excluded. Compact the specimen to the required wet bulk density after adding the required amount of water. Place the extension collar on top of the container ring and fasten the bottom of the container ring to a baseplate. Weigh the exact quantity of the processed sample to give the desired wet density when compacted to a thickness ¼ inch greater than the thickness of the container ring. Compact the specimen to the desired thickness by the compaction hammer. Remove the extension collar and trim the excess material flush with the container ring surface with a straight-edge cutting tool. Remove the ring and specimen from the baseplate and cover the specimen surfaces with glass plates until the specimen is placed in the loading device. If, after weighing and measuring the specimen and computing the wet density in accordance with section 35–3.2.4, the wet density is not within 1.0 pound per cubic foot of that required, repeat the preparation of the remolded specimen until the required accuracy is obtained.

35–3.2.3 CALIBRATION OF DIAL GAUGE FOR HEIGHT MEASUREMENTS

Prior to filling the container ring with the soil specimen, place a ring gauge in the specimen container with the same arrangement of porous plates and load plates to be used when testing the soil specimen. Place the assembly in the loading machine in the same position it will occupy during the test. After the apparatus has been assembled with the ring gauge in place, apply a load equivalent to a pressure of 0.35 psi. (pounds per square inch) (or 0.025 kg. per square cm.) on the soil specimen. The dial reading at this time will be that for the exact height of the ring gauge. Mark the parts of the apparatus so that they can be matched in the same position for the test.

35–3.2.4 INITIAL HEIGHT AND WEIGHT OF SOIL SPECIMEN

Clean and weigh the specimen container ring and glass plates, and weigh them to 0.01 g. before the ring is filled. After filling and trimming is completed, weigh the soil specimen, ring, and glass plates to 0.01 g. Determine the weight of the soil specimen. Assemble the specimen container and place it in the loading device. If the specimen is not to be saturated at the beginning of the test, place a rubber sleeve around protruding porous plates and load plates to prevent evaporation. Apply the small seating load of 0.35 psi. (or 0.025 kg. per square cm.) to the specimen. By comparing the dial reading at this time with the dial reading obtained with the ring gauge in place, determine the exact height of the specimen. Use this information to compute the initial volume of the specimen, the initial density, void ratio, water content, and degree of saturation. The true water content of the specimen will be determined when the total dry weight of the specimen is obtained at the end of the test (section 35–3.2.7).

35–3.2.5 LOAD-CONSOLIDATION AND TIME-CONSOLIDATION

As a general procedure, load the specimen consecutively to values of ⅛, ¼, ½, and 1 times the maximum load desired. Use a greater number of increments if greater detail in the test curves is required. When adding loads to the specimen, perform the operation expeditiously to obtain the early dial readings. Allow each load increment to remain on the specimen for 24 hours or until consolidation is complete. During this period, make dial readings at time intervals frequent enough to give a good distribution of points for plotting a time-consolidation curve on semilogarithmic paper. If settlement after 24 hours continues to such an extent that additional readings are required, make the additional readings at 24-hour intervals until settlement is approximately complete. The difference between the initial reading and the final reading for each increment of load shows the magnitude of consolidation for that loading, and the initial and final time-consolidation readings for each increment show the rate of consolidation for that loading increment.

35–3.2.6 EFFECT OF SATURATION AND PERMEABILITY

Make this part of the test after the final consolidation has been reached for maximum load, prior to loading, or at other loadings, when the effect of wetting and permeability is to be observed. Attach the percolation tube standpipe, fill it with water, and wet the specimen. Take care to remove any air that may be entrapped in the system by slowly wetting the lower porous stone and draining the stone through the lower drain cock. After the specimen is wetted, fill the pan in which the consolidometer stands with water. To make permeability readings, fill the percolation tube standpipe to an initial reading and allow the water to percolate through the specimen. Measure the amount of water flowing through the sample in a given time by the drop in head. If the material is relatively impervious, giving a drop of the water level in the tube of only a few inches in 24 hours, make two or three tube readings at 24-hour intervals to establish the rate of flow. If the material is relatively pervious and the percolation tube empties in a few hours, determine the time interval required to cause a drop in head of a certain amount at least three times to establish an average permeability value.

35–3.2.7 REBOUND

Reduce the load to the seating load of 0.35 psi. (or 0.025 kg. per square cm.), and allow the specimen to rebound. It is important, during the rebound period, that the specimen be completely surrounded with water, so that only water will be taken into the void space when it expands; the volume of the air in the void space then will be the same after rebound as that following the determination of permeability. Allow sufficient time (at least 24 hours) to elapse, so that the pressure of the pore fluid will equalize with the outside air pressure. Remove the sample from the ring container and weigh it immediately and again after drying to 105°C. From the water content, dry bulk density, and specific gravity of the specimen, calculate the volume of air and, assuming it to be the same as the volume of air following the determination of permeability, calculate the water content and degree of saturation for the conditions of section 35–3.2.6.

35–3.3 Calculations

Calculate the results as illustrated in the data sheets of a typical example in Fig. 35–7, 35–8, and 35–9. The general methods of calculation are shown in the example.

Calculate the void ratio as follows:

$$e = \frac{\text{volume of voids}}{\text{volume of solids}} = \frac{h - h_0}{h_0}$$

where

e = void ratio,
h = height of the specimen, and
h_0 = height of the solid material at zero void content.

Calculate the consolidation, as a percentage of the original height, as follows:

$$\Delta, \text{percent} = \frac{h_1 - h_2}{h_1} \times 100$$

where

Δ = consolidation in percentage of initial volume,
h_1 = the initial height of the specimen, and
h_2 = the height of the specimen under the load in question.

Calculate the permeability rate by means of the following basic formula for the variable head permeameter:

$$k = \frac{A_p \times L_s}{A_s \times 12} \times \frac{1}{t} \log_e \frac{H_i}{H_f}$$

where

k = permeability rate in feet per year,
A_p = area of standpipe furnishing the percolation head in square inches,
A_s = area of the specimen in square inches,
L_s = length of the specimen in inches,
H_i = initial head, difference in head between headwater and tailwater in inches,
H_f = final head, difference in head between headwater and tailwater in inches, and
t = elapsed time in years.

ONE-DIMENSIONAL CONSOLIDATION TEST
LOAD-CONSOLIDATION DATA SHEET 2

SAMPLE NO. 51-58   SPECIMEN NO. 1

PRESSURE (psi)	FINAL DIAL	Δ DIAL	$h = h_1 - \Delta$	VOIDS $h - h_0$	VOID RATIO $= (h - h_0)/h_0$	DRY DENSITY (pcf)	% CONSOLIDATION	REMARKS
0.35	.2705		.2490	.5689	.8365	90.75	0.0	Seating load
10.0	.1948	.0757	.1733	.4932	.7252	96.61	6.06	
37.5	.1619	.1092	.1398	.4597	.6759	99.45	8.74	
75.0	.1189	.1517	.10973	.4172	.6134	103.30	12.15	Water access at end of period
150.0	.0732	.1973	.10517	.3716	.5464	107.78	15.80	
150.0	.0732	.1973	.1051	.3716	.5464	107.78	15.80	
0.35	.1331	.1374	.1116	.4315	.6345	101.97	11.00	Expanded under water

	INITIAL CONDITIONS	EXPANDED CONDITIONS	MAX. LOAD CONDITIONS
DRY DENSITY, pcf.	90.75	101.97	107.78
TOTAL HEIGHT, in., = h	1.2490	1.1116	1.0517
HEIGHT OF SOLIDS, in., = h_0	.6801	.6801	.6901
HEIGHT OF WATER, in., = h_w	.5489	.4315	.3714
HEIGHT OF AIR, in., = h_a	.0200	.0002	.0002
MOISTURE CONTENT, PERCENT OF DRY WEIGHT	50.23 w_i	23.75 w_e	20.45
DEGREE OF SATURATION, %	96.48	99.95	99.95

$D = \text{DRY DENSITY} = \dfrac{\text{WT. DRY SPEC. IN GRAMS}}{(3.724)(h)} = \dfrac{422.10}{(3.724)(h)} = \dfrac{(422.10)(w_r)}{(91.52)(2.54)}$

$h_w = \text{HEIGHT OF WATER} = \dfrac{(\text{WT. DRY SPEC., IN GRAMS})(w_r \text{ or } w_e)}{(\text{AREA cm.}^2)(2.54)}$

$h_a = \text{HEIGHT OF AIR} = h - h_w - h_0 =$

$\text{DEGREE OF SATURATION, } S = \dfrac{h_w}{h - h_0} \times 100 \text{ or } \dfrac{(G)(w)}{e}$

*AIR HEIGHT ASSUMED TO REMAIN CONSTANT AFTER SATURATION OF SPECIMEN
**COMPUTED BY -

Fig. 35-8. Sample of load-consolidation data sheet.

ONE-DIMENSIONAL CONSOLIDATION TEST-PLACEMENT DATA, SHEET 1

PROJECT Knife River-Unit N.R.S.   FEATURE Broncho Dam   SAMPLE NO. 51-58

SPECIMEN NO. 1   SPECIMEN TYPE Undisturbed   CONTAINER NO. 2   LOADING UNIT NO. 2

TESTED BY W.H.T.   COMPUTED BY C.L.P.   CHECKED BY R.P.W.   DATE 12-17-46

SPECIFIC GRAVITY 2.67   CONTAINER: HEIGHT 1.25 in. DIAMETER 4.25 in. AREA IN. 186 IN.² = 91.52 cm.²

TYPE OF SOIL: CLAY (CL), some organic matter very moist, black color

WEIGHT OF SOIL (Complete assembly, see Eq(1) text)	16.5 POUNDS
WEIGHT OF SPECIMEN CONTAINER AND SPECIMEN (Complete assembly, see Eq(1) text)	
WEIGHT OF SPECIMEN RING, COVER PLATES, AND WET SOIL	1622.5 GRAMS
WEIGHT OF SPECIMEN RING AND COVER PLATES	1072.8 GRAMS
WEIGHT OF WET SOIL	549.7 GRAMS

r_1 = DIAL READING WITH GAGE RING IN PLACE (with .035 p.s.i. applied)   0.2715 INCH

r_2 = DIAL READING WITH NO LOAD ON SPECIMEN (used only in Expansion Test)   INCH

r_3 = DIAL READING WITH 0.35 p.s.i. ON SPECIMEN   0.2705 INCH

h_1 = INITIAL SPECIMEN THICKNESS = 1.25 + ($r_3 - r_1$) = 1.25 + (.2705 - .2715)   1.2490 INCH

h_0 = HEIGHT OF SOLIDS = $\dfrac{\text{WT. DRY SPECIMEN IN GRAMS}}{(\text{AREA cm.}^2)(2.54)(G)} = \dfrac{422.10}{(91.52)(2.54)(2.67)}$ .06801 INCH

MOISTURE DETERMINATION	MOISTURE SPECIMEN BEFORE TEST	WHOLE SPECIMEN AFTER TEST
DATE	12-17-46	1-2-47 *
CONTAINER NO.	221	72
WET WEIGHT OF SPECIMEN + CONTAINER, GRAMS	421.9	625.35
DRY WEIGHT OF SPECIMEN + CONTAINER, GRAMS	359.2	539.90 217.00
WEIGHT OF CONTAINER, GRAMS	151.8	180.10 154.70
WEIGHT OF WATER, GRAMS	62.7	85.45
DRY WEIGHT OF SPECIMEN, GRAMS	207.4	359.80 + 63.30 = 422.10
MOISTURE CONTENT, PERCENT OF DRY WEIGHT	30.23 w_i	23.75 w_e

*THIS COLUMN FOR DETERMINING w_i.
**THIS COLUMN FOR DETERMINING DRY WEIGHT OF ALL MATERIAL ADHERING TO SPECIMEN RING, TRIMMED FROM SPECIMEN, AND WASHED OUT OF POROUS PLATES.
REMARKS:

Fig. 35-7. Sample of placement data sheet.

ONE-DIMENSIONAL CONSOLIDATION TEST TIME-CONSOLIDATION DATA, SHEET NO. 3   SAMPLE NO. _5L - 58_

SPEC. NO. ____1____

PRESSURE IN POUNDS PER SQUARE INCH		TIME ELAPSE	0:00	4	10	20	40	1:20	1:40	3:20	6:40	13:20	16:40	33:20	1:06:40	2:13:20	2:46:40	5:33:20	2:00:00		
0.35		DATE TIME	12-17-46 3:00																	12-18-46 8:30	22
		% CONS. DIAL	2705																	0.18 2682	
19.0		DATE TIME	12-18-46 8:30						8:31	8:33										12-19-46 8:30	300
		% CONS. DIAL	0.18 2682	3.12 2315	3.31 2291	3.64 2250	4.08 2196	4.51 2142	—	5.07 2072	5.35 2037	5.52 2015	—	5.70 1993	5.80 1981	5.87 1972	—	5.88 1970	6.06 1948	
37.5		DATE TIME	12-19-46 8:30																	12-20-46 8:30	575
		% CONS. DIAL	6.06 1948	6.41 1904	6.57 1885	6.74 1863	6.92 1841	7.15 1812	—	7.53 1765	7.79 1732	7.96 1711	—	8.17 1685	8.29 1670	8.41 1655	—	8.53 1639	8.74 1613	
75.0		DATE TIME	12-20-46 8:30																	12-23-46 8:30	1134
		% CONS. DIAL	8.74 1613	9.23 1552	9.39 1532	9.61 1505	9.82 1748	10.19 1432	—	10.50 1393	10.99 1332	11.23 1302	—	11.44 1276	11.59 1258	11.70 1244	11.84 1226	12.15 1188		
150.0		DATE TIME																		12-26-46 8:30	2252
		% CONS. DIAL	12.15 1188	12.67 1122	12.83 1103	13.05 1075	13.35 1038	13.76 0986	—	14.28 0922		14.84 0852	—	15.05 0825	15.16 0812	15.25 0800	—	15.40 0782	15.80 0732	
150.0		DATE TIME	12-26-46 8:30																	12-30-46 8:30	2254
		% CONS. DIAL	15.80 7.32																	15.80 0732	
0.35		DATE TIME	12-30-46 8:30																	12-31-46 8:30	24
		% CONS. DIAL	0732																	11.00 1331	

PERMEABILITY COMPUTATIONS

HEAD (Hi)	DATE	TIME	TUBE READ	R	t'	c	k
16.75	12-23	2:10 3:50	0.0 0.44	0.44	1.66	0.09	0054
	12-24	4:00 8:20	0.0 3.50	3.50	16.33	0.87	0053
		8:20 10:40	0.0 0.50	0.50	2.33	0.12	0052
$k = 0.053$ ft/yr				Avg.			

Fig. 35–9. Sample of time-consolidation data sheet.

35–3.4 Plotting Consolidation Data

Plot the consolidation data by the general method shown in Fig. 35–10 to 35–12. These curves are adapted to further detailed calculations, if desired, of the compression index C_c, the coefficient of consolidation C_v, and the coefficient of compressibility a_v, as defined by the Tentative Definitions of Terms and Symbols Relating to Soil Mechanics (ASTM Designation: D653-67, Part 11, Standards; Am. Soc. Testing Mater., 1968).

35–3.5 Report

Include the following information on the soil specimens tested in the report:

(1) Identification of the sample (hole number, depth, location).

(2) Description of the soil tested and size fraction of the total sample tested.

(3) Type of sample tested (remolded or undisturbed—if undisturbed, describe the size and type, as extruded core, hand-cut, or other).

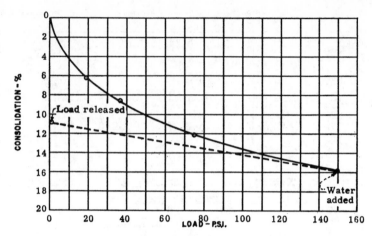

Fig. 35–10. Example of load-consolidation curve.

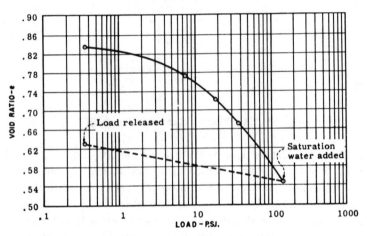

Fig. 35–11. Example of void ratio-load curve.

(4) Initial moisture and density conditions and degree of saturation [if remolded, give the comparison to maximum density and optimum water content—ASTM Designation D698-66T, Part 11, Standards (Am. Soc. Testing Mater., 1968) or other].

(5) Type of consolidometer (fixed or floating ring, specimen size), and type of loading equipment.

(6) Load versus volume-change data (as in Fig. 35–10 and 35–11).

(7) Time versus volume-change data (as in Fig. 35–12).

(8) Provide load and time versus volume-change data in other forms if specifically requested.

(9) Final water content, bulk dry density, and saturation degree data.

(10) Report permeability data and any other data specifically requested.

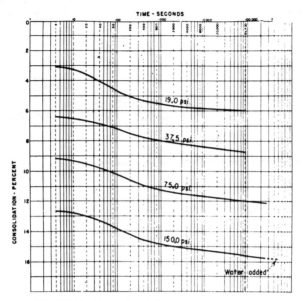

Fig. 35–12. Example of time-consolidation curve.

35–4   METHOD FOR EXPANSION [3]

35–4.1   Special Apparatus

Same as in section 35–3.1.

35–4.2   Procedure

Prepare the test specimen, calibrate the dial gauge, and determine the initial height and weight of specimen as described in section 35–3.2.

To measure expansion characteristics where the soil specimen is saturated under full load and then allowed to expand, apply the seating load of 0.35 psi. (or 0.025 kg. per square cm.) to Specimen No. 1, and secure initial dial readings. Then saturate the soil specimen by filling with water the pan in which the consolidometer stands and by partially filling the permeameter tube. (The permeameter tube head should be sufficiently low so that the specimen is not lifted.) As the specimen begins to expand, increase the load as required to hold the specimen at its original height. Then reduce the load to ½, ¼, and ⅛ of the maximum load and finally to the seating load of 0.35 psi. (or 0.025 kg. per square cm.), and meas-

[3] Holtz and Gibbs, 1956.

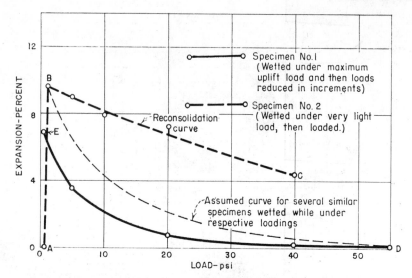

Fig. 35–13. Effect of wetting and loading on expansion.

ure the height with each load. Use a greater number of loadings if greater detail in the test curve is required. Maintain all loads for 24 hours, or longer if needed, to obtain constant values of height. Perform the remainder of the test in conformance with section 35–3.2.7.

To measure expansion characteristics where the soil is allowed to expand before loading, apply the seating load of 0.35 psi. (or 0.025 kg. per square cm.) to Specimen No. 2, and secure initial dial gauge readings. Then saturate the specimen as described in the preceding paragraph. Allow the specimen to expand under the seating load for 48 hours or until expansion is complete. Load the specimen successively to ⅛, ¼, ½, and 1 times the maximum load found in the preceding paragraph for Specimen No. 1, to determine the reconsolidation characteristics of the soil. Use a greater number of loadings if greater detail in the test curve is required. Follow the procedure specified in section 35–3.2.5 for making loadings and measurements.

Calculate and plot the test results as described in sections 35–3.3 and 35–3.4. Report the results as described in section 35–3.5; in addition, plot load versus volume-change data as in Fig. 35–13.

35–4.3   Comments

The expansion characteristics of an expansive-type soil vary with the loading history, so that it is necessary to perform a separate test for each condition of loading at which exact expansion data are required (Holtz and Gibbs, 1956). In some laboratories, it is common procedure to test only two specimens: (*1*) loaded-and-expanded, and (*2*) expanded-and-loaded. From these data, an estimate of expansion can be made for any load condition as shown by Curve *BD,* Fig. 35–13, in which Specimen No. 1 was loaded and expanded (*Curve ADE*) by saturation with water, and Specimen No. 2 was expanded by saturation with water and then loaded (Curve *ABC*).

35-5 METHOD FOR SHRINKAGE

35-5.1 Special Apparatus

Same as section 35–3.1.

35-5.2 Procedure

When measurements of shrinkage on drying are needed, prepare an additional specimen as described in section 35–3.2.1 or 35–3.2.2. Cut this specimen from the same undisturbed soil sample as the expansion specimens, or remolded to the same bulk density and water content conditions as the expansion specimens (section 35–4.2). Place the specimen in the container ring, and measure the initial volume and height as described in section 35–3.2.4. Determine the water content of the soil specimen by weighing unused portions of the original sample of which the specimen is a part, drying the material in an oven to 105°C. and reweighing it.

If the height of the air-dried specimen is desired, place the specimen and ring container in the loading machine. Apply the seating load of 0.35 psi. (or 0.025 kg. per square cm.), and then read the dial gauge.

To measure volume shrinkage, allow the specimen in the ring to dry in air completely or at least to the water content corresponding to the shrinkage limit [ASTM Standard Method of Test for Shrinkage Factors of Soils, Designation D427-61, Part 11, Standards (Am. Soc. Testing Mater., 1968)]. After the specimen has been air-dried, remove it from the ring container, and obtain its volume by the mercury-displacement method.

To perform the mercury displacement measurement, place a glass cup with a smoothly ground top in an evaporating dish. Fill the cup to overflowing with mercury, and then remove the excess mercury by sliding a glass plate over the rim. Pour the excess mercury into the original container and place the glass cup in the evaporating dish. Then immerse the air-dried soil specimen in the glass cup filled with mercury, using a special glass plate with three prongs for holding the specimen in the mercury [see ASTM Designation D427-61 for general scheme of test and equipment (Am. Soc. Testing Mater., 1968)]. Transfer the displaced mercury into a graduated cylinder, and measure the volume. If the shrinkage specimen is cracked into separate parts, measure the volume of each part, and add the individual volumes to obtain the total. (A paper strip wrapped around the specimen side and held by a rubber band is effective in holding the specimen intact during handling.)

35–5.3   Calculations and Report

Calculate the volume shrinkage as a percentage of the initial volume as follows:

$$\Delta_s = \frac{v_1 - v_d}{v_1} \times 100$$

where

Δ_s = volume shrinkage in percentage of initial volume,

v_1 = initial volume of specimen (height of specimen times area of ring container), and

v_d = volume of air-dried specimen from mercury displacement method.

Calculate the shrinkage in height as follows:

$$\Delta h_s = \frac{h_1 - h_d}{h_1} \times 100$$

where

Δh_s = height of shrinkage in percentage of initial height,

h_1 = initial height of specimen, and

h_d = height of air-dried specimen.

To calculate the total percentage change in volume from "air-dry to saturated conditions," add the percentage shrinkage in volume on air drying Δ_s to the percentage expansion in volume on saturation Δ, as described in section 35–3.3. This figure is used as an indicator of total expansion but is based on initial conditions of density and water content. Since expansion volume data are determined for several conditions of loading, the total volume change can also be determined for several conditions of loading.

To calculate the total percentage change in height from saturated to air-dry conditions, add the percentage shrinkage in height Δh_s to the percentage expansion Δ when the specimen is saturated under load (sections 35–4.2 and 35–3.3).

The report on shrinkage includes data on the decrease in volume from the initial to air-dried condition and, if desired, other information such as the total change in volume and total change in height. Report the load conditions under which the volume change measurements were obtained. Include also Items *1, 2, 3, 4, 5,* and *9,* given in section 35–3.5.

35–6 LITERATURE CITED

American Society for Testing and Materials. 1968. 1968 Book of Standards, Including Tentatives. Part 11. Am. Soc. Testing Mater., Philadelphia.

Casagrande, A., and Fadum, R. E. 1940. Notes on soil testing for engineering purposes. Harvard Univ., Grad. School of Eng., Soil Mechanics Series No. 8, pp. 37–49.

Gibbs, H. J. 1950. The effect of rock content and placement density on consolidation and related pore pressure in embankment construction. Am. Soc. Testing Mater. Proc. 50:1343–1360.

Gibbs, H. J., 1953. Estimating foundation settlement by one-dimensional consolidation tests. U. S. Bureau of Reclamation, Engineering Monograph No. 13.

Holtz, W. G., and Gibbs, H. J. 1956. Engineering properties of expansive clays. Trans. Am. Soc. Civil. Eng. 121:641–677.

Holtz, W. G., and Gibbs, H. J. 1958. Suggested method of test for consolidation of soils. Procedures for Testing Soils, pp. 296–306. Am. Soc. Testing Mater., Philadelphia.

Holtz, W. G. 1959. Expansive clays—properties and problems. Quart., Colorado School of Mines. 54(4):90–117.

Lambe, T. W. 1951. Soil Testing for Engineers. pp. 74–87. John Wiley & Sons, Inc., New York.

Taylor, D. W. 1951. Fundamentals of Soil Mechanics. pp. 212–247. John Wiley & Sons, Inc., New York.

Terzaghi, K. 1953. Theoretical Soil Mechanics. pp. 118–136, 265–290. John Wiley & Sons, Inc., New York.

Terzaghi, K., and Peck, R. B. 1948. Soil Mechanics in Engineering Practice. pp. 56–57, 61–65. John Wiley & Sons, Inc., New York.

U. S. Bureau of Reclamation. 1968. One-dimensional consolidation test. Earth Manual, Ed. 1, Rev. pp. 492–507. U. S. Bureau Reclamation, Denver.

United States National Committee, Subcommittte 3. 1948. Comprehensive report on the earth laboratories in the United States. Proc. Second Intern. Conf. Soil Mech. 6:242–291.

Van Zelst, T. W. 1948. An investigation of the factors affecting laboratory consolidation of clay. Proc. Second Intern. Conf. Soil Mech. 7:52–61.

36

Modulus of Rupture

R. C. REEVE
United States Salinity Laboratory
Riverside, California

36–1 INTRODUCTION

The cohesion exhibited by soil material upon drying is a soil property that relates particularly to surface crusting and clod formation. The modulus of rupture, a concept relating to the breaking strength of beams and one used extensively for predicting strength of materials, is applied for evaluating the cohesion of dry soil.

In the following procedure, a soil briquet, specially molded to have a rectangular cross section and supported as a simple beam (ends supported with no constraint), is loaded to failure with a concentrated load at the center of the beam span. From the load or force required to break the beam, and from the appropriate dimensions of the sample, the modulus of rupture for the soil briquet is calculated.

Shrinkage of soil material on drying is also a pertinent property. Shrinkage can be determined from the dimensions of the briquet before and after drying.

36–2 PRINCIPLES

The modulus of rupture is an index of the strength of materials and is used for comparing the binding strength of structural materials or to determine the probable breaking load on a beam. It is expressed as the maximum stress in the material when failure occurs in bending. The derivation of the modulus of rupture equation is given in a number of standard textbooks on strength of materials. For instance, see Laurson and Cox (1938, pp. 118–123).

For a beam of rectangular cross section, as is used in this test, the modulus of rupture s is given by the equation

$$s = 3FL/2bd^2 \qquad [1]$$

where F = the breaking force applied at the center of the briquet beam span, L = the distance between the briquet end supports, b = the width of the briquet, and d = the depth or thickness of the briquet (the dimension of the briquet parallel with the direction of the applied load). If F is measured in dynes (gram-weight × 980) and L, b and d are in centimeters, s will be in dyne cm.$^{-2}$. Modulus of rupture may be conveniently expressed in bars or millibars (1 bar = 1,000 millibar = 10^6 dyne cm.$^{-2}$).

The following procedure is designed to simulate soil crust formation in the field under conditions that obtain where soil is irrigated (as from a furrow) and dried by direct heating from the sun. For additional information, the papers by Richards (1953) and Allison (1923), Handbook 60 of the USDA (U. S. Salinity Laboratory Staff, 1954), and Reeve et al. (1954) should be consulted.

36–3 METHOD [1]

36–3.1 Special Apparatus

The apparatus required for this test and details of construction are given in Fig. 36–1. The major items are:

	Number recommended
1. Briquet support and knife-edge assembly (made from parts Nos. 1 to 14, and 17).	1
2. Drying tray (No. 15).	2
3. Briquet mold (No. 16).	24
4. Tremie.	1
5. Strike-off tool.	1
6. Drying rack.	2
7. Soaking tank.	1

The briquet molds are precision-made from ⅜-inch brass strip with inside dimensions of 3.5 cm. by 7 cm. by 0.952 cm. high. A rectangle of hard, white, photographic blotting paper is cut to the size 5 cm. by 8.5 cm. to serve as a bottom for each briquet mold.

The briquet-support and knife-edge assembly (the machine for breaking the sample) makes use of two parallel bars 5 cm. apart for supporting the sample. The breaking force is supplied from a third overlying bar that is centrally located and parallel with respect to the supporting bars. The bar above and one bar below are self-aligning to accommodate to any slight lack of parallelism in the lines of bearing of the sample. The bars are coated on the edge that is in contact with the briquet with a strip of soft rubber having a cross section 0.16 cm. by 0.16 cm.

A beam balance is used to measure and apply the load to the briquet-breaking apparatus (a "solution balance" with a capacity of 20 kg. is sat-

---

[1] Richards (1953); U. S. Salinity Laboratory Staff (1954).

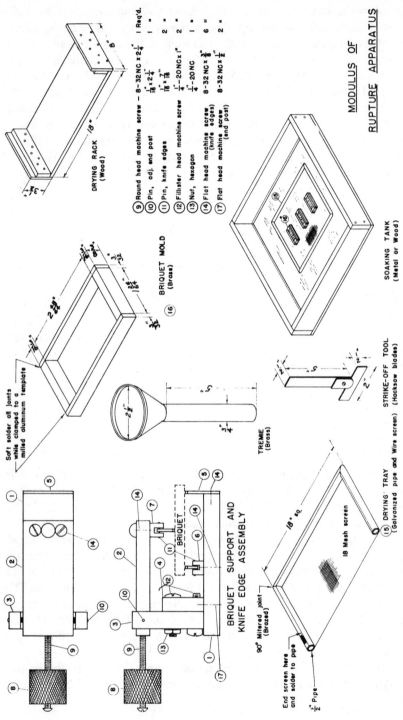

Fig. 36–1. Details for construction of modulus of rupture apparatus (Richards, 1953), continued on next page.

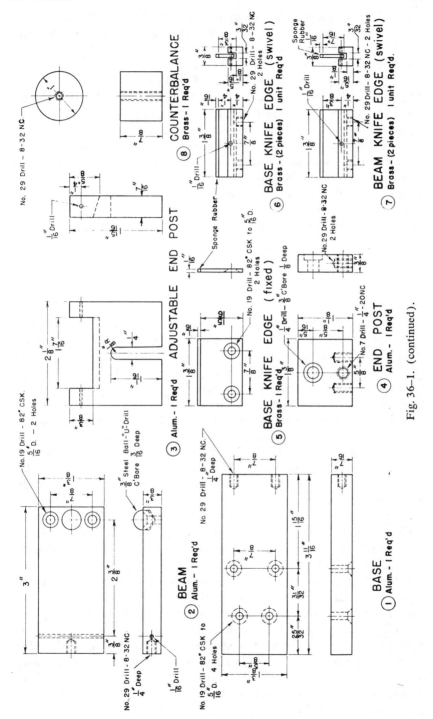

Fig. 36–1. (continued).

isfactory). The briquet-breaking apparatus is mounted on the balance platform. Upward motion of the upper bar is constrained by a cross frame that is anchored externally and located above the balance platform. The briquet is broken by upward motion of the two lower bars, which are supported by the platform of the balance. The breaking force on the briquet is applied at the rate of 1.96×10^6 dynes per minute by water accumulating in a vessel hung from the end of the balance beam. A jet of water is directed toward a deflector on the end of the beam that intercepts the water and directs it into the vessel, where it accumulates as long as the briquet remains unbroken. The vertical drop of the end of the balance beam that occurs when the briquet breaks is used to stop automatically the accumulation of water in the vessel. As the vessel drops, the jet of water is no longer intercepted. Two valves are used on the line that supplies the jet of water, one to regulate the flow rate and the other as a shut-off.

36–3.2 Procedure

With the aid of equation [5] in section 36–3.3, calculate the weight of water that must be added per minute to the vessel on the balance arm to apply a breaking force on the briquet at the rate of 1.96×10^6 dynes per minute. Then, by repeated trial, adjust the flow-rate valve to control the rate of accumulation of water in the vessel from the water jet to apply the breaking force at the desired uniform rate.

Make the determination of modulus of rupture on 5 replicate samples of soil that have been passed through a 2-mm., round-hole sieve. Make the volume of each sample slightly larger than that of the molds. Cover the inside of the molds (part No. 16, Fig. 36–1) with a thin layer of vaseline, so that the soil will not stick to the mold. Place the screen-bottomed drying tray (part No. 15, Fig. 36–1) in the pan or soaking tank. Place the molds on the blotting paper on the screen. Rest the tremie on the blotting paper at one end of the mold. Dump all of a soil sample into the tremie. Move the tremie around inside the mold, raising it continuously to give a uniform smooth filling of the mold.

Strike off excess soil level with the upper surface of the mold. Add water to the pan until free water surrounds every mold. Allow the samples to stand for 1 hour after the soil samples become wet. Raise the screen very carefully, so as not to jar the samples, and transfer it to a forced-draft oven at 50°C. After drying the briquets to a constant weight, remove them from the molds, measure the dry length and width, and determine the weight of water accumulated in the vessel on the balance when each briquet breaks. After the briquet has been broken, measure the depth or thickness across the ruptured face.

36-3.3 Calculations

If the breaking force F is applied with a beam balance that requires W_1 grams on the weight hanger on the end of the beam to counter-balance 1,000 grams on the platform, and if W_2 is the grams of water added to the vessel on the weight hanger to break the sample, we have

$$F = 980 \times \frac{1000}{W_1} \times W_2 \text{ dynes .} \qquad [2]$$

Substituting [2] in [1] gives, on rearrangement,

$$s = 1.47 \times 10^6 \frac{W_2}{W_1} \frac{L}{bd^2} . \qquad [3]$$

If W_3 is the weight of water that must be added to the vessel on the weight hanger in 1 minute by a steady jet to increase F at the rate of 1.96×10^6 dynes per minute, we have

$$1.96 \times 10^6 = \frac{980 \times 1000}{W_1} W_3 \qquad [4]$$

or

$$W_3 = \frac{1.96 \times 10^6}{0.980 \times 10^6} W_1 = 2W_1 \text{ grams .} \qquad [5]$$

Calculate the modulus of rupture s using equation [1] or [3].

36-3.4 Comments

Five replicates have been found to give satisfactory precision. The average of 96 coefficients of variation (8 soils with 12 exchangeable cation levels) based upon 5 replicates in each case was 6.0%. The coefficients ranged from 0.5 to 15%. For 96 standard errors of the mean, each based upon 5 replicates and expressed as a percentage of the mean, the average was 2.7% and the range was 0.2 to 6.7%.

36-4 LITERATURE CITED

Allison, R. V. 1923. The modulus of rupture of a soil as an index of its physical structure. J. Am. Soc. Agron. 15:409–415.

Laurson, P. G., and Cox, W. J. 1938. Mechanics of Materials. John Wiley and Sons, Inc., New York.

Reeve, R. C., Bower, C. A., Brooks, R. H., and Gschwend, F. B. 1954. A comparison of the effects of exchangeable sodium and potassium upon the physical condition of soil. Soil Sci. Soc. Am. Proc. 18:130–132.

Richards, L. A. 1953. Modulus of rupture as an index of surface crusting of soil. Soil Sci. Soc. Am. Proc. 17:321–323.

U. S. Salinity Laboratory Staff. 1954. Diagnosis and improvement of saline and alkali soils. U. S. Dept. Agr. Handbook 60.

37 | Penetrometer Measurements

DONALD T. DAVIDSON
Iowa State University
Ames, Iowa

37–1 GENERAL INTRODUCTION

Any device forced into soil to measure its resistance to vertical penetration may be called a "penetrometer." In a static penetration test, the penetrometer is pushed steadily into the soil. In a dynamic penetration test, the penetrometer is driven into the soil by a hammer or falling weight.

The earliest soil penetrometers—fists, thumbs, fingernails, pointed sticks, or metal rods—are still used for qualitative measurements of relative density of cohesionless soils or consistency of cohesive soils. Results of such tests are commonly expressed by terms such as "loose" or "soft," "stiff" or "hard." Many varieties of penetrometers have been designed to give quantitative measurements of soil penetration resistance for a more precise correlation with soil physical properties such as tilth or crop yields, relative density, unconfined compressive strength or shear strength, bearing value or safe soil pressure; or for a better correlation with the rolling resistance or trafficability of wheels or crawler tracks on soil.

Although most penetrometers were developed for a particular use, each can be adapted to other uses. The test procedure and associated correlations and interpretations, however, generally will be different for each use. For example, the Proctor penetrometer and test procedure were developed for controlling field compaction of soils in embankments and other earth structures. The Proctor penetrometer can be used also in cultivated fields to predict the rolling resistance of tractor wheels, or to measure soil compaction or hardness caused by such wheels, but widely accepted test procedures covering these agricultural uses have not been developed.

Although there are many varieties of penetrometers in existence, only those which have gained wide acceptance are described in detail here. Other tests which, broadly viewed, could be classed as penetrometer-type tests are covered in section 38.

37–2 POCKET PENETROMETER

37–2.1 Introduction

The pocket penetrometer is a hand-operated, calibrated-spring penetrometer, originally developed as an improvement on the first thumb-fingernail technique for estimating consistency ("soft," "medium," "stiff," "hard") of cohesive, fine-grained soils. The maximum deformation of the spring, as the piston needle is pushed into silty clay or clay soil in the prescribed manner, has been correlated with unconfined compressive strength of soil in tons per square foot or kilograms per square centimeter. The latter values are calibrated directly on a scale on the piston barrel. Unconfined compressive strength is a quantitative expression of clayey soil consistency, and in foundation engineering may be taken as the approximate safe soil pressure for design of footings on clays (Peck et al., 1953).

The pocket penetrometer is simple to operate. It can be pushed into the surface in agricultural fields, into soil in a sampling tube, into an undisturbed block sample, into soil in an open pit excavation, into soil at footing elevation, or into molded soil specimens.

Although the pocket penetrometer is considered reliable only to approximately ±20%, the test can be very useful, when intelligently used and interpreted, in evaluating the safe soil pressure or the shearing strength of soils in field investigations and in preliminary laboratory studies. However, this penetrometer test is primarily supplemental, and usually does not eliminate the need for more precise field and laboratory testing and analysis.

37–2.2 Method [1]

37–2.2.1 SPECIAL APPARATUS

Direct-reading pocket penetrometers in several different models and sizes are commercially available (Fig. 37–1). They weigh from 4 to 7 ounces, and are from 6⅛ to 7⅝ inches in length. All have a diameter of ¾ inch and a piston needle diameter of ¼ inch.

Commercial sources of penetrometers include the following: Hogentogler & Co., 5218 River Road, Washington 16, D. C.; Humboldt Manufacturing Co., 4466 North Harlem Ave., Chicago 31, Ill.; Karol-Warner, Inc., 261 South Adelaide Ave., Highland Park, New Jersey; Soiltest, Inc., 2205 Lee St., Evanston, Ill. 60202; Testlab Corp., 564 West Monroe St., Chicago 6, Ill.

---

[1] Van Zelst (1957); Cordova (1957).

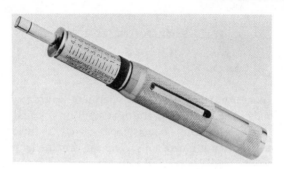

Fig. 37–1. A pocket penetrometer.

37–2.2.2 *PROCEDURE*

Grip the handle, and push the piston needle, with steady pressure, vertically into the soil surface until penetration reaches the calibration groove (approximately ¼ inch). Read the unconfined compressive strength, in tons per square foot or kilograms per square centimeter, on the penetrometer scale. In some models the scale has a sliding indicator which holds the reading when the piston is released. Clean the needle, and return the sliding indicator to its zero position. Repeat the test several times in different areas to find an average value for unconfined compressive strength.

37–3 PROCTOR PENETROMETER

37–3.1 Introduction

For engineering purposes, soil "density" is considered to be the weight in pounds of 1 cubic foot of soil material, including voids. The density may be expressed as pounds of oven-dry soil per cubic foot (dry unit-weight or dry density) or pounds total weight of moist soil material per cubic foot (wet unit-weight or wet density).

The Proctor penetrometer (Fig. 37–2) ordinarily is used as a quick check on degree of compaction of fine-grained soils in fills or embankments. If the water content is known or measured, the wet density and dry density may be estimated from the resistance to penetration. The test is particularly practicable for measuring the effects of additional passes of rollers used for compaction. In an alternative method, wet density is measured, and the resistance to penetration is used to estimate the water content.

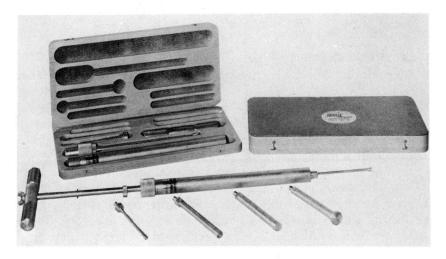

Fig. 37–2. Proctor penetrometer set.

The principal advantages of the Proctor penetrometer as an aid in con-trolling field compaction of soil with rollers are the low cost of the instrument, and the simplicity and rapidity with which measurements can be made. The Proctor penetrometer gives closer control than the "feel and heel" method of estimating soil water content and in-place density; but it is limited to fine-grained soils because pebbles and stones interfere with the measurement of penetration resistance. Also, the soils cannot be dry. Correctly used and supplemented as needed by more precise methods for determining water content and in-place density, Proctor penetrometer measurements are sufficient for most compaction jobs. By appropriate correlation studies, the Proctor penetrometer can be adapted to uses other than compaction of soils—for example, to prediction of rolling resistance of wheels or crawler tracks on agricultural soils (McKibben and Hull, 1940) or to measurements of compactness of agricultural soils (Swanson and Jacobson, 1956).

In practice, curves are first established for the relations of water content to density and to penetration resistance (Fig. 37–3) for the soil in question after the soil has been compacted by a standard technique. The curve for water content versus penetration resistance is obtained by the procedure in section 37–3.2.2, based on Am. Soc. Testing Mater. Tentative Method D 1558. The corresponding curve for water content versus density is obtained as described in section 32–3. Applications to the control of compaction are given in sections 37–3.2.3 and 37–3.2.4.

37–3.2   Method [2]

37–3.2.1   SPECIAL APPARATUS

1. Apparatus for determining relation of water content to density; see section 32–3.1.
2. Proctor penetrometer (Fig. 37–2): This instrument has a special spring dynamometer with pressure-indicating scale on the stem of the handle. The pressure scale is graduated to at least 90 pounds in 2-pound divisions, with a line encircling the stem at each 10-pound interval. A sliding ring on the stem indicates the maximum pressure obtained in the test. The apparatus is available commercially (see section 37–2.2.1).
3. Set of penetrometer needles: Each penetrometer needle (Fig. 37–2) has a shank with a circular head of known end-area. Am. Soc. Testing Mater. Tentative Method D 1558 specifies a set of seven needles having end-areas of 1, 3/4, 1/2, 1/3, 1/5, 1/10, and 1/20 square inch. Another widely used set contains five needles having end-areas of 1, 1/2, 1/4, 1/10, and 1/20 square inch. The needle shank is at least 4 inches in length, not including the threaded portion, and has graduations inscribed at intervals of 1/2 inch to indicate the depth of penetration.

37–3.2.2   PROCEDURE FOR DETERMINING RELATION OF WATER CONTENT
TO PENETRATION RESISTANCE

Prepare the soil sample as described in section 32–3.2 or 32–3.3. After preparation, the fraction passing the No. 4 (4,760-micron) sieve must have at least 20% passing the No. 200 (74-micron) sieve.

Compact the soil in the mold in accordance with the procedure given in section 32–3.2 or 32–3.3.

Determine the resistance of the soil specimen to penetration by use of the Proctor penetrometer with attached needle of known end-area, using a needle size that will give readings between 20 and 75. To make the test, place the mold containing the soil specimen on a smooth space on the floor between the feet. Place the needle on the surface of the soil away from the edge of the mold. Hold the penetrometer in a vertical position and control the rate of penetration by steadying the arm against the front of the legs while applying pressure to the penetrometer handle. Apply pressure sufficient to cause penetration of the soil specimen at a rate of ½ inch per second for a distance of not less than 3 inches. Record the penetrometer reading. Then take two more measurements at other locations that will not be influenced by the edge of the mold or previous trials. Average the three readings. Measure the water content of the soil by drying a representative sample of 100 g. or more in an oven at 110° ± 5°C. for at least 12 hours or to constant weight.

---

[2] Am. Soc. Testing Mater. (1958); Gregg (1960); Proctor (1933).

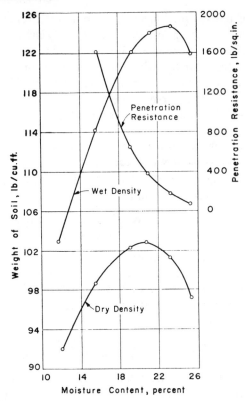

Fig. 37-3. Typical curves illustrating the relation of water content of soil to "density" and penetration resistance.

Repeat the foregoing procedure after increasing the water content of the soil as described in section 32–3.2 or 32–3.3. Continue to add water and repeat the measurement of penetration resistance and water content until enough data are obtained to cover the desired range.

Multiply the average penetrometer reading of each soil specimen by the reciprocal of the end-area of the penetration needle used, and record the resulting value as the penetration resistance of the soil in pounds per square inch. Calculate the percentage content of water in each soil specimen at the time of penetration, using the dry-weight basis. On a graph with the curve showing the relation of water content to density, plot penetration resistance as another ordinate (Fig. 37–3).

37–3.2.3 PROCEDURE FOR ESTIMATING WATER CONTENT IN THE FIELD FOR USE IN COMPACTION CONTROL

Sample the soil from the layer under consideration, and compact it in the mold (as described in section 32–3.2 or 32–3.3) with the sample at the water content of the sampled layer. Determine the average penetration resistance of the soil specimen in pounds per square inch, following the same procedure described in section 37–3.2.2. Use the average value of penetration resistance for estimating the water content of the soil from the curve showing penetration resistance versus water content. Then use the water content to find from the curve of density versus water content whether the desired degree of compaction has been attained.

37–3.2.4 PROCEDURE FOR ESTIMATING DENSITY IN THE FIELD
FOR USE IN COMPACTION CONTROL

Measure the wet density of the soil using the excavation method (section 30–3). Calculate the wet density of the compacted layer as follows:

$$\text{Wet Density} = \frac{\text{Weight of Soil Removed}}{\text{Volume of Hole}}$$

Measure the penetration resistance of the soil after compaction as described in section 37–3.2.2. Use the value of penetration resistance to find the corresponding water content from the curve prepared in section 37–3.2.2. Then use the wet density and the water percentage to estimate the dry density according to the relation,

$$\text{Dry Density} = \frac{\text{Wet Density}}{1 + (\text{Percent Water}/100)}$$

Alternatively, where measurements of the water content of the soil by rapid drying, neutron moderation or other rapid method (section 7) are made, find by interpolation in the curves described in section 37–3.2.2 the penetrometer reading for compacted soil that corresponds to the observed water content. In this instance, make the penetrometer readings directly on the embankment or subgrade soil using the procedure in the third paragraph of section 37–3.2.2. Take at least three readings at each location, and record the average value. Make measurements at enough locations selected at random within the confines of the area being rolled to obtain the desired degree of precision. Compare the resulting penetrometer readings with the value for compacted soil. If the penetration resistance is too low, make repeated measurements as needed after further compaction of the soil.

37–4   CONE PENETROMETER

37–4.1   Introduction

The cone penetrometer was developed by the U. S. Army Corps of Engineers for predicting the carrying capacity of cohesive, fine-grained soils for army vehicles in off-road military operations. The trafficability of

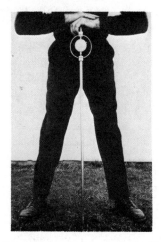

Fig. 37–4. Cone penetrometers (military model, left; commercial model, right).

a soil depends on its bearing capacity and traction capacity, both being functions of the shear resistance or strength of the soil. The applied force required to press the cone penetrometer into a soil is an index of the shear resistance of the soil and is called the "cone index." Cone index capacity, or trafficability, is measured in terms of cone index. Cone index readings taken at depths up to 24 inches permit plotting of a "cone index curve," which, in addition to its significance in trafficability studies, gives quantitative information on soil compactness or density that can be correlated with other soil physical properties or with crop yields.

37–4.2 Method [3]

37–4.2.1 SPECIAL APPARATUS

The cone penetrometer (Fig. 37–4; military model, left; commercial model, right, see section 37–2.2.1), consists of a handle, proving ring and dial gauge, 36-inch rod graduated in 6-inch or 12-inch intervals, and a stainless steel cone. The cone is about 1½ inches in height and has a 30-degree apex angle and a base area of ½ square inch.

37–4.2.2 PROCEDURE

The test procedure is best performed by two persons: an operator, who presses the cone penetrometer into the soil and calls out times for readings, and a recorder, who records the dial readings.

Select the location of the test and prepare a flat, clean soil surface for

[3] Davidson et al. (1960); Foster et al. (1958).

testing. Avoid unnecessary disturbance of the in-place soil structure. Set the dial gauge to zero position. Depending on the model used, hold the penetrometer in a vertical position (Fig. 37–4). Push the cone point slowly downward into the soil at a uniform rate, and take readings of the dial gauge at desired vertical increments—for. example, when the base of the cone is at ground level, and at 3- or 6-inch intervals to a depth of 24 inches. (It should take about 15 seconds to reach a depth of 24 inches.) Withdraw the cone from the soil and wipe it clean.

Repeat the test several times at each location investigated to obtain at least three sets of consistent and reliable readings. Space the individual penetrations so that they do not interfere with one another. Average the dial readings obtained at each depth increment for at least three penetration tests. Using the proving-ring calibration chart, convert the average dial readings to penetrometer force in pounds or in kilograms. Plot the cone-index curve for the test location (abscissa scale, penetrometer force in pounds or kilograms; ordinate scale, depth of penetration in inches).

37–4.2.3 INTERPRETATION OF RESULTS

The layer of soil for which the cone index is considered a measure of trafficability is termed the "critical layer." The depth of this layer varies with the weight of the vehicle, but for many military vehicles the critical layer is 6 to 12 inches below ground surface. The average cone index for the critical layer is correlated with trafficability.

Early attempts to predict trafficability from the average cone index of the critical layer of the undisturbed soil were not always successful. The reason is that many soils with low undisturbed strengths become even weaker under the remolding effect of a vehicle. This led to the development of a remolding test to determine a "remolding index" for soil cored from the critical layer. The remolding test consists of measuring the cone index of the core sample confined in a cylindrical container before and after it has received 100 blows of a 2.5-pound hammer falling 12 inches. The remolding index is obtained by dividing the cone index of the soil after pounding by its cone index before pounding. A "rating cone index," the final measure of a soil's trafficability, is the cone index of the critical layer of the undisturbed soil multiplied by the remolding index. Table 37–1 illustrates the

Table 37–1. Rating cone index required for different vehicles.

Vehicle	Rating cone index required	
	For 1 pass	For 50 passes
M 29C Weasel	20	25
D 7 engineer tractor	30	40
M 48 tank	40	50
3/4-ton weapons carrier	50	65
2 1/4-ton cargo truck	45	60

use of the rating cone index, showing the rating cone indexes necessary in off-road operations for completion of one pass and 50 passes of some typical military vehicles.

37–4.2.4 COMMENTS

The rating cone index and trafficability of a cohesive, fine-grained soil is an inverse function of water content. Therefore, in humid climates, trafficability measurements are made during the wet season.

Generally, a tall, strong operator on the cone penetrometer will produce the best test results. Unless the soil is very soft, small operators have difficulty pushing the penetrometer into the soil at the desired slow, steady rate. In dry or hard soils, or in soils containing pebbles and stones, any operator will find it difficult to obtain consistent and reliable penetrometer measurements, especially as penetration depth increases.

37–5 STANDARD SPLIT-SPOON PENETROMETER

37–5.1 Introduction

In subsurface soil exploration with a drill rig, as for foundation design, a dynamic penetration test can be made at different depths by driving an ordinary sampling spoon into the soil and counting the number of blows of a drop hammer required to produce a given penetration. When conducted as a part of soil-boring and sampling operations, this kind of penetration test provides useful information at little extra cost. The penetration resistance of the subsurface materials can be correlated in a general way with desired physical properties. A widely used test of this kind, the "standard penetration test," is performed in accordance with ASTM Tentative Method D 1586.

37–5.2 Method [4]

37–5.2.1 SPECIAL APPARATUS

All equipment described here is available commercially (see section 37–2.2.1), and most drilling contractors are fully equipped to perform the standard penetration test.

1. Drilling equipment: The equipment should provide a reasonably clean hole and should permit driving a sampler to obtain the sample and penetration record according to the procedure described below. When

---

[4] Am. Soc. Testing Mater. (1958); Peck et al. (1953); McAlpin and Hofmann (1960).

drilling is done in sand or in soft clay or other material that will not allow a hole to stay open, drilling mud or casing is needed. The hole should be at least 2½ and not over 6 inches in diameter.

2. Split-spoon sampler: The dimensions of the sampler are important and are shown in Fig. 37–5. The drive shoe is of hardened steel and must be replaced or repaired when it becomes dented or distorted. The coupling head has four ½-inch (minimum diameter) vent ports for water or has a ball check-valve and no ports.

3. Drive-weight assembly: The drive-weight assembly consists of a driving head and a 140-pound weight with a 30-inch free fall. (A heavier hammer may be used for driving casing.)

37–5.2.2 PROCEDURE

Clean out the hole to the sampling elevation without disturbing the material to be sampled. In reaching the sampling elevation, side-discharge fishtail drilling is suitable, but not bottom-discharge fishtail drilling. The process of jetting through an open-tube sampler and then sampling at the desired depth likewise is unsuitable. Take samples at every change in stratum but at intervals not greater than 5 feet. Where casing is used, do not drive it below the sampling elevation. Record any loss of circulation in drilling fluid during advancing of the hole.

With the split-spoon sampler resting on the bottom of the hole, and the water level in the boring at the ground-water level or above, drive the split-spoon through undisturbed soil 6 inches with a few light taps. Then drive it 12 inches more, or to refusal, by dropping the 140-pound hammer 30 inches. Record the number of blows required to cause the final foot of penetration. Refusal is defined as a penetration less than 1 foot for 100 blows.

Raise the split-spoon sampler to the surface, and open it. Place a typical sample or samples of soil from the open spoon into jars without ramming.

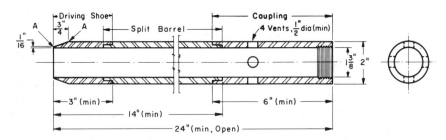

Notes: Coupling head with ball check valve and no vents may be substituted for coupling shown.
Split barrel may be 1½ in. I.D. and may contain a liner.
A spring-type core catcher in the driving shoe to prevent loss of sample is permitted.
Corners at A may be slightly rounded.

Fig. 37–5. Standard split-spoon penetrometer and sampler assembly.

Note on the jars the job designation, boring number, sample number, depth, penetration record, and length of the recovery. Store the jars in suitable containers for shipment; protect samples from freezing and direct exposure to the sun.

Record water-table information on the field logs, including ground-water level, elevations at which the drilling water was lost, or depths at which water under excess pressure was encountered. Measure ground-water levels before and after pulling the casing, where used. In sands, determine the water level as the casing is pulled, and then measure it again at least 30 minutes after the casing is pulled; in silts, measure the water level at least 24 hours after the casing is pulled. No accurate water-level determination is possible in clays, unless there are pervious seams. However, record the 24-hour level for clays. When drilling mud is used and the water level is desired, remove the mud from the hole by bailing or preferably by jetting with clean water. As an alternative where casing is needed to maintain the hole, lower casing (perforated at the lower end) into the hole, and do the bailing inside the casing. Determine the ground-water levels at time intervals of 30 minutes and 24 hours after bailing. In cased holes, repeat the bailing until all traces of drilling mud are removed from inside the casing.

Prepare the data thus obtained as a soil profile to show the nature and extent of the soil strata over the area under consideration. As supplementary information, include such items as date of sampling, drilling method, and casing used.

37–5.2.3 INTERPRETATION OF RESULTS

At best the standard penetration test is a crude method of measuring the penetration resistance of soil. However, where correlations between soil N values (blows per foot) and relative density or consistency have been established, the test is a practical and economical method of obtaining useful information on subsurface materials, which in many instances may be sufficient for final design by foundation engineers. Table 37–2 gives a widely used correlation of N values and soil properties. Although the cor-

Table 37–2. Correlation of N values and soil properties.

Sands		Clays		
N, blows /foot	Relative density	N, blows /foot	Consistency	Unconfined compressive strength, tons/sq. ft.
0-4	Very loose	0-2	Very soft	< 0.25
4-10	Loose	2-4	Soft	0.25-0.5
10-30	Medium	4-8	Medium	0.5 -1.0
30-50	Dense	8-15	Stiff	1.0 -2.0
> 50	Very dense	15-30	Very stiff	2.0 -4.0
		> 30	Hard	> 4.0

relation is fairly reliable for sands, it is not so reliable for clays. The N values of very fine or silty sands below a water table should be corrected by the formula

$$N = 15 + 1/2(N' - 15)$$

before using the correlation. (N' is the recorded field value.) Boulders in granular deposits are another source of misleading N values.

The use of spoon or core samplers as penetrometers is not restricted to foundation investigations. A dynamic penetration test of this kind with a small, portable drill rig may also be used, for example, to find the effects of soil compaction or hardness on crop growth (Swanson and Jacobson, 1956).

37–6 LITERATURE CITED

American Society for Testing and Materials. 1958. *In* Book of ASTM Standards, Part 4. Am. Soc. Testing Mater., Philadelphia.

Cordova, F. J. 1957. Field application of the pocket penetrometer. Am. Soc. Testing Mater. Spec. Tech. Publ. 232:372–375.

Davidson, D. T., Roy, C. J. et al. 1960. The geology and engineering characteristics of some Alaskan soils. Iowa Eng. Exp. Sta. Bull. 186.

Foster, C. R., Knight, S. J., and Rula, A. A. 1958. Soil trafficability. Proceedings of seminar on tillage and traction equipment research. U. S. Dept. Agr. Publ. ARS 42-16.

Gregg, L. E. 1960. Earthwork. *In* K. B. Woods, ed. Highway Engineering Handbook. Section 14. McGraw-Hill Book Co., Inc., New York.

McAlpin, G. W., and Hofmann, W. P. 1960. Soil Explorations. *In* K. B. Woods, ed. Highway Engineering Handbook. Section 10. McGraw-Hill Book Co., Inc., New York.

McKibben, E. G., and Hull, D. O. 1940. Transport wheels for agricultural machines. VIII. Soil penetration tests as a means of predicting rolling resistance. Agr. Eng. 21:231–234.

Peck, R. B., Hansen, W. E., and Thornburn, T. H. 1953. Foundation Engineering. John Wiley & Sons, Inc., New York.

Proctor, R. R. 1933. Description of field and laboratory methods. Engineering News-Record 111:286–289.

Swanson, C. L. W., and Jacobson, H. G. M. 1956. Effect of soil hardness and compaction on corn growth. Soil Sci. Soc. Am. Proc. 20:161–167.

Van Zelst, T. W. 1957. New developments in soil sampling and rock coring equipment. Am. Soc. Testing Mater. Spec. Tech. Publ. 232:1–10.

38 — Bearing Capacity

W. A. GOODWIN
University of Tennessee
Knoxville, Tennessee

38-1 GENERAL INTRODUCTION

Ultimately any structure which rests on the earth's surface must be supported by the underlying soil. The ability of the underlying soil to support the loads produced by the structure is dependent upon many variables such as soil type, ground-water table, depth and size of footing, and type of structure. Failure of the underlying soil to support the structure may occur through excessive settlement and/or shearing of the foundation soils.

For many years the ability of foundation soils to carry building and traffic loads was based largely upon the past experience of the designer. However, within recent years more emphasis has been placed upon the actual determination of bearing capacities through the use of laboratory and field bearing tests. Although many types of bearing tests are in use, none is adaptable to all situations. It is not uncommon that supposedly standard tests must be changed to accommodate the situation under investigation. For example, a shallow-type California-Bearing-Ratio (CBR) test would not be suitable for investigating foundations for deep footings.

Figure 38–1 contains a schematic drawing of a type of shear failure which may occur under building foundations. In this figure, it may be seen that three separate failure zones exist under the footing. Zone I directly under

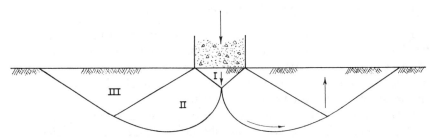

Fig. 38–1. Types of shear failure which may occur under building foundations.

the footing moves downward, Zone II is the shear zone, and Zone III provides the resisting force to the movement of Zones I and II. The bearing capacity of the footing indicated in the figure is dependent upon the volume and weight of Zone III and the shearing resistance along the failure arc. If the footing is well below the surface, then Zone III offers considerably more resistance. If the footing is of a shallow type and is located near the surface, there is less resistance to sliding from Zone III. More comprehensive treatment of the theoretical considerations involved in bearing capacity analysis may be obtained by referring to recent texts on soil mechanics.

The bearing capacity of a foundation has been defined by the Committee on Glossary of Terms and Definitions in Soil Mechanics of the Soil Mechanics and Foundations Division (1958) of the American Society of Civil Engineers as follows:

Allowable bearing value—The maximum pressure that can be permitted on foundation "soil" giving consideration to all pertinent factors with adequate safety against rupture of the "soil" mass or movement of the "foundation" of such magnitude that the structure is impaired.

Ultimate bearing capacity—The average load per unit of area required to produce failure by rupture of the supporting "soil" mass.

Bearing capacity may be investigated by a study of case histories of the behavior of similar foundations under similar structures, by a study of the performance and analysis of bearing tests, and by a theoretical analysis based upon physical properties of the foundation material. For a preliminary investigation the traditional approach of examining existing structures and of studying case histories is perhaps sufficient; however, the purpose of this chapter is to present methods of determining bearing capacities through laboratory and field tests. The most important methods are as follows:

(*1*) Penetration (see section 37).
    a. Pocket penetrometer.
    b. Proctor penetrometer.
    c. Cone penetrometer.
    d. Standard split-spoon penetrometer.
(*2*) California bearing ratio (CBR).
(*3*) Plate bearing.
(*4*) Unconfined compression (see section 34–6).

Penetrometer tests are frequently used as a measure of bearing capacity; the difference between penetration and plate-bearing tests is one principally of scale. Ideally, a bearing test should be made on a scale approximating that of the foundation in question. Since this is usually impracticable, the smaller scale tests are used rather extensively.

Bearing-capacity measurements are also of value in estimating soil compactness. Hard, dry soils will obviously have a higher bearing value than will soft, saturated ones. Information on bearing values is useful to the agriculturist in estimating tillability of farm land. In addition, an agriculturist's efforts made in reducing the binding effectiveness of clay may be measured by bearing tests.

Either of two loading procedures, static or repetitive, may be used in the determination of bearing capacities. The static method is more convenient, due to ease of loading, and involves the same general techniques as does the repetitive method. Repetitive load tests are sometimes used on bases and subgrade materials for airports and highways, whereas static tests are used for evaluating most foundation soils for buildings.

38–2 CALIFORNIA BEARING RATIO (CBR)

38–2.1 Introduction

The California-Bearing-Ratio test, herein referred to as the CBR test, involves application of a vertical load in increasing amounts at some predetermined rate, and measurement of the accompanying penetration or settlement of the loaded area. The vertical loads are usually applied well above the design load, and each increment is permitted to remain for some arbitrary period or until a fixed amount of penetration has occurred. The CBR test may be used in either the laboratory or the field. In the laboratory the test is conducted on a compacted or an "undisturbed" sample, whereas in the field the test is conducted under *in situ* soil conditions. It is a flexible test and may be conducted on materials ranging from clay soils to fine gravels. Test conditions may be varied, within limits, to approach the characteristics of the structure foundation under consideration. For example, surcharge weights may be placed around the test area to simulate the effect of footing depth or of overburden loads. This may be done in the field as well as in the laboratory. In its present state of development, the test is mostly used in the design of highway and airport pavements; however, Baker and Drake (1949) and Kerkhoven and Dorman (1953) have attempted correlations with other types of bearing tests. Only the laboratory test will be described here.

38–2.2 Principle

The California Bearing Ratio is an arbitrary value which attempts to express the relationship of load and penetration as a single value. It is calculated from the following equation:

$$CBR = \frac{\text{Test Load per Unit Area}}{\text{Standard Load per Unit Area}} \times 100$$

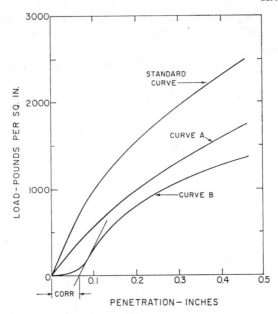

Fig. 38–2. Load-penetration curves for standard sample and tests *A* and *B*.

The curve for the standard load per unit area is shown in Fig. 38–2 (plotted from values in Table 38–1). These values are for loads required to produce the indicated penetration in a sample of crushed stone established as a standard when the procedure was developed. It may be observed that the CBR is a ratio of the penetration resistance of the material under test to that of the crushed stone. The standard sample is defined as having a CBR of 100%. The CBR is calculated from the corrected load values taken from the load-penetration curve at the desired penetrations. Usually these penetrations are 0.10 and 0.20 inch.

38–2.3   Method [1]

38–3.2.1   SPECIAL APPARATUS [2]

Special apparatus needed for the laboratory test is described briefly below. Specifications of most items are given with the schematic diagrams in Fig. 38–3. A typical laboratory setup is shown in Fig. 38–4.

1. Mold, made of metal, cylindrical in shape, with an internal diameter of 6.0 ± 0.005 inches and a height of 7.0 ± 0.005 inches, and provided with (*a*) a metal extension or collar 2 inches in height, and (*b*) a base

---

[1] Am. Soc. Testing Mater. (1961a).

[2] Commercially available from all except the third source listed in section 37–2.2.1.

Table 38–1. Load-penetration values for standard CBR curve.

Load, lb. /sq. in.	Penetration, inches
1,000	0.1
1,500	0.2
1,900	0.3
2,300	0.4
2,600	0.5

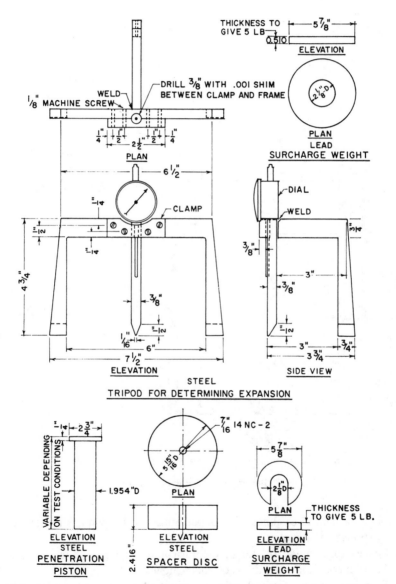

Fig. 38–3. Bearing-ratio test apparatus (Am. Soc. Testing Mater., 1961a), cont. p. 490.

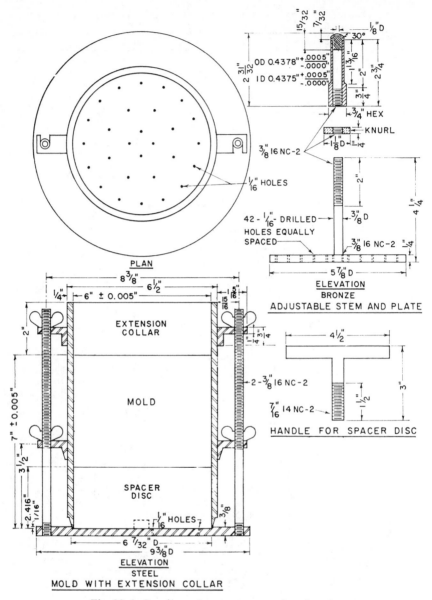

Fig. 38–3. Bearing-ratio test apparatus (continued).

plate ⅜ inch in thickness that is perforated with openings not exceeding 1/16 inch in diameter.

2. Spacer disc, made of metal, cylindrical in shape, with a diameter of 5.938 inches and a thickness of 2.416 inches.

3. Rammer, made of metal, with a weight of 5.5 pounds and a circular

LOAD APPLICATION MACHINE

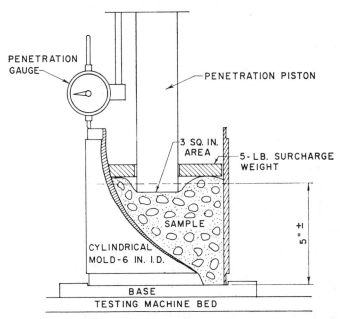

Fig. 38–4. Typical set-up for laboratory CBR test.

face 2 inches in diameter, and with provision for controlling the height of drop to a free fall of 1 foot above the elevation of the soil. The foregoing specifications are for low-density compaction. For high-density compaction, change the weight to 10 pounds and the height of free fall to 1.5 feet.

4. Device for measuring expansion, consisting of an adjustable metal stem, a perforated metal plate (with perforations not exceeding 1/16-inch diameter), and a metal tripod to support the dial gauge used for measurement.

5. Surcharge weights, including one annular lead weight and several slotted lead weights, each with a diameter of 5⅞ inches, a center hole 2⅛ inches in diameter, and a thickness sufficient to give a weight of 5 pounds.

6. Penetration piston, made of metal, with a diameter of 1.95 inches (cross section area = 3 square inches), and a length not less than 4 inches.

7. Two dial gauges, calibrated in units of 0.001 inch.

8. Loading machine, capable of applying a uniformly increasing load up to 10,000 pounds at a uniformly even rate of penetration of 0.05 inch per minute, and equipped with a load-indicating device that can be read to 10 pounds or less.

Table 38–2. Specimen fabrication methods.

Method	Sample size, lb.	Maximum particle size	Mold diameter, in.	Rammer weight, lb.	Height of drop, in.	Blows per layer	Number of layers
A	14	No. 4 sieve, 4.76 mm.	6.0	5.5	12	56	3
B	22	3/4-inch sieve	6.0	5.5	12	56	3
C	16	No. 4 sieve, 4.76 mm.	6.0	10.0	18	56	5
D	25	3/4-inch sieve	6.0	10.0	18	56	5

38–2.3.2 PROCEDURE

The test procedure described in the following paragraphs applies to test method A in Table 38–2. The procedure is applicable for the other methods shown in the table if due recognition is given to the test variables as tabulated.

Dry the field sample in air or at a temperature not over 60°C. until it becomes friable. Pulverize the soil aggregates in such a manner as to avoid reducing the natural size of individual particles. Pass a sufficient quantity of the pulverized soil through a No. 4(4.76-mm.) sieve to produce a representative sample weighing approximately 14 pounds. Discard material larger than the No. 4 sieve.

Thoroughly mix the sample with sufficient water to attain the optimum water content, as attained for the soil in the compaction test referred to in section 32. If a curing period was used in obtaining the optimum water content, place the mixture in a covered container until uniform distribution of the mixing water is obtained (usually 5 minutes or longer). Following the curing period, and immediately prior to compaction, place the spacer disc inside the mold (with collar attached) on the perforated base plate, and place a coarse filter paper on the spacer disc. Then compact the sample in the mold in three uniform layers with a 5.5 pound rammer, using 56 blows per layer.

After compaction, remove the extension collar, and carefully trim the compacted soil even with the mold top by a straightedge. Lift the mold containing the specimen from the base plate and spacer disc; then weigh the mold and specimen. Place a coarse filter paper on the perforated base plate. Then invert the mold and compacted sample over the base plate so that the soil is in contact with the filter paper. Clamp the perforated base plate to the mold.

Place the adjustable stem and attached perforated plate on the compacted soil specimen in the mold, and apply weights to produce the desired surcharge weight. This is normally, in the case of pavements, equal to the weight of the material above the soil under test and should in no case be

less than 10 pounds. Then immerse the mold and weights in water, allowing free access of water to both ends of the specimen. Measure the swelling
that occurs initially and during a 96-hour period while the specimen is
allowed to soak at a constant water level. (Shorter soaking periods may be
used if, upon investigation, they are found not to alter the test results.)
Calculate the swelling as a percentage of the initial specimen height.

Following the measurements for swell, remove the free water from the
mold, and allow the specimen to drain downward for about 15 minutes.
Avoid disturbing the specimen during water removal. Remove the perforated plate and surcharge weights; then weigh the mold containing the
specimen, and record the result.

Preparatory to performing the penetration test, place surcharge weights
on the specimen to produce an intensity of loading equal to that used during the soaking period. First, place the 5-pound annular weight on the soil
surface. Next, seat the penetration piston with the smallest possible load,
but in no case in excess of 10 pounds. Then add the remaining surcharge
weights. Set the depth-penetration gauge to zero, and note the initial load
on the load-application machine. (The small initial load required to seat
the piston is ignored when determining the load-penetration relation.)
Apply the load on the penetration piston at a rate of approximately 0.05
inch per minute. Record the load-indicator values at each 0.025-inch depth
of penetration up to a total penetration of 0.500 inch. Note and record the
maximum load and penetration if it occurs for a penetration less than
0.500 inch.

After the test is completed, remove the soil from the mold, and take a
250-g. sample directly in the penetrated area from the top 1 inch of the
specimen. Determine the water content of this sample. Take additional
samples throughout the specimen if an average value for water content is
desired.

38-2.3.3 CALCULATION AND PRESENTATION OF RESULTS

Obtain the load-penetration curve by plotting on rectangular coordinate
paper the load in pounds per square inch as the ordinate and the accompanying penetration in inches as the abscissa. Curves A and B in Fig. 38–2
are for typical tests on two different materials. In some instances, as in
Curve B, the load-penetration curve is initially concave upward because of
surface irregularities, lack of zero adjustment of measurement dials, or other
causes. In such instances, adjust the curve before use by projecting the
straight-line portion to the penetration axis and then shifting the curve
horizontally until it passes through the origin of the graph shown in Fig.
38–2.

Using corrected load values taken from the load-penetration curve at
penetrations of 0.100 and 0.200 inch, calculate the bearing ratios by divid-

ing the corrected loads by the standard loads (Table 38–1) of 1,000 and 1,500 pounds per square inch, respectively, and multiplying by 100 to obtain the bearing ratio in percent. If the penetration is less than 0.200 inch, use the maximum test load to calculate a bearing ratio, interpolating the standard load for the penetration at maximum load.

The bearing ratio is normally reported as the one calculated at 0.100-inch penetration. When the bearing ratio at 0.200-inch penetration is greater than that at 0.100 inch, run a check test. If the check test gives similar results, report the bearing value at the 0.200-inch penetration.

Include in the test report the method of sample preparation, the dry unit weight before and after soaking, the water content before and after soaking, the water content of the top 1 inch layer after the test, the swelling, and the bearing ratio.

38–2.3.4 COMMENTS

If desired, the water content of the sample after penetration may be determined by the relationship presented in section 32.

In the analysis of CBR data, it is important to recognize that the degree of compaction of the laboratory test sample will influence the test results. Sample preparation should be such as to prepare specimens duplicating field conditions. Even if field conditions are duplicated in the laboratory, the lateral restraint of the laboratory mold may cause much greater load values than those obtained by *in situ* testing.

Considerable judgment and experience are needed before CBR bearing values can be projected to loading conditions expected for shallow footings and highway and airport loadings. It is also necessary to consider the effect of differences in size of the test-loaded and structure-loaded areas.

38–3 FIELD PLATE-BEARING TEST

38–3.1 Introduction

Plate-bearing tests may be of either the nonrepetitive or repetitive static-load type. They may be conducted on compacted soils, as existing in high-way and airport embankments, or on soils in their natural state, as commonly encountered in highway and airport cuts and building foundations. In either type of bearing test, the measured deflections are related to the compressibility and elasticity of the soil; whereas, in the penetration test discussed in section 37, the deflections indicate the resistance of the soil to shear deformations. In the plate-bearing and penetrometer tests, a compressive load is applied to the soil by a rigid bearing area, and the accompanying deflection or penetration is measured as the load is varied.

From the viewpoint of application, plate-bearing tests may be used to evaluate soils for static loads applied by spread footings used in building foundations or to obtain data on subgrade soils for use in design of rigid or flexible airport and highway pavements. The tests for the two purposes are essentially the same except that the static-load test for spread footings is made over a longer time interval and at greater depths below the ground surface than is the test for design of pavements. The latter type is discussed herein.

The field plate-bearing test for evaluating subgrade soils consists of loading a rigid circular plate of 30-inch diameter with an axial compressive load. During loading, measurements are taken to determine the average deflection or penetration of the rigid plate into the soil surface. Loading of the plate may be of the nonrepetitive or repetitive static type. In the nonrepetitive type, the load is applied at a moderately rapid rate in uniform increments until the desired penetration is obtained or until the capacity of the loading equipment is reached. The repetitive static-loading procedure consists of applying a load until a given penetration is reached and then completely releasing the load and again applying and releasing the load until six cycles have been made. The load is then increased to give a greater desired penetration, and the procedure of applying and releasing the load is resumed. The endpoint of the test occurs when a certain rate of penetration is achieved.

In either of the tests, the load is transmitted to the rigid plate by a jack arrangement which has as its reaction a heavily loaded truck or some type of heavy construction equipment usually located at the job site. If a hydraulic jack is used, the load increments can be measured by a pressure gauge located on the output side of the jack. Other types of load-measuring devices such as proving rings and electrical strain-gauge load cells have also proved satisfactory.

Penetration of the rigid plate during load application is measured with reference to an independent datum plane. Such a plane usually consists of a beam at least 16 feet long, resting on supports located at least 8 feet from the bearing plate, or the nearest supporting element of the reaction load. The dial gauges are arranged symmetrically around the periphery of the plate and are attached to the datum beam in such a way as to show the movement of the rigid bearing plate relative to that of the beam (see Fig. 38–5).

Data obtained during the test are plotted in the form of load (average bearing pressure) versus vertical movement (average vertical deformation) of the rigid plate. Typical test results are shown in Fig. 38–6.

The method described herein may be used for conducting nonrepetitive static load tests on bases or subgrade soils in either the compacted or natural state. Data derived from use of this method are employed in the evaluation and design of airport and highway pavements.

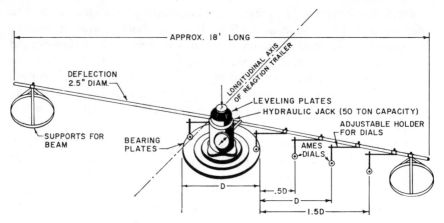

Fig. 38–5. Diagram showing arrangement of equipment for plate-bearing test (Courtesy of The Asphalt Institute).

38–3.2   Method [3]

38–3.2.1   SPECIAL APPARATUS [4]

1. Loading device: A heavily loaded truck or construction equipment to produce the desired reaction for test loads.
2. Hydraulic jack, equipped with a gauge for measurement of the applied load and a spherical bearing-cap for transmitting the applied load normal to the bearing plate.
3. Four or more circular steel bearing plates not less than 1 inch in thickness and having diameters ranging from 6 inches to 30 inches. Machine the plates so that they may be arranged in pyramid fashion to ensure rigidity.
4. Three or more dial gauges graduated in units of 0.001 inch and capable of recording a maximum penetration of 1 inch.
5. Reference datum, consisting of a steel beam or pipe at least 16 feet long, resting on supports located at least 8 feet from the bearing-plate edge or the nearest support of the loading device.
6. Miscellaneous items, including a stop watch, dial gauge clamps, a spirit level, a thermometer, plaster of paris, and fine sand.

38–3.2.2   PROCEDURE

If the tests are to be performed at some distance below the ground or pavement surface, and if an unconfined bearing test is desired, remove the surrounding materials to provide a clearance equal to one and one-half

---

[3] Am. Soc. Testing Mater. (1961b).
[4] Commercially available from all except the third source listed in section 37–2.2.1.

times the bearing-plate diameter from the edge of the bearing plate; however, if a confined test is desired, excavate just enough material to accommodate the actual bearing plate.

Level the surface to be tested to permit proper application of the test loads. Then place the bearing plate in position, and check for levelness of the test surface. If high points exist, trim the surface, and again check for levelness. In the case of coarse-grained soils which are difficult to level, seat the plate in a ¼-inch layer of fine sand. (In some instances plaster of paris can be used to obtain a level and uniform surface interface with the bearing plate.)

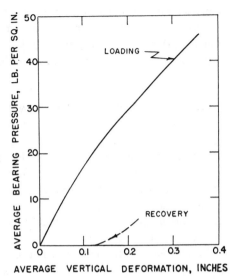

Fig. 38-6. Typical plate-bearing test results showing loading and recovery curves.

Once the test is leveled, set the bearing plate in position, and place the remaining plates of small diameter concentric with, and on top of, the bearing plate. Space three dial gauges on the upper surface near the edge of the bearing plate and 120 degrees apart to indicate the average penetration of the plate. Attach the dial gauges to the reference datum beam, and allow the dial stems to rest on the upper surface of the bearing plate. After the plate and gauges have been properly arranged, and after the hydraulic jack is positioned under the reaction or loading device, seat the bearing-plate assembly by the quick application and release of a load sufficient to produce a penetration of not less than 0.01 inch nor more than 0.02, as indicated by the dial gauges. When the dial needles come to rest following release of the load, reseat the plate by applying one-half the recorded load producing the 0.01- to 0.02-inch penetration. When the dial needles again come to rest, set each dial accurately at its zero mark, and record the seating load.

Continue the test by applying loads at a moderately rapid rate in uniform increments, so that at least six points are obtained for a load-deformation curve. After each load increment is applied, allow its action to continue until a rate of penetration not more than 0.001 inch per minute has been maintained for 3 consecutive minutes. Record load and penetration readings for each load increment. Continue this procedure until the selected total penetration is obtained. After application of the final load, maintain it until an increased penetration of not more than 0.001 inch per minute for

3 consecutive minutes occurs, at which time record the total penetration. Release the load to the load at which the dial gauges were set at zero, and maintain this zero-setting load until the rate of recovery does not exceed 0.001 inch for 3 consecutive minutes. Record the deformation at the zero-setting load.

38–3.2.3 CALCULATION AND PRESENTATION OF RESULTS

Report the test data in graphical form by plotting the load in pounds per square inch for each increment against the corresponding average vertical deformation in inches. Also plot the recovery after full release of load. Correct the graph for the zero deformation point by taking into account the dead weight of the equipment and the seating load. Information may be obtained from this graph relative to the total deformation (penetration) under the maximum load and relative to the elastic and permanent deformation for the maximum load.

In addition to the load-deformation data, keep a record of the date, the time of beginning and completing the test, the weather conditions, and any unusual conditions observed at the site or during test.

38–3.2.4 COMMENTS

In a plate-loading test, only a portion of the desired foundation information may be obtained. At best, the test indicates the bearing capacity of the soil at the water content and time-rate of loading used in the test. The loading test should not be used to estimate slow settlement caused by consolidation of the soil by drainage of water unless time effects are considered.

38–4   LITERATURE CITED

American Society for Testing and Materials. 1961a. Tentative method of test for bearing ratio of laboratory-compacted soils. *In* 1961 Book of ASTM Standards Including Tentatives. Part 4, pp. 1380–1385. Am. Soc. Testing Mater., Philadelphia.

American Society for Testing and Materials. 1961b. Nonrepetitive static load tests of soils, for use in evaluation and design of airport and highway pavements. *In* 1961 Book of ASTM Standards, Including Tentatives. Part 4, pp. 1387–1391. Am. Soc. Testing Mater., Philadelphia.

Baker, R. F., and Drake, W. B. 1949. Investigation of field and laboratory methods for evaluating subgrade support in the design of highway flexible pavements. Kentucky Eng. Exp. Sta. Bull. 13.

Committee on Glossary of Terms and Definitions in Soil Mechanics of the Soil Mechanics and Foundations Division. 1958. Glossary of terms and definitions in soil mechanics. Am. Soc. Civil Eng. Proc. 84, No. SM4, Paper 1826.

Kerkhoven, R. E., and Dorman, G. M. 1953. Some consideration on the California Bearing Ratio method for the design of flexible pavements. Shell Res. Centre, London.

39

Size Distribution of Aggregates[1]

W. D. KEMPER

Agricultural Research Service, USDA, and Colorado State University
Fort Collins, Colorado

W. S. CHEPIL

Agricultural Research Service, USDA
Manhattan, Kansas

39–1 INTRODUCTION

39–1.1 Aggregate Defined

If the aggregate-size distribution is to be determined, the term "aggregate" must be defined. An aggregate is a group of two or more primary particles which cohere to each other more strongly than to surrounding particles. Generally, all adjacent particles cohere to some degree. Therefore, the disintegration of the soil mass into aggregates implies the imposition of some disrupting force. The units of the soil mass which maintain their identity as aggregates will be those in which the cohesive forces among particles are greater than the disruptive force. Consequently, a major factor determining the aggregate-size distribution of a soil is the manner in which the soil mass is broken into aggregates.

If comparisons are to be made among aggregate-size distributions of soils, it is necessary that the procedure by which the soil mass is broken into aggregates be standardized. If the measurements are to have practical field significance, the forces causing disintegration should be related to forces expected in the field. The better methods to determine aggregate-size distribution have evolved as a result of efforts to standardize the disruptive forces and make them comparable to those in field phenomena.

39–1.2 Significance of Size Distribution of Aggregates

The size distribution of soil aggregates is important because the size of the aggregates determines their susceptibility to movement (erosion) by

[1] Contribution from the Soil and Water Conservation Research Division, ARS, USDA, in cooperation with the Colorado and Kansas Agr. Exp. Sta., Ft. Collins and Manhattan, respectively.

499

wind and water, and because their size is important in determining the dimensions of the pore space in cultivated soils. The size of the pores, in turn, affects the movement and distribution of water and air in the soil, which are major factors affecting plant growth.

Immediately after cultivation, the dimensions of large pores in the soil are a function of the size distribution of aggregates and clods. The water content of the aggregates then is usually relatively low. However, when rain or irrigation increases the water content of the soil to high levels, the aggregates slake to some extent, and the soil settles. The size distribution of the soil aggregates when the soil is wet is a major factor determining the amount of large pores persisting in the soil. Thus, the choice of conditions under which the aggregate-size distributions are to be measured is largely determined by the purpose of the analysis.

Since the purposes of the analysis have often been different, a variety of procedures have been used. No single method meets the requirements of all investigators. Consequently, several methods are discussed here. Some of them may be more applicable to the problems of some investigators than the one method which is outlined in detail.

39–1.3 Separation and Measurement of Dry Aggregates

Mechanical disruption during the course of preparing and sieving the sample is used to break the soil mass into "aggregates" in this procedure. The various size fractions are collected on screens of successively smaller size, and the amount in each fraction is determined by weighing. Puchner (1911), Mangelsdorff (1929), Keen (1933), and Nekrossov (1934), as quoted by Russell (1938), used various methods of dry sieving. All these early methods employed sieving by hand with a nest of flat sieves. The flat-sieve method in its various forms is simple but suffers from several draw-backs. Skill and care are required during sieving because manual sieving introduces a nonconsistent factor which can cause variations in the results. Clogging of sieves is often a serious problem.

Cole (1939) attempted to avoid personal judgment in sieving by passing air-dry soil through a nest of flat sieves operated mechanically by a motor giving a standard number of shakes and jolts. Clogging of fine sieves was prevented, but the treatment was rather severe and tended to break up weak aggregates. To overcome some of the difficulties of the flat-sieve method, Chepil and Bisal (1943) devised a rotary-sieve machine. It had six concentric sieves bolted together and not interchangeable. This and other limitations were overcome later with an improved rotary sieve that could be equipped with from 1 to 14 sieves (Chepil, 1952). Chepil (1962) presented a detailed plan for the construction of this machine. Edwards (1956) designed a larger rotary sieve for more convenient sieving of large volumes of soil to investigate the association of sizes of dry aggregates with crop yields.

Some advantages of the rotary sieve are: (*1*) it is the most consistent dry-sieving method thus far devised; (*2*) it is not subject to a personal factor; (*3*) it gives fairly consistent results irrespective of the size of soil sample used; (*4*) it causes less breakdown of clods than the mechanical flat-sieve method; (*5*) it virtually eliminates clogging; and (*6*) it is well suited to resieving soil any number of times to determine the relative resistance of the soil to breakdown by mechanical forces.

One limitation is that the cost of a rotary sieve is somewhat higher than the cost of flat sieves. The number and size of the sieves used influences the amount of aggregate breakdown. Therefore, it is necessary to have the same sizes and number of sieves in all comparable tests.

Chepil (1951, 1958) showed that the mechanical stability of dry aggregates or clods is a good index of the susceptibility of soil to erosion by winds. In other work, Chepil (1953) found close relationships between the size distribution of dry aggregates and the susceptibility of soils to erosion by wind.

Samples for dry sieve analysis should be taken when the soil is reasonably dry to avoid breakdown or change in structure. A flat, preferably square-cornered, spade is pushed under the sample to lift it and place it in a suitable tray. Air- or oven-drying have given virtually the same results. Since clod structure varies with depth, the same depth of sampling must be used for all results expected to be comparable. Usually no special preparation for sieving is given. The soil is merely placed in the rotary sieve, the sieve is turned on, and the various sizes of dry aggregates are caught in pans and weighed.

39–1.4 Separation and Measurement of Wet Aggregates

The wetting process usually causes considerable disruption of previously dry aggregates. The size of the aggregates after this disruption is apparently an important soil parameter. Several methods have been devised to obtain a quantitative measurement of the size distribution of these aggregates. Rate of sedimentation, elutriation, and sieving have been used to determine size distributions.

39–1.4.1 SEDIMENTATION

According to Stokes' law, the velocity with which a small sphere settles through a viscous fluid is proportional to the square of its radius, proportional to the difference between its density and the density of the fluid, and inversely proportional to the viscosity of the fluid.

The dependency of settling velocity on particle radius can be used to separate aggregates of various equivalent sizes in the same manner that it is used to separate primary particles into various size fractions (see section 43). Quantitative separation of aggregates into distinct size groups by this method would require that aggregates have the same density. Indications are that this is more nearly true of aggregates than of primary particles. Chepil (1950) found that the densities of aggregates in a given sample are not greatly different from each other but may be markedly different from the densities of the primary particles. He described a method to measure the densities. Although aggregates are not spherical, as assumed in use of Stokes' law, they approximate spherical shape more closely than do most clay particles.

The major limitation of sedimentation procedures is that aggregates >1 mm. in diameter settle too rapidly to be measured precisely. Yoder (1936), Kolodny and Joffe (1940) and others have used sedimentation techniques to determine the amounts of small aggregates in soils.

Davidson and Evans (1960) have extended the sedimentation technique to measure the amounts of aggregates in the larger size range by using liquid (1 part water to 9 parts glycerol) that had a viscosity about 140 times that of water. Settling rate was measured photometrically. The method yields reproducible results and is easily adapted to automatic recording. Stability of aggregates in glycerol-water mixtures is correlated (Davidson and Evans, 1960) with stability of aggregates in water. Whether the correlation is close enough to justify widespread use of their glycerol-water sedimentation method has not been determined as of this writing.

39–1.4.2 ELUTRIATION

Water flowing upward tends to carry aggregates with it. However, if the aggregates are large enough and dense enough that their velocity of settling with respect to the water is as fast or faster than the upward movement of the water, they will not be carried upward.

Kopecky (1914) connected a series of successively larger tubes, placed the sample in the smallest tube and passed water upward through the series of tubes at a set volume per unit time. The upward velocity of the water was smaller in the larger tubes; hence, successively smaller equivalent sizes of particles remained in the successively larger tubes. Baver and Rhoades (1932) and others used the elutriation method in aggregate analyses.

Elutriation methods have been criticized because it is difficult to avoid turbulence in water flowing in wide columns, and some aggregates that would stay in the tube if only laminar flow occurred are carried out of the tube as a result of turbulence. Aggregate density should be determined if actual sizes of aggregates are to be calculated. Water flowing upward in a tube normally has a parabolic velocity distribution, with water adjacent to the sides moving more slowly than water at the center of the tube. While there is a sound basis for all of these criticisms, elutriation may still be used to make a separation of aggregates into several approximate size fractions. If care is used and good equipment is available, the separation of aggregates < 2 mm. in diameter will be fairly accurate.

39–1.4.3 SIEVING

This technique involves wetting the sample and then separating aggregates into various sizes by sieving the sample through a nest of sieves under water. Care is taken to cause as little mechanical disruption of the aggregates as possible. Tiulin (1928) and Yoder (1936) were among the early workers to use this procedure extensively.

A major factor affecting the size of the water-stable aggregates is the method by which they are wetted. Direct immersion of dry soil in water at atmospheric air pressure causes a great disruption of large aggregates into smaller aggregates. A much smaller degree of disruption is caused when soils are wetted slowly under tension, by spraying with a fine mist, or by adding water under a vacuum.

For a discussion regarding the mechanisms involved in the disruption of dry soils when immersed in water, reference may be made to section 40. The immersion wetting process is fairly comparable to wetting the soil surface by irrigation. If the purpose of the aggregate analysis is related to the formation of soil crusts, immersion wetting is probably the preferred procedure. On the other hand, soils below the surface are wet more slowly under tension and, therefore, are disrupted much less. Wetting the dry soils under a tension is preferred when the geometry of soil particles and voids below the immediate surface is being studied. Kemper and Koch (1965) found that soils wet under tension had about the same aggregate stabilities whether the tension in the water was 0.5 or 15 millibars. Aggregate stability of soils wet under a vacuum was found to be closely correlated with aggregate stability of soils wet under a tension. Since the vacuum wetting procedure produced more reproducible results and was faster, it was used to approximate disruptive forces involved in wetting soil below the soil surface.

A study concerning the reproducibility of aggregate-size distribution values was reported by the Soil Science Society of America Committee on Physical Analysis (Van Bavel, 1953). Analyses were made at several laboratories using a Yoder-type procedure and using both immersion at atmospheric air pressure and vacuum-wetting techniques. They found extreme variability of size distribution of a given soil when it was measured by different laboratories using their vacuum-wetting technique. This technique involved transferring wet soils from nonstandardized containers, in which they were wet under vacuum, to the sieves. The committee believed that the great variation using the vacuum-wetting technique probably resulted from nonuniform handling procedures. Some of the variation probably was caused by wetting the samples when only a partial vacuum had been achieved. It was assumed that the pressure in the vacuum desiccator had reached the vapor pressure of water when water left in the desiccator began to boil. It is probable that some of the technicians mistook the formation of air bubbles and their escape from the water for the onset of boiling. This mistaken assumption that the proper degree of vacuum had been reached would cause them to wet the samples when appreciable air was left in the desiccator.

If water brought to equilibrium with room conditions is used to wet the samples in the evacuated desiccators, air begins to come out of the water as it enters the desiccators. When the water contacts the soil, the soil seems to catalyze the release of the remaining air from the water. Formation of a bubble in water in or near an aggregate causes some disruption of the particle. The degree of disruption depends on how fast the water enters the desiccator and other factors. Kemper and Koch (1965) found that the average aggregate stability and the reproducibility of the measurement were both improved if the samples were wet by de-aerated water.

Aggregate-size distribution often is measured to gain information on the size of the aggregates as they exist in the mass of soil. This requires a wetting treatment less drastic than direct wetting at atmospheric pressure. Consequently, vacuum wetting is proposed as an alternative to immersion at atmospheric air pressure.

39–1.5 Representation of Size Distribution of Aggregates

Multiple-sieve techniques give data on the amount of aggregates in each of several size groupings. To evaluate treatments, or to rank soils, a single parameter to represent a soil sample is necessary. The problem then is to decide on the importance of each size group to the final parameter. If equal weights of the different size groups of aggregates were of equal importance, the quantities of the different sizes should be added, so that making a number of separations would provide no advantage over a single separation obtained using the smallest size screen and determining the weight of all the aggregates retained. It is generally considered, however, that a unit weight of large aggregates is more indicative of good structure for most agricultural purposes than is an equal weight of small aggregates, and this concept is incorporated in certain mathematical techniques for expressing aggregation data in the form of a single parameter.

39-1.5.1 MEAN WEIGHT-DIAMETER

Van Bavel (1949) proposed that equal weights of aggregates be assigned an importance or weighting factor that is proportional to the size of the aggregates. The parameter which he called the mean weight-diameter (MWD) is equal to the sum of products of (1) the mean diameter $\bar{x}_i$ of each size fraction and (2) the proportion of the total sample weight w_i occurring in the corresponding size fraction, where the summation is carried out over all n size fractions, including the one that passes through the finest sieve:

$$MWD = \sum_{i=1}^{n} \bar{x}_i w_i. \qquad [1]$$

The entire sample is passed through an 8-mm. sieve prior to analysis. In his original definition, Van Bavel used an integration, which is equivalent to a summation made over a very large number of very small increments.

Van Bavel's (1950) concept of the MWD has been used widely. However, its calculation in the integral form involves plotting points on a graph and determining the area enclosed. This is a fairly tedious process. Youker and McGuinness (1956) suggested that the summation-type calculation in the above equation be used in place of the graphical approach. The summation equation shown above generally overestimates the original MWD when only five fairly broad size fractions are used. However, the correlation between MWD's found by graphical means and MWD's calculated from the summation using five size fractions is very good. Because of the general shape of the curve, overestimation of the MWD from use of the summation equation is generally somewhat less if sieves with openings of 4.76, 2.00, 1.00, and 0.21 mm. are used rather than sieves with openings of 2.00, 1.00, 0.50, and 0.20 mm.

39-1.5.2 GEOMETRIC MEAN DIAMETER

Mazurak (1950) suggested that the geometric mean diameter (GMD) be used as an index of the aggregate-size distribution. The geometric mean diameter is calculated approximately by the equation

$$GMD = \exp \left[\frac{\sum_{i=1}^{n} w_i \log \bar{x}_i}{\sum_{i=1}^{n} w_i} \right] \qquad [2]$$

where w_i is the weight of aggregates in a size class with an average diameter $\bar{x}_i$ and $\sum_{i=1}^{n} w_i$ is the total weight of the sample. The use of the GMD is supported by Gardner's (1956) finding that the aggregate-size distribution in most soils is aproximately log-normal rather than normal. This log-normal distribution provides the opportunity to describe the actual aggregate-size distribution of most soils with two parameters, the geometric mean diameter and the log standard deviation (Gardner, 1956). If data are summarized in the form of these two parameters, the *MWD* and other aggregate-size indexes may be calculated from these parameters. The main disadvantage of expressing data in terms of the *GMD* and log standard deviation is the extensive work involved in obtaining them. The log standard deviation must be obtained by either graphical or differential interpolation from the data.

39–1.5.3 OTHER PROPOSALS

Other parameters which have been developed to express aggregate-size distribution in terms of one or two numbers are the weighted mean diameter and standard deviation (Puri and Puri, 1939) and the coefficient of aggregation (Retzer and Russell, 1941). Recently, De Boodt et al. (1961) have shown that the change in mean weight-diameter when dry soil samples are wetted is correlated with crop yields under some conditions. They obtained correlation coefficients that averaged about 0.9.

39–1.5.4 COMPARISON AND EVALUATION

Schaller and Stockinger (1953) compared five methods for expressing aggregation data on several soils. The best methods for presenting aggregate-size distribution data seemed to be *MWD* or *GMD* and the log standard deviation. The correlation coefficient between *MWD* and *GMD* was about 0.9. The *GMD* and the log standard deviation give a more complete description of the size distribution than the *MWD*. However, the *MWD* is easier to calculate and easier for most individuals to visualize. Both the *MWD* and *GMD* can be used to represent aggregate-size distribution for statistical analysis. Stirk (1958) maintains that the reliability of a mean is questionable if the aggregate distributions are extremely skewed. Consequently, he favors the use of a *GMD* and a log standard deviation on basic considerations. However, he points out that use of these parameters may complicate the calculations to a point beyond that which is most efficient for interpreting individual experiments.

39–2   METHOD FOR WATER-STABLE AGGREGATES [2]

39–2.1   Special Apparatus

1. Nests of sieves 5 inches in diameter and 2 inches in height, with mesh No's. 4, 9, 16, and 25 (i.e., hole widths of 4.76, 2.00, 1.00, and 0.21 mm., respectively), and one 2½-mesh screen (hole widths of 8 mm.).

---

[2] This method is similar to that proposed by the Soil Science Society of America Committee on Physical Analyses (Van Bavel, 1953) with some important variations.

2. A Yoder (1936) type sieving machine which raises and lowers the nests of sieves through water 1.5 inches, approximately 30 times per minute.
3. Vacuum desiccators and small barometers. The latter consist of a piece of glass tubing, 6 cm. in length, closed at the upper end, open at the lower end, and filled with mercury, with the lower end immersed in a container of mercury.
4. Mechanical stirrers.

39–2.2 Procedure

Take the sample when the soil is moist and friable. Sieve it through an 8-mm. (2½-mesh) screen. Pull apart clods larger than 8 mm. until their subunits are small enough to go through the sieve, breaking the large clods so that practically all the subunits are retained on a 4-mesh (4.76-mm.) screen. Avoid compacting, puddling or powdering the soil during sampling and transportation.

Air-dry the sample at room temperature. Weigh three representative 25-g. subsamples. Oven-dry and weigh one sample. Assume that the other two subsamples contain the same amount of oven-dry soil. Use the two samples not oven-dried as duplicates in the following determination.

Base the decision as to which wetting method to use on the purpose of the analysis. Use water at a temperature between 20° and 25°C. to wet and sieve the samples.

To wet the samples under vacuum, place the samples on 75-mm. watch glasses on the perforated ceramic plate in a vacuum desiccator with 5 or 10 ml. of water in the bottom of the desiccator and a small barometer on the ceramic plate. Evacuate the desiccator for 5 minutes after the pressure has been reduced to less than 3 cm. of mercury. Allow de-aerated water (see section 40–3.3) to enter the desiccator until it comes up over the edges of the watch glasses and wets all samples. Remove the watch glasses and samples from the desiccators, and immediately place them on separate nests of sieves which are immersed in salt-free ($<10^{-5}$ mhos per cm.) water. Then gently slide the samples off the lower lip of the watch glass onto the top sieve, distributing the sample evenly over the sieve. Lower the water level so that it just covers the sample when the sieve is in its highest position.

If it is decided to wet the samples at atmospheric pressure instead of under vacuum, fill the container in which the sieving is to take place with salt-free ($<10^{-5}$ mhos per cm.) water to a level somewhat below that of the screen in the top sieve. Distribute the air-dry sample evenly over the top sieve. Immediately prior to sieving, raise the water level rapidly to a point where it barely covers the sample when the sieves are in their highest position. Allow <3 seconds to elapse between the time the water first touches the sample and the time it completely covers the sample.

Begin sieving approximately 10 minutes after the samples are wetted. Sieve the samples for 10 minutes. Remove the sieves from the water, and determine the oven-dry weight of the material on each sieve. Part of the material on each sieve usually is sand too large to go through the sieve. Determine the amount of sand in each sieve by dispersing the material with a mechanical stirrer and dispersing agent and washing the material through the sieve, which retains the sand larger than the sieve holes. Then oven-dry the sand and weigh it. Determine the weight of aggregates in each sieve by subtracting the weight of the sand from the weight of the oven-dry material retained after the first sieving. Calculate the quantity of material smaller than 0.21 mm. by subtracting the sum of the oven-dry weights of material retained on each sieve from the oven-dry weight of the original sample.

39–2.3 Calculation of Results

Divide the weight of aggregates in each of the five size classes by the weight of the oven-dry sample, minus the weight of the sand remaining on all the sieves, to obtain a decimal fraction for each size class. For erosion studies and some other purposes it may be advisable to leave the data in this form.

Approximate the mean weight-diameter (MWD) using equation [1], or approximate the geometric mean diameter (GMD) using equation [2]. For most practical work the MWD gives an adequate basis for comparisons. Alternatively, express the data in terms of the more analytic GMD and log standard deviation. Gardner (1956) gives details of calculation. This method of representation is not recommended for general use because of the extensive work of calculating the results.

39–2.4 Comments

One of the greatest sources of variation lies in the sampling procedure at the point where lumps of soil >8 mm. are broken into aggregates to pass through the 8-mm. sieve. If a major portion of the lumps is broken so small as to pass the 4.76-mm. sieve, the MWD will be considerably below its value if nearly all the aggregates broken from the lump are >4.76 mm. Another source of variation is segregation of the sample so that the aggregate-size distribution in the subsamples of the dry soil is not representative.

Segregation occurs even when the samples are separated into subsamples by good mechanical dividers. The coefficient of variation can often be decreased by counting the large-size aggregates in the dry subsamples and making sure that there are approximately the same number of large aggregates in each subsample.

The coefficient of variation of the MWD for replicate subsamples should be <7% for both wetting procedures if reasonably good care is taken to follow the procedure.

39-3 LITERATURE CITED

Baver, L. D., and Rhoades, H. F. 1932. Aggregate analysis as an aid in the study of soil structure relationships. Agron. J. 24:920–930.

Chepil, W. S. 1950. Methods of estimating apparent density of discrete soil grains and aggregates. Soil Sci. 70:351–362.

Chepil, W. S. 1951. Properties of soil which influence wind erosion: III. Effect of apparent density on erodibility. Soil Sci. 71:141–153. IV. State of dry aggregate structure. Soil Sci. 72:387–401. V. Mechanical stability of structure. Soil Sci. 72:465–478.

Chepil, W. S. 1952. Improved rotary sieve for measuring state and stability of dry soil structure. Soil Sci. Soc. Am. Proc. 16:113–117.

Chepil, W. S. 1953. Factors that influence clod structure and erodibility by wind: I. Soil texture. Soil Sci. 75:473–483. II. Water-stable structure. Soil Sci. 76:389–399.

Chepil, W. S. 1958. Soil conditions that influence wind erosion. U. S. Dept. Agriculture Tech. Bul. 1185.

Chepil, W. S. 1962. A compact rotary sieve and the importance of dry sieving in physical soil analysis. Soil Sci. Soc. Am. Proc. 26:4–6.

Chepil, W. S., and Bisal, F. 1943. A rotary sieve method for determining the size distribution of soil clods. Soil Sci. 56:95–100.

Cole, R. C. 1939. Soil macrostructure as affected by cultural treatments. Hilgardia 12:429–472.

Davidson, J. M., and Evans, D. D. 1960. Turbidimeter technique for measuring the stability of soil aggregates in a water-glycerol mixture. Soil Sci. Soc. Am. Proc. 24:75–79.

De Boodt, M., De Leenheer, L., and Kirkham, Don. 1961. Soil aggregate stability indexes and crop yields. Soil Sci. 91:138–146.

Edwards, R. S. 1956. A mechanical sieve designed for experimental work on tilths. Empire J. Exp. Agr. 24:317–322.

Gardner, W. R. 1956. Representation of soil aggregate-size distribution by a logarithmic-normal distribution. Soil Sci. Soc. Am. Proc. 20:151–153.

Kemper, W. D., and Koch, E. J. 1965. Aggregate stability of soils from the western portions of the United States and Canada. (In process for publication as a U. S. Department of Agriculture Technical Bulletin.)

Kolodny, L., and Joffe, J. S. 1940. The relation between moisture content and micro-aggregation or the degree of dispersion in soils. Soil Sci. Soc. Am. Proc. (1939) 4:7–12.

Kopecky, J. 1914. Ein Beitrag zur Frage der neuen Einteilung der Körnungsprodukte bei der Mechanischen Analyse. Int. Mitt. Bodenk. 4:199–202.

Mazurak, A. P. 1950. Effect of gaseous phase on water-stable synthetic aggregates. Soil Sci. 69:135–148.

Puri, A. N., and Puri, B. R. 1939. Physical characteristics of soils: II. Expressing mechanical analysis and state of aggregation of soils by single values. Soil Sci. 47:77–86.

Retzer, J. L., and Russell, M. B. 1941. Differences in the aggregation of a Prairie and a Gray-Brown Podzolic soil. Soil Sci. 52:47–58.

Russell, E. W. 1938. Soil structure. Imperial Bur. Soil Sci., Tech. Commun. 37.

Schaller, F. W., and Stockinger, K. R. 1953. A comparison of five methods for expressing aggregation data. Soil Sci. Soc. Am. Proc. 17:310–313.

Stirk, G. B. 1958. Expression of soil aggregate distributions. Soil Sci. 86:133–135.

Tiulin, A. F. 1928. Questions on soil structure: II. Aggregate analysis as a method for determining soil structure. Perm. Agr. Exp. Sta. Div. Agr. Chem. Report 2:77–122.

Van Bavel, C. H. M. 1950. Mean weight diameter of soil aggregates as a statistical index of aggregation. Soil Sci. Soc. Am. Proc. (1949) 14:20–23.

Van Bavel, C. H. M. 1953. Report of the committee on physical analyses 1951–1953, Soil Science Society of America. Soil Sci. Soc. Am. Proc. 17:416–418.

Yoder, R. E. 1936. A direct method of aggregate analysis of soils and a study of the physical nature of erosion losses. J. Am. Soc. Agron. 28:337–351.

Youker, R. E., and McGuinness, J. L. 1956. A short method of obtaining mean weight-diameter values of aggregate analyses of soils. Soil Sci. 83:291–294.

40

Aggregate Stability[1]

W. D. KEMPER

Agricultural Research Service, USDA, and Colorado State University
Fort Collins, Colorado

40–1 INTRODUCTION

Any determination of aggregate-size distribution is also, in one sense, a determination of aggregate stability. This follows because some force is necessary to disintegrate the soil mass into aggregates, and the aggregates still intact are those in which the primary particles cohere strongly enough to be stable against the applied force. The forces involved in aggregate-size and stability studies are generally (*1*) impact and shearing forces administered while taking and preparing the samples, (*2*) abrasive and impact forces during sieving, and/or (*3*) forces involved in the entry of water into the aggregate. These forces can generally be related to (*1*) cultivation, (*2*) erosion (wind and water), and (*3*) wetting of soils, respectively. Although the disintegrating forces used in the laboratory may simulate those in the field, it cannot be said that the forces used in the laboratory duplicate those occurring in the field. Consequently, the relationship between aggregate-size distribution in the laboratory and field is empirical. Recognizing the empiricism involved in relating aggregate-size measurements to field phenomena, many investigators have decided to use the stability of the aggregates rather than aggregate-size distribution as an index of soil structure in the field. The bases of these decisions have generally been (*1*) that a much simpler procedure involving only one size fraction may be used for stability analysis, (*2*) that the results of stability analysis are highly correlated with aggregate-size distributions and field phenomena, or (*3*) that the ability of the aggregates to resist breakdown by continuing or increasing disruptive forces is important to the solution of the problem under study.

Large pores in the soil generally favor high infiltration rates, good tilth, and adequate aeration for plant growth. Immediately after cultivation, most soils contain an abundance of these large pores. Their continued

---

[1] Contribution from Soil and Water Conservation Research Division, USDA, ARS, in cooperation with the Colorado Agr. Exp. Sta., Ft. Collins.

existence in the soil depends on the stability of the clods and aggregates. Several factors may play a part in the breakdown of the clods and aggregates.

In determining aggregate stability, known amounts of some size fraction (or fractions) of aggregates are commonly obtained. The aggregates are subjected to a disintegrating force designed to simulate some important field phenomenon. The amount of disintegration is measured by determining the portion (by weight) of the aggregates which is broken down into aggregates and primary particles smaller than some selected size. This determination is usually made by sieving or sedimentation. Since the disintegrating forces of interest range from wind erosion to slaking by water, no single type of disintegrating force can be recommended for all objectives. In the following section, the principles underlying the development of methods for measuring aggregate stability will be considered, and these will be followed by description of a single method that appears to have relatively broad application.

40–2 PRINCIPLES

40–2.1 Disintegration of Aggregates by Water

The flow of water over the surface of the soil provides energy by which individual particles and groups of particles may be detached and carried away. The solid particles in the moving water provide an abrasive action that greatly enhances the disintegrating effect of the water.

Much less obvious than the foregoing but probably of greater significance in most instances are several other ways in which water promotes the disintegration of aggregates.

On wetting of aggregates by water, many of the bonding substances become weaker, more flexible or elastic, and actually dissolve in some cases. This weakens the aggregates, which may then slump because of gravitation and the weight of soil lying above.

Water between closely adjacent mineral surfaces usually has a free energy less than water in bulk. Consequently, more water tends to move in between the mineral surfaces. The entry of water between soil particles forces the particles apart. This may result in breakage of some or all of the bonds which were holding the particles together, and in consequent slumping of the aggregate. In the process of wetting, one side of the aggregate may become wet and swollen while the other side is still dry. This differential swelling often causes fractures just behind the wetting front, weakening the aggregate.

When air is trapped within the aggregate during wetting, it is compressed as water is drawn into the aggregate by capillary forces. This air bursts out of the aggregate when the aggregate structure is sufficiently weakened by hydration, causing breakdown of the aggregates (Emerson and Grundy, 1954). These miniature explosions cause a major portion of the disintegration of aggregates on the soil surface when the land is flooded and are, therefore, largely responsible for the dense, unaggregated surface crusts often found on flooded soils. Soil below the surface is wet slowly from one side under a tension; and, consequently, there is very little entrapment of air involved in the wetting of aggregates in the main body of the soil.

40–2.2 Selection of Disrupting Forces

Where the objective of the work is to investigate the resistance of soil to erosion by water, the forces involved in the field may be simulated in part by applying abrasive forces to wet soil in the laboratory. Wet sieving of aggregates for successively longer periods of time was used by Russell and Feng (1947) to determine the resistance of aggregates to continued abrasion. They used an immersion method of wetting, which simulates disintegrating forces found in flooding conditions and sheet erosion. Those interested in studying water erosion should read Russell and Feng's paper for details. Gully-type erosion, where the erosion channel goes down more than 1 or 2 mm., would involve wetting the deeper soil under tension. Vacuum or tension wetting may be more applicable if gully-type erosion is being studied.

Erosion of soil by wind occurs when the soil is dry; hence, to simulate the field phenomenon, laboratory studies are made on dry soils. Chepil (1958) has shown that the mechanical stability of dry aggregates or clods is a good index of the ability of soils to resist wind erosion. The mechanical stability of soils against abrasion by wind action may be determined by continued sieving of the soil sample, with evaluation of the size fractions from time to time. The rotary sieve described by Chepil (1962) is an excellent piece of equipment for this purpose.

Where formation of surface crusts is to be investigated, the laboratory techniques may make provision to bring into play the effect of entrapment of air in disintegrating aggregates under rapid wetting. Disintegration of aggregates in this way is known to be an important factor in formation of surface crusts. Direct immersion of dry soil, followed by wet sieving, would provide a reasonable combination of laboratory techniques to simulate important forces involved in the field phenomenon. The vacuum-wetting procedure outlined in section 40–3.3 would not permit the entrapment of air to play a part in the disintegration of the aggregates. If raindrop impact is furthering the disintegration of surface aggregates under field conditions, a wetting method involving simulated raindrops may be desirable.

As discussed in the introduction, the most common type of aggregate disintegration in cultivated soils occurs in the bulk of the soil as slumping or slaking during the first wetting after cultivation. This wetting occurs under a tension, and thus wetting the sample under tension would appear to be the best method of wetting soil to simulate forces involved in the most common type of aggregate disintegration. However, wetting soils under tension is a fairly time-consuming process; and, when this wetting procedure is used, the results of aggregate-stability analyses are often not sufficiently reproducible (Kemper and Koch, 1965). Wetting under a vacuum with de-aerated water precludes the entrapment of air bubbles within the aggregates. The absence of these destructive entrapped bubbles is common to both the tension-wetting and vacuum-wetting techniques. Wetting under a vacuum has been found (Kemper and Koch, 1965) to yield more reproducible results than wetting under tension. The results are highly correlated with and have about the same average value as those obtained where the aggregates are wet under a tension. On the basis of these findings and because of the importance and common occurrence of disintegration while soils are being wet under tension, vacuum wetting is suggested as the method of wetting for the procedure outlined in detail in section 40–3.3.

40–2.3 Correction for Sand

Large sand particles must be differentiated from aggregates if meaningful estimates of aggregate stability are to be obtained. Better correlations between aggregate stability and clay, organic matter, etc. are found, and lower standard deviations are encountered when the sand >60 mesh is not considered as aggregates. The standard procedure is to calculate the percent aggregate stability as:

$$\%AS = \frac{100[(\text{Weight of Aggregates} + \text{Sand}) - (\text{Weight of Sand})]}{\text{Weight of Sample} - \text{Weight of Sand}}.$$

Since only those sand particles >60 mesh are retained as individual particles on the sieve in the procedure in section 40–3.3, "sand" in this equation will refer to sand >60 mesh.

The procedure for determining the weight of the sand involves reusing the material left on the sieve after wet sieving. After the dry weight of this material has been determined, the material is placed back in the sieve and sieved in sodium hexametaphosphate solution. Sodium hexametaphosphate is very effective in replacing Ca^{2+} by Na^+ in initially Ca^{2+}-saturated soils. Most Ca^{2+}-saturated soils disperse completely when treated in this manner and sieved for 5 minutes. Only the sand >60 mesh is left in the sieves when complete dispersion has taken place. Sodium hydroxide is a good dispersing agent in soils containing large amounts of hydrogen ion.

40–3 METHOD [2]

40–3.1 Special Apparatus

1. A mechanical sieving machine that will raise and lower a sieve holder through a distance of 0.5 inch 42 times each minute. Sieving machines giving a maximum sieve velocity between 0.6 and 0.8 inches per second with a total stroke length of at least 0.4 inch will yield results sufficiently close, for most practical purposes, to those obtained with the recommended equipment.
2. Sieves with 60-mesh screen (holes 0.25 mm. in diameter). An inside diameter of the sieves of 3.8 cm. is suggested but is not critical.
3. Sieves with 2-mm. and 1-mm. openings.
4. Vacuum desiccator having an inlet through which water can be brought to the bottom of the desiccator from the outside. Keep a small barometer in the desiccator. Prepare the barometer by sealing one end of a glass tube 6 to 8 cm. in length, filling the tube with mercury, and placing the tube, open end down, in a small open container of mercury.

40–3.2 Reagents

1. Dispersing solutions: sodium hexametaphosphate, 5 g. per liter, for Ca-saturated soils; or sodium hydroxide, 4 g. per liter, for acid soils.
2. Hydrochloric acid, 1.0 N.
3. Sodium hydroxide solution, 0.5 N.

40–3.3 Procedure

Take the sample when the water content is between the field capacity and the wilting point. Dry the sample at room temperatures. Grind and sieve the sample, saving the aggregates which pass through a 2-mm. sieve and are retained on a 1-mm. sieve.

Place 4 g. of each sample in a weighing dish. (If the relative humidity in the laboratory is above 30%, oven-dry an extra 4-g. subsample to determine the water content of the sample.) Make weighings to the nearest 0.01 g. Transfer the air-dry subsample to a 60-mesh sieve 1.5 inches in diameter, and place the sieve on filter paper on the ceramic plate in the vacuum desiccator containing a few cubic centimeters of water.

Evacuate the desiccator, and allow the water to boil for 2 or 3 minutes after the height of mercury in the barometer has been reduced to <3 cm.

[2] This method was developed largely on the basis of data reported by Kemper and Koch (1965).

Leave the sample in the evacuated (except for water vapor) desiccator for at least 10 minutes.

De-aerate a supply of water by reducing the pressure over it in a desiccator so that boiling takes place for 10 minutes. Then allow the water to come to room temperature. Let de-aerated water flow through a tube into the bottom of the evacuated desiccator containing the soil samples until the aggregates are covered with water.

Place the sieve containing the sample in a sieve holder, and sieve the sample in salt-free ($<10^{-5}$ mhos per cm.) water at 22° to 25°C. for 5 minutes ($\pm$5 seconds) at 42 cycles per minute. In each cycle, the sieve goes down and up 0.5 inch. Maintain the water at a level high enough to keep the sample covered when the sieve is at the top of the stroke.

At the end of 5 minutes, remove the sieve from the holder, and wash the retained aggregates and sand into a weighing dish. Pour off excess water and dry the material in an oven at 105°C. Weigh the dish containing the aggregates and sand. Then wash the aggregates and sand back into the sieve, and operate the sieve for 5 minutes in one of the dispersing solutions. At the end of this time only the >60-mesh sand should remain. Break any remaining aggregates with a rubber-tipped rod or a jet of water from a wash bottle. When only the sand remains, wash it back into the weighing dish, pour out the excess water, and oven-dry the sand. Weigh the sand and dish.

40–3.4 Calculation and Interpretation of Results

The data sheet should have the following columns:

1	2	3	4	5	6	7	8	9
Sample No.	Dish No.	Dish weight	Dish + aggregates + sand	Dish + sand	Sand Col. 5 − Col. 3	Aggregates Col. 4 − Col. 5	*Initial sample − sand 4.00 − Col. 6	% Aggregation $=\dfrac{100 \times \text{Col. 7}}{\text{Col. 8}}$
		g.	g.	g.	g.	g.	g.	%

* Use the weight of the duplicate subsample which was oven-dried if the relative humidity in the laboratory is >30%.

Soils containing aggregates which are highly stable will generally have high infiltration rates and adequate aeration. High aggregate stability is favorable to the production of most crops.

40–3.5 Comments

The results obtained depend very much on the procedure employed. Hence, if reproducible results are to be obtained, it is important to follow closely all details of the procedure described in the preceding section or to follow closely whatever modification may be decided upon. Knowledge of causes of differences in results is helpful in avoiding difficulties and in adjusting procedures for the desired purposes.

Compression of samples when they are taken from the soil causes some variation in aggregate stability; consequently, sampling instruments such as shovels and tubes that cause little compression are to be preferred to augers. Compression is more likely to affect the results obtained with samples taken from soil that is relatively moist than from soil that is dry. Where proper care is exercised in sampling, similar results may be obtained with samples taken at any water content between the field capacity and the permanent wilting point (Kemper and Koch, 1965).

Drying the soil at high temperatures sometimes causes irreversible or slowly reversible dehydration of the bonding materials and clay particles. This dehydration is particularly important in soils containing considerable exchangeable sodium. In such soils, oven-drying may cause a transient stability of otherwise unstable aggregates. This transient stability decreases with increasing time allowed for rehydration before sieving (Kemper and Koch, 1965). The stability of samples dried at room temperatures does not change appreciably with time allowed for rehydration (Russell and Feng, 1947; Emerson and Grundy, 1954). Apparently, dehydration at room temperatures is not too severe, or else it is rapidly reversible. Consequently, drying at room temperatures is suggested.

There is a tendency for stability to increase with time of storage (Kemper and Koch, 1965). Increases in aggregate stability occurring following the incorporation of fresh organic material into soil are detected more easily if the analyses are made within 2 weeks after the sample is dried (Miller and Kemper, 1962). For these reasons, it is recommended that analyses be made as soon as feasible after air-drying is completed.

In choosing the size of aggregates to be used in the analysis, it may be noted that the larger an aggregate is when dry, the smaller is the probability that it will pass through a sieve of given size when it is wet. Consequently, results are more reproducible if aggregates of a limited size range are selected for the determination of stability. Aggregates 1 to 2 mm. in diameter have been found to be best suited to the screen size and sieving speed employed in the procedure described in section 40-3.3. Observations of Bryant et al. (1948) and data by Strickling (1951), Schaller and Stockinger (1953), and Panabokke and Quirk (1957) all indicate that results from simple one- and two-sieve methods of determining aggregate stability are closely correlated with results using several size ranges of aggregates and sieves, and expressed in terms of mean weight-diameters. Consequently, a single size-range of aggregates is employed in preference to more time-consuming methods such as that of De Boodt et al. (1961), using several size ranges of aggregates and sieves.

The purpose of sieving the samples after wetting is to separate the fine slaked material from the stable aggregates without undue disruption of the aggregates. The choices of length and frequency of stroke for the sieving are based on an empirical study (Kemper and Koch, 1963) to determine optimum values. In that study, it was found that 5 minutes of sieving were adequate to separate the fines from the aggregates in all cases.

Kemper and Koch (1965) found a slight tendency for aggregate stability to decrease when the temperature of water used to wet and sieve the samples was increased from 20° to 30°C. Consequently, there is some reason for maintaining the temperature of the water within the range of 22° to 25°C.

Appreciable salt in the water can cause changes in the ionic status and stability of the soils; therefore, it is suggested that the salt content of the water be low enough so that the electrical conductivity is $<10^{-5}$ mhos per cm.

Some soils, especially those containing large amounts of free iron oxides, are nearly 100% stable when wet by the vacuum-wetting technique and sieved gently. If differences in aggregate stability among such soils are to be determined, the disrupting force must often be increased. Wetting by immersion at atmospheric pressure accomplishes this purpose by allowing entrapment of air within the aggregates. The suggested procedure may be modified for this purpose by letting air back into the desiccator just before the samples are flooded. Aggregate stability, determined when the soil is wet at atmospheric pressure, is highly dependent on initial water content. The initial water content can be standardized by leaving the samples in the evacuated (except for water vapor) desiccator for at least 1 hour before flooding them. Sieving more violent and prolonged than that described in section 40–3.3 may also provide sufficient disruption of aggregates to detect differences among these highly stable soils.

The question of how to treat concretions requires additional discussion. Those aggregates which do not break down under a rubber-tipped rod or a jet of water from a wash bottle are referred to as concretions. They obviously contain many soil particles and are held together by $CaCO_3$, iron oxides, and so forth. They may be considered and treated in two ways:

(1) Since concretions are extremely stable and will not break down under normal cultivation practices, they may be considered as sand >60 mesh. If this is done, no further treatments should be used to break them down and wash them through the sieve.

(2) On the other hand, since concretions usually have some porosity and appreciable internal surface area and exchange capacity, they may be treated as stable aggregates. If they are considered in this way, they must be broken down when separating out the sand, so that the fine particles can pass through the sieve or be dissolved. Soaking $CaCO_3$-bonded concretions in $1N$ HCl causes complete disintegration. Concretions bonded with

organic matter and iron usually disintegrate when soaked in $0.5N$ NaOH. It is suggested that concretions be treated as stable aggregates unless the investigator has some definite reason for considering them as sand.

The reproducibility of the measurement varies with the texture of the soil. Where extreme care was used, aggregate-stability measurements carried out on coarse-textured soils on successive days were found to have coefficients of variation of 4.0% (Kemper and Koch, 1965). Under the same conditions, aggregate-stability measurements on fine-textured soils had an average coefficient of variation of 1.2%. Where large numbers of samples have been handled in routine fashion, somewhat higher coefficients of variation have been obtained for duplicate runs on different dates. It is recommended that duplicate subsamples be analyzed on different dates for all analyses.

40–4 LITERATURE CITED

Bryant, J. C., Bendixen, T. W., and Slater, C. S. 1948. Measurement of the water-stability of soils. Soil Sci. 65:341–345.

Chepil, W. S. 1958. Soil conditions that influence wind erosion. U. S. Dept. Agriculture Tech. Bull. 1185.

Chepil, W. S. 1962. A compact rotary sieve and the importance of dry sieving in physical soil analysis. Soil Sci. Soc. Am. Proc. 26:4–6.

De Boodt, M., De Leenheer, L., and Kirkham, Don. 1961. Soil aggregate stability indexes and crop yields. Soil Sci. 91:138–146.

Emerson, W. W., and Grundy, G. M. F. 1954. The effect of rate of wetting on water uptake and cohesion of soil crumbs. J. Agr. Sci. 44:249–253.

Kemper, W. D., and Koch, E. J. 1965. Aggregate stability of soils from the western portions of the United States and Canada. U. S. Dept. Agriculture Tech. Bull. (In process).

Miller, D. E., and Kemper, W. D. 1962. Water stability of aggregates of two soils as influenced by incorporation of alfalfa. Agron. J. 54:494–496.

Panabokke, C. R., and Quirk, J. P. 1957. Effect of initial water content on stability of soil aggregates in water. Soil Sci. 83:185–195.

Russell, M. B., and Feng, C. L. 1947. Characterization of the stability of soil aggregates. Soil Sci. 63:299–304.

Schaller, F. W., and Stockinger, K. R. 1953. A comparison of five methods for expressing aggregation data. Soil Sci. Soc. Am. Proc. 17:310–313.

Strickling, Edward. 1951. The effect of soybeans on volume weight and water stability of soil aggregates, soil organic matter content and crop yield. Soil Sci. Soc. Am. Proc. (1950) 15:30–34.

41 Air-to-Water Permeability Ratio

R. C. REEVE

U. S. Salinity Laboratory, ARS, USDA
Riverside, California

41–1 INTRODUCTION

The ratio of the permeability of soil to air and to water is an index of stability of soil structure. The permeability of a soil is first measured by using air, a fluid that has little effect on structure, followed by a measurement of permeability using water. Water, being a polar liquid, reacts with soil to cause a change in structure, resulting usually in a decrease of permeability. This decrease results from swelling, slaking, deflocculation, dispersion, and other structure-disrupting processes. The ratio of air-to-water permeability is a dimensionless number which reflects the magnitude of the breakdown of structure as a result of wetting. A value of one, which is rarely, if ever, obtained with soils, indicates no change in structure. Values greater than one signify a deterioration of soil structure.

A knowledge of the stability of structure is useful in predicting the irrigability of soils and assessing the effects of management practices and various treatments on the physical condition of soil. The wet-sieving method of Yoder has been used extensively for evaluating soil structure. It involves the determination of size distribution of water-stable aggregates after agitation in water, whereas the air-water permeability method involves flow through the pore openings of the soil. The latter method is perhaps more directly related to the physical problems that involve the movement of gases and water into and through soils.

41–2 PRINCIPLES

Darcy's law forms the basis for permeability measurements of permeable media using viscous fluids. In the generalized vector form, it may be written as

$$\bar{v} = -\nabla\phi \tag{1}$$

where $\bar{v} = Q/A$ = fluid flux or macroscopic flow velocity, Q = volume flow rate, A = cross sectional area normal to the flow direction and

$$\phi = (k'/\eta)(p + \rho gz)^1 \qquad [2]$$

where k' = permeability of the medium, η = fluid viscosity, p = fluid pressure, ρ = fluid density, g = acceleration of gravity and z = distance from some reference elevation along the z coordinate which is oriented in the direction of the gravity force field. The negative sign of equation [1] is used to indicate that the velocity vector increases in the direction of the negative potential gradient. Assuming isotropic media and isothermal flow, Darcy's law, from equations [1] and [2], may be written as

$$v_s = -(k'/\eta)(d/ds)(p + \rho gz) \qquad [3]$$

where v_s = volume flow rate or volume flux in the direction s.

For all practical cases for liquids, ρ and g may be considered constant. Equation [3] then becomes

$$v_s = -(k'\rho g/\eta)(dh/ds). \qquad [4]$$

Solving for k'

$$k' = (Q\eta/A\rho g)[1/(dh/ds)] \qquad [5]$$

where $h = p/\rho g + z$ = hydraulic head, where $p/\rho g$ = pressure head and z = position head. Hydraulic head has the dimensions of length (L) and represents energy per unit weight of fluid (see section 11). The permeability k' is a property of the medium, independent of the fluid, and has the dimensions of length squared (L^2).

It is sometimes helpful and convenient to combine the permeability constant with the properties of the fluid into a single proportionality constant as follows:

$$v_s = -k\,dh/ds \qquad [6]$$

where

$$k = k'\rho g/\eta. \qquad [7]$$

For water, this proportionality factor k between the flow velocity and the hydraulic gradient is termed "hydraulic conductivity" and has the dimensions of velocity (L/T). Methods for measuring the hydraulic conductivity are given in sections 13, 14, 15, and 16.

In the case of viscous flow of gases through a permeable medium, equation [3] must be modified to take into account gas compressibility.

In all practical gas-flow cases, the gravitational term is negligible compared to the pressure term. The gas-flow equation may, therefore, be written as

---

[1] The kinetic energy term, $\rho v^2/2$, which relates to the inertial forces in fluid-flow systems as treated in classical hydrodynamics, is negligible for viscous flow in permeable media.

$$v_s = -(k'/\eta)(dp/ds). \qquad [7a]$$

At steady state and for isothermal flow, the mass flow velocity (v_s multiplied by the density ρ) is constant. From this and the ideal gas law, $p = \rho RT$, R being the gas constant and T the constant Kelvin temperature, the permeability equation for gases becomes

$$pv_s = \text{const} = -(k'/\eta)p(dp/ds). \qquad [8]$$

Equation [8] can be integrated for any number of special cases, depending upon the flow geometry and the boundary conditions. Integration of this equation for a cylindrical tube of length L, with ends at pressures p_1 and p_2, yields

$$pv_s L = (k'/\eta)(p_1^2 - p_2^2)/2. \qquad [9]$$

By taking $p = p_2$, the exit pressure of the tube, and $v_s = Q_2/A$, where $Q_2 = $ volume of gas per unit time leaving the tube at the exit pressure, the equation for permeability measurements using gases may be written as

$$k' = \frac{2\eta Q_2 p_2}{A(p_1^2 - p_2^2)/L}. \qquad [10]$$

If the average flow rate Q_{avg} and the average pressure $p_{avg} = (p_1 + p_2)/2$ are substituted, the equation becomes

$$k' = \frac{\eta Q_{avg}}{A(p_1 - p_2)/L} \qquad [11]$$

Thus, the permeability k' may be obtained for gas flow in the same way as for the flow of liquids, provided that the volume outflow rate at the conditions of measurement is reduced to the equivalent volume at the algebraic mean pressure and constant temperature, and provided that viscous flow prevails during the measurement. The steady-state methods for measuring air permeability make use of equations [10] and [11]. Such methods are described by Corey (1957), Grover (1955), American Petroleum Institute (1956) and Brooks and Reeve (1959).

By use of equation [8] and the ideal gas law, and with a few simplifying assumptions, Kirkham (1947) developed an equation and a non-steady-state method whereby the flux and pressure measurements are combined into a single measurement of pressure as a function of time as air is discharged through a soil sample from a closed air chamber of constant volume. Space does not permit the derivation of this equation here, but Kirkham's final working equation, which is used for air permeability in the procedure herein described, is given in section 41–3.3. The reader is referred to the original paper (Kirkham, 1947) for this derivation.

Regardless of the air permeability method used, the measurement of permeability of soil with either air or water involves the preparation and placement of the soil in a suitable container with provision for determining the hydraulic head, or for air, the pressure differential across the sample, and the rate of flow of fluid through it. For the steady-state case, this involves a measure of both the inlet and outlet pressures, and the volume flux; for the non-steady-state method of Kirkham mentioned above, this involves a measure of pressure change with time. The air-to-water permeability ratio is easily obtained from properly determined values for air and water permeability by simply expressing the values as a ratio, k'_a/k'_w.

Either fragmented samples or soil cores may be used; however, with soil cores there are several problems that are not involved when fragmented samples are used. For example, the higher water content required for securing and maintaining suitable cores may affect the air permeability determination. The effect of water content on air permeability is negligible for air-dried soils. Therefore, it is not a problem with fragmented soil samples. Also, the problems associated with encasing the sample to eliminate air leakage through channels that occur between the soil and the encasing material, or through cracks that may develop in the soil, must be considered with soil cores, but are negligible with fragmented soils. For this reason the procedures outlined herein are for air-dried, fragmented soils. However, the general principle of the air-to-water permeability ratio applies also to cores if the necessary precautions are taken in making the measurements.

The effect of water contained in the soil on permeability, where air is used as the measuring fluid, is somewhat analogous to the effect of entrapped air in the soil when water is used. Permeability measurements for two- and three-phase systems have been made as a function of percentage saturation for various liquids and gases (Wyckoff and Botset, 1936; Corey 1957; see also Carmen, 1956). These measurements have been made mostly for sands and various consolidated sediments in connection with oil production, where absolute values are particularly important and high precision is required. The results show that both liquid and gas permeabilities decrease as the percentage saturation with the other fluid increases. In the very low water content range, air permeability is affected only slightly; but, beyond a certain water content, depending upon the soil, air permeability falls off markedly as water content is increased. Likewise, with water permeability, there is a range of water contents slightly below saturation where permeability does not change appreciably; but, below a certain water content, depending again upon the soil, there is a marked reduction in permeability. It is well to keep in mind that these factors are involved in air and water permeability measurements, but for purposes of this method, these are not major factors, especially where the results are expressed as a ratio. In this case, errors due to blocking of air flow by water in the soil and those due to air entrapment for water flow are compensating.

The permeability of soils to water is greatly affected by the chemistry of the soil-water system. Both the exchangeable cation status of the soil and the concentration and composition of salts in the water greatly influence the water permeability. The concentration effect alone has been observed to cause changes in permeability as great as several hundredfold. This is particularly true where soils having high exchangeable sodium are involved. The quality of the water to be used will depend upon the purpose of the test. In general, it may be stated that the quality of the water should coincide with that of the water to which the soil is subjected in the field. If the stability of soil structure under rainfall conditions is being investigated, then demineralized or distilled water would be appropriate. If the effect of irrigation on the physical condition of soils is being studied, then a water of the composition and concentration of the irrigation water should be used. In any case, the concentration and composition of the water are very important considerations and should be reported along with the water permeability data.

For additional information, the papers of Reeve (1953), Reeve and Brooks (1953), U. S. Salinity Laboratory Staff (Handbook 60) (1954), Kirkham (1947), and Brooks and Reeve (1959) should be consulted.

41–3 METHOD FOR PERMEABILITY OF SOIL TO AIR [2]

41–3.1 Special Apparatus

1. Compressed-air source.
2. Air-storage tank: Fit a 213-liter air tank (55-gallon drum) with a valve and inlet tube from a compressed-air supply and with an outflow tube with a full opening control valve (diameter $\geq$ ½ inch) for discharging air through the soil sample. Connect a water manometer about 100 cm.

---

[2] Reeve (1953), after Kirkham (1947).

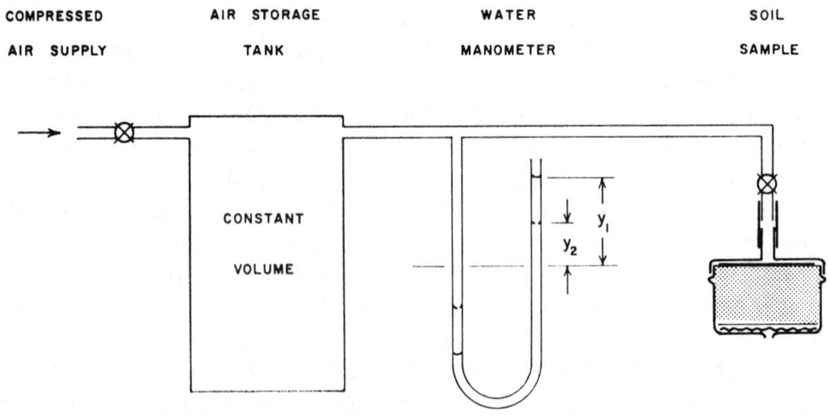

COMPRESSED   AIR STORAGE   WATER   SOIL

AIR SUPPLY   TANK   MANOMETER   SAMPLE

Fig. 41–1. Non-steady-state method for air permeability (After Kirkham, 1947).

in length to the air outflow tube. This apparatus is shown diagrammatically in Fig. 41–1.

3. Soil container: Punch a hole of diameter $\geq 5/32$ inch in the bottom of a 1¾-inch-diameter tinned-iron can (size designation $= 3$ ounce) with the flare of the hole outward. In the bottom of the can, place first a disc of brass screen, with 20 to 40 meshes per inch, and then one or more layers of fiberglass sheet as a support and filter. In the center of the lid that fits the can, bore a hole of diameter $\geq$ ½ inch. Solder a short length of brass or copper tubing (diameter $\geq$ ½ inch) into the central hole in the lid. Make a top extension for the can from a 4-cm. section of brass tubing 2¼-inch in diameter by 0.042-inch wall thickness, counterbored on the lower inside to allow it to fit snugly on the top of the can.

41–3.2 Procedure

Pass air-dried soil through a wire-mesh sieve with 1-mm. openings. Obtain a representative sample by quartering or by taking at random a large number of small scoopsful from the soil pile. As indicated in Fig. 41–2, part 1, place brass cylinder extension B on top of can A, and fill the container thus formed about three-fourths full of soil. To reduce segregation, dump in the soil rather than pouring it in or scooping it in. Pack the soil in the container by dropping the soil-filled container from a height of 2.5 cm. 200 times on a solid wooden block. Remove the brass cylinder extension from the can, and use a spatula to strike the soil off level with the top of the can. As indicated in Fig. 41–2, part 2, cover the soil with a disk of filter paper, place the lid with the metal-tubing air connection C on the can, complete the seal of the lid to the can with a tight, broad rubber band or with a mixture of 50% paraffin and 50% beeswax.

Admit compressed air to the tank until a manometer displacement y_o is attained ($y_o = 30$ cm. is a convenient value). Record the temperature of the air in the tank and the barometric pressure of the atmosphere. Open the outflow valve to allow air to flow from the tank through the soil sample, and record the time in seconds and the manometer level in centimeters at approximately 2-cm. intervals from about $y_1 = 20$ to $y_2 = 10$.

41–3.3 Calculations

Calculate the permeability of the soil using air by the equation

$$k'_a = \frac{2.30 L V S \eta}{A P_a} \qquad [12]$$

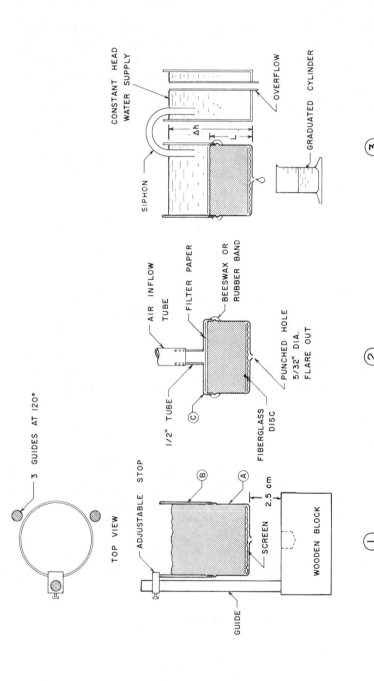

Fig. 41-2. Equipment for air and water permeability of fragmented soils. 1. The soil is compacted by dropping the soil-filled container on a wooden block. Three parallel upright rods guide the container. 2. For air-permeability measurements, the cylinder extension *B* is removed, the soil in can *A* is struck off level, and lid *C* with air-inlet tube is sealed to the can with beeswax or a rubber band. 3. For water-permeability measurements, lid *C* is replaced with cylinder extension *B*, and water is supplied to the container with a siphon from a constant-level water-supply tank.

in which

k'_a = permeability with air, cm.^{2},

L = length of soil column, cm.,

V = volume of tank, cm.^{3},

η = viscosity of air at the temperature at which determination was made, dyne second cm.$^{-2}$ (poises) (Values of viscosity η may be obtained from the *Handbook of Physics and Chemistry* or other such handbooks.),

A = cross sectional area of sample, cm.^{2},

P_a = atmospheric pressure, dynes per cm.^{2},

S = slope of log y vs. time curve = $(\log_{10} y_1 - \log_{10} y_2)/\Delta t$ (the constant 2.30 in equation [12] is consistent with the use of logarithms to the base 10 in calculating S; for natural logarithms, the value of the constant is 1),

y = displacement of the water surface in one arm of the manometer, cm.,

Δt = time interval in seconds for the water surface in the manometer to drop from y_1 to y_2.

The units of air permeability k'_a as calculated above are cm.^{2} Because of the extremely small number for soils, it is convenient to express results in square microns μ^2 or milli square microns $m(\mu^2)$ as follows:

$$1\mu^2 = 1 \times 10^{-8} \text{ cm.}^2$$
$$1m(\mu^2) = 1 \times 10^{-11} \text{ cm.}^2$$

Air permeability values encountered for soils as determined by this method have ranged from about 0.10 to $18\mu^2$ or from 100 to 18,000 m(μ^2).

41–3.4 Comments

The air-flow line and all valves and fittings in the line of the pressure apparatus should be ½ inch in diameter or larger to reduce frictional losses in the flow line to a negligible level.

The size of tank can be varied to allow a suitable rate of pressure drop, depending upon the permeability of the soil. Two tanks, $V = 200$ liters (approximately) and $V = 25$ liters, have been used to cover the range of $k'_a = 0.1$ to $20\mu^2$. For the size of sample described above and for manometer readings, $y_1 = 20$ cm. and $y_2 = 10$ cm., the time interval has ranged approximately as follows:

V (liters)	k'_a (μ^2)	Δt (sec.)
200	1 — 20	20 — 400
25	0.1 — 1.0	50 — 500

The approximate volume required can be calculated from the equation

$$V = (k'_a \, \Delta t)/2 \qquad\qquad [13]$$

where V is in liters, k'_a is in square microns (μ^2), and Δt is in seconds. For the purpose for which this measurement is made, i.e., to compare with water permeability as an index of soil structure, it is not necessary to strive for a high degree of precision in measurement. It is well to keep in mind that the scale of values for air to water permeability ratio is extremely large, ranging from 2 or 3 for very stable soils to as much as 50,000 for unstable soils. Errors associated with air-permeability determinations, which mostly will be of the order of 10 to 20%, are therefore of little consequence for this use of the air-permeability values. If the air-permeability value is used for other purposes where a higher order of precision is required, then special attention should be given to sources of measurement error. In any case, it would be desirable to check the method and equipment with an independent method. This can be done by use of a stable permeable medium such as a carbon or ceramic core, using water or other viscous fluid. If water is used, care should be exercised to ensure complete saturation. Displacement of air in the pores with CO_2 prior to wetting is a convenient and effective method of attaining saturation.

Air-permeability values for soils as determined by this method have ranged from 0.10 to $18\mu^2$. In one trial where the air-permeability determination was repeated on a given sample, the average deviation from the mean (duplicate runs on a large number of samples) was $\pm 1.25\%$, with a coefficient of variation of $\pm 1.14\%$. Adding the variation from sampling and packing, i.e., the reproducibility of air-permeability determinations on different samples of a given soil, the average deviation from the mean was $\pm 9\%$ with a coefficient of variation of $\pm 9.3\%$.

"Gas slippage" is a factor involved in the flow of gases in porous media and consequently is involved in air-permeability measurements. Errors of from 10 to 30% from this source have been reported for air-permeability measurements (Corey, 1957; American Petroleum Institute, 1956). Correction for this can be made by extrapolation of the air-permeability determinations at known pressures to a value at infinite pressure. For the usual application of this method, a correction is not required; however, if more precise values are desired, the correction should be made as described by Corey (1957) and American Petroleum Institute (1956).

41–4 METHOD FOR PERMEABILITY OF SOIL TO WATER

41–4.1 Special Apparatus

Prepare a soil container as described in section 41–3.1. For use in the water-permeability measurement, arrange a constant-level water supply as illustrated in Fig. 41–2, part 3.

41–4.2 Procedure

Follow the procedure of section 41–3.2 for preparing and packing samples. Following the air-permeability determination, remove the lid from the soil-filled can, and place a brass-cylinder extension on top of the can. Seal it in place with an elastic band or with wax. Place the soil sample on the rack, cover the soil surface with a disc of filter paper, and admit water to the sample from the supply reservoir with the siphon. Adjust the water level in the supply reservoir so that the height of the soil-plus-water column is approximately two times the soil-column length.

Record the temperature of the water, the time at which water is admitted to the container, and the time at which water first percolates through the sample. Measure the volume of percolate obtained during a number of successive time intervals as dictated by the purpose of the determination.

41–4.3 Calculations

Permeability of the soil to water is given by the equation

$$k'_w = \frac{\eta}{\rho_w g} k = \frac{\eta}{\rho_w g} \frac{VL}{A \, \Delta h \, \Delta t} \qquad [14]$$

in which

k'_w = intrinsic permeability with water, cm.^{2},

k = hydraulic conductivity, cm. per sec.,

V = volume of percolate in time Δt, cm.^{3},

L = length of soil column, cm.,

Δh = difference in hydraulic head between the inflow and outflow ends of the soil column, cm.,

A = cross sectional area of the soil column, cm.^{2},

Δt = time interval for volume of percolate V to pass through the soil, sec.,

η = viscosity of water at the recorded temperature, dyne sec. cm.$^{-2}$ (poises),

ρ_w = density of water, g. per cm.^{3}, and

g = acceleration of gravity, cm. sec.$^{-2}$

Values for η, ρ_w and g can be obtained from the *Handbook of Physics and Chemistry*.

41–4.4 Comments

The amount of water passed through the soil and the number of volume measurements made will depend upon the purpose of the determination.

The permeability of soil to water is not constant for most soils but varies with time or with the amount of water passing through the soil. Therefore, measurements of time and volume of percolate should be continued until the changes dictated by the purpose for which the tests are being made have taken place. The total depth of water passed through the soil may correspond to the depth of water applied in an irrigation, which may be from 3 to 6 inches. For comparing one soil with another, or for determining the effect of various treatments on a given soil, it is frequently desirable to use a value obtained after the hydraulic conductivity has become essentially constant. From 70 to 80 hours usually are required before constancy of values is obtained.

41-5 EXPRESSION AND INTERPRETATION OF RESULTS

Both the absolute value of permeability of soil to water k'_w and the air-to-water permeability ratio k'_a/k'_w should be reported. The former is an absolute measure of the soil physical condition, and the latter is an index of stability or the susceptibility of soil structure to deterioration as a result of wetting with water. As an aid in interpretation of results, water permeability values may be converted to hydraulic conductivity at a specified temperature, usually 25°C. This is done by multiplying water permeability by $\rho_w g/\eta$.

A value of $k'_a/k'_w = 1$ indicates a stable medium. A value of one has been measured for carbon cores and glass beads; but, for soils, measured values always have been greater than one. Values as low as 2.5 have been measured for soils of low clay content and low exchangeable sodium. Values as great as 50,000 have been obtained where distilled water was used with problem soils having high exchangeable sodium.

In all cases the salt concentration and composition of the water used should be reported. Salt content may be expressed in milliequivalents per liter, or the electrical conductivity may be given. The concentration of the individual ions should be reported. In the absence of a complete analysis, a minimum report should include the total salt concentration and the sodium adsorption ratio (SAR) where $SAR = Na^+/[(Ca^{2+} + Mg^{2+})/2]^{1/2}$ (cation concentrations expressed in milliequivalents per liter).

Individual determinations of k'_a/k'_w are satisfactory for most purposes. Seventy-five percent of the time, individual determinations can be expected to lie within $\pm 10\%$ of the mean, and 80% of the time within $\pm 20\%$.

41-6 LITERATURE CITED

American Petroleum Institute. 1956. Recommended practice for determining permeability of porous media. Code No. 27, third issue. Am. Petrol. Inst., Dallas, Tex.

Brooks, R. H., and Reeve, R. C. 1959. Measurement of air and water permeability of soils. Am. Soc. Agr. Eng. Trans. 2:125–126, 128.

Carmen, P. C. 1956. Flow of Gases through Porous Media. Academic Press, Inc., New York.

Corey, A. T. 1957. Measurement of water and air permeability in unsaturated soil. Soil Sci. Soc. Am. Proc. 21:7–10.

Grover, Ben L. 1955. Simplified air permeameters for soil in place. Soil Sci. Soc. Am. Proc. 19:414–418.

Kirkham, D. 1947. Field method for determination of air permeability of soil in its undisturbed state. Soil Sci. Soc. Am. Proc. (1946) 11:93–99.

Reeve, R. C. 1953. A method for determining the stability of soil structure based upon air and water permeability measurements. Soil Sci. Soc. Am. Proc. 17:324–329.

Reeve, R. C., and Brooks, R. H. 1953. Equipment for subsampling and packing fragmented soil samples for air and water permeability tests. Soil Sci. Soc. Am. Proc. 17:333–336.

U. S. Salinity Laboratory Staff. 1954. Diagnosis and improvement of saline and alkali soils. U. S. Dept. Agr. Handbook 60.

Wyckoff, R. D., and Botset, H. G. 1936. The flow of gas-liquid mixtures through unconsolidated sands. Physics 7:325–345.

42

Specific Surface

M. M. MORTLAND

Michigan State University
East Lansing, Michigan

W. D. KEMPER

Agricultural Research Service, USDA, and Colorado State University
Fort Collins, Colorado

42-1 INTRODUCTION

Physical and chemical properties of a material may be greatly influenced by the extent of its surface area. Soils differ markedly in surface area as a result of differences in texture, types of clay minerals, and amount of organic matter. Such important properties as water retention and cation-exchange capacity have been shown to be highly correlated with the surface area of soils. The term "specific surface" refers to area per unit weight of soil or clay and is usually expressed in square meters per gram (m.^{2} per g.).

Several absolute methods of measuring the specific surface have been derived from fundamental principles of thermodynamics, electrostatics, and kinetics. Data obtained when such methods are employed usually have a firm theoretical basis. Some relative methods of estimating the specific surface of soil and clay minerals have been developed which are much more convenient to use than the absolute methods. Most relative methods are based on retention of a polar organic molecule such as ethylene glycol or glycerol by the material in question. Data using these relative methods have been related to figures obtained with one of the absolute methods by some workers, and to the theoretical surface area of certain clay minerals by other workers.

Because of their fine state of subdivision, clays contribute the greatest amount of surface of any of the mineral constituents of soil. Clay minerals differ a great deal in specific surface. Nonswelling clays like kaolinite have only an external surface, but swelling clays like montmorillonite and ˘vermiculite have a great deal of internal as well as external surface. The specific surface of clay minerals ranges from 10 to 30 m.^{2} per g. for kaolinite to about 800 m.^{2} per g. for montmorillonite and vermiculite. Consequently the type of clay mineral present in soil is of major importance in determining the effect of clay on soil properties.

In this section, a method for measurement of specific surface of soils and clays on the basis of sorption of ethylene glycol will be described.

42–2   PRINCIPLES

42–2.1   Adsorption Isotherms

Adsorption of a gas by a solid exists when there is a higher concentration of the gas at the surface of the solid than in the bulk of the gas. All gases tend to be adsorbed on surfaces. When gas molecules strike a surface, they ordinarily do not rebound elastically but are attracted by the force field arising from the surface atoms of the solid phase. The adsorbed molecules may eventually obtain enough energy to go back into the gaseous state. However, in the time interval between adsorption and desorption, gas accumulates on the surface. The degree of polarity of the gas molecules influences their response to the force field of the surface. A clear picture of adsorption phenomena is given by de Boer (1953).

Data obtained from the adsorption of certain gases and vapors at constant temperatures may be used to estimate the surface area of soils and soil colloids. At sufficiently low gas pressures, the relationship of the extent of adsorption per unit area σ to pressure P, temperature T, and heat of adsorption Q is: $\sigma = k_1 Pe^{Q/RT}$, where R is the gas constant and k_1 is a constant also. From this equation it can be observed that as the pressure increases the adsorption increases, and as the temperature increases the adsorption decreases.

Taking into consideration that an adsorbent has a finite surface area and that the molecules already adsorbed influence the adsorption of more molecules, results in the Langmuir (1918) equation,

$$\frac{P}{V} = \frac{1}{k_2 V_m} + \frac{P}{V_m}$$

where V is the volume of gas adsorbed per gram of adsorbent at pressure P, k_2 is a constant, and V_m is the volume of gas adsorbed per gram when a complete monomolecular layer has been formed on the adsorbent. A value for surface area may be obtained by applying the Langmuir equation to adsorption data obtained at constant temperature and calculating V_m. This is usually done by ploting P/V versus P, the slope of the resulting curve being equal to $1/V_m$. Once this value is known, the specific surface of the adsorbent may be calculated by determining the number of molecules in V_m and multiplying this figure by the cross sectional area of the adsorbate molecules. Two important assumptions in the Langmuir equation are that (*1*) only one layer of molecules is adsorbed, and (*2*) the heat of adsorption is uniform during adsorption of the monomolecular layer.

Brunauer, Emmett, and Teller (1938) derived an equation (BET) from multimolecular adsorption theory from which the number of molecules in a monolayer of adsorbate can be calculated. The BET equation is

$$\frac{P}{V(P_0 - P)} = \frac{1}{V_m C} + \frac{(C - 1)P}{V_m C P_0}$$

where V is the volume of gas sorbed at pressure P, V_m is the volume of gas required for a single layer of molecules over the entire surface of the adsorbent, P_0 is the pressure of the gas required for saturation at the temperature of the experiment, and $C = \exp[(E_1 - E_2)/RT]$, where E_2 is the heat of liquefaction of the gas, E_1 is the heat of adsorption of the first layer of adsorbate, R is the gas constant, and T is the absolute temperature. Two assumptions in the BET equation are that (1) the heat of adsorption of all molecular layers after the first is equal to the heat of liquefaction E_2, and (2) at equilibrium, the rate of condensation on the surface is equal to the rate of evaporation from the first or higher layers.

The BET equation at low pressures reduces to the Langmuir equation. Since the most active parts of the surfaces of most adsorbents are heterogeneous, with widely varying heats of adsorption, the Langmuir equation is often not obeyed. For the determination of the surface area of most adsorbents, the BET equation is most useful between relative pressures (P/P_0) of 0.05 to 0.45. By plotting $P/V(P_0 - P)$ versus P/P_0 one can calculate V_m from the intercept and slope of the linear portion of the curve. Once V_m is known, the surface area of the adsorbent may be calculated if the cross-sectional area of the adsorbate molecules is known. The density of the adsorbate is usually assumed to be either that of the liquefied or solidified gas. Since the calculated area per molecule will be different, depending upon which density is used, the absolute surface areas measured by this method are uncertain to this extent.

The BET method of analysis has been applied to adsorption isotherms of nitrogen, ethane, water, ammonia, and other gases on soils and clay minerals by a number of workers (Emmett et al., 1938; Makower et al., 1938; Nelson and Hendricks, 1943; Eschard, 1950; Teichner, 1950; Mooney et al., 1952; Bering et al., 1952; Orchiston, 1953; Brooks, 1955; Mortland, 1955; and Zettlemoyer et al., 1955). The apparent surface area of montmorillonites has been shown to depend upon the nature of the adsorbate used. Weakly adsorbed nitrogen, for instance, will not penetrate the interlayer surfaces of clay minerals such as montmorillonite, so that the measurement obtained is only that of the external surface. On the other hand, the more polar molecules, water and ammonia, are strongly adsorbed and penetrate between the interlayer surfaces, thus leading to much higher values for specific surface.

The use of the BET equation in determining surface area of clays from water adsorption isotherms has been criticized (Quirk, 1955). The water molecules may tend to cluster around the cation sites with the result that the assumption of hexagonal close packing, which is supposed to hold for molecules which are approximately symmetrical, may not hold for water. Also it has been demonstrated rather conclusively that the density of water decreases as the surface of montmorillonite is approached, indicating that the assumption made in many papers as to the density of the adsorbed monolayer of water may be in error (Anderson and Low, 1958). The criticisms expressed for use of the BET equation with water adsorption data may apply also where ammonia has been used as the adsorbate (Mortland, 1955; Zettlemoyer et al., 1955). Here again assumptions regarding the density of the adsorbed molecules may be in error.

Harkins and Jura (1944) and Harkins (1952) described a method for the determination of the surface area of solids by measuring heats of immersion. The theoretical basis of the method is derived from thermodynamics and has an advantage over the BET equation in the respect that assumptions regarding the density of the adsorbate are not required. The method involved the measurement of the energy change during immersional wetting of a finely divided solid which is in equilibrium with the vapor of the liquid in which it is to be immersed. Consequently, the free energy of the adsorbed film is equal to that of the liquid, so that when the solid is immersed in the liquid the energy given up is attributable only to the loss of surface or the heat of immersion. Under these circumstances, the heat given off by unit area of the solid upon immersion in the liquid corresponds to that which would be given off if many small drops of liquid of an equivalent total area were immersed in the same liquid. This "absolute method" works well for nonporous solids, but is probably not applicable to soils or soil colloids because the interstices and interlayer spaces are filled with molecules of the adsorbate during equilibration and hence do not have a heat of immersion.

The "relative method" of Harkins and Jura utilizes the equation,

$$\log P/P_0 = B - (A/V^2)$$

in which A and B are constants, P/P_0 is the relative pressure, and V the volume of gas or vapor adsorbed. At low relative pressures, a plot of log P/P_0 against $1/V^2$ yields a straight line with intercept B and slope A. The area of a solid S is proportional to the square root of the slope ($A^{1/2}$), i.e., $S = kA^{1/2}$ The parameter k is a constant for a given adsorbate at a given temperatu e and is evaluated on a nonporous solid by the absolute method described in the preceding paragraph. Orchiston (1953) obtained remarkably good agreement between the Brunauer, Emmett and Teller analysis and the relative Harkins and Jura method in the determination of surface area of some New Zealand soils from water adsorption isotherms.

42–2.2 Retention of Polar Liquids

Clay minerals adsorb polar molecules from the liquid as well as from the gaseous phase. Clay-water complexes are examples of such adsorption phenomena in the natural state. Polar organic molecules possessing alcoholic groups complex with clay minerals in a similar manner (Bradley 1945; MacEwan, 1948). Ethylene glycol and glycerol have been shown to be held in two layers in the expanding portion of montmorillonite resulting in a c-spacing of 17.1$\mathring{A}$. and 17.7$\mathring{A}$., respectively. Vermiculite, on the other hand, adsorbs only one layer of these polar molecules giving about a 14$\mathring{A}$. c-spacing. This difference in complexation properties with polar molecules has been used as a basis for differentiation between montmorillonite and vermiculite by X-ray diffraction.

The fact that ethylene glycol will form a monomolecular layer on clay surfaces has been utilized in a method for the estimation of specific surface (Dyal and Hendricks, 1950). The rate of ethylene glycol evaporation decreases when all the free glycol is gone and only that adsorbed in a monomolecular layer is left. The quantity of glycol retained at the moment the rate of evaporation decreases was suggested as proportional to the surface area. From the theoretical surface area of bentonite and ethylene glycol retention measurements, it was found that 0.00031 g. of ethylene glycol was needed to form a monolayer on each square meter of clay surface.

It has been suggested that the glycol[1] molecules may be clustered around the cation exchange sites and that assumptions regarding their cross sectional area may be in error (Quirk, 1955; Diamond and Kinter, 1956).[2] Considerable evidence shows, however, that glycol retention is not a function of cation-exchange capacity alone.

The vapor pressure of ethylene glycol is of critical importance in gravimetric methods utilizing this molecule for estimation of specific surface. Where the glycol-saturated sample is evacuated over dry $CaCl_2$, the vapor pressure is maintained at a low level. Consecutive weighings will show the transition from the rate of loss of free glycol to the lower rate of loss of that bound to the surface of the clay (Bower and Gschwend, 1952). At this point the amount of bound ethylene glycol may be determined. A specific surface estimation may then be made by assuming that the bound glycol is present in a monomolecular layer in which each molecule occupies an average cross sectional area. Where a free surface of glycol is included with the soil or clay sample and $CaCl_2$ in a desiccator, the vapor pressure is comparatively high. Using this environment, however, results in a steady-state system in which the amount of glycol retained reaches a con-

---

[1] The term "glycol" is used here to denote the compound "1,2,ethanediol" or ethylene glycol as it is commonly called.

[2] B. McNeal (1964) has made similar conclusions.

stant value and remains there as long as the free glycol surface and the $CaCl_2$ are both present (Martin, 1955). The amount of glycol retained is more than enough to form a monomolecular layer, and specific surface cannot be calculated from the resulting data. Comparisons between samples can be made on the basis of the amount of glycol retained.

A large quantity of bentonite, containing just enough ethylene glycol to form a monolayer on all surfaces, has been used as a "buffer" to maintain a glycol vapor pressure in an evacuated desiccator equal to that necessary for formation of a monolayer of glycol on the surfaces of small samples. A definite equilibrium value is reached with this method (Sor and Kemper, 1959).

A $CaCl_2$-ethylene glycol complex has been used to maintain the vapor pressure slightly less than that required for a monolayer on clay mineral surfaces (Bower and Goertzen, 1959). The $CaCl_2$ "monoglycolate," when in the presence of excess $CaCl_2$ appears to maintain a constant glycol vapor pressure as long as these are the only two solid phases in the system. (For an explanation of this type of phenomenon, see Prutton and Maron, 1951, pp. 372–375.) The presence of these two materials apparently stabilizes the glycol vapor pressure in the presence of small soil or clay samples initially saturated with glycol so that equilibrium weights are obtained. Comparisons between the glycol retained by samples over the bentonite-glycol buffer and the $CaCl_2$ monoglycolate plus $CaCl_2$ have shown a slightly smaller retention in the latter environment. Thus the vapor pressure of glycol over $CaCl_2$ monoglycolate appears to be approximately equal to, or slightly less than, the vapor pressure of glycol in equilibrium with a monomolecular layer of glycol on soil surfaces. The use of $CaCl_2$ monoglycolate with $CaCl_2$ to stabilize the glycol vapor pressure in an equilibrium procedure combines the advantages of using pure, commercially available materials with the advantages of the equilibrium type of procedure. The amount of ethylene glycol retained by samples with this method is approximately the same as the amount the samples would contain under carefully controlled conditions with the Bower and Gschwend procedure.

Although the retention and sorption of glycol is one of the easiest and most precise ways to estimate total surface areas of clay and soil samples, it involves some assumptions and has limitations which should be made clear. To obtain their value of 0.00031 ± 0.00002 g. of glycol per m.[2] for the amount of glycol adsorbed in a monomolecular layer per unit surface area, Dyal and Hendricks (1950) divided their experimental value for glycol retention by the total theoretical surface area of the bentonite they employed. In making this calculation, it was assumed that glycol covered all the surfaces and that it penetrated between all molecular layers. Because these assumptions are satisfied in different degree with different materials, the appropriate factor depends on the nature of the material. Investigators generally have used the value 0.00031 g. per m.[2], however, because of the difficulty of checking it and the lack of a way to verify its accuracy with clays or soils. One indication that the assumptions may not have held exactly for the bentonite employed in deriving the value 0.00031 may be observed in some calculations of density of adsorbed glycol. Using the assumptions mentioned above, together with the value of $3.7\mathring{A}$. as the thickness of the adsorbed layer of glycol, the density of glycol is found to be 0.83 g. per cm.³ as compared with 1.11 g. per cm.³ in the bulk liquid. This difference in density may be due to (1) a more open packing of glycol molecules on the clay surface, or (2) failure of the glycol molecules to form complete layers on all platelet surfaces.

Hydrated halloysite adsorbs only one layer of glycol or water between structural units. It is irreversibly collapsed, as far as entry of glycol or water molecules between structural units is concerned, if the sample is heated at 75°C. for 12 hours. If one prefers to disregard this internal halloysite surface, the samples may be dried at 75°C. for 12 hours instead of over P_2O_5. The other minerals are not collapsed irreversibly at this temperature if they are saturated with calcium.

Vermiculite likewise adsorbs only one layer of glycol molecules between adjacent molecular layers of clay, although it takes up two layers of water. Thus, the assumption that all surfaces are covered with a single layer of glycol does not hold with hydrated halloysite and vermiculite. An estimate of the amount of vermiculite may be obtained by determining the amount of glycol retained before and after saturating samples of the material with potassium. The potassium collapses the vermiculite, and thus the change in amount of glycol retained may be associated with internal vermiculite surfaces. To express the specific surface in terms of both sides of the interlayer spaces of vermiculite, the change in weight of glycol retained per gram of sample may be added to the weight of glycol retained per gram by the sample before the material was saturated with potassium. This sum is then divided by 0.00031 to obtain the estimated total surface area in m.² per g. of sample.

Glycol is adsorbed readily by soil organic matter. Bower and Gschwend reported that removal of organic matter from several soils reduced the glycol retention by an amount equivalent to 558 to 803 m.² of surface per g. of organic matter removed. There is a question as to whether the glycol-organic matter association should be considered in the same light as the glycol-clay association as far as indicating surface area is concerned. Since several chemical reactions are possible between the alcoholic groups of the ethylene glycol and other organic groups which might be present in soil organic matter, sorption by this soil component may differ in nature from sorption by soil minerals. However, the assumption must be made that relationship between surface area and glycol sorption is the same with organic matter as with soil minerals if the organic matter is not removed prior to measurement of glycol sorption.

There are indications that glycol forms a monolayer on external surfaces and that this monolayer has approximately the same vapor pressure as that in monolayers on internal surfaces. If it does not, there may not be a time, or a unique glycol vapor pressure, at which a complete monolayer exists on all surfaces, with no extra glycol on any surface. This assumption of approximately equal vapor pressure of glycol on all types of mineral surfaces is implicit in any glycol sorption or retention method of determining surface area.

Glycerol has been used as the polar molecule in the measurement of surface area of clay minerals by Diamond and Kinter (1956). They found that in the presence of glycerol vapor at high temperatures, montmorillonite forms a stable complex with glycerol in which a single layer of adsorbed molecules occurs between the molecular layers of the clay. Mehra and Jackson (1959) utilized glycerol retention as a means of quantitatively determining the amounts of montmorillonite and vermiculite in mixtures. In one environment, both montmorillonite and vermiculite retain a single layer of glycerol molecules between the molecular layers of the clay, whereas in another, vermiculite retains one layer of glycerol molecules and montmorillonite retains two.

42–2.3 Negative Adsorption

In dilute solutions of electrolytes, clay minerals usually possess a negative electrical charge and therefore attract cations and repel anions. The concentration of cations in the bulk of the solution is less than that in the solution immediately adjacent to the clay surfaces, and the reverse is true of anions. This effect of clays on the concentration of anions in the adjacent solution has been called negative adsorption. The amount of negative adsorption is a function of the extent of the electrically charged surface.

Schofield (1949), utilizing Gouy's theory of the electrical double layer associated with charged particles, developed a method for calculating the surface area of clays from measurements of the increase in anion concentration in the bulk of the solution.

Bower and Geortzen (1955) measured negative adsorption of salts by a group of soils and related it to the specific surface as determined by the ethylene glycol retention method. They obtained a high correlation between the two measurements, but they did not calculate surface area directly from their negative adsorption data.

A comparison of values for the specific surface of bentonite obtained by Schofield (1949), using the negative adsorption method with values obtained by others using the ethylene glycol technique, suggests that smaller values will be found by the first method. The values obtained by Schofield, however, do compare favorably with those obtained by use of the BET equation on adsorption isotherms of polar molecules such as ammonia and water. Schofield (1949) found that essentially the same value for the specific surface of kaolinite was obtained from negative adsorption data as from nitrogen adsorption data.

42–3   METHOD [3]

42–3.1   Special Apparatus

1. Pyrex vacuum desiccator 25 cm. in diameter with porcelain plate.
2. Vacuum pump capable of reducing the pressure to 0.025 mm. of Hg.
3. Aluminum boxes having a diameter of 6 to 7 cm. and a height not exceeding 2 cm.
4. Culture chamber consisting of glass dish with cover, having a diameter of 20 cm. and a height of 7.5 cm.
5. Support for holding aluminum boxes in culture chamber approximately 2 cm. above the bottom of the chamber. The support consists of a circular piece of ¼-inch mesh hardware cloth having three legs, which are 8/32 by ¾-inch brass machine screws attached at equal distances near the perimeter of the hardware cloth by means of nuts and washers.

42–3.2   Chemicals

1. Ethylene glycol (Eastman): Take reasonable care to prevent contamination of the glycol by water vapor. If large amounts of contamination are suspected, redistill the glycol under reduced pressure, discarding the first and last 10% of the distillate.
2. Phosphorus pentoxide (P_2O_5).
3. Calcium chloride ($CaCl_2$), 40-mesh anhydrous reagent grade.

42–3.3   Procedure

42–3.3.1   PREPARATION OF $CaCl_2$–GLYCOL SOLVATE

Weigh approximately 120 g. of 40-mesh $CaCl_2$ into a 1-liter Pyrex beaker, and place the beaker in a drying oven at 210°C. to remove all traces of H_2O. After the $CaCl_2$ has been in the oven 1 hour or more, weigh 20 g. of glycol into a 400-ml. Pyrex beaker. Remove the $CaCl_2$ from the oven, weigh out 100 g. of the salt without cooling, and add it to the beaker containing the glycol. Mix the contents immediately and thoroughly with a

---

[3] Bower and Goertzen (1959) and unpublished work by K. Sor and W. D. Kemper.

spatula. The heat of the $CaCl_2$ facilitates solvation. After the solvate has cooled, transfer it to a culture chamber, and spread it uniformly over the bottom. Store the chamber and contents in a sealed desiccator.

42–3.3.2 SAMPLE PRETREATMENT

Treat the sample with H_2O_2, as described in section 44–3.2, to remove organic matter. Saturate the sample with Ca by leaching or repeated centrifuging with an excess of $1.0N$ $CaCl_2$. Remove the excess $CaCl_2$ with water, air-dry the sample, and pass it through a 60-mesh sieve, using a grinder if necessary. If a measure of only the external surface is desired, heat the sample at 600°C. for 2 hours to suppress interlayer swelling.

42–3.3.3 SORPTION TECHNIQUE

Weigh 0.3 g. of clay or 1.1 g. of soil into a tared aluminum box. Spread the sample evenly over the bottom of the box. Place the box with lid removed in a vacuum desiccator over about 250 g. of P_2O_5, evacuate the desiccator by applying a vacuum pump for 1 hour, close the stopcock, and dry the sample to constant weight. Constant weight usually is attained within 5 to 6 hours when no more than four samples are in the desiccator. Weigh the dried sample, using care to minimize adsorption of atmospheric H_2O. Wet the sample with a minimum amount of glycol (1 ml. or less) by distributing the liquid dropwise from a pipette over the surface of the sample. Wetting may be facilitated by warming the box for a few minutes in an oven at 50° to 60°C. Place the box, with lid under it, in a culture chamber on a hardware cloth support over approximately 120 g. of $CaCl_2$-glycol solvate. Cover the chamber and place it in a desiccator. The sample and $CaCl_2$-glycol solvate are enclosed in a culture chamber within a desiccator to shorten the mean diffusion path of the glycol vapor and thus hasten equilibration. Evacuate the desiccator by applying a vacuum pump for 1 hour, close the stopcock and allow the desiccator to stand at a temperature of 25 ± 1°C. After 16 to 24 hours apply the vacuum pump again for 30 minutes to remove any foreign vapors which may have reduced the vacuum.

When the box has been in the desiccator for about 48 hours, release the vacuum, open the desiccator and culture chamber, and place the lid on the aluminum box to prevent adsorption of atmospheric H_2O by the sample. Weigh the assembled box, lid and sample; then place the lid under the box, and return the assembly to the culture chamber. Cover the culture chamber, evacuate the desiccator by applying a vacuum pump for 30 minutes, and close the stopcock. After the desiccator has been allowed to stand at 25 ± 1°C. for an additional 8 to 16 hours, weigh the box again. Repeat these operations at 8- to 16-hour intervals until two successive weighings agree within a few tenths of a milligram. If surface area determinations are made on several samples concurrently, a point is often reached when some samples appear to gain and some to lose a fraction of a milligram of weight between two successive weighings. This is a good indication that equilibrium has been attained. Use the mean of two successive weights that agree within a few tenths of a milligram to calculate the amount of glycol retained by the sample.

42–3.3.4 CALCULATION OF SPECIFIC SURFACE

Calculate the specific surface by the equation, $A = W_g/(W_s \times 0.00031)$, where A = specific surface in m.^{2} per g., W_g = weight of glycol retained by the sample, W_s = weight of P_2O_5-dried sample in g., and 0.00031 is the Dyal-Hendricks value for the grams of glycol required to form a monolayer on a square meter of surface.

42–3.4 Comments[1]

The vacuum pump and desiccators should be connected by means of tight-fitting, vacuum-type rubber tubing, a glass tube filled with 8-mesh anhydrous $CaCl_2$ being inserted in the line to prevent undesirable vapors from entering the pump. High-vacuum stopcock lubricant should be used to seal glass joints.

Adsorption of atmospheric H_2O by the sample during weighing operations is controlled by allowing air to flow through the $CaCl_2$ tube into the desiccator when releasing vacuum, by placing the lid on the box promptly after releasing the vacuum, and by weighing rapidly. Determinations may be made on as many as four samples concurrently.

It is desirable to prepare fresh $CaCl_2$-glycol solvate for each set of determinations, as some absorption of atmospheric H_2O with continuing use is unavoidable. The P_2O_5 employed for drying may be used until it absorbs sufficient water to develop a syrupy consistency.

According to Diamond and Kinter (1956), some montmorillonites re-expand after being heated at 600°C. Therefore, measurements on samples which have received this pretreatment do not always provide an unbiased estimate of external surface.

The coefficient of variation of determinations on subsamples from a large sample will depend on the homogeneity of the sample. In samples containing coarse sand, the inclusion or exclusion of a few more or less large sand grains can cause the values of surface area to be less or greater than the average by several percent. The average coefficient of variation of determinations on sub-samples from large samples of homogeneous clays has been about 1.9% when duplicate determinations were made by different operators on different days. Greater coefficients of variation should be attributed to heterogeneity of the material being measured or to careless technique.

---

[1] R. E. Morin and H. S. Jacobs (1964) have published an apparently useful modification of the method presented here.

42–4 LITERATURE CITED

Anderson, Duwayne M., and Low, Philip F. 1958. The density of water adsorbed by lithium-, sodium-, and potassium-bentonite. Soil Sci. Soc. Am. Proc. 22:99–103.

Bering, B. P., Dreying, V. P., Kiselev, A. V., Serpinskii, V. V., Surova, M. D., and Shcherbakova, K. D. 1952. Adsorption properties of montmorillonite clays. Kolloid. Zhur. 14:399–407.

Boer, J. H., de. 1953. The Dynamical Character of Adsorption. Oxford Univ. Press, London.

Bower, C. A., and Goertzen, J. O. 1955. Negative adsorption of salts by soils. Soil Sci. Soc. Am. Proc. 19:147–151.

Bower, C. A., and Goertzen, J. O. 1959. Surface area of soils and clays by an equilibrium ethylene glycol method. Soil Sci. 87:289–292.

Bower, C. A., and Gschwend, F. B. 1952. Ethylene glycol retention by soils as a measure of surface area and interlayer swelling. Soil Sci. Soc. Am. Proc. 16:342–345.

Bradley, W. F. 1945. Molecular association between montmorillonite and some polyfunctional organic liquids. J. Am. Chem. Soc. 67:955–981.

Brooks, C. S. 1955. Nitrogen adsorption experiments on several clay minerals. Soil Sci. 79:331–347.

Brunauer, S., Emmett, P. H., and Teller, E. 1938. Adsorption of gases in multimolecular layers. J. Am. Chem. Soc. 60:309–319.

Diamond, S., and Kinter, E. B. 1956. Surface areas of clay minerals as derived from measurements of glycerol retention. In Clays and Clay Minerals, pp. 334–347. Nat. Acad. Sci., Nat. Res. Council Publ. 566.

Dyal, R. S., and Hendricks, S. B. 1950. Total surface of clays in polar liquids as a characteristic index. Soil Sci. 69:421–432.

Emmett, P. H., Brunauer, S., and Love, K. S. 1938. The measurement of surface areas of soils and soil colloids by the use of low temperature van der Waals adsorption isotherms. Soil Sci. 45:57–65.

Eschard, J. 1950. Adsorption de l'azote a'basse temperature par la montmorillonite; influence de l'eau residuelle et des cations exchangeables. Trans. Intern. Congr. Soil Sci. 4th Amsterdam. 3:71–74.

Harkins, W. D. 1952. The Physical Chemistry of Surface Films. Reinhold Publishing Corp., New York.

Harkins, W. D., and Jura, G. 1944. Surface of solids: XIII. J. Am. Chem. Soc. 66:1366–1373.

Langmuir, I. 1918. The adsorption of gases on plane surfaces of glass, mica, and platinum. J. Am. Chem. Soc. 40:1361–1402.

MacEwan, D. M. C. 1948. Complexes of clays with organic compounds, I. Trans. Faraday Soc. 44:349–367.

Makower, B., Shaw, T. M. and Alexander, L. T. 1938. The specific surface and density of some soils and their colloids. Soil Sci. Soc. Am. Proc. (1937) 2:101–109.

Martin, R. T. 1955. Ethylene glycol retention by clays. Soil Sci. Soc. Am. Proc. 19:160–164.

McNeal, Brian L. 1964. Effect of exchangeable cations on glycol retention by clay minerals. Soil Sci. 97:96–102.

Mehra, O. P., and Jackson, M. L. 1959. Specific surface determination by duo-interlayer and mono-layer glycerol sorption for vermiculite and montmorillonite analysis. Soil Sci. Soc. Am. Proc. 23:351–354.

Mooney, R. W., Keenan, A. G., and Wood, L. A. 1952. Adsorption of water vapor by montmorillonite: II. J. Am. Chem. Soc. 74:1371–1374.

Morin, R. E., and Jacobs, H. S. 1964. Surface area determination of soils by adsorption of ethylene glycol vapor. Soil Sci. Soc. Am. Proc. 28:190–194.

Mortland, M. M. 1955. Adsorption of ammonia by clays and muck. Soil Sci. 80:11–18.

Nelson, R. A., and Hendricks, S. B. 1943. Specific surface of some clay minerals, soils, and soil colloids. Soil Sci. 56:285–296.

Orchiston, H. D. 1953. Adsorption of water vapor: I. Soil Sci. 76:453–465.

Prutton, C. F., and Maron, S. H., 1951. Fundamental Principles of Physical Chemistry. Macmillan Publ. Co., New York.

Quirk, J. P. 1955. Significance of surface areas calculated from water vapor sorption isotherms by use of the B.E.T. equation. Soil Sci. 80:423–430.

Schofield, R. K. 1949. Calculation of surface area of clays from measurements of negative adsorption. Trans. Brit. Ceram. Soc. 48:207–213.

Sor, Kamil, and Kemper, W. D. 1959. Estimation of surface area of soils and clays from the amount of adsorption and retention of ethylene glycol. Soil Sci. Soc. Am. Proc. 23:105–110.

Teichner, S. 1950. Sur la mesure des surfaces specifiques de certaines argiles. Comp. Rend. 231:1063–1064.

Zettlemoyer, A. C., Young, G. J., and Chessick, J. J. 1955. Studies of the surface chemistry of silicate minerals III: Heats of immersion of bentonite in water. J. Phys. Chem. 59:962–966.

43

Particle Fractionation and Particle-Size Analysis

PAUL R. DAY

University of California
Berkeley, California

43–1 INTRODUCTION

Soil particles, or "ultimate soil particles," are the discrete units which comprise the solid phase of the soil. They generally cluster together as aggregates, but can be separated from one another by chemical and mechanical means. The particles have diverse composition and structure, and generally differ from one another in both size and shape. They may be organic or inorganic, crystalline or amorphous. The methods described herein will apply only to the inorganic particles, the typical ones being single crystalline fragments.

Particle size is a parameter having the dimension of length, and defined by one or another of several arbitrary criteria, such as (*1*) the width of the smallest square opening, or the diameter of the smallest circular opening, through which the particle can pass, (*2*) the diameter of a circle having an area equal to the maximum projected area of the particle, (*3*) the diameter of a sphere whose volume is equal to that of the particle, and (*4*) the diameter of a sphere whose density and settling velocity (in a given fluid) are equal to those of the particle. These criteria all agree for spherical particles, but not for the anisometric particles commonly found in the soil. Hence, the recorded results of a particle-size measurement should always be accompanied by a notation of the method used.

The particle-size distribution of a soil expresses the proportions of the various sizes of particles which it contains. The proportions are commonly represented by the relative numbers of particles within stated size classes (i.e., by their frequency ratios), or by the relative weights of such classes. The determination of a particle-size distribution is commonly referred to as a particle-size analysis, a term which has largely superseded the older and somewhat ambiguous term "mechanical analysis" (Soil Sci. Soc. Am., 1946, 1949; Am. Soc. Testing Mater., 1959; Inst. Chem. Eng., 1947, p. 114).

The term fractionation refers in the present context to any process used to sort the soil particles into distinct classes according to size. Sieving and sedimentation are the most common methods. Fractionation is employed in most methods of particle-size analysis, and is also used independently in the preparing of soil materials for detailed physical, chemical, or mineralogical study. The fractions are often referred to as separates.

Particle-size distribution is one of the most stable soil characteristics, being little modified by cultivation or other practices. Although the usefulness of particle-size analysis in practical agriculture has sometimes been questioned (Schofield and Russell, 1947), its indirect benefits have been extensive. It has been used in many countries as a basis of soil textural classification, particularly in the United States (Soil Survey Staff, 1951). Particle-size analysis is a valuable research method in problems dealing with weathering, segregation of soil particles by leaching, soil structure, and sediment transport by water and wind.

The methods of fractionation and particle-size analysis described herein are limited to sieving and sedimentation procedures. The extraction of clay by gravitational sedimentation is the most common method for separating this fraction of the soil. In this procedure, sedimentation and decantation to a fixed depth are repeated a sufficient number of times to achieve almost a complete separation.

The pipette method of particle-size analysis is a sedimentation procedure which utilizes pipette sampling at controlled depths and times. It was developed simultaneously in three different countries (Jennings et al., 1922; Krauss, 1923; Robinson, 1922), and was later adopted by the Intern. Soc. Soil Sci. (1929). Further developments have put special emphasis on methods of dispersion (Olmstead et al., 1930; Robinson, 1933; Tyner, 1940; Kilmer and Alexander, 1949).

Another sedimentation procedure, the hydrometer method, was introduced by Bouyoucos (1926), who subsequently published many articles about it. Casagrande (1934) improved the method and put it on a more firm theoretical basis by demonstrating the manner in which Stokes' equation applies. This method is sufficient for many purposes, but less accurate than the pipette sampling method.

The early history of particle-size analysis has been discussed by Keen (1931) and Krumbein (1932). The following works contain reviews and developments of more recent date: Am. Soc. Testing Mater. (1959), Cadle (1955), Dallavalle (1948), Inst. Chem. Eng. (1947), Irani and Callis (1963), Orr and Dallavalle (1959), Williams et al. (1958).

43–2 PRINCIPLES

43–2.1 Pretreatment and Dispersion

The usual methods of fractionation and particle-size analysis require that the particles be dispersed in an aqueous solution, i.e., that they be detached from one another and suspended in the liquid. Shaking the soil in a dilute alkaline solution of sodium metaphosphate is sufficient, in many cases, for the dispersion of all except the finest colloidal aggregates. However, soils which contain considerable amounts of readily soluble salts, gypsum, or organic matter may not disperse adequately unless these components are removed first. Removal can be accomplished by treating the soil with peroxide to destroy organic matter, followed by filtration and washing with enough water to dissolve the gypsum. A method for removing iron oxide is described in section 44–4.

Dispersion usually requires the addition of a reagent such as NaOH, Na_2CO_3, $Na_2C_2O_4$ (sodium oxalate), $Na_4P_2O_7$ (sodium pyrophosphate), $NaPO_3$ (sodium metaphosphate), or various mixtures of these, in dilute concentration. The effectiveness of these dispersing agents depends upon the adsorption of sodium in exchange for other cations, and the resultant development of strong electrical repulsion forces between the soil particles. Mixtures of $NaPO_3$ and Na_2CO_3 have proved particularly effective, and have made it possible to disperse calcareous soils without the prior removal of alkaline earth carbonates (Tyner, 1940; Kilmer and Alexander, 1949).

Finally, the particles must be separated by shearing action or turbulent mixing, using such devices as mechanical shakers or electric mixers. However, the mixing should not be too vigorous, since the rupture of individual particles should be avoided.

43–2.2 Sieving

Sieving is a convenient procedure for segregating particles coarser than 0.05 mm. Although outwardly simple, it has limitations that are not always recognized (Dallavalle, 1948, pp. 104–113; Herdan, 1960; Whitby, 1958). The probability of a particle passing a given sieve in a given time of shaking depends upon the nature of the particle and the properties of the sieve. For example, a particle whose shape permits its passage only in a certain orientation has a limited chance of getting through, except after prolonged shaking. Furthermore, sieve openings are generally unequal in size, requiring extensive shaking before all particles have had the opportunity of approaching the largest openings. In fact, the requirement that sieving be continued to "completion" can rarely be met in practical times of shaking. Good reproducibility requires careful standardization of procedure.

43–2.3 Sedimentation

Small spherical particles of density ρ_s and diameter X are known to settle through a liquid of density ρ_L and viscosity η at a rate of $v = X^2 g(\rho_s - \rho_L)/18\eta$, where g = acceleration of gravity. This relationship between the size of a spherical particle and its settling velocity, known as Stokes' equation, furnishes an arbitrary measure of the sizes of nonspherical particles. Thus, the separation of the clay fraction $(0 < X < 0.002$ mm.$)$ by sedimentation can be accomplished by homogenizing a soil suspension and decanting all of that which remains above the plane $z = -h$ after time $t = 18\eta h/g \ (\rho_s - \rho_L)X^2$. (See Table 43–1.) Quantitative separation by decantation requires that the residue be resuspended and decanted repeatedly to salvage those particles that had not previously been at the top of the suspension at the start of the sedimentation period.

43–2.4 Theory of the Pipette Sampling Method

The pipette method of analysis depends upon the fact that sedimentation eliminates from the depth h in a time t all particles having settling velocities greater than h/t, while retaining at that depth the original concentration of particles having settling velocities less than h/t. The taking of a small volume element by a pipette at a depth h at time t furnishes a sample from which all

Table 43–1. Sedimentation times* for particles of 2, 5 and 20μ diameter, settling through water for a depth of 10 cm.

Temperature °C.	Settling time with indicated particle diameter					
	2 microns		5 microns		20 microns	
	hr.	min.	hr.	min.	min.	sec.
20	8	0	1	17	4	48
21	7	49	1	15	4	41
22	7	38	1	13	4	35
23	7	27	1	11	4	28
24	7	17	1	10	4	22
25	7	7	1	8	4	16
26	6	57	1	7	4	10
27	6	48	1	5	4	4
28	6	39	1	4	4	0
29	6	31	1	3	3	55
30	6	22	1	1	3	49
31	6	14	1	0	3	44

* Values calculated from Stokes' equation, assuming a particle density of 2.60 g./cm³. The figure for particle density is arbitrary and has been chosen to satisfy simultaneously the two definitions of the clay fraction, viz., particles having an effective diameter of 2 microns and a settling velocity of 10 cm. in 8 hours at 20° C. (International Society of Soil Science, 1929).

particles coarser than X (as determined by Stokes' equation) have been eliminated, and in which all particles finer than that size are present in the same amount as initially. The volume element at depth h has, in effect, been "screened" by sedimentation, so that the ratio of the weight w of particles present in that volume at time t, divided by the weight w_o of particles present in it initially, is equal to $P/100$, where P is the percentage of particles, by weight, smaller than X. Now, the ratio w/w_o can also be written as the concentration ratio c/c_o, giving $c/c_o = P/100$. This equation connects the concentration c of the pipette sample, in grams per liter, to the parameter P of the particle-size distribution, c_o being the weight of solids in the entire sample divided by the volume of the suspension.

43–2.5 Theory of the Hydrometer Method

The theory of the hydrometer method is similar to that of the pipette method except for the manner of determining the concentration of solids in suspension. Letting φ represent the suspension density, ρ_L the density of liquid, and ρ_s the particle density, all in grams per liter, we have the equation $\varphi = \rho_L + (c/1,000)(1 - \rho_L/\rho_s)$, where c is the concentration of suspended solids in grams per liter. Although the buoyant force on a hydrometer is determined directly by the suspension density φ, hydrometer scales can be calibrated in terms of c for particular values of ρ_L and ρ_s. The large size of hydrometer bulb necessary to give adequate sensitivity reduces the depth discrimination of the instrument, but this limitation can be overcome by a simple correction (Casagrande, 1934; Day, 1956).

The hydrometer method, like the pipette method, depends fundamentally upon Stokes' equation, which may be written as

$$X = \theta/(t)^{1/2}, \text{ where } \theta = 1000 \left[\frac{30\,\eta h}{g(\rho_s - \rho_L)} \right]^{1/2}.$$

The sedimentation parameter θ is not constant during sedimentation be-because the depth of immersion of the hydrometer bulb is variable. By equating the settling depth h to the distance in centimeters from the surface of the suspension to the center of the hydrometer bulb, it is possible to relate measured values of h to the stem readings R, making θ a determinate function of R. This functional relation is displayed in Table 43–7 for the particular hydrometer prescribed in section 43–5.1 (Am. Soc. Testing Mater., 1961b; Day, 1956).

Table 43–7 is based upon the above equation, using the following constants: $\eta = \eta_{30}$ = viscosity of water at 30°C. = 0.008007 poise, ρ_L = density of 0.5% Calgon solution = 0.99949 g. per ml., ρ_s = particle density = 2.650 g. per ml., g = 980.7 cm. per sec.^{2}. The factor 1,000 arises from converting diameter in millimeters to diameter X in microns.

When a temperature other than 30°C. is used, θ should be multiplied by a correction factor $(\eta/\eta_{30})^{1/2}$. When particle densities differ from 2.650 g. per ml., θ should be multiplied by the factor $[(2.650 - 0.99949)(\rho_s - 0.99949)]^{1/2}$.

43–3   METHOD FOR SEPARATION OF CLAY, SILT, AND SAND FRACTIONS

43–3.1   Special Apparatus

1. Siphon: Prepare a siphon tube from a 30-cm. length of glass tubing having an inner diameter of 6 mm. Make a 90° bend in one end (the upper) and a short U-shape bend in the other, giving an upturned opening to serve as an entry port. Connect a 50-cm. length of rubber tubing to the bent end, and close the free end of the rubber tubing with a screw clamp. Using a support rod and adjustable clamp, mount the glass tube in a vertical position to allow its insertion to a measured depth in a suspension.
2. Suction filtration apparatus:[1] Using rubber tubing with heavy walls, connect a Pasteur-Chamberland filter (fineness F) to a suction flask and to a pressure bulb through a 3-way stopcock (Fig. 43–1). Attach the suction flask to a suction pump.
3. Sieve, 47μ, 300-mesh phosphor bronze wire cloth, 0.0015-inch wire, in a 5-inch or 8-inch frame.

43–3.2   Reagent

1. Dissolve 50 g. of Calgon in water, and dilute the solution to a volume of 1 liter.[2]

43–3.3   Procedure

Prepare a 7% aqueous suspension of soil in a straight-sided jar, keeping the upper surface of the suspension well below the top of the jar to avoid losses during stirring. Add 250 ml. of Calgon solution per 100 g. of soil, allow the soil to slake for a few minutes, and stir the suspension for 3

---

[1] See Perry (1944) for a description of a multiple-assembly rack suitable for routine analysis.

[2] Calgon is a commercial preparation of sodium metaphosphate ($NaPO_3$) containing sufficient Na_2CO_3 to give a pH of 8.3 in a 10% aqueous solution. A weight of 50 g. per liter gives a concentration of sodium slightly greater than $0.5N$. Procedures for preparing sodium metaphosphate from monosodium phosphate have been described by Tyner (1940) and Kilmer and Alexander (1949).

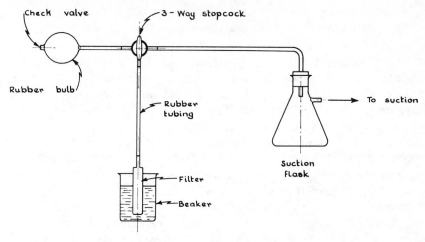

Fig. 43–1. Filtration apparatus.

minutes with an electric mixer. Cover the jar, and store it in a locker to reduce temperature fluctuations and to avoid direct sunlight.

Record the temperature. Determine from Stokes' equation (or from Table 43–1) the time required for a spherical particle 0.002 mm. in diameter to fall through a definite distance h, equal to about 80% of the depth of the suspension. Move the jar (carefully) to the bench top at the proper time, insert the siphon tube to the predetermined depth h, and siphon the suspension into another jar, proceeding very slowly to reduce disturbance. Continue siphoning until the supernatant liquid has been removed to the depth h.

Remove the siphon, add distilled water again to the original level, mix the suspension thoroughly as before, and repeat the sedimentation and siphoning.

While the second period of sedimentation is in progress, use the filtration apparatus to concentrate the clay that has already collected in the receiver. When a coherent layer of clay has formed on the surface of the filter candle, disconnect the suction and apply air pressure to the interior of the filter by squeezing the rubber bulb. Touch the filter candle to the side of the receiver to initiate the expulsion of the clay, which will slide off as an intact mass. Continue the filtration until no free water remains.

Collect all the siphonings in the same jar, and repeat the operations until the yields become negligible. Save the clay fraction as a concentrated paste if needed in that form, or dry it in air and store it in the dry state.

Separate the silt and sand fractions by wet-sieving the residue on a 47μ sieve as described in section 43-4.3.3. Dry the fractions as needed.

43–3.4 Comments

The procedure for dispersing the soil prior to sedimentation may be varied in accordance with the use to be made of the clay. For example, Calgon would introduce unsuitable contamination of clay intended for experiments on phosphorus nutrition, and some other dispersing agent would have to be used. Dispersing agents can be omitted entirely when their presence is objectionable, although the yields of clay in each settling period will usually be smaller in the early stages. (In the later stages, when the electrolyte content has been reduced to a low level, the yields may be much more abundant than at first.)

The use of hydrogen peroxide to destroy organic matter may cause the formation of calcium oxalate unless certain precautions are taken (see section 43–4.4.1). Such contamination is undesirable when the extracted clay is intended for mineralogical study.

The concentrating of the clay may be greatly accelerated by flocculating it chemically as soon as it has entered the receiver. The supernatant liquid can then be decanted instead of filtered, and the suspension can be dialyzed in a thin cellophane bag to remove electrolyte.

43–4 PIPETTE METHOD OF PARTICLE-SIZE ANALYSIS [3]

43–4.1 Special Apparatus

1. Suction filtration apparatus (see section 43–3.1).
2. Pipette sampling apparatus: Construct a special pipette (Fig. 43–2), and determine its volumetric capacity from the weight of mercury that it will hold. Prepare a pipette holder (e.g., a cathetometer or a support stand

---

[3] Taken, with minor modifications, from Kilmer and Alexander (1949).

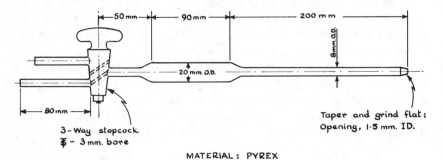

MATERIAL : PYREX

Fig. 43–2. Special pipette.

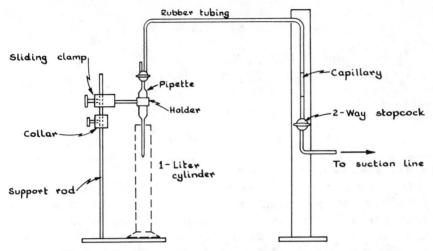

Fig. 43-3. Sampling apparatus using special pipette of Fig. 43-2.

with a sliding clamp) for lowering and positioning the pipette at a controlled depth 10 to 13 cm. below the upper mark of a 1-liter graduated cylinder. Connect the pipette by a 2-foot length of rubber tubing to the suction line through a fine glass capillary and a 2-way stopcock (Fig. 43-3). Try different capillaries until one is found which permits the pipette to fill in about 30 seconds under full suction.

3. Brass plunger: On the center of a circular brass plate 1/16 inch in thickness and 2⅛ inches in diameter, fasten vertically a brass rod 20 inches in length and 3/16 inch in diameter.

4. Sedimentation cabinet or constant-temperature room.

5. Shaker, horizontal reciprocating type, 2½-inch stroke, 120 strokes per minute.

6. Sieve shaker, ½-inch vertical and lateral movements, 500 strokes per minute, with automatic timer.

7. Sieves, set of 6, 3-inch diameter frame, with cover and pan:

Sieve opening, mm.	Specifications
1.0	Perforated brass plate, round holes, number 3 straight, 0.04-inch diameter holes, 240 holes per square inch.
0.5	Perforated brass plate, round holes, number 00 staggered, 0.02-inch diameter holes, 714 holes per square inch.
0.25	60-mesh, Bureau of Standards (phosphor bronze wire cloth)
0.177	80-mesh, Bureau of Standards (phosphor bronze wire cloth)
0.105	140-mesh, Bureau of Standards (phosphor bronze wire cloth)
0.047	300-mesh, phosphor bronze wire cloth, 0.0015 wire.

43–4.2   Reagents

1. Hydrogen peroxide (H_2O_2), 30%.
2. Calgon solution: Dissolve 50 g. of Calgon in water, and dilute the solution to 1 liter (see section 43–3.2).

43–4.3   Procedure

43–4.3.1 SAMPLING AND PRETREATMENT

Dry and crumble the field sample. Separate the "fine earth" fraction by hand-sieving through a 2-mm. sieve. Use a mortar and rubber-tipped pestle to break up those aggregates which are larger than 2 mm. When all the fine earth has passed the sieve, leaving only the gravel, weigh both fractions and discard the gravel. (Omit the weighings if the gravel content is not required.)

Mix the soil on a flexible plastic sheet by raising one corner at a time, causing the particles to lift, turn, and tumble over one another until thoroughly intermingled. When subsamples are required, take small, representative portions from several different parts of the sample, and combine them to obtain the desired weight.

Place a subsample weighing approximately 10 g. in a tared 250-ml. beaker, and weigh it to the nearest 0.01 g.[4] Dry the sample overnight[5] at 105°C., cool it in a desiccator, and reweigh it. Add 30 ml. of water, cover the beaker with a watch glass, and stir the contents by swirling the beaker. Cautiously add a few ml. of 30% H_2O_2, and swirl the suspension if necessary to reduce foaming. (Precaution: do not allow concentrated H_2O_2 to come in contact with the skin.) When the reaction subsides, add additional amounts of H_2O_2 in the same manner; and complete the digestion by heating the beaker for 1 hour or more at 90°C. on a hotplate, water bath, or oven top. Repeat the treatment if visual inspection indicates that the reaction has not been completed.

43–4.3.2 FILTRATION

Remove the excess liquid by the filtration apparatus shown in Fig. 43–1. When the filter candle has become coated with soil to a thickness of 1 or 2 mm., reverse the stopcock, and apply pressure with the rubber bulb, touching the candle lightly against the inner wall of the beaker to dislodge the soil from the filter candle. Resume the filtration process, removing the coatings frequently to reduce the impedance to flow.

---

[4] All weighings should be to the nearest 0.01 g. unless indicated otherwise.

[5] Alternatively, take a second sample for determination of water content, and omit the oven drying of the test sample.

After the free water has been removed, add additional water, and mix the suspension by a jet of water. Filter the suspension again, and repeat the mixing and filtering several times. Dislodge as much of the soil as possible from the filter candle by applying pressure as before, and wash the last traces of soil back into the beaker from the filter by rubbing the latter with a rubber stopper fitted on the end of a glass rod, using a jet of water when needed. Finally, remove the filter, dry the beaker and contents in the oven at 105°C., cool the beaker in a desiccator, and weigh the dry sample and beaker.

43–4.3.3 DISPERSION AND WET-SIEVING

Add exactly 10 ml. of Calgon solution, and swirl the beaker to bring the contents into suspension. Transfer a 10-ml. sample of Calgon solution to a tared weighing bottle, dry the bottle overnight at 105°C., cool it in a desiccator, and weigh the bottle and contents to the nearest milligram. (One such determination is sufficient for each stock of reagent.) Transfer the suspension through a funnel into a 250-ml. shaker bottle (an 8-ounce Pyrex nursing bottle), add water to bring the volume of suspension to 180 ml., stopper the bottle firmly, and shake the bottle and suspension overnight in a horizontal reciprocating shaker. Remove the bottle from the shaker, place it in an upright position, and let the suspension settle for a few minutes.

Put a wide-mouth funnel in a 1-liter graduated cylinder, using the rim of the latter as a support. Inspect the 47μ sieve for cleanliness and mechanical condition. Moisten it on both sides with water, and place it in the funnel. Then, without shaking or swirling the mixture, pour the suspended portion into the sieve. Add more water to the residue in the bottle, stir the mixture, allow it to settle for 1 or 2 minutes, and decant the suspended portion into the sieve as before. Repeat the mixing and decanting several times until most of the fine material has been transferred.

Tilt the bottle, neck downward, over the sieve. Direct a jet of water upward into the bottle, sweeping the soil particles downward into the sieve by the force of the effluent stream. Do not rub the screen at any time. When the transfer has been completed, agitate the residue on the sieve with a jet of water (cautiously, to avoid damage to the screen), and obtain as complete a separation of the coarse and fine fractions as possible. Add distilled water to bring the volume of suspension to 1 liter, insert a rubber stopper,[6] and transfer the cylinder to the sedimentation cabinet or constant temperature room.

43–4.3.4 DRY SIEVE ANALYSIS

Put the screen and contents in a tared evaporating dish, and dry them in the oven. Cool the screen, and transfer the coarse fraction from the screen

---

[6] Losses of water by evaporation before or during sedimentation may affect results seriously.

to the dish, using a soft brush to complete the transfer. Dry the dish and contents for 2 hours at 105°C., cool them in a desiccator, and weigh the dish and sand to the nearest 0.01 g.

Inspect the set of sieves for cleanliness and mechanical condition, and repair or replace any which are defective. (The finer ones are particularly susceptible to spreading of wires and tearing of the wire cloth around the edges.) Arrange the sieves on the pan in the sequence, 1,000, 500, 250, 177, 105, and 47μ, reading from top to bottom. Transfer the coarse fraction from the dish into the top screen, using a brush to complete the transfer. Put the cover in place, and fasten the nest of sieves firmly in the shaker. Shake the sieves for 3 minutes.

Transfer the separates, one at a time, into the tared evaporating dish, starting at the top and working downward, and weighing the dish and cumulative contents after each addition. Include the weight of "residual silt" which collects in the pan, since this will be reported as a part of the coarse silt fraction (50 to 20μ). Compare the cumulative weight with the total weight of the coarse fractions previously determined.

43–4.3.5 SEDIMENTATION ANALYSIS WITH PIPETTE SAMPLING

Record the temperature of the suspension when it has become constant. Insert the plunger in the suspension, and move it up and down to mix the contents thoroughly. (Caution: hold the cylinder firmly in place with the free hand when the plunger is pulled upward.) Move the plunger cautiously near the top of the suspension during both upstroke and downstroke to avoid spilling the contents. Use strong upward strokes of the plunger near the bottom to lift into suspension any particles that may have lodged there. Dislodge any sediment that remains in the lower corners by inclining the rod slightly and rotating it to impart a spinning motion to the disk. Finish with two or three slow, smooth strokes and remove the plunger, tipping it slightly to remove adhering drops. Record the time immediatley.

Move the cylinder into position in the pipette stand (Fig. 43–3), clamp the clean, *dry,* pipette in its holder, attach the tubing, and make the adjustments required to immerse the pipette 10 cm. in the suspension when the proper time has arrived. Record the volume of the particular pipette used. Note the temperature, and determine from Table 43–1 the sedimentation time required for a 20-micron sampling.[7] Lower the pipette to its proper depth 30 seconds before sampling time.

At the chosen time, open the suction stopcock, and be ready to close the pipette stopcock at the instant the liquid has filled the pipette. After closing the stopcock, raise the pipette, wipe the stem with a soft towel, and by re-

---

[7] Omit this sampling if not required, and proceed directly to the 5μ and/or 2μ sampling. The coarsest sample must always be taken first, followed by the finer ones in sequence.

versing the stopcock run the suspension into a tared weighing bottle (accurate to the nearest milligram). Rinse the pipette, and add the washings to the bottle.

Close the suction stopcock, and detach the pipette from the tubing.

Clean the pipette, and dry it by attaching it to a suction line.

Place the weighing bottle in an oven at 105°C. for 12 hours, cool it in a desiccator, and weigh the bottle and contents to the nearest milligram.

Take 5μ and/or 2μ samples in the same manner, restirring the suspension each time or not as desired, but always counting time from the moment of the most recent stirring. *Always measure the sampling depth from the existing surface of the suspension,* and not from the level used for an earlier sampling.

43-4.3.6 CALCULATION OF RESULTS

Let w = dry weight of the pipette sample, v = volume of the pipette, and V = total volume of the suspension (Table 43-2). Calculate the apparent (uncorrected) weight of particles in the given (cumulative) size range from the formula wV/v. Deduct the weight of dispersing agent per liter of suspension, using the data obtained by drying a 10-ml. sample of the 0.5N reagent. The result will be the cumulative weight ΣW. Determine by difference the weights W of the individual fractions.

Determine, as shown in Table 43-3, the weights of the sand separates.

Table 43-2. Sample calculations in pipette analysis.*

Particle size	Sample wt.	Sample vol.	Suspension vol.	wV/v	ΣW	W
mm.	g.	cm.^{3}	cm.^{3}	g.		
0.020	0.114	26.49	1,000	4.30	3.81	1.54
0.005	0.073	26.49	1,000	2.76	2.27	0.61
0.002	0.057	26.49	1,000	2.15	1.66	1.66

* Concentration of dispersing agent = 0.49 g./liter.

Table 43-3. Sample calculations in sieve analysis.

Nominal size	Weight of sand	Weights of separates
mm.	g.	g.
2	0.00	0.00
1	0.01	0.01
0.5	0.03	0.02
0.25	0.06	0.03
0.10	0.58	0.52
0.05	2.02	1.44
0.00	2.31	0.29

Table 43–4. Sample calculations in particle size analysis.

	grams
Initial weight of sample	10. 21
Oven-dry weight of sample	9. 93
Weight of washed soil	9. 72
Difference = solution loss	0. 21
Weight of coarse fractions:	
(1) After wet sieving	2. 33*
(2) After dry sieving	2. 31*
Sieving loss	0. 02
Weight of residual silt	0. 29
Weight of sand (= 2. 33 - 0. 29)	2. 04
Weight of silt plus clay, by difference, (= 9. 72 - 2. 04)	7. 68*
Weight of 20-μ fraction	3. 81
Difference = weight of coarse silt (50 μ to 20 μ)	3. 87*

* Includes residual silt.

Calculate the solution loss and sieving loss, as shown in Table 43–4. (The term "solution loss" refers not only to the solutes removed by leaching but also to losses of organic matter by volatilization and mechanical losses on the filter.) Calculate the weight of coarse silt (Table 43–4).

Summarize the data, as shown in Table 43–5 and Figs. 43–4 and 43–5.

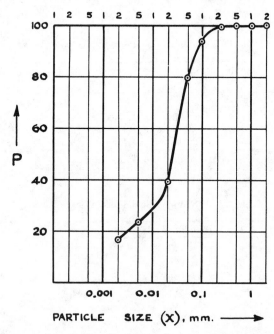

Fig. 43–4. Summation curve, plotted from the data of Table 43–5, using a logarithmic scale of particle size.

Table 43–5. Summary of sample calculations in particle size analysis.

Nominal size	Fraction wt.	p*	P†
mm.	g.	%	%
2-1	0.01	0.1	99.8‡
1-0.5	0.02	0.2	99.7
0.5-0.25	0.03	0.3	99.5
0.25-0.1	0.52	5.4	99.2
0.1-0.05	1.44	14.8	93.8
0.05-0.02	3.87	39.8	79.0
0.02-0.005	1.54	15.8	39.2
0.005-0.002	0.61	6.3	23.4
0.002-0	1.66	17.1	17.1

* p = (wt. of fraction) (100/wt. of washed soil).
† P = percentage of particles, by weight, smaller than the upper size limit in column 1.
‡ Sieving loss 0.2%.

43–4.4 Comments

43–4.4.1 DESTRUCTION OF ORGANIC MATTER

Hydrogen peroxide attacks the colloidal, or humidified organic matter, but not the fibrous (cellulosic) residues (Robinson and Jones, 1925). A

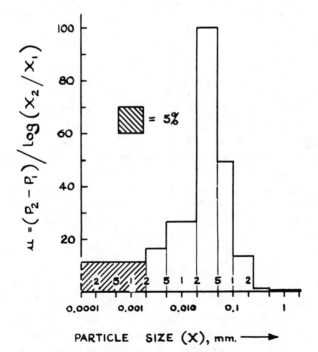

Fig. 43–5. Distribution diagram plotted from the data of Table 43–5. The grid lines of the logarithmic scale are identified by the numbers 1, 2, 5 above the base line.

large part of the colloidal organic matter is oxidized to CO_2 and volatilized. Some of the remainder is converted to soluble compounds of low molecular weight which can be washed out. However, one of the decomposition products is oxalate ion, which reacts with dissolved or exchangeable calcium to form crystals of calcium oxalate monohydrate or trihydrate (Brown, 1953; Martin, 1954). The obvious remedy for this difficulty is to remove calcium salts, including $CaCO_3$ before treating the soil with H_2O_2.

Another undesirable effect of the H_2O_2 treatment is the exfoliation of weathered mica and vermiculite caused by the catalytic decomposition of the reagent between the plates of the mineral (Drosdoff and Miles, 1938).

The effectiveness of H_2O_2 in decomposing soil organic matter is much reduced in the presence of MnO_2. This disadvantage can be eliminated (at least, in noncalcareous soils) by reducing the MnO_2 to the manganous form by acetic acid (Olmstead et al. 1930) or sodium bisulfite (Robinson, 1933). Furthermore, the exfoliation of mica is less likely after such treatment. However, the effects of these reagents upon calcareous soils containing MnO_2 is uncertain, since carbonates will be dissolved, removing a part of the solid phase being analyzed, and making calcium available for precipitation with oxalate during peroxidation.

Although H_2O_2 treatment is effective when used judiciously, it has disadvantages and creates additional problems. Nevertheless, H_2O_2 is useful where it is desired to report results on the basis of the inorganic fraction only.

43–4.4.2 DISPERSION

It should not be expected that the dispersion procedure given herein, or any other procedure, will serve equally well for all soils. Additional trials should be made with other dispersing agents and perhaps other pretreatments whenever it is thought that the given treatment may not be adequate.

The reciprocating shaker is only one of several methods of agitation that have been used successfully. Others include simple boiling, rubbing (triturating), air-jetting (Chu and Davidson, 1953) and stirring with electric mixers (see section 43–5.1). Any of these methods, including the one recommended above, may abrade or fracture individual particles by impacts with one another and with stirring blades or container walls, particularly if the particles are abnormally weak (Låg, 1953).

43–4.4.3 CLASSIFYING AND NAMING OF FRACTIONS

The classifying and naming of the different fractions is arbitrary, and a number of different systems are used. The scheme adopted by the Intern. Soc. Soil Sci. (1929), following Atterberg, is shown in Table 43–6. It is a geometric progression of sizes with common ratio 10, except for the fourth fraction, whose range encompasses all particles finer than 0.002 mm. The scheme used by the U. S. Department of Agriculture (Table 43–6) is a

Table 43-6. Size limits of soil separates from two schemes of analysis
(Soil Survey Staff, 1951, p. 207).

U. S. Department of Agriculture Scheme		International Scheme	
		Fraction	Diameter (range)
Name of separate	Diameter (range)		
	mm.		mm.
Very coarse sand	2.0 -1.0	I	2.0 -0.2
Coarse sand	1.0 -0.5		
Medium sand	0.5 -0.25		
Fine sand	0.25-0.10	II	0.2 -0.02
Very fine sand	0.10-0.05		
Silt	0.05-0.002	III	0.02-0.002
Clay	< 0.002	IV	< 0.002

geometric progression within the sand fractions, except for an irregularity in the interval from 0.25 to 0.10 mm.

The fine-sieve series of the U. S. Bureau of Standards, which has been adopted by the Am. Soc. Testing Mater. (1961a), is used in many soil laboratories. The members of this series form a geometric progression based upon the fourth root of 2. Since the sieves specified by the American Society for Testing and Materials are of woven wire cloth, they are not precisely interchangeable with the perforated plate sieves prescribed by the U. S. Department of Agriculture (Tanner and Bourget, 1952).

43-4.4.4 GRAPHICAL REPRESENTATION

Figure 43-4 shows the most common and most direct method of plotting particle-size distributions. The particles are assumed to be infinite in number, and particle size is considered to be a continuous variate. The plotting of the summation percentage P as a continuous function of X (or of log X) is consistent with these assumptions. However, it should be noted that the shape of the summation curve between points is arbitrary.

A second method of representing a particle-size distribution involves the plotting of the slope u ($= dP/d \log X$) of the summation curve as a function of log X. In that case, the percentage of particles between the limits X_1 and X_2 is equal to the definite integral of $u \cdot d(\log X)$ between the given limits, and is shown geometrically by the corresponding area under the derived curve. The summation percentage is equal to the area of the derived curve over the range from $X = 0$ to X.

When the intervals are broad, as in the data of Table 43-4, the shape of the derived curve (u versus log X) depends upon the arbitrary manner in which the summation curve has been interpolated between points. The block diagram of Fig. 43-5 is simpler to construct and avoids the uncertainties of interpolation that are inherent in the corresponding continuous curve. The percentages within each fraction are represented by the areas of the corresponding rectangles, whose heights are given by the equation $u = (P_2 - P_1)/\log (X_2/X_1)$, where $X_2 > X_1$. The coefficients $\log X_2/X_1$ may be regarded as weighting factors required to correct the bias caused by the unequal widths of the intervals. The area of the shaded rectangle in Fig. 43–5 is a correct representation of the percentage of clay, even though the lower limit of 0.0001 mm. is arbitrary and has no physical significance. The maximum ordinate of 100 units in this diagram is purely coincidental, values much greater than that being obtained frequently.

43–5 HYDROMETER METHOD OF PARTICLE-SIZE ANALYSIS [8]

43–5.1 Special Apparatus

1. Standard hydrometer, ASTM No. 152H, with Bouyoucos scale in grams per liter (Am. Soc. Testing Mater., 1961b). Sources of supply are given in section 37–2.2.1.
2. Electrically driven mixer with replaceable stirring paddle (Am. Soc. Testing Mater., 1961b). Sources of supply are given in section 37–2.2.1.
3. Graduated cylinder, 1 liter, with 1,000-ml. mark 36 ± 2 cm. from the bottom on the inside.
4. Sedimentation cabinet or constant-temperature room.
5. Brass plunger (see section 43–4.1).

43–5.2 Reagent

1. Dissolve 50 g. of Calgon in water, and dilute the solution to a volume of 1 liter (see section 43–3.2).

43–5.3 Procedure

Calibrate each hydrometer in the following manner: Add 100 ml. of Calgon solution to the sedimentation cylinder, and add distilled water to make exactly 1 liter. Mix the suspension thoroughly with the plunger, and bring it to the temperature of the sedimentation cabinet. Record the temperature. Lower the hydrometer into the solution carefully, and determine the scale reading R_L at the *upper edge of the meniscus* surrounding the stem.[9]

Weigh 40.0 g. of soil for analysis and an equal quantity for determination of the oven-dry weight. Dry the latter overnight in an oven at 105°C.,

---

[8] Taken, with minor modifications, from Day (1956).
[9] See next page for footnote 9.

and reweigh it. Place the sample in a 600-ml. beaker (or directly into a dispersing cup if enough cups are available for all the samples being prepared). Add 100 ml. of Calgon solution and approximately 400 ml. of distilled water, and allow the sample to soak for at least 10 minutes.

Transfer the suspension to the dispersing cup, using a stream of distilled water from a rubber syringe to complete the transfer. *Mix the suspension for 5 minutes* with the motor mixer, transfer it to the sedimentation cylinder with the help of a stream of water from the rubber syringe, and bring the level of the liquid to the 1,000-ml. mark with distilled water. Move the cylinder into the sedimentation cabinet.

Record the temperature of the suspension when it has become constant. Insert the plunger, and move it up and down to mix the contents thoroughly. (Caution: hold the cylinder firmly in place with the free hand when the plunger is pulled upward.) Move the plunger cautiously near the top of the suspension during both the upstroke and downstroke to avoid spilling the contents. Use strong upward strokes of the plunger near the bottom to lift into suspension any particles that may have lodged there. Dislodge any sediment that remains in the lower corners by inclining the rod slightly and rotating it to impart a spinning motion to the disk. Finish with two or three slow, smooth strokes, and remove the plunger, tipping it slightly to remove adhering drops. Record the time immediately. Add a drop of amyl alcohol if the surface is covered with foam, and restir the suspension if necessary.

Lower the hydrometer carefully into the suspension, and after 30 seconds read the scale at the top of the meniscus by the highlight method.[9] Without removing the hydrometer, read it again at the end of one minute. After this and each subsequent reading, remove the hydrometer carefully, rinse the surface, and wipe it dry with a soft towel.

Without remixing the suspension between measurements, lower the hydrometer carefully into the suspension about 10 seconds before each measurement, and take hydrometer readings at 3, 10, 30, 90, 270 and 720 minutes (see section 43–5.4.1).

Record the hydrometer readings (R) taken at the various times. Calculate for each reading the concentration of suspension, in grams per liter, from the equation $c = R - R_L$, and the summation percentage from the equation $P = 100(c/c_o)$, where c_o is the oven-dry weight of soil in grams

---

[9] The customary technique of viewing the stem from beneath the surface of the liquid is not possible with soil suspensions, and the substitute method of viewing from above must be used in the calibrations, as well as in the measurements of suspensions.

The position of the meniscus can be determined accurately by viewing it from an angle of 10 to 20 degrees above the plane of the liquid and noting the bright horizontal line (diffraction image) formed on the scale by a small lamp held in front of the forehead and shielded from the eyes by a shade. Occasionally, owing to a lack of cleanliness of the stem or the presence of fatty substances in the soil, the highlight will fail to appear because of the failure of the meniscus to take on its normal contact angle of zero. In that case, it can often be reformed in the normal manner by raising and lowering the hydrometer slightly in the suspension.

per liter of suspension. Calculate the corresponding particle sizes, or "diameters," by the equation X (microns) $= \theta/(t)^{1/2}$, where t is the sedimentation time in minutes and θ is a sedimentation parameter obtained from Table 43–7 by entering the table with the observed (uncorrected) value of R.

Plot P versus X on semilogarithmic paper, as in Fig. 43–4, using the log scale for X. Interpolate from the curve the summation percentages which may be required at particular values of X, such as 2, 5, 20, and 50μ.

If a sieve analysis of the coarse fraction is required, use sieves with 5-inch frames. (The sieves with 3-inch frames used for the pipette method are too small to accommodate the size of sample required for the hydrometer method.)

Pour the suspension directly from the sedimentation cylinder into the 47μ sieve. Discard the effluent. Agitate the residue on the sieve by running ordinary tap water into it directly from the tap, or from a large rubber tube leading from the tap. When most of the fine material appears to have been washed through, dry the sieve and contents, and proceed with dry sieving as in the pipette method (section 43–4.3.4).

43–5.4 Comments

43–5.4.1 SAMPLING SCHEDULE

The time intervals specified in the instructions refer to the total time

Table 43–7. Values of θ for determination of particle size
from observed hydrometer readings (Day, 1956).

R	θ	R	θ	R	θ
-5	50.4				
-4	50.1	11	46.4	26	42.2
-3	49.9	12	46.2	27	41.9
-2	49.6	13	45.9	28	41.6
-1	49.4	14	45.6	29	41.3
0	49.2	15	45.3	30	41.0
1	48.9	16	45.0	31	40.7
2	48.7	17	44.8	32	40.4
3	48.4	18	44.5	33	40.1
4	48.2	19	44.2	34	39.8
5	47.9	20	43.9	35	39.5
6	47.7	21	43.7	36	39.2
7	47.4	22	43.4	37	38.9
8	47.2	23	43.1	38	38.6
9	47.0	24	42.8	39	38.3
10	46.7	25	42.5	40	38.0

LEGEND:
R = hydrometer scale reading, g./liter.
θ = sedimentation parameter based on a temperature of 30° C. and a particle density of 2.650 g./ml. for ASTM hydrometer 152H.

elapsed between the start of sedimentation and the time of reading the hydrometer. The sampling schedule is arbitrary, but a geometric progression of time intervals gives a convenient spread of data. The 270- and 720-minute samplings (4½ and 12 hours, respectively) could be replaced by a single 8-hour sampling, if desired, or the 4½-hour sampling could be omitted entirely.

The instructions ignore the possible disturbance to the suspension that may result from the repeated inserting and removing of the hydrometer, although Mériaux (1952) has found considerable error from this cause. This effect can be eliminated by restirring the suspension after each reading, taking the separate periods of sedimentation in any convenient sequence.

43–5.4.2 SOIL DENSITY

The accuracy of the hydrometer results depends, among other things, upon the amount of deviation of particle density from 2.65 g. per ml. Summation percentages will be affected to the extent of $\pm 3\%$ of their measured value within the normal range of variation of particle density, 2.5 to 2.8 g. per ml. This range includes the majority of soils, although soils treated with H_2O_2 to remove organic matter give somewhat higher densities (Smith, 1943). Thus, a summation percentage of 60% may be in error by $\pm 1.8\%$ of the dry weight of soil within the range of densities quoted above.

43–5.4.3 DISPERSION

Good dispersion is no less important in hydrometer analysis than in pipette analysis. Although the dispersion procedure described above is satisfactory for many soils, it should be modified for some kinds of soil. The following will require special treatment: soils containing large amounts of natural soil organic matter, soils containing polyelectrolyte soil conditioners, soils containing gypsum, and soils containing large amounts of soft, easily disintegrated rock or mineral fragments. Soils containing $CaCO_3$ will disperse satisfactorily with the above pretreatment unless there are other conditions which prevent dispersion. Any solutes added during pretreatment, except for the dispersing agent, should be removed before analysis.

The amount of dispersion is affected by the time of mixing. The most rapid changes occur during the first 2 minutes and usually reach a maximum in less than 5 minutes. Soft mineral or rock fragments may disintegrate (slowly) during mixing (Låg, 1953), and if so will increase the amount of fine material present in suspension. For this reason it is undesirable to prolong the mixing beyond the minimum time required to disperse the colloidal components.

The blades of the electric mixer deteriorate rapidly by abrasion and should be replaced as soon as they begin to show signs of wear. This may occur in 1 or 2 hours of operating time (Doolittle, 1957).

Overnight shaking in a reciprocating shaker, as prescribed in the pipette procedure, is a permissible substitute for the mechanical dispersion method described above. However, samples weighing 40 g. will often pack in the bottom of the bottle during shaking when 8-ounce bottles are used. Larger bottles containing 500 ml. of suspension are recommended if the reciprocating shaker is used at the ordinary rate of 120 strokes per minute.

43–6   LITERATURE CITED

American Society for Testing and Materials. 1959. Symposium on Particle Size Measurement. ASTM Spec. Pub. No. 234. Am. Soc. Testing Mater., Philadelphia.

American Society for Testing and Materials. 1961a. Standard specifications for sieves for testing purposes. *In* The 1961 Book of ASTM Standards, Part 4, pp. 1479–1486. Am. Soc. Testing Mater., Philadelphia.

American Society for Testing and Materials. 1961b. Tentative method for grain-size analysis of soils. *In* The 1961 Book of ASTM Standards, Part 4, pp. 1272–1283. Am. Soc. Testing Mater., Philadelphia.

Bouyoucos, G. J. 1926. Estimation of the colloidal material in soils. Science 64:362.

Brown, G. 1953. The occurrence of lepidocrocite in some British soils. Soil Sci. 4:220–228.

Cadle, R. D. 1955. Particle Size Determination. Interscience Publishers, Inc., New York.

Casagrande, A. 1934. Die Aräometer-Methode zur Bestimmung der Kornverteilung von Boden und anderen Materialien. Julius Springer, Berlin.

Chu, T. Y., and Davidson, D. T. 1953. Simplified air-jet dispersion apparatus for mechanical analysis of soils. Proc. Highway Res. Board 32:541.

Dallavalle, J. M. 1948. Micromeritics. Ed. 2. Pitman and Sons, Ltd., London.

Day, P. R. 1956. Report of the Committee on Physical Analyses, 1954–55. Soil Sci. Soc. Am. Proc. 20:167–169.

Doolittle, W. T. 1957. Wear of soil mixer paddles and effect on mechanical analysis. Soil Sci. Soc. Am. Proc. 21:662.

Drosdoff, M., and Miles, E. F. 1938. Action of hydrogen peroxide on weathered mica. Soil Sci. 46:391–393.

Herdan, G. 1960. Small Particle Statistics. Ed. 2. Butterworths, London.

Institution of Chemical Engineers. 1947. Symposium on Particle Size Analysis. Supplement to Transactions, Inst. Chem. Eng. volume 25, London.

International Society of Soil Science. 1929. Minutes of the First Commission Meetings, International Congress of Soil Science, Washington, 1927. Proc. Intern. Soc. Soil Sci. 4:215–220.

Irani, R. R., and Callis, C. F. 1963. Particle Size: Measurement, Interpretation, and Application. John Wiley and Sons, Inc., New York.

Jennings, D. S., Thomas, M. D., and Gardner, W. 1922. A new method of mechanical analysis of soils. Soil Sci. 14:485–499.

Keen, B. A. 1931. The Physical Properties of the Soil. Longmans, Green and Co., London.

Kilmer, V. J., and Alexander, L. T. 1949. Methods of making mechanical analyses of soils. Soil Sci. 68:15–24.

Krauss, G. 1923. Über eine neue Methode der mechanischen Bodenanalyse. Int. Mitt. Bodenk. 13:147–160.

Krumbein, W. C. 1932. A history of the principles and methods of mechanical analysis. J. Sedimen. Petrol. 2:89–124.

Låg, J. 1953. Observations on overdispersing in the preparation of soil samples for mechanical analysis. Acta Agricultura Scandinavica III: 113–119.

Martin, R. T. 1954. Calcium oxalate formation in soil from hydrogen peroxide treatment. Soil Sci. 77:143–145.

Mériaux, Suzanne. 1952. Observations sur la méthode densiometrique dans l'analyse granulometrique. Comptes Rendus, Acad. Sci. (Paris), 235:381–383.

Olmstead, L. B., Alexander, L. T., and Middleton, H. E. 1930. A pipette method of mechanical analysis of soils based on improved dispersion procedure. U. S. Dept. Agr. Tech. Bull. 170.

Orr, C. Jr., and Dallavalle, J. M. 1959. Fine Particle Measurement. Macmillan Co., New York.

Perry, E. P. 1944. Equipment for facilitating mechanical analysis of soils. Soil Sci. Soc. Am. Proc. (1943) 8:372–373.

Robinson, G. W. 1922. A new method for the mechanical analysis of soils and other dispersions. J. Agr. Sci. 12:306–321.

Robinson, G. W. 1933. The dispersion of soils in mechanical analysis. Imp. Bur. Soil Sci. Tech. Comm. 26.

Robinson, G. W., and Jones, O. W. 1925. A method for determining the degree of humification of soil organic matter. J. Agr. Sci. 15:26–29.

Schofield, R. K., and Russell, E. W. 1947. The significance of particle size in relation to soils. In Institution of Chemical Engineers, Symposium on Particle Size Analysis. Supplement to Transactions, Inst. Chem. Eng. (London). 25:94–95.

Smith, W. O. 1943. Density of soil solids and their genetic relations. Soil Sci. 56:263–272.

Soil Survey Staff. 1951. Soil survey manual. U. S. Dept. Agr. Handbook 18.

Soil Science Society of America. 1946. Report of Committee on Terminology: Mechanical analysis. Soil Sci. Soc. Am. Proc. 1945 10:274.

Soil Science Society of America. 1949. Report of Committee on Terminology: Particle size analysis. Soil Sci. Soc. Am. Proc. 1948 13:573.

Tanner, C. B., and Bourget, S. J. 1952. Particle-shape discrimination of round and square holed sieves. Soil Sci. Soc. Am. Proc. 16:88.

Tyner, E. H. 1940. The use of sodium metaphosphate for dispersion of soils for mechanical analysis. Soil Sci. Soc. Am. Proc. 1939 4:106–113.

Whitby, K. T. 1958. The mechanics of fine sieving. Am. Soc. Testing Mater. Special Tech. Publ. 234:3–25.

Williams, J. W., van Holde, K. E., Baldwin, R. L., and Fujita, H. 1958. The theory of sedimentation. Chem. Rev. 58:715–806.

44 | Pretreatment for Mineralogical Analysis

G. W. KUNZE

Texas A & M University
College Station, Texas

44–1 GENERAL INTRODUCTION

The use of pretreatments involves the risk of altering or destroying fractions of the soil other than those for which the treatments are intended. In many cases, however, the investigator has very little choice; either pretreatments are utilized or the obtainable data are very much limited. The pretreatments are designed to have a minimum effect on constituents other than those to be eliminated. Even so, the philosophy of using a minimum of pretreatments remains sound.

The removal of free iron oxides was initially employed to clean the coarser fractions of the soil for study with the petrographic microscope and to eliminate aggregates of particles resulting from the cementing action of these materials. Iron-rich soils often require removal of free iron oxides for particle-size-distribution studies. Removal of free iron oxides is in many cases desirable and sometimes necessary to obtain definitive X-ray diffraction patterns. Differential thermal, infrared, and other mineralogical analyses are many times simplified and aided by the removal of free iron oxides. The removal of organic matter, soluble salts, and calcium carbonate has also proven advantageous for most mineralogical studies.

44–2 REMOVAL OF SOLUBLE SALTS AND CARBONATES

44–2.1 Introduction

Soil samples containing soluble salts, including gypsum, may be difficult or impossible to disperse and fractionate as a result of the flocculating action of the salts. If the nature of the salts is such that the soil suspension is alkaline, hydrogen peroxide will decompose readily, and removal of organic matter will be difficult or impossible. The presence of soluble salts also makes it impossible to saturate the exchange complex with a specific cation for the purpose of determining cation-exchange capacity. Removal of these soluble constituents will simplify X-ray diffraction and differential thermal analyses as well as other mineralogical analyses. Since these soluble constituents may be readily identified and measured quantitatively (section 62–3), removal does not constitute destroying a portion of the sample which cannot be accounted for.

The carbonates commonly encountered in soils in quantities sufficient to cause difficulties are those of calcium and magnesium. As in the case of soluble salts, the carbonates may be accounted for quantitatively (section 91); thus their removal does not detract from characterization of the sample. If positive identification of the carbonates is desired through X-ray diffraction or other mineralogical techniques, this may be accomplished with a sample prepared specifically for this purpose.

The more crystalline, concretionary forms of the carbonates are less troublesome than the poorly crystalline, finely divided forms. It is not uncommon to find horizons, particularly the Cca horizon, containing 50% or more of finely divided carbonates. Unless these are removed, it is impossible to achieve any meaningful separation of silt and clay by centrifugation (section 49–3.3), due to continual breakdown of the carbonate particles. Furthermore, the presence of carbonates, in many cases, causes a great deal of scatter and, in general, a poor X-ray diffraction pattern. In the case of X-ray diffraction samples, the degree of orientation of clay particles is reduced in the presence of significant quantities of finely divided carbonates, resulting in a less definitive diffraction pattern. The presence of carbonates also needlessly increases the complexity of differential thermal analysis patterns. Cation-exchange capacity and surface area measurements for genetic studies can be made more meaningful through removal of carbonates and soluble salts. Finally the efficiency of hydrogen peroxide is extremely low in an alkaline medium, which requires that carbonates be removed if organic matter is to be oxidized by this reagent.

Soluble salts are most simply removed by dissolution in water. Carbonates may be removed by treatment with acid sodium acetate, acid, or disodium dihydrogen ethylenediaminetetraacetate. Soluble salts may be removed as part of the same treatment.

44–2.2 Methods

44–2.2.1 TEST FOR GYPSUM AND SOLUBLE SALTS [1]

44–2.2.1.1 Reagent

1. Acetone, reagent grade.

---

[1] The method is, in part, that described by U. S. Salinity Laboratory Staff (1954) with modifications based upon the experience of the author.

44–2.2.1.2 Procedure. To test initially for the presence of gypsum, place 10 to 20 g. of air-dried soil into an 8-ounce bottle, 250-ml. centrifuge tube or 250-ml. Erlenmeyer flask, and then add 100 to 150 ml. of distilled water. Stopper the container, and shake it by hand 6 times at 15-minute intervals, or agitate it for 15 minutes in a mechanical shaker. Filter the extract through a paper of medium porosity. Place about 5 ml. of the extract in a test tube, add an approximately equal volume of acetone, and mix the solutions. The formation of a white (gel-like) precipitate indicates the presence of gypsum in the soil.

In the absence of gypsum, check another portion of the supernatant liquid for soluble salts with a conductivity bridge (section 62–2) to determine the need for pretreatment.

44–2.2.1.3 Comments. Because of the variations in the properties of the soluble salts found in soils, it is not feasible to suggest a lower limit below which removal is not necessary. For example, a soil concentration of 500 to 1,000 ppm. of NaCl would have little if any effect on dispersion or oxidation of organic matter with hydrogen peroxide, but the same would not be true for a similar concentration of $CaCl_2$. To convert conductivity values to quantities of salt, reference should be made to Figures 2 to 4 in *Agricultural Handbook 60* (U. S. Salinity Laboratory Staff, 1954). In the absence of knowledge of the behavior of the samples under investigation, it is good routine practice to treat all samples to remove excess soluble salts as described in the next section.

44–2.2.2 DISSOLUTION OF SOLUBLE SALTS [2]

44–2.2.2.1 Reagent
1. Magnesium chloride ($MgCl_2 \cdot 6H_2O$), $1N$, 102 g. per liter.

44–2.2.2.2 Procedure. Place the required amount of sample, ground to pass a 2-mm. sieve, into a beaker of sufficient size to allow for the addition of water at the rate of 100 ml. of distilled water to 1 g. of soil. Cover the beaker with a watchglass, and stir the suspension at intervals of 15 to 20 minutes over a period of 2 hours. Allow the suspended material to settle. If clay remains suspended after 2 or more hours, add a minimum of $1N$ $MgCl_2$ to flocculate the clay. Decant or siphon off the supernatant liquid, being careful not to lose any soil material.

Repeat the above procedure as many times as necessary to dissolve the gypsum and/or other soluble salts. Check for dissolution and removal of gypsum by treating an aliquot of the supernatant solution according to the procedure described in section 44–2.2.1.2.

Following dissolution of the gypsum and the subsequent final decantation, transfer the sample with the aid of a powder funnel and wash bottle to a

---

[2] The method is essentially that described by Kunze and Rich (1959).

centrifuge tube of appropriate size for washing to remove the soluble salts. Balance pairs of tubes with distilled water, centrifuge the tubes at 1,600 to 2,200 rpm. for 5 to 10 minutes, and decant the supernatant liquid. Fill the tube half full with distilled water, stopper it tightly, jar the soil loose from the walls by striking the bottom of the tube on a large rubber stopper, and then shake the tube for 5 minutes in a reciprocating shaker. Wash adhering soil particles from the stopper and walls of the tube with a fine jet of distilled water, balance pairs of tubes, centrifuge the tubes for 10 to 15 minutes at 1,600 to 2,200 rpm. and decant the supernatant liquid. Continue to wash the sample in this manner until clay remains suspended after centrifuging for 10 to 15 minutes at 1,600 to 2,200 rpm. Mix several drops of $1N$ $MgCl_2$ *with the supernatant* liquid to flocculate the suspended clay without disturbing the sedimented material. Repeat the centrifuging, and decant the supernatant liquid. Without drying, transfer the sample with a minimum of distilled water to a beaker of appropriate size for removal of organic matter.

44–2.2.3 DISSOLUTION OF CARBONATES AND SOLUBLE SALTS WITH SODIUM ACETATE BUFFER [3]

44–2.2.3.1 Reagent.
1. Sodium acetate ($NaC_2H_3O_2 \cdot 3H_2O$), $1N$, 136 g. per liter, adjusted to pH 5 with acetic acid.

44–2.2.3.2 Procedure. Place a suitable amount of sample, ground to pass a 2-mm. sieve, into a dialysis membrane (cellulose casing available from Visking Company, Division of Union Carbide Corp., 6733 West 65th Street, Chicago 38, Ill.), one end of which is tied with a rubber band. Add several hundred milliliters (depending upon size of sample and size of casing used) of Na-acetate buffer solution. Tie the top of the dialysis membrane around a glass "breather" tube (approximately 4 inches long), and hang the sample in a reservoir of the Na-acetate buffer solution contained in a plastic or glass container. (A 20-gallon plastic garbage can containing 60 liters of buffer solution serves well for samples of a kilogram or larger.)

Knead the membrane after several days. If carbonates are still being dissolved, bubbles of CO_2 will be released. (The time required for dissolution of carbonates is dependent upon particle size, percentage, and type of carbonate, and sample size.) When bubbles of CO_2 are no longer evident on kneading, open the dialysis membrane, and check some of the coarser particles with strong acid for the presence of carbonates. When the sample is free of carbonates, transfer it (still in the dialysis membrane) to another container; and desalt it against tap water flowing continuously through the container. Check the ionic concentration inside the membrane by conduc-

---

[3] The method is essentially that described by Grossman and Millet (1961).

tivity measurements on a small volume of the supernatant liquid poured out through the breather tube. Continue dialysis until the salt concentration drops below 10 me. per liter. Remove excess water in the membrane with a filter candle.

As an alternative procedure for removing excess salt, and if the sample size permits, transfer the sample to one or more centrifuge tubes, and wash the sample as outlined in section 44–2.2.2.2.

Following removal of excess salts, transfer the sample without drying and with a minimum of distilled water to a beaker for removal of organic matter.

44–2.2.3.3 Comments. Grossman and Millet (1961) reported that holding noncalcareous samples in contact with the buffer for 9 weeks did not affect the particle-size distribution, cation-exchange capacity, organic carbon, nitrogen, and free iron values.

The rate of carbonate removal is strongly affected by the concentration of alkaline earth ions in the buffer solution. By changing the buffer in the reservoir well before the buffer capacity has been exhausted, and thereby keeping the alkaline-earth ion concentration low, the rate of carbonate removal can be markedly increased.

Jackson (1956) described basically the same method for removal of carbonates, except that it is carried out in beakers, and the samples are heated in a boiling water bath to expedite dissolution.

44–3 REMOVAL OF ORGANIC MATTER

44–3.1 Introduction

Organic matter has an aggregating effect; hence removal is necessary if the analysis requires dispersion of the sample. Removal of organic matter is required for, or at least expedites, most mineralogical analyses, such as differential thermal, X-ray diffraction, infrared, et cetera.

Hydrogen peroxide, first used by Robinson (1922), is now generally used to oxidize organic matter. Efficient use of H_2O_2 requires an acid medium, which means that the soil needs prior treatment for removal of carbonates and soluble salts imparting an alkaline reaction to the soil suspension. To overcome the effects of the manganese oxides, Olmstead et al. (1930) proposed the addition of a small amount of glacial acetic acid, while Jackson (1956) suggested that the reaction be carried out in the presence of a sodium acetate solution adjusted to pH 5.

Atterberg (1912) and Troell (1931) proposed the use of sodium hypo-bromite to oxidize organic matter. With this reagent, it is not necessary to remove carbonates.

44–3.2 Method [4]

44–3.2.1 REAGENTS

1. Hydrogen peroxide (H_2O_2), 30%.
2. Magnesium chloride ($MgCl_2 \cdot 6H_2O$), $1N$, 102 g. per liter.

44–3.2.2 PROCEDURE

If the sample was treated previously to remove soluble salts and/or carbonates, transfer it to a beaker with a minimum of distilled water. The beaker should be of sufficient size to eliminate loss of sample resulting from moderate to strong frothing. Cover the beaker with a ribbed watchglass, place it on a steam bath or hot plate, and allow excess water to evaporate until a soil-to-water ratio of 1:1 to 1:2 is obtained. Remove the beaker, and allow it to cool.

If the sample required no other treatment prior to removal of organic matter, grind it to pass a 2-mm. sieve, and place the required amount into a beaker. The beaker should be of sufficient size to eliminate loss of sample resulting from moderate to strong frothing. Add distilled water to the sample to give a 1:1 to 1:2 soil-to-water ratio, and cover the beaker with a ribbed watchglass.

If necessary, make the suspension acid to litmus paper with a few drops of $1N$ HCl. Initially add 30% H_2O_2 in increments of 5 to 10 ml. or less, stir the suspension, and allow time for any strong effervescence or frothing to subside. Control reactions that are too vigorous by cooling the beaker in a water bath. Continue adding H_2O_2 in small amounts until the sample ceases to froth; then transfer it to a steam bath or hot plate at low heat (65° to 70°C.), and observe it closely for 10 to 20 minutes or until danger of any further strong reaction has passed. Add additional H_2O_2 in amounts to give approximately a 10% solution. Evaporate excess liquid between additions of H_2O_2 to maintain a soil-to-water ratio of 1:1 to 1:2. Do not allow the sample to evaporate to dryness.

The reaction of soil with H_2O_2 is essentially complete when the soil sample loses its dark color or when conspicuous effervescence ceases. Some effervescence will always be present due to the decomposition of the H_2O_2. The majority of soils will show some color as a result of highly colored mineral particles and free iron oxides.

Transfer the sample with the aid of a powder funnel and wash bottle to a centrifuge tube of appropriate size, balance pairs of tubes, centrifuge the tubes at 1,600 to 2,200 rpm. for 10 to 15 minutes, and decant and discard the supernatant liquid. If clay remains suspended, add a few drops of $1N$ $MgCl_2$, mix the suspension without disturbing the sedimented material, centrifuge the tubes, and decant the supernatant liquid. Further wash-

---

[4] The method is a modification of that described by Kunze and Rich (1959).

ing is not necessary. If, however, a clear supernatant liquid is obtained without the addition of any flocculating agent, fill the tube approximately one-third or less with distilled water, stopper it tightly, jar the soil loose from the walls of the tube by striking the bottom of the tube on a large rubber stopper, and then shake the tube for 5 minutes in a reciprocating shaker. Wash adhering particles from the stopper and walls of the tube with a fine jet of distilled water. Balance pairs of tubes, centrifuge them for 10 to 15 minutes at 1,600 to 2,200 rpm., and decant the supernatant liquid. Flocculate suspended clay by the addition of a few drops of $1N$ $MgCl_2$ as outlined above. The sample is now ready for removal of free iron oxides, dispersion, et cetera.

44–3.2.3 COMMENTS

Hydrogen peroxide is a strong oxidizing agent, and contact with the skin should be avoided. If contact is made, affected parts should be washed with copious quantities of water.

Elevated temperatures result in decomposition of the H_2O_2, which is the reason for not heating the sample in excess of 70°C.

Normally the deeper samples in the profile contain very little organic matter; however, it is here that the manganese oxides, if present, occur in greatest abundance. Therefore, any vigorous reaction of H_2O_2 with samples from the lower portion of the profile is very likely due to something other than organic matter.

If H_2O_2 is present in the sample at the time of the washing and centrifuging operation, it will be difficult to obtain a clear supernatant liquid to decant because of a slow, continuous release of oxygen resulting from decomposition of the H_2O_2. To dispose of an excess of H_2O_2, make the suspension basic with NH_4OH, and place it in a warm water bath.

44–4　REMOVAL OF FREE IRON OXIDES

44–4.1　Introduction

Free iron oxides, occurring as discrete particles or as coatings, are frequently removed from soil or its fractions to expedite mineralogical studies. Observation of the optical properties with a petrographic microscope is greatly facilitated if the particles are clean or free of coatings. Iron-containing samples, such as Latosols, are generally very difficult to disperse unless the free iron oxides are removed. Particles coated with iron oxides will not allow for a satisfactory heavy mineral separation. Iron oxides fluoresce when a copper target is used for X-ray diffraction analyses, resulting in an increased background count, and a general decrease in the quality or clarity of the diffraction pattern. This, however, does not mean that each sample requires treatment for iron oxide removal to obtain a satisfactory pattern. It has been the writer's experience in working with soil profile samples that less than 10% required removal of free iron oxides for the purpose of obtaining satisfactory X-ray diffraction patterns. Removal of iron oxides would, of course, allow for a greater degree of parallel orientation of the clay particles and would release iron-clogged exchange sites. Electron microscope observations and differential thermal analysis could possibly be improved. Hence, individual judgment needs to be exercised concerning the necessity or desirability for removing free iron oxides.

The most successful methods for removing free iron oxides, though none remove magnetite and ilmenite (Jackson, 1956), involve the chemical reduction of the iron to the ferrous form (Deb, 1950; Jeffries, 1947). Other methods have utilized biological reduction (Allison and Scarseth, 1942), or solution of the iron with oxalic acid (Robinson and Holmes, 1924; Schofield, 1949) or one of its salts (Drosdoff, 1935; Tamm, 1922). The earlier methods required subjecting the sample to highly acid conditions in the presence of high concentrations of cations such as potassium, ammonium, or aluminum which are fixed rather strongly by certain of the clay minerals. The sodium dithionite-citrate procedure (Mehra and Jackson, 1960) which follows, overcomes these objectionable features and removes free iron oxides with a minimum of destructive action to the clay minerals. Even so, silica and alumina are common components of the extract and are thought to be contributed primarily by the amorphous and poorly crystalline fractions.

Sodium citrate serves as the chelating agent for ferrous and ferric forms of iron. The sodium bicarbonate buffers the solution, while the sodium dithionite (also known as sodium hydrosulfite and sodium hyposulfite) reduces the iron.

44–4.2 Method [5]

44–4.2.1 REAGENTS

1. Na-citrate dihydrate, $0.3M$, 88 g. per liter.
2. Sodium bicarbonate ($NaHCO_3$), $1N$, 84 g. per liter.
3. Sodium dithionite ($Na_2S_2O_4$).
4. Sodium chloride ($NaCl$) solution, saturated.
5. Acetone, reagent grade.

44–4.2.2 PROCEDURE

Transfer to a 100-ml. centrifuge tube a suitable amount of sample (4 g. of many soils or 1 g. of clay) that has been treated to remove organic

---

[5] The method is essentially that described by Mehra and Jackson (1960) with minor modifications of the writer.

matter, soluble salts, and preferably carbonates. The sample should contain no more than 0.5 g. of extractable Fe_2O_3. Add 40 ml. of $0.3M$ Na-citrate solution and 5 ml. of $1N$ $NaHCO_3$ solution to the sample. Warm the suspension to 80°C. in a water bath, and then add 1 g. of solid $Na_2S_2O_4$ (½ g. suffices for clays low in free iron oxides); stir the suspension constantly for 1 minute and occasionally for a total of 15 minutes. Avoid heating above 80°C. because FeS forms. Following the 15-minute digestion period, add 10 ml. of a saturated NaCl solution. If the suspension fails to flocculate with the NaCl, add 10 ml. of acetone. Mix the suspension, warm it in a water bath if needed to expedite flocculation, and centrifuge the tube for 10 to 15 minutes at 1,600 to 2,200 rpm. If Si, Fe, and Al determinations are to be made (sections 64, 65, and 67), decant the clear supernatant liquid into a 500- or 1,000-ml. volumetric flask; otherwise discard it.

Repeat the above treatment once or twice for samples which originally contained more than 5% extractable Fe_2O_3 (the sample may be combined into fewer tubes for the second treatment). Combine extracting and washing solutions with those of the first treatment if Fe, Al, and Si are to be determined. Wash (two or more times for samples of more than 1 g. of residue) the sample finally with the Na-citrate solution (with NaCl and acetone if necessary for flocculation), and combine the washings with the previous decantates. Avoid HCl and $CaCl_2$ solutions as flocculants. (Caution: exercise care to prevent solutions containing acetone from boiling.) The sample, freed of extractable Fe_2O_3 but not dried at any time during the procedure, is now ready for further processing as prescribed by the procedure for the specific analysis to be made.

44–4.2.3 COMMENTS

Because many minerals are rather strongly colored, and because it is impossible to remove the last trace of organic matter with H_2O_2, samples freed of extractable Fe_2O_3 generally do not have a pure white color.

44–5 PARTICLE-SIZE SEPARATIONS

Mineralogical analyses are normally performed on specific size fractions of the soil such as 2 to 0.2μ (coarse clay). For mineralogical work, the particle-size separations are usually made after application of pretreatments such as those described in section 44. A method for separating sand, silt, and clay by a combination of sieving and sedimentation under gravity is given in section 43–3. A method for separating different fractions of the sand by sieving is given in section 43–4. The use of a centrifuge to separate different particle-size fractions of clay is described in section 49–3.3.

44–6 LITERATURE CITED

Allison, L. E., and Scarseth, G. D. 1942. A biological reduction method for removing free iron oxides from soils and colloidal clay. J. Am. Soc. Agron. 34:616–623.

Atterberg, A. 1912. Die mechanische Bodenanalyse und die Klassifikation der Mineralböden Schwedens. Int. Mitt. Bodenk. 2:312–342.

Deb, B. C. 1950. The estimation of free iron oxides in soils and clays and their removal. J. Soil Sci. 1:212–220.

Drosdoff, M. 1935. The separation and identification of the clay mineral constituents of colloidal clay. Soil Sci. 39:463–478.

Grossman, R. B., and Millet, J. C. 1961. Carbonate removal from soils by a modification of the acetate buffer method. Soil Sci. Soc. Am. Proc. 25:325–326.

Jackson, M. L. 1956. Soil Chemical Analysis—Advanced Course. Publ. by the author, Dept. of Soils, Univ. of Wis., Madison 6, Wis.

Jeffries, C. D. 1947. A rapid method for the removal of free iron oxides in soil prior to petrographic analysis. Soil Sci. Soc. Am. Proc. (1946) 11:211–212.

Kunze, G. W., and Rich, C. I. 1959. Mineralogical methods. In C. I. Rich, L. F. Seatz, and G. W. Kunze, ed. Certain properties of selected southeastern United States soils and mineralogical procedures for their study. Southern Coop. Series Bul. 61:135–146.

Mehra, O. P., and Jackson, M. L. 1960. Iron oxide removal from soils and clays by a dithionite-citrate system buffered with sodium bicarbonate. In Clays and Clay Minerals, Proc. 7th Conf., pp. 317–327. Natl. Acad. Sci.-Natl. Res. Council Publ.

Olmstead, L. B., Alexander, L. T., and Middleton, N. E. 1930. A pipette method of mechanical analysis of soils based on an improved dispersion procedure. U. S. Dept. Agriculture Tech. Bull. 170.

Robinson, G. W. 1922. Note on the mechanical analysis of humus soils. J. Agri. Sci. 12:287–291.

Robinson, W. O., and Holmes, R. S. 1924. The chemical composition of soil colloids. U. S. Dept. Agriculture Bull. 1311.

Schofield, R. K. 1949. Effect of pH on electric charges carried by clay particles. J. Soil Sci. 1:1–8.

Tamm, O. 1922. Eine Methode zur Bestimmung der anorganischen Komponenten des Gelkomplexes in Boden. Meddel. Statens Skogsförsöksanst (Sweden). 19:385–404.

Troell, E. 1931. The use of sodium hypobromite for the oxidation of organic matter in mechanical analyses of soils. J. Agr. Sci. 21:476–484.

U. S. Salinity Laboratory Staff. 1954. Diagnosis and improvement of saline and alkali soils. U. S. Dept. Agriculture Handbook 60.

45

Free Oxides, Hydroxides, and Amorphous Aluminosilicates[1]

M. L. JACKSON
University of Wisconsin
Madison, Wisconsin

45-1 GENERAL INTRODUCTION

Free oxides and hydroxides of soils include crystalline and amorphous compounds of silicon (quartz, etc.), aluminum (gibbsite, etc.), iron (hematite, goethite, etc.), titanium (anatase, etc.), and manganese (pyrolusite, etc.). Small amounts of various other elements are usually present in free oxides and hydroxides of soils. The amorphous and finely divided crystalline compounds are hydrous. The term "free" refers to compounds having mainly a single species of coordinating cation such as oxides of silicon or aluminum. Hydrous oxides containing two or more coordinating cation species are spoken of as "combined" oxides, the most abundant kinds in soils being aluminosilicates. The amorphous combined oxides as well as free hydrous oxides of soils take part in many important chemical reactions; for example, they exhibit cation-exchange capacity, phosphate retention, and reactions with lime.

Amorphous aluminosilicates of soils include noncrystalline gel-like compounds containing mainly aluminum, silicon, oxygen, and water, but usually containing more or less of iron, magnesium, hydroxyl, and occasionally phosphate and possibly other ions. Some of the amorphous aluminosilicate compounds have been designated allophane. The common presence in soils of various amorphous aluminosilicates that have properties distinct from

[1] This contribution from the Department of Soil Science, University of Wisconsin, was supported in part by grants of funds from the National Science Foundation and through the Research Committee of the Graduate School from the Wisconsin Alumni Research Foundation. Sincere thanks are extended to the many research assistants who have worked with the author with the study of selective-dissolution and cation-exchange methods for free oxides and amorphous aluminosilicates; particularly engaged with these studies have been: N. H. Aguilera, D. G. Aldrich, S. Aomine, O. L. Baykan, B. E. Brown, G. A. Borchardt, S. C. Chang, R. B. Corey, L. E. DeMumbrum, H. D. Dion, J. B. Dixon, E. J. Evans, D. S. Fanning, R. C. Glenn, A. B. Hanna, I. Hashimoto, P. H. Hsu, P. V. Kiely, J. A. Kittrick, O. P. Mehra, M. H. Milford, R. P. Pennington, F. Saatci, V. A. K. Sarma, B. L. Sawhney, W. R. Schmehl, L. D. Swindale, T. Tamura, R. C. Vanden Heuvel, K. Wada, J. L. White, and L. D. Whittig.

those of allophane is also coming to be recognized. One class of such compounds is thought to be highly disordered (three-dimensionally), subcrystalline, clay-like, and clay-relic materials, transitional to crystalline clay minerals being destroyed or synthesized by weathering. A highly precise analytical distinction of amorphous from crystalline materials of soils is at present impossible because of the transitional nature of the boundary between the two categories. The class of layer-silicate lattice disorder (a kind of amorphousness) along the Z-axis dimension involved in random interstratification or mixed layering is excluded from the present consideration and left to the X-ray diffraction analysis approach (section 49).

The crystalline free oxides of soils can be identified qualitatively and estimated semiquantitatively by X-ray diffraction analysis (section 49). Those containing hydroxyl can sometimes be determined fairly quantitatively by differential thermal analysis (section 50–3). Integral thermal analysis (section 50–4) can also be used. Coarser particles of the sand and silt can be counted by petrographic methods (section 46).

The diagnostic properties of the hydrous oxides, as measured by the above techniques, vary a great deal with variation in particle size and degree of crystallinity of the oxides. For example, fine-grained goethite (limonite) has its differential endotherm in the range of 300° to 350°C., overlapping the endotherm of gibbsite (Jackson, 1956, p. 267), instead of 400°C. which is typical of highly crystalline goethite. Thus the selective dissolution of free iron oxides from a ferruginous gibbsite sample provides for more accurate differential thermal analysis for gibbsite. The above example illustrates one general objective of selective dissolution methods, namely, to free the remaining mineral materials of certain amorphous or free oxide material. Sensitive chemical methods are needed for independent determinations of various inorganic constituents of soils also because difficulty is experienced with many physical analytical methods in estimating or even recognizing amorphous free oxides and amorphous aluminosilicates mixed with crystalline components of soils. Such determinations can be carried out for some constituents by the selective or differential dissolution methods and cation-exchange capacity methods to be detailed in this section.

Free MnO_2 (pyrolusite, etc.) is selectively dissolved in acid H_2O_2 (Jackson, 1956, p. 31) during the usual preparations of soil for mineralogical analysis (section 44–3.2). Free Fe_2O_3 (hematite), $FeOOH$ (goethite), and amorphous iron oxides are selectively dissolved by the dithionite-citrate-bicarbonate method (given in connection with the allophane determination in section 45–4.3). The elegant elemental analysis methods available for iron and manganese selectively dissolved make possible specific and precise determination of the total of these free oxides based on analysis of the elements in the extracts. The physical methods for mineralogical analysis are the most useful in identifying the crystalline mineral species of these oxides. Free oxides, for which no specific selective dissolution methods are available, include $ZrSiO_4$ (zircon), $FeO \cdot TiO_2$ (ilmenite), Fe_3O_4 (magnetite), $AlOOH$ (boehmite, diaspore), Al_2O_3 (corundum), and most of the trace element oxides. If the presence of these minerals is determined by X-ray diffraction or other methods, the percentages of them are estimated from total elemental analysis of the residues after removal of substances for which selective dissolution methods are available such as TiO_2—anatase and rutile (section 45–5).

The selective dissolution methods to be presented include (*1*) the $Na_2S_2O_7$–HCl–NaOH method for quartz and feldspars, and (*2*) the flash-heating NaOH-dissolution method for allophane, gibbsite, and amorphous oxides of aluminum and silicon. The determination of allophane by the cat-ion-exchange capacity method is also given.

45–2   QUARTZ

45–2.1   Introduction

Crystalline SiO_2 occurs in soils mainly as the mineral quartz. Opal ($SiO_2 \cdot nH_2O$) is common in some soils. Crystalline cristobalite (also SiO_2) may make up appreciable percentages of some soils and, together with quartz, can dominate (95%) even the clay fraction in strongly podzolized soils (Swindale and Jackson, 1956, 1960). Coesite and stishovite are high-pressure polymorphs of SiO_2 found around meteor craters (Sclar et al., 1962). The resistance of coarser particles of quartz and opal to chemical weathering results in their common occurrence in soils. The resistance of quartz sand and silt makes possible the use of quartz in these soil fractions as a reference index to the weathering of other minerals (Barshad, 1955). Quantitative determination of quartz in soils is therefore frequently wanted.

Quartz, cristobalite, and other crystalline forms of SiO_2 can be estimated by the internal-standard X-ray diffractometric method, and quartz also can be estimated by infrared absorption (Tuddenham and Lyon, 1960) or from its alpha-beta inversion differential endotherm at 573°C. (Grim, 1953; Sysoeva, 1958). Quartz in sand and silt sizes can be determined by count in a petrographic microscope (section 46–2). A high degree of variability is experienced in the diffraction intensity of standard quartz (Pollack et al., 1954; Nagelschmidt, 1956; Brindley, 1961); the reasons probably arise (*1*) from the great variations in the degree of crystallinity of quartz specimens, and (*2*) from the effect of the amorphous surface layer which forms on quartz particles. For simplicity, determination of quartz and opal by chemical methods based on their relative resistance to dissolution in acid reagents which decompose aluminosilicates is increasing in favor in many laboratories. Alternatively, free silica has been selectively dissolved away from aluminosilicates by fusion of the sample in equal parts of $KHCO_3$

and KCl, or $NaHCO_3$ and NaCl (Polezhaev, 1958), the Si from free SiO_2 subsequently being determined colorimetrically. Work on selective dissolution in laboratories concerned with ceramics, geochemistry, silicosis, and soils extends back many decades. The persistent interest in and improvements of chemical determination of quartz has resulted in the development of methods with a fairly high degree of accuracy.

45–2.2 Principles

Quartz determination as a residue from acid decomposition of aluminosilicates is based on its relatively slow solubility in acid. The metallic cations are liberated from many aluminosilicates by digestion in mineral acids. The amorphous silica released by the action of hot acids on aluminosilicates forms a gelatinous precipitate which in the past was often separated from the quartz by its passage through a filter paper as a sol and solution. A better procedure of separating the released silica is its rapid dissolution in $0.5N$ NaOH solution during 2 or 3 minutes of boiling. Quartz is only slowly soluble in this reagent.

The quartz is determined in the residue after acid treatment and washing or alkali treatment, on the basis of (1) the weight of SiO_2 lost from the residue on volatilization by HF, or (2) the difference between the original total SiO_2 and the SiO_2 dissolved in NaOH. From this determined amount of SiO_2, an amount must be deducted corresponding to any nonquartz silicate remaining with the quartz residue prior to HF treatment. Feldspars constitute the most frequently occurring nonquartz mineral remaining in significant amounts in the residue. Cristobalite, the occasional presence of which is determined by X-ray diffraction (section 49), and opal behave in a manner similar to quartz though having higher and more variable solubility correction factors. The term quartz will be used below to include quartz, cristobalite, and opal.

Hot aqueous acids that have been used for decomposition of the nonquartz minerals include a tri-acid mixture which is 2:4:1 by volume of concentrated hydrochloric, sulfuric, and nitric acids (Hardy and Follett-Smith, 1931); phosphoric acid (Talvitie, 1951; Jophcott and Wall, 1955); perchloric acid (Medicus, 1955; Jackson, 1956); $9N$ H_2SO_4 (Shaw, 1934; Nagelschmidt, 1956); concentrated HCl followed by boiling in a solution of Na_2S and digestion in $6N$ HCl–HNO_3 (Shchekaturina and Petrashen, 1958). The tri-acid mixture of HCl–HNO_3–H_2SO_4 (above) has greater effectiveness than $HClO_4$ in decomposing some layer silicates, particularly unheated kaolinite;[2] anorthoclase resists[3] decomposition during digestions in

---

[2] Corey, R. B. 1952. Allocation of elemental constituents to mineral species in poly-component colloids of soils. Ph.D. thesis, University of Wisconsin library, Madison.

[3] Hashimoto, I. 1961. Differential dissolution analysis of clays and its application to Hawaiian soils. Ph.D. thesis, University of Wisconsin library, Madison.

either acid. The use of a hot $HClO_4$ digestion in later stages of an acid digestion procedure has the advantage that the acid-released silica is quantitatively dehydrated; the metallic cations then can be washed out with HCl; finally, the silicon from the aluminosilicate can be dissolved in dilute NaOH for determination by the molybdosilicate colorimetric method. Phosphoric acid interferes with molybdosilicate colorimetry. Talvitie (1951) found that the minerals albite, pyrophylite, sillimanite, kyanite, tourmaline, beryl, and topaz resisted decomposition in H_3PO_4. Appreciable dissolution of quartz in H_3PO_4 was reported (Jophcott and Wall, 1955). Digestion of silicate dusts in pyrophosphoric acid ($H_4P_2O_7$; mp., 61°C.; digestion temperature, 250°C.) decomposed most aluminosilicates (Dobrovol'skaya, 1958) leaving beryl, topaz, tourmaline, and zircon along with quartz little attacked. Previous ignition of some dust samples was required to obtain the desired aluminosilicate decomposition by $H_4P_2O_7$ digestion (Bulycheva and Mel'-nikova, 1958), and even then subsequent treatment with concentrated HCl was required to decompose some rock powders.

Dehydroxylation of kaolinite and dioctahedral micas by heating has been found necessary to ensure their complete decomposition and dissolution in the several acid-NaOH dissolution routines that preserve the quartz. An efficacious way to effect this dehydroxylation of layer silicates, while at the same time providing a rigorous acid treatment to which quartz is resistant, is fusion of the sample in $Na_2S_2O_7$ or $K_2S_2O_7$. The fusion begins at about 300°C., and the dehydroxylation is promoted by the presence of a hot acid flux consisting of free SO_3 (sulfuric acid anhydride) liberated as the temperature is elevated to full red heat. Gibbsite and various oxides, which tend to be rendered acid- and alkali-insoluble by dry heating (pre-ignition has frequently been recommended), are dissolved in the fusion. The pyrosulfate fusion method of dehydroxylation is not only more effective but also is several steps simpler than the various aqueous and low-temperature acid procedures (Shaw, 1934; Nagelschmidt, 1956), which call for extraction of the sample by aqueous acid, drying the residue, heating the residue for dehydroxylation, and re-extraction with acid.

Fusion of mineral samples in $Na_2S_2O_7$ or $K_2S_2O_7$ has been employed for the analytical decomposition of certain minerals for over 100 years (Smith, 1865; Hillebrand and Lundell, 1929, p. 705), and fusion in $K_2S_2O_7$ has long been employed in the field of ceramics according to Trostel and Wynne (1940). Fusion in $NaHSO_4$ (which forms $Na_2S_2O_7$) has been employed for quartz and opal determination in rocks (Astaf'ev, 1958); pretreatments consisting of digestion in concentrated HCl, washing, drying, and ignition, were given before the fusion. Trostel and Wynne (1940) employed $K_2S_2O_7$ fusion for refractory clays, materials which are high in alumina and kaolinite (and which these authors considered usually to be free of feldspars), to determine the quartz in the insoluble residue. The $K_2S_2O_7$ fusion cake was slaked in hot water, and the resulting suspension was made alkaline by the addition of NaOH pellets. After digestion for ½ hour at 90°C. in this approximately 2N NaOH, the suspension was filtered through paper. The residue on the paper was washed successively with H_2O, 6N HCl, and H_2O, and then dried and recovered by ignition of the paper. Incomplete removal of iron oxides by this procedure was experienced by Florentin and Heros (1947) when applying the procedure to quartz determination in rocks rich in iron, and these authors consequently employed two successive pyrosulfate fusions and digestions of the residue in concentrated HCl.

These difficulties were also experienced for soils in the author's laboratory; also, the filtration of an alkaline suspension on paper was found to be unsatisfactory for fine-grained rocks and soils. Moreover, the presence of feldspars must be considered in the quartz determination in soils. Potassium and sodium feldspars are relatively resistant to both $Na_2S_2O_7$ and $K_2S_2O_7$ fusion and to HCl and NaOH washings. The K of the $K_2S_2O_7$ was found to penetrate the $NaAlSi_3O_8$ (albite) lattice to an appreciable extent, exchanging for Na during the fusion. This exchange reaction tended to vitiate the separation of K of mica or illite from that of K feldspars by means of the $K_2S_2O_7$–HCl–NaOH procedure, which is one important objective of the method. The J. Lawrence Smith (1865) $Na_2S_2O_7$ fusion procedure was tested and found to involve much less exchange of Na for K than the reverse exchange of K for Na in the $K_2S_2O_7$ fusion. Fusion in $Na_2S_2O_7$ instead of $K_2S_2O_7$ was adopted. The subsequent HCl and NaOH treatments also were completely redesigned as follows: (1) the fusion cake is taken up in 3N HCl (instead of NaOH) so as to keep in solution the Fe, Mg, and other metallic cations liberated by the fusion; (2) the residue is washed with 3N HCl to free the residue of Fe and Mg which would precipitate in the subsequently used NaOH solution; (3) centrifugation is used instead of filtration on paper; and (4) the residue is digested in 0.5N NaOH for 2.5 minutes (Hashimoto and Jackson, 1960), which is ample for dissolution of amorphous silica in the absence of precipitated Fe and Mg (Fe and Mg, if present, inhibit the dissolution of amorphous silica and alumina). This NaOH treatment is less destructive to fine-grained quartz and feldspars than longer digestion in stronger solutions employed previously.

45-2.3 Method [4]

45-2.3.1 REAGENTS

1. Sodium pyrosulfate: Use reagent-grade $Na_2S_2O_7$, or gently heat $NaHSO_4$

---

[4] The procedure adopted is essentially that described by P. V. Kiely and M. L. Jackson, Research Report No. 7, Department of Soils, University of Wisconsin, March 15, 1962, and employed at the National Science Foundation Advanced Science Seminar on Soil Clay Mineralogy at Virginia Polytechnic Institute, Blacksburg, Virginia, July 2-27, 1962 (Kiely and Jackson, 1964, 1965; Jackson, 1964).

until the melt is quiet and SO_3 begins to be evolved; then cool the melt, giving $Na_2S_2O_7$; crush the solid to a powder before use.

2. Hydrochloric acid (HCl): Dilute concentrated HCl (approximately 12N) with water to give stocks of approximately 6N, 3N, and 0.05N HCl.

3. Sodium hydroxide (NaOH): Dissolve 2 g. of reagent-grade NaOH pellets in 100 ml. of water to give approximately 0.5N NaOH.

4. Perchloric acid ($HClO_4$): Use reagent-grade 60% $HClO_4$.

5. Sulfuric acid (H_2SO_4): Cautiously add 50 ml. of reagent-grade concentrated H_2SO_4, a few drops at a time with constant stirring, to 50 ml. of water to give approximately 18N H_2SO_4.

6. Hydrofluoric acid (HF): Use reagent-grade 48% HF.

45–2.3.2 PROCEDURE

The sample should be a powder, not coarse aggregates. To prepare a clay sample, wash it successively with 0.05N HCl, acetone, and benzene, by centrifugation. Dry the clay in a centrifuge tube, and then powder the clay with a spatula and a rubber-tipped rod. Silt or fine sand fractions may be used directly. Grind rock, gravel, or coarse sand in an agate mortar, so that the powder passes a 60-mesh (per inch) sieve.

Weigh 0.2 g. of powdered clay, silt, or sand fraction (dried at 105°C.), and transfer the sample into a 50-ml. vitreous silica crucible. Add 10 to 12 g. of $Na_2S_2O_7$ powder, and mix it with the sample by means of a glass rod. Working with the crucible in a fume hood, fuse the $Na_2S_2O_7$ with a Meker burner, using a low flame at first until vigorous bubbling ceases and thereafter using the full flame. With some samples it is advisable to cover the crucible to avoid loss by spattering. Much SO_3 will be evolved. The fusion is complete when some Na_2SO_4 crystals float on the surface of the $Na_2S_2O_7$ melt while in the full heat. It should *not* go to complete crystallization of the melt. Grasp the crucible with tongs, and rotate the crucible so as to spread the melt on the crucible sides as the melt solidifies, and then allow the crucible to cool.

Add a little 3N HCl to the crucible, and carefully transfer the cake to a 150-ml. beaker with the aid of a rubber-tipped rod. Slake the fusion cake in about 50 ml. of 3N HCl, and heat the suspension just to boiling. When the fusion cake has disintegrated, transfer the resulting suspension to a 70-ml. pointed centrifuge tube. Centrifuge the tube at 1,800 rpm. for 4 minutes or longer if necessary to make the supernatant liquid clear. Decant the supernatant solution, and discard it. Wash the crucible to complete the transfer of the residue (consisting of quartz, feldspars, and amorphous silica) again with 3N HCl, and break up the residue in the tube with a glass rod. Centrifuge the residue, and decant the solution as before. Give the residue a third washing with 3N HCl as before. Transfer the residue from the tube into a 500-ml. Ni or stainless steel beaker with the aid of a little 0.5N NaOH, and add 0.5N NaOH to a total volume of 100 ml. Bring the suspension rapidly to boiling over a Meker burner, and boil it for exactly 2.5 minutes to dissolve amorphous silica (and a little alumina). Cool the solution by placing the beaker in a water bath. Transfer the solution to centrifuge tubes, scrub and wash the beaker with 0.5N NaOH to ensure complete transfer of the residue from beaker to tube, and centrifuge down the residue (usually mostly quartz and feldspars). Discard the supernatant solution. Wash residue and tube thoroughly 4 times with 3N HCl to remove soluble Na and other soluble components. Transfer the residue in the tube into a tared platinum crucible (or Teflon beaker), dry it at 105°C., and weigh the crucible or beaker on an analytical balance.

To the weighed residue in the platinum crucible (or Teflon beaker), add two drops of 60% $HClO_4$, 1 drop of 18N H_2SO_4, and 10 ml. of 48% HF. In a fume hood, evaporate this solution to dryness on a sand bath at a temperature not greater than 225°C. The solution must not be boiled vigorously, or spattering and loss of sample will occur. When the HF is gone, cool the crucible or beaker, and add 5 ml. of HF. Evaporate the solution as before. Remove the crucible or beaker, cool it, and reweigh it on an analytical balance.

Next, add 1.7 ml. of 6N HCl. Scrub the crucible or beaker with a rubber-tipped rod to obtain contact of HCl with the residue, warming the solution slightly. Rinse the rod with 10 ml. of H_2O. Warm the HCl solution nearly to boiling for 5 minutes to complete the dissolution of the perchlorates and sulfates in the residue. Make the solution to a volume of 25 ml. in a volumetric flask. Determine the K and Na of this solution *immediately* (to minimize contamination from glass) with methods described in section 54–6. Determine Ca on an aliquot of the 25 ml. of solution (section 54–6), with provision for elimination of Al interference in flame photometry.

45–2.3.3 CALCULATION OF RESULTS

Calculate the K, Na, and Ca content found in the residue as oxide percentages of the original sample employed. Then the percentages of feldspars left in the residue are given by:

Microcline-orthoclase content = $\% K_2O \times X$ [1]

Albite content   = $\% Na_2O \times Y - Y' \times \%$ Microcline [2]

Anorthite content   = $\% CaO \times Z$ [3]

in which values for X, Y, Y' and Z for different size fractions are given in Table 45–1. The albite and anorthite contents obtained represent the equivalent end-members of the high Na plagioclase present since high anorthite feldspars are largely dissolved by the fusion.

Calculate the residue weight percentage of the original sample from the weighing before the HF treatment. This is "% residue." When only quartz and feldspar are present in the residue, as is substantially the case in soils from acid rocks and sedimentary rocks, the following relation holds:

$$\% \text{ quartz} = \frac{100}{D} \left[\% \text{ residue} - \frac{A \times \% \text{ K feldspar}}{100} \right.$$

$$\left. - \frac{B \times \% \text{ Na feldspar}}{100} - \frac{C \times \% \text{ Ca feldspar}}{100} \right] \quad [4]$$

in which values for A, B, C, and D for the different particle-size fractions are given in Table 45–2. Substitute D' for D if X-ray diffraction evidence establishes the presence of cristobalite and the absence of quartz.

45–2.3.4 COMMENTS

The chief positive error in the quartz determination arises from the presence of nonquartz silicates other than feldspars (for example, zircon, $ZrSiO_4$) which resist the $Na_2S_2O_7$–HCl–NaOH treatments. The quantities of such minerals present in most soils are inappreciable, but the possibility

Table 45–1. Factors* for converting the quantities of K_2O, Na_2O, and CaO in the residue of different particle-size fractions to the corresponding quantities of end-member potassium, sodium, and calcium feldspar.

Particle size, microns	Residue K_2O to microcline X	Residue Na_2O to albite Y	Y'	Residue CaO to anorthite Z
500–50	6.1	8.9	0.0	5.2
50–20	6.5	9.1	0.02	5.2
20–5	7.0	9.5	0.04	5.5
5–2	8.4	10.3	0.12	6.0
2–0.2	13.2	13.7	0.20	8.1

* These factors differ from the theoretical (X = 5.9, Y = 8.5, Z = 4.95) for 16.9% K_2O in microcline-orthoclase, 11.8% Na_2O in albite, and 20.2% CaO in anorthite, respectively, because of dissolution of feldspars, surface loss of K, Na, and Ca and exchange of Na for K and Ca during the Na pyrosulfate fusion; Y' is used in equation [2] to correct for the Na uptake by microcline during the fusion.

Table 45–2. Factors to be applied in equation [4] to obtain the quartz content in different particle-size fractions.

Particle size, microns	Weight percentage recovery				
	Microcline A	Albite B	Anorthite C	Quartz D	Cristobalite* D'
500–50	96.5	95.2	95.2	99.6	98
50–20	96.0	94.5	94.5	99.4	97
20–5	93.6	92.7	92.7	99.1	93
5–2	84.4	86.2	86.2	98.2	77
2–0.2	64.0	68.3	68.3	96.5	53

* D' is based on one cristobalite sample (purity not determined) from Ward's Scientific Establishment.

of their being present must be considered for a given sample. Tremolite is fairly resistant to the treatment; its Ca content makes it appear mainly as "feldspar" by the Ca analysis after the HF treatment of the residue. Trostel and Wynne (1940) recommended examination of the residue with a microscope prior to the HF treatment. Examination by X-ray diffraction has been found to be highly useful in the author's laboratory; quartz and feldspar peaks are the only peaks present in most of the residues from soils. Shaw (1934) and Nagelschmidt (1956) used a $9N$ H_2SO_4 digestion, and took twice the residue weight after HF (assuming 50% SiO_2 was lost from the nonquartz minerals that were present in the residue) as an approximation of the resistant nonquartz minerals that had been present before HF treatment.

The chief negative errors for feldspars and quartz arise from variations of the determined minerals from the standards used in determining the factors given in Tables 45–1 and 45–2. Excessive losses in the fusion occur with altered feldspars. The losses may represent dissolution of alteration products such as sericite and carbonate but may reflect excessive porosity in the macrocrystal. The correction factors for quartz represent chiefly dissolved silica but include slight manipulative losses. Other forms of SiO_2 such as cristobalite (rare in soils except certain ones derived from some rhyolites) are less resistant and more variable from specimen to specimen. Quartz is the form of SiO_2 commonly found in soils and a wide variety of rocks, and the correction factors given for quartz should invariably be employed unless positive evidence of other crystalline forms of SiO_2 is obtained by X-ray diffraction. The overall error in the determination mainly reflects variations from those represented in the correction factors and those of the emission spectrophotometric determinations (section 54). The overall error of the quartz determination is generally of the order of 1 to 5% (increasing with decreasing particle size) of the sample when only quartz and feldspars are present in the residue.

45–3 AMORPHOUS ALUMINOSILICATES, SILICA, AND ALUMINA

45–3.1, Introduction

Amorphous mineral colloids occur extensively in soils (Jackson, 1956; Kanehiro and Whittig, 1961). The commonly used method of characterizing them is to determine their relative resistance to dissolution in various alkaline solutions. Alumina and silica, and amorphous (high specific surface) aluminosilicates, form soluble sodium silicates and sodium aluminates in NaOH solutions. Historically, both NaOH and Na_2CO_3 solutions have been employed for dissolving silica and alumina cements, for cleaning mineral grains, and for dispersing clays. A 2% Na_2CO_3 solution has a pH value of about 10.7, which is about the same as that of $0.0003N$ NaOH (Jackson, 1956, p. 72); it is buffered at this pH by hydrolysis. A 2% solution of Na_2CO_3, though dissolving only small amounts of silica, has a remarkably favorable dispersion effect on soils and clays (Jackson et al. 1950), when used after the removal of exchangeable Ca and Mg (Jackson, 1956). It has a moderate solvent effect for free amorphous silica when not too much alumina is to be dissolved (Hillebrand and Lundell, 1929). It is ineffective in simultaneously dissolving appreciable amounts of both free silica and alumina from soils (Hashimoto and Jackson, 1960) and the amorphous aluminosilicates of dehydroxylated kaolinite (Hislop, 1944). Alumina tends to precipitate when the amount of silica dissolved from soil increases.[5]

Sodium hydroxide solutions have long been used for selective dissolution of various constituents of soils. A boiling solution of $0.5N$ NaOH was used for the dissolution of amorphous silica from soils (Hardy and Follett-Smith, 1931). This solution was used for a 4-hour digestion at 100°C. to dissolve free silica and (or) alumina in montmorillonitic samples (Foster, 1953) and in soils (Dyal, 1953; Whittig et al., 1957). Treatment with $0.5N$ NaOH dissolved 2 to 15 times as much "free Al_2O_3" as "free SiO_2" from one $<0.3\mu$ soil fraction high in both aluminum phosphate and amorphous silicate (Dyal, 1953). Gibbsite was dissolved from soil samples high in goethite and halloysite by digestion of the samples in $1.25N$ NaOH on a steambath for 20 minutes (Muñoz Taboadela, 1953; Mackenzie and Robertson, 1961). Rapid dissolution of crystalline layer silicates such as kaolinite and montmorillonite in a dilute suspension in boiling $0.5N$ NaOH has been demonstrated (Hashimoto and Jackson, 1960). Extensive treatment of clays in $6N$ NaOH decomposed most of the layer silicate clay minerals except mica, which became enriched in the sample (Reynolds, 1960).

45–3.2 Principles

Use of a high ratio of $0.5N$ NaOH volume to sample weight (Hashimoto and Jackson, 1960), so as to avoid saturation of the solution with respect to silica and alumina, brings about an entirely different selective dissolution result with this reagent as compared to results with higher sample to solution ratios often employed. Boiling a soil or clay for only 2.5 minutes in a large excess of $0.5N$ NaOH causes dissolution of free amorphous silica, free alumina, and large percentages of amorphous combined aluminosilicates including allophane. A similar treatment with a small volume of NaOH solution may dissolve all of the free amorphous silica or free alumina but not both; amorphous aluminosilicates are dissolved only to a limited extent

---

[5] Whittig, L. D. 1950. Chemistry of dispersion of soils by boiling in sodium carbonate solution. M.S. Thesis, University of Wisconsin library, Madison.

in concentrated suspensions. Clay fractions of soils may contain from 30% (Tamura et al., 1953) to nearly 100% (Aomine and Yoshinaga, 1955; Aomine and Jackson, 1959) of amorphous materials, and therefore a large capacity factor in a selective dissolution analysis method is important.

Selective dissolution of hydrous silica and alumina and of amorphous aluminosilicates depends upon the fact that these materials have higher specific surface (giving a higher dissolution rate) than crystalline clays. Careful limitation of treatment time is essential because the crystalline clays are appreciably soluble during an hour or so of treatment of dilute suspensions in NaOH (Hashimoto and Jackson, 1960). Crystalline quartz is not extensively dissolved in the brief extraction time (150 seconds of boiling) given in the procedure, and thus can be determined otherwise (as given in section 45–2). Halloysitic allophane (SiO_2/Al_2O_3 molar ratio of 1.5 to 2.3) dissolves (but see section 45–1) although it gives little CEC delta value (section 45–4).

Heating the sample to 400°C. followed by extraction with 0.5N NaOH dissolves some interlayer alumina (Dixon and Jackson, 1959, 1962; Jackson, 1963a, 1963b), which frequently occurs in expanded layer silicates of soils. An increment of alumina, silica, and iron oxide often becomes soluble as a result of heating to 400°C., suggesting that an allophane-like interlayer precipitate may be characteristic of expanded layer silicates of some soils (Dixon and Jackson, 1962). The extraction of the additional amounts of Al_2O_3, SiO_2, and Fe_2O_3 after the 400°C. heating treatment (in excess of amounts extracted before the heating treatment) causes the expanded layer silicates of many soils to have different properties from those of clays not subjected to thermal plus NaOH treatment. The treated clays undergo more complete thermal collapse at 300°C., have an increase in the measurable interlayer specific surface, and have an increase in cation-exchange capacity. Scarcely recognizable 18Å. montmorillonite diffraction peaks of Tama soil clay, for example, became clearly resolved after 0.5N NaOH extraction of quickly soluble constituents from the clay (Glenn et al., 1960). Free alumina, including gibbsite, should be extracted from samples by 0.5N NaOH treatment prior to heating to 400°C., since dehydroxylated alumina is not quickly soluble in NaOH (Hashimoto and Jackson, 1960).

45–3.3 Method [6]

45–3.3.1 REAGENTS

1. Sodium hydroxide (NaOH), approximately 0.5N: Prepare a fresh solution for each use by dissolving 2 g. of reagent-grade NaOH pellets in 100 ml. of water in a nickel or stainless steel beaker.
2. Acetone, 99% reagent grade.

---

[6] Hashimoto and Jackson (1960).

3. Benzene, technical grade.
4. Sodium citrate, approximately $0.3M$: Dissolve 88 g. of trisodium citrate per liter of solution in water.
5. Sodium bicarbonate ($NaHCO_3$), approximately $1M$: Dissolve 8.4 g. per 100 ml. of solution in water.
6. Sodium dithionite ("hydrosulfite") ($Na_2S_2O_4$): Use purest grade.
7. Sodium chloride ($NaCl$), saturated solution: Shake 80 g. of reagent-grade $NaCl$ in 200 ml. of water.
8. Hydrochloric acid (HCl), approximately $0.05N$: Dilute 4 ml. of concentrated HCl to 1 liter with water.

45–3.3.2 PROCEDURE

Transfer a volume of clay suspension containing 100 mg. of Na-saturated [7] sample (base the weight on drying a separate aliquot) from which free iron oxides have been removed (section 44–4.2, or next paragraph) into a 500-ml. nickel or stainless steel beaker. (Alternatively, crush the aggregates of dried clay, silt, soil, or deposit sample in a small mortar, or dry the sample from a nonpolar solvent such as benzene, and rub it with a rubber-tipped rod in a beaker. Then weigh a 0.100-g. sample, and transfer it to the nickel or stainless steel beaker.) Add 100 ml. of $0.5N$ NaOH, immediately heat the solution to boiling, and boil it for 2.5 minutes (the total heating time is approximately 5 minutes). Promptly cool the beaker to room temperature in a water bath, and remove the supernatant liquid by centrifugation. Immediately determine the dissolved Si colorimetrically as molybdosilicate (section 64–3), and determine the dissolved Al colorimetrically as the salt of aurin tricarboxylic acid (section 67–3.3).

Extract the iron oxide released (now giving a brown stain to the residue) by the $Na_2S_2O_4$-citrate-bicarbonate method as follows: Add 40 ml. of $0.3M$ Na citrate solution and 5 ml. of $1M$ $NaHCO_3$ solution to the sample in the tube. Shake the tube to mix the contents, and then heat the tube in a water bath at 80°C. for several minutes, stirring the contents of the tube with a thermometer. When the suspension temperature reaches 80°C. (no higher), add 1 g. of $Na_2S_2O_4$ powder measured with a calibrated spoon, and immediately stir the suspension vigorously for 1 minute. Heat the tube for 15 minutes with intermittent stirring. Add 10 ml. of saturated NaCl, mix the suspension, and promptly centrifuge the tube. (Occasionally, addition of 10 ml. of acetone may be necessary to obtain complete flocculation as indicated by a clear supernatant solution after centrifugation.) Determine the iron by orthophenanthroline (section 65–1.3.3) or KSCN on the clear supernatant solution. Examine the undissolved residue by means of X-ray diffraction, since the removal of amorphous materials frequently discloses interesting crystalline components in the residue, such as mica, montmoril-

---

[7] Use of a Na-saturated sample instead of a dried H-saturated sample is less destructive of fine-clay layer silicates (Hanna and Jackson, unpublished).

lonite, or chlorite, which were not clearly revealed in the diffractogram of the material before the above treatments were given.

To determine amorphous interlayer material, H-saturate a second sample (by washing it with 0.05N HCl, acetone, and benzene). Dry the sample, heat it at 400°C. for 4 hours, and allow it to cool. Then powder it, and extract it by the same procedures as given above, including both the NaOH and dithionite procedures.

45–3.3.3 CALCULATION OF RESULTS

Calculate the percentages of SiO_2, Al_2O_3, and Fe_2O_3 dissolved in the extractions. If the cation-exchange capacity indicates the presence of allophane (section 45–4), add 21% H_2O to the total percentage of allophane-derived SiO_2 plus Al_2O_3 plus Fe_2O_3 extracted, to give the percentage of allophane dissolved (100°C. basis). If other evidence indicates the presence of gibbsite, add 35% H_2O to the percentage of gibbsite-derived Al_2O_3 extracted to give the percentage of gibbsite dissolved. Free amorphous alumina and (or) silica (uncombined) in the sample are also represented in the dissolved constituents.

Multiply the difference in % Al_2O_3 extracted before and after heating at 400°C. by 4.40 to obtain the theoretical chlorite equivalent of the interlayer alumina extracted.

45–3.3.4 COMMENTS

An aluminosilicate precipitate may form in the NaOH solution if the solution after the extraction is allowed to stand for an appreciable time prior to the Si and Al determinations. Also serious contamination with these elements occurs if the NaOH solution stands in contact with glass before or after the extraction.

Selective dissolution in 0.5N NaOH of amorphous aluminosilicates, silica, and alumina does not give a complete differentiation of the crystalline from the amorphous state because of the transitional nature of the boundary, as pointed out in the introduction. For example, poorly crystalline halloysite minerals, closely related genetically with allophane (Sudo, 1954), are appreciably attacked by 0.5N NaOH,[8] and this must be taken into consideration. The separation of amorphous from truly crystalline materials is accurate to within about 5% of the amount present.

Highly crystalline gibbsite may require two or more successive NaOH treatments for its complete dissolution (Hashimoto and Jackson, 1960). Magnesium hydroxide is, of course, not dissolved by NaOH. Magnesium-containing silicate minerals apparently are protected by $Mg(OH)_2$ formation at surfaces during treatment with NaOH, for they are relatively stable to the NaOH treatment. Such protection may account for the remarkable

[8] Hashimoto, I. 1961. *Op. Cit.*

resistance of chlorite to dissolution (Hashimoto and Jackson, 1960). Since kaolinite and halloysite are converted to amorphous aluminosilicates by heating to 500°C. (525°C. in practice, Hashimoto and Jackson, 1960), they can be dissolved in NaOH after such heating, and can be sharply differentiated from chlorite minerals. The kaolinite plus halloysite can be determined quantitatively on the basis of the difference in amorphous Al_2O_3 dissolved from samples preheated at 525° and 400°C., calculated from the 39.5% Al_2O_3 in kaolinite. This result may be checked by taking the difference between amorphous silica dissolved from samples preheated at these two temperatures, based on 46.5% SiO_2 in kaolinite (Dixon and Jackson, 1959 and 1962). Good checks between the Al_2O_3 basis and the SiO_2 basis are generally found (agreement to 1 or 2% of the sample). The percentage of NaOH-dissolved amorphous product which results from kaolinite plus halloysite decomposition between 525° and 400°C. checks well (Andrew et al., 1960) with the lattice-expansion method for these minerals, a fact that further supports the NaOH-dissolution method for amorphous aluminosilicates in general.

45–4 ALLOPHANE

45–4.1 Introduction

Allophane is a general term for amorphous aluminosilicate gels of a wide range in composition (Ross and Kerr, 1934; White, 1953). The Al_2O_3/SiO_2 mole ratio falls in the range of 0.5 to 1.3 or 2.0. Other constituents include H_2O and OH; iron oxides are frequently combined in allophane. Sometimes up to 10% P_2O_5 (White, 1953) may be present. In relatively pure allophane deposits, the refractive index falls in the range of 1.480 to 1.483, varying with water content. The water is lost progressively with rise in temperature to over 400°C. Allophane occurring in surface soils as a product of weathering of volcanic ash characteristically is strongly associated with humus (Aomine and Yoshinaga, 1955), giving dark-colored soils known (Thorp and Smith, 1949) as the Ando great soil group (*Ando* in Japanese means *dark soil*). Differential thermal analysis (section 50–3) indicates surface soil allophane by a carbon-burning exotherm in the range of 450° to 550°C. as well as a low temperature endotherm (160°C.). Allophane gives a stable porous structure to soils, predisposing them to high permeability, exhaustive leaching (Jackson, 1959), and hence, infertility. The porosity of freely drained sandy soils subjects the limited amount of clay present to intensive leaching in humid climates, and can result in production of amorphous clay (Dyal, 1953; Whittig and Jackson, 1955; Jackson, 1959), with cation-exchange properties of allophane. The high specific surface and high aluminum activity of allophane cause a problem of high phosphate fixation (Wada, 1959).

Markedly different values of cation-exchange capacity (CEC) have been reported for allophane and allophanic clays (Ross and Kerr, 1934; Birrell and Fieldes, 1952; Fieldes, Swindale, and Richardson, 1952; Aomine and Yoshinaga, 1955; Aomine and Kodama, 1956). Allophane is spectacular in the degree to which exchangeable cations hydrolyze from the exchange positions during washing with aqueous alcohol (Birrell and Gradwell, 1956), and this is one reason for variability in CEC reported. Another reason for variability of CEC of allophane is the alteration of surface composition and net negative charge that occurs in response to differences in pH of the solution in which it has been equilibrated prior to the determination of CEC. This latter property is employed as described in following paragraphs for the analytical determination of allophane.

45–4.2 Principles

It was noticed (Aomine and Jackson, 1959) that the CEC of allophanic clay separates, measured by using washing solutions having a pH value of 7, varied a great deal according to the pH of the dispersion reagents employed for separation. The clay fraction originally separated in an alkaline medium (about pH 10.7) showed a high (150 me. per 100 g.) exchange capacity, while the clay fraction from the same soil originally separated with an acid dispersion medium (about pH 3.5) had an exchange capacity only about one-third that of the sample receiving alkaline dispersion. The CEC of the acid-dispersed sample was increased to equal that of the former on treatment with a mildly alkaline buffer. This characteristic increase in CEC, exhibited by a number of allophanic soils developed on rapidly weathered volcanic ash and also by two standard allophanes of Ross and Kerr (1934), and designated the CEC delta value (Fig. 45–1), has been used as a basis for quantitative determination of allophane content in soils (Jackson, 1956, pp. 856–857; Aomine and Jackson, 1959).

Hydrolysis of metallic cations dissociated from acid-pretreated allophane and from alkali-pretreated allophane was found (Aomine and Jackson, 1959) to be nearly constant; hence the delta value remained constant with varying water concentration in the washing solutions. The reproducibility obtained is sufficiently high for quantitative determination, provided solutions of the same kind, same volume, and same strength are used for washing out the excess of salt solution in a standardized procedure.

The CEC of organic matter is greatly affected by the reference pH of the washing solution and the cation species employed. Also, organic matter forms soluble humate substances in the Na_2CO_3 solution of pH 10.7 involved in a 100°C. digestion of the soil sample, and thus some of the soil organic matter content of the sample would be lost in the supernatant solution were it to be left in the soil. To avoid these sources of error, organic matter is removed from the soil sample by H_2O_2 digestion (Jackson, 1958, p. 63) prior to the CEC delta value determination.

Free iron oxides in soils lower the CEC delta value of allophane to a considerable extent (Aomine and Jackson, 1959); to eliminate this variable, the free iron oxides are removed prior to the measurement. The removal of the free iron oxides by $Na_2S_2O_4$ reduction in neutral citrate-bicarbonate solution (Aguilera and Jackson, 1953; Jackson, 1956; and Mehra and Jackson, 1960) is important for selective dissolution of free iron oxides without removal of combined iron of allophane and nontronite. Iron oxide removal methods involving acid solutions dissolve the allophane itself (Birrell and Fieldes, 1952).

Evolution of CO_2 by the reaction of "neutral" allophane with $NaHCO_3$ in solution (Aomine and Jackson, 1959) was interpreted (Jackson, 1960) as indicating a fundamental reaction involving structural proton or hydronium release from the allophane surface structure (and to a limited

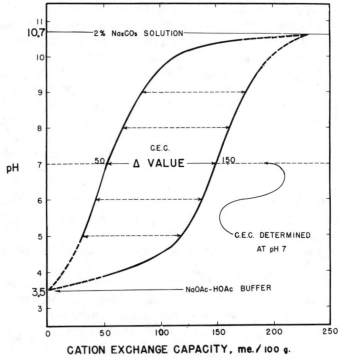

Fig. 45–1. Cation-exchange capacity hysteresis loop of allophane. The "CEC delta value" of allophane is the 100 me. per 100 g. spread in the loop across the pH 7 reference line between two curves, one originating at pH 3.5 and the other at pH 10.7, when each of the corresponding samples was washed with pH 7 KOAc solution.

extent from montmorillonite and halloysite edges). Through this reaction, a net negative exchange charge is created which is measurable as CEC at pH 7. The action of Na_2CO_3 buffer is seen as the same except that CO_2 is not evolved from this carbonate solution having an alkalinity of pH 10.7. The reciprocal reaction in dilute HOAc buffer (pH 3.5) restores the proton to the allophane surface structure, and eliminates the corresponding amount of net negative charge. Changes of the amounts of Si–OH and Al–OH_2 groups at surfaces are probably involved, inasmuch as small percentages of Si and Al are dissolved in each buffer solution (Aomine and Jackson, 1959) applied to sesquioxidic allophane of SiO_2/Al_2O_3 molar ratios in the range of 0.8 to 1.4.

The measurement must be distinguished from a simple change in CEC as measured at different pH values, since the CEC measurements are all made at pH 7, following neutral KOAc buffer washings. Two pH-dependent CEC curves (Fig. 45–1), corresponding to each of the 2 buffers, form a hysteresis loop characteristic of allophane, crossing the reference line for CEC at pH 7 with a 100 me. per 100 g. spread (the delta value). The CEC delta value was measured (Aomine and Jackson, 1959, p. 212) as 18 for halloysite, 0 for kaolinite, 10 for Wyoming montmorillonite, 0.5 for gibbsite, and 0 for quartz. The method provides a specific criterion for sesquioxidic allophane, supplementing the selective dissolution of various types of amorphous aluminosilicates including halloysitic allophane having higher SiO_2/Al_2O_3 molar ratios (section 45–3.2) and lower CEC delta values, along with free SiO_2 and Al_2O_3 (section 45–3). The CEC delta value involves a newly associated property of sesquioxidic allophane but has been observed with a rather wide variety of soils in a number of laboratories. It recalls the earlier observations of "build-up and break-down of soil zeolites" (Burgess, 1929) and CEC of undried amorphous hydrous oxides (Fieldes et al., 1952).

45–4.3   Method [9]

45–4.3.1 REAGENTS

1. Acetate buffer of pH 5: Dissolve 82 g. of NaOAc salt in water, add 27 ml. of glacial HOAc, and dilute the solution to a volume of 1 liter to give a solution approximately $1N$ with respect to NaOAc and of pH 5.
2. Hydrogen peroxide (H_2O_2), 27 to 35% reagent grade.
3. Acetone, 99% reagent grade.
4. Sodium citrate, approximately $0.3M$: Dissolve 88 g. of trisodium citrate per liter of solution in water.

[9] Aomine and Jackson (1959) and Jackson (1956, pp. 57, 856; 1958, p. 168). Thanks are extended to Dr. O. L. Baykan for help with testing the procedure and with making minor modifications of it in this laboratory during 1961.

5. Sodium bicarbonate ($NaHCO_3$), approximately $1M$: Dissolve 8.4 g. of reagent-grade $NaHCO_3$ per 100 ml. of solution in water.

6. Sodium dithionite ("hydrosulfite") ($Na_2S_2O_4$): Use purest grade.

7. Sodium chloride (NaCl), saturated solution: Shake 80 g. of reagent-grade NaCl in 200 ml. of water.

8. Acetone: Dilute acetone with water to give 50% and 75% acetone by volume.

9. Acetone-methanol mixture: Dilute acetone with 99% methanol to give 50% and 75% acetone by volume.

10. Sodium carbonate (Na_2CO_3), approximately 2% (or $0.2M$): Dissolve 2 g. of reagent-grade Na_2CO_3 in 100 ml. of water.

11. Acetate buffer of pH 3.5: To 57 ml. of reagent-grade glacial HOAc, add 900 ml. of water, and then add 60 ml. of $1N$ NaOH. Adjust the pH to 3.5 (glass electrode) by addition of HOAc or NaOH as needed, and dilute the solution to 1 liter.

12. Potassium acetate (KOAc), approximately $1N$: Dissolve 98 g. of reagent-grade KOAc per liter of solution in water. Adjust the pH to 7 with glacial HOAc.

13. Ammonium acetate (NH_4OAc), approximately $1N$: To 57 ml. of glacial HOAc, add 500 ml. of water and then NH_4OH to obtain pH 7. Dilute the solution to 1 liter.

45–4.3.2 PROCEDURE

Wash each of two 5-g. soil samples with $1N$ NaOAc of pH 5 in 100-ml. centrifuge tubes. Then treat the samples several times with 10-ml. increments of 27 to 35% H_2O_2 on a steam plate in 400-ml. beakers until the color of organic matter has been destroyed. Wash the samples twice with acetone by centrifugation. Transfer one sample (Sample A) into a weighed porcelain dish, dry it at 105°C., and weigh the dish for residual mineral matter.

Remove the free iron oxides from the second sample (Sample B), contained in a centrifuge tube, as follows: Add 40 ml. of $0.3M$ Na citrate solution and 5 ml. of $1M$ $NaHCO_3$ solution, shake the tube to mix the contents, and heat the tube in a water bath at about 80°C. for several minutes, stirring the suspension with a thermometer. When the temperature of the soil suspension rises to 80°C. (it must not go higher), add about 1 g. of $Na_2S_2O_4$ powder with a calibrated spoon, and immediately stir vigorously for 1 minute. Continue to heat the tube at 80°C. for 15 minutes, with intermittent stirring. Then mix in 10 ml. of saturated NaCl solution, and promptly centrifuge the suspension. (Occasionally, addition of 10 ml. of acetone may be necessary to obtain complete flocculation, as indicated by a clear solution after centrifugation.) Decant the clear supernatant solution into a 500-ml. volumetric flask. Repeat the iron removal treatment, decanting the solution into the same flask as before. Determine the extracted iron by the orthophenanthroline method (section 65–1.3.3) or by KSCN. Wash the sample in the tube three times, using successively 50% and 75% water-diluted acetone, and finally 99% acetone.

Transfer the sample into a 500-ml. nickel or stainless steel beaker with 200 ml. of 2% Na_2CO_3 solution, stir the suspension thoroughly, cover the beaker with a watchglass, and boil the contents for 5 minutes. Recover the residual sample by centrifuging, and wash it successively with methanol-diluted 50% and 75% acetone and with 99% acetone. Transfer the residue to a tared porcelain dish, and dry the dish and contents in an oven at 105°C. Determine the weight of the dried residue (Sample B).

Mix Sample B (previously treated with H_2O_2, $Na_2S_2O_4$, and Na_2CO_3) with a spatula, and transfer 0.1-g. subsamples into each of four 15-ml. centrifuge tubes (alternatively, use 0.3-g. subsamples of soil low in allophane). Add 5 ml. of 2% Na_2CO_3 solution to each of two tubes and 5 ml. of acetate buffer of pH 3.5 to each of the other two tubes. Place all tubes in a boiling water bath, and mix each intermittently by a Vortex stirrer. After 15 minutes, remove the tubes containing the pH 3.5 buffer; and, after 1 hour, remove the tubes containing the Na_2CO_3 solution. Mix 1 ml. of saturated NaCl into the contents of each tube, and centrifuge the tubes to sediment the solids.

Determine the usual (pH 7) cation-exchange capacity (CEC) by the K method, washing 5 times with neutral $1N$ KOAc and successively with 5 ml. of each of the following solvents to remove salts: once with 99% methanol, once with 50% acetone (diluted with 99% methanol), once with 75% acetone (diluted with 99% methanol), and once with 99% acetone. Then replace the exchangeable K by 5 washings, each consisting of an 8-ml. quantity of neutral $1N$ NH_4OAc; and collect the decantate. Determine K in the decantate (section 71–3).

45–4.3.3 CALCULATION OF RESULTS

The difference (in me. per 100 g.) obtained by subtraction of the CEC of the samples treated at pH 3.5 from that of the samples treated in 2% Na_2CO_3 is the cation-exchange capacity "delta value" of the sample (Sample B weight basis). The allophane percentage, in the first approximation, equals the CEC delta value.

Total matter dissolved by the citrate-dithionite-bicarbonate and carbonate treatments is the difference between the final dry weights of Samples A and B. Dissolved allophane matter is this difference less the ratio of extracted Fe_2O_3 to 0.85, where 0.85 is the ratio of the weight of Fe_2O_3 to that of hydrated goethite or limonite. Add dissolved allophane thus calculated to that indicated by the CEC delta value determined on Sample B. Subtraction of CEC delta values attributable to other minerals improves the result. To do this, allocate the observed CEC delta value to allophane at 100 me. per 100 g. (it varies from 90 to 110, averaging about 100), to halloysite at 18, to montmorillonite and vermiculite at 10, and to illite and chlorite at 5 me. per 100 g. To make this calculation, the contents of these minerals must be known from other types of analysis.

45–4.3.4 COMMENTS

Dispersion during washing is more of a problem with allophanic soils than with those containing crystalline clays, and it is for this reason that acetone solutions are employed in the washings. It is easy to separate some of the allophane from highly allophanic Ando soils, but it is practically impossible to separate all of it. The possibility is available of standardizing the CEC delta value for separated soil allophane from a given locality. The range of values given covers two allophanes of Ross and Kerr (1934) and several Ando soil allophanes of Kyushu Island (Japan). A few highly leached soils of the USA, including a sandy soil of Wisconsin (Whittig and Jackson, 1955), have been found to give CEC delta values indicative of a considerable allophane content in the clay fraction.

Use of K as the saturating cation provides a sensitive measure of CEC although K fixation may occur in vermiculitic clays. This fixation usually is not a problem in the CEC delta value determination, since it occurs in both the acid- and alkali-treated samples. The use of Ca gives a less sensitive measure and requires washing of the Na_2CO_3-treated samples with neutral $1N$ NaOAc prior to $Ca(OAc)_2$ washing to prevent the precipitation of $CaCO_3$.

The allophane determination by CEC gives duplicates falling within about 10%, and the mean values agree well with the percentage of allophane derived from thermal dehydration data (Aomine and Jackson, 1959). Although not a highly accurate method, the CEC delta value method contributes a moderately rapid and reliable quantitative estimate of allophane, which may otherwise be missed altogether or merely suspected to be present in a mixture with crystalline minerals and (or) amorphous free oxides of aluminum or silicon.

45–5 RUTILE AND ANATASE

45–5.1 Introduction

The titanium oxide minerals, rutile and anatase, often termed "accessory minerals," are usually present in soils and sediments, and because of their high resistance to weathering are used as index minerals. Their content in soils may vary widely, from 0.5% in young or little weathered soils, to about 4% in many soils of the tropical and temperate regions; unusually high contents of TiO_2 up to 25% have been reported in the highly weathered Humic Ferruginous Latosols of Hawaii (Sherman, 1952). The usual method employed for their identification is X-ray diffraction; but detection of their presence is often missed in diffraction patterns, as their contents are relatively low, and the X-ray peaks (3.51Å. for anatase and 3.25Å. for rutile) fall very close to those of various silicates in soils. Isolation of the free oxide minerals, rutile and anatase, is necessary to verify that the Ti they contain is present in the form of the oxide and not in the octahedral position in layer silicates. In the absence of such information, Mankin and Dodd (1963) allocated the entire Ti content of their proposed reference illite to octahedral positions. Recent analysis by X-ray and electron microscope methods has shown (see footnote 10, below) that almost the entire Ti content is present in this sample as rutile needles.

45–5.2 Principles

Qualitative detection of the presence of rutile and anatase in small amounts is made possible by the selective dissolution of the siliceous materials in the sample by treatment with cold HF, which leaves the accessory minerals relatively unattacked. The presence of rutile and anatase is detected by X-ray techniques. Exchangeable bases are replaced with hydrogen, and free $(Ca, Mg)CO_3$ is dissolved prior to the HF treatment to eliminate the formation of insoluble Ca and Mg fluorides. These fluorides would coat the siliceous minerals and impede dissolution of the latter by HF. Anatase shows a diffraction peak at 3.51Å. and rutile at 3.25Å. These spacings change slightly with isomorphous substitutions in the lattice.

45–5.3 Method [10]

45–5.3.1 REAGENTS

1. Hydrochloric acid (HCl): Dilute concentrated HCl (approximately $12N$) with water to give a stock of approximately $6N$.
2. Hydrofluoric acid (HF): Use reagent-grade 48% HF.
3. Perchloric acid $(HClO_4)$: Use 60% reagent.
4. Tiron reagent: Prepare the reagent daily by dissolving 4 g. of Tiron in 75 ml. of distilled water and diluting the solution to 100 ml.
5. Buffer solution of pH 4.7: Mix equal volumes of $1N$ HOAc (60 ml. of glacial acetic acid per liter) and $1N$ NaOAc (82 g. of anhydrous NaOAc per liter) and adjust to pH 4.7 using a glass electrode.
6. Standard Ti solution: Prepare the solution by fusion of 0.1668 g. of standard TiO_2 in $K_2S_2O_7$, taking up the melt with 10 ml. of $6N$ HCl.

---

[10] The procedure adopted is essentially that described by K. V. Raman and M. L. Jackson, Research Report No. 3, Department of Soil Science, University of Wisconsin, Madison, Feb. 21, 1963; Tiron method (Jackson, 1958).

Dilute the solution to 1 liter with 50 ml. of 6N HCl and water. The concentration is 100 mg. of elemental Ti per liter of 0.4 N HCl. After thorough mixing, dilute 10 ml. of this solution to 100 ml. with 0.4 N HCl, to give a standard Ti solution of 10 ppm. Aliquots (2, 4, 6, 8 and 10 ml.) of this standard are taken for the standard curve, giving 20 to 100 μg. of Ti.

45–5.3.2 PROCEDURE

Grind the sample lightly in an agate mortar and transfer a weighed 0.5-g. sample to a polypropylene centrifuge tube (50-ml. capacity). Wash the sample three times with 30 ml. of 6N HCl. Use a centrifuge to throw down the sample. Treat the sample with 30 ml. of HF at room temperature; and allow it to stand 24 hours, with occasional stirring in the initial few hours. Centrifuge the sample, decant off the supernatant liquid, and then wash the sample twice with 30 ml. of distilled water, once with 30 ml. of 6N HCl, and twice more with distilled water. Dry and weigh the residue. X-ray the residue, and index the peaks to detect the presence of rutile or anatase.

Decompose the residue by treatment with $HClO_4$, H_2SO_4, and HF as described in paragraph four of section 45–2.3.2. Dilute the extract of the Ti test sample to 25 ml. as described in paragraph five of section 45–2.3.2.

To develop the color, first, pipette out 10 ml. of pH 4.7 buffer solution into a clean 50-ml. volumetric flask. Adjust the volume to approximately 30 ml. with water, and add 5 ml. of the Tiron solution. Add an aliquot of the Ti test sample solution, containing 10 to 100 μg. of Ti in 0.4N HCl, to the volumetric flask; swirl the solution, and dilute it to the mark with water. Read the percentage light transmission of the yellow Ti complex within 10 minutes at a wavelength of 400 mμ. The concentrations of Ti (μg. per 50 ml.) are then obtained from the standard curve.

45–5.3.3 CALCULATIONS OF RESULTS

About 93% of the Ti from rutile and anatase is recovered by this procedure. The total TiO_2 content determined is therefore multiplied by 1.08 to obtain the percentage of rutile plus anatase.

45–5.3.4 COMMENTS

Rutile and anatase have been found by this method in the clay fraction of several soils where they were not detected in diffraction patterns of the bulk sample. Electronoscopic observations indicate the presence of euhedral crystals of different sizes in some samples before the HF treatment, though they are diluted by siliceous components. The morphology of the crystals was not changed by repeated HF treatment, indicating nonsynthesis by this treatment.

45–6 LITERATURE CITED

Aguilera, N. H., and Jackson, M. L. 1953. Iron oxide removal from soils and clays. Soil Sci. Soc. Am. Proc. 17:359–364 (also 18:223 and 350, 1954).

Andrew, R. W., Jackson, M. L., and Wada, K. 1960. Intersalation as a technique for differentiation of kaolinite from chloritic minerals by X-ray diffraction. Soil Sci. Soc. Am. Proc. 24:422–424.

Aomine, S., and Jackson, M. L. 1959. Allophane determination in Ando soils by cation-exchange capacity delta value. Soil Sci. Soc. Am. Proc. 23:210–214.

Aomine, S., and Kodama, I. 1956. Clay minerals of some arable soils in Miyazaki Prefecture. J. Fac. Agr. Kyushu Univ. 10:325–344.

Aomine, S., and Yoshinaga, N. 1955. Clay minerals of some well-drained volcanic ash soils in Japan. Soil Sci. 79:349–358.

Astaf'ev, V. P. 1958. Method of determination of quartz and opal in rocks. Opredelenie Svobodnoĭ Dvuokisi Kremniya v Gorn. Porodakh i Rudn. Pyli, Akad. Nauk S.S.S.R., Inst. Gorn. Dela, Sbornik Stateĭ. 1958:51–53.

Barshad, I. 1955. Soil development. In F. E. Bear, ed. Chemistry of the Soil, pp. 1–52. Reinhold Publishing Corp., New York.

Birrell, K. S., and Fieldes, M. 1952. Allophane in volcanic ash soils. J. Soil Sci. 3:156–166.

Birrell, K. S., and Gradwell, M. 1956. Ion-exchange phenomena in some soils containing amorphous mineral constituents. J. Soil Sci. 7: 130–147.

Brindley, G. W. 1961. Quantitative analysis of clay mixture. In G. Brown, ed. The X-ray Identification and Crystal Structures of Clay Minerals, pp. 489–516. Mineralogical Society, London.

Bulycheva, A. I., and Mel'nikova, P. A. 1958. Determination of free silica in the presence of silicates with pyrophosphoric acid. Opredelenie Svobodnoĭ Dvuokisi Kremniya v Gorn. Porodakh i Rudn. Pyli, Akad. Nauk S.S.S.R., Inst. Gorn. Dela, Sbornik Stateĭ. 1958:23–32.

Burgess, P. S. 1929. The so-called "build-up" and "break-down" of soil zeolites as influenced by reaction. Arizona Agr. Exp. Sta. Tech. Bull. 28:101–135.

Dixon, J. B., and Jackson, M. L. 1959. Dissolution of interlayers from intergradient soil clays after preheating at 400°C. Science, 129:1616–1617.

Dixon, J. B., and Jackson, M. L. 1962. Properties of intergradient chlorite-expansible layer silicates in soils. Soil Sci. Soc. Am. Proc. 26:358–362.

Dobrovol'skaya, V. V. 1958. Determination of free silica in dust by a method with pyrophosphoric acid. Opredelenie Svobodnoĭ Dvuokisi Kremniya v Gorn. Porodakh i Rudn. Pyli, Akad. Nauk S.S.S.R., Inst. Gorn. Dela. Sbornik Stateĭ. 1958:15–22.

Dyal, R. S. 1953. Mica leptyls and wavellite content of clay fraction from Gainesville loamy fine sand of Florida. Soil Sci. Soc. Am. Proc. 17:55–58.

Fieldes, M., Swindale, L. D., and Richardson, J. P. 1952. Relation of colloidal hydrous oxides to the high cation-exchange capacity of some tropical soils of the Cook Islands. Soil Sci. 74:197–205.

Florentin, M. D., and Heros, M. 1947. Dosage de la silice libre (quartz) dans les silicates. Bull. Soc. Chim. France, 1947M:213–215.

Foster, M. D. 1953. Geochemical studies of clay minerals. III. The determination of free silica and free alumina in montmorillonite. Geochim. Cosmochim. Acta 3:143–154.

Glenn, R. C., Jackson, M. L., Hole, F. D., and Lee, G. B. 1960. Chemical weathering of layer silicate clays in loess-derived Tama silt loam of southwestern Wisconsin. In Clays and Clay Minerals, 8th Conf., pp. 63–83. Pergamon Press, New York.

Grim, R. C. 1953. Clay Mineralogy. McGraw-Hill Book Co., New York.

Hardy, F., and Follett-Smith, R. R. 1931. Studies in tropical soils. II. Some characteristic igneous rock soil profiles in British Guiana, South America. J. Agr. Sci. 21:739–761.

Hashimoto, I., and Jackson, M. L. 1960. Rapid dissolution of allophane and kaolinite-halloysite after dehydration. *In* Clays and Clay Minerals, 7th Conf. pp. 102–113. Pergamon Press, New York.

Hillebrand, W. F., and Lundell, G. E. F. 1929. Applied Inorganic Analysis. pp. 705 and 715, tenth printing (1948). John Wiley and Sons, New York.

Hislop, J. F. 1944. The decomposition of clay by heat. Trans. Brit. Ceram. Soc., 43:49–51.

Jackson, M. L. 1956. Soil Chemical Analysis—Advanced Course. Published by the author, Department of Soils, Univ. of Wis., Madison, Wis.

Jackson, M. L. 1958. Soil Chemical Analysis. Prentice-Hall, Inc., Englewood Cliffs, New Jersey.

Jackson, M. L. 1959. Frequency distribution of clay minerals in major great soil groups as related to the factors of soil formation. *In* Clays and Clay Minerals, 6th Conf., pp. 133–143. Pergamon Press, New York.

Jackson, M. L. 1960. Structural role of hydronium in layer silicates during soil genesis. Trans. Intern. Congr. Soil Sci., 7th Madison. 2:445–455.

Jackson, M. L. 1963a. Interlayering of expansible layer silicates in soils by chemical weathering. *In* Clays and Clay Minerals, 11th Conf., pp. 29–46. Pergamon Press, New York.

Jackson, M. L. 1963b. Aluminum bonding in soils: A unifying principle in soil science. Soil Sci. Soc. Am. Proc. 27:1–10.

Jackson, M. L. 1964. Soil clay mineralogical analysis. *In* C. I. Rich and G. W. Kunze, ed. Soil Clay Mineralogy, pp. 245–294. University of North Carolina Press, Chapel Hill, N. C.

Jackson, M. L., Whittig, L. D., and Pennington, R. P. 1950. Segregation procedure for the mineralogical analysis of soils. Soil Sci. Soc. Am. Proc. (1949) 14:77–81.

Jophcott, C. M., and Wall, H. F. V. 1955. Determination of quartz of various particle sizes in quartz-silicate mixture. Arch. Ind. Health, 11:425–430.

Kanehiro, Y., and Whittig, L. D. 1961. Amorphous mineral colloids of soils of the Pacific region and adjacent areas. Pacific Sci. 40:477–482.

Kiely, P. V., and Jackson, M. L. 1964. Selective dissolution of micas from potassium feldspars by sodium pyrosulfate fusion of soils and sediments. Am. Mineralogist, 49:1648–1659.

Kiely, P. V., and Jackson, M. L. 1965. Quartz, feldspar, and mica determination for soils by sodium pyrosulfate fusion. Soil Sci. Soc. Am. Proc. 29: (in press).

Mackenzie, R. C., and Robertson, R. H. S. 1961. The quantitative determination of halloysite, goethite, and gibbsite. Acta Universtatis Carolinae—Geologica Supplementum 1:139–149.

Mankin, C. J., and Dodd, C. G. 1963. Proposed reference illite from the Ouachita mountains. *In* Clays and Clay Minerals, 10th Conf., pp. 372–379. Pergamon Press, New York.

Medicus, K. 1955. Schnellbestimmung der Kieselsäure im Bauxite nach der Perchlorsäure method. Zeit. anal. Chemie, 145:337–338.

Mehra, O. P., and Jackson, M. L. 1960. Iron oxide removal from soils and clays by a dithionite-citrate system with sodium bicarbonate buffer. *In* Clays and Clay Minerals, 7th Conf., pp. 317–327. Pergamon Press, New York.

Muñoz Taboadela, M. 1953. The clay mineralogy of some soils from Spain and from Rio Muni (West Africa). J. Soil Sci., 4:48–55.

Nagelschmidt, G. 1956. Inter-laboratory trials on the determination of quartz in dusts of respirable size. Analyst, 81:210–219.

Polezhaev, N. G. 1958. New method of determination of free silica in presence of silicates. Opredelenie Svobodnoĭ Dvuokisi Kremniya v Gorn. Porodakh i Rudn. Pyli, Akad. Nauk S.S.S.R., Inst. Gorn. Dela, Sbornik Stateĭ. 1958:33–43.

Pollack, S. S., Whiteside, E. P., and Varowe, D. E. Van. 1954. X-ray diffraction of common silica minerals and possible applications to studies of soil genesis. Soil Sci. Soc. Am. Proc. 18:268–272.

Reynolds, R. C., Jr. 1960. Separating illite for geochemical analysis. U. S. Patent 2,946,657.

Ross, C. S., and Kerr, P. F. 1934. Halloysite and allophane. U. S. Geol. Survey, Prof. Paper 185 G:135–148.

Schwertmann, U., and Jackson, M. L. 1963. A third buffer range in the potentiometric titration of H-Al-clays. Science 139:1052–1054.

Sclar, C. B., Carrison, L. C., and Schwartz, C. M. 1962. Relation of infrared spectra to coordination in quartz and two high-pressure polymorphs of SiO_2. Sci. 138:525–526.

Shaw, A. 1934. The determination of free silica in coal-measure rocks. Analyst, 59:446–461.

Shchekaturina, L. G., and Petrashen, V. I. 1958. Determination of free silica in coal dust. Opredelenie Svobodnoĭ Dvuokisi Kremniya v Gorn. Porodakh i Rudn. Pyli, Akad. Nauk S.S.S.R., Inst. Gorn. Dela, Sbornik Stateĭ. 1958:54–57.

Sherman, G. D. 1952. The titanium oxide content of Hawaiian soils and its significance. Soil Sci. Soc. Am. Proc. 16:15–18.

Smith, J. L. 1865. On the use of the bisulphate of soda as a substitute for the bisulphate of potash in the decomposition of minerals, especially the aluminous minerals. Am. J. Sci. and Arts 40:248–249.

Sudo, T. 1954. Clay mineralogical aspects of the alteration of volcanic glass in Japan. Clay Min. Bul. 2:96–106.

Swindale, L. D., and Jackson, M. L. 1956. Genetic processes in some residual podzolised soils of New Zealand. Trans. Intern. Congr. Soil Sci., 6th Paris. 5:233–239.

Swindale, L. D., and Jackson, M. L. 1960. A mineralogical study of soil formation in four rhyolite-derived soils from New Zealand. N.Z.J. Geol. Geophys., 3:141–183.

Sysoeva, R. S. 1958. Test of parallel determination of the free silica in the dust of a crushing mill by chemical, petrographic, X-ray spectral and thermal methods. Opredelenie Svobodnoĭ Dvuokisi Kremniya v Gorn. Porodakh i Rudn. Pyli, Akad. Nauk S.S.S.R., Inst. Gorn. Dela, Sbornik Stateĭ. 1958:103–110.

Talvitie, N. A. 1951. Determination of quartz in presence of silicate using phosphoric acid. Anal. Chem. 23:623–626.

Tamura, T., Jackson, M. L., and Sherman, G. D. 1953. Mineral content of low humic, humic, and hydrol humic latosols of Hawaii. Soil Sci. Soc. Am. Proc. 17:343–346.

Thorp, J., and Smith, G. D. 1949. Higher categories of soil classification: order, suborder and great soil group. Soil Sci. 67:117–126.

Trostel, L. J., and Wynne, D. J. 1940. Determination of quartz (free silica) in refractory clays. J. Am. Ceram. Soc. 23:18–22.

Tuddenham, W. M., and Lyon, R. J. P. 1960. Infrared techniques in the identification and measurement of minerals. Anal. Chem. 32:1630–1634.

Wada, K. 1959. Reaction of phosphate with allophane and halloysite. Soil Sci. 87:325–330.

White, W. A. 1953. Allophanes from Lawrence County, Indiana. Am. Mineralogist, 38:634–642.

Whittig, L. D., and Jackson, M. L. 1955. Interstratified layer silicates in some soils of northern Wisconsin. In Clays and Clay Minerals, Nat. Acad. Sci.-Nat. Res. Council Publ. 395:322–336.

Whittig, L. D., Kilmer, V. J., Roberts, R. C., and Cady, J. G. 1957. Characteristics and genesis of Cascade and Powell soils of northwestern Oregon. Soil Sci. Soc. Am. Proc. 21:226–232.

46

Petrographic Microscope Techniques

JOHN G. CADY

Soil Conservation Service, USDA
Beltsville, Maryland

46-1 · GENERAL INTRODUCTION

The microscope was first used in soils studies to make an inventory of the minerals found in a variety of soils. Early examples of this approach are in publications by McCaughey and Fry (1913, 1914). Among the objectives of the early work were determination of source of parent materials and estimation of potential fertility reserves. Most of the work of this period was geological-mineralogical and was not applied to solution of soil development problems.

Several soil scientists and geologists made and studied thin sections of soils before and during the 1920's, but they were hampered by lack of suitable impregnating media. The greatest impetus to the study of micromorphology in thin sections was given by Kubiena (1938). This subject has developed rapidly in America, Europe, and Australia within the past few years under the influence of a number of workers. Osmond (1958) and Stephen (1960) have published reviews that indicate the scope of the work. The recent Soil Classification System (Seventh Approximation) by the Soil Survey Staff of the U. S. Dept. Agr. (1960) puts considerable emphasis on soil mineralogy and micromorphology.

The microscope is a simple, direct observational tool; the user sees the features himself without intermediate calculations or inferences. However, the observations must be analyzed and their meanings synthesized and interpreted; hence, the results are affected by the bias, experience, skill, and aptitude of the observer. The petrographic microscope may be used in soils investigations for the study of (*1*) identity, size, shape, and condition of single grains and mineral aggregates in the silt and sand size range, and (*2*) the distribution and interrelations of constituents of the soil in thin sections. Observations with the petrographic microscope are often valuable when used to interpret data obtained by other physical and mineralogical methods.

The petrographic microscope differs in two ways from the basic or biological microscope: it has devices for polarizing light, one below the condenser and one above the objective; and it has a rotating stage, graduated in degrees, for measuring angles. Other special refinements exist, but the foregoing two are the essential ones. Descriptions of petrographic microscopes and instructions for their use are in many standard mineralogy texts, including those by Winchell (1937), Kerr (1959), Wahlstrom (1951), and Johannsen (1918).

The purpose of this chapter is not to repeat information and instructions easily found in standard texts on optical mineralogy and petrography, particularly sedimentary petrography, but to describe methods, minerals, and structures that are peculiar to soils, based on the writer's experience in the application of microscopy to soil genesis and classification.

46–2 GRAINS

46–2.1 Introduction

Single grains of sand and silt size may be identified and described by examination under a petrographic microscope. Knowledge of the nature and condition of the minerals in these fractions provides information on the source of the parent material; on the presence of lithological discontinuities or overlays in the solum or between the solum and the underlying material; and on the degree of weathering in the soil as a key to its history, genetic processes, and possible fertility reserve. Examples of applications of such studies of sand or silt can be found in publications by Haseman and Marshall (1945), Marshall and Jeffries (1946), Ruhe (1956), and Cady (1940).

Many of the preparation and identification procedures are identical with those used in sedimentary petrography (Milner, 1962; Krumbein and Pettijohn, 1938). Modifications applicable to soils work are concerned with sampling, types of observations for purposes peculiar to soils, and noting of grain types and mineral bodies and aggregates that are more characteristic of soils than rocks.

The first step in the study of grains is the separation of the desired size fraction from the remaining material. Procedures for dispersion and separation are given in sections 43–3 and 43–4. Combined with this step, or subsequent to it, is the cleaning of the mineral grains, for which procedures are given in section 44. It is sometimes desirable to examine soil separates before rigorous cleaning treatments are applied, because aggregates, concretions, partly weathered mineral grains, and other types of grains that are worth attention and study may be removed by the cleaning treatments.

All the fractions from coarse sand to fine silt can be studied, but the most suitable ones are those in the middle part of this size range. There are usually too few grains of coarse sand on a slide to constitute a good sample, and it is difficult to observe optical properties on large grains; the grains in the fine silt range may be too small for observation of all their important optical properties. Smithson (1961) published some special instructions for studying the silt fraction.

Selection of the sample depends on the purpose of the analysis. For most work, such as checks on discontinuities or estimation of degree of weathering in different horizons, one usually selects one or two of the size fractions that make up a relatively large weight percentage of the soil. Examination of more than one size fraction is necessary in such problems as checking for an admixture of wind-blown material in dominantly coarse-textured residuum, and studying weathering where the process might cause minerals formerly dominant in one size class to shift to a smaller one.

The sample must be well mixed because the subsample on the slide is small. If a sample of sand is in a beaker or a vial, for example, shaking or jarring may cause heavy grains to settle and platy or prismatic grains to accumulate toward the top. Stirring with a small flat-bladed implement will usually mix the sample sufficiently. Steel needles or spatulas should be avoided because they will attract the magnetic minerals. Small sample-splitting devices are available that effectively subdivide sand and silt samples down to amounts suitable for single slides or replicates.

A sample of the whole fraction should be examined first; and then, if the nature of the material and requirements of the problem justify it, the heavy and light minerals can be separated. With some types of specimen it is advantageous to separate and weigh the magnetic fraction, either before or after the heavy liquid separation. Wrapping a thin sheet of flexible plastic around the magnet facilitates making this separation quantitative. Such separations can be done on either dry material or dispersed suspensions of silt and clay.

46–2.2 Heavy-Liquid Separations

The sand and silt fractions of most soils are dominated by quartz or by quartz and feldspars. These minerals have a relatively low specific gravity (2.57 to 2.76). The large number of "heavy" mineral species (sp. gr. above 2.8) with a wide range in weatherability and diagnostic significance may make up only a small percentage of the grains. To facilitate the study of these important but less abundant grains, it is common practice to concentrate them by specific-gravity separations in a heavy liquid such as tetra brom ethane or bromoform. These liquids can be diluted with toluene or other organic solvents to make separations in other density ranges, so that one can concentrate mica or calcic plagioclase, for example. A light liquid (<2.5) would be useful for concentrating volcanic ash, plant opal, or sponge spicules. Procedures and apparatus for these separations are numerous and are well covered in standard references. Separations in the sizes larger than 0.10 mm. can usually be carried out by gravity alone in separatory funnels or various types of tubes. Smaller size grains require centrifuging. A pointed, 15-ml. centrifuge tube has been found to be generally satisfactory. A glass rod with a smooth bulb on the end can be used to stop off the tapered end of the tube while the light fraction is poured off, or the contents of the lower part of the tube can be frozen (Matelski, 1951) to keep the heavy and light minerals separated.

Micas may be difficult to separate and may appear in both fractions because of their shape and because a little weathering, especially in biotite, can decrease the specific gravity measurably. It is possible to make use of such differences to concentrate weathered biotite in various stages of alteration (leRoux et al., 1963).

Heavy-liquid separations are most effective on well-cleaned grains. Organic matter may prevent wetting and cause grains to clump or raft together. Light coatings may cause heavy grains to float, and iron oxide coatings may increase the specific gravity.

46–2.3 Slide Preparation

With a microspatula, enough sample is taken so that an area about 22 mm. square on a slide can be covered uniformly without having individual grains touch each other. A few drops of water containing a little alcohol to reduce surface tension are added, and the grains are spread uniformly in the liquid with a pointed nonmagnetic instrument. After the slide has dried, the spacing of the grains can be checked with a microscope; and, if satisfactory, the mounting medium is applied. If this procedure is followed, the grains will lie in one plane and will not drift out when the cover glass is applied. They can be fixed more securely if a little gelatin or gum arabic is added to the water.

A number of media are used for permanent grain mounts. Canada balsam is the most generally used and is the best all-purpose medium. Its refractive index, about 1.53, is close to that of quartz, and this aids in distinguishing quartz from other colorless minerals, particularly the feldspars. Other commercial media are available, in the refractive index range from 1.53 to 1.55. Piperine, with a refractive index of 1.68, is the best substance for mounting heavy minerals; its refractive index is close to that of many of the common heavy minerals, and this facilitates their identification. Directions for preparation of slides with balsam and piperine are available in the standard reference works.

Permanent mounts are necessary where the same slide is needed for several purposes; they can be kept as records, and they are almost essential for percentage analysis by counting. There are, however, several advantages in the use of immersion liquids of known refractive index (Larsen and Berman, 1934). The refractive indexes of minerals can be determined exactly, and identification is aided in other ways as well. Permanent mounts may have all the prismatic or platy grains in a preferred-orientation position. In an oil a given grain can be moved into different orientations by moving the cover slip. The optical properties of anisotropic minerals vary with the crystallographic directions, and so it is often a valuable aid in identification to see the same grain in different positions and to observe these variations.

46–2.4 Mineralogical Analysis

46–2.4.1 GENERAL PROCEDURE

The first step is a survey of the slide with a low-power objective to become familiar with the grain assemblage and to make a rough estimate of the relative abundance of the minerals and other grains present. It is helpful to become familiar with the minerals first, whether they are identified or not, so that the observer can be sure he is recognizing the same mineral each time he sees it. This serves two purposes: it avoids wasting time going through identifying criteria, and it enables one to appraise mineral properties as seen in grains of different shapes and sizes in different positions. The most abundant minerals should be identified first. These will probably be the easiest to identify, and their elimination will decrease the number of possibilities to consider when the difficult ones are to be attacked. Furthermore, there are certain likely and unlikely assemblages of minerals, and awareness of the overall types present gives clues to the minor species that may be expected. Practical working procedures for identifying soil mineral grains were outlined by Fry (1933).

In actual practice, one ultimately learns to identify minerals by a combination of familiarity with a few striking features and a process of elimination. If one sees a dog with very short legs, it is either a dachshund, a basset, or a corgi. If it is solid colored, it is a dachshund; spotted, a basset; and, if its ears stand up, a corgi. It is not necessary to make a number of observations on the length of the hair or the configuration of the teeth. At least 80% of the sand and silt grains in soil are identified like this, by a combination of a few distinctive features. Unfortunately, one does have to cope with some nontypical specimens. Minerals modified by weathering, secondary minerals, aggregate grains, and other grains not identifiable as specific minerals are common in many soils, and may be among the important characteristics of the soils in which they occur. They should be accurately described even if they can not be identified.

A mineralogical analysis of a sand or silt fraction may be entirely qualitative, or it may be quantitative to different degrees. For many purposes a list of minerals is sufficient information. It is easy to accompany such a list with an estimate of relative abundance. A crude scale, such as one based on numbers from 1 to 10, can be used to express the amounts. Presence, absence, scarcity or abundance of certain minerals or mineral groups can sometimes confirm the source of the soil parent material, the presence of overlays, and the reserve of weatherable minerals.

To detect more subtle distinctions among samples, analysis is based on a count of grains, from which a volume percentage can be obtained. Weight percentages then can be calculated using specific gravity, and various useful ratios can be calculated from count percentages.

The counting procedure and number of grains counted depend on the requirements of the job, the number and proportions of minerals present, and the distribution on the slide. Uniform coverage of the whole area of the mount is important because grains may be segregated by shape, size, or density in spite of care taken in slide preparation. Because of the natural variations in soils, and because of the opportunity for sampling error by the time a heavy mineral concentrate is mounted on a slide, differences in amounts of minerals must be large and consistent to be interpreted with confidence. Mineral count percentages should usually be reported in whole numbers only, with no more than two significant figures.

Counting of numbers of grains of individual species can proceed on arbitrarily or regularly spaced traverses. If the grains are large or sparsely distributed, all grains can be counted. Various sampling methods may be used where only a portion of the grains is to be counted. In work on 20 to 50μ fractions with well-populated slides, the writer frequently counts all grains in individual fields evenly spaced over the slide in a preset grid pattern. Another method is to count all the grains lying within an arbitrarily selected quadrant of the field of vision as the slide is moved past the objective. Still another method is to count all the grains touched by the cross hair intersection in a continuous traverse.

If only a few species are present, identification of 100 to 300 grains will provide a good approximation to the composition. As the number of species increases, the count should increase, within limits of practicability. It is rarely necessary to count more than 1,000 grains, however; in most work, 500 to 600 is a more usual number. A multi-unit laboratory counter can be used to tally the most abundant species without having to take one's eyes from the microscope. Some of these counters sum the count and ring whenever 100 counts have been accumulated. Noting the composition of the first 100 will provide an idea of the number of grains that should be counted to give a good sample. Discussions of the statistics of analysis of mineral separates by counting may be found in the books by Krumbein and Pettijohn (1938) and Milner (1950, 1962).

The detail of the analysis can be adjusted to fit the need. In some instances one may be concerned only about the proportion of one mineral. In others, one may be interested in the ratio between two minerals as an indicator of source or in ratios between certain known weatherable minerals and known resistant minerals as indicators. of weathering or age. For purposes other than a complete enumeration, the occurrence of several minor species of uncertain identity should not cause undue concern about the validity of the count on which interest is centered.

In addition to identity and amount of the different grains in the sand and silt fractions, it is often important to record their morphology and condition. Evidence of wear or abrasion and evidence of chemical alteration or weathering is the most frequently sought information.

Wear during transportation shows as rounding, especially in chemically resistant minerals such as quartz that do not have good cleavage. Zircon and rutile also are good mineral species to examine for evidence of mechanical abrasion.

Easily weathered minerals can be rounded by solution; apatite, for example, is often found in ovoid grains.

In connection with observations of rounding, it should be noted that a grain may have a round outline but still be a flat plate. If a truly rounded grain is observed in crossed polarized light, the interference colors will rise smoothly without steps or interruption from low orders at the periphery to high order in the thickest part. Interference colors can be read like the contour lines on a map.

Weathering can have several manifestations ranging from slight bleaching of color, or slight lowering of refractive index, to replacement of one mineral by another or complete removal of a species. Effects depend upon the chemical composition, crystal structure, and habit of the mineral and upon the environment. Corrosion or solution results in etching and pitting of surfaces. Minerals with pronounced cleavage or a fibrous or columnar habit are usually attacked most along these planes of weakness, as shown in Fig. 46–2C. Hornblende, for example, appears to weather most readily at ends of the columnar grains and in a direction parallel to the long axis. The ends of the grains become forked and pinnacled, and pits in the sides are elongated with the length. Garnet is isometric and corrosion is random. Decomposition of feldspars follows cleavage and twinning planes.

Weathering can produce coatings of clay or mixed oxides, can open channels which may be filled with clay, iron oxide, or gibbsite, or can completely alter the mineral to another mineral with little change in form (Fig. 46–2A and 46–2B, Fig. 46–3D).

Observations on weathering in single grains are best made in two or more mounting media. A medium that closely matches the refractive index of the grain enables one to see the interior of the grain well and will show up contrasting coatings. A medium having a refractive index some few hundredths of a unit away from that of the grain will show the condition of the grain surfaces. Resistance to both dissolution and alteration to secondary minerals varies greatly. Some minerals, magnetite for example, may be resistant in some environments and easily weathered in others. Such differences in weathering can exist between horizons in a soil profile. Lists of minerals arranged in order of resistance are given in many publications and are valuable guides; but, like all generalizations, they must be used with caution. Observations on weathering will be discussed further in section 46–3.5.

46–2.4.2 MINERALS

46–2.4.2.1 Criteria Used in Identification. Properties important in grain identification are listed below in approximate order of ease and convenience of determination. Often estimates of several or even two or three of these properties will allow identification of a grain, so that it is seldom necessary to resort to detailed or extremely accurate measurements. In the finer soil separates, it may be impossible to find grains large enough or in the right position to permit measurement of some properties such as optic angle or optic sign. It is helpful to crush, sieve, and mount a set of known minerals for practice in estimating properties and for standards to compare with unknowns.

Refractive index can be estimated by relief or determined accurately by use of calibrated immersion liquids. When relief is used to estimate refractive index, allowance must be made for grain shape, color, and surface texture. Thin platy grains may be estimated low; colored grains and grains with rough, hackly surface texture may be estimated high. Estimation is aided by comparing unknown with nearby known minerals.

Birefringence, the difference between highest and lowest refractive index of the mineral, is estimated by interference color (see the chart in Kerr, 1959), taking into account grain thickness and orientation. Several grains of the same species must be observed because they may not all lie in positions that show the extremes of refractive index. Mica, for example, has high birefringence, but the refractive indexes of the two crystallographic directions in the plane of the plates are very close together, so that the birefringence appears low when the plate is perpendicular to the microscope axis. The carbonate minerals have extremely high birefringence (0.17 to 0.24), most of the ferromagnesian minerals are intermediate (0.015 to 0.08), orthoclase feldspar is low (0.008), and apatite is very low (0.005).

Color aids in discriminating among the heavy minerals. Pleochroism, the change in color or light absorption with stage rotation when one polarizer is in, is a good diagnostic characteristic for many colored minerals. Tourmaline, hypersthene, and staurolite are examples of pleochroic minerals.

Shape, cleavage, and crystal form are characteristic or unique for many minerals. Cleavage may be reflected in the external form of the grain, or may appear as cracks within it showing as regularly repeated straight parallel lines or sets of lines intersecting at definite repeated angles. The crystal shape may be quite different from the cleavage-fragment shape. Plagioclase feldspars, kyanite, and the pyroxenes have strong cleavage. Zircon and rutile usually appear in crystal forms.

Extinction angle and character of extinction observed in crossed polarized light are valuable criteria for some groups. The grain must show its cleavage or crystal form for extinction angles to be measured, and the angle may be different along different crystallographic axes. Some minerals have sharp, quick total extinction; in others extinction is more gradual; and in some minerals with high light dispersion, a dimming and change of interference color takes place at the extinction position.

Optic sign, optic angle, and sign of elongation are useful, sometimes essential, determinations but are often difficult to make unless grains are large or in favorable orientation. To determine optic sign, grains that show dim, low-order interference colors or no extinction must be sought. Grains with bright colors and sharp, quick extinction will rarely give usable interference figures.

46–2.4.2.2 Useful Differentiating Criteria for Particular Species. The following are the outstanding diagnostic characteristics of the most common minerals and single-particle grains found in the sand and silt fractions of soils. The refractive indexes given are the intermediate values. If these minerals and the ones in section 46–2.4.3.2 can be learned, it is safe to say that one can identify over 80% of the grains in most soil mineral assemblages.

Quartz has irregular shapes. The refractive index, 1.54, is close to that of balsam. The interference colors are of low order but are bright and warm. There is sharp extinction within a small angle of rotation ("*blick* extinction"). Crystal forms are sometimes observed and usually indicate derivation from limestone, or other low-temperature secondary origin.

Feldspars: Orthoclase may resemble quartz, but the refractive index is about 1.52 (well below that of balsam), birefringence is lower, and the mineral may show cleavage. *Microcline* has a refractive index of 1.53, and twinning intergrowth produces a plaid or grid effect in crossed polarized light. The refractive indexes in the *plagioclase* group increase with increasing proportion of calcium. The refractive index of albite, 1.53, is below that of quartz, but the refractive index of anorthite, 1.58, is noticeably above. Plagioclase feldspars almost always show a type of twinning that appears as alternating dark and light bands in crossed polarized light. Cleavage is good. Lath and prismatic shapes are common.

Mica occurs as platy grains that often are very thin. The plate view shows very low birefringence; the edge view, very high birefringence. Plates are commonly equidimensional and may appear as hexagons or may have some 60° angles. *Biotite* is green to dark brown. Paler colors, lowering of refractive index, and distortion of extinction and interference figure indicate weathering to *hydrobiotite* or *vermiculite. Muscovite* is colorless and has a moderate refractive index (about 1.59 in the plate view). If the identification is in doubt, it is desirable to use an oil mount, so that the grains can be seen from different angles.

Amphiboles are fibrous to platy or prismatic minerals with parallel to slightly inclined extinction. Color and refractive index increase as the iron content increases. They have good cleavage at angles of about 56 and 124 degrees. Refractive index in the group ranges from 1.61 to 1.73. *Hornblende* is the most common; it is slightly pleochroic, has refractive index close to piperine, and usually has a distinctive color close to olive-green. It is often used as an indicator of weathering.

Pyroxenes: Enstatite and *hypersthene* are prismatic and have parallel extinction; hypersthene has unique and striking green-pink pleochroism. *Augite* and *diopside* have good cleavage at angles close to 90 degrees and large extinction angles; colors are usually shades of green. Refractive indexes of the pyroxenes are in a somewhat higher range than the amphiboles (1.65 to 1.79).

Olivine is colorless to very pale green, is usually irregular in shape (weak cleavage), has vivid, warm interference colors, and has a refractive index close to that of piperine. It is an easily weathered mineral and may have cracks filled with serpentine or seams or crack fillings of goethite.

Staurolite is pleochroic yellow to pale brown; it sometimes contains holes, giving a "Swiss cheese" effect. Its refractive index is about 1.74. All the grains seen by the writer have had a foggy or milky appearance, possibly caused by colloidal inclusions.

Epidote is a common heavy mineral, but the forms occurring in soils may be hard to identify positively. Typical epidote, with its high refractive index (1.72 to 1.76), strong birefringence, and pleochroism that includes the pistachio-green color, is unmistakable. However, epidote is modified by weathering or metamorphism to colorless forms with lower birefringence and lower refractive index; and, furthermore, close relatives of epidote, *zoisite* and *clinozoisite,* are more abundant than some of the literature indicates. These minerals of the epidote group commonly appear as colorless, pale-green, or bluish-green, irregularly shaped or roughly platy grains with high (1.70 to 1.73) refractive index. Most show anomalous interference colors (bright pale blue) and no complete extinction. They can be confused with several other minerals such as kyanite and diopside. Identification usually depends on establishing properties on many grains.

Kyanite is common but seldom abundant. Its pale blue color, platy, angular cleavage flakes, large cleavage angles, and large extinction angles can usually be observed and make it easy to identify.

Sillimanite and *andalusite* are two fibrous to prismatic minerals with straight extinction that resemble each other; however, their sign of elongation is different, and sillimanite is colorless, but andalusite commonly has a pink color.

Garnet is in irregularly shaped, equidimensional grains that are isotropic and have high refractive index (1.77 and higher). Garnet of the size of fine sand and silt is often colorless; pale pink colors are diagnostic in larger grains.

Tourmaline has a refractive index close to piperine. Prismatic shape and strong pleochroism are characteristic; some tourmaline is almost opaque when at right angles to the vibration plane of the polarizer.

Zircon occurs as tetragonal prisms with pyramidal ends, has very high refractive index (>1.9), straight extinction and bright, strong interference colors. Broken and rounded crystals are found frequently. Zircon crystals and grains are almost always clear and fresh appearing.

Sphene in some forms resembles zircon, but the crystal forms have oblique extinction; and the common form, a rounded or subrounded grain, has with crossed polarizers a color change through ultra blue instead of extinction because of its high dispersion. It is the only pale-colored or colorless high-index mineral that gives this effect. The refractive index is slightly lower than that of zircon, and the grains are often cloudy or rough-surfaced.

Rutile grains have prismatic shape. The refractive index and birefringence are extremely high (2.6 and 0.29). The interference colors are usually obscured by the brown, reddish-brown or yellow colors of the mineral. Other TiO_2 minerals, *anatase* and *brookite,* also have very high refractive indexes and brown colors and may be difficult to distinguish in small grains. The latter two usually occur as tabular or equidimensional grains.

Apatite is fairly common in youthful soil materials. It has a refractive index slightly below that of piperine (1.63) and very low birefringence. Crystal shapes are common and may appear as prisms; rounding by solution produces ovoid forms. It is easily attacked by acid and may be lost in pretreatments.

Carbonates: Calcite, dolomite and *siderite,* in their typical rhombohedral cleavage forms, are easy to identify by their extremely high birefringence. In soils they have other forms—scales and chips, cementing material in aggregates, microcrystalline coatings and other fine-grained masses often mixed with clay and other minerals. The extreme birefringence always is the clue to identification; it is shown by the bright colors in crossed polarized light and by marked change in relief when the stage is rotated with one polarizer in. The three can be distinguished by refractive index measurements; siderite is the only one with both indexes above balsam.

Gypsum occurs in platy or prismatic flat grains with refractive index about the same as orthoclase.

Opaque minerals, of which *magnetite* and *ilmenite* are the most common, are difficult to identify, especially when they are worn by transportation or

Fig. 46–1.

A. Longitudinal section of a tubular clay skin. Plain light, 60×.

B. The same field as A in crossed polarized light. The sides of the split tube are bright because the stacked aggregate of platy grains is seen from the edge or normal to the *c* axis. The center of the tube is dark because the view is down the composite *c* axis of the aggregate. The tube forks around the large quartz grain at the lower right. The empty area at the lower left is the edge of the thin section. 60×.

C. Pressure orientation of clay in a grumusol. In plain light, orientation or segregation of clay is not visible. When the stage is turned, other sets of bright lines corresponding to other shear directions appear. Crossed polarized light, 60×.

D. Natural channel, either a crack or a tube, lined with oriented, translocated clay. Plain light, 60×.

Fig. 46–2.

A. Weathering effects and clay arrangement in a residual soil derived from gabbro. Plagioclase feldspar (lower left and upper right) has weathered in place to clay, leaving the grain outlines and twinning planes still visible. The augite (upper left and right center) is weathering, but the clay produced has moved to form clay skins around the adjacent pores (center). Plain light, 60×.

B. Same field as A in crossed polarized light. The clay replacing the feldspars is almost isotropic, indicating that it is not organized into oriented aggregates; however, some of the clay in these bodies is halloysite, which shows only weak birefringence, if any. The bright areas are oriented clay aggregates (clay skins) and unweathered augite. 60×.

C. Plagioclase feldspar weathering in place in A horizon of a Non-Calcic Brown soil. Alteration follows the cleavage and twinning planes. The matrix is a mixture of silt, clay and organic matter; note the large pores and inter-grain bridging. Plain light, 60×.

D. Large pore coated with translocated iron-stained kaolinite in crossed-polarized light. The dark bands or brushes (left and upper center) through the clay deposit indicate where the composite *a* and *b* axes and the composite *c* axis are parallel to the planes of polarization of light. The bands will sweep through the aggregate when the stage is rotated. 60×.

Fig. 46–3.

A. Clay skin on present ped face (right). Old clay skin on former face that is being reworked into the matrix (upper left) is barely distinguishable in plain light. Crossed polarized light, 60×.

B. Coarse vermicular, accordion-like and book-like aggregates of well crystallized residual kaolinite, center and lower part. Large pore lined with clay-size, iron-stained, translocated kaolin, top. In crossed polarized light the pore is dark, and the complex pattern of extinction bands in the pore lining can be seen. The larger kaolinite aggregates resemble mica but have lower birefringence. 60×.

C. Clay-filled tubule in a fragipan. The morphology suggests that the pore was filled from the left in several stages. Note the close packing of the matrix. The white areas are quartz grains. At the top is an opaque concretion. Plain light, 60×.

D. Weathering and clay formation in soil derived from gabbro. Plagioclase weathers first, largely to halloysite (top) and the clay stays more or less in place. The ferromagnesian mineral weathers later; montmorillonite is synthesized and accumulates as oriented skins in voids (lower right). Plain light, 60×.

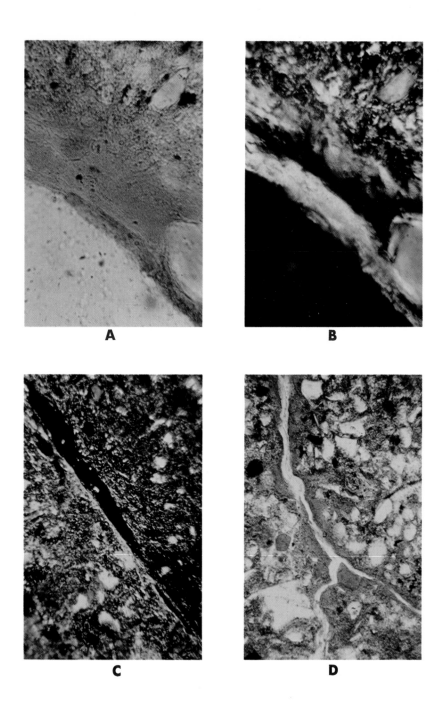

Fig. 46–1.

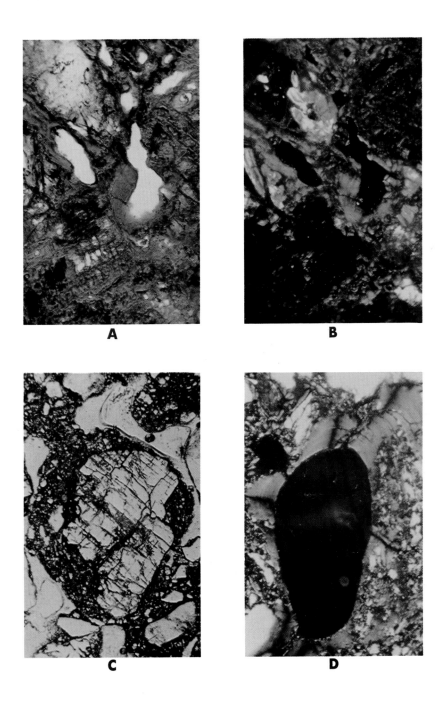

Fig. 46–2.

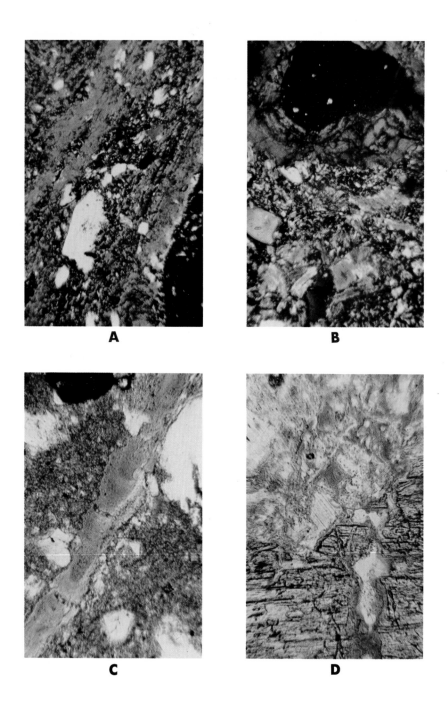

Fig. 46–3.

otherwise affected by weathering. Observations on color and luster by reflected light, aided by crystal form if visible, are the best procedures. Magnetic separations will help confirm the presence of magnetite and ilmenite. Many grains that appear opaque by plain light can be seen to be translucent if viewed in strong crossed polarized light. Most grains that behave in this way are altered grains or aggregates, not opaque minerals.

46–2.4.3 MICROCRYSTALLINE AGGREGATES AND AMORPHOUS SUBSTANCES

46–2.4.3.1 Criteria Useful in Identification. Most microcrystalline aggregates have one striking characteristic feature: they show birefringence but do not have definite, sharp, complete extinction in crossed polarized light. Extinction may occur as dark bands that sweep through the grain or parts of the grain when the stage is turned, or it may occur in patches of irregular size and shape. In all positions, some part of the grain is bright except in a few types of grains such as well-oriented mineral pseudomorphs and certain clay-skin fragments. Aggregates and altered grains should be examined with a variety of combinations of illumination and magnification in both plain and polarized light. The principal properties that can be used to identify or at least characterize aggregates are given below.

Color, if brown to bright red, is usually related to iron content and oxidation of the iron. Manganese and organic matter may contribute black and grayish-brown colors.

Refractive index is directly related to density; elemental composition, atom packing, water content, and porosity all influence refractive index.

Strength of birefringence is a clue to identity of the minerals. Even though the individual units of the aggregate are small, birefringence can be estimated by interference color and brightness.

Morphology may provide clues to the composition or origin of the aggregate. Some aggregates are pseudomorphs after primary mineral grains; and characteristics of the original minerals, such as cleavage traces, twinning, or crystal form can still be observed. Morphology can sometimes be observed in completely altered grains—even in volcanic ash shards and basalt fragments. Other morphological characteristics may be observable in the individual units or overall structure; for example, the units may be plates or needles, or there may be banding.

46–2.4.3.2 Useful Differentiating Criteria for Particular Species. For purposes of studies of soil genesis, the aggregates present in sand and silt fractions are not of equal significance. Some are nuisances, but must be accounted for, and others are particles with important diagnostic value. Useful differentiating criteria for some of the commonly found types of aggregates are given below.

Rock fragments include chips of shale, slate, schist, and fine-grained igneous rocks like rhyolite. Identification depends on recognition of structure and individual components, and consideration of possible sources.

Clay aggregates may be present in a wide variety of forms. Silt and sand bound together into larger grains by a nearly isotropic brownish material usually indicates faulty dispersion. Clay skins may resist dispersion and consequently may appear as fragments in grain mounts. Such fragments are usually brown or red and translucent, with wavy extinction bands. Care may be needed to distinguish them from weathered biotite. Clay aggregates may be mineral pseudomorphs. Kaolin pseudomorphs after feldspar are found fairly commonly, and montmorillonite aggregates, pseudomorphic after basic rock minerals, have been observed. Montmorillonite in this form shows its high birefringence, and its extinction is mottled or patchy on a small scale. Coarse kaolinite flakes, books, and vermicular aggregates resist dispersion and may be abundant in sand and silt; these particles may resemble muscovite, but they are cloudy, show no definite extinction, and have very low birefringence. Many cases of anomalously high cation-exchange capacity of sand and silt fractions, calculated from the exchange capacity of the whole soil and the percentage content and exchange capacity of the clay, no doubt can be accounted for by the occurrence of such aggregates in the sand and silt fractions.

Volcanic glass is isotropic and has a low refractive index—lower than most of the silicate minerals, ranging from 1.48 in the colorless siliceous glasses to as high as 1.56 in the green or brown glasses of basalt composition. Shapes vary, but elongated, curved shard forms, often with bubbles, are fairly common. This glassy material may be observed sticking to other minerals, and particles may contain small crystals of feldspar or incipient crystals with needle and dendritic forms. The basic glasses weather easily, and so the colorless siliceous types are more common in soils.

Allophane is present in many soils derived from volcanic ash. It can seldom be identified directly, but its presence can be inferred when sand and silt are cemented into aggregates by isotropic material with low refractive index, especially if volcanic ash shards are also present.

Opal, an isotropic material, occurs as a cementing material and in separate grains, some of which are of organic origin (plant opal, sponge spicules, diatoms). Its refractive index is very low (<1.45, which is lower than the value for volcanic ash). Identification may depend in part on form and occurrence.

Iron oxides may occur separately or as coatings, cementing agents and mixtures with other minerals. They impart brown and red colors and raise the refractive index in the mixtures. *Goethite* is yellow to bright red. The refractive index and birefringence are higher in the red varieties, which seem to be better crystallized, often having a prismatic or fibrous habit. Aggregates have parallel extinction. In oriented aggregates, the interference colors often have a greenish cast. *Hematite* has higher refractive index than goethite and is granular rather than prismatic. Large grains of hematite are nearly opaque.

Gibbsite often occurs as separate, pure, crystal aggregates, either alone or inside altered mineral grains. The grains may appear to be well-crystallized single crystals, but close inspection in crossed polarized light shows patchy, banded extinction, indicating intergrown aggregates. It is colorless, and the refractive index (1.56 to 1.58) and birefringence are higher than the values for quartz. The bright interference colors and aggregate extinction are characteristic.

Chert occurs as aggregate grains with patchy extinction. The refractive index is slightly lower than that of quartz, and the birefringence is lower than that of gibbsite. It sometimes occurs in pseudomorphs after fossils and sometimes in grains with the exterior form of quartz crystals.

Glauconite occurs in the form of an aggregate of small micaceous grains with high birefringence. When fresh, it is dark green and almost opaque, but it weathers to brown and more translucent forms. It is difficult to identify on optical evidence alone.

TiO_2 aggregates have been tentatively identified in the heavy mineral separates of many soils. These bodies have an extremely high refractive index and high birefringence like rutile, and the yellow to gray colors are similar to those of anatase. They are granular and rough-surfaced. This habit of growth, with its little spurs and projections, suggests that TiO_2 aggregates may be secondary.

46–3   THIN SECTIONS

46–3.1   Introduction

Thin sections are studied to observe the soil constituents in their natural, undisturbed arrangement. Examination of thin sections with a microscope can be regarded an extension of morphological studies of field soil profiles. Soil structural features should be examined with the naked eye, with the hand lens, with the stereoscopic microscope, and, finally, with the petrographic microscope. Observations on thin sections are always most meaningful when correlated with these other observations. Effort should be made, where pertinent and where possible, to relate the micromorphology to the field profile or hand specimen.

There are two mutually supporting aspects of the study of thin sections, namely, identification of constituents, and observation of morphology. Morphological investigations can stand alone, but they are strengthened greatly as more minerals and other substances are identified. Support from X-ray diffraction analysis, differential thermal analysis, and chemical analysis should be obtained if feasible. Observations made on thin sections often are useful in interpreting the results of these bulk analyses.

Information to be sought depends upon the problem and the type of material, and so there can be no rules for a routine examination of thin sections. Recording and expressing results has been a problem because of the lack of descriptive terms that have the same meaning to everyone. It is difficult to separate objective observation from interpretation, and perhaps it is not always necessary to do so. However, a narrative type of description can be used (Yassogou and Whiteside, 1960; Thorp et al., 1959). Descriptions can be accompanied by photomicrographs and sketches (Grossman et al., 1959; Flach, 1960;[1] Altemueller, 1961, 1962; Soil Survey Staff, 1960; Alexander and Cady, 1962). Brewer (1960) and Brewer and Sleeman (1960) have made advances in developing terminology for describing and interpreting morphological features in thin sections.

Some features are so gross that their meaning may be missed at high magnifications, and so the first step should be to look at the section with a hand lens or other low-power magnifier. A check should be made for large-scale structural units, presence and shape of soil peds, mottles, concretions, contrasts of color or density, banding, bedding, or other evidence of stratification or alignment of the coarse grains. Both reflected light and transmitted light should be used.

Examination should proceed from lower to higher power in both plain and crossed polarized light. As in the study of grains, it is desirable to become familiar with the overall features of the section before identification or interpretation begins. Since many problems requiring use of thin sections are concerned with movement of clay or other substances and differences among horizons caused by soil-forming processes and weathering, it is helpful to scan all the sections from a profile or all connected with the problem to see what important features might be worth the most emphasis. A variety of types of illumination should be used with each magnification. Strong, convergent light with crossed polarizers brings out structures in dense or weakly birefringent material that at first might appear opaque or isotropic. Structures in translucent specimens become more clearly visible if plain light is used and if the condensers are stopped down. Everything should be viewed in several positions of the stage or during slow rotation with crossed polarized light.

A thin section is essentially a two-dimensional slice through a three-dimensional body. Mineral grains and structural features are seen in one plane, and the shapes seen must be extrapolated into their true shapes. A grain that appears needle shaped may be a needle or the edge of a flat plate. An elliptical pore may be an angular slice through a tube with a circular cross section. A circular structural unit is probably a ball. Repeated viewing of similar features that appear to be cut at different angles, with

---

[1] Flach, Klaus W. 1960. Sols Bruns Acides in the Northeastern United States; genesis, morphology, and relationships to associated soils. Ph.D. thesis. Cornell University, Ithaca, N. Y.

the potential third-dimensional appearance in mind, is the best way to accustom oneself to a volume, rather than a planar interpretation of shape. The observer must also keep the facts about the thickness of the section in mind. A well-prepared section is 20 to 30μ thick. Grains smaller than this may be stacked and hence not observable as individuals, and pores much smaller than the section thickness can not be seen clearly.

46–3.2 Sampling

Samples may be natural clods, cores, or any other block or unit of soil volume that can be collected without breaking up. Fine-textured soils may hold together well when they are wet but fall apart into smaller aggregates when dry. Coarser-textured materials may not hold together under any condition. Therefore samples can be coated immediately in the field with paraffin or synthetic resin (Brasher et al., 1965). Intermediate-textured material free of stones can be collected with a core-cutter, packed in boxes, and transported gently. Alternatively, clods can be cut out with a knife and packed in boxes with a soft material or loose soil from the same horizon as a cushion, or the samples can be partially impregnated in the field with a water-soluble resin (Cymel, obtainable from the American Cyanamid Co., is suitable for such use). Many problems require that the orientation of the specimen be known. A tag with appropriate arrows can be affixed. Two ordinary pins placed in line with the vertical axis make a good orientation marker.

46–3.3 Impregnation

Impregnating media of several types are readily available. The most commonly used ones are polyester resins that are diluted with monomeric styrene to a water consistency when used. They harden after addition of an organic oxidant catalyst. These various resins and the other ingredients can be obtained from several of the major chemical companies and from some of the scientific supply houses. Small lots are often available at hobby shops. Names and sources of some of the resins that have been used are given in the references cited. For impregnation with these materials, samples must be dry. Clods are impregnated by immersing them in the liquid after addition of the catalyst, placing the container in a vacuum chamber and pumping out the air. After a few hours the plastic hardens. Hardening is hastened and made more complete by heating at about 70°C. Procedures for impregnating samples with plastics of this type have been given by Lockwood (1950), Bourbeau and Berger (1948), Buol and Fadness (1961), and Jongerius and Heintzberger (1963).

A second impregnation method employs resins like Canada balsam, which polymerize or harden after heating. This method is excellent for quick jobs on small clods (Dalrymple, 1957). A small amount of the resin is cooked in a dish on a hot plate until a withdrawn drop will harden on cooling. Slow cooking at a low temperature is desirable to prevent the resin from darkening and becoming too brittle. The sample is placed in the resin and left until it appears to be thoroughly soaked, or until evolution of air bubbles stops. The sample can then be either lifted out to cool, or the resin can be cooled with the block in it to prevent the liquid from draining out of pores.

Other resins are mixed with a volatile solvent such as acetone. Again, they are diluted to a watery consistency, and the samples are impregnated under vacuum. After the solvent has evaporated, heating for a few hours at 70° to 80°C. completes the hardening.

The water-soluble plastics, such as Cymel and Carbowax (available from Union Carbide Co.), have several important advantages. They can be used to achieve at least partial impregnation in the field, which permits or facilitates the study of loose material. They have a potential for impregnating materials such as Ando soils, peat soils, and some soils high in montmorillonite that change their structure radically when dried.

Each different kind of soil behaves somewhat differently in the various impregnating media, and so in actual practice each worker must develop his own procedure. In general, soils of medium and coarse textures and those containing predominantly kaolin clays are easy to impregnate. Medium- and fine-textured samples containing swelling clays are difficult to work with and require special handling at all stages. Developments are rapid in the plastics field, and new and better materials may well appear in the future.

46–3.4 Cutting and Finishing

If the sample can be successfully impregnated, the rest of the process of cutting, polishing, mounting, and finishing is essentially the same as that used by geologists for preparing rock sections. A complete set of general instructions for making sections of a variety of materials is given in an article by Reed and Mergner (1953). Sometimes reimpregnation of surfaces with one of the balsam-like cements is needed after cutting. Samples containing montmorillonite often must be cut, ground, and polished in the absence of water—either dry or in kerosene or mineral oil.

Making thin sections is an art and requires some practice and patience. Essentially it consists of the following steps after impregnation.

(1) A rectangular block or slab is cut with the dimensions of a finished section or a little larger.

(2) One side of this block is ground and polished flat and smooth. The condition can be checked with a binocular microscope or hand lens.

(3) After the block has been polished, it is cleaned and cemented to a microscope slide.

(4) The specimen is then ground to the required thickness with successively finer grades of abrasive powder. A useful slide holder for this stage has been devised by Cochran and King (1957). Again, the specimen is cleaned and dried. Then it is painted with a thin coat of flexible collodion with a fine, soft brush to prevent splitting and drifting of the section, and a cover glass is applied.

The individual worker will soon make his own adaptations of this general procedure and will continually change it to cope with new kinds of soil and new problems.

A few additional notes may be made on questions that may arise:

Often, impregnation will be incomplete, or the plastic will not reach the center of the specimen. After the clod has been cut into rough blocks for finishing, the faces can be reimpregnated if soft spots are seen. Re-treatment with the same plastic may not be successful because the liquid styrene may soften the previously set plastic. Another method is simple and direct. The block is dried well, and the surface to be finished is coated with a thick layer of precooked balsam or one of the synthetic balsam-like resins and placed in an oven at about 100°C. for a few hours. The balsam will seep into the empty pores. Polishing to prepare the block for mounting must be done with care for it is necessary to grind away the layer of balsam but not to grind into the block past the depth of penetration of the balsam.

It is desirable to have two rotating cast-iron laps, one for coarse grinding, one for fine. Large, slow-turning laps are best; one can use the part near the circumference for higher-speed work and the part near the center when more caution is needed. Great care is sometimes needed at the last stages— the last 20 or 30μ may disappear in a few seconds on a fast lap. Final polishing is often done on a piece of plate glass 1 foot square.

Abrasive powders are obtained from scientific supply houses or optical-goods companies. A supply of emery paper should be on hand for dry grinding and polishing of montmorillonite materials (200, 400 and 600 fineness is a good working range of sizes).

Thickness is usually checked by interference colors of sand grains, but many fine-textured soils and high-iron-oxide materials that are opaque or have very fine structural elements must be ground thinner than the standard 30μ. Thickness control depends on repeated examination and grinding until one can see as much of the fine structure as possible without losing the section. When the thickness is being checked, the section should be wet to avoid the strong contrast in refractive index between air and section that may make it look thicker and more featureless than it really is. Most sections are thinner at the edges than the center because of the motions used in grinding; but this may be an advantage, enabling one to see morphology in a third dimension to a slight degree.

It is important to have the block firmly and closely cemented to the slide with no, or few, flattened air bubbles or iridescent films visible. A set of clamps or spring clothespins helps at this point because block and slide must be handled while hot.

Hot balsam or other resin is used to cement on the cover glass. Soil thin sections are very fragile at this stage. The coat of flexible collodion will help to protect them. It is possible also to cook the balsam on a cover glass and then to invert the glass on the slightly warmed section.

It is possible to make thin sections with very simple equipment. They have been made with a hacksaw, a few files, a glass plate, and some emery powder.

Cleanliness of a sort is essential. When a shift from coarser to finer abrasive is made, the sample must be washed, brushed, or air-blasted to remove coarser grit to prevent tearing the section. When the block is mounted on the slide it should be as clean as possible, and the finished section should be well cleaned before the cover glass is applied.

There are a number of commercial, custom thin-section makers available for those who do not have the time or equipment for the work. There are several advantages in making one's own: a large number of sections can be made from any sample at a variety of orientations; the specimen can be studied at all stages of the work—as a polished section by reflected light, for example; structural features of interest that are noted can be preserved in the sections; and special treatments such as staining, or acid washes to remove carbonates obscuring other structures can be applied.

46–3.5 Observations and Interpretations

46–3.5.1 IDENTIFICATION

46–3.5.1.1 Grains. Identification of sand and silt grains in thin sections is carried out by standard methods given in petrography texts (Kerr, 1959; Winchell, 1937). The general approach is the same as that outlined in sections 46–2.4.2 and 46–2.4.3 except that refractive index can be used only roughly, and more weight is placed on the other optical and morphological properties. It is rarely necessary to be concerned with minerals that occur in small quantities or to attempt quantitative mineralogical analysis with a thin section. The usual soil thin section contains too few grains to be usable for such work. Rough information on particle-size distribution can be obtained in some materials with replicate sections, however.

The thickness of the section limits the size of grain that can be identified. If the section is 30μ thick, grains smaller than this will be overlapping or buried in the matrix and can not be seen clearly enough to be identified, unless they have some outstanding property such as extremely high birefringence or refractive index (calcite and rutile, for example).

If identification and mineralogical analysis are important for the problem being studied, it is best to do this work on separated size fractions and to use the thin sections mainly for information about the arrangement of the components. The methods and types of samples supplement each other: grains in thin sections are seen as slices in random orientation; cleavage and interior structure can often be seen best in the sections; and one sees the whole range of sizes as well.

Visible grains will be in part single minerals, most commonly quartz, but aggregates and compound grains are common, especially in transported material like loess and till. Recognition of aggregates, concretions, pseudomorphs, and weathered grains is more important in thin-section studies than in sand and silt petrography. It can be easier because interior structures are exposed. Grains of this type may be important in soil genesis studies but are often destroyed or eliminated by sample preparation procedures that separate sand, silt, and clay. Most sections are thinnest at the edge, and examination here with high power will enable one to see the patchy aggregate extinction, to estimate birefringence and refractive index, and to observe morphology of aggregates and small structural features.

46–3.5.1.2 Matrix. When the skeletal grains of coarse silt and sand size have been accounted for, there will remain a matrix consisting of the finer silt fractions, clay, free oxides, and often organic matter. Some of this material can be identified, but some can only be described and placed into groups. It is very helpful to have a list of the minerals in the fine fractions and estimates of the relative amounts found by X-ray diffraction studies and differential thermal analysis.

Clay will occur not only in the form of aggregates but also in a variety of massive interstitial fillings, coatings, bridges, and general groundmass. Even though the particles are submicroscopic, the clay can be described and characterized and sometimes identified; at least the 1:1 and 2:1 lattice types can be distinguished. Completely randomly arranged clay $<1\mu$ in size will exhibit no birefringence and will appear isotropic in crossed polarized light. Seldom is all the clay in a soil random and isotropic. It develops in oriented bodies during its formation or becomes oriented by pressure or translocation. If enough of the plate-shaped particles are together and oriented in a body large enough to see, the birefringence can be observed.

Except for halloysite, the silicate clay minerals found in soils have a platy shape. The a and b crystallographic axes are within the plane of the plate, and the c axis is almost perpendicular to this plane. The crystals are monoclinic, but the distribution of atoms along the a and b axes is so nearly the same, and the c axis is so nearly perpendicular to the other axes, that the minerals are pseudo-hexagonal. The optical properties as well as the crystal structure and general habit of clay particles are analogous to those of the micas, and the micas can be used as a model in thinking about and describing the properties of clays.

The speed of light traveling in the direction of the *c* axis and vibrating parallel to the *a* axis is almost the same as that vibrating parallel to the *b* axis; therefore, the refractive indexes are very close together, and interference effects seen in crossed polarized light will be small when the observer is looking along the *c* axis.

Light vibrating parallel to the *c* axis travels faster than in other directions, and hence the refractive index is lower. If the edge of the crystal, or aggregate of crystals, is viewed along the *a-b* plane between crossed polarizers there will be two straight extinction positions, and interference colors will show in other positions.

Figures 46–1A and 46–1B illustrate these optical properties of clay aggregates.

If a concentration of clay is organized so that the plates are predominantly parallel, the optical effects can be observed. How completely or satisfactorily they can be observed depends on the purity and continuity of the clay body and the process that oriented it.

Kaolinite has refractive indexes slightly higher than quartz and has low birefringence. In the average thin section, interference colors are gray to pale yellow. In residual soils derived from coarse-grained igneous rocks, it often occurs as book-like and accordion-like aggregates of silt and sand size (see Fig. 46–3B).

Halloysite, because of tubular habit, should not show birefringence even though it could form oriented aggregates. It sometimes does have very faint patternless birefringence, possibly caused by impurities or refraction of light at interfaces between particles.

The 2:1 lattice minerals have high birefringence and show bright intermediate-order interference colors when the edges of the aggregates are viewed. It is seldom possible to distinguish between clay-size montmorillonite, mica, vermiculite, and chlorite in thin section. The latter clay minerals rarely occur pure in soils; there is usually a mixture of the minerals themselves, and they are often stained by and mixed with iron oxide and organic matter.

46–3.5.2 MORPHOLOGY

46–3.5.2.1 Skeletal Grains. Shape, size, and spacing of the primary mineral grains may be related to source of parent material, mode of deposition, and changes caused by weathering and soil development. Large, angular quartz grains suggest granite or related rocks, and material in place or transported only a short distance. Rounding indicates water transportation, and rounding plus frosting and pitting indicates movement by wind. These latter observations, however, can be made more easily on cleaned separates with a stereoscopic microscope than in thin sections. Stratification of coarse and fine particles usually indicates alluvium. Alignment of platy particles can indicate depositional stratification but can also be caused by pressure or shear. Spacing of primary or skeletal grains can be a valuable reference datum for volume changes in weathering and for interhorizontal and local losses and gains; leaching or removal of material leaves the resistant grains closer together; additions such as translocated clay or iron oxide may force them apart.

46–3.5.2.2 Pore Space. Size, shape, spacing, and location of pores and other openings must be described. In making such observations, the observer must remember that the two-dimensional slice can intersect openings of various shapes at any angle, that some features can be artifacts, and that the lower end of the size range of structures observable is limited by the thickness of the section. The condition and composition of the walls of the openings and the adjoining material should be noted as well as the morphology of the opening itself. Pores and holes are distinguished from colorless grains by checking for anisotropism when the stage is rotated with polarizers crossed. Grains viewed down an optic axis will appear isotropic, and a check for interference figure should be made if this is suspected. Some of the impregnating plastics show anisotropism in crossed polarized light because of strain, but this will not be confused with a mineral after a little thought and practice.

Visible pore space can range from essentially none, as in some fragipans (Fig. 46–3C) and glacial tills, to situations where large pores or open space make up a large part of the section area, as in A horizons of Brunizems with well-developed structure and in coarse, well-sorted sands.

Tubular pores are common in some soils. Seen in cross section they are often perfectly round, but in sections cut in other directions they may exhibit a variety of shapes. Such pores are seldom straight for any appreciable distance. Repeated observation and examination of the whole void or pore may be needed to distinguish a tubular pore from a crack or ped face if the section happens to cut the pore longitudinally.

Ped faces can be straight over distances up to several millimeters, and they often intersect at angles. Surfaces are generally smooth, and they may or may not have a coating. Cracks, or more or less straight openings, may be either ped faces or simple cleavage channels. It may be necessary to refer back to the structure of the hand specimen or appearance with very low magnification to distinguish them.

Holes or vesicles that are isolated can be the result of weathering of a soluble mineral. These are seldom round, although they may have smooth surfaces. Clues to formation of pores in this manner might be shape, residues from the mineral, or presence of an easily weathered mineral of similar size in deeper horizons.

Large scale pore space can be described by its relation to shapes of the grains or aggregates and by estimates of percentage. Areas can be measured with a grid eyepiece or by various transect-measuring statistical methods like those used for modal analysis of rocks (Anderson and Binnie, 1961). Although only areas are measured, the volume of various constituents can be estimated in this way. If pore area or volume and pore arrangement are important aspects of the study, it is helpful to add a soluble dye to the impregnating plastic (Lockwood, 1950). This makes it readily possible to separate colorless sand grains from pores without crossed polarized light. Various types of pores and channels are shown in the figures.

46–3.5.2.3 Clay Arrangement. By far the greatest interest in micromorphology, in the USA at least, has centered on the arrangement of clay as an indication of the genetic processes that have operated and on the relation of the clay to soil structure. The features of the several common types of clay arrangement are summarized in the following few paragraphs.

Residual clay has been in place since its formation by weathering or since deposition of a transported soil parent material. Local adjustment of position may have occurred, but such clay has not moved separately. It may be completely unoriented, and thus isotropic, but more often it shows some birefringence. In transported materials, silt-size flakes and other small aggregates are common. In residual materials, clay is often arranged in forms pseudomorphic after rock minerals (as in Fig. 46–2A and Fig. 46–2B) or in crystal aggregates in definite bodies such as the vermicular or accordion-like kaolin books shown in Fig. 46–3B. Regular, intact arrangement of these materials generally is diagnostic for residual material.

The clay becomes rearranged by pressure applied differentially to produce shear. Platy particles may become oriented by slip along a plane, as in the slickenside faces in a Grumusol or in fine-textured glacial till, and they will also be oriented inside the blocks or peds. Root pressure, wetting and drying, and mass movement can produce pressure orientation.

Pressure orientation can be inferred when smooth faces with no separate coating are seen on structural units. But otherwise it can not be observed in plain light. In plain light, the clay in the section may be homogeneous and rather featureless. In crossed polarized light, a reticulate pattern of orientation appears, consisting of bright lines showing aggregate birefringence often intersecting at regular angles. The effect is that of a network in a plaid pattern. There may be numerous sets of these slip planes that will appear in different positions as the stage is turned. Pressure-oriented clay is illustrated in Fig. 46–1C.

Pressure-oriented clay may appear around rigid bodies, such as quartz grains, or along root channels, and it is often strongly developed on ped faces. Pressure can also orient the mica flakes and any other small platy grains.

Translocated clay has several features that distinguish it from residual clay. It occurs in separate bodies, usually with a distinct boundary, and it is located on present or former pore walls or ped faces.[2] Several common forms of translocated clay are shown in Fig. 46–1A, 46–1B, 46–1D, 46–2A, 46–2B, 46–2D, 46–3A, 46–3B, and 46–3C. It is more homogeneous than matrix clay and is usually finer (see Fig. 46–1, 46–2, and 46–3). It is often of different composition from the matrix, especially if it came from another horizon. It shows lamination, indicating deposition in successive increments. And, finally, these bodies of translocated clay will show birefringence and extinction, indicating that they are oriented aggregates. If they are straight, they will have parallel extinction; if curved, a dark band will be present wherever the composite c axis and composite a and b axes are parallel to the vibration planes of the polarizers. These dark bands sweep through the clay aggregate when the stage is rotated. Features of such curved clay deposits are shown in Fig. 46–2D.

Swelling, slump, and movement in soils may cause clay skins to become distorted and broken. Pores may collapse, and the lining then becomes an oblong block of oriented clay. New faces and openings develop, and the old clay skins are found as isolated fragments in the matrix; ultimately they may be re-incorporated into the matrix and disappear (see Fig. 46–3A).

46–3.5.2.4 Organic Matter. Amorphous coatings of organic matter with or without admixed iron and aluminum are common, especially in Podzols or soils influenced by the podzolization process. This material is dark brown to black, isotropic or faintly birefringent, and often flecked with minute opaque grains. It occurs as the bridging and coating material in B horizons of sandy Podzols and also as a thin coating or stain on faces of pores and peds in other soils (Flach, 1960).[3]

Organic residues such as living and partly decomposed roots are usually recognizable by their cellular structure. The birefringence of many plant fibers often causes them to be confused with minerals. Chitinous remains of arthropods and egg capsules also may resemble an inorganic structure. Anything with an unusually symmetrical shape or regular cellular form should be suspected to be of organic origin.

46–3.5.2.5 Mottles, Concretions, and Nodules. Mottles are continuous with the matrix. The spacing and size of the sand and silt grains is the same inside and out; and clay orientation, if present, is a continuous pattern. Color is caused by a high content of iron oxide or iron and manganese oxides. Sometimes a central pore or tubule is visible. These local, patchy concentrations usually are irregular and have diffuse boundaries.

Concretions have a concentric, banded structure. Commonly they are

---

[2] Substances other than clay may form pore linings and coatings in some soils. The most common of these substances are goethite, gibbsite, the carbonate minerals, and gypsum, and these may be identified by their mineralogical properties.
[3] Flach, Klaus W. 1960. *Op. Cit.*

high in MnO_2 and nearly opaque, although they may have alternate light and dark bands.

A somewhat related type of dense body is illustrated by the residual lumps or nodules of B-horizon material left isolated in the lower A horizon, as the A horizon tongues down into the B horizon. These have a higher clay content than the surrounding matrix, and boundaries are regular and usually rather sharp. Such nodules may become centers of accumulation of iron and manganese. With development, they may become smaller and rounder and ultimately may become "shot."

Mottles, concretions, and nodules are cemented to varying degrees, and so they may move as sand or gravel when material is transported. Comparing their interior composition with that of the surrounding matrix, and examining the continuity, or lack of it, at their boundaries will enable one to decide whether these aggregates are formed in place or not.

46–3.5.2.6 Artifacts. Artifacts are caused by grains tearing out of the section, by scratches during grinding, and by splitting of the section when the cover glass is pressed down. These features usually have unnatural looking boundaries with a ragged appearance. Splitting may follow natural structural lines; if it does, the face will show some evidence of a coating or of compression or alignment of grains. If it is a random split, it will cross natural features. In some soils, sand grains have compressed, oriented clay coatings. Such grains may fall out during grinding and leave a smooth, coated hole. Recognition of such holes may depend on comparison of their shape and lining with the situation around grains of similar size. Other artifacts that may cause some confusion if one is not aware of the possibilities are: grains of the abrasive grinding powder (carborundum, Al_2O_3, garnet); cellulose fibers, hairs and bristles from cleaning tissues, towels and brushes (these often have high birefringence, but their fibrous structure is apparent); and air bubbles, which have high negative relief.

46–4 APPLICATIONS

Microscope petrography may be useful in investigating the origin of soil parent material. Certain suites of minerals are associated with specific rock sources; hence, overlays and unconformities may be suspected from certain kinds of discontinuities in the mineralogical composition of samples taken at different depths in a given profile. For example, fresh feldspar and hornblende in the silt fraction in the A and B horizons and only resistant minerals in the C horizon may indicate an overlay of loess younger than the underlying material. Evidence of volcanic ash (glassy shards, plagioclase feldspar types) may be critical in explaining some soil properties.

Ratios between resistant minerals can serve as a check on the homogeneity of the original parent material in a soil development study and as a base for calculations of loss and gain.

Effects of weathering in formation of parent materials and in soil profiles can be investigated by microscope petrography. Decrease or disappearance of minerals or groups when compared against resistant minerals provides an index of weathering. The condition of remaining minerals also answers some questions; for example, one can tell whether the minerals are altering to clay or other secondary products or whether the products are being carried away in solution. Observations of thin sections enable one to see minerals in the process of alteration with the products in place. Halloysite has been seen forming from feldspar, montmorillonite from augite, kaolinite from feldspar and from mica, and vermiculite from mica. Stages of weathering can be followed, and the source of secondary minerals can be observed directly.

Clay illuviation can be observed in sequences of thin sections from the clay-depleted A horizon, to the tongued transition zone at the top of the B horizon, to the B horizon with its variety of clay accumulation features, and to the C horizon with its residual clay. Clay distribution and arrangement vary greatly among different soil groups, and much work remains to be done on origin of soil clay and reasons for its distribution and concentration.

Petrographic studies may aid in understanding the development of certain types of concretions, laterite, and pans. Rearrangement and recrystallization of oxides to cause cementation, and sequences of changes whereby mottles become hard plinthite nodules may be investigated.

The view of the soil in a thin section through a microscope approaches the view seen by the plant root and permits close, direct investigation of the physical and mineralogical environment of roots. Thus, microscope petrography is useful also in investigations of tilth, seedling emergence, and penetration of air, water, and roots. The shape and sometimes the binding agent of soil aggregates can be observed. Arrangement and continuity of pore space can be traced. Compaction and orientation of particles in "traffic" pans can be confirmed. Surface crusts can be observed directly.

Microscopy gives information about the form and location of chemical elements in the soil. It provides a direct look at the interior arrangement of the soil—the location and condition of the sand, silt and clay, and the distribution and character of the secondary minerals. Such information is a helpful adjunct to classification and mapping of soils and to the development of improved systems that will serve more accurately to extend the knowledge obtained on specific areas to other areas having similar properties.

46–5 LITERATURE CITED [1]

Alexander, Lyle T., and Cady, John G. 1962. The genesis and hardening of laterite in soils. U. S. Dept. Agriculture Tech. Bull. 1282.

Altemueller, H. J. 1961. Beitrag zur micromorphologischen Differenzierung von durchschlammter Parabraunerde, Podsol-Braunerde und Humus-Podsol. Zeitschr. Pfl., Düng. Bodenk. 98:247–258.

Altemueller, H. J. 1962. Mikromorphologische Untersuchung an Bodenprofilen des mittleren fränkischen Jura. Bayerisches Landwirtschaftliches Jahrbuch 39:98–109.

Anderson, D. M., and Binnie, R. R. 1961. Modal analysis of soils. Soil Sci. Soc. Am. Proc. 25:499–503.

Bourbeau, G. A., and Berger, K. C. 1948. Thin sections of soils and friable materials prepared by impregnation with the plastic "Castolite." Soil Sci. Soc. Am. Proc. (1947) 12:409–412.

Brasher, B. R., Davidson, S. E., and Valassis, V. 1965. Volume measurement and bulk density of Saran-coated soil fragments. Soil Sci.

Brewer, R. 1960. The petrographic approach to the study of soils. Trans. Intern. Congr. Soil Sci. 7th Madison. I:1–13.

Brewer, R., and Sleeman, J. R. 1960. Soil structure and fabric: their definition and description. J. Soil Sci. 11:172–185.

Brewer, R. 1960. Cutans: Their definition, recognition, and interpretation. J. Soil Sci. 11:280–292.

Buol, S. W., and Fadness, D. M., 1961. New method of impregnating fragile material for thin sectioning. Soil Sci. Soc. Am. Proc. 25:253.

Cady, John G. 1941. Some mineralogical characteristics of Podzol and Brown Podzolic forest soil profiles. Soil Sci. Soc. Am. Proc. (1940) 5:352–354.

Carozzi, Albert V. 1960. Microscopic Sedimentary Petrography. John Wiley and Sons, Inc., New York.

Cochran, Manning, and King, A. G. 1957. Two new types of holders used in grinding thin sections. Am. Mineralogist. 42:422–425.

Dalrymple, J. B. 1957. Preparation of thin sections of soils. J. Soil Sci. 8:161–165.

Fry, W. H. 1933. Petrographic methods for soil laboratories. U. S. Dept. Agriculture Tech. Bull. 344.

Grossman, R. B., Stephen, I., Fehrenbacher, J. B., and Beavers, A. H. 1959. Fragipan soils of Illinois: III. Micromorphological studies of Hosmer silt loam. Soil Sci. Soc. Am. Proc. 23:73–75.

Haseman, J. F., and Marshall, C. E. 1945. The use of heavy minerals in studies of the origin and development of soils. Missouri Agri. Exp. Sta. Res. Bull. 387.

Johannsen, Albert. 1918. Manual of Petrographic Methods. Ed. 2. McGraw-Hill Book Co., Inc., New York.

Jongerius A., and Heintzberger, G. 1963. The preparation of mammoth-sized thin sections. Soil Survey Papers No. 1, Netherlands Soil Survey Inst., Wageningen.

Kerr, Paul F. 1959. Optical Mineralogy. McGraw-Hill Book Co., Inc., New York.

Krumbein, W. C., and Pettijohn, F. J. 1938. Manual of Sedimentary Petrography. Appleton-Century-Crofts, New York.

---

[1] Just before this book was printed, the following additional reference work on the subject was published:

Brewer, R. 1964. Fabric and Mineral Analysis of Soils. John Wiley and Sons, Inc., New York.

The material covered in the references listed in section 46–5 for Brewer and Brewer and Sleeman can all be obtained from the more recent reference work.

Kubiena, W. L. 1938. Micropedology. Collegiate Press, Ames, Iowa.

Kubiena, W. L. 1953. The Soils of Europe. Murby, London.

Larsen, Esper S., and Berman, Harry, 1934. The microscopic determination of the nonopaque minerals. U. S. Dept. Interior, Geol. Surv. Bul. 848.

leRoux, F. H., Cady, J. G., and Coleman, N. T. 1963. Mineralogy of soil separates and alkali-ion exchange sorption. Soil Sci. Soc. Am. Proc. 27:534–538.

Lockwood, William N. 1950. Impregnating sandstone specimens with thermosetting plastics for studies of oil-bearing formations. Bull. Am. Assoc. Petrol. Geol. 34:2061–2067.

Marshall, C. E., and Jeffries, C. D. 1946. The correlation of soil types and parent materials, with supplementary information on weathering processes. Soil Sci. Soc. Am. Proc. (1945) 10:397–405.

Matelski, R. P. 1951. Separation of minerals by subdividing solidified bromoform after centrifugation. Soil Sci. 71:269–272.

McCaughey, W. J., and Fry, W. H. 1913. The microscopic determination of soil-forming minerals. U. S. Dept. Agriculture Bur. Soils Bull. 91.

McCaughey, W. J., and Fry, W. H. 1914. In W. O. Robinson: The inorganic composition of some important American soils. U. S. Dept. Agriculture Bull. 122:16–27.

Milner, H. B. 1962. Sedimentary Petrography. Ed. 4. The Macmillan Co., New York.

Osmond, D. A. 1958. Micropedology. Soils and Fertilizers 21:1–6.

Reed, Frank S., and Mergner, John L. 1953. Preparation of rock thin sections. Am. Mineralogist 38:1184–1203.

Ruhe, R. V. 1956. Geomorphic surfaces and the nature of soils. Soil Sci. 82:441–455.

Smithson, F. 1961. The microscopy of the silt fraction. J. Soil Sci. 12:145–157.

Soil Survey Staff. 1960. Soil Classification, A Comprehensive System, 7th Approximation. U. S. Govt. Printing Office, Washington, D. C.

Stephen, I. 1960. Clay orientation in soils. Sci. Progr. (London) 48:322–330.

Thorp, J., Cady, J. G., and Gamble, E. E. 1959. Genesis of Miami silt loam. Soil Sci. Soc. Am. Proc. 23:156–161.

Wahlstrom, Ernest E. 1951. Optical Crystallography, Ed. 2. John Wiley and Sons, Inc., New York.

Winchell, Alexander N. 1937. Elements of Optical Mineralogy. Part I. Principles and Methods. Part II. Descriptions of Minerals. John Wiley and Sons, Inc., New York.

Yassoglou, N. J., and Whiteside, E. P. 1960. Morphology and genesis of some soils containing fragipans in northern Michigan. Soil Sci. Soc. Am. Proc. 24:396–407.

47

Electron Microscope Techniques[1]

J. A. KITTRICK[2]

Washington State University
Pullman, Washington

47–1 INTRODUCTION

The electron microscope is similar to the light microscope in that it is a combination of lenses for creating magnified images of minute objects. It can provide information as to size, shape, and arrangement, with great resolving power being its chief advantage. It represents about the same amount of improvement in resolving power over the optical microscope as is attained by the optical microscope over the unaided eye. Although the electron microscope has been generally available to scientists for only about 20 years, improvements in equipment and technique have been so rapid that its field of usefulness is already large.

The value of the electron microscope for mineral identification work is limited by the fact that it cannot be used to obtain refractive indexes, and it does not have the polarizing features of the petrographic microscope. However, selected-area electron diffraction, a technique which is just starting to develop, may someday compensate for these deficiencies. A special disadvantage is the high cost of electron microscopes and the difficulty of their maintenance for peak performance. Further, certain specimens may become distorted under bombardment by the electron beam or through desiccation in the evacuated system. Electron microscopy has not had time to develop a literature as extensive as the one built up through 300 years of light microscopy, but with the current rapid pace of improvement, applications of the instrument to problems in soil science are certain to increase.

Applications of the electron microscope can be grouped into three general categories. The first includes studies of the structure of materials in which there is a degree of organization, such as clay particles in suspension. The second includes the study of processes, such as phosphate fixation. These

[1] Accepted for publication May 1959.

[2] The author wishes to express his appreciation to Dr. P. J. Kaesberg, Biochemistry Department, University of Wisconsin, and to Drs. H. W. Smith and C. D. Moodie, Agronomy Department, Washington State University, for their helpful criticism of the manuscript.

two categories have been largely ignored by soil scientists. The study of particle sizes and shapes constitutes the third category and includes most of the work that has been done in soils.

The electron microscope first became available to German soil scientists who started publishing work based on its use in 1940; the first such U. S. work was published in 1941. These early papers confirmed the plate-like character of many of the clay minerals, which had been predicted previously by colloid chemists. Most of the work was on "type" clays, and there was considerable optimism as to the possibility of identifying clay minerals on the basis of their shape. Later it was found that particle shape is not highly useful as a differentiating characteristic because it changes with conditions of formation and degree of weathering. In a few years, the volume of work diminished in which the electron microscope was the primary analytical tool, and most electron micrographs published by soil scientists today are concerned with mineralogical studies in which the electron microscope is only one of the analytical tools used.

Most of the clay-mineral particles in soils appear flat and plate-like, but relatively irregular in outline and, therefore, without characteristic crystal form, even though "type" minerals of similar composition may have diagnostic form. The one really useful exception to this seems to be halloysite, which frequently can be differentiated from kaolinite with the electron microscope when other methods are inconclusive (compare Fig. 47–1 and 47–2). The electron microscope also has contributed considerable information on the structure of halloysite.

47–2 PRINCIPLES AND INSTRUMENTATION

47–2.1 Resolution

Resolution of a microscope can be defined as the smallest distance that can exist between two separate objects before they appear as one under the microscope. In light microscopy, the resolution is limited by the nature of light. The way in which radiation and matter interact (diffraction) limits resolution to about one-half the wavelength of the light used. The best light microscopes can use light of about 4,000Å., which will give a resolution limit of about 2,000Å.; that is, if two objects are 2,000Å. apart, they will appear to be only one object. In the electron microscope, it is possible to use electrons that have a wavelength of 0.05Å., which gives a theoretical resolution limit of about 0.025Å. It can be seen then that the great difference in resolving power between electron microscopes and light microscopes results from the difference in wavelength of the radiation employed.

The first electron microscopes provided a resolution of about 100Å.; refinements of the last two decades have improved this figure to 5 or 6Å.

Fig. 47–1. Kaolin. Well-crystallized material from Georgia. Line indicates 1μ. (L. A. Woodward, Georgia Institute of Technology, Atlanta, Georgia. By permission of the National Academy of Sciences, National Research Council.)

in experimental microscopes. But since resolving power is critically dependent upon the specimen, these latter figures apply only under the most favorable circumstances. Several instrumental factors prevent achievement of the theoretical resolution limit of the electron microscope, but contamination of the specimen and all surfaces exposed to the electron beam through build up of carbonaceous deposits is currently the greatest single hindrance (Cosslett, 1956). The carbon appears to originate from organic vapors contributed by lubricated parts, photographic film, etc. In spite of these limitations, direct images of certain crystal structures have been obtained when circumstances are particularly favorable (Fig. 47–3). The ultimate goal of electron microscopy is a general resolving power of atomic order.

47–2.2 Magnetic Lenses and the Electron Optical System

Magnetic lenses are the heart of the optical system of the electron microscope, which uses electrons instead of visible light. When light passes from

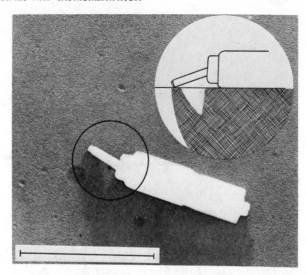

Fig. 47–2. Halloysite, Silver City, New Mexico. Notice light shadow (gold-manganin alloy at 14°). Inset is side view of indicated area predicted on the basis of shadow evidence. Line indicates 1μ. (M. S. Taggart, Humble Oil & Refining Co., and W. O. Milligan and H. P. Studer, Rice Institute, Houston, Texas. By permission of the National Academy of Sciences, National Research Council.)

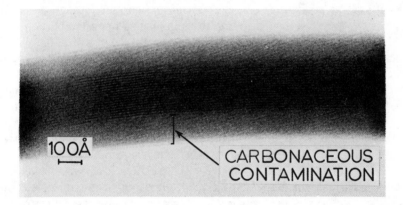

Fig. 47–3. Bent platinum phthalocyanine crystal, showing (20$\bar{1}$) planes 12.0Å. apart. Conditions are such that only this particular set of planes is resolved. The carbonaceous contamination arises from inside the microscope, with a deposition rate of the order of 1Å. per second. (J. W. Menter, Tube Investments Research Laboratories, Hixton Hall, Cambridge, England. By permission of the Royal Society.)

one medium to another of different density, it is refracted. Similarly, a beam of electrons is refracted when it passes from one area to another having a different density of magnetic lines of force; this is the basis of the optical system of electron microscopes.

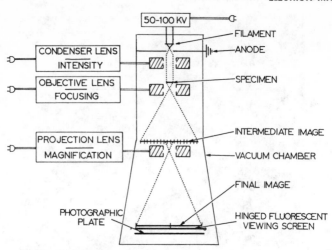

Fig. 47–4. Diagram indicating some of the components of the electron microscope. Many microscopes have an intermediate lens where the intermediate image is indicated above. Voltages are usually controlled on the order of 1 part in 10^5.

In Fig. 47–4, the filament with its associated electronics provides a stable, high-intensity source of electrons of uniform wavelength. Changing the focal length of the condenser lens (by varying the current through its electromagnet) varies the number of electrons impinging upon the portion of the specimen being viewed, and hence controls the intensity of the electron beam. The objective lens produces an enlarged electron image of the object, and a portion of this intermediate image is enlarged further and projected on the fluorescent screen by means of the projection lens. The magnification provided by the objective lens is constant (about 100 diameters), but its strength can be varied through narrow limits to produce focusing of the object. The focal length of the projection lens is variable over a wide limit and, as a result, largely determines the magnification of the image.

Since particulate matter (such as air) scatters electrons, the electron microscope column must be evacuated. However, scattering of electrons by the specimen is the primary source of image contrast. Electrons are scattered either by loss of speed (and their consequent change of path in the magnetic field) or by outright change in direction by deflection. Various parts of the specimen will appear light or dark, depending upon differential scattering of electrons, since most of the scattered electrons are not imaged by the lenses and, therefore, do not appear on the viewing screen.

47–2.3 Apertures, Depth of Focus, and Beam Intensity

If the severe aberrations of present-day magnetic lenses were not compensated for in some manner, they would more than counteract the advantages obtained from the small wavelength of electrons. Fortunately, even the worst lens approaches perfection if only its central core is used, so that the high quality of electron microscopes has been achieved by the simple artifice of using lenses with relatively small apertures. Fortunately sufficient beam intensity for very high magnifications remains in spite of small apertures. The small apertures result in a depth of focus that is many times greater than that in the light microscope, so that all of a relatively high specimen will be in focus at once.

47–2.4 Commercial Electron Microscopes and Supplies

Electron microscopes are manufactured in all the major industrial countries, with Japan producing the largest number. There are about 1,000 electron microscopes in operation throughout the world excluding the Soviet Bloc (Cosslett, 1955b), and all the leading countries of the world have electron microscope societies. The Electron Microscope Society of America is one of the largest, with about 700 members. Recent trends in the design of commercial electron microscopes have been toward two types, the instrument of limited performance and cost for routine purposes (Fig. 47–5), and the instrument of highest possible resolving power (Fig. 47–6).

In addition to the companies that manufacture and sell electron microscopes, a number of firms furnish special accessories, supplies, and information to electron microscopists. Some of them are: Canal Industrial Corporation, 4940 St. Elmo Ave., Bethesda 14, Md.; E. F. Fullam, Inc., P.O. Box 444, Schenectady 1, N. Y.; C. O. Jelliff Mfg. Corp., Southport, Conn.; and Ladd Research Industries, Inc., 159 Wagon Rd., Roslyn Heights, N. Y.

47–3 SPECIMEN PREPARATION

The way in which an electron microscope facility is administered has much to do with its usefulness to an organization. In some fields a microscope is used by one person or by a small group of specialists in electron microscopy. Since soil scientists usually do not have enough work to warrant this degree of specialization, some kind of central service organization run by an electron microscope specialist is desirable. For example, two contributors of electron micrographs to this section, H. L. Nixon of Rothamsted and J. J. Comer of Pennsylvania State University, run such organizations with outstanding success. In such instances, the potential electron microscope user can consult the specialist concerning his particular problem. If such a consultant is not available, one must make the inevitable mistakes of manipulation and judgment in sample preparation and

Fig. 47–6. Electron microscopes of relatively high resolving power. Purchase prices in 1958 were about $24,000 for the Philips EM 100B (*left*) and $27,000 for the RCA EMU-3 (*right*). Both have a guaranteed resolution of better than 20Å. (Philips Electronics, Inc., and Radio Corporation of America.)

Fig. 47–5. An electron microscope intermediate in price and performance. This Philips EM 75B costs about $12,000 and has a guaranteed resolution of better than 50Å. (Philips Electronics)

interpretation as well as be responsible for the operation, performance, and maintenance of the microscope itself—a burden that stops most research with the electron microscope before it begins. Assuming then, that a satisfactory electron microscope facility is available, *successful application of the electron microscope to a problem in soil science will depend almost entirely upon the investigator's skill and ingenuity in specimen preparation.*

A number of specimen preparation techniques have been used often enough so that they can be described in general terms in this article. But one must always keep in mind a statement by Hall (1953): "No method is so excellent that judgment, initiative, and imagination become unnecessary. At present, almost every noteworthy published account of an application in electron microscopy contains some innovation in technique."

47–3.1 Support of Specimen in Electron Beam

The specimen is usually supported in the electron beam on a thin film. The best supporting films are of substances containing only atoms of low atomic weight, because these produce the least scattering of electrons. Supporting films are commonly made from collodion, carbon, and Formvar (polyvinyl formal). The film itself is supported on a wire grid, and the specimen is observed between the meshes of the grid, suspended in the electron beam by the supporting film (Fig. 47–7).

Although carbon films are more difficult to prepare than collodion or Formvar films, they are smoother and stronger. Their great strength permits use of films as thin as 25Å. Such films contain relatively little electron-scattering matter and hence permit high-resolution microscopy. The unusually high-quality micrograph of montmorillonite (Fig. 47–8) in which the edges of plates one unit cell in thickness are resolved was made using a carbon film. Many electron micrographs of montmorillonite have such poor resolution that they resemble a mass of clouds; even large aggregates are poorly defined.

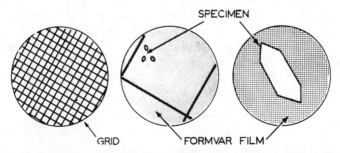

Fig. 47–7. Diagram illustrating how the specimen is supported in the electron beam. Increasing magnification of supporting grid from left to right.

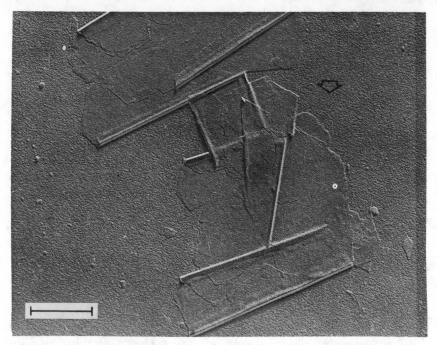

Fig. 47–8. Montmorillonite from Unter-Rupsroth in the Rhöngebirge, Germany. An exceptionally distinct electron micrograph of this mineral. Carbon substrate, platinum shadow at 7° to clay surface in the direction of arrow. Shadow measurements indicate the thinnest layers to be only 10Å. thick. Line indicates 1μ. (H. L. Nixon and R. H. Weir, Rothamsted Exp. Sta. Harpenden, Herts, England. By permission of the Mineralogical Society.)

There is as much art as there is science in preparing specimens for the electron microscope. For example, Formvar films are said to be stronger than collodion films, but collodion is much more frequently used. Collodion can be spread on water, whereas Formvar films must be spread on glass and are very difficult to remove from the glass. However, a thin film of oil from the outside of one's nose will prevent the Formvar from sticking to the glass. For reasons unknown, the same glass slide cannot be used twice. Unfortunately, information of this type is frequently omitted from technical papers and books, which probably explains why sometimes a method is a spectacular success in one laboratory but a dismal failure in another.

47–3.2   Application of Specimen to Support

The simplest and most commonly used method for placing a highly stable specimen on a grid is to suspend the material in water and allow a drop of

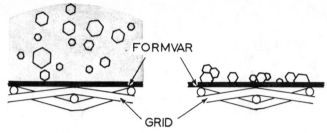

Fig. 47–9. Diagram of the placement of a sample on a Formvar-covered grid by drying a drop of suspension.

the suspension to dry on the grid (Fig. 47–9). Where one is interested only in size and shape, which is usually the case with clay mineral particles for example, excellent results can be obtained by this method (Fig. 47–1). Alternatively, spraying the specimen on the grid as very fine droplets will give a somewhat more uniform sampling of the suspension in a smaller area of the grid.

Under certain circumstances it may be possible to allow a reaction to proceed directly on the specimen grid. If size, shape, or arrangement are sufficient to distinguish between reactants and products, or various reaction

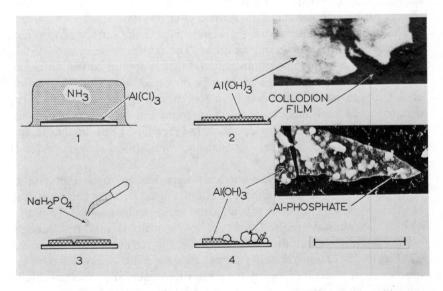

Fig. 47–10. Diagram illustrating various stages in the formation of thin films of Al(OH)₃ and their reaction with phosphate to form an aluminum phosphate. Specimens were washed with distilled water to remove soluble salts preparatory to electron microscope examination of stages 2 and 4. Line indicates 1μ on the electron micrographs. (J. A. Kittrick and M. L. Jackson, University of Wisconsin, Madison, Wis.)

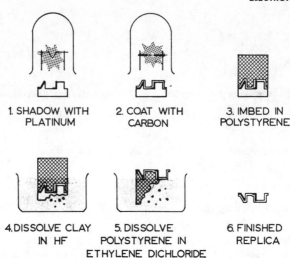

1. SHADOW WITH
PLATINUM

2. COAT WITH
CARBON

3. IMBED IN
POLYSTYRENE

4. DISSOLVE CLAY
IN HF

5. DISSOLVE
POLYSTYRENE IN
ETHYLENE DICHLORIDE

6. FINISHED
REPLICA

Fig. 47–11. Diagram of the steps in the preparation in a single-stage replica of the surface of a clay aggregate. This method was used by Bates and Comer to produce the replicas in Figs. 47–12 and 47–13.

stages, it may be possible to follow the course of a reaction when circumstances permit no other analytical method (Fig. 47–10).

The replica technique allows the examination of the surface of materials that are too dense to transmit electrons. The replica is an extremely thin mold or cast of some amorphous material that is applied to the surface to be examined. The specimen may then be dissolved away from the replica, or the replica may be stripped from the specimen. Depending upon the material to be replicated, the one-stage replica can be shadowed and examined in the electron microscope directly (Fig. 47–11) or another replica can be made of the first one. Occasionally, even a third stage is prepared from the second.

Until recently, most replica methods were limited to a resolution of about 200Å. by structure in the replica itself. However, when carbon is used as the replicating substance, this difficulty seems to be avoided. Now that high-quality replicas are produced routinely in many laboratories throughout the world, its application to problems in soil science should not be far off. Figure 47–12 immediately suggests the possibility of investigating the weathering of mineral grains by the replica technique. It is also possible to investigate clay skins and the fine structure of bedding with the replica technique as suggested by an electron micrograph such as Fig. 47–13. By the same technique one might also study the formation and rupture of soil aggregates.

Fig. 47–12. One-stage replica of microcline surface showing hexagonal crystals (indicated by arrows) which are presumed to be kaolinite. Line indicates 1μ. (T. F. Bates and J. J. Comer, The Pennsylvania State University, University Park, Pa. By permission of the National Academy of Sciences, National Research Council.)

47–3.3 Maintenance of Specimen Structure

Depending upon the specimen, the three attributes of size, shape, and arrangement that can be observed in the electron microscope may be distorted during specimen preparation; arrangement and shape are usually the more sensitive properties. When a specimen is dried from water suspension, surface tension forces may exceed 1 ton per square inch, markedly distorting the shape and arrangement of the more fragile specimens. If the specimen is first frozen and the water removed by sublimation, the liquid state and hence surface tension is avoided (Fig. 47–14). An idea of the magnitude of the distortion owing to drying can be obtained by comparing the freeze-dried and nonfreeze-dried specimens in Fig. 47–15 and 47–16.

Figure 47–15 compares some diagrams of the hypothetical configuration of clay platelets with some electron micrographs of clays, suggesting that it may be possible to follow the change in configuration of clay mineral platelets as a function of water stress using the freeze-dry technique. It may also be possible to study the flocculation and dispersion of soil colloids with this technique. The technique has already been used to study the mechanism by which soil conditioners aggregate soil particles (Fig. 47–16 and 47–17).

The surface structure of materials that are unstable in the electron microscope can be preserved in ways other than freeze-drying, such as with a replica. Where this is not practicable, it may be possible to cover the specimen with metal in the shadowing chamber and then observe essentially the metal coating in the microscope. If necessary, volatilization of the specimen in the shadowing chamber can be prevented by cooling. Certainly, imagination is the ingredient most necessary to success in specimen preparation.

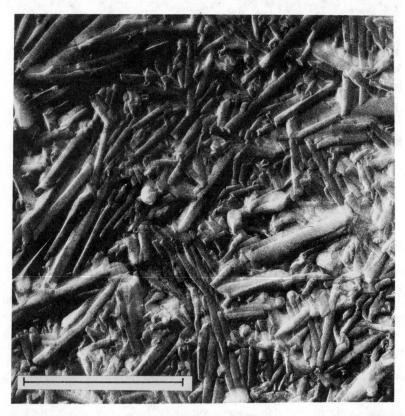

Fig. 47–13. One-stage replica of halloysite from Wendover, Utah, showing arrangement of tubular crystals. Line indicates 1μ. (T. F. Bates and J. J. Comer, The Pennsylvania State University, University Park, Pa. By permission of the National Academy of Sciences, National Research Council.)

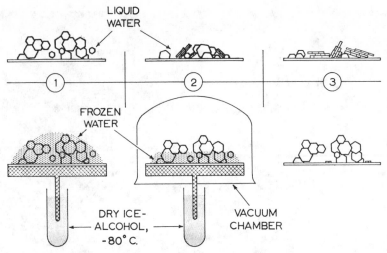

Fig. 47–14. Diagrammatic comparison of regular specimen preparation (upper sequence) with freeze drying: (1) initial specimen, (2) partial removal of water, and (3) dry specimen.

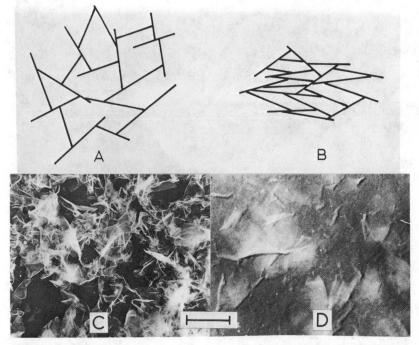

Fig. 47–15. Comparison of electron micrographs of clay particle configurations with theoretical diagrams based on physical measurements. (Diagrams after Kemper, 1958.) (A) Flocculated clay after complete dispersion. (B) Partial collapse of clay structure owing to applied pressure. (C) Freeze-dried Wyoming bentonite. (D) Wyoming bentonite collapsed by surface tension of ordinary drying. Line indicates 1μ on the electron micrographs.

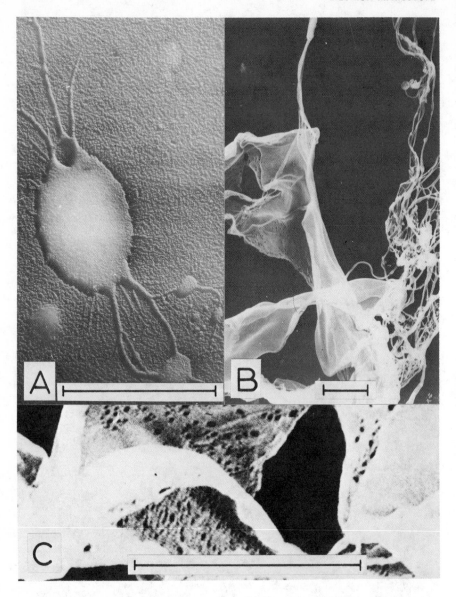

Fig. 47–16. VAMA soil conditioner (the copolymer of vinyl acetate and the partial methyl ester of maleic acid): (A) ordinary drying, (B) freeze drying, and (C) enlargement of a portion of (B) showing the arrangement of fibers which appear to form the film. Lines indicate 1μ. (S. L. Rawlins, Washington State University, Pullman, Wash.)

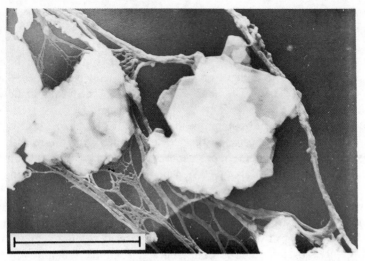

Fig. 47-17. Kaolinite treated with IBMA soil conditioner (copolymer of isobutylene and half-ammonium, half-amid salt of maleic acid). Strands that appear to bond kaolinite particles one to another have actually been observed to do so when the supporting Formvar film ruptures. Line indicates 1μ. (S. L. Rawlins, Washington State University, Pullman, Wash.)

47-4 ENHANCING SPECIMEN DEFINITION

47-4.1 Shadowing

In early studies with the electron microscope, there was often insufficient contrast between the specimen and the supporting film to make the object sufficiently visible. This was particularly true of biological specimens because they are composed of atoms of low atomic weight and do not scatter electrons much more effectively than does the supporting film. Image contrast of a specimen and surface relief can be accentuated enormously by depositing a thin layer of heavy metal atoms on the surface of the specimen as shown in Fig. 47-18. For relatively thick clay particles the technique

Fig. 47-18. Diagrammatic representation of the shadowing process. In the vacuum chamber (*left*), the hot filament is shown vaporizing a heavy metal. The heavy metal coats the near side of the specimen as shown in the enlarged portion of specimen (*right*). The area where no heavy metal is deposited is later observed from above in the electron microscope as "shadow."

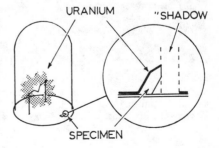

is not so dramatic as with biological specimens, but it is still effective (compare Fig. 47–2 in this section with Fig. 48–9*A* in section 48). As shown in Fig. 47–2, shadowing allows one to obtain information about the vertical dimension of objects. Specimen heights above the substrate can be calculated readily from the length of the shadow, provided that the relative positions of the specimen and the heavy metal source during shadowing are known.

According to a private communication from H. L. Nixon, use of the shadowcasting technique can be expected to decline in the future as better electron microscopes become more generally available. These instruments have a resolution limit of about 10Å., whereas the best shadowcasting deposits seem to have a lower grain-size limit of about 20 to 30Å., so that shadowing diminishes the effective resolution in these instruments. Fortunately, these electron microscopes also produce much higher image contrast than the older instruments; thus the improved resolution is actually usable. Figure 47–19 is an electron micrograph of a type of montmorillonite taken on such an instrument (without shadow). Compare Fig. 47–19 with similar material in Fig. 47–8 that has been shadowed and examined on an instrument of lower resolving power (keep in mind that in the author's

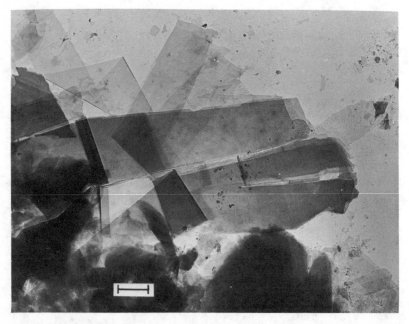

Fig. 47–19. Beidellite. This micrograph was taken by H. L. Nixon with a new Siemens electron microscope. High image contrast was obtained without the use of shadowcasting, permitting extremely high resolution. Line indicates 1μ. (H. L. Nixon and R. H. Weir, Rothamsted Exp. Sta., Harpenden, Herts, England.)

opinion, Fig. 47–8 is by far the best electron micrograph of montmorillo-nite ever published prior to Fig. 47–19).

47-4.2 Stereophotography

If a specimen has extreme vertical dimensions or a complex geometry that is not well displayed by shadowing, the great depth of focus of the electron microscope permits stereophotography. Tilting the specimen holder allows one to take two successive photographs of a specimen from slightly different viewpoints. When the two photographs are observed through a stereoscopic viewer, the 3-dimensional image is reconstituted (Fig. 47–20 and 47–21).

47-5 SOURCES OF INFORMATION

Over half of the applications of the electron microscope are biological and medical, and most of the others are metallurgical and chemical. About half the electron microscopes are in industrial laboratories, so that much work in applied science and technology probably is not published.

For someone unfamiliar with the electron microscope, but considering its use in a research project, the best initial source of information usually is the specialist in charge of the microscope (assuming the microscope facility is run on a service basis). If the project then appears feasible, a general knowledge of the instrument and specimen preparation technique can be obtained from one or two of the excellent books available. Details of speci-men preparation techniques can then be obtained from research articles or perhaps from the article by Drummond (1950). The New York Society of Electron Microscopists bibliography is the best general source of research articles. Other bibliographies are available, and *Chemical Abstracts* may be helpful. Once started in electron microscopy, one has a number of review sources available which will help him keep abreast of the literature.

The following is a description of material in English considered likely to be most useful to soil scientists. Books on the subject of electron mi-croscopy have been published by Burton and Kohl (1946), Cosslett (1951), Drummond (1950), Fisher (1953), Hall (1953), and Wyckoff (1949). Of these, the books by Burton and Kohl and by Fisher are the least technical. In addition, book sections devoted to microscopy have been written by Cosslett (1955a), Davis et al. (1950), Hamm (1954), Jackson (1956, pp. 411–469), and Trillat (1959). Recent reviews include those by Cosslett (1955b, 1956), and the biennial reviews of fundamental devel-opments in analysis published in *Analytical Chemistry*. The latest of three

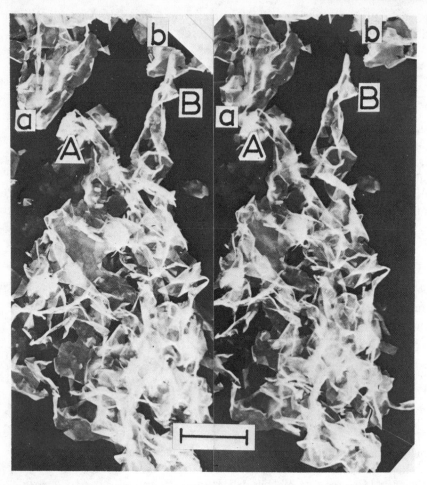

Fig. 47–20. Stereo pair of freeze-dried Wyoming bentonite (montmorillonite). Notice the relative positions of the pairs of *A*'s and *B*'s. Photos taken with specimen tilted 7° to either side of vertical and displayed here for a lens-type stereo viewer. Line indicates 1μ.

in *Analytical Chemistry* is by Rochow et al. (1960). Reviews dealing with applications to clay minerals include those by Bates (1955, 1958), Dwornik and Ross (1955), Hillier (1946), and Kinter et al. (1952). The best collection of electron micrographs of clays will be found in the review by Bates (1958). A bibliography of electron microscopy edited by Cosslett (1950) covers literature through 1948 and includes a short abstract of most of the articles. Abstracts of literature subsequent to this date appear in the *Journal of the Royal Microscopical Society, Series* III. A bibliography issued by the National Bureau of Standards (1950) covers the years from 1933 through 1949. The New York Society of Electron Microscopists

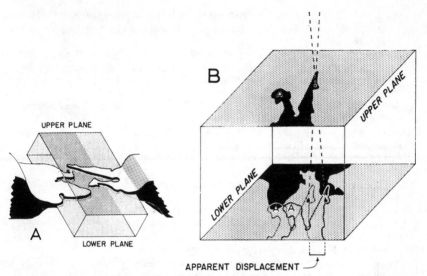

Fig. 47–21. Diagrammatic explanation of the relative positions of the pairs of *A*'s and *B*'s in Fig. 47–20. Stero viewing reveals that the clay mass indicated by the upper case letters of each pair in Fig. 47–20 (opposite page) is at a level in space *above* the other clay mass as is indicated by *UPPER PLANE* in part *A* (Figures in part *A* rotated 90° for clarity). Projecting the object in the UPPER PLANE onto the LOWER PLANE results in an apparent relative displacement of the object, depending upon the angle of view as indicated in part *B*. This is equivalent to compressing the three-dimensional scene of part *A* into the two-dimensional stereo photos of Fig. 47–20.

(NYSEM) publishes a quarterly *Bibliography of Electron Microscopy* in the form of keysort cards punched according to subject and author. This bibliography is available from the Society, 2 East 63rd St., New York 21, N. Y. It includes entries from 1950 to date.

47–6 LITERATURE CITED

Bates, T. F. 1955. Electron microscopy as a method of identifying clays. Proc. Natl. Conf. on Clays and Clay Tech. 1:130–150.

Bates, T. F. 1958. Selected electron micrographs of clays and other fine-grained minerals. Mineral Ind. Exp. Sta. Circ. 51. Pennsylvania State Univ.

Burton, E. F., and Kohl, W. H. 1946. The Electron Microscope. Ed. 2 Reinhold Publ. Co., New York.

Cosslett, V. E. (Ed.) 1950. Bibliography of Electron Microscopy. Edward Arnold and Co., London.

Cosslett, V. E. 1951. Practical Electron Microscopy. Academic Press, Inc., New York.

Cosslett, V. E. 1955a. Electron Microscopy. *In* G. Oster and A. W. Pollister, ed. Physical Techniques in Biological Research. Vol. 1, pp. 461–531. Academic Press, Inc., New York.

Cosslett, V. E. 1955b. Recent developments in electron microscopy. Res. 8:48–56.

Cosslett, V. E. 1956. Electron microscopy: its scope and limitations. Endeavour 15:153–165.

Davis, W. D., Rochow, T. G., Rowe, F. G., Fuller, M. L., Kerr, P. F. and Hamilton, P. K. 1950. Electron micrographs of reference clay minerals, Preliminary Report No. 6. *In* Reference Clay Minerals, Am. Petrol. Inst. Res. Proj. 49. Columbia University, New York.

Drummond, D. G. ed. 1950. The Practice of Electron Microscopy. Royal Microscopical Society, London. Also in J. Roy. Microscop. Soc. (1950) 70:1–141.

Dwornik, E., and Ross, M. 1955. Application of the electron microscope to mineralogic studies. Am. Mineralogist 40:261–274.

Fisher, R. B. 1953. Applied Electron Microscopy. Indiana University Press, Bloomington.

Hall, C. E. 1953. Introduction to Electron Microscopy. McGraw Hill Book Co., New York.

Hamm, F. A. 1954. Electron microscopy. *In* Arnold Weissberger, ed. Physical Methods of Organic Chemistry. Vol. 1, Part III. pp. 2097–2178. Interscience Publishers, New York.

Hillier, J. 1946. Electron microscopy. Am. Ceramic Soc. Bull. 25:439–448.

Jackson, M. L. 1956. Soil Chemical Analysis—Advanced Course. Published by the author, University of Wisconsin, Madison 6, Wisconsin.

Kemper, W. D. 1958. Structural implications of moisture retention by clay-size soil materials. Soil Sci. Soc. Am. Proc. 22:5–8.

Kinter, E. B., Wintermeyer, A. M., and Swerdlow, M. 1952. Electron microscopy of soil clays and related materials. Public Roads 27:89–100.

National Bureau of Standards. 1950. Bibliography of electron microscopy. Natl. Bur. Stand. Circ. 502.

Rochow, T. G., Thomas, Ann, and Botty, M. C. 1960. Electron microscopy. Anal. Chem. 32:92R–103R.

Trillat, J. J. 1959. Exploring the Structure of Matter. Interscience Publishers, New York. Translated from the 1956 French edition by F. W. Kent.

Wyckoff, R. W. G. 1949. Electron Microscopy, Technique and Applications. Interscience Publishers, New York.

48

Electron-Diffraction Techniques for Mineral Identification[1]

J. A. KITTRICK[2]

Washington State University
Pullman, Washington

48–1   INTRODUCTION

Electron diffraction has definite advantages for investigating poorly diffracting materials and thin surfaces; yet the technique has seldom been used by soil scientists. Though many soil scientists have had access to electron microscopes that could be converted to electron diffraction, the quality of the results obtainable usually did not justify the effort. Furthermore, the person in charge of the electron microscope may have been unable to give much advice on the subject. As electron-diffraction units, some of the newer electron microscopes are much more satisfactory than the earlier models.

Commercial electron-diffraction equipment is available (Fig. 48–1), but few soil scientists have had access to it. Fewer still have known how to use it when they did, since soil scientists seldom have had an opportunity to become acquainted with the technique as part of their college training. For a technique that requires one to be self-taught, the literature situation in electron diffraction is not promising at present. Summary-type literature (as listed in section 48–5) is relatively rare and is usually written for specialists in this branch of physics. The widespread application of electron diffraction to problems in soil science awaits the production of electron microscopes better suited to electron diffraction, and books on techniques written by specialists in such a way that they can be readily understood by soil scientists.

---

[1] Accepted for publication May 1959.

[2] The author wishes to express his appreciation to Dr. F. V. Schossberger, Scientific Advisor, Armour Research Foundation, and to Drs. H. W. Smith and W. H. Gardner, Agronomy Department, Washington State University, for their helpful criticism of the manuscript.

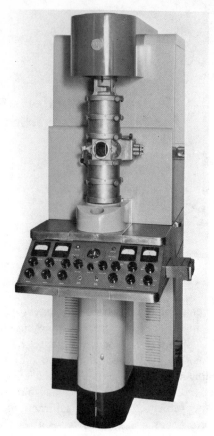

Fig. 48–1. A commercial electron-diffraction unit, the RCA type EMD. (Radio Corporation of America.)

48–2   PRINCIPLES

Nuclei as well as electrons are responsible for electron diffraction, whereas X-rays are diffracted only by the electrons in the atoms composing matter. The interaction between electrons and matter is, therefore, about 10^7 times greater than the interaction of X-rays with matter. An electron-diffraction pattern of a sample might represent the surface 0.05μ or less (Fig. 48–2), whereas the penetrating power (lack of interaction) of X-rays causes them to represent a relatively thick portion of the sample, let us say 50μ.

Less repetition of units within a structure is required to produce electron-diffraction effects because of the intense interaction of electrons with matter. This accounts for the major advantage and the major limitation of electron diffraction as an analysis tool. Electron diffraction can be used to investigate

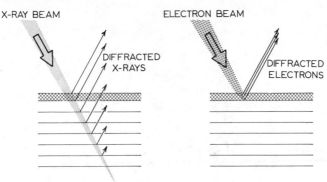

Fig. 48–2. Diagrammatic comparison of X-ray and electron diffraction. Notice how the lack of penetration of electrons, owing to their much more intense interaction with matter, permits their use in the investigation of surface layers.

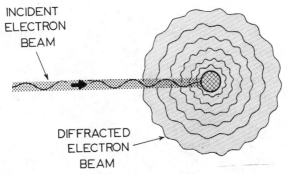

Fig. 48–3. Diagrammatic representation of the diffraction of electrons from a "single atom."

the composition and structure of thin surfaces and poorly crystalline materials (where X-ray diffraction cannot be used), but at the same time electron-diffraction patterns are frequently complicated by the fact that too few repetitions of a given configuration are involved to ensure "ideal" diffraction effects. The extreme sensitivity of electron diffraction to surface layers can also be a disadvantage in that contamination from many sources, such as the fingers, the air, etc., may alter the pattern. Operationally then, compared with X-ray diffraction, it is relatively difficult to produce, record, and interpret electron-diffraction patterns. However, one should not think of electron diffraction as a competitor of X-ray diffraction, but rather as its complement.

To appreciate some of the differences that exist between X-ray and electron diffraction, it will be necessary to consider a more detailed description of the electron-diffraction process. Electrons diffracted from a "single atom" are emitted in all directions as shown in Fig. 48–3. However, when

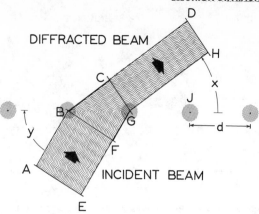

Fig. 48–4. Diagrammatic representation of the diffraction of electrons from a single "row of atoms." That portion of the incident beam that is not diffracted is omitted in this diagram.

electrons are diffracted from a "row of atoms," [3] interference between electron beams diffracted from the various atoms in the row limits emission of diffracted beams to certain directions only (Fig. 48–4). The beam diffracted from the row of atoms will exist only if its component rays are in phase; that is, the path difference (*BC* minus *FG*) between rays *ABCD* and *EFGH* must be some multiple of the wavelength (the distance between wave crests) as shown in Fig. 48–4. For a given distance between atoms, this will be the case for multiple values of angle *x,* representing path differences of one, two, and three or more times the wavelength. In Fig. 48–4, the incident beam can meet the lattice row at an angle *y* from many directions. The locus of these possible directions is a cone concentric with the atom row, with angle *y* as the apex angle (Fig. 48–5). Similarly, the loci of the various orders of diffracted beams are cones concentric about the atom row (Fig. 48–5).

Thus far the only diffraction considered has been from a single atom or from a single row of atoms (essentially a one-dimensional lattice). In actual practice, of course, one must deal with a three-dimensional lattice, which can be considered in terms of three mutually perpendicular rows of atoms. As shown in Fig. 48–6, where the atom rows are represented by axes, diffraction from a three-dimensional lattice can be visualized as resulting from the interaction of three perpendicular sets of diffraction cones. These sets of diffraction cones intersect a given plane in space (photographic film for example) as two families of mutually perpendicular hyperbolas plus a family of circles. Diffracted waves from a three-dimensional lattice will be in phase only where the three diffraction cones of Fig. 48–6

---

[3] For a more complete discussion see Klug and Alexander (1954, p. 113).

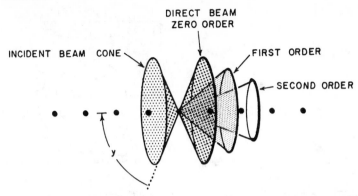

Fig. 48-5. Diagrammatic representation of the loci of first- and second-order diffracted electron beams from a "row" of atoms, resulting in a family of cones concentric about the atom row. The undiffracted portion of the incident beam (direct beam, zero order) is also shown in this diagram.

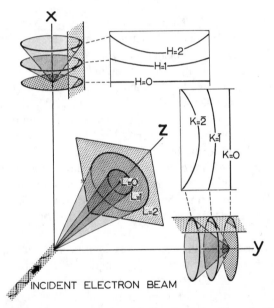

Fig. 48-6. Diagrammatic representation of the three families of diffraction cones originating along the three axial atom rows of a three-dimensional crystal. Zero orders, which originate at the origin, have been displaced along the axes for clarity, displacing negative orders along the −y axis to the y axis as shown.

mutually intersect. At these points of intersection, electron waves diffracted from all three atom rows are in phase with each other, because all the path differences between them are some multiple of the wavelength. These intersections are recorded as spots on a photographic film as indicated in Fig. 48-7.

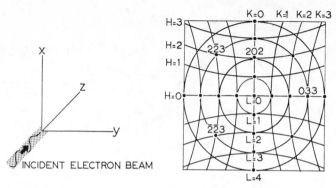

Fig. 48–7. The mutual intersection of the three diffraction cones (whose origin was depicted in the previous figure) with the photographic plate produces the spot pattern indicated. Each spot represents a point at which the diffracted waves from all three atom rows are in phase. Only positive orders of the diffraction cones are labeled. The *Miller indexes* of several spots are given.

Now we come to the essential difference between X-ray diffraction and electron diffraction. In ideal diffraction from a three-dimensional lattice, intensities of the diffracted beams are zero everywhere, except where all three interference conditions (path difference $= n\lambda$) are fulfilled. Intensity maxima are shown in Fig. 48–7 lying at the intersection of two hyperbolas and a circle. This applies *strictly* in the case of X-ray diffraction, but not for electron diffraction. Because of the intense interaction of electron waves with atoms, their penetrating power is very low and only a relatively few atomic layers normal to the beam diffract electrons. It will be necessary to re-examine Fig. 48–4 to see how this affects diffraction. For Fig. 48–4 to be strictly correct, among other things the row of atoms must be infinite in length. Of course, in nature the length of atom rows is limited, and so let us consider the effect of relatively short atom rows on the interference between electron waves.

To be in phase, the diffracted waves in Fig. 48–4 must differ in path length by an integral number of wavelengths. But suppose that the path difference between the rays scattered by atoms B and G is only ¼ wavelength. These waves do not completely cancel one another, but simply unite to form a beam of smaller amplitude (less intense) than that formed by two rays which are completely in phase. Rays diffracted from the next atom at J would also be a quarter out of phase with the ray at G, but would be ½ wavelength out of phase with the ray scattered by atom B, *completely cancelling* it. A ray diffracted from the atom after J would then completely cancel the one at G and so on. However, if the path difference between rays scattered by the first two atoms were only slightly out of phase (much less than ¼), then the diffracted ray that would completely cancel it would lie a considerable distance along the atom row from atoms B and G. If the atom row is not sufficiently long, complete cancellation of such a scattered ray cannot result. If the atom row in question happens to be normal to the crystal surface, and if electrons do not penetrate sufficiently deep, the same relation holds. The result is a broader area over which diffracted electrons are in phase (or more strictly, not completely out of phase). This gives a certain "thickness" to the diffraction cones about the atom row in question, broadening the area over which they intersect the photographic plate, as shown in Fig. 48–8. This is described in the literature by saying that one of the Laue conditions is relaxed or that the resolution in a certain direction in the crystal is poor.

As shown in Fig. 48–8, broadening of one of the diffraction cones allows more mutual intersections of the three diffraction cones, resulting in more

Fig. 48–8. Diagrammatic represen- tation of the mutual intersection of the three families of electron- diffraction cones with the photo- graphic plate. In *A* the diffrac- tion effects are strictly three-di- mensional, while in *B* one of the Laue conditions has been relaxed due to lack of penetration of the beam normal to the crystal sur- face, resulting in more diffrac- tion spots.

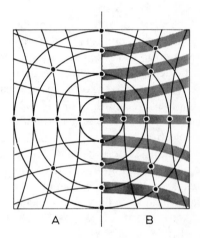

A   B

diffraction spots. The indexing of electron diffraction patterns is carried out as in the case of X-ray diffraction, but their interpretation in terms of atomic structure must take into account the relaxation of certain diffraction conditions. It can be seen then that the relatively intense interaction of elec- trons with matter limits their penetrating power and frequently prevents their diffraction effects from equally representing all three dimensions in a structure.

48–3 TRANSMISSION METHOD

In transmission electron-diffraction, the electrons pass directly through the specimen, which of course must be very thin. If the crystals are relatively thick but with thin edges, most of the transmission diffraction will occur at the edges. The diffraction patterns obtained depend upon whether the specimen is a powder or a single crystal.

48–3.1 Powder

The powder sample is usually supported in the electron beam on a thin plastic film as in electron microscopy. If the crystals are very small and randomly oriented, a pattern of circular diffraction rings is formed that is similar in appearance to the one in Fig. 48–10*B*. These are frequently called Debye-Scherrer rings. When the crystals are relatively large and few, they give rise to a pattern in which the rings are broken up into irregularly distributed spots. As in X-ray diffraction, the grain size of small crystals can be estimated from the breadth of the diffraction line, with the line-broadening effect obtained from crystals roughly 20 times smaller than in X-ray diffraction.

The electron-diffraction powder transmission pattern is the one most similar to its counterpart in X-ray diffraction. If the powder-pattern rings are uniformly blackened and the pattern does not change when the angle of incidence of the electron beam is changed, the crystals in the powder are randomly oriented (no preferred orientation). Transmission diffraction patterns that are arced as in Fig. 48–9 always indicate preferred orientation. If the crystals are oriented about a crystallographic axis that is parallel to the electron beam, the electron-diffraction pattern will consist of normally shaped rings, but some rings will be absent, and the intensities of others may be abnormal (Fig. 48–10). Inclining the sample to the beam will produce arcs from this type of sample because the axis of orientation is then no longer parallel to the electron beam.

According to Finch et al. (1935), the ring pattern obtained in electron diffraction, unlike X-ray diffraction, really arises mainly from two-dimensional effects. In spite of this, the pattern can be interpreted according to the Bragg formula as in X-ray diffraction, but the precision in *d*-spacing measurements is usually much less. One cannot look up *d*-spacings for a known wavelength as in X-ray diffraction, because the wavelength usually cannot be calculated with sufficient accuracy from the voltage. It is necessary to compare the diffraction pattern with a standard pattern of some substance such as gold foil. Identification may then be carried out by use of the ASTM X-ray card index, although line intensities may be different, and one may encounter difficulties from the lower precision of the *d*-spacing measurements.

Electrons generated at 50,000 v. have a wavelength of 0.05Å. as compared to say 1.5Å. for CuKα X-rays. Because of the short wavelength of the electrons, the diffraction rings are confined to a very narrow range of angles around the primary beam (Fig. 48–11). Even though the distance from specimen to plate in an electron-diffraction camera may be 10 times or more the distance in an X-ray diffraction camera, long spacings are recorded with difficulty or not at all. This is a distinct disadvantage in work

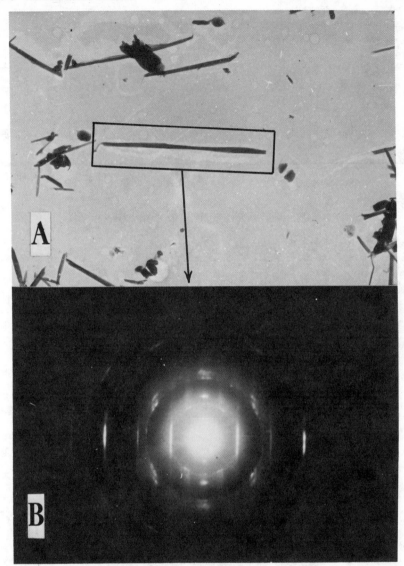

Fig. 48–9. Halloysite, Silver City, New Mexico. Electron micrograph (A) of an unshadowed single crystal (4μ long) and its transmission electron-diffraction pattern in (B). The arced pattern indicates that the single crystal is composed of a number of smaller crystallites with preferred orientation. (M. S. Taggart, Humble Oil & Refining Co., and W. O. Milligan and H. P. Studer, The Rice Institute, Houston, Tex. By permission of the National Academy of Sciences, National Research Council.)

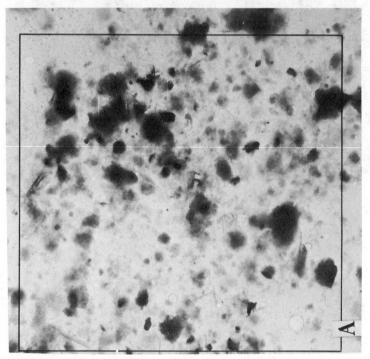

Fig. 48–10. Transmission electron-diffraction pattern from a portion of the surface clay fraction of the Beaumont formation, a South Texas Outcrop. Electron micrograph (A) of sample area (10 by 10μ) yielding the electron-diffraction pattern in B. The clay platelets are doubtless oriented with the c axis normal to the electron beam, resulting in loss of rings corresponding to d-spacings in that crystallographic direction. However, the clay platelets must be randomly oriented in the other two crystallographic directions because the diffraction pattern is not arced. (M. S. Taggart, Humble Oil & Refining Co., and W. O. Milligan and H. P. Studer, The Rice Institute, Houston, Tex. By permission of the National Academy of Sciences, National Research Council.)

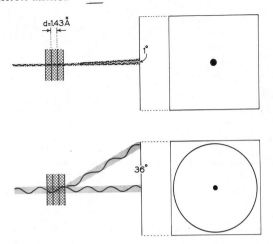

Fig. 48–11. Diagrammatic comparison of transmission diffraction of 0.05Å. electrons (*upper*) and 1.5Å. X-rays from a set of planes 1.43Å. apart. The indicated angles represent the respective Θ values in the Bragg equation ($n\lambda = 2d \sin \Theta$).

with clay minerals, since most of their diagnostic spacings are relatively long spacings along the *c* axis. Furthermore, most clay particles will orient with their *c* axis parallel to the electron beam so that only hk0 spacings (that is, none along the *c* axis) are obtained.

In spite of these difficulties, most future applications of electron diffraction to soil science will doubtless be of the powder transmission type. With this method specimens are relatively easy to prepare. Results are relatively easy to interpret and are the most comparable to the type of X-ray diffraction patterns with which many soil scientists are already familiar. Inorganic substances that diffract X-rays very poorly (collectively called allophane) are likely to be among the first to be investigated by this method.

48–3.2 Single Crystal

Most single crystals are actually composed of small individual units which are slightly out of orientation with each other. This condition is called mosaic structure (Fig. 48–12). The whole assemblage can be viewed as a powder with all grains oriented the same way. If the single crystal is very thin, electron-diffraction transmission patterns from it will consist of a pattern of spots. As the "grains" of the crystal become less perfectly oriented, the spots elongate into arcs. A completely random orientation is equivalent to a random powder and will, of course, produce the powder pattern of concentric rings. Thus there is a gradation in structure and in resultant electron-diffraction pattern between single crystals and random powders.

A FEW SECONDS OF ARC

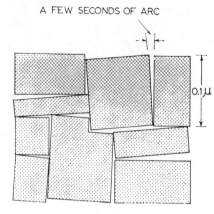

0.1 μ

Fig. 48–12. Diagram of mosaic structure in a crystal, with approximate dimensions.

As the thickness of the crystal increases, a new type of diffraction pattern appears—the Kikuchi line pattern (Fig. 48–13). Kikuchi lines consist of pairs of bright and dark straight lines generated only from single crystals of considerable perfection. Sharp Kikuchi lines indicate relatively clean surfaces with well-oriented surface atoms; slightly deformed surfaces give diffuse Kikuchi lines or none at all. They may be seen in both transmission and reflection patterns and appear primarily from specimens which are relatively thick. Their origin is complicated and beyond the scope of this article. It will have to suffice to say that the distance between the lines of a pair corresponds to some d-distance in the sample. There is a gradation then in single-crystal transmission patterns from spots only for very thin crystals, to a combination of spots and an increasing proportion of Kikuchi lines as the thickness of the crystal increases.

Crystal thickness has another important influence on the single-crystal transmission pattern. Thin crystals of the order of 10 to 100Å. thick give strictly two-dimensional spot patterns such as Fig. 48–14 (frequently called a cross-grating pattern). Although the spot pattern in Fig. 48–14 is from an unknown crystal, it is typical of the pattern obtained from very thin mica crystals when the electron beam is nearly parallel to the c axis. An analogous situation would occur in Fig. 48–7 if the third diffraction condition were completely relaxed, making it unnecessary to consider the series of concentric circles at all. A spot pattern would then be obtained at every intersection of the horizontal and vertical lines in Fig. 48–7. As the crystals become thicker, the third diffraction (Laue) condition comes into play, and the spots lying on the intersection of the concentric circles with the horizontal and vertical lines become more intense than the others. With crystals so thick that the central beam is almost extinct (about 1,000Å.). Kikuchi lines are very pronounced and the 2-dimension diffraction effects are reduced to a minimum.

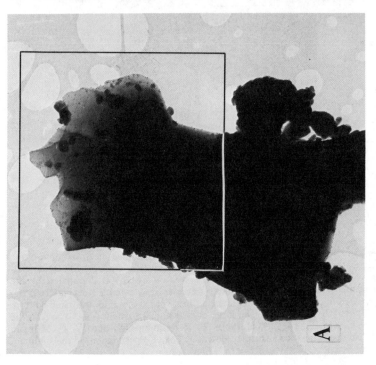

Fig. 48–13. Kikuchi line pattern from quartz (ground Ottawa Sea Sand). The marked area (2.5 by 3μ) in the electron micrograph in (A) gave the electron-diffraction pattern in (B). Weak Debye-Scherrer rings arising from the small crystal fragments adhering to the crystal plate are also visible. (M. S. Taggart, Humble Oil & Refining Co., and W. O. Milligan and H. P. Studer, The Rice Institute, Houston, Tex. By permission of the National Academy of Sciences, National Research Council.)

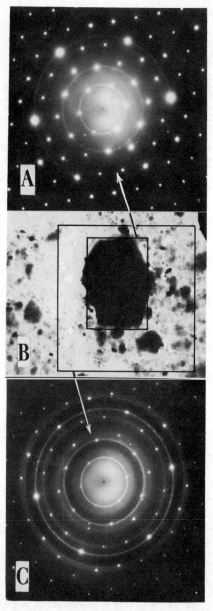

Fig. 48–14. Another area of Beaumont formation sample. The electron micrograph in (B) indicates the areas that produced the transmission electron-diffraction patterns in (A) and (C). The smaller marked area (4 by 6μ) is dominated by the two-dimensional spot pattern of the large single crystal, whereas the pattern from the larger area includes more small crystallites contributing to the ring pattern. Since the spots fall on the rings, the large crystal and the smaller ones must be the same mineral. (M. S. Taggart, Humble Oil & Refining Co.; and W. O. Milligan and H. P. Studer, The Rice Institute, Houston, Tex. By permission of the National Academy of Sciences, National Research Council.)

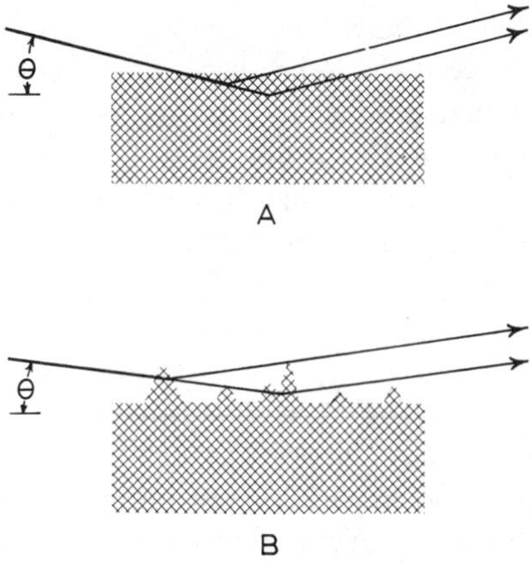

Fig. 48–15. Diagram of reflection electron diffraction: (A) true reflection
diffraction from a smooth surface (angle Θ is about 1°), and (B) by transmission through surface projections.

48–4   REFLECTION METHOD

Reflection electron-diffraction patterns are obtained from an electron
beam oriented nearly parallel to the surface of the specimen (Fig. 48–15).
Patterns of rings, arcs or spots, as well as Kikuchi lines, are obtained in
reflection diffraction, but the bottom half of the pattern is masked by the
shadow of the specimen (Fig. 48–16). The reflection method is chiefly
advantageous where it is necessary to examine surface material that cannot
be removed from a substrate that is opaque to electrons. Much thinner
surfaces can be examined by reflection diffraction than by transmission

Fig. 48–16. Reflection electron-diffraction pattern of mica (Radio Corporation of
America).

diffraction because the path length of the electron beam *in the crystal* greatly exceeds the *depth* of penetration of the beam (by a factor of about 15 in actual practice). The necessary volume of diffracting planes is then encountered in a much smaller depth of crystal. In some cases the electron beam is also slightly refracted, but this phenomenon is beyond the scope of the present discussion.

48–4.1   Single-Crystal Surface

In transmission through a single crystal, two of the Laue conditions are rigid, whereas the relaxation of the third Laue condition parallel to the beam depends upon the thickness of the crystal (the number of atom rows in the beam direction). In reflection diffraction, where the electron beam is grazing the crystal face, only one of the Laue conditions is rigid, whereas two of the three Laue conditions are partially relaxed (Fig. 48–17).

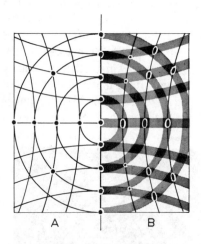

Fig. 48–17. Comparison of the mutual intersection of diffraction cones from three-dimensional diffraction in (A) with those generated during reflection electron diffraction in (B). In reflection electron diffraction two of the Laue conditions are relaxed, resulting in a large number of spots, some of which are elongated (after Finch et al., 1935).

First, the depth of penetration of the electron beam normal to the crystal surface is of the order of 20 to 40Å., clearly insufficient for sharp extinction effects. Second, the atom rows parallel to the beam have a lower resolving power than the atom rows perpendicular to the beam in the plane of the crystal surface. It is in the crystallographic directions normal to the crystal face and parallel to the electron beam then that the two Laue conditions are relaxed. It is doubtful that soil scientists will ever do much structure work involving interpretation of the spot patterns obtained from true reflection electron-diffraction, but will leave this relatively complex application to crystallographers.

48–4.2 Polycrystalline Surface

Very few surfaces are smooth and flat from the standpoint of an electron beam incident at a grazing angle of about 1°. As a consequence, most reflection-diffraction patterns do not result from the electrons penetrating and emerging from the same crystal face as diagramed in Fig. 48–15A, but rather from the diffraction of electrons from small crystallites on the surface of the specimen as in Fig. 48–15B. The latter is essentially a case of transmission diffraction, and frequently these crystallites are intentionally produced by etching or abrasion. Depending upon the orientation of the crystallites (varying from all orientations exactly the same, to random), patterns of spots, arcs, or concentric circles will be obtained, analogous to regular transmission-diffraction.

Since the projections diffract electrons for several millimeters parallel to the beam, the crystal-to-photographic-plate distance is somewhat indeterminate, resulting in relatively diffuse rings. The projections should be relatively sharp and narrow at the base (of the order of 100Å.) for best results. If the projections are much wider at the base, a high proportion of inelastically scattered electrons will contribute to a high background. Another disadvantage of "reflection" ring patterns is the difficulty in locating the central beam accurately, which complicates the measurement of the diameters of arcs. However, soil scientists may find this method useful for investigating certain surfaces that cannot be removed from their substrates for regular transmission experiments. Most likely the surface will be abraded in an attempt to obtain a ring pattern that can be more simply interpreted.

48–5 SOURCES OF INFORMATION

A number of sources of general information on electron diffraction are available, all of a relatively technical nature. Books on the subject have been published by Bauer (1958), Pinsker (1953), and Thomson and Cochrane (1939). The one by Pinsker provides the most recent complete treatment of the subject available in English. Book sections devoted to electron diffraction have been published by Barret (1952, pp. 581–600), Fisher (1954, pp. 217–231), Raether (1957), Sproull (1946, pp. 536–559), and Trillat (1959). Review papers have been published by Finch et al. (1935), Reisner (1958), and Ross and Christ (1958).

48–6 LITERATURE CITED

Barret, C. S. 1952. Structure of Metals, McGraw-Hill Book Co., New York.
Bauer, E. 1958. Electronenbeugung. Verlag Moderne Industrie, München.

Finch, G. I., Quarrell, A. G., and Wilman, H. 1935. Electron diffraction and surface structure. Trans. Faraday Soc. 31:1051–1080.

Fisher, R. B. 1954. Applied Electron Microscopy. Indiana Univ. Press, Bloomington.

Klug, H. P., and Alexander, L. E. 1954. X-ray Diffraction Procedures. John Wiley & Sons, Inc., New York.

Pinsker, Z. G. 1953. Electron Diffraction. Butterworths, London. Translated from the 1948 Russian edition by J. A. Spink and E. Feigl.

Raether, H. 1957. Elektroneninterferenzen. *In* S. Flugge, ed. Handbuch der Physik. Springer-Verlag, Berlin. 23:443–551.

Reisner, J. H. 1958. Electron diffraction on the electron microscope. Sci. Inst. News. 3:1–5.

Ross, M., and Christ, C. L. 1958. Mineralogical applications of electron diffraction. Am. Mineralogist. 43:1157–1178.

Sproull, W. T. 1946. X-Rays in Practice, McGraw-Hill Book Co., New York.

Thomson, G. P., and Cochrane, W. 1939. Theory and Practice of Electron Diffraction. Macmillan and Co., London.

Trillat, J. J. 1959. Exploring the Structure of Matter. Interscience Publishers, New York. Translated from the 1956 French edition by F. W. Kent.

49

X-Ray Diffraction Techniques for Mineral Identification and Mineralogical Composition

L. D. WHITTIG

University of California
Davis, California

49–1 GENERAL INTRODUCTION

Both the physical and chemical properties of any soil are controlled to a very large degree by the minerals of the soil, and especially by those constituting the clay fraction. Identification, characterization, and an understanding of properties of the different minerals materially aid in evaluation of soils in relation to classification, agronomic practices, and engineering properties.

The clay fraction of soils is commonly composed of a mixture of one or more secondary layer-silicate minerals together with primary minerals inherited directly from the parent material. Positive identification of mineral species and quantitative estimation of their proportions in such polycomponent systems usually require the application of several complementary qualitative and quantitative analyses. One of the most useful methods is X-ray diffraction analysis. Hadding (1923) and Rinne (1924) were the first to apply X-rays to the study of clay minerals, and Hendricks and Fry (1930) and Kelley et al. (1931) were the first to demonstrate that soil clays contain crystalline mineral components that yield X-ray diffraction patterns. Investigation of the structure, properties, and occurrence of soil clay minerals by X-ray diffraction methods has become a major effort in soil science.

Continued improvement in X-ray instrumentation, techniques of sample preparation, and definition of criteria for identification and characterization of clay mineral species in recent years has advanced the field of clay mineralogy to a point where mineralogical analyses yield a wealth of information relative to the properties and genesis of soils. X-ray diffraction has contributed more to mineralogical characterization of clay fractions of soils than has any other single method of analysis.

49–2   PRINCIPLES OF X-RAY DIFFRACTION

The nature and properties of X-rays and principles of X-ray diffraction are discussed thoroughly in a number of excellent texts (Buerger, 1942; Sproull, 1946; Henry et al., 1951; Klug and Alexander, 1954; Clark 1955; Cullity, 1956). The reader is referred to these works for detailed discussion of basic principles of X-ray diffraction.

Crystalline structures are characterized by a systematic and periodic arrangement of atoms (or ions) in a three-dimensional array. Because crystals are composed of regularly spaced atoms, each crystal contains planes of atoms which are separated by a constant distance. The distances between planes are characteristic of the crystalline species.

X-rays are electromagnetic radiations of short wavelength (of the order of 0.01 to 100Å.). Laue, in 1912, reasoned that if crystals were composed of regularly spaced atoms which might act as centers of scattering for X-rays, and if X-rays were electromagnetic waves of wavelength about equal to the interatomic distances in crystals, then it should be possible to diffract X-rays with crystals. Experiments designed to test his theories were successful, and he established the wave nature of X-rays and the periodicity of the arrangement of atoms within crystals.

The phenomenon of diffraction involves the scattering of X-rays by atoms of a crystal and the reinforcement of scattered rays in definite directions away from the crystal. Reinforcement of the scattered rays is quantitatively related to the distance of separation of atomic planes as defined by Bragg's law,

$$n\lambda = 2d \sin \theta$$

When a collimated beam of monochromatic X-rays of wavelength λ strikes a crystal, the rays penetrate and are partially scattered from many successive planes within the crystal (Fig. 49–1). For a given interplanar

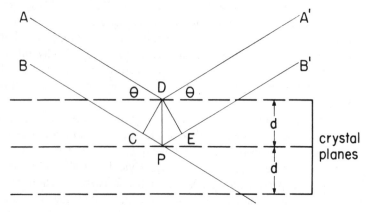

Fig. 49–1. Diffraction from crystal planes according to Bragg's law, $n\lambda = 2d \sin \theta$.

spacing d, there will be a critical angle θ at which rays scattered from successive planes will be in phase along a front as they leave the crystal. A ray following the path BPB', for example, will have traveled some whole number of wavelengths $n\lambda$ farther than a ray traveling along the path ADA'. The angle between the normal to the emerging wave front and the atomic planes will equal the angle between the normal to the primary wave front and the atomic planes. Diffraction from a succession of equally spaced lattice planes results in a diffraction maximum which has sufficient intensity to be recorded.

When n is equal to 1, diffraction is of first order. At other angles, where n is equal to 2, 3, or a greater number, diffraction is again possible, giving rise to second, third, and higher orders of diffraction. Although d remains the same, d/n values will be different depending upon the value of n.

Since no two minerals have exactly the same interatomic distances in three dimensions, the angles at which diffraction occurs will be distinctive for a particular mineral. The interatomic distances within a mineral crystal then result in a unique array of diffraction maxima which serves to identify that mineral.

Diffraction can occur whenever the Bragg law, $n\lambda = 2d \sin \theta$, is satisfied. The wavelength of radiation is characteristic and constant for the particular X-ray tube used. The angle of incidence θ of the primary radiation with the crystal planes can be varied, however.

With an X-ray spectrometer, the angle of incidence is varied by rotating the sample in the path of the primary X-ray beam. A Geiger-counter detector, used to intercept and measure the diffracted rays, also moves in such a way as to maintain an angle with the sample which is equal at all positions to the angle of incidence of the primary beam. From the chart of a direct-recording X-ray spectrometer, the value of 2θ (with reference to the primary beam) is available directly.

The angle θ may be effectively varied by analysis with stationary sample and recorder, the recorder in this case being a photographic film. Crystals to be analyzed are reduced to a very fine powder and placed in the path of a beam of monochromatic X-rays. The particles of the powder are tiny crystals oriented at random with respect to the primary beam. Because of the large number of crystals in the mass of fine powder, there will be sufficient crystals properly oriented so that every set of lattice planes will be capable of diffraction. The mass of powder is equivalent to a single crystal rotated, not about one axis, but about all possible axes. In the event that several crystal species are present in the powder mixture, each component species registers its own diffraction maxima independently. The diffracted rays from a powder mixture may be registered on a photographic film or plate that is geometrically so placed in relation to the sample as to allow determination of the angle of diffraction for each maximum, and subsequent calculation of interatomic spacing.

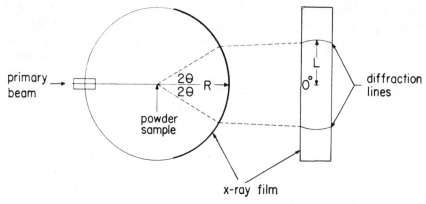

Fig. 49–2. Registration of diffraction lines on film in a cylindrical camera.

A cylindrical film pattern registers diffraction-cone intercepts at angles θ from the diffracting crystal planes (2θ as measured from the primary beam) as shown in Fig. 49–2. The geometry of cylindrical camera systems requires that θ be related to the camera radius R and the distance between the primary beam position and each line position L, as measured on the film in a flat position, by the equation

$$L/2\pi R = 2\theta/360°.$$

Knowing both the radius of the camera and the measured value of L in centimeters, one may readily calculate θ for each diffraction line.

After determining θ, or more usually 2θ, for each diffraction line on either a chart-recorded or film-recorded pattern, d may be calculated from Bragg's equation. Operation manuals of the various commercial diffraction instruments usually contain tables for ready conversion of θ or 2θ to d values.

Efficiency of diffraction from a mineral sample is dependent upon the wavelength of radiation used and the physical and chemical nature of the sample. Selection of the proper wavelength of radiation and careful sample preparation are factors to be considered by the analyst to ensure that maximum diffraction intensity and quality may be obtained in any particular analysis.

49–3   PREPARATION OF SAMPLES

49–3.1   Introduction

Because of the necessity for application of several diagnostic tests for positive identification of layer-silicate species, a sample may have to be analyzed two or more times. The number of analyses, preparatory treatments, and manner of presentation of a sample to the X-ray diffractometer will depend upon the particular mineral assemblage in a sample.

To ensure detection of mineral species in a soil or clay sample by X-ray diffraction analysis, it is distinctly advantageous to concentrate the individual species as much as possible. Although it is impossible to separate mineral species physically from polycomponent systems, it is possible in many cases to concentrate species by fractionation of samples according to particle size.

Segregation of size-fractions in polycomponent mineral samples can be accomplished only if the samples are thoroughly dispersed. To achieve dispersion, it is imperative that flocculating and aggregate-cementing agents be removed from the samples.

Great dependence is placed on diffraction from (00l) planes of layer-silicate species, since diffraction intensities from these planes are normally highest per unit of clay. Both the distances between crystal layers and the intensity of diffraction from expandable layer-silicates vary with the nature of the liquid present between layers. Preparation of unknown clay samples for X-ray analysis should always be designed to allow detection of expandable layer-silicates which may be present.

Both film-recorded and chart-recorded X-ray patterns of a sample are normally obtained if both types of equipment are available. A film-recorded X-ray pattern of a random powder sample is especially advantageous for identification of species other than layer-silicates. One or more patterns of oriented aggregates are taken with the direct-recording spectrometer for most efficient identification of layer-silicate species. Although this sequence is most convenient, all analyses can be performed with either type of equipment. The procedures described are designed to allow the necessary sequence of analyses with either or both methods.

49–3.2 Removal of Flocculating and Cementing Agents

Common cementing agents in soils include alkaline-earth carbonates, organic matter, oxides and hydroxy oxides of iron, oxides of manganese, and amorphous silica and alumina. Removal of these materials is of advantage not only from the standpoint of obtaining efficient dispersion of soil particles prior to size fractionation, but also from the standpoint of improving X-ray diffraction quality from segregated samples. Unless removed, these cementing agents may (1) prevent effective dispersion and ultimate segregation of mineral particles, (2) act as diluents, thus reducing diffraction intensity of crystalline species present, (3) prevent efficient orientation of layer-silicate species during preparation of an oriented aggregate specimen, (4) cause attenuation of the primary X-ray beam, and

(5) cause an increase in the general level of scatter of X-rays from the sample being analyzed.

Items (4) and (5) deserve special comment. It is a common observation that materials amorphous to X-rays cause nondirectional scatter of X-radiation from a sample, resulting in a general increase in background radiation. Such an effect lowers the ratio of diffraction maxima to background and thus decreases the sensitivity of an analysis. Organic matter, amorphous alumina, and amorphous silica produce this effect.

Removal of oxides of iron can greatly improve diffraction intensity if copper radiation is employed. Iron will absorb copper radiation, the amount of absorption more or less depending upon the concentration of iron. This will reduce the intensity of both primary and diffracted radiation. As a result of the absorption, the iron in turn will fluoresce and emit its own characteristic X-radiation, which will be nondirectional and will add to the general background level.

Preparation of samples for X-ray diffraction analysis should include treatments designed to remove such aggregating agents and amorphous materials as may be present. These treatments, normally given before size fractionation of samples, are described in sections 44–2 through 44–4.

49–3.3 Separation of Particle-Size Fractions

49–3.3.1 PRINCIPLES

In accordance with the recommendations of Truog et al. (1937a; 1937b), Jackson et al. (1948), and Jackson and Sherman (1953), soil clay samples are normally separated into coarse (2 to 0.2μ), medium (0.2 to 0.08μ), and fine ($<0.08\mu$) fractions before X-ray diffraction analysis.

The tendency of particular soil mineral species to occur within rather well-defined size limits has been demonstrated by a number of investigators (Marshall, 1930; Truog et al. 1937a, 1937b; Nagelschmidt, 1939; Jackson and Hellman, 1942; Jackson et al. 1948). According to Jackson and Sherman (1953), the tendency for specific colloidal mineral species to concentrate within specific size fractions is a function of their resistance to weathering and of intensity of weathering. Minerals which are more resistant to chemical weathering, such as members of the montmorillonite series, tend to persist in greater quantities in the finer clay fractions. Weathering susceptibility of less resistant minerals, such as feldspars and micas, results in their extinction before they reach fine-clay dimensions.

The intensity of diffraction from a particular mineral species is affected by a number of factors in addition to the concentration of the mineral. Included among these factors are crystal size and crystal perfection. Since finer particles within the clay-size fractions yield weaker diffraction intensities than larger particles of the same species, and since finer particles might be expected to exhibit crystal imperfections to a greater extent, it is especially important that samples be separated according to size and that each fraction be analyzed separately. It has been a common practice of many investigators to analyze, without further separation, the entire clay fraction (particles $<2\mu$ diameter). Such practice may lead to serious error in identification of species present and in estimation of relative proportions of the various species. Analysis of various size fractions of a sample, rather than analysis of bulk samples, will often enable detection of small amounts of a mineral or minerals which may otherwise be obscured by the more abundant or more easily detected species present.

In preparation of oriented aggregate specimens (section 49–3.6), it is especially advantageous to separate size fractions. Oriented aggregate mounts are prepared by sedimentation of suspended mineral material onto a flat surface. If a clay sample contains minerals with a relatively wide range of particle size, there will be differential settling as a function of size, with resulting stratification. Diffraction effects obtained from such a sample will be largely contributed by smaller particles near the surface of the mount.

The procedure for separation of fractions to a limit of 2μ diameter is given in sections 43–3 and 43–4. The $<2\mu$ fraction, as obtained, may be subdivided further into coarse (2 to 0.2μ), medium (0.2 to 0.08μ), and fine ($<0.08\mu$) fractions.

Separation of small quantities of clay fractions specifically for X-ray analysis may be accomplished using small quantities of soil and with elimination of several steps involved in complete fractionation.

Subdivisions within the clay fraction are accomplished by differential sedimentation of particles under centrifugal force. The reader is referred to Svedberg and Nichols (1923) and Jackson (1956) for principles involved in separation of fractions with a tube centrifuge and to Jackson (1956) for principles involved in separation of fractions with a supercentrifuge.

An integrated form of Stokes' law, as proposed by Svedberg and Nichols (1923), allows calculation of the time required for sedimentation of particles of particular diameter and specific gravity under centrifugal acceleration. The formula takes the following form for separation of particles in a tube centrifuge:

$$t = \frac{n \log (R/S)}{3.81 N^2 r^2 (\Delta S)} \qquad [1]$$

where t is the time in seconds, R is the radius in cm. of rotation of the top of the sediment in the tube, S is the radius in cm. of rotation of the surface of the suspension in the tube, N is revolutions per second, r is the particle radius in cm., n is the viscosity of the liquid in poises at the existing temperature, and ΔS is the difference in specific gravity between the particles and the suspension liquid.

The proper flow rate F for separation of fractions with a Sharples super-centrifuge can be calculated by the following formula [derivation of this formula is given in detail by Jackson (1956)]:

$$F \text{ (in ml. per min.)} = \frac{60 A_w C_w \, \Delta S (D_L)^2}{18n} \qquad [2]$$

where A_w is the area of the inner wall of the supercentrifuge bowl in cm.^{2}, C_w is centrifugal force in dynes, ΔS is the difference in density between the particles and the suspension liquid (in g. cm.$^{-3}$), D_L in the particle limiting diameter in microns, and n is the viscosity of the liquid in poises at the existing temperature.

49–3.3.2 METHOD

49–3.3.2.1 Special Apparatus.

1. International No. 2 centrifuge (International Equipment Co., Boston, Mass.) equipped with a No. 240 head and 100-ml. centrifuge tubes.
2. Centrifuge speed indicator.
3. Supercentrifuge (The Sharples Corp., Philadelphia, Pa.) equipped with a cellulose acetate liner (made by Eastman Kodak Co. and sold by Transilwrap Co., 281 W. Fullerton Ave., Chicago, Ill.).
4. Waring Blendor (Winsted Hardware Manufacturing Co., Winsted, Conn.)
5. Time clock.

49–3.3.2.2 Reagents.

1. Sodium carbonate (Na_2CO_3) solution, pH 9.5.
2. Sodium chloride (NaCl).
3. Methanol, 95%.

49–3.3.2.3 Procedure.
Start with enough soil to ensure separation of an adequate amount of each clay fraction (150 mg. of each is sufficient for all analyses usually performed). Remove the soluble salts, carbonates, organic matter, and free iron oxides as described in section 44. Separate the sand and coarse silt from the sample (as outlined below) to remove the bulk of the coarse fractions and facilitate subsequent separation of clay.

Transfer the pretreated soil to a 100-ml. tall-form beaker (if the quantity of soil taken is large, distribute the soil between two or more beakers to limit the sediment volume and, hence, facilitate subsequent separation by sedimentation and decantation). Stir the suspension and allow it to stand for at least 3 minutes for each 5 cm. of depth. Make a mark on the side of the beaker with a wax pencil at a point exactly 5 cm. above the top of the sediment in the bottom of the beaker. Decant the supernatant liquid (containing particles $<20\mu$ in diameter) into an appropriate vessel. Add Na_2CO_3 solution to the sediment in the beaker to just below the 5-cm. mark, and stir the suspension thoroughly with a stirring rod equipped with a rubber policeman. When the suspension is thoroughly mixed, remove the stirring rod, wash the adhering mineral particles into the suspension with water from a wash bottle, and make the suspension to the 5-cm. mark with a jet of water from the wash bottle. Allow the suspension to stand for about 3 minutes [determine the exact time at the existing temperature by calculation from Stokes' law or from the nomograph given by Tanner and Jackson (1948) and Jackson (1956)]. After the appropriate sedimentation time, decant the supernatant suspension into the vessel reserved for the $<20\mu$ particles. Resuspend the sediment in Na_2CO_3 solution, stir the suspension thoroughly, and repeat the sedimentation and decantation until the supernatant liquid is practically free of suspended material. As many as 5 to 8 repetitions of the procedure may be required to effect nearly complete separation (if only the clay fractions are desired, complete separation of particles at 20μ is not necessary).

Particles $<2\mu$ in diameter may be separated directly by centrifugation and decantation as described below. It is usually advantageous, however, first to reduce the suspension volume by allowing particles $>2\mu$ in diameter to sediment by gravity.

If the latter procedure is followed, allow the suspension containing particles $<20\mu$ in diameter to stand for at least 8 hours for each 10 cm. of depth. Decant the supernatant liquid containing suspended particles $<2\mu$ in diameter into an appropriate vessel. The sediment will contain all particles $>2\mu$ in diameter and some particles $<2\mu$ in diameter. Resuspend the sediment in Na_2CO_3 solution, and transfer the suspension to 100-ml. centrifuge tubes, keeping the suspension depth exactly 10 cm. To facilitate subsequent separation, limit the depth of sediment in each tube (as determined after the first centrifugation) to approximately 1 cm. Centrifuge the suspension in an International No. 2 centrifuge at the appropriate speed and for the time required to allow all particles $>2\mu$ in diameter to settle to the bottom of the tube. Calculate the speed and time with the aid of equation [1], or use the nomograph given by Tanner and Jackson (1948) and by Jackson (1956). Decant the supernatant liquid into the vessel reserved for $<2\mu$ particles. Resuspend the sediment in Na_2CO_3 solution, mix the suspension thoroughly, centrifuge it for the appropriate time, and decant the supernatant liquid. Repeat the procedure until separation is essentially complete, as indicated by constant turbidity of the supernatant liquid after successive centrifugations. From 5 to 8 repetitions of the resuspension, centrifugation, and decantation procedures are usually required. Gradual physical breakdown of silt particles during the process of resuspension prevents complete clearing of the supernatant liquid.

A preliminary separation of particles $<0.08\mu$ in diameter may be desirable as a means of reducing suspension volume. If the suspension volume is less than about 2 liters, however, it is usually more efficient to proceed with separation of particles $>0.2\mu$ in diameter.

To start the separation at 0.2μ, transfer the suspension of $<2\mu$ clay to a group of 100-ml. centrifuge tubes, keeping the depth of suspension in the tubes exactly 10 cm. Centrifuge the suspensions in the International No. 2 centrifuge for the appropriate time and speed to allow particles $>0.2\mu$ in diameter to sediment to the bottom. Determine the time and speed by calculation from equation [1] or from the nomograph given by Tanner and Jackson (1948) and Jackson (1956). Decant the supernatant liquid containing particles $<0.2\mu$ in diameter into an appropriate vessel. Continue the procedure until all the clay suspension has been collected in the tubes. Resuspend the sediment in the tubes in Na_2CO_3 solution, make the suspension to volume, and repeat the centrifugation and decantation until separation is essentially complete. From 5 to 8 repetitions are usually sufficient.

After the last decantation, transfer the sediment in the bottom of the tubes (coarse clay, 2 to 0.2μ) to a small flask, and save it for X-ray analysis.

Because of the fine size of the particles remaining in supension and the force required to effect sedimentation, the separation of particles $<0.08\mu$ in diameter is accomplished with a supercentrifuge. Operation of the supercentrifuge and adjustment of flow rate are outlined in the Instruction Manual supplied by the manufacturer.

The suspension of medium and fine clay decanted in the previous separation is then placed in the feed reservoir of the supercentrifuge. Fit a wetted cellulose acetate liner around the interior of the clarifier bowl, and install the bowl in the supercentrifuge. Place a 6-liter flask under the upper delivery spout of the separator assembly, and start the supercentrifuge. When the desired speed is attained, start the flow of suspension through the bowl, and catch the effluent containing particles $<0.08\mu$ in diameter in the collection flask. When nearly all the suspension has passed from the reservoir, wash down the sides of the reservoir with Na_2CO_3 solution from a wash bottle. When the wash solution has nearly drained away, add about 300 ml. of Na_2CO_3 solution to the reservoir, and allow it to flush out the suspension remaining in the bowl. When the effluent flow ceases, allow the centrifuge to coast freely to a stop, remove and open the bowl, and extract the cellulose acetate liner holding the sedimented particles. Carefully wash the sediment from the liner and from the interior of the bowl into a Waring Blendor. Add Na_2CO_3 solution, and mix the suspension in the Blendor for 1 to 2 minutes. Dilute the suspension to a concentration of 1% or less, and repeat the entire supercentrifugation. A total of 4 to 5 repetitions of the resuspension and centrifugation procedure allows essentially complete separation of particles at the 0.08μ-diameter limit. After the last centrifugation, collect the sedimented particles (medium clay, 0.2 to 0.08μ diameter), and save this fraction for X-ray analysis.

Add sufficient NaCl to the effluent from the supercentrifugation to render it approximately $1N$ with respect to NaCl. Let the suspension stand until the clay flocculates and settles; then remove the clear supernatant liquid with a siphon or by careful decantation. Transfer the flocculated clay to 100-ml. centrifuge tubes, and centrifuge them at 1,500 rpm. for 5 minutes. Decant the supernatant liquid, and wash the clay 5 times with 95% methanol to remove most of the NaCl. Save the clay for X-ray diffraction analysis.

49-3.4 Saturation of Exchange Complex

49-3.4.1 PRINCIPLES

Since different cations may retain different amounts of water of hydration (Barshad, 1950; Norrish, 1954; Mielenz et al., 1955), it is imperative that a clay sample prepared for diffraction analysis be homoionic to ensure that expansion as a result of hydration will be uniform within all crystals of a species. Also, since clay samples are commonly analyzed after drying in air, it is advisable to exchange-saturate the clay with a cation which will minimize changes in interlayer water adsorption due to fluctuations in relative humidity. Magnesium (Mg), which allows relatively uniform interlayer adsorption of water by expandable layer-silicates, and potassium (K), which specifically restricts interlayer adsorption of water by vermiculite, are most commonly used for exchange-saturation (Hellman et al., 1943; MacEwan, 1946; Walker, 1957).

Formation of a stable, two-layer water complex between plates of air-dried, Mg-saturated members of the montmorillonite and vermiculite series results in an interatomic spacing of approximately 14Å. between (001) planes. This spacing, which results from expansion of the layers, allows the distinction of these species from the nonexpanding 2:1 layer-silicates, the interatomic spacing of which is approximately 10Å.

Detection of nonexpandable 14Å. chlorites (2:2 layer-silicates) which may be present requires further diagnostic tests for positive differentiation from 14Å. vermiculite. Vermiculite will collapse to an essentially non-expanded structure (10Å.) when saturated with K (Barshad, 1948), whereas chlorites will be unaffected. The difference in behavior of these species when saturated with K is utilized as a means for their differentiation.

Rich and Obenshain (1955), Tamura (1955), and Klages and White (1957) have found that some soil vermiculites contain nonexchangeable interlayer aluminum (as a hydroxy complex) which inhibits lattice contraction on saturation with K. Heating a K-saturated sample at 500°C. for 2 hours will destroy the hydroxy complex and permit contraction of the vermiculite layers. The heat treatment will not affect chlorite.

Effects of heating of samples will be discussed in greater detail in section 49-5.

As many as four Mg-saturated samples and two K-saturated samples may be required for the complete succession of analyses, depending upon the mineral species present and the manner of presentation of the sample to the X-ray equipment. The procedure for exchange-saturation with Mg or K is the same for all preparations regardless of subsequent treatments. It is usually convenient to prepare sufficient Mg- and K-saturated samples to allow the maximum number of analyses that may be necessary.

49–3.4.2 METHOD [1]

49–3.4.2.1 Reagents.

1. Hydrochloric acid (HCl), $0.1N$.
2. Magnesium chloride ($MgCl_2$), $1N$ and $10N$.
3. Magnesium acetate [$Mg(OAc)_2$], $1N$.
4. Potassium chloride (KCl), $1N$.
5. Silver nitrate ($AgNO_3$), $0.1N$.
6. Methanol, 50% and 95%.
7. Acetone, 95% and 100%.
8. Brom phenol blue indicator, 0.04% in ethanol.

49–3.4.2.2 Procedure. To saturate the clay with Mg, transfer an aliquot of dispersed clay suspension containing approximately 25 mg. of clay to a beaker. Add $0.1N$ HCl dropwise with stirring until the pH of the suspension is between 3.5 and 4.0, as determined by a spot-plate test with brom phenol blue indicator. [The suspension is acidified before addition of Mg solutions to prevent precipitation of $Mg(OH)_2$.] Add sufficient $10N$ $Mg(OAc)_2$ to render the suspension approximately $1N$ with respect to Mg. Transfer the clay suspension into a 15-ml. centrifuge tube, centrifuge the tube for 5 minutes at 1,500 revolutions per minute (rpm), and decant and discard the clear supernatant liquid. Complete the exchange-saturation with Mg by washing the sample two times with $1N$ $Mg(OAc)_2$, which is effective in removing H^+ ions from the acidified suspension, and then two times with $1N$ $MgCl_2$. To effect each washing, add approximately 10 ml. of the salt solution, mix the suspension thoroughly, centrifuge the suspension, and decant the supernatant liquid. After exchange-saturation is complete, remove excess salts from the sample by washing (centrifugation and decantation) once with 50% methanol, once with 95% methanol, and finally with 95% acetone until the clear decantate gives a negative test for chloride with $0.1N$ $AgNO_3$. If the sample is to be analyzed as a random powder, transfer it to a large watchglass with acetone, and allow it to dry. Do not dry samples which are to be prepared as oriented aggregates.

To saturate a sample of clay with K, transfer an aliquot of dispersed clay suspension containing approximately 25 mg. of clay to a 15-ml. centrifuge

---

[1] The method is essentially that given by Jackson (1956). The method described allows preparation of both random-powder and oriented-aggregate specimens.

tube. Add enough $1N$ KCl to the suspension to flocculate the clay. Centrifuge the suspension, and discard the supernatant solution. Wash the sample four times (centrifugation and decantation) with $1N$ KCl to complete saturation of the clay with K (the suspension need not be acidified before treatment with KCl since there is no danger of precipitation of K during the treatments). Remove excess salts from the sample by washing once with 50% methanol, once with 95% methanol, and finally with 95% acetone until the decantate gives a negative test for chloride with $AgNO_3$.

If the sample is to be analyzed as a random powder, transfer it to a watchglass with acetone, and allow it to dry. Do not dry the sample if it is to be analyzed as an oriented aggregate.

49–3.5   Solvation with Glycerol

49–3.5.1   PRINCIPLES

The similarity in basal spacing of Mg-saturated vermiculite and montmorillonite species necessitates further differentiation to distinguish between the two groups of minerals. The ability of montmorillonite members to adsorb double sheets of glycerol $[C_3H_5(OH)_3]$ molecules between adjacent layers to yield a basal spacing of approximately 17.7Å. (MacEwan, 1944; Bradley, 1945; White and Jackson, 1947) is utilized as a means of differentiating the two groups. Solvation of vermiculite with glycerol does not materially change its interlayer expansion (Walker, 1950; Barshad, 1950).

Montmorillonite readily forms complexes with many other polar molecules of moderate size, including monohydric alcohols (MacEwan, 1946); polyhydric alcohols, benzene, and ethers (Bradley, 1945); and amines and polyamines (Gieseking, 1939; Bradley, 1945). The glycerol complex, however, offers the maximum number of advantages. As summarized by MacEwan (1946), the main advantages of glycerol are given below.

(1) Resolution of diffraction maxima:
  a. The intense, first-order, basal-diffraction maximum of glycerol-montmorillonite (17.7Å.) is particularly well separated from other maxima likely to occur in clay diffraction patterns.
  b. None of the other glycerol-montmorillonite, basal-diffraction maxima interfere seriously with reflections from other likely minerals.

(2) Stability of the complex:
  a. The spacings and intensities of the glycerol-montmorillonite, basal-diffraction maxima are unaffected by wide variations in water content.
  b. The extremely low volatility of glycerol causes the complex which it forms to be extremely stable.

49–3.5.2.1   Reagents.

1. Benzene.
2. Glycerol.
3. Benzene-ethanol, 10 to 1 by volume and 200 to 1 by volume.
4. Benzene-ethanol-glycerol, 1,000 to 100 to 4.5 by volume.

49–3.5.2.2   Procedure. To prepare a glycerol-solvated, random-powder sample, add 10 ml. of 10-to-1 benzene-ethanol to a Mg-saturated sample as prepared in section 49–3.4.2. Mix the suspension thoroughly, centrifuge it for 5 minutes at 1,500 rpm., and decant the supernatant liquid. Repeat the benzene-ethanol washing once. Wash the sample three times with 10-ml. portions of the ternary mixture of benzene, ethanol, and glycerol to effect solvation of the clay with glycerol. Wash the sample once with 200-to-1 benzene-ethanol solution to remove most of the excess glycerol. Resuspend the sample in benzene and transfer the mixture to a large watchglass. After evaporation of the benzene, the sample is ready for analysis as a Mg-saturated, glycerol-solvated, random-powder sample (section 49–3.6).

To prepare a glycerol-solvated, oriented-aggregate sample, add approximately 2 ml. of distilled water and 2 drops of glycerol to a Mg-saturated sample as prepared in section 49–3.4.2. Thoroughly mix the suspension to ensure complete dispersion. The sample is ready for mounting as an oriented aggregate (section 49–3.6).

49–3.5.2.3   Comment. The correct amount of glycerol to add to a sample being prepared as an oriented aggregate will depend upon the proportion of expandable layer-silicates present and the particle-size range of the mineral particles. Two drops of glycerol per 25-mg. sample is sufficient without excess in most cases. The correct amount may have to be determined by trial and error, however.

49–3.6   Mounting

Two different methods of sample mounting are commonly used in diffraction analysis of clay samples—the sample may be mounted either as a random powder or as an oriented aggregate. There are several ways in which a random powder may be mounted and at least two ways in which an oriented aggregate may be mounted. Both the random-powder and oriented-aggregate mounts have advantages for particular purposes.

---

[2] Jackson (1956) and White and Jackson (1947)

In a random-powder sample, in which crystals lie in all possible positions, there will be a sufficient number of crystals properly oriented to yield diffraction maxima from all atomic planes within the crystals. Different sets of crystals simultaneously register the diffraction maxima corresponding to all interatomic plane distances within each crystal species. The random sample, therefore, enables one to obtain all possible diffraction spacings from minerals present in a sample. This often assists in identification of species since a family of diffraction maxima is obtained for each species. Relative intensities of diffraction maxima obtained from a random powder are more nearly proportional to the number of crystals present than are the maxima obtained from an oriented aggregate.

Preferential orientation of layer-silicate species, as attained in an oriented aggregate, results in enhancement of basal (001) diffraction maxima. This often allows detection of small quantities of layer-silicate species which might otherwise be obscured among more crystalline or more perfect diffracting species in the sample. MacEwan (1946) has reported detection of as little as 1% montmorillonite in polycomponent mixtures using such a mount. The oriented mount has the further advantage that variation in basal spacings may be examined more critically and minor variations more easily detected. Preferential orientation of species, on the other hand, decreases the number of hkl planes in position to diffract X-rays.

The oriented-aggregate mount is especially advantageous when a direct-recording X-ray spectrometer is employed. If both film-recording and direct recording equipment are available, both types of mounts are used to advantage in conjunction with each other.

An oriented aggregate mounted on a porous ceramic plate offers some distinct advantages. Clay on a porous plate may be saturated with Mg or K or solvated with glycerol by applying successive portions of the appropriate solution to the surface and pulling the solution through the plate by suction. A single sample mounted on a porous plate can be Mg-saturated, glycerol-solvated, K-saturated, and heated by successive treatments and X-rayed after each treatment, thus eliminating the need for preparation of a separate mount for each treatment.

49–3.6.2 ROD METHOD FOR RANDOM ORIENTATION

Random powder samples are commonly formed into a rod 0.3 to 0.5 mm. in diameter for analysis. Dried glycerol-solvated samples are slightly sticky and may be readily formed into a thin rod without addition of a binding substance. A binder usually must be added to nonsolvated samples before they can be formed into a rod, however. Gum tragacanth, which offers little interference to X-rays, is a suitable binding substance.

To form such a rod, mix a small amount of the dry clay sample with one-fifth to one-tenth its volume of powdered gum tragacanth, and add enough water to form a thick paste. After a few moments, shape the mixture into a rough rod with the fingers. Perfect the rod to the desired diameter by rolling it back and forth between two glass slides.

Although the above described rod is the most commonly used form of cylindrical mount, alternative mounts may be employed. For example, the sample may be enclosed in a borosilicate-glass capillary or coated on a gummed glass fiber (Henry et al., 1951).

49–3.6.3 WEDGE METHOD FOR RANDOM ORIENTATION [3]

Powder samples are frequently mounted in a specially designed metal wedge (Jeffries and Jackson, 1949). To form the mount, place a small quantity of sample on a clean glass slide, and gently push it into the recess of the wedge with a spatula or with the edge of another glass slide. Carefully smooth the surface of the mounted sample, so that it forms a sharp edge flush with the tip of the wedge.

49–3.6.4 GLASS-PLATE METHOD FOR ORIENTED AGGREGATES [3]

Oriented aggregate specimens may be formed directly from Mg-saturated, K-saturated, or Mg-saturated, glycerol-solvated samples as prepared in sections 49–3.4 or 49–3.5.

Add sufficient water to the sample (or samples) to make a suspension of approximately 2-ml. volume. Thoroughly mix the suspension to ensure complete dispersion. Extract the suspension with a pipette, and carefully transfer it to a glass microscope slide (2.6 by 4.6 cm.) resting on a level surface. Add as much suspension to the slide as can be held by film tension. The total amount of clay per slide should be between about 15 and 25 mg. Allow the suspension to dry completely on the slide before the sample is analyzed.

49–3.6.5 POROUS-CERAMIC-PLATE METHOD FOR ORIENTED AGGREGATES

An alternative method for preparation of oriented aggregates employs a porous ceramic plate as a mounting surface. Unglazed tile is commonly used for this purpose. The tile may be cut with a diamond or carborundum saw or scored with a diamond pencil and broken to appropriate dimensions (approximately 2.6 by 4.6 by 0.5 cm.). The surface should be smoothed by wet-grinding on a glass plate with fine-grade corundum abrasive.

The reader is referred to Kinter and Diamond (1956) for specific details of the procedure and special apparatus needed for preparation of the porous-ceramic-plate-mounted aggregate. In general, the procedure involves the following:

A dilute suspension of clay (containing between 15 and 25 mg. of clay) is added to the surface of a porous ceramic plate. The liquid is separated

---

[3] Jackson (1956).

from the clay by applied suction or by centrifugal force. After the liquid is removed through the plate, the clay remains oriented on the surface.

49–3.6.6 PREPARATION OF CLAY FILMS AND CLAY RODS FROM SALTED CLAY PASTES

An alternative procedure for analysis of clay samples involves preparation of clay films and clay rods from glycerol-ethanol-treated, salted clay pastes. The reader is referred to Barshad (1960) for specific details of the procedure for preparation of the pastes, clay films, and clay rods.

In general, the procedure for preparation of rods for analysis by film techniques involves extrusion of the salted paste from a hypodermic needle. For analysis by the diffractometer method, the clay paste may be spread on the surface of a microscope slide with a smooth-edged instrument.

The rods formed by extrusion from a hypodermic needle present both oriented and unoriented clay particles to the X-ray beam. Particles closest to the surface of the rods are preferentially oriented in the direction parallel to the axis of the rods, whereas those in the interior of the rods are unoriented.

49–4 X-RAY EXAMINATION OF SAMPLES

49–4.1 Special Apparatus

Commercial X-ray diffraction equipment includes a high-voltage generator, an X-ray source, an X-ray beam collimating system, and a detecting and recording system. Film-recording systems require suitable X-ray film (no-screen medical X-ray film is most commonly used) and film-developing reagents and equipment.

49–4.2 Procedure

Clay samples prepared for analysis should be examined in the following order for most efficient identification and differentiation of species: (*1*) Mg-saturated, air-dried sample; (*2*) Mg-saturated, glycerol-solvated sample; (*3*) K-saturated, air-dried sample; and (*4*) K-saturated, heated sample (500°C.).

49–4.2.1 EXAMINATION WITH CYLINDRICAL CAMERA

Cylindrical cameras are equipped with a bracket for mounting either a cylindrical or a wedge-mounted sample. Film is loaded after mounting the sample in some cameras. In others, film is loaded before mounting the samples.

If a cylindrical sample is analyzed, carefully position the sample squarely in the path of the X-ray beam. If a wedge mount is employed, position the wedge so that the sample intercepts approximately two-thirds of the primary beam. Expose the sample to X-rays for sufficient time to yield a sharp contrasting pattern of diffraction maxima. (The proper time of exposure will depend upon the radius of the camera used, the wavelength of radiation employed, the instrument voltage and current settings, and the chemical and mineralogical composition of the sample. Appropriate exposure times must be determined experimentally with each type of equipment.) After exposure, develop the X-ray film according to the procedure recommended by the film manufacturer.

49–4.2.2 EXAMINATION·WITH DIRECT-RECORDING SPECTROMETER

Place a sample in the sample holder provided on the instrument, and position the goniometer to start its angular scan. The practical lower limit for most analyses for 2θ is two degrees. The upper limit for 2θ is dictated by the geometry of the goniometer system (maximum allowable is 180°) and the mineral assemblage in the sample. Start the goniometer in synchronism with the chart recorder, and scan through the desired angular range.

49–4.3 Comments

The principal components which the analyst must consider for his particular applications are the X-ray tube and the detecting and recording system.

The characteristic wavelength produced by an X-ray tube will depend on the metal used in plating the anode target. Metals commonly used for the purpose include molybdenum (Mo), copper (Cu), nickel (Ni), cobalt (Co), iron (Fe), and chromium (Cr). The wavelength of the characteristic radiation produced is different for each metal and is inversely related to atomic number of the metal. The choice of wavelength for diffraction analysis will be dictated by the minerals present in samples to be analyzed, the elemental composition of the samples, the resolution required, and the amount of absorption of the particular wavelength by air.

Chromium radiation ($K\alpha$, 2.28Å.) suffers relatively high absorption by the air that it must pass through between the source and the detector. Elements within a sample such as alumium (Al), iron (Fe), and calcium (Ca) (present in relatively high concentrations in most soil or clay samples) also have relatively high absorption coefficients for Cr radiation. Absorption of the radiation in the air path or within the sample decreases the intensity of diffraction maxima obtained and increases the general background level registered by a detector. The relatively long wavelength of Cr radiation, on the other hand, provides a high degree of resolution in a diffraction pattern. For a given interatomic spacing, the angle at which diffraction occurs will increase with the wavelength used, thus allowing a greater distance between recorded diffraction maxima.

Molybdenum radiation (Kα, 0.71Å.), in contrast to that of Cr, is little affected by absorption by air or by elements within a soil or clay sample. Offsetting these advantages, however, is the relatively poor resolution attainable with Mo radiation. This is of particular significance in detection and separation of maxima at low angles of diffraction.

Copper radiation (Kα, 1.54Å.) is almost universally used in diffraction work because it is not greatly affected in most cases by air or sample absorption, and it provides adequate resolution for most mineral analyses. Absorption of Cu radiation is significant, however, in samples with a high content of Fe. This problem can often be alleviated by selective removal of free iron oxides from samples (section 44–4) before X-ray analysis.

The most common detecting-recording systems used for mineral analysis are cylindrical film-loaded cameras and Geiger-counter detectors with chart recorders. As mentioned in section 49–3.6, these two systems have their particular advantages for specific applications. If both systems are available, they may both be used to advantage in analysis of a sample.

49-5 CRITERIA FOR DIFFERENTIATION OF LAYER-SILICATE SPECIES

Soils nearly always contain a number of mineral species. Many of the species can be identified easily by their distinctive diffraction maxima from a single X-ray pattern. Tables of diffraction spacings for crystalline substances (Hanawalt et al., 1938; Am. Soc. Testing Mater., 1945) and for soil minerals specifically (Brown, 1961) are adequate for identification of species other than layer-silicates. Layer-silicate species, however, have many similar or identical structural features which make their differentiation and identification more difficult. Differentiating analyses and criteria for identification of layer silicate species are discussed in detail by Warshaw and Roy (1961).

The criteria for species differentiation as presented here concern only the layer-silicates, and specifically those most commonly found in soils. The criteria, as furnished by diagnostic diffraction maxima from the specially treated samples, are presented in diagrammatic form (Table 49–1) for ready reference. Only the more pertinent basal (001) diffraction spacings are listed.

Table 49–1. X-ray diffraction spacings obtained from (001) planes of layer-silicate species as related to sample treatment.

Diffraction spacing (Å.)	Mineral (or minerals) indicated
	Mg-saturated, air-dried
14-15	Montmorillonite, vermiculite, chlorite
9.9-10.1	Mica (illite), halloysite
7.2- 7.5	Metahalloysite
7.15	Kaolinite, chlorite (2nd-order maximum)
	Mg-saturated, glycerol-solvated
17.7-18.0	Montmorillonite
14-15	Vermiculite, chlorite
10.8	Halloysite
9.9-10.1	Mica (illite)
7.2- 7.5	Metahalloysite
7.15	Kaolinite, chlorite (2nd-order maximum)
	K-saturated, air-dried
14-15	Chlorite, vermiculite (with interlayer aluminum)
12.4-12.8	Montmorillonite
9.9-10.1	Mica (illite), halloysite, vermiculite (contracted)
7.2- 7.5	Metahalloysite
7.15	Kaolinite, chlorite (2nd-order maximum)
	K-saturated, heated (500° C.)
14	Chlorite
9.9-10.1	Mica, vermiculite (contracted), montmorillonite (contracted)
7.15	Chlorite (2nd-order maximum)

As seen in Table 49–1, a diffraction spacing of approximately 14Å. obtained from a Mg-saturated, air-dried sample may be contributed by montmorillonite, vermiculite, or chlorite, or by a mixture of these species. Solvation with glycerol allows separation and positive identification of montmorillonite. Saturation with K similarly allows separation of vermiculite from chlorite, which does not collapse.

Heating of a sample to 500°C. serves two important functions. It effects collapse of vermiculite which contains nonexchangeable interlayer aluminum hydroxy complexes, and it destroys the kaolin minerals. When chlorite is present in a sample, it normally yields a second-order maximum at nearly the same position as the first-order maximum of kaolinite (7.15Å.). If a 7.15Å. spacing, obtained from an unheated sample, disappears or decreases in intensity after heating at 500°C., the presence of kaolinite is confirmed.

An efficient technique for differentiation of kaolinite from chlorite has been described by Andrew et al. (1960). Kaolinite may be expanded to 14Å. by intersalation with potassium acetate. Replacement of the interlayer potassium acetate with NH_4NO_3 results in a spacing of 11.6Å. for kaolinite. This spacing does not coincide with spacings of other common clay minerals.

Soil clays often contain interstratified mixtures of layer-silicate species. Two or more species may be interstratified within a single crystal in either a regular or random manner. Diffraction effects from mixed crystals are quite different from those obtained from crystals containing only a single species. Diffraction from a few of the more common interstratified mixtures will be considered here.

Regular alternation of two species within a crystal produces repeating diffraction planes at a distance equal to the sum of the (001) distances of the two species. Thus, a regular alternation of Mg-saturated montmorillonite and mica, chlorite and mica, or vermiculite and mica yields a diffraction spacing of 24Å. (14Å. + 10Å. in each case). Regular alternation of montmorillonite with either chlorite or vermiculite, or of chlorite with vermiculite, yields a spacing of approximately 28Å. (14Å + 14Å. in each case).

Individual species in regularly alternating binary mixtures can be identified by the succession of analyses of samples treated as prescribed in section 49–4. Species within each possible mixture will give the normal response to glycerol solvation, K-saturation, and heat treatment.

Two species randomly interstratified yield a well-defined spacing intermediate between the normal (001) spacing of the two individual members (Hendricks and Teller, 1942). Randomly interstratified mica and vermiculite, for example, yield an "average" spacing between 10 and 14Å. The exact spacing distance will depend upon the relative proportions of the two species in the mixture. A randomly interstratified mixture of vermiculite and chlorite yields a single spacing of 14Å. Potassium-saturation of such a sample will collapse the vermiculite to 10Å. and will leave the chlorite at 14Å., resulting in an average spacing someplace between 10 and 14Å.

Other random binary combinations can be differentiated by the succession of analyses of samples treated as prescribed in section 49–4. The reader is referred to Brown (1961) for a detailed discussion of diffraction effects from randomly interstratified systems.

Table 49–2. X-ray diffraction spacings (Å.) obtained from (001) planes of binary, regularly alternating, layer-silicate species as related to sample treatment.

Interstratified mixture	Mg-saturated, air-dried	Mg-saturated, glycerol-solvated	K-saturated, heated (500° C.)
		diffraction spacings, Å.	
Mica-vermiculite	24	24	10
Mica-chlorite	24	24	24
Mica-montmorillonite	24	28	10
Vermiculite-chlorite	28	28	24
Vermiculite-montmorillonite	28	32	10
Montmorillonite-chlorite	28	32	24

More complicated interstratified mixtures involving three or more species do occur in soils, but they are practically impossible to differentiate into individual component species. Such mixtures usually yield only broad, indistinct diffraction effects.

Diffraction maxima obtained from common regularly alternating interstratified binary mixtures are given in Table 49–2.

49–6   QUALITATIVE INTERPRETATION OF DIFFRACTION PATTERNS

Qualitative interpretation of diffraction patterns involves identification of crystalline species from the array of diffraction maxima obtained from a sample. Identification may be accomplished by either (1) direct comparison of diffraction patterns of unknown samples with patterns obtained from known minerals, or (2) measurement of diffraction spacings and comparison of these spacings with known spacings of standard minerals.

49–6.1   Direct Comparison

In the direct-comparison method a film or chart-recorded pattern is compared, edge to edge, with patterns obtained from standard minerals. Lines on the pattern of the unknown which match lines on the known pattern, both in position and relative intensities, can be identified in this way. When more than one mineral is present, comparison with patterns of several known minerals may be necessary to identify all species present.

49–6.2   Measurement of Diffraction Spacings

When several minerals are present in a sample, identification of species is usually accomplished most easily and positively by determining the interatomic spacings giving rise to the various maxima and by comparing these with known spacings of minerals. Each maximum will represent either a specific interatomic distance d or a diffraction order d/n of a given distance.

The position of diffraction maxima on a pattern is determined by the geometry of the analyzing system, the wavelength of radiation used, and the distance between diffracting planes within crystals in the sample. In any particular analysis, the geometry of the system and the wavelength are fixed. Therefore, the angle of diffraction from diffracting planes will be directly dependent upon the interplanar distances. Interception of diffraction cones at a known distance from the sample provides a means for determination of diffraction angles and, hence, interplanar spacings.

Diffraction angles may be determined directly in terms of 2θ from a direct-recording spectrometer pattern. By reference to standard conversion tables, one may obtain the corresponding diffraction spacings.

Determination of diffraction angles from film patterns requires physical measurement of the position of each maximum on the film with respect to zero degrees θ (position of undiffracted primary beam) and conversion of these measured values to angular displacements.

Measurement of the distance of a diffraction maximum from the position of the undiffracted beam is done on a film placed in a flat position on an illuminated viewing device fitted with a ruler and a vernier cross-hair indicator. The exact center of the pattern is found by determining the midpoint between two corresponding maxima (representing arcs of a single diffraction cone) equidistant on both sides of the center. The distance between each maximum and the focus of the pattern is measured in centimeters. The diffraction angle θ, corresponding to each maximum can then be calculated directly by the equation $\theta = 360°L/2\pi R$, where R represents the radius of the camera in centimeters. Interatomic spacings d can then be obtained by reference to standard conversion tables or by calculation from Bragg's equation.

49–6.3 Identification of Mineral Species

Both the diffraction spacings and the intensity of each maximum are recorded to enable one to identify species. Intensities of maxima obtained with Geiger-counter records should be recorded directly as counts per second. Maxima from photographically recorded patterns are usually measured visually and assigned relative intensities as very strong, strong, medium, weak, or very weak.

Identification of layer-silicate species in clay samples can be accomplished by comparing maxima obtained from Mg-saturated, K-saturated, and glycerol-solvated samples as tabulated in section 49–5. Identification of other species may require reference to the Hanawalt tables (1938) or the ASTM card file. Standard minerals are indexed in the Hanawalt tables and in the ASTM card file system on the basis of their three strongest diffraction maxima. Identification of minerals in a sample is accomplished by selecting from the card system a number of cards which correspond to the spacing of the most intense line of a diffraction pattern. The spacing of the second most intense line is next found on some of the cards, thus eliminating some of the cards. The third most intense line occurs on only one of the cards, thus identifying the mineral. For a more detailed description of the procedure for identification of species with the card system, the reader is referred to Jackson (1956) and Henry et al. (1951).

49–7 QUANTITATIVE INTERPRETATION OF DIFFRACTION PATTERNS

The intensities of diffraction maxima are related to the number of corresponding diffraction planes in a sample. Thus, the relative intensities of maxima provide a basis for estimation of concentrations of mineral species present. There are a number of factors relative to the physical and chemical nature of samples, however, which can also greatly influence diffraction intensities and, hence, the validity of quantitative estimation of mineral species. These factors will be considered briefly before discussion of methods of quantitative estimation of diffraction patterns to acquaint the reader with some of the difficulties inherent in the methods.

According to Jackson (1956), the principal factors which influence diffraction intensities, in addition to concentration of species, are particle size, crystal perfection, chemical composition, variations in sample packing, crystal orientation, and presence of amorphous substances.

When particles are greater than about 10μ in diameter, X-ray patterns became spotty in character because there are not sufficient crystals in all possible orientations to yield continuous diffraction-cones. If particles are less than about 0.02μ in diameter, the diffraction maxima become broad and diffuse. Diffraction intensity decreases simply as a function of very fine particle size in this range. Soil clays can be expected to have a relatively wide range in particle size, and the size of a particular species may be different in different samples.

The degree of crystal imperfection can vary within members of a species, and it depends upon conditions of formation of the mineral, conditions of weathering of its mineral grains, or both. Any discontinuities due to crystal imperfections will reduce X-ray intensities.

Layer-silicate clays frequently occur as interstratified mixtures. In such mixtures there may be too few planes of one species in any one zone to allow detection or to be represented by proportional diffraction intensity (Jackson et al. 1952).

The chemical composition of a sample can affect diffraction intensities in two principal ways. The presence of an element or elements in a sample capable of absorbing the wavelength of radiation employed for the analysis will reduce diffraction intensities. Diffraction intensities from a particular species will be affected also by the constituent elements of the species, since atoms vary in their ability to scatter X-rays.

The density of packing of a powder sample will also affect the intensity of diffracted rays. In general, the more dense (tightly packed) a sample is, the more planes will contribute to diffraction. If a sample is too tightly packed, however, the absorption of both primary and diffracted rays increases.

The degree of orientation or, on the other hand, the degree of randomness of the crystals of a powder will cause a variation in diffraction intensity independent of the quantity of a mineral species present.

The presence of amorphous substances, acting as nondiffracting diluents, will also lead to an erroneous estimation of the mineral composition of a sample. If the amorphous substances cannot be detected, one is apt to conclude that the sample is composed entirely of the detectable crystalline components.

If it were possible to hold each of these variables constant, or if one were able to evaluate properly the influence of these variables, a precise quantitative estimation of species would be possible. Unfortunately, these factors cannot be controlled in most cases.

In specific cases, where variations in diffraction intensities from these causes can be considered negligible, quantitative estimations of clay mineral percentages can be made by comparison of intensities of diffraction maxima contributed by minerals in a sample to diffraction intensities obtained from the same species in artificial standard mixtures (Willis et al. 1948; Talvenheimo and White, 1952). By this method, standard mineral mixtures, composed of two or more minerals in various proportions, are prepared and analyzed. Calibration curves, equating diffraction intensities obtained from component minerals in the mixtures to known concentrations of the minerals, are then prepared. Quantitative estimates of minerals in test samples are made by measuring the intensities of their diffraction maxima and by comparing these intensities to those obtained from known concentrations in the prepared standards.

The use of an internal standard, in conjunction with the standard mineral mixtures, is an effective means of compensating for errors caused by X-ray absorption within a sample (Phillippe and White, 1951; Whiteside, 1948). A known quantity of some mineral not already present in a sample is added and thoroughly mixed with each standard mixture. The mixtures are analyzed, and the intensities of diffraction maxima of the added internal standard mineral and of each component mineral in each standard mixture are measured. The ratio of the diffraction intensity of each mineral of the standard mixture to the diffraction intensity of the internal standard is plotted against the weight ratio of standard mineral to internal standard for each case. The internal standard is then added to each test sample in the same weight ratio as in the standard mixtures, and the test mixtures are analyzed. The diffraction-intensity ratios (intensity of mineral being analyzed to intensity of internal standard) are determined and compared to the plot obtained for the standard-mineral internal-standard mixtures to obtain the weight ratio of mineral to internal standard. Finally, by multiplying the weight of internal standard added to the test sample by the weight ratio of mineral to internal standard, the weight of the mineral in the sample is obtained. Knowing the total weight of the test sample, the percentage of the determined mineral (or minerals) can be calculated.

The internal standard chosen should have diffraction maxima as close as possible to diffraction maxima of minerals in the sample, and it should have absorption characteristics similar to the sample. If the standard is properly chosen, absorption effects will be the same for the internal standard and the component minerals in the sample.

Quantitative analysis of minerals by X-ray diffraction can be reliable in some cases, but generally speaking, variations in chemical composition, crystal perfection, amorphous substances, and particle size are very difficult to evaluate and compensate for in analysis of soil or clay samples. In most cases, estimation of mineral percentages from X-ray diffraction patterns is only semiquantitative at best. For the most reliable and accurate estimation, the use of X-ray diffraction analysis in conjunction with other methods, such as differential-thermal, integral-thermal, infrared, surface-area, and elemental analysis, is advisable.

49–8   LITERATURE CITED

American Society for Testing and Materials. 1945. Alphabetical index of X-ray diffraction patterns. Am. Soc. Testing Mater., Philadelphia.

Andrew, R. W., Jackson, M. L., and Wada, K. 1960. Intersalation as a technique for differentiation of kaolinite from chloritic minerals by X-ray diffraction. Soil Sci. Soc. Am. Proc. 24:422–423.

Barshad, I. 1948. Vermiculite and its relation to biotite as revealed by base exchange reactions, X-ray analysis, differential thermal curves, and water content. Am. Mineralogist 33:655–678.

Barshad, I. 1950. The effect of the interlayer cations on the expansion of the mica-type crystal lattice. Am. Mineralogist 35:225–238.

Barshad, I. 1960. X-ray analysis of soil colloids by a modified salted paste method. Proc. Natl. Conf. Clays Clay Minerals. 5:350–364.

Bradley, W. F. 1945. Molecular associations between montmorillonite and some polyfunctional organic liquids. J. Am. Chem. Soc. 67:975–981.

Brown, G. 1961. The X-Ray Identification and Crystal Structures of Clay Minerals. The Mineralogical Society, London.

Buerger, M. J. 1942. X-Ray Crystallography. John Wiley and Sons, Inc., New York.

Clark, G. L. 1955. Applied X-Rays. McGraw-Hill Book Co., Inc., New York.

Cullity, B. D. 1956. Elements of X-Ray Diffraction. Addison-Wesley Publishing Co., Reading, Mass.

Gieseking, J. E. 1939. The mechanism of cation exchange in the montmorillonite-beidellite-nontronite type of clay minerals. Soil Sci. 47:1–13.

Hadding, A. 1923. Eine röntgenographische Methode kristalline und kryptokristalline Substanzen zu identifizieren. Ztsch. Krist. 58:108–112.

Hanawalt, J. D., Rinn, H. W., and Frevel, L. K. 1938. Chemical analysis by X-ray diffraction. Ind. Eng. Chem., Anal. Ed. 10:457–512.

Hellman, N. N., Aldrich, D. G., and Jackson, M. L. 1943. Further note on an X-ray diffraction procedure for the positive differentiation of montmorillonite from hydrous mica. Soil Sci. Soc. Am. Proc. (1942) 7:194–200.

Hendricks, S. B., and Fry, W. H. 1930. The results of X-ray and microscopical examinations of soil colloids. Soil Sci. 29:457–480.

Hendricks, S. B., and Teller, E. 1942. X-ray interference in partially ordered layer lattices. J. Chem. Phys. 10:147–167.

Henry, N. F. M., Lipson, H., and Wooster, W. A. 1951. The Interpretation of X-Ray Diffraction Photographs. Macmillan and Co., Ltd., London.

Jackson, M. L. 1956. Soil Chemical Analysis—Advanced Course. Published by the author, Department of Soils, Univ. of Wis., Madison 6, Wis.

Jackson, M. L., and Hellman, N. N. 1942. X-ray diffraction procedure for positive differentiation of montmorillonite from hydrous mica. Soil Sci. Soc. Am. Proc. (1941) 6:133–145.

Jackson, M. L., Hseung, Y., Corey, R. B., Evans, E. J., and Vanden Heuvel, R. C. 1952. Weathering sequence of clay-size minerals in soils and sediments: II. Chemical weathering of layer silicates. Soil Sci. Soc. Am. Proc. 16:3–6.

Jackson, M. L., and Sherman, G. D. 1953. Chemical weathering of minerals in soils. Adv. Agron. 5:219–318.

Jackson, M. L., Tyler, S. A., Willis, A. L., Bourbeau, G. A., and Pennington, R. P. 1948. Weathering sequence of clay size minerals in soils and sediments. I. Fundamental generalizations. J. Phys. Colloid Chem. 52:1237–1260.

Jeffries, C. D., and Jackson, M. L. 1949. Mineralogical analysis of soils. Soil Sci. 68:57–73.

Kelley, W. P., Dore, W. H., and Brown, S. M. 1931. The nature of the base exchange material of bentonite, soils, and zeolites, as revealed by chemical investigations and X-ray analysis. Soil Sci. 31:25–55.

Kinter, E. B., and Diamond, S. 1956. A new method for preparation and treatment of oriented-aggregate specimens of soil clays for X-ray diffraction analysis. Soil Sci. 81:111–120.

Klages, M. G., and White, J. L. 1957. A chlorite-like mineral in Indiana soils. Soil Sci. Soc. Am. Proc. 21:16–20.

Klug, H. P., and Alexander, L. E. 1954. X-Ray Diffraction Procedures. John Wiley and Sons, Inc., New York.

Marshall, C. E. 1930. The orientation of anisotropic particles in an electric field. Trans. Faraday Soc. 26:173–189.

MacEwan, D. M. C. 1944. Identification of the montmorillonite group of minerals by X-rays. Nature 154:577–578.

MacEwan, D. M. C. 1946. The identification and estimation of the montmorillonite group of minerals, with special reference to soil clays. J. Soc. Chem. Ind. 65:298–305.

Mielenz, R. C., Schieltz, N. C., and King, G. E. 1955. Effects of exchangeable cation on X-ray diffraction patterns and thermal behavior of a montmorillonite clay. Proc. Natl. Conf. Clays Clay Minerals. 3:146–173.

Nagelschmidt, G. 1939. The identification of minerals in soil colloids. J. Agr. Sci. 29:477–501.

Norrish, K. 1954. The swelling of montmorillonite. Discussions Faraday Soc. 18:120–134.

Phillippe, M. M., and White, J. L. 1951. Quantitative estimation of minerals in the fine sand and silt fractions of soils with the Geiger counter X-ray spectrometer. Soil Sci. Soc. Am. Proc. (1950) 15:139–142.

Rich, C. I., and Obenshain, S. S. 1955. Chemical and mineral properties of a red-yellow podzolic soil derived from sericite schist. Soil Sci. Soc. Am. Proc. 19:334–339.

Rinne, F. 1924. Röntgenographische Untersuchungen an einigen feinzerteilten Mineralien, Kunstprodukten und dichten Gesteinen. Ztschr. Krist. 60:55–69.

Sproull, W. T. 1946. X-Rays in Practice. McGraw-Hill Book Co., Inc., New York.

Svedberg, T., and Nichols, J. B. 1923. Determination of size and distribution of size by centrifugal methods. J. Am. Chem. Soc. 45:2910–2917.

Talvenheimo, G., and White, J. L. 1952. Quantitative analysis of clay minerals with the X-ray spectrometer. Anal. Chem. 24:1784–1789.

Tamura, T. 1955. Weathering of mixed-layer clays in soils. Proc. Natl. Conf. Clays Clay Minerals. 4:413–422.

Tanner, C. B., and Jackson, M. L. 1948. Nomographs of sedimentation times for soil particles under gravity or centrifugal acceleration. Soil Sci. Soc. Am. Proc. (1947) 12:60–65.

Truog, E., Taylor, J. R., Pearson, R. W., Weeks, M. E., and Simonson, R. W. 1937a. Procedure for special type of mechanical and mineralogical soil analysis. Soil Sci. Soc. Am. Proc. (1936) 1:101–112.

Truog, E., Taylor, J. R., Simonson, R. W., and Weeks, M. E. 1937b. Mechanical and mineralogical subdivision of the clay separate of soils. Soil Sci. Soc. Am. Proc. (1936) 1:175–179.

Walker, G. F. 1950. Vermiculite-organic complexes. Nature 166:695–697.

Walker, G. F. 1957. On the differentiation of vermiculites and smectites in clays. Clay Mineral Bull. 3:154–163.

Warshaw, C. M., and Roy, R. 1961. Classification and a scheme for the identification of layer silicates. Bull. Geol. Soc. Am. 72:1455–1492.

White, J. L., and Jackson, M. L. 1947. Glycerol solvation of soil clays for X-ray diffraction analysis. Soil Sci. Soc. Am. Proc. (1946) 11:150–154.

Whiteside, E. P. 1948. Preliminary X-ray studies of loess deposits in Illinois. Soil Sci. Soc. Am. Proc. (1947) 12:415–419.

Willis, A. L., Pennington, R. P., and Jackson, M. L. 1948. Mineral standards for quantitative X-ray diffraction analysis of soil clays. Soil Sci. Soc. Am. Proc. (1947) 12:400–406.

50

Thermal Analysis Techniques for Mineral Identification and Mineralogical Composition

ISAAC BARSHAD

University of California
Berkeley, California

50–1 GENERAL INTRODUCTION

The clay-size separates of soils and mineral deposits and many coarse-grained minerals undergo several reactions upon heating. Some reactions, such as evaporation of imbibed and adsorbed water, occur at low temperatures; some reactions, such as oxidation of organic constituents and metallic ions in a reduced state, occur at intermediate temperatures; and some reactions, such as loss of crystal-lattice OH^- as H_2O and CO_3^{2-} as CO_2, occur at high temperatures.

In the course of these reactions, a change in state or crystal structure may occur in one or more of the constituents present. The reactions may be either exothermic or endothermic in nature. Moreover, it has long been recognized that the different minerals which may be present in clay-size separates react differently at different temperatures. Consequently, advantage has been taken of these differences to develop thermal analysis techniques by which the different mineral species can be identified both qualitatively and quantitatively.

The thermal analysis techniques may be divided into three broad groups: those that measure changes in weight from loss or gain in gaseous substances, those that measure energy changes, and those that measure changes in the solid phase. Changes in weight caused by loss of water or CO_2 or gain in oxygen are measured by thermogravimetric analysis and by integral and differential thermogravimetric analyses; energy changes are measured by differential thermal analysis; and changes in crystallinity, volume, color, and various physical-strength properties are measurements performed by X-ray analysis, infrared analysis, and other analyses employed in the ceramic industry. The latter analyses will not be discussed in the present paper; for further information on these methods, the reader is referred to sections 49 and 51 and to a review of this subject by Henry (1955).

A voluminous amount of literature deals with thermal analysis of clays, but a large proportion of this literature is devoted to the analysis of clays from clay deposits and not of clays from soils. That soil clays differ from clay deposits in many respects is usually not emphasized sufficiently. These differences are particularly brought out by differential thermal analysis and will be indicated in the present section.

<h2 style="text-align:center">50–2 GENERAL PRINCIPLES</h2>

The water driven off by heating a clay is present in two distinct forms: OH^- ions and H_2O molecules. Customarily, the OH^- ions are referred to as "crystal-lattice water," and their removal from the mineral is termed "dehydroxylation"; the H_2O molecules are referred to as "water of hydration" and "water of adsorption," and their removal is termed desorption or dehydration.

The OH^- ions are present in fixed positions, either as individual ions among the oxygens at the apices of the tetrahedra or as continuous sheets as in the 1:1 and 2:2 mineral species. Their removal from the clay, as a rule, is irreversible and is accompanied by an irreversible change or a complete destruction of the clay mineral structure. The H_2O molecules, on the other hand, are present either on the external surfaces of the clay particles only, as in kaolinite, or on both external and internal surfaces, as in montmorillonite, vermiculite, and hydrated halloysite. Their removal from a clay particle may or may not cause a reversible change in the crystal-lattice, depending on the clay mineral. For example, upon removal and readsorption of H_2O molecules, the crystal-lattice is not changed in kaolinite but is changed in a reversible manner in montmorillonite and vermiculite. Most of the adsorbed water molecules tend to be organized into sheets of monomolecular layers on the oxygen surfaces and to be grouped around the exchangeable ions. This form is termed here "layer-water." Some water molecules, however, are present as individual molecules inside the cavities of the oxygen surfaces which form the bases of the tetrahedra. This water is termed here "cavity-water."

The ratio of crystal-lattice water to crystal-lattice oxygen is constant for each clay mineral, but the ratio of adsorbed water to crystal-lattice oxygen varies with the vapor pressure at which the mineral is equilibrated. At a given vapor pressure, the amount of adsorbed water depends on the total surface area, on the ratio of internal to external surface area, on the nature and amount of the exchangeable ions, and on the history of the clay with respect to wetting and drying (Barshad, 1955).

The loss of water, as a rule, is measured by loss in weight of the clay mineral upon heating. With soil clays, gross errors may occur in this measurement unless organic matter and carbonates are eliminated. In minerals which contain reduced ions, such as ferrous iron, some of the loss in weight from loss of water is counterbalanced by a gain of oxygen upon oxidation of the reduced element. It is obvious that for such minerals a correction must be applied to obtain reliable values for crystal-lattice water. In certain temperature ranges, both crystal-lattice water and adsorbed water may be lost simultaneously. The temperature at which the major amount of the crystal-lattice water is lost differs greatly among the different species and is the most singular property for the identification of the species. Because organic matter interferes in the determination of the crystal-lattice water, it is important to ascertain that it is absent from the sample to be analyzed. Absence of organic matter can be verified by differential thermal analysis—even traces can be detected by this method. Differential thermal analysis is useful also for ascertaining the critical temperature range within which water losses occur. It is recommended, therefore, that differential thermal analysis precede thermogravimetric analysis.

The pretreatment of a soil clay required before thermal analysis depends on the objective of the analysis and on the nature of the soil in which the clay occurs. To obtain qualitative information, it may be possible to analyze the whole soil by the differential thermal method, even without removal of organic matter, particularly if the soil is high in clay and low in organic matter. However, for quantitative analysis of all constituents present in a clay, as for the purpose of evaluation of soil profile development and for the purpose of soil classification, the sample must be treated in various ways prior to the analysis. These treatments are described in sections 43, 44, and 45.

50–3 DIFFERENTIAL THERMAL ANALYSIS

50–3.1 Principles

Because of reactions which may occur in a clay sample as it is heated, its temperature at a given time may be lower or higher than that of the furnace or of a sample in which no reactions occur. This difference in temperature may be recorded in two ways: (*1*) by two thermometers, one of which records the temperature of the clay sample and the other the temperature of the furnace or an inert sample heated in the same furnace under comparable conditions; or (*2*) by a single thermometer, which records only the difference in temperature between the clay sample and the furnace or inert sample. The latter method is generally used. The thermometer employed is the readily available thermocouple, which consists of two dissimilar metals joined at two ends to form a circuit with two junctions. When one junction is warmer than the other, an electric current is set up with a small electromotive force (emf). This electric current may be recorded by use of a galvanometer that reflects a beam of light on a photographic paper or by amplifying it and using the amplified output to operate an automatic pen-and-ink recorder. The record of the differences in temperatures thus obtained has been termed a "differential-thermal-analysis curve" or a DTA curve (Le Chatelier, 1887; Orcel, 1927; Norton, 1939; Hendricks and Alexander, 1939).

The occurrence of a lower temperature in the clay than in the inert sample indicates that an endothermic reaction is taking place, and the occurrence of a higher temperature indicates that an exothermic reaction is taking place. These temperature differences are records of net heat changes, and they do not exclude the possibility that both exothermic and endothermic reactions are occurring simultaneously. Hence, the absence of a "break," "loop" or "peak" (as they are termed) in a DTA curve does not indicate necessarily the absence of a reaction or reactions. It is conceivable that an endothermic and an exothermic reaction with equal heat changes might occur simultaneously, thus cancelling each other. Such a cancellation is thought to occur in DTA curves of vermiculite in the temperature region between 700° and 900°C. and in some forms of chlorites in the temperature region between 700° and 800°C. (Martin, 1955).

The temperature at which thermal reactions occur upon heating a clay sample may be determined either by a thermocouple, which continuously records either the temperature of the furnace or the inert sample, or by the same thermocouple which records the difference in temperature. The latter is accomplished by incorporating in the inert sample or the clay sample small quantities of temperature-indicator substances which cause temperature breaks at known temperatures such as at melting points or at inversion points (Barshad, 1952). Such a DTA curve is complete in itself and greatly simplifies the instrumentation.

The points on DTA curves which indicate maximum temperature differences have been termed peak temperatures. They are, of course, situated within the "thermal breaks" (the regions in the curves which show the differences in temperature). The shape, size, and temperature of the thermal breaks are affected not only by the heats of reaction but also by various instrumental factors such as rate of heating, nature of thermocouples, size, shape, and nature of sample holder, position of the differential thermocouple in the sample hole, nature of the recording instrument, and other details of the instrument itself (Arens[1]; Mackenzie, 1957).

DTA apparatus can be used as a calorimeter for measuring the various heats of reaction which occur during heating of a clay. To accomplish this the instrument is calibrated by using substances with known heats of reaction which yield DTA curves having thermal breaks similar to those of clay minerals. Such an application was made by Barshad (1952, 1960b) and by De Bruijn and Van Der Marel (1954).

---

[1] Arens, P. L. 1951. A study on differential thermal analysis of clays and clay minerals. Ph.D. Thesis, Landbouw-Hogeschool, Wageningen, Holland.

50–3.2 Method

50–3.2.1.1 Basic Requirements. A DTA apparatus consists of three sections: a heating section, a sample and thermocouple holder section, and a recording section (Fig. 50–1).

The heating section includes a furnace that can be heated to about 1,100°C. at a constant rate of 9° to 10°C. per minute. A constant rate of heating may be attained by varying the voltage applied to the furnace by use of a variable transformer (Variac) and/or a variable wire resistor in series with the furnace. Either of these operations may be made automatic. It is possible also to use a program controller (Mackenzie, 1957), which applies a constant voltage to the furnace but varies the proportion of the time the circuit is closed.

The sample holder consists of either a rectangular or circular nickel or ceramic block with cylindrical holes in which the samples and the thermocouples are placed. It is important that the depth of hole bearing the sample is equal to its diameter and that the thermocouple be placed exactly in the center of the hole. For quantitative analysis, it is preferable to make the depth of the hole in the block about 2 mm. greater than the diameter but to place the thermocouple junctions in the center of a cylinder with a depth

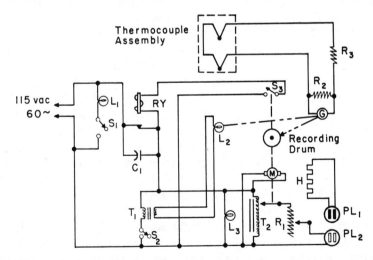

Fig. 50–1. A schematic diagram for a differential thermal analysis apparatus: S_1, safety lamp switch; S_2, galvanometer lamp switch; S_3, shut off switch (wiping type); L_1, safety lamp; L_2, galvanometer lamp; L_3, Pilot lamp; C_1, Capacitor; R_1, rheostat; R_2, galvanometer shunt resistance; R_3, galvanometer sensitivity resistance; RY, mercury relay (latching type); T_1, filament transformer; T_2, variac transformer; M, timing motor; G, galvanometer; H, furnace; PL_1, male plug; PL_2, female plug.

equal to its diameter, measured from the bottom of the hole. The hole is then filled only to within 2 mm. of the top with the test sample. The upper 2 mm. are filled with the inert reference material. Such an arrangement decreases the possibility that some of the sample will be lost while the hole is being packed. A hole 9 mm. deep and 7 mm. in diameter is convenient for general use.

The thermocouple is placed in the hole either from its side or from its bottom. The thermocouple wires should be cemented in place, so that the junction cannot be displaced easily from a fixed position. It is for this reason that fairly sturdy thermocouple wires of about No. 22 gauge should be used, even though such wire is not as sensitive to temperature differences as finer wires. The thermocouple elements in most common use are made from platinum and platinum (90%)-rhodium (10%) or from chromel-P and alumel. For use with soil clays, the former elements are preferable because they are more resistant to corrosion and consequently last longer. The sensitivity to temperature differences can be controlled by choosing a galvanometer that has the desired sensitivity, by varying the resistance in the thermocouple circuit, or by amplifying the output. The size of the two thermocouples in the DTA circuit must be identical; otherwise, the DTA curves tend to drift either upward or downward from the base line.

The recording of the temperature differences and furnace temperature is accomplished by placing in the thermocouple circuit either a reflecting galvanometer, which records the variation in emf. on photographic paper fastened to a rotating drum, or a pen-and-ink recorder. In most instruments, the temperature differences and the furnace temperature are recorded separately; but, by using temperature indicators, the temperature differences and the furnace temperature can be recorded as an integral part of the DTA curve (Barshad, 1952). For a given thermal reaction the galvanometer may be made to deflect the spot of light or the recording pen either upward or downward from the base line depending on the position of the reacting sample with respect to the two thermocouples. In general practice in DTA, the deflection due to an endothermic reaction is directed downward and that due to an exothermic reaction upward from the base line. However, where the DTA apparatus is being calibrated for temperature, a given thermal reaction is recorded in either direction from the base line, depending solely on the position of the temperature-indicator with respect to the two thermocouples.

50–3.2.1.2 Automation and Modifications. To improve efficiency of operation and reproducibility of DTA curves, the instrument may be automated by motorizing the rotating drum and the Variac and by inserting a mercury latch-type relay switch that opens automatically when the desired temperature in the furnace is reached (Fig. 50–1).

A multiple-sample holder, together with additional thermocouples and recording devices, makes it possible to analyze more than one sample at a time. Because after completion of an analysis, the furnace cools to room temperature much more slowly than the sample holder, addition of a second furnace to the instrument assembly makes it possible to analyze nearly twice as many samples during the course of a day as with one furnace.

A modification of the furnace so that the interior can be evacuated or filled with an inert gas or with the gas evolved during the decomposition of the sample is an important innovation in DTA (Whitehead and Breger, 1950; Rowland and Lewis, 1951; Stone, 1952 and 1954). Where the furnace is evacuated or where an atmosphere of nitrogen is introduced during an analysis, the curve of a sample containing organic matter does not have the exothermic break associated with its oxidation; hence, for qualitative DTA the elimination of organic matter is unnecessary (Whitehead and Breger, 1950).

The use of a furnace similar to that employed for total carbon (section 89), but modified to the extent that the gases evolved during heating can be trapped at various temperature ranges, enables the measurement of the actual losses of water and CO_2 during a DTA. The modification consists in attaching to the outlet of the furnace a pyrex glass tube fitted with several stopcocks, to each of which is connected a train for trapping quantitatively the water and CO_2 evolved during heating.

Mauer (1954) developed an analytical balance that permits simultaneous recording of the weight-loss curves and the DTA curves during the course of heating a sample from room temperature to ignition.

50–3.2.2 MATERIALS

1. Temperature indicators (all powdered): (*a*) ammonium nitrate (NH_4NO_3), (*b*) sodium nitrate ($NaNO_3$), (*c*) sodium molybdate (Na_2MoO_4) that has been preheated to 500°C., (*d*) silver nitrate ($AgNO_3$), (*e*) silver chloride (AgCl), and (*f*) silver-aluminum oxide ($Ag-Al_2O_3$) mixture. To prepare powdered AgCl, add $1N$ HCl solution to $1N$ $AgNO_3$. Wash the precipitated AgCl thoroughly with water in a crucible with a sintered-glass bottom. To prepare a mixture of Ag and Al_2O_3, mix 1 part of powdered $AgNO_3$ with 10 parts of finely powdered and ignited Al_2O_3, and heat the mixture in a porcelain crucible to a temperature of at least 700°C. or higher for about 1 hour. During the heating process the $AgNO_3$ decomposes, and metallic silver is left behind. The temperatures which these indicators register on a DTA curve are given in Table 50–1.
2. Calibration substances for heats of reaction: calcium sulfate ($CaSO_4 \cdot 2H_2O$), $AgNO_3$, $NaNO_3$, and calcium carbonate ($CaCO_3$) (Table 50–1).
3. Inert reference substances: either finely powdered and ignited Al_2O_3 or ignited kaolinite.

Table 50–1. Temperatures and heats of reaction of substances for temperature and
heat-of-reaction calibration of the DTA apparatus.

Substance	Temperature for calibration	Heat of reaction	Temperature range for heat-of-reaction calibration
	° C.	cal. /g.	° C.
NH_4NO_3	32		
	85		
	125		
	170		
$AgNO_3$	160	210	370–470
	212		
Ag (from $AgNO_3$)	961		
AgCl	455		
$NaNO_3$	314	770	600–720
Na_2MoO_4	642		
	687		
$CaSO_4 \cdot 2H_2O$		160	50–200
$CaCO_3$		468	720–820

4. Reference clay minerals: Homoionic sodium (Na)- and magnesium
   (Mg)- or calcium (Ca)-saturated kaolinite, halloysite, gibbsite, goethite
   and representative species of the 2:2 minerals (chlorites), as indicated
   in Table 50–2. Prepare these samples for analysis by the same method
   as the soil clays, and then standardize them by X-ray analysis and thermogravimetric analysis. The standardization consists in determining the
   exact amount of the represented species, as described in section 50–5.
5. Homoionic Na- and Mg- or Ca-saturated soil clays equilibrated with
   water vapor in a desiccator containing a saturated solution of magnesium
   nitrate $[Mg(NO_3)_2]$ or in the room atmosphere.
6. Air-dry and finely sieved (200-mesh) soils.
7. A brass or stainless steel block with a cylindrical hole which is slightly
   smaller than the hole in the sample block of the DTA apparatus.
8. Developing equipment for photographically recorded DTA curves: (a)
   8-by-10-inch, portrait-proof, single-weight R photographic paper, (b)
   solutions for developing, stopping, and fixing the photographic paper,
   and (c) a three-compartment developing tank large enough to accommodate the 8-by-10-inch paper, each compartment having a capacity of
   900 to 1,000 ml.

50–3.2.3 PROCEDURE

50–3.2.3.1 Calibration for Temperature. Pack firmly in each of the
sample holes 150 to 200 mg. of Al_2O_3, so that in one hole the thermocouple
junction is slightly above and in the other slightly below the surface of the

Table 50–2. Adsorbed and crystal-lattice water of clay minerals, and the temperature at completion of desorption and at start and completion of dehydration.

Clay mineral	Adsorbed water*		Crystal-lattice water	Temperature at completion of desorption		Temperature at start of dehydroxylation	Temperature at completion of dehydroxylation
	Layer water	Cavity water		Layer water	Cavity water		
	%†	%†	%†	°C	°C	°C	°C
Ca Montmorillonite	20.16	3.37	5.08	250	370	370	1,000
Na Montmorillonite ‡	14.00	0.00	5.05	150	–	150	1,000
Ca Vermiculite‡	20.00	3.08	4.80	250	700	250	1,000
Na Vermiculite	10.14	4.66	4.76	150	700	150	1,000
Ca Illite ‡	5.16	1.06	4.97	150	370	370	1,000
Na Illite	3.45	0.66	5.07	150	370	370	1,000
Muscovite ‡	1.00	0.45	4.74	250	350	370	1,000
Phlogopite ‡	0.4–1.0		4.51		350	350	1,000
Biotite ‡	0.4–1.5		4.17		350	350	1,000
Talc ‡	0.7–1.0		4.99		350	350	1,000
Pyrophylite ‡	0.5–1.5		5.26		350	350	1,000
Kaolinite §	0.2–1.2		16.20	350		350	1,000
Halloysite (hydrated)	13.2		16.20	250		350	1,000
Chrysotile and antigorite	1.0–2.0		14.95	250		350	1,000
Clinochlore¶	0.2–0.5		14.81	250		370	1,000
Ripidolite	0.2–0.5		13.39	250		370	1,000
Sheridinite	0.2–0.5		14.81	250		370	1,000
Gibbsite	0.5–0.6		52.95	100		150	350
Goethite	0.0–0.1		33.80	100		200	370
Brucite	0.5–0.6		44.70	170		200	370

* See text for meaning of terms. † On the ignited basis. ‡ 2:1 minerals. § 1:1 minerals. ¶ 2:2 minerals.

packed Al_2O_3. Place 5 mg. of NH_4NO_3 in the hole in which the junction is below the surface of the Al_2O_3, and then firmly pack the rest of the hole with Al_2O_3. Thoroughly mix 20 mg. of the Al_2O_3 containing the powdered Ag, 3 mg. of AgCl and 2 mg. of $NaNO_3$, and place them in the other hole around the thermocouple junction. Cover this mixture with a firmly packed thin layer of Al_2O_3, and then place 5 mg. of the Na_2MoO_4 indicator above this layer. Fill the rest of the hole with Al_2O_3.

Before completing the DTA of these indicators, or of any other substance, it is necessary to establish the base line for the resulting curve. This is a curve which would result in the absence of any reaction during DTA. It is established as follows: Turn on the light which the galvanometer mirror reflects onto the photographic paper, and then rotate the drum quickly, with three short stops, so that three points are registered along the paper. The line connecting the three points is the base line. Where a pen-and-ink recorder is used, the base line is the horizontal line which passes through the initial point of the DTA curve. After the three points are registered, the DTA curve for the temperature indicators is made. The temperature scale is then established by dropping perpendicular lines to the base line from each temperature-indicating point. Each temperature point is at the start of a thermal break. From the known difference in temperature between successive temperature points, and from the distance measured along the base line between these points, the number of degrees rise in temperature per unit length may be calculated, thereby establishing the complete temperature scale. This scale will indicate also whether or not the rate of heating per unit time is constant because the drum rotates at a constant speed. An illustration of such a calibration is given in Fig. 50–2.

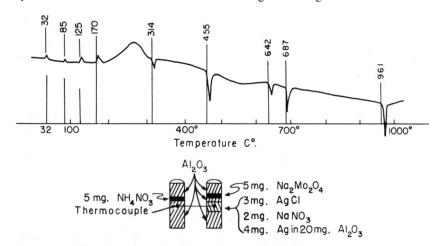

Fig. 50–2. Differential thermal curve illustrating the method of temperature calibration by use of "temperature indicators." NH_4NO_3 registers 32°, 85°, 125°, and 170°C.; $NaNO_3$ registers 314°C.; $Na_2Mo_2O_4$ registers 642° and 687°C.; AgCl registers 455°C.; and Ag registers 961°C.

By incorporating two temperature indicators (AgCl and Ag) in the DTA curves of each sample, the temperature at any point on the curve can readily be determined from the fully calibrated scale.

50–3.2.3.2 Calibration for Clay Mineral Content. Weigh 50-, 100-, 150-, and 200-mg. quantities of each sample of the air-dry, Na-saturated, 1:1 and 2:2 reference clay minerals, and 20-, 60-, and 100-mg. quantities of each sample of gibbsite, goethite and brucite. (The 2:1 minerals are not amenable to quantitative DTA.)

Place each weighed amount in turn in the hole of the brass or stainless steel block, and fill the remainder of the hole with the inert substance (ignited Al_2O_3 or ignited kaolinite). Firmly pack the sample and the inert substance in the hole by placing them in the hole in small increments and by tamping each increment with a glass rod. After the hole is completely filled with the inert substance, empty the contents on a glazed paper, and thoroughly mix them before packing them in the sample hole of the DTA apparatus. While packing the mixture in the sample hole, be careful not to displace the thermocouple from its fixed position. Use the inert substance to complete the filling of the sample hole and also to fill the reference-thermocouple hole. Place 2 to 3 mg. of AgCl and 10 mg. of the Ag-Al_2O_3 indicator in the reference hole just above the thermocouple junction.

Alternatively, add to each weighed amount of sample enough inert substance to make a total weight of 600 mg.—an amount which is more than needed to fill the sample hole. Then thoroughly mix the sample and the inert substance. Weigh the mixture, fill the sample hole, and weigh the material left over. The amount placed in the sample hole is the difference between the last two weighings.

In the DTA curves thus obtained, draw a straight line from the point on the curve where each thermal peak begins to the point where it ends. Then measure the area by using a planimeter. Alternatively, trace the area on transparent, cross-section paper, cut out the delineated area, and weigh the paper. Calculate the area of the thermal breaks from the ratio between the total weight of paper representing the break and the weight of paper per unit area. Plot peak area against quantity of pure clay used. The characteristic of a good calibration curve is a straight line that extrapolates to zero area for a zero amount of clay, as shown in Fig. 50–3.

50–3.2.3.3 Calibration for Clay Mineral Species. Weigh 200-mg. quantities of each of the Ca-saturated 1:1, 2:2, and 2:1 minerals and 50-mg. quantities of gibbsite, goethite, and brucite. Thoroughly mix 200- to 300-mg. quantities of Al_2O_3 with each sample. Complete the DTA as described in 50–3.2.3.1.

Mix 100-mg. quantities of the following minerals: kaolinite with antigorite, kaolinite with chrysotile, kaolinite with each of the chlorites, and each of the serpentine minerals with each of the chlorites. To each of the mixed samples add 200- to 300-mg. quantities of Al_2O_3. Mix each sample thoroughly with the Al_2O_3, and complete the DTA.

50–3.2.3.4   DTA of Soil Clays for Qualitative Results.   Mix 300-mg. quantities of Ca- or Mg-saturated soil clay samples with an equal amount of Al_2O_3, and complete the DTA in the same manner as for the reference samples. Where whole soils are analyzed, do not dilute them with Al_2O_3.

50–3.2.3.5   DTA of Soil Clays for Quantitative Results.   Weigh 100-, 200-, and 300-mg. quantities of the Na-saturated clay samples prepared for thermogravimetric analysis, and proceed as described in section 50–3.2.3.2.

Plot the area of each diagnostic thermal break against the amount of clay used. Compare the straight part of the curve which extrapolates to zero with the appropriate calibration curve obtained in section 50–3.2.3.2 to determine the clay mineral content.

50–3.2.3.6   Calibration for Heats of Reaction.   Weigh 50-, 100-, and 200-mg. quantities each of $CaSO_4 \cdot 2H_2O$ and $AgNO_3$, and 25-, 50-, and 100-mg. quantities of $NaNO_3$ and $CaCO_3$. Carry out the DTA of each quantity as described in section 50–3.2.3.2. To complete the calibration, measure the peak area of each quantity of each substance, and plot peak area against quantity of the substance. From the heats of reaction in Table 50–1, convert the curve to peak area versus calories.

50–3.2.4   COMMENTS

For the purpose of standardization of DTA curves, it is recommended that a heating rate of $10° \pm 1°C$. per minute be used (Mackenzie and Farquharson, 1952). The higher is the rate of heating, the higher is the temperature at the thermal peaks (Barshad, 1952; Kissinger, 1956).

Very small amounts of temperature indicators are used to ensure that very small thermal breaks are produced. The temperature reference point is at the start of the thermal break.

Peak area is plotted versus amount of reference clay mineral used rather than percentage composition of the mixture because the area is proportional to the amount of the material per unit volume and because the amount of sample present in the sample hole depends on the bulk density and firmness of packing. As long as the weight of the tested sample is known, the percentage composition with respect to a known reference sample can be calculated.

Because the sensitivity, that is, the response of the galvanometer to a given difference in temperature, differs for different instruments, it is advisable to calibrate one's own instrument with a standard reference substance, such as $CaSO_4 \cdot 2H_2O$, in terms of calories per unit area. When this is done, DTA curves obtained by different instruments for the same mineral can be compared. Such a calibration is described in section 50–3.2.3.6.

Although the reference inert material and the temperature indicators

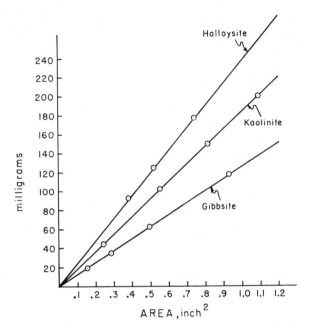

Fig. 50–3. Illustration of calibration curves for the determination of kaolinite, halloysite, and gibbsite content.

(AgCl and Ag) remain the same for each DTA of a tested sample, it is recommended that the reference material should be repacked for each run. Without repacking, the DTA curve tends to deviate considerably from the base line after two or more runs.

DTA cannot be used for quantitative determination of montmorillonite, vermiculite, and illite, or the other mica-like clay minerals in soil clays, because DTA curves for these species often do not show any endothermic breaks associated with loss of crystal-lattice water.

The larger is the sample hole (and, consequently, the greater is the sample size), the larger are the thermal breaks, and the higher are the temperatures at the peaks (Kissinger, 1956). It is for this reason that each DTA instrument should be calibrated for both qualitative and quantitative work with a set of standard reference minerals.

The inert reference material is added to all soil clays before analysis to overcome the tendency for samples to harden into a brick and to shrink during heating. The hardening makes it difficult to remove the sample after analysis without damage to the thermocouple junction. The shrinkage often causes a shifting of the DTA curve from the base line and thus causes inaccuracies in quantitative DTA.

The diagnostic characteristics of DTA curves are the position and shape of the thermal breaks rather than the size. The relative size of different breaks in a DTA of an unknown sample, however, indicates semiquantitatively the relative abundance of the different mineral species. For qualitative analysis, therefore, it is advisable to obtain a DTA curve of each reference sample and of mixtures of closely related minerals. This is the reason for the many mixtures analyzed in section 50–3.2.3.3.

Where DTA is used in conjunction with thermogravimetric analysis for quantitative evaluation of clay mineral composition, samples from the same batch of clay must be used for both of these analyses. The sample should be equilibrated with the water vapor of the room atmosphere so that no change in sample weight will occur during the various operations.

Where the amounts of sample available are of the order of only 10 to 50 mg., one may fill the lower half of the sample hole with the inert substance, place the sample around the thermocouple junction, and fill the rest of the hole with the inert substance. This method of packing yields maximum peak areas for a minimum amount of sample (Barshad, 1952). Because of the difficulty of duplicating the packing, the results are essentially qualitative; however, by constructing a sample holder with a very small sample hole, micro-DTA may be carried out quantitatively.

50–3.2.5 INTERPRETATION OF RESULTS

It is important to emphasize that DTA curves of clay minerals extracted from deposits such as bentonite and kaolin beds and of clay-size particles of mica and vermiculite obtained by grinding the coarse-grained minerals may differ considerably from the DTA curves of the corresponding minerals occurring in soils. All the DTA curves, however, possess certain common features that are of importance for identification of the mineral species. These features can best be described where the DTA curves of the minerals are arranged in accordance with the two broad classification groups, namely, the 2:1 minerals and the 1:1 and 2:2 minerals. As an aid to interpretation, characteristic DTA curves of these minerals are discussed in the following sections. Further information may be found in the book by Mackenzie (1957).

50–3.2.5.1 DTA Curves of 2:1 Minerals. The most distinguishing feature of DTA curves of 2:1 minerals—montmorillonites (smectites), vermiculites, and micas—is the size and shape of the low-temperature endothermic break that represents the loss of adsorbed water. The size and shape of this break are affected by the amount of adsorbed water and the nature of the exchangeable ions, as may be seen in Fig. 50–4, 50–5, 50–6, 50–7, 50–8, and 50–9.

The size of the endothermic break caused by loss of adsorbed water is extremely useful for distinguishing between mica minerals on the one hand and montmorillonite and vermiculite on the other. Regardless of the nature of the exchangeable ion and the relative humidity at which the clay is equilibrated prior to analysis, the size of the endothermic break is con-

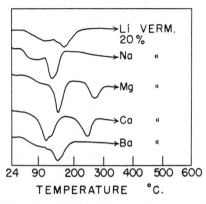

Fig. 50–4. Differential thermal curves of water desorption from an air-dry vermiculite saturated with various cations. A mixture of 0.1 g. of vermiculite and 0.4 g. of ignited Al_2O_3 was used in the sample hole.

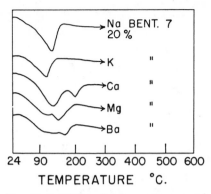

Fig. 50–5. Differential thermal curves of water desorption from an air-dry montmorillonite saturated with various cations. A mixture of 0.1 g. of montmorillonite and 0.4 g. of ignited Al_2O_3 was used in the sample hole.

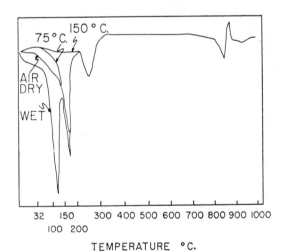

Fig. 50–6. Differential thermal curves of water desorption from a Mg-saturated vermiculite at various states of hydration. A 0.5-g. sample was used in sample hole.

siderably smaller for the former minerals than for the latter. The shape of the break for the Ca- or Mg-saturated minerals is useful for distinguishing among the mica, montmorillonite, and vermiculite minerals. The break for the mica minerals is nearly symmetrical and has essentially only one peak and a slight shoulder on the higher temperature end. The break for montmorillonite contains two and possibly three distinct peaks but with a common origin at the base line; whereas, for vermiculite, the peaks resolve

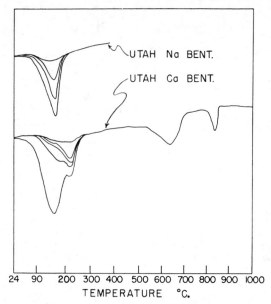

Fig. 50–7. Differential thermal curves of water desorption from a Ca- and a Na-saturated montmorillonite at various states of hydration. A 0.5-g. sample was used in the sample hole.

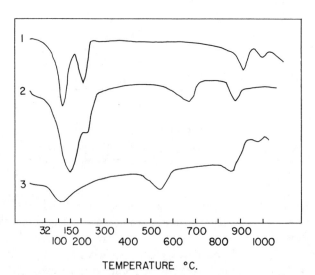

TEMPERATURE °C.

Fig. 50–8. Differential thermal curves of water desorption of an air-dry Ca-saturated sample of vermiculite (curve 1), of montmorillonite (curve 2), and of illite (curve 3). A 0.5-g. sample was used in the sample hole.

Fig. 50–9. Differential thermal curves of vermiculite and montmorillonite illustrating the effect of saturation with hydroxyaluminum ions and subsequent resaturation with Mg^{2+} ions: (*1*) naturally occurring Mg-saturated vermiculite; (*2*) $Al(OH)^{2+}$-saturated vermiculite; (*3*) Mg-saturated vermiculite after being saturated with $Al(OH)^{2+}$; (*4*) Mg-saturated vermiculite after being saturated with $Al(OH)_2^+$; (*5*) Al^{3+}-saturated montmorillonite; (*6*) $Al(OH)_2^+$-saturated montmorillonite; and (*7*) Mg-saturated montmorillonite after being saturated with $Al(OH)_2^+$.

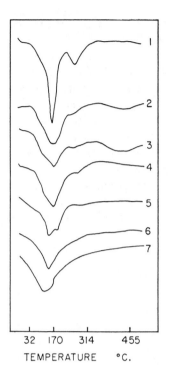

TEMPERATURE   °C.

into two or three distinct breaks, depending on the water content, as seen in Fig. 50–8.

The effect of the degree of hydration on the endothermic break is shown in Fig. 50–6 and 50–7 by the progressive dehydration of a Na- and a Ca-montmorillonite and a Mg-vermiculite. The DTA curves for the various states of hydration are superimposed to show that the variation in water content affects mostly the part of the curve at the lowest temperatures.

With all three mineral species, exchangeable Na^+ ions cause the initial thermal break to contain a single peak and to return to the base line at about 150°C. as contrasted to nearly 300°C. for the Ca- or Mg-saturated clays. This difference indicates that it is easier to distinguish between adsorbed water and crystal-lattice water for Na-saturated than for Ca- or Mg-saturated clays (Mielenz et al. 1955; Barshad, unpublished).

In naturally occurring acid soils, exchangeable aluminum (Al^{3+}) and hydroxyaluminum ions are often the major exchangeable ions. These ions alter the shape of the low-temperature endothermic break, so that the double or triple peaks are eliminated from the DTA curves of both montmorillonite and vermiculite, as seen in Fig. 50–9. It is also seen in this figure that the double endothermic break is not restored in vermiculite upon resaturation with Mg^{2+} ions, even though the sample has been treated with an alkaline solution to aid in removing adsorbed Al^{3+} ions prior to resaturation with Mg^{2+}. It appears, therefore, that montmorillonite and vermiculite extracted from acid soils are indistinguishable from one another by their DTA curves (Figs. 50–10 and 50–12) even though they are saturated with Mg^{2+} or Ca^{2+} ions prior to analysis.

It is necessary to point out that although the DTA curves of the pure 2:1 mineral species do contain endothermic peaks associated with the loss of crystal-lattice water, the equivalent soil clay minerals rarely do have such breaks. Whenever such breaks occur, they are attributable to the presence of 1:1 or 2:2 mineral species (Fig. 50–10 and 50–12).

Whenever DTA curves of soil clays have a very small endothermic break at low temperatures (between 20°C. and 200°C.) and no endothermic breaks, or very small ones, at higher temperatures (above 450°C.), they indicate the presence of large amounts of the mica-type (illitic) clay minerals.

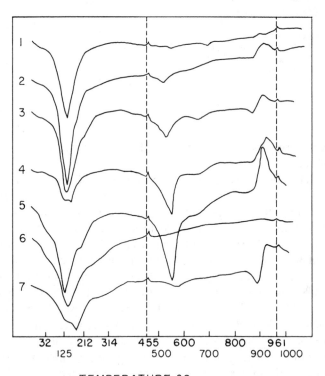

TEMPERATURE °C.

Fig. 50–10. Differential thermal curves of soil clays containing montmorillonite or allophane: (*1*) Venada, almost a pure montmorillonite; (*2*) Yolo, a montmorillonite with about 5% kaolinite; (*3*) Cayucos, a montmorillonite with about 10% kaolinite; (*4*) Corning, a mixture of montmorillonite and hydrated halloysite in about equal proportions; (*5*) Lassen, a mixture of montmorillonite and kaolinite in about 2:1 proportions; (*6*) Hillo, a soil allophane; and (*7*) Sweeney, a mixture of montmorillonite and vermiculite in about 1:1 proportions.

Exothermic breaks at high temperature are small in the DTA curves of
2:1 soil clays. In the curves for the Mg-saturated forms, a broad exothermic
break occurs between 850° and 950°C., but for the K-saturated forms it
is nearly absent (Barshad, 1950).

Soil allophane may be mistaken for montmorillonite or vermiculite because its DTA curve is also typified by a fairly large endothermic break at
low temperatures—particularly for the Na-saturated clays. However, when
the clays are either Mg- or Ca-saturated, the DTA curve of allophane
still retains an endothermic break with a single peak; whereas the montmorillonite and vermiculite curves possess an endothermic break with
double or triple peaks (Fig. 50–10, curve 6).

50–3.2.5.2 DTA Curves of 1:1 and 2:2 Minerals. The DTA curves of
1:1 minerals are characterized by a relatively small endothermic break at
low temperatures and a large endothermic break at higher temperatures.
The latter represents loss of crystal-lattice water, which is present as OH^-
ions at the octahedral position. The curves also have exothermic peaks at
high temperatures, which represent the formation of new mineral species.

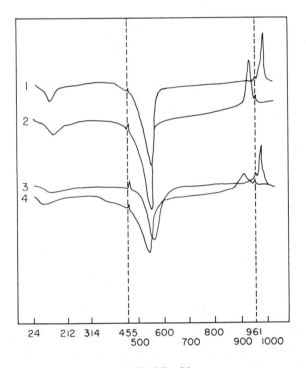

TEMPERATURE °C.

Fig. 50–11. A comparison between DTA curves of kaolinite and halloysite from clay
mineral deposits and from soils: (*1*) halloysite from a clay deposit, (*2*) halloysite
from a soil, (*3*) kaolinite from a clay deposit, and (*4*) kaolinite from a soil.

By the position and shape of these high temperature breaks, it is possible to distinguish the various minerals, as illustrated in Fig. 50–11 and 50–12 and as described below.

The distinction between kaolinite and halloysite is made primarily on the basis of the shape of the endothermic break starting at about 455°C. The break for kaolinite is a symmetrical V, whereas for halloysite it is an asymmetrical V. The peak temperature is about 20° to 30°C. higher for kaolinite than halloysite, and the break ends at 625°C. for kaolinite and 595°C. for halloysite. The variation in the shape of the break is often measured in terms of the ratio of the difference between the peak temperature and the temperature at the start of the break to the difference between the temperature at the end of the break and the peak temperature. For kaolinite this ratio is small, whereas for halloysite it is high.

As a rule the degree of asymmetry of the main endothermic break is a

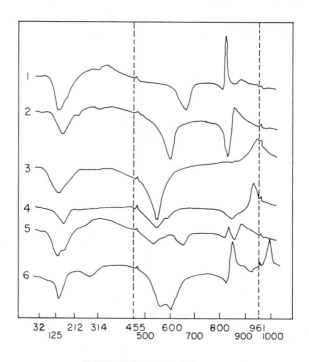

Fig. 50–12. Differential thermal curves of soil clays containing large amounts of the 1:1 and 2:2 clay minerals: (*1*) Montara, a mixture of chrysotile and montmorillonite in about 1:1 proportion; (*2*) Yorkville, a mixture of chlorite and vermiculite in about 1:1 proportion; (*3*) Josephine, a mixture of kaolinite and vermiculite in about 1:1 proportion; (*4*) Polebar, a mixture of kaolinite, chlorite, and vermiculite in about equal proportions; (*5*) Clear Lake, a montmorillonite containing 10% kaolinite and 10% chrysotile; and (*6*) an artificial mixture of equal proportions of a vermiculite, a chlorite, and a kaolinite.

good diagnostic feature for distinguishing between halloysite and kaolinite, even for soil clays. When the asymmetry is considerable, the presence of halloysite is probable, and confirmation should be obtained by X-ray diffraction and electron micrographs. There are exceptions, however, where DTA curves of soil kaolinites have very asymmetric endothermic breaks, as was found by the author in laterite crusts. Electron micrographs indicated that this exception might be caused by the extreme smallness of the clay particles.

DTA curves of hydrated halloysite (endellite) and halloysite differ at low temperatures, where hydrated halloysite has a distinct endothermic break and halloysite does not.

DTA curves for the serpentine minerals, the Mg 1:1 minerals, are distinguished readily from those for the kaolinitic minerals by the position of the main endothermic break. The break starts at about 610°C.—very near the end of the break in the kaolinite curve—and rejoins the base line at about 750°C., with a peak ranging between 660° and 680°C.

The DTA curves for the chlorites, the 2:2 minerals, have a main endothermic break between those of the kaolinite and serpentine minerals. The break starts at about 520°C. and ends at 685°C., with a peak at about 600°C. Thus, the DTA curve of a mixture of kaolinite and chlorite minerals has a very broad endothermic break extending from 455° to 685°C., with a double peak or two shoulders or inflection points, depending on the relative and absolute amounts of each mineral (Fig. 50–12, curves 4 and 6). A DTA curve of a mixture of kaolinite and serpentine minerals, however, has two distinct endothermic breaks adjoining at the base line (Fig. 50–12, curve 5). A DTA curve of a mixture of chlorite and serpentine minerals also has a very broad endothermic break starting at 520°C. and ending at 750°C., with either two peaks or inflection points. In California soils, mixtures of kaolinite and chlorite and mixtures of chlorite and serpentine minerals have been found, but none have been found to contain a mixture of kaolinite and serpentine minerals.

DTA curves of chlorite minerals usually have a second endothermic break starting at 750°C., with a peak at about 812°C., which often tends to cancel the preceding endothermic break. DTA curves of kaolinite and serpentine minerals, however, usually do not have a second endothermic break; and, if they do, it is very small (Fig. 50–12).

The exothermic break in the DTA curves of pure kaolin minerals starts at 960°C. with a peak at 1,000°C.; but, in the soil kaolin minerals, the break starts at about 850°C., with a peak at 900°C., and ends at 960°C. The height of the break of soil kaolins is much lower than that of pure kaolins (Figs. 50–10, 51–11, and 50–12). Sharp exothermic peaks occur also in DTA curves of serpentine minerals but at a lower temperature than for the kaolin minerals. The break starts at about 810°C. and ends at 850°C. and has a peak between 820° and 830°C. This break is often preceded by a small endothermic break. In some DTA curves of soil serpentine clay minerals, however, the exothermic reaction is completely absent or very small.

50–3.2.5.3 DTA Curves of Free Oxides. Gibbsite is commonly present in soils containing halloysite, but goethite and brucite are rarely present. Because all three oxides contain relatively large amounts of crystal-lattice water (Table 50–2), their DTA curves have large and sharp endothermic breaks. Consequently, the presence of very small quantities of these minerals in a clay sample can readily be detected by DTA. The endothermic break in DTA curves for gibbsite starts at about 258°C. and ends at 360°C., with a peak at 328°C.; in goethite the break starts at 314°C. and ends at 400°C., with a peak at 368°C.; and in brucite it starts at 356°C. and ends at 455°C., with a peak at 437°C. No exothermic breaks occur in the DTA curves of any of these minerals.

Organic matter oxidizes in the temperature range over which the endothermic breaks occur in the DTA curves of gibbsite, goethite, and brucite. This exothermic reaction may completely cancel an endothermic break occurring in the same temperature range. Therefore, to determine or detect gibbsite, goethite, or brucite in soil clays, a pretreatment must be employed to destroy the organic matter.

50–3.2.5.4 DTA Curves of Clay Carbonates. The endothermic break associated with decomposition of carbonates (in particular calcite) in soil clays departs from that of standard pure carbonate as follows. The initial temperature of the break is about 100° to 200°C. lower; the break extends over a broader range of temperatures—from 600° to 950°C. instead of 800° to 900°C.; and, instead of a single peak, the break may contain two or three peaks. This departure is attributable to three factors: (*1*) smallness of particle size, (*2*) presence of $MgCO_3$, and (*3*) occurrence of endothermic and exothermic breaks in this temperature range associated with minerals other than the carbonates (Barshad et al., 1956). It is recommended that clay samples containing carbonates should be analyzed with and without the carbonates. The removal of the clay carbonates is readily accomplished with cold $0.1N$ HCl with little effect on the clay minerals.

50–4 THERMOGRAVIMETRIC ANALYSIS

50–4.1 Principles

To determine the temperature range over which adsorbed water is completely eliminated and the loss of crystal-lattice water begins, it is necessary to heat individual samples of clay to constant weight at successively increasing temperatures. The temperature intervals should be of the order of 25° to 50°C. in the critical range. From such an analysis of pure clay species, it is possible to determine this range by comparing the accumulated water losses with the theoretical crystal-lattice water that should be present.

To calculate the theoretical amount of crystal-lattice water of a given pure species, it is necessary first to determine the chemical composition of the species and then to calculate its formula and molecular weight on a water-free basis. The theoretical number of moles of water is then added to the formula, and the composition is recalculated on a basis of percentage by weight, either on the formula weight with the water or without the water (on the ignited basis). For determining the temperature range above which all crystal-lattice water is removed, the ignited basis is the more convenient; this is the basis used in Table 50–2.

Two significant facts are brought out by this table; namely, that the crystal-lattice water for all the important silicate clay minerals is lost by heating between about 150° or 350°C. and 1,000°C., and that the clay minerals can be divided into two distinct groups on the basis of the total amount of crystal-lattice water, namely, the 2:1 minerals and the 1:1 and 2:2 minerals. Among the 2:1 minerals, i.e., montmorillonites, vermiculites, and micas, the water content lies in the range from 4.2 to 5.1%. Among the 1:1 and 2:2 minerals, it lies in the range from 13.4 to 16.2%. It may readily be seen, therefore, that on the basis of only a crystal-lattice water analysis, i.e., total water loss by heating between either 150°C or 350°C. and 1,000°C., it is possible to determine approximately the relative content of 2:1 minerals and of 1:1 or 2:2 minerals in a clay sample. If an X-ray analysis and a chemical analysis are available also, it is possible to determine the amount of each mineral species present.

Although it is well established that the major portion of the crystal-lattice water for the various minerals is lost at different temperature ranges, particularly as indicated by differential thermal analysis, there is a sufficient overlap among them to preclude the use of thermogravimetric analysis in a particular temperature range for a quantitative determination of a single mineral.

The determination of water content of clay samples in a paste form at onset of gelation and in the air-dry state at about 50% relative humidity are also useful for differentiating among the different clay mineral species. At onset of gelation, depending on the exchangeable ion, the montmorillonites take up 5 to 30 g. of water per gram of clay, whereas the kaolinite and illite minerals take up only 0.5 to 1.5 g. of water per gram of clay (Barshad, 1955). Large differences exist also in the air-dry state, where montmorillonites adsorb 20 to 30 times more water per gram of clay than do kaolinites.

From the position and size of the endothermic breaks in DTA curves, it may be inferred that the adsorbed water and the crystal-lattice water require different amounts of energy for their separation from the solid phase and that several energy levels exist for both the adsorbed and the crystal-lattice water (Barshad, 1952, 1955, 1960b).

To find the activation energy involved in release of water in a particular endothermic reaction, it is necessary to know both the calorie equivalent of the reaction, from differential thermal analysis, and the quantity of water released, from thermogravimetric analysis carried out under comparable conditions. Measurements of the quantity of water released may be made by means of an automatic recording balance (Chevenard et al. 1944; Merveilli and Boureille, 1950; Mauer, 1954).

By plotting the accumulated weight-loss measurements against temperature, one obtains what are known as "weight-loss" or "integral-thermal-analysis curves." By plotting the loss in weight per degree rise in temperature against temperature, however, one obtains a "differential-thermogravi-metric-analysis (DTgA) curve." This latter curve is essentially a plot of the slope of the corresponding "integral-thermogravimetric-analysis (ITgA) curve."

In the literature of clay analysis, however, the term "differential thermogravimetric analysis" is restricted to the process of obtaining the differential curves directly by an instrument rather than the process of plotting the slope of integral curves. Instruments for DTgA have been developed by De Keyser (1953) and also by Erdley et al. (1954). The De Keyser instrument measures the difference in loss of weight between two identical samples while they are being heated simultaneously at identical rates in two furnaces which consistently differ in temperature by 4°C. throughout the heating period. The instrument of Erdley et al. automatically records the emf. of an electric current necessary to keep a balance at zero position while a sample suspended from one pan of the balance is being heated at a constant rate of rise in temperature. Curves obtained with these instruments are similar to DTA curves.

A careful comparison of DTA curves with ITgA and DTgA curves of identical samples which were heated at approximately the same rate reveals that endothermic breaks in DTA curves correspond to relatively large water losses at a rapid rate and that small water losses at slow rates are not recorded at all on DTA curves. Therefore, in studying heats involved in desorption of water from clays by DTA, it is necessary to determine only the water losses between the initial and final temperatures of the desired endothermic break in DTA curves. The water losses in the temperature region between the endothermic breaks should be ignored in such a study.

The rate of heating during thermogravimetric analysis and the temperature at which weight losses are measured, when automatically recording balances are not available, depend upon the purpose for which the analysis is made. For studying heats of reactions in conjunction with DTA, the rate of heating should be the same as during DTA, and the measurements of loss in weight should be made at the initial and final temperature of each endothermic break. For the purpose of differentiating between adsorbed and crystal-lattice water, however, the heating should be at a rate such that the adsorbed water is lost before the loss in crystal-lattice water begins. For this purpose, heating samples at known fixed temperatures for periods between 3 and 12 hours is more practical than is heating them at a continuously rising temperature. The number of weight-loss measurements can thus be reduced to a small number. For Na-saturated samples, these measurements can be made at temperatures of 150°C., 370°C., and 1,000°C.

The best condition of a sample to be analyzed depends also upon the purpose of the analysis. A Na-saturated sample freed of organic matter is most suitable for differentiating between adsorbed and crystal-lattice water, whereas a Mg- or Ca-saturated sample is more suitable for differentiating between the 2:1 and 1:1 minerals on the basis of adsorbed water.

Thermogravimetric analysis can be used also to determine organic matter content of a soil or of a clay separate, provided that the soil or clay separate is available in the naturally occurring state and in a state without the organic matter.

The method to be used in thermogravimetric analysis, therefore, depends upon the purpose of the analysis and on the available equipment.

50–4.2 Method for Crystal-Lattice Water and Organic Matter

50–4.2.1 SPECIAL APPARATUS

1. Oven with adequate temperature controls for the range between 20° and 250°C.
2. Muffle furnace with adequate temperature controls for the range between 200° and 1,000°C.
3. Bunsen burners capable of heating a crucible to about 1,000°C.
4. Desiccators with silica gel desiccant.

50–4.2.2 PROCEDURE A

By use of the procedures in section 44–3.2.2, treat the samples with H_2O_2 to remove organic matter; then prepare them in Na-saturated condition. Alternatively, by a combination of these procedures with those of sections 44–4.2.2 and 45–3.3.2, remove organic matter, allophane, and uncombined Fe_2O_3, Al_2O_3, and SiO_2.

Analyze two 1- to 2-g. quantities of each sample. Place one aliquot in a weighed weighing bottle and the other in a weighed platinum crucible, and weigh them.

Heat the samples in weighing bottles in an oven at a temperature of 150°C. for at least 24 hours. Cover the bottles, and place them in a desiccator containing a silica gel desiccant. Weigh the samples as soon as they are cooled to room temperature. Repeat the heating at 150°C. and weighing until the sample weight remains constant. Heat the samples in the platinum crucibles either in a muffle or on bunsen burners. Raise the temperature gradually to about 1,000°C., and maintain this temperature for about 1 hour or longer. Cover the crucibles, place them in a desiccator to cool, and then weigh them. Repeat the heating and weighing until the sample weight remains constant. Keep the cooling period before weighing constant and between 30 and 45 minutes.

50–4.2.3 PROCEDURE B

Use this procedure for untreated samples; for samples in their natural state of cation saturation but freed of organic matter by H_2O_2 (section 44–3); and for Mg- or Ca-saturated samples that have been freed of organic matter by H_2O_2 and equilibrated with water vapor over a saturated $Mg(NO_3)_2$ solution. Use the same weighing procedure as in A, but heat the samples in weighing bottles at 150° and 250°C. and in crucibles at 370° and 1,000°C.

50–4.2.4 INTERPRETATION OF RESULTS

50–4.2.4.1 Crystal-Lattice Water. For organic-matter free, Na-saturated clays other than vermiculite, the loss in weight between 150° and 1,000°C. is crystal-lattice water; for vermiculite it is the sum of crystal-lattice water and adsorbed water present in cavities of the oxygen network of the interlayer surfaces.

The loss in weight above 370°C. with naturally occurring samples free of organic matter and with Mg- or Ca-saturated samples free of organic matter is caused by loss of crystal-lattice water for all the clay minerals except vermiculite. In the latter, some adsorbed cavity water is included in this loss. The loss in weight between 150° and 370°C. is derived from OH^- of gibbsite, goethite, and hydroxyaluminum ions, and from adsorbed cavity water present in vermiculites and in Ca- or Mg-saturated montmorillonite (Table 50–2).

The loss in weight in vermiculites (Barshad, 1948) after their interlayer water has been removed, that is, after the $d(001)$ X-ray spacing is about 10Å., is equal to 7.88% (on the ignited basis) for the Ca- or Mg-saturated samples when heated between 250° and the ignition temperature, and 9.42% (on the ignited basis) for the Na-saturated form when heated between 150°C. and the ignition temperature. The 7.88% loss is equal to about $1.6 \times$ crystal-lattice water, and the 9.42% loss is equal to about $2.0 \times$ crystal-lattice water. This excess water, that is, the 3.08% in the Mg- or Ca-saturated forms and the 4.66% in the Na-saturated forms, was shown to be present in the cavities of the hexagonal oxygen network, which also accommodate the exchangeable ions. The water molecules are either in the empty cavities, that is, the cavities from which exchangeable ions are absent (as in the Mg- or Ca-forms), or in the same cavity with exchangeable Na or other monovalent ions. Similar cavity water is present also in Ca- and Mg-saturated montmorillonites.

The quantity of water lost from air-dry samples in the temperature range between 20° and 150°C. or 350°C. and between 150° or 350°C. and 1,000°C. indicates qualitatively the kind of minerals present. Losses up to 20% at the lower temperatures and <5% at the higher temperatures indicate the presence of montmorillonite, vermiculite, or a mixture of the two. Losses <5% at the lower temperatures and >12% at the higher temperatures indicate the presence of 1:1 or 2:2 minerals. Losses of 10 to 15% at the lower temperatures and <2% at the higher temperatures indicate the presence of allophane.

50–4.2.4.2 Organic Matter Content. The difference in loss of weight between the samples with and without organic matter when heated between 150°C. and the ignition temperature is equal to the organic matter content.

50–4.3 Method for Integral and Differential Thermogravimetric Curves

50–4.3.1 SPECIAL APPARATUS

Automatic recording analytical balance, together with a furnace, the rate of heating of which can be regulated as desired (Mauer, 1954). In the absence of such equipment, use the same equipment as described for crystal-lattice water determination (section 50–4.2). The oven and the furnace, however, should be of a quality such that the heating can be regulated precisely.

50–4.3.2 PROCEDURE

By use of the H_2O_2 method described in section 44–3, treat the samples to remove organic matter. Prepare the samples in homoionic condition by leaching them with the desired salt solution in $1N$ concentration and washing out the excess salt with water and alcohol. Then prepare subsamples of each sample with differing content of water by exposing them to water vapor of various partial pressures or by heating samples with a relatively high water content (as in samples equilibrated with water vapor over distilled water) at 70°C. for various lengths of time.

If automatic recording equipment is employed, place the sample in the holder, adjust the heating regulator to the desired rate, and run the analysis. The curve obtained is either an integral- or a differential-thermogravimetric-analysis curve, depending on the type of equipment employed. From the integral curve construct the differential curve or vice versa.

To prepare a weight-loss curve by heating clay to constant weight at different temperatures with conventional equipment, accurately weigh as many samples of approximately 1-g. size into glass weighing bottles and platinum crucibles as are desired to obtain the curve (each sample provides one point). Use weighing bottles for samples that are to be heated at temperatures up to 250°C. and platinum crucibles for higher temperatures. Heat the samples at the desired constant temperatures for a period of 3 hours or longer. Then stopper the weighing bottles, and place the bottles and crucibles in a desiccator. Weigh the samples as soon as they have cooled. Repeat the heating and weighing until constant weight is attained. Plot the loss in weight against the temperature of heating to obtain a weight-loss curve.

To prepare a weight-loss curve with conventional equipment under conditions of continuously rising temperature, weigh samples as described in the preceding paragraph. Place the samples in an oven or furnace, and heat them at the desired rate. Remove individual samples as the desired temperature is reached, and place them in a desiccator for cooling and weighing. Weigh the samples as soon as they have cooled. Plot the loss in weight against the temperature to obtain a weight-loss curve.

50–4.3.3 *INTERPRETATION OF RESULTS*

The curves obtained by the procedure with conventional equipment are more properly called weight-loss curves than integral-thermogravimetric-analysis curves because the weight loss is determined at intervals and not continuously. True differential curves cannot be derived from such curves, but they can be obtained from the continuous record of loss in weight provided by an automatic recording analytical balance operating during continuous heating of a single sample of clay.

Integral and differential thermogravimetric curves of clay samples equilibrated at known water-vapor pressures, together with DTA curves obtained by procedure 50–3.2.3.6, can be used for evaluating the thermodynamic quantities of heat (ΔH), free energy (ΔF), and entropy (ΔS) for the reaction of water desorption from clay minerals (Barshad, 1960b). A similar combination of the two methods can be used for determining the mean integral heat, in calories per mole or per gram of water, for the dehydroxylation reaction at the different temperature ranges at which endothermic breaks appear in the DTA curves. Such data, when available, could be used for differentiating minerals having endothermic breaks in the same temperature range but having different mean integral heats of dehydroxylation. One such example is given by Barshad (1952) for the endothermic break in the DTA curves of a kaolinite, an halloysite, and an illite occurring in the temperature range between 400° and 695°C. The mean integral heat of decomposition, in calories per gram of H_2O lost, was found to be 1,983 for kaolinite, 1,385 for halloysite, and 1,025 for illite. As yet, little use has been made of this application.

50–5 QUANTITATIVE MINERALOGICAL COMPOSITION
BY THERMAL ANALYSIS

By combining quantitative DTA for kaolinite, halloysite, and gibbsite with thermogravimetric analysis, it is possible to determine not only the amount of each clay mineral present but also the total amount of substances such as quartz, feldspars, and free oxides that do not contain crystal-lattice water. The following examples illustrate the application of the concepts involved.

In the first example, it may be assumed that thermogravimetric analysis established that a Na-saturated clay sample containing kaolinite and montmorillonite lost 9.25% water upon heating between 150°C. and ignition. Differential thermal analysis established that the sample contained 50% kaolinite. The content of montmorillonite and of substances containing no crystal-lattice water can then be calculated as follows: If X is the percentage content of montmorillonite, the amount of substances containing no crystal-lattice water is equal to $(50 - X)$. Taking into consideration the content of crystal-lattice water of kaolinite and montmorillonite (Table 50–2), the following relationship holds true:

$$\frac{50 \times 16.20}{100} + \frac{X \times 5.05}{100} + \frac{(50 - X) \times 0}{100} = 9.25$$

Solving for X, the montmorillonite content, we find that it is equal to about 22.8%; therefore, the amount of substances containing no crystal-lattice water is equal to $50 - 22.8$ or 27.2%. In the second example, it may be assumed that the clay minerals present were found by X-ray analysis to be kaolinite and vermiculite. The relationship would then be as follows:

$$\frac{50 \times 16.20}{100} + \frac{X \times (4.76 + 4.66)}{100} + \frac{(50 - X) \times 0}{100} = 9.25$$

Solving for X, the vermiculite content, we find that it is equal to 12.2%; therefore, the amount of substances containing no crystal-lattice water is equal to $50 - 12.2$ or 37.8%.

To calculate the percentage values on the air-dry basis, the percentage content of each constituent on the ignited basis is multiplied by 100 and divided by the sum of 100 and the percentage content of water expressed on the ignited basis.

Hydrous oxides and allophane, which contain crystal-lattice water, must be removed from clay samples containing a mixture of kaolinite, montmorillonite, vermiculite, and the mica-like (illite) minerals before the relative amounts of each can be determined. Removal can be accomplished by the methods described in sections 44–4 and 45–3. In such a purified sample, after the kaolinite content has been determined by DTA, the sum of montmorillonite and mica minerals is determined as a single constituent, and vermiculite is determined separately by assigning an average content of 4.9% crystal-lattice water to the former minerals and 9.4% to the latter.

Where the substances other than silicate clay minerals are removed or determined by chemical and X-ray analysis, the relative amount of 1:1 and 2:1 minerals can be determined by thermogravimetric analysis alone by assuming that in the Na-saturated clay samples the loss in weight upon heating between 150°C. and 1,000°C. represents only crystal-lattice water and by assigning 16.2% crystal-lattice water to the 1:1 group and 4.9% to the 2:1 group.

Objections may be raised to the use of DTA for the quantitative determination of kaolinite and halloysite on the ground that there are no standard reference kaolinite or halloysite minerals (Van der Marel, 1960). Reference samples differ in shape and size of the diagnostic endothermic break in the temperature range between 400° and 600°C. These differences found by Van der Marel are exaggerated because he did not use the technique for calibration described in section 50–3.2.3.2, particularly with respect to confining the samples to a constant volume, and he did not determine precisely the actual water lost for the temperature range delineated by the characteristic endothermic break. To ensure, nevertheless, that DTA can be used quantitatively for kaolinite and halloysite, a number of reference samples of each of these minerals should be analyzed according to procedure 50–3.2.3.2. The calibration curves plotted for each sample should include a description of the slope ratio of the endothermic break and the initial and final temperature delineating the thermal break. When a DTA is made on an unknown sample containing kaolinite or halloysite, the endothermic break should be described similarly. A calibration curve of a reference sample having the same slope ratio and the same initial and final temperatures may then be chosen.

50–6 QUANTITATIVE MINERALOGICAL COMPOSITION BY USE OF THERMAL ANALYSIS AND OTHER ANALYTICAL METHODS

50–6.1 Introduction

For a complete quantitative determination of the mineralogical composition of a soil clay fraction, the combined use of several methods of analysis described in this monograph may be required. Besides the thermal analysis techniques just described, X-ray analysis, total elemental analysis, differential dissolution techniques, cation-exchange measurements, and glycol- or glycerol-adsorption measurements may be useful. For any specific clay sample, the number of analyses needed to evaluate its mineralogical composition on a quantitative basis is dependent on the number of mineral species present. The species are identified by qualitative X-ray analysis. As a rule the number of different analyses needed is equal to the number of mineral species present.

To facilitate application of the various methods of analysis for the evaluation of the mineralogical composition, it is preferable that samples be sodium-saturated, free of organic matter, and air-dry; that is, in the same state of preparedness as for quantitative differential thermal and thermogravimetric analyses.

50–6.2 Use of Individual Methods

50–6.2.1 THERMAL ANALYSIS

The use of thermal analysis for evaluating mineralogical composition is described in section 50–5.

50–6.2.2 X-RAY ANALYSIS

The use of X-ray analysis as an aid for quantitative mineralogical analysis is many fold: (1) To identify the minerals present, (2) to differentiate the montmorillonite and vermiculite species with respect to cation-exchange capacity, (3) to measure the $d(001)$ spacing of montmorillonite and vermiculite in conjunction with surface-area analysis by glycol- or glycerol-adsorption techniques, (4) to measure the $d(001)$ spacing of regularly and randomly interstratified 2:1 clay mineral species in order to determine the relative amount of each species present (MacEwan et al. 1961), and (5) to measure quantitatively the content of quartz, cristobalite, gibbsite, and feldspars when present in amounts less than about 15%.

To accomplish item 5, suspensions of each mineral having particle sizes in the same range of values as those of the clay minerals are prepared. Various amounts of these suspended minerals are then added to known amounts of known mixtures of clay minerals, which are also in a suspended state, and are X-rayed by the procedure described in section 49–4 (or by the method of Barshad, 1960a). Because of difference in swelling properties, known mixtures of clay minerals in various proportions which are of greatest usefulness in quantitative X-ray analyses are mixtures of (1) kaolinite and montmorillonite, (2) halloysite and montmorillonite, (3) kaolinite and mica, (4) kaolinite and vermiculite, (5) halloysite and vermiculite, and (6) kaolinite, mica, and vermiculite.

50–6.2.3 FREE OXIDE, HYDROXIDE, AND AMORPHOUS ALUMINOSILICATE ANALYSES

The methods of analysis for these clay components are inherently quantitative (section 45), and consequently the results obtained need only be expressed on the same sample-weight basis as the other mineral components.

50–6.2.4 CATION-EXCHANGE CAPACITY AND EXCHANGEABLE BASES

The cation-exchange capacity (CEC) of a clay can be an aid in determining quantitatively its mineralogical composition. For estimating the mineralogical composition, it is important that the appropriate values of CEC are employed for the mineral components of the mixture (X-ray analysis can be used to obtain an index of the CEC of montmorillonite and vermiculite, as indicated in table 50–3). Moreover, the method for measuring the CEC should not be influenced by cation fixation, cation trapping, hydrolysis, adsorption of divalent ions as monovalent ions, or occlusion of free salts, and it should ensure replacement of the strongly adsorbed hydroxy-aluminum ions present in clays from acid soils (see sections 57, 59, and 67–3). The CEC measurement is particularly useful as an aid in mineralogical analysis of samples containing amounts of montmorillonite or vermiculite in excess of about 15%. The values of CEC listed in table 50–3 may be used in evaluating the mineralogical composition.

Variation in particle size does not affect the CEC of montmorillonites or

Table 50–3. X-ray $d(001)$ spacing of montmorillonite and vermiculite with different pretreatments, and cation-exchange capacity of these and other clay minerals.

Mineral	Cation-exchange capacity*	d(001) spacing found with indicated pretreatment			
		Glyceration of water-wet sample		Glyceration of oven-dry sample	
		Na saturated	K saturated	Na saturated	K saturated
	me./100 g.	Å	Å	Å	Å
Montmorillonite	100	18	18	17.7	14.2
	115	18	16	17.7	14.2
	135	18	14.5	17.7	14.2
Vermiculite	160	14.2	14.0	14.2	13.3
	210	14.2	13.3	14.2	10.6
	260	14.2	10.4	14.2	10.4
Soil mica	50				
Illite mica	30				
Soil kaolinite	8				
Clay kaolinite	5				
Soil halloysite	20				
Clay halloysite	14				
Feldspars ($< 2\mu$)	10				
Quartz ($< 2\mu$)	5				
Silica (silicic acid)	15				
Allophane†	50				
Allophane†	150				

* Based on the weight after ignition.   † See section 45-4.

vermiculites, but it does affect the CEC of kaolinite, halloysite, and micas: the smaller the particles, the higher their CEC. But because of the relatively small contribution of the latter group of minerals to the total CEC of clay samples that are high in vermiculite or montmorillonite, even a two- or threefold variation in CEC of kaolinite or halloysite produces only small errors in mineralogical composition.

The determination of exchangeable bases is needed to permit calculation of the nonexchangeable bases from the total bases determined by total elemental analysis.

50–6.2.5 TOTAL ELEMENTAL ANALYSIS

Total elemental analysis, together with analyses for exchangeable bases, free oxides, hydroxides, and amorphous aluminosilicates, permits a quantitative evaluation of a number of mineral constituents that may be identified in clay samples by X-ray analysis. The smaller is the number of such constituents, the more correctly can their amounts be calculated. To facilitate these calculations, the major elemental composition of the minerals occurring most frequently in soil clays is given in table 50–4.

The total analyses for K_2O, Na_2O, and CaO are used most frequently for the determination of the feldspar and mica contents. Most soil clays do not contain feldspars; but, if they do, the feldspars are present in very small quantities. Micas, however, may frequently be present in fairly large amounts; and the amounts present can be calculated from the content of

Table 50–4. Chemical composition of the most abundant soil clay minerals and of some important accessory minerals.

Mineral	Composition on basis of weight of ignited mineral							$\frac{SiO_2}{Al_2O_3}$
	SiO_2	Al_2O_3	Fe_2O_3	MgO	CaO	Na_2O	K_2O	
				%				
Na-montmorillonite	67.10	20.20	2.33	5.66		4.12		5.64
Na-montmorillonite	67.55	22.50	3.92	2.50		3.10		5.09
Na-montmorillonite	65.80			31.09		3.16		
Na-montmorillonite	51.50	7.50	37.30			3.51		11.65
Na-vermiculite	47.50	16.11		29.72		6.54		5.0
Na-muscovite	47.37	40.18				1.55	10.04	2.0
Na-phlogopite	45.10	12.75		30.30		1.55	9.45	6.0
Na-biotite	36.49	10.32	43.65			1.55	7.20	6.0
Kaolinite or halloysite	54.1	45.9						2.0
Gibbsite		100.0						
Quartz	100.0							
Orthoclase or microcline	64.7	18.4					16.9	6.0
Albite	68.7	19.5				11.8		6.0
Anorthite	43.2	36.6			20.2			2.0

the nonexchangeable K_2O, as determined by the difference between total and exchangeable K_2O. Since the K_2O content of a mica depends on the composition of its octahedral layer, it is important to verify the latter by X-ray analysis (section 49–6). The nonexchangeable K_2O content of clay micas is affected also by the extent of its replacement by other ions. Thus, if we assume that soil clay micas have an average CEC of 50 me. per 100 g. (Barshad, 1951), the nonexchangeable K_2O content is 10% in muscovite, 9.45% in phlogopite, and 7.20% in biotite of the species having only iron in the octahedral layer. In biotites in which both iron and magnesium are present, the K_2O content is determined from that of the two end-members. If the X-ray analysis of a clay indicates that all the feldspars and calcite are absent, all the nonexchangeable K_2O, Na_2O, and CaO are assigned to the mica minerals, and their sum is equated to the values of nonexchangeable K_2O content listed above for the various micas. This approximation suffices because the Na_2O and CaO are present in most micas in only minor amounts.

If X-ray analysis indicates the presence of a potassium feldspar, the amount is then determined by quantitative X-ray analysis. The K_2O content of the feldspar is calculated by multiplying the feldspar percentage by 0.169 and is then subtracted from the total K_2O content to yield the K_2O content present in the clay mica. If X-ray analysis indicates the presence of plagioclase or orthoclase feldspars and the absence of mica, the nonexchangeable Na_2O, CaO, and K_2O can be used to evaluate the content of albite by multiplying the Na_2O percentage by 8.5, the anorthite content by multiplying the CaO percentage by 4.95, and the orthoclase content by multiplying the K_2O percentage by 5.9 (based on 11.8% Na_2O in albite, 20.2% CaO in anorthite, and 16.9% K_2O in orthoclase or microcline).

With clay samples containing only dioctahedral clay minerals (muscovite, kaolinite, and dioctahedral vermiculite), which are characterized by a silica-to-alumina ratio of 2.0, it is possible to calculate from the total SiO_2 and Al_2O_3 of the samples the amount of uncombined silica or alumina which may be present. Thus, if the SiO_2/Al_2O_3 ratio is greater than 2.0, and if all the Al_2O_3 is present in a combined form, one obtains the combined silica by multiplying the Al_2O_3 percentage by 1.18 [derived from $(2 \times 60.06)/101.94$]. If the SiO_2/Al_2O_3 ratio is less than 2.0, and if all the silica is in a combined form, one obtains the combined Al_2O_3 by multiplying the SiO_2 percentage by 0.848 [derived from $101.94/(2 \times 60.06)$]. By subtracting the calculated amounts of combined Al_2O_3 or SiO_2 from the total Al_2O_3 or SiO_2 found by analysis, one obtains the "free" Al_2O_3 or SiO_2 present in excess of a SiO_2/Al_2O_3 ratio of 2.0. Where the content of quartz and gibbsite in such samples is determined directly by analysis, the SiO_2 and Al_2O_3 associated with the quartz and gibbsite is subtracted from the total SiO_2 and Al_2O_3 before the calculations described above are made. Frequently soil clays contain uncombined SiO_2 and Al_2O_3 in forms other than quartz and gibbsite. The foregoing calculations are particularly useful for clays occurring in latosolic or lateritic soils.

The total MgO content is often useful in detecting and verifying the presence of trioctahedral clay mineral species, but it cannot be used to determine the content of any given species because of the large variation of MgO content among minerals of the same species. Where the content of MgO and combined Fe_2O_3 is known, it is possible to calculate the relative abundance of the end-members of minerals containing either Mg or Fe in octahedral positions.

50–6.2.6 GLYCOL- OR GLYCEROL-ADSORPTION MEASUREMENTS

Measurements of adsorption of glycol or glycerol are particularly applicable as an aid in evaluating the mineralogical composition of clays containing montmorillonite and/or vermiculite. But because the amount of adsorbed glycol or glycerol that characterizes a montmorillonite or vermiculite depends on the degree to which the mineral is expanded (measured by the $d(001)$ X-ray spacing given in table 50–5), it is important to control the expansion. The most suitable procedure appears to be one in which montmorillonite is induced to adsorb a duolayer and vermiculite a monolayer on interplanar surfaces (section 42–3), and in which the $d(001)$ spacing is measured immediately after the adsorption measurement is completed.

Table 50–5. Quantities of glycol and glycerol adsorbed by montmorillonite and vermiculite as a function of the thickness of the adsorbed layers and of the percentage of the total planar surface occurring on the exterior of the particles.

Adsorbate	d (001) X-ray spacing	Thickness of duolayer	Thickness of monolayer	Adsorbate per gram of oven-dry clay with indicated percentage of total surface on exterior of particles			
				Montmorillonite		Vermiculite	
				10*	20†	10*	20†
	Å.	Å.	Å.	g.	g.	g.	g.
Glycol	17.1	7.2	3.6	0.3117	0.3117		
	16.8	6.9	3.45	0.2980	0.2980		
	14.3		4.4	0.2081	0.2263	0.1951	0.2122
	14.2		4.3	0.2041	0.2228		
	13.8		3.9	0.1869	0.2164		
Glycerol	18.4	8.5	4.25	0.4110	0.4110		
	17.7	7.8	3.9	0.3780	0.3780		
	14.3		4.4	0.2349	0.2562	0.2294	0.2393
	14.2		4.3	0.2302	0.2522	0.2153	0.2358
	14.1		4.2	0.2272	0.2494	0.2122	0.2328

* Assumed for clay particles < 2μ in diameter.
† Assumed for clay particles < 0.1μ in diameter.

Table 50–6. Quantities of glycol and glycerol adsorbed by various clay minerals.

Mineral	Adsorbate	Quantity of adsorbate per gram of oven-dry mineral of indicated particle diameters		
		2 to 1μ	< 2μ	< 0.1μ
			g.	
Kaolinite	Glycol	0.011	0.016	0.027
	Glycerol	0.014	0.023	0.033
Halloysite	Glycol	0.0209	0.0342	0.0476
	Glycerol	0.0255	0.0418	0.0580
Illite	Glycol	0.0430	0.0610	0.0790
	Glycerol	0.0500	0.0730	0.0960
Quartz	Glycol		0.0040	
	Glycerol		0.0033	
Allophane	Glycol	0.1200	0.1300	0.1400
	Glycerol	0.1470	0.1509	0.1700

Only a small percentage error results from introducing into the calculation of the mineralogical composition of a clay sample the minimum, maximum, or average values of the "characteristic" amounts of glycol or glycerol adsorbed by clay minerals other than montmorillonite or vermiculite (table 50–6) because the amounts of glycol or glycerol adsorbed by these minerals are several-fold smaller than the amounts adsorbed by montmorillonite or vermiculite.

50–6.3 Examples of Calculations

The combined use of the various methods of analysis for calculating the mineralogical composition of clays can best be demonstrated by presenting a number of examples of such calculations. Except as otherwise specified, all numerical values given are expressed on the basis of the weight of the sample after ignition.

50–6.3.1 EXAMPLE 1

The following information is available for a sample of Ca-saturated clay for which the mineralogical composition is to be calculated: (*1*) From total chemical analysis, the chemical composition is $SiO_2 = 51.75\%$, $Al_2O_3 = 25.50\%$, $Fe_2O_3 = 13.23\%$, $TiO_2 = 0.93\%$, $MnO = 0.20\%$, $P_2O_5 = 0.28\%$, $CaO = 1.76\%$, $MgO = 3.67\%$, $K_2O = 2.36\%$, and $Na_2O = 0.40\%$. (*2*) By thermogravimetric analysis (loss of weight between 350° and 1,000°C.), $H_2O = 8.04\%$. (*3*) From X-ray analysis, the quartz content is 3%. (*4*) By free-oxide analysis, the free iron oxide content is 3.23%. (*5*) Exchangeable Ca^{2+} and CEC are identical and are 54.2 me. per 100 g., which is equivalent to 1.52% CaO. (*6*) From X-ray analysis, the minerals present include biotite, montmorillonite, vermiculite, kaolinite, hematite, quartz, and plagioclase feldspar. The montmorillonite and vermiculite are of the species with CEC values of 135 and 260 me. per 100 g. From this information, calculation of the mineralogical composition then may proceed in the manner indicated in the following paragraphs.

Because the sample was in a Ca-saturated state, the K_2O and Na_2O found by total chemical analysis are nonexchangeable. The nonexchangeable CaO is $1.76 - 1.52 = 0.24\%$.

The nonexchangeable CaO and Na_2O are assumed to be present as plagioclase feldspar. The albite content is then $(0.40)(8.5) = 3.40\%$, and the anorthite content is $(0.24)(4.95) = 1.18\%$.

Constituents without crystal-lattice water are quartz, feldspar, and free Fe_2O_3. Their sum is $3.0 + 3.40 + 1.18 + 3.23 = 10.81\%$.

To calculate the nonexchangeable K_2O characteristic of the type of biotite occurring in the sample, it is necessary to determine the Fe/Mg ratio in the octahedral layer. For this sample it is justifiable to assume that the Fe_2O_3/MgO ratio is the same for all the 2:1 minerals, and that it is equal to the ratio of combined Fe_2O_3 to MgO, namely, $(10.0/3.67)(40.32/159.7)(2) = 1.376$. In terms of percentage composition, $(1.376/2.376)(100) = 58\%$ of the iron end-member, and $100 - 58 = 42\%$ of the magnesium end-member. The K_2O content of the mica species in the sample thus is equal to $(9.45)(0.42) + (7.20)(0.58) = 8.15\%$. The biotite content of the sample, as calculated from the K_2O content, is then $(100/8.15)(2.36) = 29.0$.

The content of crystal-lattice water in the 2:1 species is calculated on the assumption that all species have the same value as does biotite. The crystal-lattice water in the biotite species present in the sample is calculated from the values for the end-members: That of phlogopite, the magnesium end-member, is 4.74%; and that of the iron end-member is 3.65%. Thus, $(4.74)(0.42) + (3.65)(0.58) = 4.01\%$ crystal-lattice water in all the 2:1 minerals in the sample.

The content of kaolinite is calculated from the 8.04% loss of weight found by thermogravimetric analysis upon heating the sample between 350° and 1,000°C. The crystal-lattice water is attributable entirely to the 2:1 and 1:1 minerals, the sum of which is equal to $100 - 10.81 = 89.19$ or 89.2%. Kaolinite contains 16.20% crystal-lattice water. If $x =$ percent kaolinite, the sum of the 2:1 minerals with a crystal-lattice water content of 4.01% is equal to $89.2 - x$. The content of kaolinite is then calculated from the equation,

$$(x)(16.20/100) + (89.2 - x)(4.01/100) = 8.04,$$

from which $x = 36.6\%$ kaolinite. Therefore, the sum of the 2:1 minerals is equal to $89.2 - 36.6 = 52.6\%$. Because the biotite content is 29.0%, the sum of montmorillonite and vermiculite is equal to $52.6 - 29.0 = 23.6\%$

The contents of montmorillonite and vermiculite are calculated with the aid of information on the CEC. If x is the CEC of the sum of montmorillonite and vermiculite, the total CEC of the sample per 100 g. is given by the equation,

$$(x)(23.6/100) + (50)(29.0/100) + (8)(36.6/100) = 54.15,$$

where 50 and 8 are the CEC values for the biotite and kaolinite. From this equation, $x = 155.5$ me. per 100 g. If y is the percentage content of vermiculite with a CEC of 260 me. per 100 g., and if $100 - y$ is the percentage content of montmorillonite with a CEC of 135 me. per 100 g. in a mixture of these two minerals only, the CEC of 155.5 me. per 100 g. for the mixture is given by the equation,

$$(y)(260/100) + (100 - y)(135/100) = 155.5,$$

from which $y = 18\%$ vermiculite and $100 - y = 82\%$ montmorillonite. The clay sample thus contains $(23.6)(18/100) = 4.25\%$ vermiculite and $(23.6)(82/100) = 19.35\%$ montmorillonite.

The mineralogical composition of the sample of clay as found by these calculations is as follows:

Kaolinite	36.6%
Biotite	29.0%
Montmorillonite	19.4%
Vermiculite	4.3%
Quartz	3.0%
Anorthite	1.2%
Albite	3.4%
Hematite	3.2%
TOTAL	100.1%

50–6.3.2 EXAMPLE 2

The following information is available for a sample of a base-unsaturated lateritic soil clay for which the mineralogical composition is to be calculated: (1) From total chemical analysis, the chemical composition is $SiO_2 = 35.38\%$, $Al_2O_3 = 42.49\%$, $Fe_2O_3 = 17.71\%$, $TiO_2 = 1.55\%$, $Mn_3O_4 = 0.08\%$, $CaO = 0.09\%$, $MgO = 2.12\%$, $Na_2O = 0.07\%$, $K_2O = 0.18\%$, and $P_2O_5 = 0.08\%$. (2) By thermogravimetric analysis (loss of weight between 150° and 1,000°C.), $H_2O = 17.70\%$. (3) The CEC is 3.2 me. per 100 g. (4) X-ray analysis and differential thermal analysis indicate that the sample contains kaolinite, gibbsite, hematite, and very small amounts of trioctahedral mica and vermiculite, and that feldspars are absent. From this information, calculation of the mineralogical composition may proceed in the manner indicated in the following paragraphs.

The sum of the contents of mica and vermiculite is calculated from the MgO content on the assumptions that both contain only Mg^{2+} in octahedral positions and that the MgO content is 30.41%. On this basis, (2.12)(100/30.41) = 6.96% mica plus vermiculite.

The phlogopite content is calculated from the sum of CaO, Na$_2$O, and K$_2$O (=0.34%) and from the nonexchangeable K$_2$O of phlogopite (=9.45%). On this basis, (0.34)(100/9.45) = 3.60% phlogopite; and 6.96 − 3.60 = 3.36% vermiculite.

From the values in the preceding paragraph and from table 50–4, the amounts of SiO$_2$ and Al$_2$O$_3$ present in the phlogopite and vermiculite are calculated to be 3.26% and 1.02%. These values are subtracted from the total SiO$_2$ and Al$_2$O$_3$ in the sample to obtain 35.38 − 3.26 = 32.12% SiO$_2$ and 42.49 − 1.02 = 41.47% Al$_2$O$_3$ that may be attributed to kaolinite and gibbsite.

The content of kaolinite is calculated on the assumption that the 32.12% SiO$_2$ obtained in the preceding paragraph is present entirely in kaolinite. On this basis, the content of kaolinite is (32.12)(100/54.1) = 59.37%.

The content of gibbsite is calculated on the assumption that it contains all the Al$_2$O$_3$ not present in phlogopite, vermiculite, or kaolinite. The amount of Al$_2$O$_3$ present in the kaolinite may be calculated from the preceding paragraph and from table 50–4 to be (59.37/100)(45.9) = 27.25%. The Al$_2$O$_3$ present in the gibbsite thus is 41.47 − 27.25 = 14.22%. From this figure for Al$_2$O$_3$ and from table 50–4, the content of gibbsite is (14.22/100)(100) = 14.22%.

The sum of Fe$_2$O$_3$ and TiO$_2$ is represented arbitrarily as hematite: 17.71 + 1.55 = 19.26% hematite.

The mineralogical composition of the sample of clay as found by these calculations is as follows:

Kaolinite	59.4%
Hematite (+TiO$_2$)	19.3%
Gibbsite	14.2%
Phlogopite	3.6%
Vermiculite	3.4%
TOTAL	99.9%

To check the accuracy of the results obtained by the foregoing calculations, one may calculate the crystal-lattice water for each of the mineral components and compare the sum with the crystal-lattice water determined analytically:

Kaolinite	(59.4)(0.162)	=	9.6
Gibbsite	(14.2)(0.5295)	=	7.5
Phlogopite	(3.6)(0.055)	=	0.2
Vermiculite	(3.4)(0.0942)	=	0.3
TOTAL			17.6

The calculated total 17.6 agrees satisfactorily with the observed total 17.7.

50–6.3.3 EXAMPLE 3

The following information is available for a sample of Na-saturated latosolic soil clay for which the mineralogical composition is to be calculated: (*1*) From total chemical analysis, the chemical composition is $SiO_2 = 39.35\%$, $Al_2O_3 = 39.23\%$, $Fe_2O_3 = 18.14\%$, $K_2O = 2.08\%$, and $Na_2O = 1.35\%$. The silica/alumina ratio, derived from the percentages of SiO_2 and Al_2O_3, is 1.70. The CEC, derived from the Na_2O percentage, is 43.5 me. per 100 g. (*2*) From free-oxide analysis, the free iron oxide is 13.83%. (*3*) From quantitative differential thermal analysis, kaolinite = 30.9% and gibbsite = 4.7%. (*4*) From quantitative X-ray analysis, potassium feldspar = 1.0% and quartz = 5.0%. (*5*) From qualitative X-ray analysis, the minerals present include kaolinite, dioctahedral mica, dioctahedral vermiculite, gibbsite, hematite, quartz, and feldspar. The vermiculite is the species with a CEC of 160 me. per 100 g. From this information, calculation of the mineralogical composition may proceed in the manner indicated in the following paragraphs.

The SiO_2 present as quartz is subtracted from the total SiO_2 to obtain the combined SiO_2: $39.35 - 5.00 = 34.35\%$ combined SiO_2.

The Fe_2O_3 present as hematite is subtracted from the total Fe_2O_3 to obtain the combined Fe_2O_3: $18.14 - 13.83 = 4.31\%$ combined Fe_2O_3.

The K_2O present in the mica is obtained by subtracting the K_2O present in feldspar from the total K_2O: $2.08 - (1)(0.17) = 1.91\%$ K_2O present in mica. The mica content is then calculated as soil muscovite on the basis that this mineral contains 10.0% K_2O: $1.91/0.10 = 19.1\%$ muscovite.

From the feldspar percentage and the chemical analyses in table 50–4, the SiO_2 and Al_2O_3 present in feldspar are subtracted from the combined SiO_2 and total Al_2O_3: $34.35 - (1)(0.65) = 33.70\%$ combined SiO_2 exclusive of feldspar SiO_2; $39.23 - (1)(0.18) = 39.05\%$ Al_2O_3 exclusive of feldspar Al_2O_3.

Because X-ray analysis indicates that all the clay minerals are the dioctahedral type having a SiO_2/Al_2O_3 ratio of 2.0 (that of kaolinite, muscovite, and dioctahedral vermiculite), the amount of combined Al_2O_3 may be calculated from the combined SiO_2 exclusive of feldspar SiO_2: $(33.70)(0.848) = 28.60\%$ combined Al_2O_3. The combined Al_2O_3 is then subtracted from the total Al_2O_3 exclusive of feldspar Al_2O_3 to obtain the free Al_2O_3: $39.05 - 28.60 = 10.45\%$ free Al_2O_3. The content of crystalline Al_2O_3 (gibbsite) is then subtracted from the free Al_2O_3 to obtain the noncrystalline Al_2O_3: $10.45 - 4.7 = 5.75\%$ noncrystalline Al_2O_3.

The content of vermiculite is calculated as the difference between the total and the sum of the known components: $100 - (30.9\%$ kaolinite + 19.1% muscovite + 5% quartz + 1.0% feldspar + 13.8% free Fe_2O_3 + 4.7% gibbsite + 5.75% noncrystalline Al_2O_3) = 19.7% vermiculite.

The foregoing calculations may be checked by comparing the measured CEC with the sum of the CEC values calculated for the components:

Vermiculite	$(19.7)(1.60) =$	31.5 me. per 100 g.
Muscovite	$(19.1)(0.50) =$	9.5 me. per 100 g.
Kaolinite	$(30.9)(0.08) =$	2.3 me. per 100 g.
TOTAL		43.3 me. per 100 g.

The total of 43.3 me. per 100 g. compares satisfactorily with the observed value 43.5 me. per 100 g.

50–6.3.4 EXAMPLE 4

The following information is available for a naturally occurring sample of clay for which the mineralogical composition is to be calculated: (*1*) From total chemical analysis, the chemical composition is 47.43% SiO_2, 11.77% Al_2O_3, 18.78% Fe_2O_3, 1.41% TiO_2, 0.11% MnO, 11.97% MgO, 5.82% CaO, 0.71% K_2O, 1.57% Na_2O, and 0.37% P_2O_5. (*2*) The CEC of the clay is 120.0 me. per 100 g. (*3*) The exchangeable bases per 100 g. of clay are 95.0 me. of Ca, 23.3 me. of Mg, 1.3 me. of Na, and 0.5 me. of K. The nonexchangeable bases are thus $5.82 - (95.0)(0.028) = 3.16\%$ nonexchangeable CaO, $0.71 - (0.5 \times 0.047) = 0.69\%$ nonexchangeable K_2O, and $1.57 - (1.3)(0.031) = 1.53\%$ nonexchangeable Na_2O. (*4*) No free oxides are present. (*5*) X-ray analysis indicates that plagioclase feldspar, montmorillonite, and vermiculite are the only minerals present and that the montmorillonite and vermiculite are the species with CEC values of 135 and 210 me. per 100 g. (*6*) Glycol adsorption is 0.1755 g. per g. of clay, and the $d(001)$ spacing of the glycolated montmorillonite and vermiculite are 17.1Å and 14.3Å. From this information, calculation of the mineralogical composition may proceed in the manner indicated in the following paragraphs.

The contents of anorthite, albite, and K-feldspar are calculated from the percentages of nonexchangeable CaO, Na_2O, and K_2O, together with the percentage composition data for the minerals in table 50–4: (3.16) (4.95) = 15.6% anorthite, (1.53)(8.5) = 13.0% albite, and (0.69) (5.9) = 4.1% K-feldspar.

The sum of the contents of montmorillonite and vermiculite is obtained by subtracting the sum of the feldspar contents from 100, as follows: $100 - (15.6 + 13.0 + 4.1) = 67.3\%$ montmorillonite plus vermiculite. The contents of montmorillonite and vermiculite are calculated on the basis of the CEC. If x is the CEC in me. per 100 g. of a mixture of the montmorillonite and vermiculite present in the sample, and if the CEC of the feldspars in the sample is 10 me. per 100 g. (from table 50–3), then $(x)(67.3/100) + (10)(32.7/100) = 120$, from which $x = 173.5$ me. per 100 g. From this value for the CEC of the montmorillonite + vermiculite, together with the CEC of the species of montmorillonite and vermiculite present, the proportionate contents of the individual minerals may be calculated. Letting y equal the percentage of montmorillonite and $(100 - y)$

equal the percentage of vermiculite in the mixture of montmorillonite + vermiculite, $(y)(135/100) + (100 - y)(210/100) = 173.5$, from which $y = 48.7\%$ montmorillonite and $(100 - y) = 51.3\%$ vermiculite. Because the content of montmorillonite + vermiculite is 67.3% of the sample, the content of montmorillonite is $(48.7)(0.673) = 32.8\%$ of the sample; and the content of vermiculite is $(67.3 - 32.8) = 34.5\%$ of the sample.

The values calculated for montmorillonite and vermiculite in the preceding paragraph may be verified by calculating the glycol adsorption and comparing the calculated value with the observed value. From the percentage values for montmorillonite and vermiculite, together with glycol adsorption values from table 50–3, $(32.8)(0.3117) + (34.5)(0.2122) = 0.1753$ g. of glycol adsorbed per g. of clay. This value corresponds closely to the observed value 0.1755 g. The amount of glycol adsorbed by the feldspars is similar to that adsorbed by quartz and is negligible in comparison with the adsorption by montmorillonite and vermiculite.

50–6.3.5 EXAMPLE 5

The following information is available for a naturally occurring clay sample for which the mineralogical composition is to be calculated: (1) The exchangeable bases per 100 g. of clay are 119.7 me. of Na^+ and 15.1 me. of Mg^{2+}. (2) The total K_2O content is 3.65% or 87.5 me. per 100 g. (3) X-ray analysis indicates that the only minerals present are vermiculite and biotite, and that they are completely randomly interstratified. (4) The X-ray $d(001)$ spacing of an air-dry sample is 11.97Å. (5) The X-ray $d(001)$ spacing of air-dry Na-vermiculite is 12.56Å., of Mg-vermiculite 14.33Å., and of K-vermiculite (biotite) 10.27Å. (Barshad, 1948). From this information, calculation of the mineralogical composition may proceed in different ways, as indicated in the following paragraphs.

The biotite content may be calculated either by dividing the K_2O content of 3.65% by 9.45, the nonexchangeable K_2O of phlogopite (table 50–4), and multiplying by 100 to obtain 38.6%; or by calculating the K^+ content (in me.) as a percentage of the sum of K^+ plus the exchangeable Na^+ and Mg^{2+} ions to obtain $(87.5)(100)/(119.7 + 15.1 + 87.5) = 39.5\%$. The vermiculite content is obtained by difference, that is, $100 - 38.6 = 61.4\%$ or $100 - 39.5 = 60.5\%$.

As a check on the foregoing methods, one may compare the observed $d(001)$ spacing with a weighted mean spacing derived from the spacings of the Na-vermiculite, Mg-vermiculite, and K-vermiculite (biotite) indicated to be present by the X-ray and chemical analyses. From the chemical analyses, the sum of the exchangeable and nonexchangeable bases is composed of 53.8% Na^+, 6.7% Mg^{2+}, and 39.5% K^+, where the bases are expressed in terms of chemical equivalents. The weighted mean of the $d(001)$ spacings of the three components is then $(0.538 \times 12.56) + (0.067 \times 14.33) + (0.395 \times 10.27) = 11.77$Å. This calculated spacing compares favorably with the observed value of 11.97Å.

50-7 LITERATURE CITED

Barshad, I. 1948. Vermiculite and its relation to biotite as revealed by base exchange reactions, X-ray analyses, differential thermal curves, and water content. Am. Mineralogist. 33:655–678.

Barshad, I. 1950. The effect of the interlayer cations on the expansion of the mica type of crystal lattice. Am. Mineralogist. 35:225–238.

Barshad, I. 1951. Cation exchange in soils: I. Ammonium fixation and its relation to potassium fixation and to determination of ammonium exchange capacity. Soil Sci. 72:361–371.

Barshad, I. 1952. Temperature and heat of reaction calibration of the differential thermal analysis apparatus. Am. Mineralogist. 37:667–694.

Barshad, I. 1955. Adsorptive and swelling properties of clay-water system. Proc. Natl. Conf. Clays Clay Technol. 1:70–77.

Barshad, I. 1960a. X-ray analysis of soil colloids by a modified salted paste method. In Clays Clay Minerals. Proc. Natl. Conf. Clays Clay Minerals. 5(1958):350–364.

Barshad, I. 1960b. Thermodynamics of water adsorption and desorption on montmorillonite. In Clays Clay Minerals, Proc. Natl. Conf. Clays Clay Minerals. (1959) 8:84–101.

Barshad, I., Haleoy, E., Gold, H. A., and Hagin, J. 1956. Clay minerals in some limestone soils from Israel. Soil Sci. 81:423–437.

Chevenard, P., Waché, X., and de La Tullaye, R. 1944. Étude de la corrosion sèche des métaux au moyen d'une thermobalance. Bull. Soc. Chim. France, Ser. 5, 11:41–47.

De Bruijn, C. M. A., and Van Der Marel, H. W. 1954. Mineralogical analysis of soil clays. Geologie en Mijnbouw, Nw. Ser. 16: 69–83.

De Keyser, W. L. 1953. Differential thermobalance: a new research tool. Nature 172:304–365.

Erdley, L., Paulik, F., and Paulik, J. 1954. Differential thermogravimetry. Nature 174:885–886.

Hendricks, S. B., and Alexander, L. T. 1939. Minerals present in soil colloids: I. Description and methods for identification. Soil Sci. 48:257–271.

Henry, E. C. 1955. Clay technology in ceramics. Proc. Natl. Conf. Clays Clay Technol. 1:257–266.

Jackson, M. L. 1956. Soil chemical analysis—advanced course. Published by the author, Dept. of Soils, University of Wisconsin, Madison 6, Wis.

Kissinger, H. E. 1956. Variation of peak temperature with heating rate in differential thermal analysis. J. Res. Natl. Bur. Standards. 57:217–221.

Le Chatelier, H. 1887. De l'action de la chaleur sur les argiles. Soc. Franc. Mineral. Bull. 10:204–211.

MacEwan, D. M. C., Amil, A. Ruiz, and Brown, G. 1961. Interstratified clay minerals. In G. Brown, ed. The X-Ray Identification and Crystal Structure of Clay Minerals. Mineralogical Society (Clay Minerals Group), London. pp. 393–445.

Mackenzie, R. C. 1957. The Differential Thermal Investigation of Clays. Mineral. Soc. (Clay Minerals Group), London.

Mackenzie, R. C., and Farquharson, K. R. 1952. Standardization of differential thermal analysis technique. C.R. XIX Session Cong. Geol. Intern. (Algiers) 18:183–200.

Martin, R. T. 1955. Reference chlorite characterization for chlorite identification in soil clays. In Clays Clay Minerals, Proc. Natl. Conf. Clays Clay Minerals 3:117–145.

Martin, R. T. 1962. Adsorbed water on clay: a review. In Clays Clay Minerals, Proc. Natl. Conf. Clays Clay Minerals. (1960) 9:28–70.

Mauer, F. A. 1954. An analytical balance for recording rapid changes in weight. Rev. Sci. Inst. 25:598–602.

Merveilli, J., and Boureille, A. 1950. Identifications des argiles ceramique par la thermobalance. Bull. Soc. Franc. Ceram. 7:18–27.

Mielenz, R. C., Schieltz, N. C., and King, M. E. 1953. Thermogravimetric analysis of clay and clay-like minerals. *In* Clays Clay Minerals, Proc. Natl. Conf. Clays Clay Minerals 2:285–314.

Mielenz, R. C., Schieltz, N. C., and King, M. E. 1955. Effect of exchangeable cations on X-ray diffraction patterns and thermal behavior of a montmorillonite clay. *In* Clays Clay Minerals Proc., Natl. Conf. Clays Clay Technol. 3:146–173.

Norton, F. H. 1939. Critical study of the differential thermal method for identification of clay minerals. Am. Ceramic Soc. J. 22:54–63.

Orcel, J. 1927. Recherches sur la composition chimique des chlorites. Bull. Soc. Franc. Mineral. 50:75–456.

Rowland, R. A., and Lewis, D. R. 1951. Furnace atmosphere control in differential thermal analysis. Am. Mineralogist 36:80–91.

Stone, R. L. 1952. Apparatus for differential thermal analysis under controlled partial pressures of H_2O, CO_2, or other gases. Am. Ceramic Soc. J. 35:76–82.

Stone, R. L. 1954. Preliminary study of the effects of water vapor pressure on thermograms of kaolinitic soils. *In* Clays Clay Minerals, Proc. Natl. Conf. on Clays Clay Minerals 2:315–323.

Van Der Marel, H. W. 1956. Quantitative differential thermal analysis of clay and other minerals. Am. Mineralogist. 41:222–244.

Van Der Marel, H. W. 1960. Quantitative analysis of kaolinite. Revue Silicates Industriels No. 1 and No. 2:1–19.

Whitehead, W. L., and Breger, I. A. 1950. Vacuum differential thermal analysis. Sci. (new ser.) 111:279–281.

51

Infrared Spectrometry

J. L. MORTENSEN

Ohio State University
Columbus, Ohio

D. M. ANDERSON

U. S. Army Cold Regions Research & Engineering Lab.
Hanover, New Hampshire

J. L. WHITE

Purdue University
Lafayette, Indiana

51–1 GENERAL INTRODUCTION

Infrared spectrometry has been applied to the analysis of inorganic and organic compounds for over 50 years. Development of the commercial infrared spectrometer gave great impetus to the application of this technique to the study of less complex inorganic and organic systems. Application of infrared spectrometry to the study of the inorganic and organic components of soils is of recent origin (Hunt et al., 1950; Kasatochkin and Zil'berbrand, 1956; Fieldes et al., 1956; Durie and Murray, 1957). Since infrared techniques have not been used extensively in the study of soils, the purpose of this section is to emphasize potential uses.

There is much ambiguity in the interpretation of infrared spectra of organic matter preparations. Considerably more investigation will be required before structural correlations can be made with precision. The method can be of particular use to the organic matter chemist, however, in proving the identity of two compounds, in the determination of functional groups in organic matter preparations, in the study of reaction mechanisms, and in quantitative analysis. Infrared spectrometry is of greatest service as a supplement to other methods of inquiry.

Absorption in the infrared region can provide considerable information about the structure of small molecules, but caution is required when the method is applied to the mixture of heterogeneous polymers found in soil organic matter. Without preliminary separation and purification into homogeneous, ash-free fractions, and without preliminary qualitative analysis, the assignment of functional groups to particular structures is impossible. The presence of functional groups in organic matter preparations of any

743

degree of purity, however, can be ascertained by infrared spectrometry. In some instances, intensity of absorption can be used in quantitative analysis.

Durie and Murray (1957), Farmer and Morrison (1960), Johnson (1959), Kasatochkin et al. (1958), Kumada and Aizawa (1958), Schnitzer et al. (1959), and Schwendinger,[1] among others, have reported studies on soil organic matter using infrared spectrometry. General references can be found in Bauman and Clark (1957), Bellamy (1958), Conn and Avery (1960), Jones and Sandorfy (1956), Randall et al. (1949), Clark et al. (1960) and Cross (1960).

Extensive application of infrared techniques to identification and characterization of the more complex inorganic compounds in soil awaits clarification of the complex relationships between structure or composition and the infrared spectra of these minerals. A number of workers (Miller and Wilkins, 1952; Miller et al., 1960; Keller and Pickett, 1949, 1950; Hunt et al., 1950; Adler et al., 1950; Nahin, 1955; Launer, 1952; Rudnitskaya, 1956; Kakitani, 1956; Setkina and Gopshtein, 1957; Setkina, 1957, 1959; and Lehmann and Dutz, 1960) have surveyed the infrared spectra of many inorganic compounds and minerals, including the principal natural clay minerals. Recent advances in interpretation of the infrared spectra of minerals have been made by Beutelspacher (1956), Farmer (1956), Serratosa and Bradley (1958), Van Der Marel and Zwiers (1959), Kolesova (1959), Tuddenham and Lyon (1959, 1960), and Stubican and Roy (1961a, 1961b). Fripiat (1960) has recently discussed the application of infrared spectroscopy to the study of clay minerals.

Infrared spectrometry is most useful in mineralogical studies when used in conjunction with X-ray diffraction and other similar techniques. The method can be used in identifying inorganic compounds and minerals which have well-defined absorption bands, in determining whether a layer silicate is di- or trioctahedral in composition, in the study of isomorphous substitutions, in investigations of the hydration of minerals, and in quantitative analysis. Infrared techniques provide information about the nature and identity of compounds that may be amorphous to X-rays.

Other applications of infrared spectrometry in soil research include measurement of composition of soil air [carbon dioxide, nitrogen oxides, methane (Pierson et al., 1956)] and studies of the interactions between soil colloids and both inorganic and organic compounds (fertilizers, soil conditioners, pesticides, etc.). Application of infrared techniques to the study of soils will be most profitably made in cooperation with infrared spectroscopists.

---

[1] Schwendinger, R. W. 1960. Extraction, separation and characterization of the high molecular weight organic materials in soil. Ph.D. Dissertation, The Ohio State University, Columbus, Ohio.

51-2 PRINCIPLES

51-2.1 Origin of Spectra

The infrared spectrum is a region in the general spectrum of electromagnetic radiation, which includes visible light, ultraviolet light, X-rays, and cosmic rays at wavelengths shorter than those in the infrared region, and microwaves and radiowaves at wavelengths longer than those in the infrared region. The terms used to describe a position in the infrared range of the electromagnetic spectrum are the wavelength (λ), in units of microns (μ) per wavelength, and a so-called frequency or wavenumber (ν), in units of waves per centimeter (written cm.$^{-1}$). A simple reciprocal relationship exists between wavenumber and wavelength, namely,

$$\nu(\text{cm.}^{-1}) = 1/\lambda(\text{cm.}) = 10^4/\lambda(\mu).$$

The so-called frequency unit ν (cm.$^{-1}$ or waves per cm.) is used rather than the more fundamental unit of true frequency $\bar{\nu}$ (cycles or waves per second) as a matter of convenience. True frequency $(\bar{\nu})$ is related to so-called frequency or wavenumber (ν) in the following manner, $\bar{\nu}$ (sec.$^{-1}$) = $c\nu$ where c is the velocity of light (3×10^{10} cm. per sec.). The region of primary interest in the infrared range is between wavelengths of 2.5 and 50μ (wavenumbers of 4,000 and 200 cm.$^{-1}$).

Atoms and molecules oscillate about their equilibrium positions with frequencies of 10^{13} to 10^{14} cycles per second. Infrared radiation has frequencies in this range and promotes transitions in a molecule between rotational and vibrational energy levels of the ground (lowest) electronic energy state.

Bond vibration modes in simple molecules are of two types, stretching and bending (deformation), the former constituting the periodic stretchings of the bond A-B along the bond axis. Bending vibrations of the bond A-B are displacements occurring at right angles to the bond axis. These vibrations produce periodic displacements of atoms with respect to one another, causing a simultaneous change in interatomic distance. When accompanied by a change in dipole moment, vibrations give rise to absorption of radiation in the infrared region. Vibrations in symmetrical molecules that are characteristic but are not associated with a change in dipole moment do not absorb in the infrared. In more complex molecules, vibrations may be mixtures of stretching and bending motions.

A nonlinear molecule containing N atoms possesses $3N - 6$ fundamental modes of vibration which could result in $3N - 6$ fundamental absorption bands in the infrared region. Additional overtone or combination bands arise as multiples or sums and differences of fundamental frequencies.

The frequency at which an atomic group vibrates is primarily dependent on (1) the relative masses of the bonded atoms, and (2) the bond elasticity or restoring force between atoms.

When molecules of a specific kind are irradiated with infrared radiation of successive frequencies or wavelengths, there will be radiation frequencies which correspond to the characteristic molecular frequencies in value. Energy is exchanged from the radiation to the molecule, which is caused to vibrate, and the radiation is absorbed. The scanning of a compound with successive infrared frequencies shows values for which the radiation is absorbed, and these values correspond to mechanical vibration frequencies of the molecule.

51–2.2   Infrared Spectrophotometers

The most commonly used infrared spectrophotometers are double-beam instruments. The use of a reference beam in addition to the sample beam eliminates errors due to variation in radiation source and to absorption by atmospheric water vapor and carbon dioxide, and it makes possible differential analysis. In such instruments, the source provides radiation over the whole infrared spectrum; this radiation passes through the sample cell. The monochromator located beyond the sample cell disperses this light and then selects a narrow frequency range, the energy of which is measured by a detector. The detector transforms the energy received into an electrical signal, which is then amplified and recorded in synchronization with the monochromator.

Infrared sources consist of a filament such as the Nernst glower, a bonded mixture of rare earth oxides in rod form, or the globar, a bonded silicon carbide rod, electrically heated to temperatures in the range, 1,100° to 1,800°C. Sample cells must be of nonabsorbing materials such as NaCl, LiF, CaF_2, KBr, AgCl, Irtran,[2] periclase, etc. Monochromators consist of combinations of prisms, gratings, and Littrow mirror systems. Spectra are usually obtained with NaCl prisms in the 2 to 15μ [5,000 to 660 cm.$^{-1}$] region. Resolution in the 3μ (3,330 cm.$^{-1}$) region can be improved by use of an LiF prism or grating. The use of CsBr or CsI prisms extends the spectral region to 50μ (200 cm.$^{-1}$). Detectors used to measure the radiant energy include thermocouples, bolometers, thermistors, and pneumatic detectors. The spectrum is normally recorded as a pen trace on a paper chart with wavenumber or wavelength plotted versus transmittance (percent) or absorbance. More complete details of instrumentation may be found in Conn and Avery (1960) and Cross (1960).

---

[2] Irtran-2 is an infrared-transmitting, water-insoluble, optical material manufactured by Eastman Kodak Co.

Table 51-1. Characteristic infrared group frequencies
found in organic matter preparations.

Wavelength	Wavenumber	Assignment
μ	cm.$^{-1}$	
2.90	3,400	⌐O-H stretch
3.03	3,300	∟N-H stretch
3.25	3,100	NH_3^+ stretch
3.42	2,940	C-H stretch
5.70- 5.80	1,750	COOH and ester C=O
5.90- 6.00	near 1,680	COO⁻ antisymmetric stretch
6.00- 6.20	1,650-1,620	C=O stretch (Amide I)
6.27	1,600	Aromatic C=C
6.50- 6.60	1,570-1,515	N-H deformation+ C=N stretch (Amide II)
6.45	1,550	COO⁻ symmetrical stretch
6.62	1,510	Aromatic C=C
6.85	1,460	$CC-H_3$
6.90- 7.00	near 1,435	⌐C-H bend
7.10	near 1,400	∟COO⁻ antisymmetric stretch
7.70	near 1,300	C=N stretch+ N-H deformation (Amide III)
7.89	1,267	Aromatic C-O Me
8.10	near 1,230	C-O, ester linkage
8.14	1,230	Phenolic C-OH
8.50-10.50	1,170-950	C-C, C-OH, C-O-C typical of glucoside linkages and polymeric substances
9.67	1,035	O-CH_3
11.90	840	Aromatic C-H

51-2.3 Organic Spectra

The absorption spectrum of most organic molecules is not as complicated as theory would predict. Simplification of the spectrum is due to the
fact that certain groups of atoms vibrate with the same frequency irrespective of the molecule to which they are attached. These absorption bands
can be used to characterize and identify functional groups in organic molecules. Comparison of many compounds having known structures with infrared absorption spectra has resulted in the assignment of absorption frequency bands to functional groups (see Colthup, 1950; Bellamy, 1958;
and Jones and Sandorfy, 1956). Practically all of the correlations are based
on frequency values, but more emphasis is now being placed on intensity
measurements. Correlations between frequency and functional groups on
soil organic matter preparations are incomplete. Table 51-1 summarizes
the major infrared group frequencies which have been reported for organic
matter preparations.

Insignificant coupling between vibrations of adjacent groups on large
molecules permits the treatment of individual groups as if they vibrated
independently of the rest of the chain (Elliot, 1959). Groups having strong
dipole moments, however, cause high intensity absorption and may obscure
absorption bands of the aliphatic or aromatic skeleton of the molecule,

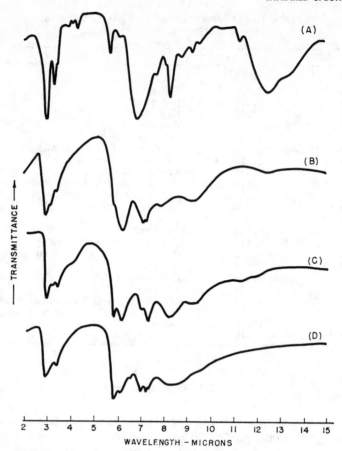

Fig. 51–1. Infrared spectra of organic matter preparations: (*A*) fluorescent fraction separated by continuous-flow paper electrophoresis from $Na_4P_2O_7$ extract of mineral soil, (*B*) humic fraction separated by continuous-flow paper electrophoresis and dialysis from $Na_4P_2O_7$ extract of mineral soil, (*C*) synthetic browning-reaction polymer (methyl glyoxal-glycine), and (*D*) humic acid precipitated from $Na_4P_2O_7$ extract of peat by HCl.

This fact must be taken into account when the spectra of polymeric organic matter preparations and model substances are compared. Figures 51–1 and 51–2 illustrate spectra which result from infrared spectrometry of organic matter preparations. They were obtained with a Perkin-Elmer Model 21 Spectrophotometer using a NaCl prism. The KBr pellet technique was used in sample preparation.

Absorption intensity of functional groups of oriented polymers increases when the bonds in the group are in a plane normal to the direction of the radiation. The orientation of the groups in this plane can be determined by use of polarized infrared radiation. Polarization is obtained either by re-

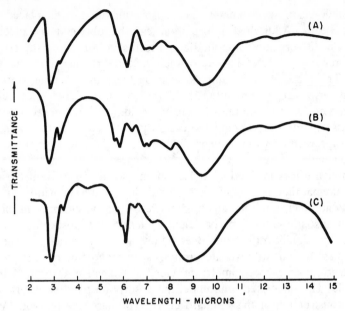

Fig. 51–2. Infrared spectra of soil polysaccharide: (*A*) copper salt of purified preparation, (*B*) preparation purified by desalting, deproteinization and dialysis, and (*C*) crude preparation before desalting.

flection at selenium mirrors or by transmission through plates of selenium or silver chloride inclined at the Brewsterian angle. Orientation of polymer films can be obtained by stroking them with a small brush.

Treatment with D_2O of compounds containing "active" hydrogen results in some replacement by deuterium of the hydrogen. The vibrational mass is thus increased, and this results in a lowering of the absorption frequency. This method is of particular use in the determination of changes in position, shape, or configuration of polymeric substances.

Perturbations in the intensity and frequency of absorption bands are of considerable use in the study of reaction mechanisms. Chelation of metals by organic compounds results in a reduction of intensity and lowering of frequency of absorption of the groups involved. The effect of complexing of copper by carboxyl and amide groups of a soil polysaccharide is illustrated in the spectra shown in Fig. 51–2.

Infrared absorption bands of both clay adsorbent and organic adsorbate may be perturbed by adsorption reactions. Functional groups involved in adsorption of organic matter on clay can thus be detected. Provided sufficient adsorption of the organic compound occurs, difference spectra are particularly revealing (Tensmeyer et al., 1960). The spectrum of the adsorbent-adsorbate surface can be obtained by placing an amount of adsorbent equal to that in the adsorption mixture in the reference beam of the double-beam spectrometer. The adsorption mixture is placed in the sample beam. Additional information can be obtained by placing an amount of the organic compound equal to that adsorbed by the adsorbent in the reference beam. The adsorption mixture is placed in the sample beam. Thickness of both samples must be the same. Sample preparation may be performed by a quantitative adaptation of the KBr pellet technique or by use of a film technique (Tensmeyer et al., 1960). Energy loss can be compensated for by scanning more slowly, by increasing the gain, or by placing a screen or variable beam attenuator in the reference beam of the spectrometer.

Although errors induced by reflection and scattering, solvent adsorption losses, nonparallel and nondispersed radiation, finite slit width, and non-linearity and inertia in the detecting and recording system prevent measurement of absolute extinction coefficients, intensities of absorption bands do not deviate significantly from Beer's Law in many instances. The usual techniques of quantitative absorption spectrophotometry can thus be applied to infrared spectrometry provided a distinctive absorption band is available. The integrated area under the absorption band is generally used in the construction of the standard curve. The base line method (Wright, 1941) can also be used to interpret infrared spectra quantitatively.

51–2.4 Inorganic Spectra

It is possible to calculate theoretically the vibration frequency of a solid; however, even for relatively simple inorganic phases, formidable mathematical difficulties are encountered. The alternative for minerals at present is to study a large number of phases in an empirical fashion and, on the basis of similarities and differences, to assign certain absorption bands to certain vibrations. Stubican and Roy (1961a) have combined the empirical approach with controlled synthesis of minerals with a high degree of success. The assignment of absorption frequency bands to functional groups common in soil minerals and selected inorganic compounds is summarized in Table 51–2.

Because of the range of wavelengths involved, particle size has a pronounced effect on the absorption spectra. For minerals of the sand and silt fractions, it is necessary to reduce the particle size by grinding to minimize this effect. The particle-size range of the clay fraction is ideal, and this fraction can be used as separated.

The percentage content of a mineral that can be detected qualitatively in a sample varies considerably, depending largely on the intensity of the diagnostic absorption bands of the mineral. Minerals having strong diagnostic bands, such as quartz and calcite, can be detected in as low as 1 to 2% concentrations. Minerals lacking strong diagnostic absorption bands,

Table 51–2. Characteristic infrared group absorption frequencies
found in minerals and other inorganic compounds.

Wavelength	Wavenumber	Assignment
μ	cm.$^{-1}$	
		O-H Vibrations
2. 70	3, 700	free O-H stretch
2. 72- 2. 76	3, 675-3, 620	O-H stretch
2. 95- 4. 00	3, 390-2, 500	bonded O-H stretch
6. 12	1, 634	H-O-H bending
10. 69-12. 20	935- 820	X^{3+}-O-H bending (dioctahedral)
		(possibly O-H libration)
		Si-O Vibrations
9. 70-12. 20	1, 031- 820	isolated SiO$_4$
9. 20-11. 60	1. 087- 862	single chain
9. 60-10. 50	1, 042- 952	double chain
9. 30-10. 40	1, 075- 961	layer
9. 60-10. 10	1, 042- 990	framework
9. 15- 9. 25	1, 093-1, 080	SiO$_2$
3. 00- 3. 30	3, 333-3, 030	NH$_4$$^+$ Vibrations
6. 73- 7. 19	1, 486-1, 391	NH$_4$$^+$ Vibrations
6. 90- 7. 09	1, 449-1, 410	CO$_3$$^{2-}$ Vibrations
11. 36-12. 50	880- 800	CO$_3$$^{2-}$ Vibrations
13. 70-14. 10	730- 709	CO$_3$$^{2-}$ Vibrations
7. 09- 7. 46	1, 410-1, 340	NO$_3$$^-$ Vibrations
11. 63-12. 50	860- 800	NO$_3$$^-$ Vibrations
8. 85- 9. 26	1, 130-1, 080	SO$_4$$^{2-}$ Vibrations
14. 71-16. 40	680- 610	SO$_4$$^{2-}$ Vibrations
9. 65-10. 00	1, 037-1, 000	PO$_4$$^{3-}$ Vibrations
9. 40- 9. 90	1, 064-1, 010	HPO$_4$$^{2-}$ Vibrations
10. 10-10. 70	990- 930	HPO$_4$$^{2-}$ Vibrations
11. 15-12. 05	900- 830	HPO$_4$$^{2-}$ Vibrations
9. 20- 9. 70	1, 090-1, 030	H$_2$PO$_4$$^-$ Vibrations
10. 50-11. 10	950- 900	H$_2$PO$_4$$^-$ Vibrations

such as many of the clay minerals, are difficult to detect in concentrations
<20%. The clay minerals illite, vermiculite, and montmorillonite are diffi-
cult to identify because the distinctive features of their spectra all overlap
in the wavelength region from 9 to 12μ (1,110 to 830 cm.$^{-1}$). The infrared spectrum of the 2 to 0.5μ fraction of the A horizon of a Crosby silt
loam is shown in Fig. 51–3. X-ray diffraction studies have shown that the
dominant mineral phase is a chlorite-like, 14Å. mineral and that small
amounts of kaolinite are present. The characteristic absorption bands for
quartz at 12.50μ (800 cm.$^{-1}$) and 12.80μ (780 cm.$^{-1}$) are readily apparent. The absorption band at 2.77μ (3,600 cm.$^{-1}$) is due to the stretching vibration of proton against oxygen in the free O–H groups of the octahedral layer of the clay minerals. The band at 2.90μ (3,450 cm.$^{-1}$) is
attributed to the stretching vibration in bonded O–H groups and appears to
be associated with the presence of water on clay surfaces; the intensity of
this band suggests water associated with internal surfaces of an expanded
2:1 layer silicate (Buswell et al. 1937). The band at 10.98μ (910 cm.$^{-1}$),

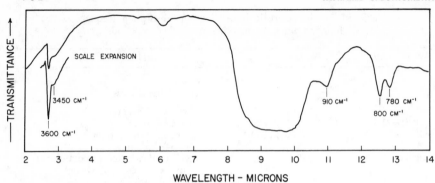

Fig. 51–3. Infrared spectrum of 2 to 0.5μ fraction of Crosby silt loam A horizon. Sample prepared as a film on Irtran-2 window; run on Perkin-Elmer Model 221 with NaCl optics.

assigned to the X^{3+} –O–H bending frequency[3] (Stubican and Roy, 1961a), is assumed to indicate dioctahedral composition for the 2:1 layer silicate but may be due, in part, to kaolinite. The sample was prepared as a film on Irtran-2, and the spectrum was obtained with a Perkin-Elmer Model 221 Spectrophotometer using a NaCl prism.

Serratosa and Bradley (1958) showed that it was possible to differentiate between dioctahedral and trioctahedral compositions in the layer silicates by examining the change in the intensity of the O–H bands in the 2.70 to 2.77μ (3,700 to 3,600 cm.$^{-1}$) range with a change in the angular relationship between a plane polarized infrared beam and the basal planes of the minerals. There is no apparent change in intensity or position of the O–H band at 2.77μ (3,600 cm.$^{-1}$) with a change in angle of incident radiation in the case of dioctahedral composition, whereas an absorption band appears or is further intensified at about 2.70μ (3,700 cm^{-1}) in the case of trioctahedral compositions. The work of Stubican and Roy (1961a) suggests that the presence of a band in the 10 to 12.5μ (1,000 to 800 cm.$^{-1}$) region (assigned to X^{3+} –O–H bending frequency) is indicative of dioctahedral composition, whereas the absence of a band in this region indicates trioctahedral composition.

Minerals which have sharp, well-defined absorption bands, such as quartz, kaolinite, orthoclase, calcite, and dolomite can be determined quantitatively. The quantitative aspects of infrared analysis of minerals have been discussed by Hunt and Turner (1953), Lyon et al. (1959), Lyon and Tuddenham (1959), Tuddenham and Lyon (1959, 1960) and Thompson and Wadsworth (1957). Reproducible grinding technique is a requirement for quantitative analysis.

[3] Dr. P. A. Giguére (personal communication) and W. Vedder (1964, Am. Mineralogist 49:741) have assigned this band to νOH libration.

51-3 SAMPLE PREPARATION

51-3.1 Gases

Infrared analysis of gaseous samples involves only the normal procedures encountered in gas analysis. A variety of sample cells for containing the gas sample while exposing it to infrared radiation is available from the manufacturers of infrared absorption apparatus. The cells usually consist of a thin, pyrex glass cylinder with a gas inlet near one end and an outlet near the other, gas flow being controlled by stopcocks. Usually the end windows through which the infrared radiation passes are made of NaCl, but they may be made of other substances which are mechanically suitable and sufficiently transparent to infrared radiation. Cell windows of many such substances are available commercially. Sample containers made of metals also are available, and special sample holders in which suitable windows may be mounted can be fabricated with relative ease for special purposes. Once the sample container is at hand, it is only necessary to empty it of air and to fill it with the sample. A vacuum line and provisions for control of the gas pressures involved is the only requirement other than the normal exercise of cleanliness and proper laboratory techniques. The observed spectra may be somewhat obscured by absorption bands due to water in the system unless precautions are taken to eliminate this contaminant.

51-3.2 Liquids

In most chemical studies, the majority of samples are analyzed as liquids. Usually, a solvent or diluent must be used in conjunction with the substance to be analyzed. The solvent or diluent must be chosen after considering the following requirements:

(*1*) In the case of a solvent, it must, of course, dissolve the substance to be analyzed. The solvent or diluent used must maintain the substance in the proper chemical form.

(*2*) The solvent or diluent must not injure the sample cell. Usually, there is a possibility of damaging the crystalline windows in the cell; adequate precautions must be taken to prevent such damage.

(*3*) The infrared absorption spectrum of the solvent or diluent must not interfere with that of the substance being investigated.

Since the desirable optical path length is much shorter for liquids than for gases, sample cells for liquids usually consist of two cell windows separated by a spacer. Narrow inlet and outlet ports are drilled through both the top metal and cell window plates for injection of solution into the sample cavity by means of a hypodermic needle and to permit the escape of trapped air bubbles. Plastic stoppers keep the liquid within the cell, and most of the sample can be recovered after the analysis has been completed. Sample preparation consists merely of obtaining the substance of interest in the solvent or diluent, filling the sample cell with the liquid and placing the cell with its contents in the path of the infrared beam.

51–3.3 Solids

51–3.3.1 INTRODUCTION

It is frequently impossible to obtain a substance, particularly most substances of interest to soil scientists, in either liquid or gaseous form, and it becomes necessary to analyze it as a solid. Even though this is the least desirable form for analysis by infrared absorption, several techniques which have proved satisfactory have been devised for the analysis.

Probably the most common method for solids is the mull technique in which the sample is mixed or ground in some weakly absorbing, nonvolatile liquid (Bradley and Potts, 1958). The resulting paste is then spread over the window of a demountable liquid cell, or in some similar manner is prepared for presentation to the infrared beam, and then analyzed. To reduce light scattering to a minimum, it has been shown desirable to use a liquid having an index of refraction near that of the solid being analyzed. Nujol and Fluorolube have been used successfully for soil and mineral samples. One must always be aware that when samples are prepared in this way, the absorption characteristics of the mulling medium must be known and allowed for in interpreting the resultant spectra. Nujol absorbs at 3.45, 6.89, and 7.28μ (2,900, 1,450, and 1,375 cm.$^{-1}$) which correspond to the CH absorption frequencies. Fluorolube absorbs at 8.75, 10.44 and 11.18μ (1,143, 957, and 895 cm.$^{-1}$). At the low thicknesses used in the mull technique, these mulling substances are otherwise transparent to infrared radiation.

Recently, several methods have been developed (Ford and Wilkinson, 1954; Dinsmore and Edmondson, 1959) for preparing pellets in which the sample is dispersed in a solid disc or plate which can then be placed directly in the infrared beam. In most cases, this kind of sample preparation is best for soils and other powdered materials. Finely powdered, spectroscopically pure potassium bromide (KBr) is usually the substance in which the sample is dispersed. Briefly, the procedure is to mix the sample with the KBr in a known weight proportion. The mixture is ground to the desired degree of fineness and then inserted into a special die and subjected to pressure and, in some cases, heat under vacuum. A nearly transparent disc is obtained for analysis in the infrared beam. The thickness of the disc can be easily measured.

Most manufacturers of infrared spectrophotometers supply dies and pellet sample holders suitable for use with their instruments. The specific directions which follow have been worked out for the analysis of soils using a Beckman ½-inch KBr die, but in all major details it will apply to other similar dies.

Several methods of presenting solids to the infrared beam as a thin film have been described (Fripiat et al., 1960; Tensmeyer et al., 1961). In cases for which it is desirable to make successive observations on a single sample after adsorption or desorption reactions (i.e., heat treatment to remove adsorbed water) the film technique is preferable to the mull or pressed pellet technique. Occasionally special circumstances may make it advisable to employ one of the following methods:

51–3.3.1.1 Film Prepared from a Liquid Suspension. Powders can be analyzed directly as a film on the window of a demountable cell if the powder can be suspended in a liquid carrier, applied to the window and the liquid carrier completely removed by evaporation. If the particle size is small enough (<2 or 3μ) to avoid high scattering losses, good results may be obtained by this means. The liquid carrier must be chosen with care so that neither the sample to be analyzed nor the cell window is damaged by its presence.

51–3.3.1.2 Film from Evaporating a Solution. In some cases, it may be desirable to analyze a solid obtained by evaporating a solution. Usually, in these cases some special reason prevents the use of techniques already described and a desirable method must be developed. Films may be evaporated onto mercury, oils, metals, glass or other substances, removed and analyzed directly in the infrared beam. Great care must be observed in handling the delicate films. Another disadvantage is the possibility of interference phenomena complicating the analysis. Instead of hanging the unsupported film in the infrared beam, it can be laid on a cell window. This procedure partially solves the problems associated with the fragility of the sample.

51–3.3.1.3 Thin Section. In some cases, particularly with plant materials, gels and gums, it is possible to cut a thin section by means of a microtome and then to analyze it by suspending it in the infrared beam.

51–3.3.1.4 Melt. Another successful but specialized technique is to melt the sample between two cell windows, press it to the desired thickness, allow the sample to solidify, and then analyze it in the infrared beam. Sample decomposition, oxidation, and other alteration are hazards in this method, and uniform thicknesses are hard to achieve. In addition, if oriented crystals develop when the sample freezes, interpretation of the results may be complicated by the appearance of polarization effects.

51–3.3.2 MULL METHOD

51–3.3.2.1 Materials.

1. Nujol, Fluorolube, or other mulling medium.
2. Carbon tetrachloride (CCl_4).

51–3.3.2.2 Procedure.
Grind 1 part of sample in 10 to 15 parts of the mulling agent with mortar and pestle. After the sample is ground in the mulling medium, smear the paste on the inside surface of one plate of a demountable cell with a small spatula. Cover it with the other plate, and assemble the cell. Adjust the sample thickness by controlling the pressure with which the plates of the cell are squeezed together. After the adsorption spectrum has been obtained, take the cell apart and clean it thoroughly with CCl_4. Store the alkali halide plates in a desiccated environment.

51–3.3.2.3 Comments.
Individual experimentation on the part of the investigator probably will be required to determine the ratio of sample to mulling medium which best suits the purpose at hand. Moreover, generally the finer the substance is ground the better the results will be, for light scattering is thus reduced, and the probability of scratching the cell windows is also reduced, but excessive grinding often alters the substance being ground and introduces impurities from the mortar and pestle. In practice, therefore, the investigator must determine for himself the extent of grinding which best suits his purpose. For routine surveys, grinding for 5 to 10 minutes usually is adequate. As mentioned above, the thickness of the mulled sample exposed to the infrared beam is controlled by adjusting the pressure on the two cell windows. With practice one can estimate the thickness sufficiently well for most purposes by viewing the visible light transmitted. Remember that the alkali halide crystals are attacked by moisture and, therefore, should be stored in desiccators and otherwise handled with care.

51–3.3.3 PELLET METHOD

51–3.3.3.1 Materials.

1. Potassium bromide (KBr), spectroscopic grade.
2. Acetone or carbon tetrachloride (CCl_4).
3. Die for making KBr pellets: The die consists of a ram and an anvil enclosed in such a way that when they are pressed together by means of a hydraulic press, the sample is compressed into a disc by the confining space. A partial vacuum may be created in this space if a vacuum pump is connected to a hose coupling which leads via carefully machined openings to the confined space. Evacuation removes entrapped air and moisture and results in a better pellet. Heat, though seldom necessary, is conducted to the sample by the metal die, which may be heated to an appropriate temperature by any of several means.

4. Laboratory press for a stroke of at least 10 cm. and capable of creating pressure on the confined sample of about 100,000 pounds per square inch. For a ½-inch ram, this is equivalent to about 20,000 pounds total force on the ram of the pellet-pressing die.

5. A small hand mortar and pestle or a Wig-L-Bug electric mortar and pestle (made by Crescent Dental Mfg. Co., 1839–45 South Pulaski Road, Chicago 23, Ill.).

6. Mechanical vacuum pump.

51–3.3.3.2 Procedure. Mix the substance to be analyzed with spectroscopic-grade KBr in a known weight proportion, usually about 1 part of soil sample to 400 parts of KBr. Grind this mixture at least 20 and preferably 30 minutes with a clean mortar and pestle to reduce the size of particles and thoroughly disperse the sample in the KBr. Grinding is more rapidly and conveniently done by means of a Wig-L-Bug, electric, stainless steel, mortar and pestle. The optimum time of grinding with the Wig-L-Bug is 10 to 20 seconds for most soil samples.

Scrupulously clean all parts of the die with acetone or CCl_4, particularly the anvil and ram, to remove impurities which otherwise would be pressed into the pellet. Assemble the die, connect the vacuum hose, and insert into the die a weighed amount, usually about 400 mg., of the sample-KBr mixture. Place the assembly in the hydraulic press, but do not apply pressure. Turn on the vacuum pump, and check the seals to make sure a partial vacuum is created in the sample, and then apply pressure on the ram until the pressure gauge just begins to indicate a positive pressure.

Continue pumping on the vacuum for 5 to 15 minutes for best results. In any case, pump not less than 1 or 2 minutes. Raise the hydraulic pressure to apply about 20,000 pounds of total force on a ram ½ inch in diameter and maintain it for 5 to 10 minutes. Release the vacuum while hydraulic pressure is still applied, and then gradually release the hydraulic pressure.

Disassemble the die, and remove the pellet with tweezers. Do not handle the pellet with bare fingers because body moisture will cloud the pellet, and impurities may be transferred from the hands to the pellet. Place the pellet in a suitable sample holder, and introduce it in the infrared beam for analysis, or place the pellet in a desiccator over $Mg(ClO_4)_2$ if it is necessary to store it. The die, KBr, and other materials can be conveniently stored in a 50°C. oven, which helps to keep them moisture free. Finally, clean the die assembly immediately with water and acetone or CCl_4 to remove corrosive KBr.

51–3.3.3.3 Comments. For many qualitative analyses or for rough survey scans, the ratio of sample to KBr need not be known with the accuracy required for more exacting studies. Care should be taken to keep the sample and KBr as dry as possible.

51–4 FUNCTIONAL-GROUP AND QUALITATIVE ANALYSIS
OF ORGANIC COMPOUNDS

51–4.1 Materials

See section 51–3.3.3.1.

51–4.2 Procedure

Desalt the organic matter extract by use of ion-exchange resins, dialysis, electrodialysis, or pressure filtration, as appropriate. Fractionate the product by precipitation techniques, electrophoresis, chromatography, ultracentrifugation, etc., as desired. Desalt the product, lyophilize it, and dry it in a vacuum desiccator over $Mg(ClO_4)_2$ for 12 hours.

Prepare a pellet of the sample with KBr as described in section 51–3.3.3.2, using 1.5 mg. of sample and 300 mg. of KBr. Prepare other pellets containing a higher or lower proportion of sample as needed if the initial pellet does not yield absorption bands of the desired intensity.

Place the pellet in the spectrophotometer and record the spectrum, operating the instrument in accordance with instructions of the manufacturer. For qualitative analysis, choose a slit program which will allow maximum resolution. If absorption bands are more intense than 100% absorption, use a pellet containing less sample.

51–4.3 Interpretation of Spectra

Considerable experience is required to understand infrared spectra and to interpret them correctly. Spectra of most organic matter preparations are generally relatively simple, however, and the correlations listed in Table 51–1 can be used to determine the presence of functional groups. There is much ambiguity in some regions of the spectrum of organic matter preparations, and considerably more investigation will be required before all correlations can be considered accurate. Infrared spectra become more complex and characteristic of pure compounds when the components of organic matter preparations are fractionated, separated, and purified.

The following procedure will be of general use in the interpretation of spectra.

Keep in mind and apply all available information about the unknown such as chemical elements known to be present or absent, physico-chemical properties, purity, and possible components.

Divide the spectrum into the characteristic-functional-group region, 2.00

to 7.41μ (5,000 to 1,350 cm.$^{-1}$), and the fingerprint region, 7.41 to 15.40μ (1,350 to 650 cm.$^{-1}$). Consider first the 2.00 to 7.41μ (5,000 to 1,350 cm.$^{-1}$) region; examine the strongest absorptions first and then the medium ones. Refer to Table 51–1 and Fig. 51–4 for information on major groups. If a band lines up for a functional group, determine whether all absorptions of the group are present.

Determine the presence and type, or absence, of C–H vibrations which occur between 3.12 and 3.57μ (3,200 and 2,800 cm.$^{-1}$). If the absorption band is above 3.33μ (3,000 cm.$^{-1}$), the C atom is unsaturated; if the absorption band is below 3.33μ (3,000 cm.$^{-1}$), the C atom is saturated. If absorption bands lie both above and below 3.33μ (3,000 cm.$^{-1}$), both unsaturated and saturated C atoms are present. A band at about 7.27μ (1,375 cm.$^{-1}$) indicates C–CH$_3$. Use Fig. 51–4 (Colthup, 1950) to determine whether ethyl, n-propyl, isopropyl or t-butyl groups are present.

Determine, if possible, the type of compound(s) present by referring to Bellamy (1958) and Jones and Sandorfy (1956). Medium-strength 6.66 and 6.25μ (1,500 and 1,600 cm.$^{-1}$) bands indicate the presence of aromatics. A medium-strength band at 6.06 to 6.21μ (1,650 to 1,610 cm.$^{-1}$) indicates the presence of olefin (in the absence of this band olefin may still be present). If CH$_2$ is present but CH$_3$–C is not, investigate the possibility of alicyclics. If CH$_2$ and CH$_3$ are present and if aromatics, olefins, and acetylenics are not, suspect the presence of aliphatic compound(s). After determining the compound type, follow through to learn the type of olefin, number and position of aromatic substituents, etc. If assignments of bands to organic compounds give little information, consider the possibility of inorganics (see Hunt et al., 1950, and Miller and Wilkins, 1952). Classify the compound as closely as possible, e.g., class of ester, type of amide, class of amine.

Concentrate next on the 7.41 to 15.40μ (1,350 to 650 cm.$^{-1}$) region, proceeding from strong bands to medium bands. When interpretation reaches the stage of suggesting the presence of one or more particular compounds, compare the spectrum of the test preparation with the spectra of samples of the suspected compounds (see Jones and Sandorfy, 1956, pp. 327–330). Spectra of known compounds can be found in the literature or in commercial spectra catalogs (Sadtler Research Laboratories, 2100 Arch Street, Philadelphia 3, Pa.).

Some general considerations that may be helpful in interpretation of spectra are the following: (1) As evidence for the occurrence or nonoccurrence of a functional group, the presence of an absorption band in the proper location is not as convincing as is the absence of an absorption band from the proper location. (2) All the bands in a spectrum cannot be interpreted. (3) Polymers in general have fewer, broader, and often less intense bands than the monomers from which they are derived. (4) Some unknowns cannot be identified.

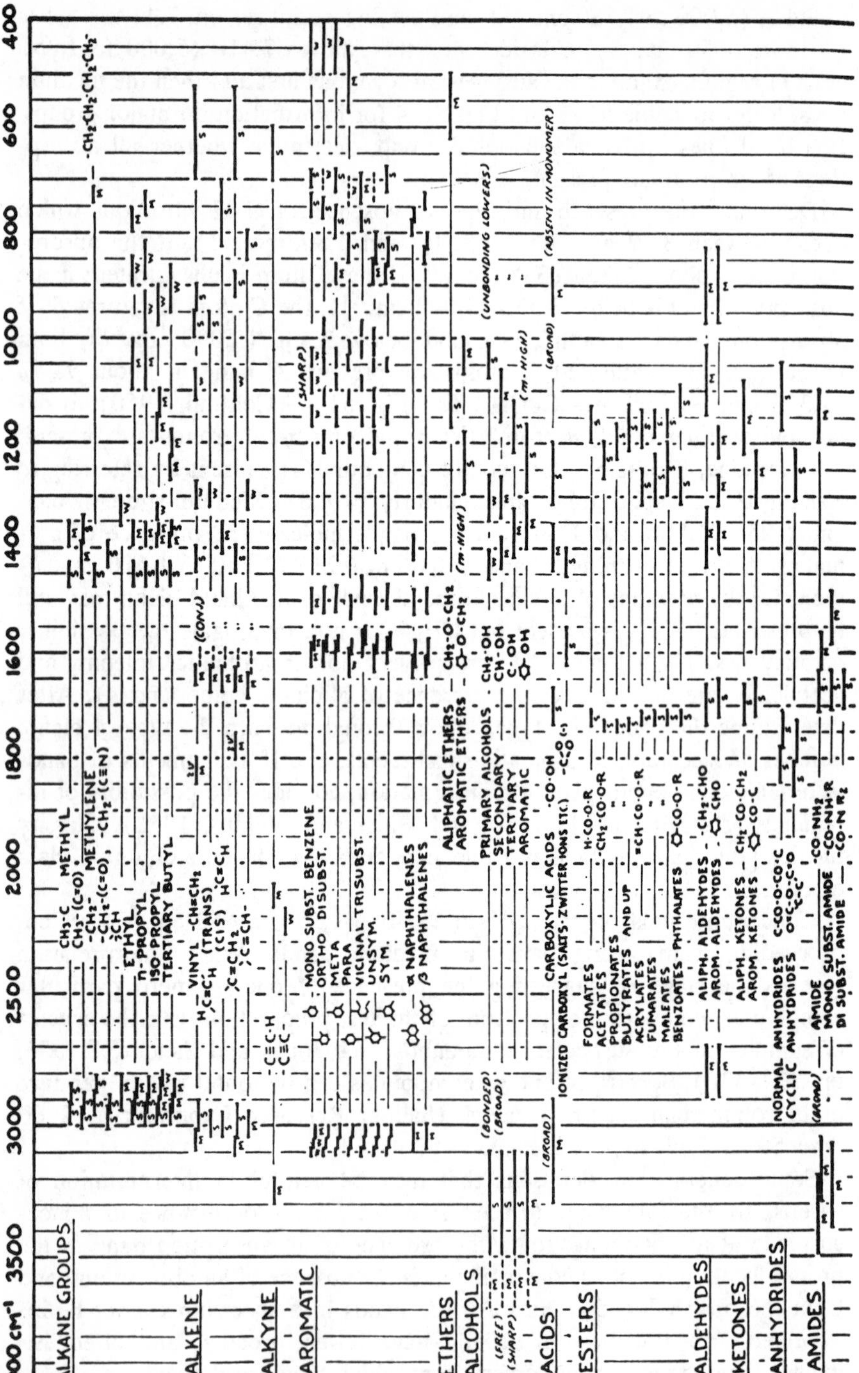
4000 cm⁻¹
3500
3000
2500
2000
1800
1600
1400
1200
1000
800
600
400
ALKANE GROUPS
METHYL
METHYLENE
ETHYL
n-PROPYL
ISO-PROPYL
TERTIARY BUTYL
ALKENE
VINYL
(TRANS)
(CIS)
ALKYNE
AROMATIC
MONO SUBST. BENZENE
ORTHO DISUBST.
META
PARA
VICINAL TRISUBST.
UNSYM.
SYM.
α NAPHTHALENES
β NAPHTHALENES
ETHERS
ALIPHATIC ETHERS
AROMATIC ETHERS
ALCOHOLS
PRIMARY ALCOHOLS
SECONDARY
TERTIARY
AROMATIC
ACIDS
CARBOXYLIC ACIDS
IONIZED CARBOXYL (SALTS·ZWITTER IONS ETC.)
ESTERS
FORMATES
ACETATES
PROPIONATES
BUTYRATES AND UP
ACRYLATES
FUMARATES
MALEATES
BENZOATES · PHTHALATES
ALDEHYDES
ALIPH. ALDEHYDES
AROM. ALDEHYDES
KETONES
ALIPH. KETONES
AROM. KETONES
ANHYDRIDES
NORMAL ANHYDRIDES
CYCLIC ANHYDRIDES
AMIDES
AMIDE
MONO SUBST. AMIDE
DI SUBST. AMIDE
(FREE)
(SHARP)
(BONDED)
(BROAD)
(SHARP)
(CONJ.)
(M·HIGH)
(UNBONDING LOWERS)
(ABSENT IN MONOMER)

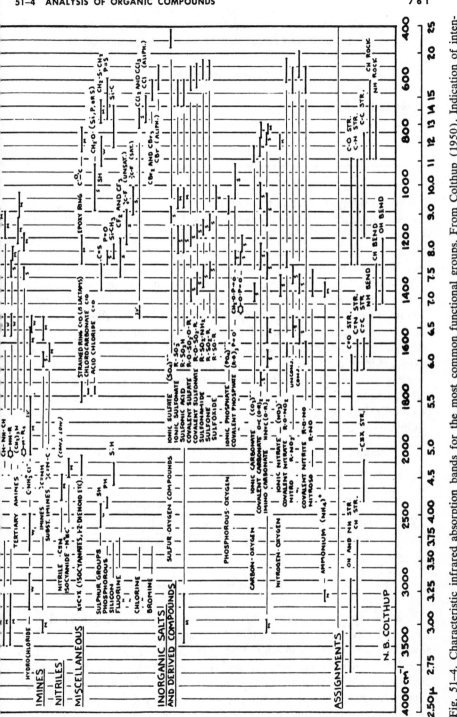

Fig. 51–4. Characteristic infrared absorption bands for the most common functional groups. From Colthup (1950). Indication of intensity: S = strong, M = medium, and W = weak. (Reprinted with permission of the Optical Society of America.)

51-5   DIFFERENCE SPECTRA OF ADSORPTION MIXTURES

51-5.1   Materials

1. See section 51-3.3.3.1.
2. Micrometer.

51-5.2   Procedure

Weigh 5.0 mg. of dried adsorption mixture of clay and organic adsorbate (or other quantity as needed for other adsorbents), and place it in a small mortar. Add 3.0000 g. of spectroscopic-grade KBr, grind the two substances together for 5 minutes, and dry the mixture overnight in vacuo over $Mg(ClO_4)_2$. Weigh 300.0 mg. of the mixture, and prepare a pellet as described in section 51-3.3.3.2. Repeat the process for preparation of a pellet containing an amount of adsorbent equal to that in the adsorption mixture. In the same manner, prepare a pellet of the adsorbate. Check the comparative thickness of the pellets by weighing them and measuring them with a micrometer. Prepare additional pellets, if necessary, until the thicknesses are identical.

Select a slit program to provide quantitative information, and compensate for energy losses, if necessary, by placing a screen in the reference beam or by increasing the gain.

Obtain spectra using the following sample arrangements:

Sample Beam	Reference Beam
Adsorption mixture	Adsorbate
Adsorption mixture	Adsorbent
Adsorption mixture	KBr
Adsorbent	KBr
Adsorbate	KBr

51-5.3   Interpretation of Spectra

Examine spectra for differences in intensity and wavelength of absorption bands. A shift in the stretching frequency of the carbonyl band of adsorbed carboxylic compounds from near 5.80μ (near 1,725 cm.$^{-1}$) to near 5.85μ (near 1,710 cm.$^{-1}$) would suggest hydrogen bonding (Kohl and Taylor, 1961) or complexing of metals by the carboxyl group (Sawyer, 1960). In difference spectra with the adsorbent in the reference beam, the presence of inverse bands (absorption bands going in the reverse direction) indicates groups on the adsorbent which are involved in adsorption (see Eyring and Wadsworth, 1956).

51-6 QUALITATIVE ANALYSIS AND STUDIES OF ISOMORPHOUS SUBSTITUTION IN CLAY MINERALS

51-6.1 Materials

See sections 51–3.3.2.1 and 51–3.3.3.1.

51-6.2 Procedure

Oxidize any organic matter in the sample with H_2O_2, and fractionate the sample to a particle size $<2\mu$ by sedimentation or centrifugation (see sections 43–3, 43–4, and 44–3). Remove the dispersing agent and any calcium oxalate that may be introduced by the reaction of H_2O_2 with organic matter (Hunt et al. 1950, p. 1491, Fig. 11, loess sample) by thoroughly washing the sample first with $0.001N$ HCl and then with water, using dialysis or pressure-filtration procedures. Dry the sample in an oven at 105° to 110°C. for 24 hours, and place it in a desiccator over $Mg(ClO_4)_2$ prior to use.

Prepare a KBr pellet (see section 51–3.3.3.2) or Nujol or Fluorolube mull (see section 51–3.3.2.2).

51-6.3 Interpretation of Spectra

Note the major absorption bands; and, by reference to Table 51–2 and Fig. 51–4, ascertain the nature of the silicates (isolated tetrahedra, single chain, etc.) and check for the presence of carbonates, sulfates, etc. The use of a template (Hunt et al., 1950), such as that illustrated in Fig. 51–5 for the 9 to 12μ (1,110 to 833 cm.$^{-1}$) region, may be helpful in recognizing layer silicates. Templates for other silicate groups may also be useful.

After making a preliminary examination of the spectrum, consult appropriate collections of mineral and inorganic infrared spectra (see section 51–1 for literature sources) for comparison of detailed features.

The effect of isomorphous substitution is usually manifested by displacement of absorption bands. In the spectra of carbonates, for example, the position of the strong band at about 11μ is displaced to successively longer wavelengths (lower frequencies) for the series Mg, Ca, Fe, Sr, Bi, which is a series of increasing atomic weight (Hunt et al., 1950). In a similar manner for the layer silicates, the absorption frequency for the O–H

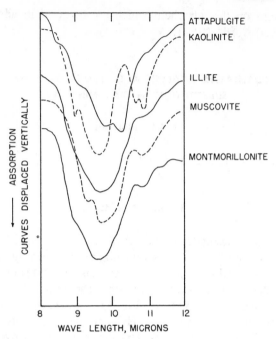

Fig. 51–5. Mineral identification template for selected clay minerals (after Hunt and Turner, 1953).

group in beidellite shifts from 10.69μ (935 cm.$^{-1}$) to 12.09μ (827 cm.$^{-1}$) in nontronite when octahedral Al^{3+} is replaced by Fe^{3+} (Stubican and Roy, 1961a). Stubican and Roy (1961a) have shown that as the amount of Mg in octahedral sites increases in the muscovite-phengite series, the band in the 18.2 to 19.2μ (550 to 520 cm.$^{-1}$) region moves toward longer wavelengths (lower frequencies).

The substitution of Al^{3+} for Si^{4+} in tetrahedral sites of both dioctahedral and trioctahedral layer silicates results in the displacement of the main Si–O stretching bands in the 9 to 11μ (1,100 to 900 cm.$^{-1}$) region toward longer wavelengths (lower frequencies). In trioctahedral structures, this substitution also strongly influences the Si–O band at 14.9μ (668 cm.$^{-1}$), which moves toward longer wavelengths (lower frequencies) with a decrease in intensity (Stubican and Roy, 1961a, 1961b).

Figure 51–6, from Stubican and Roy (1961b), shows the positions and assignments of the absorption bands with the layer structure silicates containing Al^{3+}, Fe^{3+} (dioctahedral structures), and Mg^{2+} or Fe^{2+} (trioctahedral structures) as the basic ions in the octahedral sites.

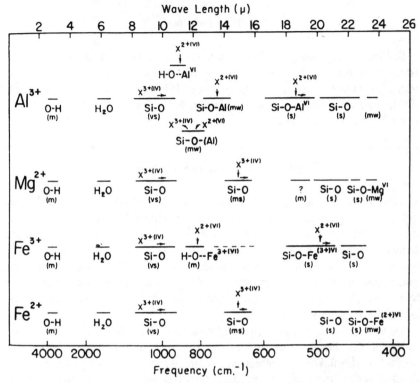

Fig. 51–6. Schematic summary of the assignments of the infrared absorption bands in layer-lattice silicates containing basically Al^{3+}, Mg^{2+}, Fe^{3+}, or Fe^{2+} in the octahedral sites. Relative intensities of the bands are described as vs = very strong, s = strong, m = medium, and w = weak. (X^{3+} and X^{2+} above the absorption bands refer to the trivalent or divalent cation, and the Roman numerals indicate the coordination sites where the substitution takes place. The perpendicular arrows indicate intensity decrease or increase, and the parallel arrows indicate the change of frequency in the indicated direction. The arrows point to (perpendicular) or start from (parallel) the frequency where a band shows maximum absorption in a specimen with no appreciable substitution. From Stubican and Roy (1961b).

51–7 DETERMINATION OF DI- AND TRIOCTAHEDRAL COMPOSITIONS, AND HYDRATION STUDIES

51–7.1 Materials

Barium fluoride (BaF_2), silver chloride (AgCl), Irtran-2[4] or other appropriate window material.

---

[4] Infrared cell windows of this material may be obtained from the Eastman Kodak Co., Special Products Sales, Rochester 4, New York.

51–7.2 Procedure

Sediment clay samples from aqueous suspension onto BaF_2, AgCl, Irtran-2 or other appropriate window material to form a highly oriented thin film having a concentration of about 0.5 mg. per cm.^{2} Progressively tilt the oriented film in the infrared beam, recording the spectra at 0°, 30°, and 60° angles of incidence.

51–7.3 Interpretation of Spectra

The presence of an absorption band at 2.76μ (3,620 cm.$^{-1}$) which does not change in intensity on tilting of the specimen in the beam indicates dioctahedral composition in both 2:1 and 1:1 layer-lattice silicates. These bands are due to OH bonds inclined about 20° to the plane of the flakes and are directed toward the unoccupied octahedra. Dioctahedral composition is also indicated by the presence of an absorption frequency at 10.69 to 12.09μ (935 to 827 cm.$^{-1}$). These bands are usually absent in trioctahedral compositions.

Development of a high-frequency shoulder at 2.70μ (3,700 cm.$^{-1}$) on tilting of the specimen is due to the presence of OH bonds which are normal to the flakes and which are relatively free of association, i.e., the O–O distances involved in hydrogen bonding are large. The development of the 2.70μ (3,700 cm.$^{-1}$) band is characteristic of trioctahedral composition in 2:1 layer silicates. However, kaolinite, a 1:1 mineral, also exhibits an OH frequency at 2.71μ (3,695 cm.$^{-1}$) which varies in intensity with orientation. This band appears to be due primarily to interlayer OH groups involved in the formation of hydrogen bonds between the hydroxyl surface and the oxygens of the adjacent tetrahedral layer.

Since kaolinite exhibits OH stretching and bending or librational frequencies at 2.76μ (3,620 cm.$^{-1}$) and 10.99μ (910 cm.$^{-1}$), respectively, characterization of a 2:1 layer silicate by infrared spectroscopy as being a dioctahedral mineral cannot be conclusive in the presence of significant amounts of kaolinite in the sample.

It is known that the formation of hydrogen bonds decreases the O–H stretching frequency. The shift in the O–H stretching frequency in the range 3.12 to 2.94μ (3,200 to 3,400 cm.$^{-1}$) as modified by hydrogen bonding in clay-water systems may be followed as a function of the degree of hydration. Protect specimens by a layer of Nujol or by enclosing them in a special cell in which the humidity may be controlled. The use of infrared to study the state of water in minerals was suggested and briefly explored by Coblentz (1911). Buswell et al. (1937) and Fripiat et al. (1960) have made detailed studies of the dehydration of montmorillonite.

51-8 QUANTITATIVE ANALYSIS

51-8.1 Materials

See section 51–3.3.3.1.

51-8.2 Procedure

If the material is $>2\mu$, reduce it to that size by wet grinding. Establish the optimum grinding procedure for specific minerals or mixtures of minerals by experimentation.

To prepare a quantity of sample in a KBr pellet so that the analytical absorption band shows a transmittance near 40%, grind 5.0 mg. or other appropriate amount of dried sample with 3.0000 g. of spectroscopic-grade KBr in a small mortar for 5 minutes, and dry the mixture overnight in vacuo over $Mg(ClO_4)_2$. Weigh 300.0 mg. of the mixture, and prepare a pellet as described in section 51–3.3.3.2. Determine the peak height or the area under the absorption band, and obtain the percentage composition from the standard curve prepared as described below.

51-8.3 Calibration Curve

From a spectrum of the compound or material under study, choose an analytical absorption band outside regions of zero or extremely low transmission percentages where bands from H_2O and CO_2 will not interfere. The band should be free from background interference (bands in carrier or contaminants), should not be too pointed (difficult to reproduce), and should be of the shape on which a good base line can be drawn (Fig. 51–7). Determine the percentage transmission or absorption in the spectral region of the analytical absorption band on a number of pellets containing varying amounts of the pure component. Percent transmission should vary between 30 and 70%.

Construct a calibration curve by plotting sample weight against peak height or area under the analytical absorption band. Obtain the area under the curve by use of a planimeter, counting squares on the chart paper, or cutting out the entire absorption band and weighing the paper on an analytical balance. Obtain the peak height of the analytical absorption band by measuring the vertical distance (in percentage transmission) from the lower tip of the absorption band up to a straight line (Lyon et al. 1959) drawn across the absorption band so that it rests on the highest percentage transmission between the absorption band being measured and the absorption band on either side (see Fig. 51–7).

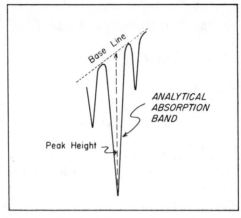

Fig. 51–7. Base-line method for obtaining peak height of analytical absorption band.

51–8.4 Comments

Reproducible grinding technique is a requirement for quantitative analysis. Tuddenham and Lyon (1960) recommend grinding 20 mg. of sample (<200 mesh) in an automatic grinder in 2.25 ml. of ethyl alcohol for 15 minutes.

51–9 LITERATURE CITED

Adler, H. H., Kerr, P. F., Bray, E. E., Stephens, N. P., Hunt, J. M., Keller, W. D., and Pickett, E. E. 1950. Infrared spectra of reference clay minerals. Am. Petrol. Inst. Res. Proj. 49, Prelim. Rept. No. 8, Columbia Univ., New York.

Bauman, R. P., and Clark, C. 1957. Biological applications of infrared spectroscopy. Ann. New York Acad. Sci. 69:1–253.

Bellamy, L. J. 1958. The Infrared Spectra of Complex Molecules. Ed. 2. John Wiley and Sons, Inc., New York.

Beutelspacher, H. 1956. Infrarot Untersuchungen an Bodenkolloiden. Trans. Intern. Congr. Soil Sci. 6th Paris Reports B (Comm. 1 and 2), 329–335.

Bradley, K. B., and Potts, W. J., Jr., 1958. The internally standardized Nujol mull as a method of quantitative infrared spectroscopy. Appl. Spectr. 12:77–80.

Buswell, A. M., Krebs, K., and Rodebush, W. H. 1937. Infrared studies. III. Adsorption bands of hydrogels between 2.4 and 3.5μ. J. Am. Chem. Soc. 59:2603–05.

Clark, G. L., ed. 1960. The Encyclopedia of Spectroscopy. Reinhold Publishing Corp., New York.

Coblentz, William W. 1911. The role of water in minerals. J. Franklin Inst. 172:309–335.

Colthup, N. B. 1950. Spectra-structure correlations in the infrared region. J. Opt. Soc. Am. 40:397–400.

Conn, G. K. T., and Avery, D. G. 1960. Infrared Methods. Academic Press, Inc., New York.

Cross, A. D. 1960. Introduction to Practical Infra-red Spectroscopy. Butterworths Scientific Publications, London.

Dinsmore, H. L., and Edmondson, P. R. 1959. Infrared microspectra of biochemical substances. II. Pressed KBr micropellets for use with reflecting microscope. Spectrochim. Acta 15:1032–1035.

Durie, R. A., and Murray, A. 1957. A study of the infrared absorption spectra of soils. Australian J. Appl. Sci. 8:335–338.

Elliot, A. 1959. The infrared spectra of polymers. Advan. in Spectr. 1:214–287.

Eyring, E. M., and Wadsworth, M. E. 1956. Differential infrared spectra of adsorbed monolayers-n-hexanethiol on Zn minerals. Mining Eng. 8:531–535.

Farmer, V. C. 1956. The infrared spectra of talc, saponite, and hectorite. Mineral. Mag. 31:829–845.

Farmer, V. C., and Morrison, R. I. 1960. Chemical and infrared studies on Phragmites peat and its humic acid. Proc. Roy. Dublin Soc. (Series A) 1:85–104.

Fieldes, M., Walker, I. K., and Williams, P. P. 1956. Clay mineralogy of New Zealand soils. III. Infrared absorption spectra of clay soils. New Zealand J. Sci. Technol. 38B:31–43.

Ford, M. A., and Wilkinson, G. P. 1954. The preparation and properties of pressed alkali halide disks with special reference to their use in spectroscopy. J. Sci. Instr. 31:338–341.

Fripiat, J. J. 1960. Application de la spectroscopie infra-rouge a l'etude des mineraux argileux. Bull. Gr. Fr. Argiles, XII, Nouvelle serie no. 7, 25–41.

Fripiat, J. J., Chaussidon, J., and Touillaux, R. 1960. Study of dehydration of montmorillonite and vermiculite by infrared spectroscopy. J. Phys. Chem. 64:1234–1241.

Hunt, J. M., and Turner, D. S., 1953. Determination of mineral constituents of rocks by infrared spectroscopy. Anal. Chem. 25:1169–1174.

Hunt, J. M., Wisherd, M. P., and Bonham, L. C. 1950. Infrared absorption spectra of minerals and other inorganic compounds. Anal. Chem. 22:1478–1497.

Johnson, H. H. 1959. Soil organic matter: I. Electrophoretic separation of acid-resistant components. Soil Sci. Soc. Am. Proc. 23:293–295.

Jones, R. N., and Sandorfy, C. 1956. The application of infrared and Raman spectrometry to the elucidation of molecular structure. In A. Weissberger, ed. Technique of Organic Chemistry, Vol. IX, pp. 247–580. Chemical Applications of Spectroscopy, Interscience Publ., New York.

Kakitani, S. 1956. Infrared absorption by some clay minerals (OH-stretching vibration of montmorillonite, kaolinite, and halloysite). (translated title) Kobutsugaku Zasshi 3:49–52.

Kasatochkin, V. I., Kononova, M. M., and Zil'berbrand, O. I. 1958. Infrared absorption spectra of humic substances of the soil. (translated title) Doklady Akad. Nauk U.S.S.R. 119:785–788.

Kasatochkin, V. I., and Zil'berbrand, O. I. 1956. X-ray and infrared spectroscopy applied to the study of the structure of soil humus. (translated title) Pochvovedenie No. 5:80–85.

Keller, W. D., and Pickett, E. E. 1949. Absorption of infrared radiation by powdered silica minerals. Am. Mineralogist 34:855–868.

Keller, W. D., and Pickett, E. E. 1950. The absorption of infrared radiation by clay minerals. Am. J. Sci. 248:264–273.

Kohl, R. A., and Taylor, S. A. 1961. Hydrogen bonding between the carbonyl group and Wyoming bentonite. Soil Sci. 91:223–227.

Kolesova, V. A. 1959. Infrared absorption spectra of the silicates containing aluminum and of certain crystalline aluminates. Opt. Spectr. 6:20–24.

Kumada, K., and Aizawa, K. 1958. The infrared spectra of humic acids. Soil and Plant Food (Tokyo) 3:152–159.

Launer, P. J. 1952. Regularities in the infrared absorption spectra of silicate minerals. Am. Mineralogist 37:764–784.

Lehmann, H., and Dutz, H. 1960. Ultrarotspektroskopisch Untersuchungen an Gläsern und kristallinen Silikaten. Silicates Indus. 25:559–566.

Lyon, R. J. P., and Tuddenham, W. M. 1959. Quantitative mineralogy as a guide in exploration. Mining Eng. 214:1–5.

Lyon, R. J. P., Tuddenham, W. M., and Thompson, C. S. 1959. Quantitative mineralogy in 30 minutes. Econ. Geol. 54:1047–1055.

Miller, F. A., Carlson, G. L., Bentley, F. F. and Jones, W. H. 1960. Infrared spectra of inorganic ions in the cesium bromide region (700–300 cm.$^{-1}$). Spectrochim. Acta 16:135–235.

Miller, F. A., and Wilkins, C. H. 1952. Infrared spectra and characteristic frequencies of inorganic ions. Anal. Chem. 24:1253–1294.

Nahin, P. G. 1955. Infrared analysis of clay and related materials. Clay and Clay Technology. Dept. Natl. Resources, Div. Mines, California, Bull. 169:112–118.

Pierson, R. H., Fletcher, A. N., and Gantz, E. S. C. 1956. Catalog of infrared spectra for qualitative analysis of gases. Anal. Chem. 28:1218–1239.

Randall, H. M., Fowler, R. G., Fuson, N., and Dangl, J. R. 1949. Infrared Determination of Organic Structure. D. Van Nostrand Co., New York.

Rudnitskaya, E. S. 1956. Use of infrared spectroscopy for the investigation of minerals. (translated title) Zapiski Vsesoyuz. Mineralog. Obshchestva 85:407–412.

Sawyer, D. T. 1960. Infrared spectra and correlations for the ethylenediamine-tetra-acetic acid metal chelates. Ann. New York Acad. Sci. 88: 307–321.

Schnitzer, M., Shearer, D. A., and Wright, J. R. 1959. A study in the infrared of high molecular weight organic matter extracted by various reagents from a Podzolic B horizon. Soil Sci. 87:252–257.

Serratosa, J. M., and Bradley, W. F. 1958. Determination of the orientation of OH bond axes in layer silicates by infrared absorption. J. Phys. Chem. 62:1164–1167.

Setkina, O. N. 1957. Infrared spectra of the clay minerals and their application. (translated title) Trudy Leningrad. Tekhnol. Inst. im. Lensoveta 40:155–162.

Setkina, O. N. 1959. Infrared spectra of minerals and their practical application. (translated title) Zapiski Vsesoyuz. Mineralog. Obschchestva 88:39–47.

Setkina, O. N., and Gopshtein, N. M. 1957. Infrared absorption spectra of clay minerals. (translated title) Trudy Leningrad. Tekhnol. Inst. im. Lensoveta 37:79–90.

Stubican, V., and Roy, R. 1961a. Isomorphous substitution and infrared spectra of the layer lattice-silicates. Am. Mineralogist 46:32–51.

Stubican, V., and Roy, R. 1961b. Infrared spectra of layer-structure silicates. J. Am. Ceram. Soc. 44:625–627.

Tensmeyer, L. G., Hoffman, R., and Brindley, G. W. 1960. Infrared studies of some complexes between ketones and calcium montmorillonite. Clay-organic studies. Part III. J. Phys. Chem. 64:1655–1662.

Thompson, C. S., and Wadsworth, M. E. 1957. Determination of the composition of plagioclase feldspars by means of infrared spectroscopy. Am. Mineralogist 42:334–341.

Tuddenham, W. M., and Lyon, R. J. P. 1959. Relation of infrared spectra and chemical analysis for some chlorites and related minerals. Anal. Chem. 31:377–380.

Tuddenham, W. M., and Lyon, R. J. P. 1960. Infrared techniques in the identification and measurement of minerals. Anal. Chem. 32:1630–1634.

Van Der Marel, H. W., and Zwiers, J. H. L. 1959. O–H stretching bands of the kaolin minerals. Silicates Indust. 24:359–369.

Wright, N. 1941. Application of infrared spectroscopy to industrial research. Ind. Eng. Chem. Anal. Ed. 13:1–8.

SUBJECT INDEX